Proceedings of the 11th International Symposium on
Ceramics in Medicine

Bioceramics

Volume 11

Proceedings of the 11th International Symposium on
Ceramics in Medicine

Bioceramics

Volume 11

New York City, New York, USA

5-8 November 1998

edited by

RZ LeGeros
JP LeGeros
New York University College of Dentistry

World Scientific
Singapore • New Jersey • London • Hong Kong

Published by

World Scientific Publishing Co. Pte. Ltd.

P O Box 128, Farrer Road, Singapore 912805

USA office: Suite 1B, 1060 Main Street, River Edge, NJ 07661

UK office: 57 Shelton Street, Covent Garden, London WC2H 9HE

British Library Cataloguing-in-Publication Data
A catalogue record for this book is available from the British Library.

BIOCERAMICS 11
Proceedings of the 11th International Symposium on Ceramics in Medicine

Copyright © 1998 by World Scientific Publishing Co. Pte. Ltd.

ISBN   981-02-3701-4

Printed in Singapore by Eurasia Press Pte Ltd

Bioceramics 11

Executive Committee (1998)

President: R. Z. LeGeros (USA)
Secretary General: W. Bonfield (UK)
Treasurer: T. Kokubo (Japan)
Members: H. Ohgushi (Japan); A. Moroni (Italy); L. Sedel (France),
       L. Hench (UK/USA); P. Ducheyne (USA); S.F. Hulbert (USA);
       H. Oonishi (Japan); G. Hastings (Singapore); T. Yamamuro (Japan);
       J. Wilson (UK)

Scientific Committee

R. Bizios (USA)   A. Gatti (Italy)   A. Ravaglioli (Italy)
A. Boskey (USA)   U.M. Gross (Germany) J. Reese (USA)
G. Daculsi (France)   S. Kim (Korea)   D. Tarnow (USA)
K. de Groot (Netherlands) R. Kijkowska (Poland) M. Vallet-Regi (Spain)
M. Filliagi (Canada)   D. Lee (USA)   A. Yii-Urpo (Finland)
C. Frondoza (USA)   S. Niwa (Japan)

Local Organizing Committee

Chairpersons: Racquel Z. LeGeros, John P. LeGeros
Editorial Assistants: Alessandra LeGeros, Lena Rettig, Katherine LeGeros Barthe
Administrative Assistants: Donna Broomfield, LaDebra Williams

Endorsing Societies

International Association for Dental Research Ceramics Society of Japan
Society for Biomaterials   Korean Society for Biomaterials
European Society for Biomaterials   Japanese Society for Biomaterials

Supported by:

National Institute for Dental Research, NIH (Grant no. R13DE12804)
New York University College of Dentistry
L. Linkow Implant Research Fund

HOWMEDICA   **OSTEONICS**   **JOHNSON & JOHNSON**

BioPlant   *Sulzer-Calcitek*   *Block Drug*
Clarkson Chemicals   *US Biomaterials*   *ETEX*

HiMED   *Biomatlante*   *CeraMED*   *Orthovita*

Acknowledgements

Bioceramics 11 gratefully acknowledges the support from **the National Institute for Dental Research** (Conference Research Grant No. R13DE12804) of the National Institutes of Health; the **New York University College of Dentistry**; the support from the **Industrial Sponsors** and of the **L. Linkow Implant Research Fund.**

Bioceramics Symposia

Year	Site
1988	Kyoto, Japan
1989	Heidelberg, Germany
1990	Terre Haute, IND, USA
1991	London, England
1992	Kyoto, Japan
1993	Philadephia, PA, USA
1994	Turku, Finland
1995	Ponte Vedra, FL, USA
1996	Otsu, Japan
1997	Paris, France
1998	New York, NY, USA

Preface

Bioceramics 11 held at New York University College of Dentistry in November 1998, continued the tradition of the preceding ten International Symposia on Ceramics in Medicine for serving as the forum for the sharing of research findings among scientists and clinicians coming from many disciplines and from academia and industry. The growing global nature of this series of symposia is reflected by participation from 25 countries compared to 9 countries in Bioceramics 1.

This book is a collection of papers presented at the Bioceramics 11 symposium reflecting research on the cutting edge of developments for bioceramics and their medical and dental applications. The evolution of ceramic materials, bioinert and bioactive, has been remarkable, as shown by the research topics covered in this symposium. Research direction towards tissue engineering reflects the growing awareness to the need to develop materials which integrate biological functions to optimize tissue response. It is interesting to note that an early application of tissue engineering is recorded in a chapter of Genesis of the Bible: the creation of Eve from Adam's rib.

What can not be included, but only implied in these pages, is that the series of Bioceramics meetings result in the strengthening of information bonds between experienced researchers and encouragement to those researchers just entering the field.

Putting together this book of Proceeding was a formidable task but was made possible with the valuable collaboration of the Local Organizing Committee, the Scientific Committee and the Executive Committee. The significant support of the New York University College of Dentistry, the National Institute of Dental Research of the National Institutes of Health, the Industrial Sponsors and the L. Linkow Implant Research Fund are gratefully acknowledged.

We hope that in this book you will find inspiration and vision for the advancement of ceramics in the field of medicine and dentistry to the ultimate goal of improving the quality of life.

God bless you.

Racquel Z. LeGeros

John P. LeGeros

NEW YORK UNIVERSITY
A private university in the public service

DAVID B. KRISER DENTAL CENTER
COLLEGE OF DENTISTRY

Office of the Dean

Arnold and Marie Schwartz Hall of Dental Sciences
345 East 24th Street, New York, NY 10010-4086
Telephone: (212) 998-9898
FAX: (212) 995-4080

November 5, 1998

Dear Colleagues:

On behalf of the New York University College of Dentistry, I am pleased to welcome you to Bioceramics 11, the Eleventh International Symposium on Ceramics in Medicine and Dentistry. For three days, the study of ceramics in the medical sciences will be the focus of your discussions here, but we hope that you will find time also to explore our facilities at the David B. Kriser Dental Center and to enjoy some of the spectacular attractions of New York City.

The College of Dentistry is delighted to host the Symposium's first visit to New York. The College is the third oldest and the largest dental education institution in the United States, and it currently instructs more dentists than any other school. From the beginning, our mission has been to train oral health practitioners in the most advanced treatment therapies and state-of-the-art techniques. It is particularly fitting, then, that the cutting-edge research of bioceramics should enhance our learning community for the next few days.

A special thank you goes to Drs. Racquel Z. LeGeros and John P. LeGeros for organizing this outstanding Symposium. Their efforts have resulted in a most interesting collection of speakers from universities and industries throughout the world. I am certain that the data presented will stimulate your scientific curiosity as well as result in collaborations that will continue to foster this exciting discipline.

Once again, welcome. Your work represents some of the most thrilling advancements for the medical and dental professions. It is an important manifestation of your commitment to research and to excellence.

Sincerely,

Michael C. Alfano, D.M.D., Ph.D.
Dean

CONTENTS

C. *Bioglass*

D. *Composites*

B. Tissue Engineering and Growth Factors

C. Drug Delivery

VII. CLINICAL APPLICATIONS

A. Dental Applications

VIII. METHODS: SPECIAL PREPARATIONS AND ANALYSES   653

A. Surface Modifications of Implant

I. BONE BIOLOGY: GENERAL

Bioceramics Volume 11, edited by R. Z. LeGeros and J.P. LeGeros
(Proceedings of the 11th International Symposium on Ceramics in Medicine)
New York, NY, USA, November 1998
© 1998 by World Scientific Publishing Co. Pte. Ltd.

CELLULAR AND MOLECULAR EVENTS IN BONE REPAIR

John M. Schmitt, Shelley R. Winn and Jeffrey O. Hollinger

Northwest Wound Healing Center, Division of Plastic and Reconstructive Surgery,
Oregon Health Sciences University, 3181 SW Sam Jackson Park Rd., Portland, OR 97201

ABSTRACT

In this brief review, the vital cellular and molecular events, which contribute to bone regeneration, will be discussed. The sequence of events that assures regeneration of the original bony structure involves a dynamic, interactive process among cells and cell products. Bone morphogenetic proteins (BMPS) as well as several other key biological molecules are integral components that activate and support the regenerative process.

The article will focus on basic BMP biology and include: The release of BMPs at the wound site; BMP binding to cells present at the injury locus leading to the activation of the Smad proteins, which in turn may directly or indirectly trigger the production of the nuclear protein Osf2. Osf2 activates osteoblast genes leading to osteoblast development. Osteoblasts are responsible for the production of new osseous tissue that restores form and function.

Keywords: bone regeneration, bone morphogenetic proteins (BMPs), Smads, Osf2

BONE INJURY AND OSTEOBLAST ORIGIN

The ability of bone to regenerate is a well-known physiological process that produces a structure that physiologically and biomechanically is indistinguishable from the original. The dynamic interactions among cells and cell-produced molecules at a fracture site ensure complete regeneration of bone. Bone morphogenetic proteins (BMPS) and other vital cell products are integral components that propel and sustain the dynamic repair process. BMPS, several other growth/differentiation factors, and cells present at the fracture site assure complete fracture healing by six to eight weeks.

Before the BMPs influence cellular differentiation, cells must be recruited to the injury locus, expanded in number, and acted upon by the proper combination of signaling factors. Immediately following osseous fracture a local population of pluripotent cells resident in the cambial layers of the periosteum, endosteum, and dura are activated and recruited to the fracture site. Another class of cells, the "inducible osteoprogenitor" cells, such as pericytes, arrive at the injury locus around three to five days after injury via transit in developing capillary sprouts (Figure 1). [4, 46, 47, 57] Pericytes may become osteoblasts following interactions with endogenous BMPS. Furthermore, according to Brighton and colleagues, a population of polymorphic mesenchymal cells can appear as early as twelve hours following fracture and become a "preosteoblast"[3]. Moreover, mesenchymal stem cells within the bone marrow contribute to the repair blastema. These cells possess multilineage potential and can convert either to cartilage-forming chondrocytes or bone-forming osteoblasts, depending on the presence of environmental cues, such as nutrient supply, BMP concentrations, growth factors, blood vessels, and mechanical stability.[5, 6] For example, marrow-derived inducible osteoprogenitors undergo osteoblastic differentiation in response to BMPs and growth factors (Figure 1). [1, 25, 35, 50, 51]

Osteoblasts are metabolically active secretary cells that have been shown to express BMP- 1, 2, 4 and 6, transforming growth factor-beta, insulin-like growth factors I and II, interleukin- 1, platelet-derived growth factor,[12] alkaline phosphatase, and osteocalcin as well as organic bone matrix.[2, 17, 19] Expression of these products by osteoblasts occurs during bone embryogenesis, maintenance (e.g., remodeling), and regeneration. Moreover, osteoblasts may express only a subset of molecules from the potential osteoblast repertoire.

The clinical relevance of BMPs and a responding cell population at the wound site represent the final common pathway of the elements, which contribute to bone regeneration. BMPs are key factors responsible for driving the cellular machinery for synthesizing new bone. Cells must be competent to respond to the BMP signal(s) and there must be a sufficient quantity of biologically active BMPs present to produce the desired outcome, for example, to regenerate form and function of bone. The types of BMPS, as well as their concentrations, will dictate the cellular responses at the injury locus.

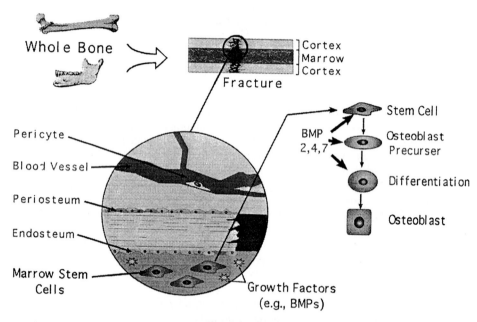

FIGURE 1

A BRIEF CLASSIFICATION OF BMPS

Wang *et al.* have supplied the details for the identification and molecular cloning of factors with BMP activity[59]. In essence, BMP-1 through BMP-9 were identified by screening human cDNA libraries to derive recombinant clones that encoded human BMPS. Moreover, BMP-2 through BMP-9 were shown to be members of the transforming growth factor beta (TGF-β) family based on amino acid sequence similarity [8, 10, 48, 49, 61]. BMP-10 through BMP-1 3 have been identified by low stringency hybridization and consensus polymerase chain reaction. The classification of the major subdivisions within the TGF-β superfamily include TGF-β 1-5 and 15 BMPs (exclusive of BMP- 1), the growth/differentiating factors (GDF) 1-10 (a subclass of BMPs4 1), the inhibins, activins, Vg-related genes, nodal-related genes, *Drosophila* genes (e.g., dpp, 60A), and glial-derived neurotropic factor.[20, 27, 28, 37, 38]

Structural studies of BMPs have revealed that they contain a mature domain, which is cleaved allowing monomeric units to dimerize by a cysteine-disulfide bridge. Following intracellular glycosylation, the dimer is expressed in an active form. Protein assembly can produce homodimers, heterodimers, and glycosylation variability, all of which may influence BMP activity and effects. Moreover, extracellular antagonists may also play a role in regulating the biological effects of BMPs at the injury site.

Studies in the *Xenopus* embryo have revealed five protein regulators of BMPS, noggin, chordin, gremlin, dan, and cerberus. These proteins bind to exogenous BMP's and eliminate intracellular BMP promoted activity[23, 64]. Moreover, BMP appears to be antagonized in a dose-dependent manner by the regulator proteins. None of the BMP regulators have been shown to play a role in BMP-inspired bone regeneration following fracture. However, BMP concentrations at the wound site profoundly influence cell differentiation. This concept is particularly relevant for the conversion of stem cells to the osteoblast phenotype. Other controlling mechanisms may come into affect during bone regeneration and repair, which are beyond the scope of this article (for review see Hollinger *et al.*[21]).

OSTEOBLASTS AND BMPs AT THE WOUND SITE

The conversion of osteoprogenitor cells to mineralizing osteoblasts by BMPs is a key event for bone regeneration. Recent studies have revealed that BMPs bind specific cell surface receptors and initiate intracellular responses, which result in a mineralizing osteoblast. BMPs at the fracture bind and initiate a cell signal through a transmembrane receptor complex formed by two related types of serine/threonine kinase proteins, designated type I and type II. For BMPS, type I and type II receptors both have low affinity for

BMP and together achieve high affinity binding[33, 42, 53]. The BMP-receptor bound complex is a heterotetramer (Figure 2). Upon BMP binding to the receptor complex, the type II receptor kinase phosphorylates a glycine-serine (GS) region on the type I receptors[62]. Type I receptor phosphorylation is required to generate an intracellular response to the bound BMP[36, 62]. For BMP signaling, two structurally related type I receptors (BMPR-IA and BMPR-IB) and a type II receptor (BMPR-II) have been identified (Figure 2). The specific combinations of type I and type II receptors in cells dictate the cell's ability to bind a particular ligand (e.g., BMPs vs. TGF-6) and elicit definitive cellular responses. Both type I and type II receptors are important for maintaining BMP signal diversity, although specific intracellular signaling is primarily determined by the type I receptor[7]. Once phosphorylated, type I receptors can propagate the intracellular signal on their own[36].

INTRACELLULAR BMP SIGNAL TRANSDUCTION

The intracellular proteins responsible for carrying (transducing) the BMP activated receptor complex responses are being elucidated. However, genetic screens of *Drosophila* proteins revealed evidence for a class of molecules responsible for transducing the BMP signal. The screens revealed an enhanced expression of the *Drosophila decapentaplegic (dpp)* gene, a homolog of vertebrate BMP-2 and BMP-4, by the gene product termed *Mothers against dpp (MAD)*[56]. MAD proteins are required for *dpp* signaling and function downstream of the *dpp* receptor.[22, 40, 60] Homologs to MAD have been identified in C *elegans, Xenopus,* mouse, and human. Our focus in this review is on mammalian MAD-related proteins preferably known as Smads. Currently, there are nine Smad proteins designated Smad1 through 9.

Smad proteins interact with BMP receptors by a L3 motif and possess conserved N-terminal (MH 1) and C-terminal (MH2) domains separated by a less conserved threonine, serine, and proline linker reuion.[22, 34, 40, 54, 56] Each of the TGF-B sub-groups appear to signal through different Smad isoforins.[22, 36] Smad1 is directly phosphorylated and "activated" on a serine residue by type I BMP receptors[30]. After Smad1 becomes activated by BMP-2 or BMP-4, Smad1 associates with Smad4 as a hetero-oligomer and rapidly accumulates in the cell nucleus (Figure 2).[22, 31, 32] Smad5 is also activated by BMP-2, associates with Smad4, and is translocated to the nucleus. The importance of Smad1 and 5 in bone formation was revealed when it was demonstrated that myoblasts over-expressing Smad1 and 5 could be converted to osteoblasts[63]. Furthermore, the Smad1 signaling pathway appears to be regulated by Smad6 which inhibits Smad1 signaling by binding to the type I receptor and by specifically competing with Smad4 for binding to receptor-activated Smad1 yielding an inactive Smadl-6 complex (Figure 2)[18, 24]. Full length Smads are latent, but initiate gene transcription upon stimulation by BMP-2. The binding of Smad-like proteins to DNA and subsequent transcriptional activation has been demonstrated in *Drosophila.* [26]

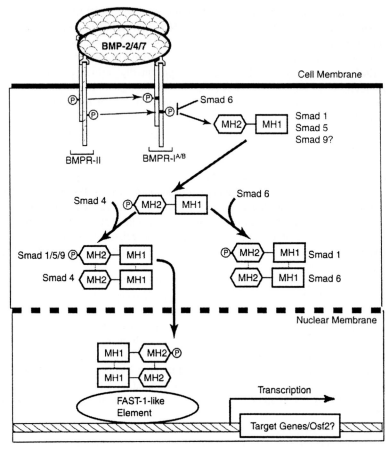

FIGURE 2

SMADS AND THE OSTEOBLAST NUCLEUS

Smads may associate with DNA binding elements to form transcriptional control complexes.[32] For example, Smad2 forms a complex with FAST-1 (forkhead activin signal transducer- 1) in an activin-dependent fashion and generates a complex that binds to the activin responsive gene element, directing transcription of the *Mix 2.* gene[11]. Therefore, we reason that Smad1 and 5 may bind FAST-1 -like elements and activate gene transcription. The authors propose that the phosphorylated Smad may either directly or indirectly activate the Osf2 (osteoblast specific factor 2) gene, which translates into the Osf2 protein. In addition, we hypothesize here and elsewhere[55], that either Smad1 or Smad5 proteins with or without a FAST-1-like complex may initiate Osf2 gene transcription (Figure 2).

The gene encoding the Osf2 protein is a highly conserved protein. The human homologs include AML-IA, AML-LB, and PEBP2u.C. Analyses of the human AML-1 (acute myeloid leukemia) genes revealed a conserved runt domain highly homologous to the corresponding region of the gene product of the *Drosophila segment* runt gene. The runt domains contain a conserved 128-amino acid peptide region, which allows Osf2 to heterodimerize with a ubiquitously expressed factor and bind DNA.[43, 44]

Recently, Osf2 was cloned and shown to bind directly and activate the osteocalcin transcriptional promoterregion.[13-15] The osteocalcin gene is a molecular marker found solely in osteoblasts.[13, 58] Importantly, BMP-treated cells expressed Osf2 before expressing other osteoblast-specific genes. [14]

The recently characterized promoter region upstream of the osteocalcin gene contains three cis-acting elements that function as transcriptional control points capable of binding transacting factors (e.g. Osf2).[13, 16] The three osteocalcin gene control points have been designated OSE1 (osteoblast specific element 1), mOCE1 (mouse osteocalcin E-box sequence 1), and OSE2 (osteoblast specific element 2).[13] Karsenty et al have shown that the OSE2 sequence is a transcriptional control point for the osteocalcin gene. Furthermore, OSE2 binds Osf2, which is present only in osteoblastic cell lines and primary osteoblasts[13, 15]. Osf2 has been shown to control the expression of several osteoblast-like genes including osteopontin osteocalcin α 1 (I) collagen, and bone sialoprotein.[14] Genetic sequence elements similar to osteocalcin OSE2 sequence have been found in the promoters of the α 1 (I) collagen, bone sialoprotein, and osteopontin.

Studies by Ducy et al have revealed Osf2 is capable of promoting osteoblast differentiation of non-osteoblastic cells. For example, when Osf2 was transfected into C3H1OT1/2 cells and mouse skin fibroblasts, bone sialoprotein and osteocalcin expression were observed.[14] Osf2 is a key molecule which activates several osteoblast phenotypes in multiple cell types. It was recently postulated that Osf2 may trigger mesenchymal stem cells to differentiate into osteoblasts during the developmental process.[14, 52] Recent data also has revealed Osf2-deficient mice lacked osteoblasts and bone, were smaller in size than non-deficient Osf2 mice, and died due to respiratory failure.[29, 45] Interestingly, Osf2 heterozygous mice exhibited skeletal abnormalities characteristic of the human heritable skeletal disorder, cleidocranial dysplasia.[39, 45] Clearly, Osf2 plays an important role in bone formation. Moreover, Osf2 is activated in response to exogenous BMPs present at the fracture site, which leads to osteoblast formation and the production of new bone.

SUMMARY

In this review we have examined the BMPs which are key cell signaling factors that are capable of promoting bone regeneration. Following BMP binding to the cell surface, intracellular Smad proteins are activated, move to the nucleus and initiate gene transcription. One gene that may directly or indirectly become activated by Smads is the nuclear protein Osf2. Osf2 production promotes osteoblast formation and, as a consequence, bone regeneration.

REFERENCES

1. Amedee, J., *et al. Differentiation* **58**, 157-164 (1994).
2. Bilbe, G., *et al. Bone* **19,** 437-445 (1996).
3. Brighton, C.T. & Hunt, R.M. *J. Bone Joint Surg.* **73** - A, 832-847 (199 1).
4. Brighton, C.T., *et al Clin. Orthop. Rel. Res.* **275,** 287-299 (1992).
5. Bruder, S.P., Fink, D.J. & Caplan, A.I. *J. Cell. Biochem.* **56,** 283-294 (1994).
6. Caplan, A.I. *J. Orthop. Res.* **9,** 641-650 (1991).
7. Carcamo, J., *et al. Mol Cell Biol* **14,** 3810-3821 (1994).
8. Celeste, A.J., *et al. Proc. Natl. Acad. Sci. U.S.A.* **8 7,** 9843-9847 (1990).
9. Celeste, A.J., *et al. J. Bone Miner. Res.* **9,** S 137 (1994).
10. Celeste, A.J., *et al Molecular cloning of BMP-8: Present in bovine bone which is highly related to BMP-51617 subfamily of osteoinductive molecules* 1-1 00 (1992).
11. Chen, X., Rubock, M. & Whitman, M. *Nature* **383,** 691-696 (1996).
12. Delmas, P.D. & Malaval, L. in *Physiology and Pharmacology of Bone* (eds. Mundy, G.R.) 673-724 (Springer-Verlag, New York, 1993).
13. Ducy, P. & Karsenty, G. *Mol Cell Biol* **15,** 1858-1869 (1995).
14. Ducy, P., *et al. Cell* **89,** 747-754 (1997).
15. Geoffroy, V., Ducy, P. & Karsenty, G. *J Biol Chem* **270,** 30973-30979 (1995).
16. Griffiths, A., *et al. An Introduction to Genetic Analysis* 1-915 (W.H. Freeman & Company, NY, 1996).
17. Harris, S., *et al. J Bone Miner Res* **10,** 178-186 (1995).
18. Hata, A., *et al. Genes Dev* **12,** 186-197 (1998).
19. Hicok, K., *et al. J Bone Miner Res.* **13,** 205-217 (1998).
20. Hogan, L.B. *Curr. Opin. Gen. Develop.* **6,** 432-438 (1996).

21. Hollinger, J.O., Buck, D.C. & Bruder, S. in *Tissue Engineering in Dentistry* (eds. Lynch, S.) (Quintessence, San Diego, In Press).
22. Hoodless, P., *et al.* *Cell* **85**, 489-500 (1996).
23. Hsu, D., *et al.* *Mol Cell* **1**, 673-683 (1998).
24. Imamura, T., *et al.* *Nature* **3 8 9**, 622-626 (1997).
25. Jaiswal, N. & Bruder, S.P. *Transactions Orthop. Res. Soc.* **22**, 524 (1997).
26. Kim, J., *et al.* *Nature* **388**, 304-308 (1997).
27. Kingsley, D. *Trends in Genetics* **10**, 16-21 (1994).
28. Kingsley, D.M. *Genes Develop.* **8**, 133-146 (1994).
29. Komori, T., *et al.* *Cell* **89**, 755-764 (1997).
30. Kretzschmar, M., *et al.* *Genes Dev.* **11**, 984-995 (1997).
31. Lagna, G., *et al.* *Nature* **383** 832-836 (1996).
32. Liu, F., *et al.* *Nature* **381**, 620-623 (1996).
33. Liu, F., *et al.* *Mol Cell Biol* **15**, 3479-3486 (1995).
34. Lo, R., *et al.* *EMBO* **17**, 996-1005 (1998).
35. Long, M.W., *et al.* *J. Clin. Invest.* **95**, 881-887 (1995).
36. Massagu6, J. *Cell* **85**, 947-950 (1996).
37. Massagu6, J. *Annual Rev. Cell Biol.* **6**, 597-641 (1990).
38. Massagu6, J., *et al.* *Cancer Surveys* **12**, 81-103 (1992).
39. Mundlos, S., *et al.* *Cell* **89**, 773-779 (1997).
40. Newfeld, S., *et al.* *Development* **122**, 2099-2108 (1996).
41. Nishitoh, H., *et al.* *J. Biol. Chem.* **271**, 21345-21352 (1996).
42. Nohno, T., *et al.* *J Biol Chem* **270**, 22522-22526 (1995).
43. Ogawa, E., *et al.* *Virology* **194**, 314-331 (1993).
44. Ogawa, E., *et al.* *Proc Natl Acad Sci USA* **90**, 6859-6863 (1993).
45. Otto, F., *et al.* *Cell* **89**, 765-771 (1997).
46. Owen, M. *Arthritis Rheum* **23**, 1073-1080 (1980).
47. Owen, M. *Lineage of osteogenic cells and their relationship to the stromal system* 1-1-25 (Elsevier Science Publishers, Amsterdam, 1985).
48. Ozkaynak, E., *et al.* *EMBO Journal* **9**, 2085-2093 (1990).
49. Ozkaynak, E., *et al.* *J. Biol. Chem.* **267**, 25220-25227 (1992).
50. Rickard, D.J., *et al.* *Dev. Biol.* **161**, 218-228 (1994).
51. Robinson, D., Bab, I. & Nevo, Z. *J. Bone Miner. Res.* **10**, 690-696 (1995).
52. Rodan, G. & Harada, S.-I. *Cell* **89**, 677-680 (1997).
53. Rosenweig, B., *et al.* *Proc Natl Acad Sci USA* **92**, 7632-7636 (1995).
54. Savage, C., *et al.* *Proc Natl Acad Sci* **93**, 790-794 (1996).
55. 55, Schmitt, J., *et al.* *J Ortho Res* (Submitted).
56. Sekelsky, J., *et al.* *Genetics* **139**, 1347-1358 (1995).
57. Takagi, K. & Urist, M.R. *Ann Surg* **196**, 100-109 (1982).
58. Towler, D., Bennette, C. & Rodan, G. *Mol Endocrinol* **8**, 614-624 (1994).
59. Wang, E.A., *et al.* *Proc. Natl. Acad. Sci. U.S.A.* **8** 5@ 9484-9488 (1988).
60. Wiersdorff, V., *et al.* *Development* **1229** 2153-2162 (1996).
61. Wozney, J.M., *et al.* *Science* **242**, 1528-1534 (1988).
62. Wrana, J.L., *et al.* *Nature* **370** 341-347 (1994).
63. Yamamoto, N., *et al.* *Biochem Biophys Res Commun* **238**, 574-5 80 (1997).
64. Zimmerman, L., Jesus-Escobar, J. & Harland, R.M. *Cell* **86**, 599-606 (1996).

Bioceramics Volume 11, edited by R. Z. LeGeros and J.P. LeGeros
(Proceedings of the 11th International Symposium on Ceramics in Medicine)
New York, NY, USA, November 1998

BIOCERAMICS, CELLS AND SIGNALS IN TISSUE ENGINEERING

A.H. Reddi

Center for Tissue Regeneration and Repair, Department of Orthopaedic Surgery, University of California, Davis, Medical Center, Sacramento, CA 95817

ABSTRACT

Tissue engineering is an evolving discipline based on principles of biology, biomaterials and engineering. Tissue engineering is the science of design and manufacture of new tissues for the functional restoration of impaired organs and lost parts due to trauma and tumors. The three principal ingredients for tissue engineering are morphogenetic signals, responding stem cells and extracellular matrix scaffolding. Bones and teeth is mineralized extracellular matrix containing tissues. The mineral phase, hydroxyapatite is a bioceramic. Bone morphogenetic proteins (BMPs) are morphogens with affinity to hydroxyapatite and collagens. In view of this bioceramics are ideal delivery systems for BMPs in the field of tissue engineering of bones and teeth including periodontium.

KEYWORDS: Tissue engineering, BMP, bone, growth factors

BONE MORPHOGENETIC PROTEINS

Bone grafts have been used for over a century by orthopaedic surgeons to aid the repair of bone. The aim of this concise article is to convey the recent excitement in the field of tissue engineering[1]. Tissue engineering may be defined as the science of design and manufacture of new tissues for the functional restoration of organs and tissues damaged or lost due to disease and trauma. The three key ingredients for tissue engineering are inductive morphogenetic signals, the responding stem cells and extracellular matrix scaffolding. Among the many tissues in the body, bone has considerable potential for repair and; therefore, a unique prototype model for insights into tissue engineering. Bone, in addition, is a tissue with encrusted bioceramic hydroxyapatite. The metabolism and remodeling of bone is governed by local and systemic factors. The former include chemical and physical signals including but not limited to cytokines, morphogens, pulsed electromagnetic fields, gravity, mechanical signals, fluid flow and deformation. The systemic factors include calcitropic hormones, ions and a variety of vitamins.
Bone morphogenetic proteins (Table 1) are the primordial morphogens for bone induction. A single recombinant protein is sufficient for the induction of the entire sequence of bone formation including chemotaxis, mitosis and differentiation[1].

BMPs regulate key steps in the sequential cascade of bone morphogenesis such as chemotaxis, mitosis and differentiation. BMP 4 is chemotactic for human monocytes at fentomolar concentration. The mitogenic response is optimal at picomolar range and differentiation is operational at nanomolar concentration. Thus BMPs are pleiotropic regulators that act in a concentration-dependent threshold[2].

Table 1. BONE MORPHOGENETIC PROTEINS

Morphogen	Other Names	Potential Function
Bone Morphogenetic Proteins		
BMP 2	BMP 2A	Cartilage Morphogenesis
BMP 4	BMP 2B	Cartilage Morphogenesis
BMP 3	Osteogenin	Bone Formation
BMP 3B	GDF 10	Membrane Bones
BMP 5	____	??
BMP 6	____	Hypertrophy of Cartilage
BMP 7	Osteogenic Protein 1	Bone Differentiation
BMP 8	Osteogenic Protein 2	Bone Formation
BMP 10	____	??
Cartilage-derived Morphogenetic Proteins (CDMPs)	Growth/Differentiation Factor	
CDMP – 1	GDF – 5	Mesenchymal Condensation
CDMP – 2	GDF – 6	Cartilage Development
CDMP – 3	GDF – 7	Ligament Development

BMPS BIND TO EXTRACELLULAR MATRIX AND HYDROXYAPATITE

A key ingredient for tissue engineering is the scaffolding of extracellular matrix (ECM). The key components of ECM are collagens, proteoglycans, and an assortment of adhesive and structural glycoproteins. BMPs play a key role in epithelial mesenchymal interactions and morphogenesis. BMPs 3, 4 and 7 bind to collagen IV, collagen I, heparan sulfate and heparin[2]. BMPs bind avidly to hydroxyapatite. The BMP – extracellular matrix interaction and affinity to hydroxyapatite may play a key role in tissue engineering of bones and teeth.

STEM CELLS

The morphogenetic proteins act on responding stem cells. The stromal cells of the marrow are plastic and may give rise to cartilage, bone, muscle, tendons and ligaments[3]. Very recently the stromal stem cells have been employed in cell and gene therapy with appropriate gene delivery vectors[4].

BIOCERAMICS AS BIOMIMETIC MATERIALS

The native biomaterial scaffolding in bones and teeth are mineralized type I collagen. The mineral phase is a modified hydroxyapatite. BMPs were purified by hydroxyapatite chromatography[2]. The geometry of the hydroxyapatite is critical for bone induction by BMPs. A comparison of hydroxyapatite beads and discs revealed that the discs are optimal for bone morphogenesis, indicating the critical role of geometry of the bioceramics[5]. In subhuman primates hydroxyapatite is both osteoconductive and osteoinductive[6]. It is likely that, in vivo hydroxyapatite binds to circulating BMPs, thus rendering an osteoconductive bioceramic into an osteoinductive substratum.

FUTURE CHALLENGES

Despite the recent advances in morphogens, bioceramics and stem cells, many challenges remain. We need to synthesize and modify ceramics for medical and dental applications with optimal properties for weight-bearing and other applications. The application of BMPs in medicine and surgery is absolutely dependent on research advances in bioceramics.

In conclusion, bioceramics may have an unlimited wide-ranging potential for delivery of morphogens for tissue engineering of a variety of tissues.

REFERENCES

1. Reddi AH. *Nature Biotechnology* 1998; 16: 247-252.
2. Reddi AH. *Cytokine & Growth Factor Reviews* 1997; 8: 11-20.
3. Caplan AI. *J Orthop Res* 1991; 9: 641-650.
4. Prockop DJ. *Science* 1997; 276: 71-74.
5. Ripamonti U, Ma, S, Reddi AH. *Matrix* 1992; 12:202-212.
6. Ripamonti, U. *Biomaterials* 1996; 17: 31-35.

Bioceramics Volume 11, edited by R. Z. LeGeros and J.P. LeGeros
(Proceedings of the 11th International Symposium on Ceramics in Medicine)
New York, NY, USA, November 1998
© 1998 by World Scientific Publishing Co. Pte. Ltd.

MONOCYTES, MACROPHAGES AND FOREIGN BODY GIANT CELLS ON BIOMATERIAL SURFACES: THE FOREIGN BODY REACTION

James M. Anderson, M.D., Ph.D.

Institute of Pathology, Case Western Reserve University, Cleveland, OH 44106

The inflammatory and healing responses to biomaterials are characterized by the development of a foreign body reaction consisting of macrophages and foreign body giant cells (FBGC) at the tissue/biomaterial interface (Figure 1). To better understand the mechanism of formation of the foreign body reaction and its potential role in the success or failure of biomaterials, we have carried out studies on lymphokine induced foreign body giant cell formation on biomaterials. These studies address the hypothesis that the monocyte/macrophage (MC/MO) is the major cellular component controlling the tissue/material inflammatory and healing responses and that surfaces with variable chemistries can selectively affect the activation, function and cytokine production of adherent macrophages and FBGCs.

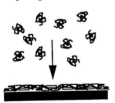

Protein Adsorption
- Affinity
- Concentration
- Denaturing
- Vroman Effect

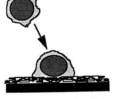

Monocyte Adhesion
- Integrins
- ECM signals

Macrophage Development
- Cytokine Signaling
- Cytoplasmic Spreading
- Cell Receptor Upregulation

FBGC Formation
- Membrane Fusion
- Phagocytic Mechanism
- Implant Degradation

Figure 1. The inflammatory response at tissue/material interfaces.

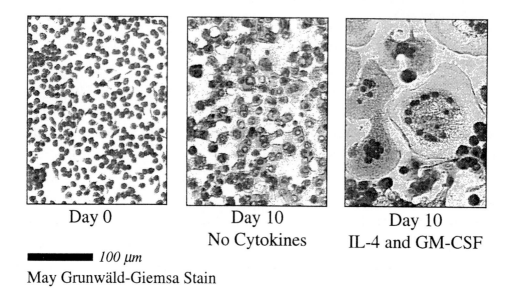

Day 0   Day 10   Day 10
                         No Cytokines   IL-4 and GM-CSF

■■■■■■ *100 μm*

May Grunwäld-Giemsa Stain

Figure 2. Typical *in vitro* results from monocyte/macrophage culture on molecular engineered surfaces which facilitate FBGC formation.

In studying the effect of preadsorbed proteins on FBGC formation, fibronectin or vitronectin do not play major roles in initial monocyte/macrophage adhesion, whereas polystyrene surfaces modified with RGD exhibited significant FBGC formation (Table II). These studies identify the potential importance of surface chemistry-dependent conformational alterations which may occur in proteins adsorbed to surfaces and their potential involvement in receptor-ligand interactions. Significantly, preadsorption of α_2-macroglobulin facilitated macrophage fusion and FBGC formation readily on the RGD surface in the absence of any additional serum proteins. As α_2-macroglobulin receptors are not found on blood monocytes but are expressed only with macrophage development, these results point to a potential interaction between adsorbed α_2-macroglobulin and its receptors on macrophages during macrophage development and fusion.

Table II. Comparison of Macrophage Fusion[a] on Polystyrene Versus
RGD-Modified Polystyrene. Effect of the Addition of Serum

Surface	% Autologous Serum Added[b]			
	0	1	5	10
PS[c]	3±3	75±5	78±9	73±3
RGD[d]	99±1	63±5	83±4	88±2

We have recently demonstrated that differential lymphokine regulation of macrophage fusion leads to morphological variants of multinucleated giant cells (FBGC). Interleukin-4 (IL-4) and interleukin-13 (IL-13) have been shown to independently promote monocyte/macrophage fusion to form FBGC, whereas interferon-ɣ has been demonstrated to form Langhans-type giant cells (1,2). IL-4 and IL-13 are secreted predominantly by Th2 lymphocytes and suggest a role for lymphocytes, present during the transient chronic inflammatory response, in the development of foreign body giant cells. *In vivo* studies using the rat cage implant system and a polyurethane together with IL-4 neutralizing antibodies and recombinant murine IL-4 demonstrated a role for IL-4 in FBGC formation (3). Confocal immunofluorescent studies demonstrated the upregulation of the macrophage mannose receptor (MMR) activity by IL-4 or IL-13 (4). IL-4 induced macrophage fusion and giant cell formation was prevented by competitive inhibitors of MMR activity, i.e. ᵅ-mannan, or inhibitors of glycoprotein processing that restrict MMR surface expression. To elucidate the mechanisms involved in monocyte/macrophage adhesion and fusion to form foreign body giant cells on molecularly engineered surfaces, we have utilized our *in vitro* culture system (Figure 2) to examine surface chemistry effects, cytoskeletal reorganization and adhesive structure development, and cell receptor-ligand interactions in *in vitro* foreign body giant cell formation. Utilizing silane-modified surfaces, monocyte/macrophage adhesion was essentially unaffected by surface chemistry, however the density of foreign body giant cells (FBGCs) was correlated with surface carbon content. An exception to the surface-independent macrophage adhesion were the alkyl-silane modified surfaces which exhibited reduced adhesion and FBGC formation. Utilizing confocal immunofluorescent techniques, cytoskeletal reorganization and adhesive structure development in *in vitro* FBGC formation was studied. Podosomes were identified as the adhesive structures in macrophages and FBGCs based on the presence of characteristic cytoplasmic proteins and F-actin at the ventral cell surface (Table I). Focal adhesion kinase (FAK) and focal adhesions were not identified as the adhesive structures in macrophages and FBGCs.

Table I. Macrophage and FBGC Podosome Protein Organization

Protein	Ring-like structure around actin core	Co-localization with actin core
Vinculin	+	-
Talin	+	-
Paxillin	+	-
Gelsolin	-	+
L-plastin	-	+
FAK	-	-

[a]Macrophage fusion values represent the percentage of nuclei in
multinucleated foreign body giant cells compared to the total
numbers of nuclei counted in three 10x objective fields.
[b]Monocytes were plated in 20% autologous serum (1).
[c]Polystyrene Plastek M (Mat Tek Corp.).
[d]RGD-modified polystyrene (Chemicon).

The overall goal of our research is to develop an understanding of the mechanisms of monocyte/macrophage adhesion, macrophage activation, macrophage fusion to form foreign body giant cells, and foreign body giant cell function on implanted biomaterial surfaces. Information and perspectives gained from these studies will provide biologically derived design criteria for surface modification of substrates which will modulate these cell/surface interactions in a fashion appropriate to the desired tissue engineered device or molecularly engineered surface.

ACKNOWLEDGMENT

This effort was supported by National Institutes of Health Grants HL-33849 and HL-55714.

REFERENCES

1.   McNally AK, Anderson JM. *Am J Pathol* 1995; **147**: 1487-1499.

2.   DeFife KM, Jenney CR, McNally AK, Colton E, Anderson JM. *J Immunol* 1997; **158**: 3385-3390.

3.   Kao WJ, McNally AK, Hiltner A, Anderson JM. *J Biomed Mater Res* 1995; **29**: 1267-1275.

4.   McNally AK, DeFife KM, Anderson JM. *Am J Pathol* 1996; **149**: 975-985.

Bioceramics Volume 11, edited by R. Z. LeGeros and J.P. LeGeros
(Proceedings of the 11th International Symposium on Ceramics in Medicine)
New York, NY, USA, November 1998
© 1998 by World Scientific Publishing Co. Pte. Ltd.

CELLS AND MATERIALS INTERACTIONS

U. Gross, C. Müller-Mai* and C. Voigt*

Institute of Pathology and Department of Traumatology and Reconstructive Surgery*
University Hospital Benjamin Franklin, Free University of Berlin
Hindenburgdamm 30, D 12200 Berlin, Germany

ABSTRACT

The interaction of cells and tissues beginns immediately after insertion of implant materials into the body of a host. The potential of reactions from the host cells and tissues are limited. The cell systems involved vary in the course of time in number and activity. Therefore, a sequence of materials can be generated according to cellular reactivity. The relative reactivity was postulated as a measure of cell number and activity. The major role of macrophages in the system of reactive cells is well established. The reason for the presence of macrophages at the interface of some specific materials and not in others is poorly understood.

From experimental and clinical data regenerating tissues near sites of cell necrosis are well known. The circumstances for tissue regeneration at sites of ceramic implant materials are investigated in this study. Examples are especially resorbable Bioglasses®, calcium phosphates and calcium carbonates. Some changes in the surface and subsurface structure of materials due to leaching and diffusion are documented. A crucial point is the sequence of interactions of different cell lines at the interface that control the development or absorption of extracellular matrix and resorbable material. There are models and suggestions for further principles in engineering "intelligent" materials.

KEYWORDS: Interface, ceramics, calcium phosphates, Bioglass®, bone development, bone resorption, .

There is only a limited body of knowledge on the early events after insertion of a foreign body into a tissue , e.g. a hole in a bone [1]. From a pathological point of view, there are four phases, 1. blood clot formation at the material surface, 2. organization of the blood clot and development of organization tissue, 3. regeneration of tissue specific for the implantation site, 4. remodeling of the regenerated tissue. These phases vary depending on the type of implant, the different materials properties and especially the surface reactivity[2]. The mechanisms involved can be divided further in host and materials response and will be observed here separately.

Tissue response
There is much more assumption and less measurements on what is occuring at the surface of a material immediately after being inserted at the implantation site. It is reasonable to assume that there is contact with blood, since the insertion of an implant into any tissue without a lesion of blood or lymph vessels can hardly be imagined. There are indeed some few experiments in which the adsorbed proteins were recovered from implant surfaces and analysed for composition of blood

constituents[3]. There is a possibility of fibrinolysis by appropriate activation of this step in the coagulation cascade. On the other hand fibrin and other proteins can be degradated by macrophages which are among the first cells to appear at the surfaces. The number of macrophages can vary considerably. There are implant materials which do attract only a few of these cells, e.g. KG Cera and Bioglass®45s5 [4]. Other materials display quite a considerable number of macrophages for a prolonged time. At the surface of the mentioned surface reactive materials the macrophages apparently loose their interest in the materials surfaces after some days. When they disappear mesenchymal cells settle in the neighbourhood of the materials and differentiate into fibroblasts or osteoblasts. The events that are observed are corresponding to the physiological process of bone remodeling.

In the case of bone remodeling a specific sequence of cellular activities is postulated and observed, i.e. activation of local mesenchymal cells, resorption of bone by osteoclasts, formation of bone by osteoblasts [5-7]. It is reasonable to assume that bone bonding to implant material whether metal, ceramic or polymer, proceeds along the lines which are in operation during the whole lifetime of an individual. During fracture healing there is a repetition of basic mechanisms of bone development during regeneration [8,9]. To discriminate between bone deposition in a field of resorption lacunae and the deposition of primary bone seems to be important. In the first case a reversal line is being made and above this line regular lamellar bone structure is observed as documented brilliantly[10]. The morphological stages are described: 1. the initial organic matrix, 2. the seeding of calcium phosphate crystallites, 3. crystal growth and collagen assembly, 4. collagen calcification and matrix mineralization. Some biochemical analysis contributed to the knowledge of these structures especially the usage of immunohistochemistry in an electron microscopical level [11]. Non-collagenous proteins of bone were accumulated at the interface of hydroxyapatite (HA), e.g. osteocalcin, osteopontin, as well as two plasma proteins alpha2HS-glycoprotein (fetuin) and albumin. The structural identity of this type of interface with a lamina limitans was documented. There are many more substances than those already demonstrated as cellular products in the extracellular matrix. They are, however, not yet clearly attributed to the cells of origin in demonstrating the whole sequence of activation of certain genes, making of transcripts, demonstration of translated products and their intracellular or extracellular appearance and interaction with other cell types. There is up to now only a limited number of investigations dealing with transcripts and with their products within cells and in the ECM [12].

The sequences of cellular activation can be influenced by material which is leached from the materials surfaces and by particles derived from the implant. An example is given with highly degradable bone bonding implant materials where typical cement lines do not develop (Figures 1 and 2).

Material response

The different solubility of materials is well known and documented quantitatively [13]. In the case of bioactive materials different processes contribute to degradation, e.g. leaching of substances and subsequent liberation of particles that can lead to severe tissue response especially by activation of macrophages after phagocytosis of particles and subsequent release of cytokines [14].

The cytokines released significantly influence the tissue response, i.e. if a certain amount of particles is released from an implant the release of factors from activated macrophages leads in turn to a release of factors from osteoblasts, e.g. interleukin 1 (IL1), IL6 or PG E_2. The latter factor is known to stimulate resorptive processes by activation of cells of the osteoclastic lineage [14,15]. This cascade of events was proposed to lead to aseptical loosening of total hip prostheses. A study using the newer technique of in-situ-hybridization demonstrated the cytokines in activated cells near the prostheses [16]. Beside the processes described, active degradation, i.e. bioresorption of implants was described. Especially hydroxyapatite, ß-tricalciumphosphate and other calcium-phosphate ceramics as well as calcium carbonate materials are targets of osteoclastic cells [17,18]. By this cellular resorption a certain surface morphology results to which osteoblasts are familiar [19].

There are deficits in knowledge regarding the interaction of different cell lines. It is not sufficient to know a specific cell product, e.g. a transcript, or a specific protein in a cell or already secreted in the extracellular matrix. It would be necessary to know the cellular targets, e.g. receptors and intracellular pathways and regulatory systems for gene activation or deactivation.

A new idea is to incorporate molecules in polymeric matrices which are doted with apatite and to observe a release of these molecules when the implants are degraded [20]. If these released molecules have a pharmacological potential, a specific effect can be seen at the implantation site [21]. By an appropriate composition of components in a material the dissolution or degradation rate can be determined and the release of components predicted. An example for such type of release is given by compounds of $Ca_2KNa(PO_4)_2$. The in vitro and in vivo degradation of the material was analysed as demonstrated in Table 1 and Figures 3 and 4. A decisive progress can be reached by engineering of such composite materials that are degraded in relation to the development of a tissue regenerate of a certain type and quality. In the case of bone the degradation should pace with the development of bone. The demonstrated $Ca_2KNa(PO_4)_2$-compounds could be together with other calciumphosphates, glasses and glass ceramics candidates in this concept.

Table 1. Composition and in vitro solubility of materials GB14 and GB18 and ß-TCP.

Material		composition wt%				solubility (mg/L)
						pH 7,4; 37 °C
	CaO	MgO	P2O5	Na2O	K2O	0,2 M TRIS-HCL
ß-TCP	54,24	0	45,76	0	0	30,6 ± 5
GB14	30,67	2,45	43,14	9,42	14,32	430 ± 40
GB18	17,72	12,74	44,86	9,79	14,88	1800 ± 80

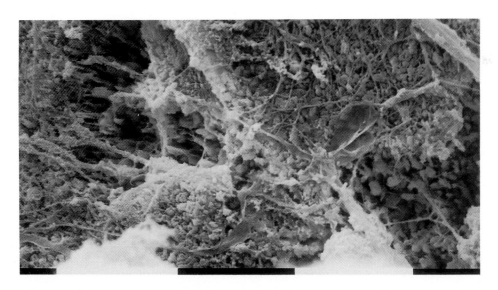

Figure 1. At 7 days natural calcium carbonate displays after implantation into the trabecular bone of the distal femur epiphysis of rabbits enlargement of the internal fine structure and deposition of granular and fibrillar material at the surface. Scanning electron micrograph. Bar 10 μm.

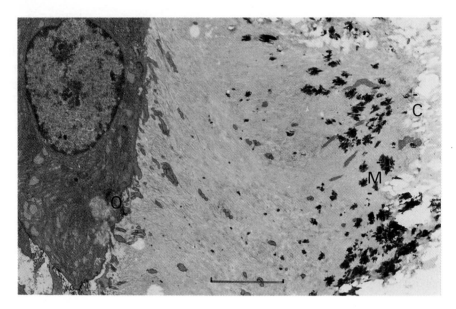

Figure 2. Natural calcium carbonate (Biocoral®) was implanted into the femur of a male rat, retrieved after 14 days and prepared for transmission electron microscopy. Voids are seen where the coral material (C) was dissolved during preparation. Adjacent deposition of collagen fibers and matrix vesicle mineralization (M). Active osteoblast (O). Bar 3.2 µm.

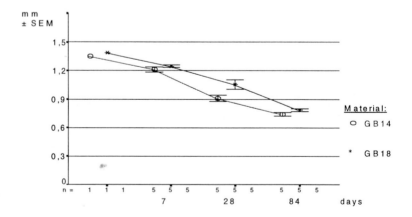

Figure 3.Particles of GB14 and GB18 were implanted in the distal femur of female adult rabbits retrieved after 7, 28 and 84 days, processed for undecalcified sawed sections and morphometrically evaluated. The boundaries are given. SEM = Standad error of the mean.

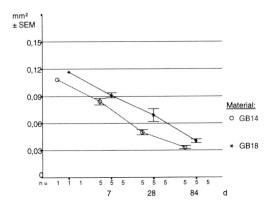

Figure 4. The areas of the particles were determined morphometrically.

AKNOWLEDGEMENTS
The material GB14 and GB18 was kindly provided by Dr. G. Berger, Federal Institute for Testing and Research of Materials, D 12200 Berlin. Biocoral® was kindly provided by Dr. J. L. Patat, Inoteb, F93400 Saint Ouen.

REFERENCES
1. Gross U, Müller-Mai C.In Yamamuro T,Hench LL,Wilson J,eds.Handbook of Bioactive Ceramics,Vol I, Boca Raton,FL,USA,1990:25-39.
2. Hench LL.In Kokubo T,Nakamura T,Miyaji F, eds. Bioceramics Vol 9 Elsevier Science,Tokyo 1996:3-6.
3.Williams DF,Askill IN,Smith R,J Biomed Mater Res 1985; **19**: 313-320.
4. Müller-Mai C,Voigt C, Knarse W,Sela J,Gross UM, Biomaterials 1991;**12**:865-871.
5. Hattner R,Epker BN,Frost HM,*Nature* (London) 1965; **206**:489-490.
6. Frost HM, Angle Orthod 1994;**64**: 175-188.
7. Frost HM, Anat Rec 1990;**226**:414-422.
8. Reddi H, J Biomed Mater Res 1985; **19**: 233-239.
9. Reddi H, Cytokine & Growth Factor Reviews 1997;**8**:11-20.
10.Davies JE, Anat Rec 1996; **245**:426-445.
11.Kawaguchi H, McKee MD, Okamoto H, Nanci A, Cells and Materials 1993; **3**: 337-350.
12.Neo M,Voigt CF,Herbst H,Gross UM, J Biomed Mater Res 1996; **30**:485-492.
13.Hench LL,Wilson J,An Introduction to Bioceramics.Singapore:World Scientific,1993:1-24.
14.Greenfield EM, Alvarez JI, et al., Calcif Tissue Int 1992;**51**:317-323.
15.Horowitz SM, Rapuano BP, Lane JM, Burstein AH, Calcif Tissue Int 1994; **54**:320-324.
16.Goodman SB, Knoblich G,O`Connor M, Song Y, Huie P, Sibley R, J Biomed Mater Res 1996; **31**:421-428.
17.Müller-Mai CM,Voigt C, Gross U, Scanning Microsc 1990; **4**:613-624.
18.Müller-Mai C, Voigt C, De Almeida Reis SR, Herbst H, Gross UM, J Mater Sci: Mater Med 1996; **7**:479-488.
19.Boyde A, Jones SJ, Microscopy Res & Technique 1996;**33**:92-120.
20.Müller-Mai C, Stupp SI, Voigt C, Gross U, J Biomed Mater Res 1995;**29**:9-18.
21.Gross UM, Stupp SI, Suhrbur M, Fang V, Müller-Mai C, Voigt C, Trans 21 Ann Meet Soc Biomaterials 1995:239.

Bioceramics Volume 11, edited by R. Z. LeGeros and J.P. LeGeros
(Proceedings of the 11th International Symposium on Ceramics in Medicine)
New York, NY, USA, November 1998
© 1998 by World Scientific Publishing Co. Pte. Ltd.

BONE/BIOCERAMIC INTERFACE

H. Oonishi[1], T. Sugihara[2], E. Tsuji[3], L. L. Hench[4] and J. Wilson[4]

[1]Dept. of Orthhopaedic Surgery, Artificial Joint Section and Biomaterial Research Laboratory,
 Osaka-Minami National Hospital, 2-1, Kidohigashimachi, Kawachinagano-Shi, Osaka, 586-0008,
 JAPAN
[2]Nitta Gelatin Inc. Research and Laboratory Center 2-22, Futamata Yao, Osaka, 581-0024, JAPAN
[3]Osaka Prefectural Industrial Engineering Research Institute, 2-7-1, Ayomino, Izumi-Shi, Osaka,
 JAPAN
[4]Dept. of Materials, Imperial College of Science, Technology and Medicine Prince Consort Road,
 London SW7 2BP,UK

ABSTRACT

Several kinds and bioceramic materials and bioactive bone cements were implanted into 6 mm diameter holes made in the femoral condyles of mature rabbits. Bioactive bioactive bone cements included: surface bioactive, all bioactive and interface bioactive bone cements. Bioceramics included were bioinert ceramics (alumina); surface bioactive ceramics (HA, A-W GC and Bioglass[R]), and resorbable bioactive ceramics (TetCP, α-TCP, ß-TCP, DCPD, DCPA, low crystaline HA and OCP). Granule sizes of 100-300 μm and 10 μm were used.

Bone/bioceramics interface reaction and bone growth behavior varied with regards to the kind of bioceramic and the size used.

Keywords: bioactive ceramics, bioglass, AW-glass, calcium phosphates, interface

INTRODUCTION

In this study the interface reactions of Ca-P bioactive bone cement and fine granules of several sizes of several kinds of bioceramics to the bone are discussed. Bioactive bone cements are classified in function into the following three groups: (1) Surface bioactive bone cement (SBBC): bioactive function only the surface; (2) All bioactive bone cement (ABBC): complete bioactive function; and (3) Interface bioactive bone cement (IBBC): bioactive function at the interface between bone and cement [1]. Bioceramics can be divided in to three categories: (1) Bioinert ceramics: alumina, zirconia etc. (2) Surface bioactive ceramics: sintered hydroxyapatite (HA); Bioglass[R] and A-W glass ceramics; and (3) Resorbable bioactive ceramics: low crystaline HA, α-TCP, ß-TCP, TetCP, OCP, DCPD, DCPA, etc. [2-7]. When bioactive cement and particles of these bioceramics are implanted into bone, interface reactions, bone growth behavior and reaction to the bone are assumed to be different due to variation in the properties and composition of the materials.

MATERIALS

A. Bioactive bone cement

(1) *Surface bioactive bone cement (SBAB)*

α-TCP was kneaded with a hardening solution containing non-fibrillar type atelocollagen 0.5%, citric acid 34.6%, and malonic acid 5.4% at a powder to liquid ratio of 2.5(g/ml) to give a cement (slurry form).

(2) *All bioactive bone cement (ABAB)*

TetCP porous particles, 300 μm diameter or less, alone and TetCP mixed with DCPD at equivalent mole ratio were kneaded with physiological saline.

(3) Interface bioactive bone cement (IBBC)

0 to 2 layers of HA particles of 100 to 300 μm are interposed between bone and bone cement (PMMA).

B. Bioceramic particles

Alumina; hydroxyapatite (HA) sintered at 1200°C ($Ca_{10}(PO_4)_6(OH_2)$; Bioglass[R], A-W glass ceramics; low crystalline HA, α-tricalcium phosphate (α-TCP, $Ca_3(PO_4)_2$), ß-tricalcium phosphate (ß-TCP, $Ca_3(PO_4)_2$), tetracalcium phosphate (TetCP, $Ca_4O(PO_4)_2$), octacalcium phosphate (OCP, $Ca_8H_2(PO_4).5H_2O$), dicalcium phosphate dihydrate (DCPD, $CaHPO_4.2H_2O$) and dicalcium phosphate anhydrous (DCPA, $CaHPO_4$) were used. The granule size was 100-300 μm in diameter. The porosity of the bioactive ceramics was near 65%.

METHODS

Drilled holes 6 mm in diameter were made bilaterally in the femoral condyles of mature rabbits, and materials were placed in sufficient amounts to fill the holes. As IBBC, PMMA bone cement was filled immediately after smearing HA particles on the bone surface. Three animals were used for each time period. The animals were killed at intervals; non-decalcified specimens were observed by light microscopy and backscattered electron imaging, and decalcified specimens observed by light microscopy. As a control, unfilled drilled holes were made.

RESULTS AND DISCUSSION

A. Bioactive Bone Cements

(1) *Surface bioactive bone cement (SBBC):* One week after implantation, the cement began to bond to the bone in some parts. Identified homogeneous substances with a thickness of 200 μm were observed between the α-TCP granules and the bone, and they directly attached to the bone. This zone was confirmed by micro X-ray diffraction analysis to be HA that had replaced the α-TCP. The boundary of the interface between bone and HA zone was indistinct. At three and six weeks, the thickness of the HA zone was about 300 and 500 μm, respectively. The periphery of the cement was surrounded by new trabecular bone even in the area where the bone did not exist anatomically (Fig. 1).

(2) *All bioactive bone cement (ABBC):* At one week, new bone tissues approached and bound to portions of the periphery of TetCP from its surrounding region. At 3 weeks, laminar new bone tissues were formed at about 200-300 μm in width from the base of the bone. TetCP in the vicinity of the new bone was found to be gradually replaced by these new bone tissues from its external circumference. TetCP fine granules gathered together and formed small trabecular-like structures, and new bone tissues grew into spaces between these small trabecular-like structures.

(3) *Interface bioactive bone cement (IBBC):* At one week, bone growth began to enter the spaces of HA particles. At six weeks, bone growth was accomplished.

B. Bioceramic particles

(1) Control: At three weeks and also at six weeks, the density of bone formation in the unfilled hole is very low. At twelve seeks, the cancellous bone formation in the cavity returned to physiological condition.

Fig. 1: Surface bioactive bone cement, 6 weeks.

(2) *Bioinert Ceramics*

     (a) Alumina , Al_2O_3, particle size, 100 μm in diameter.

At four weeks, new bone ingrowth into spaces between alumina granules to the center of the hole were observed. The new bone never contacted the alumina granules[1](Figure 2).

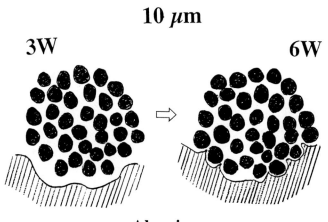

Fig. 2: Alumina (10 μm), 3, 6 weeks.

(3) *Surface Bioactive Ceramics*

     (i) Sintered Hydroxyapatite, HA, $Ca_{10}(PO_4)_6(OH)_2$, particle size, 100-300 μm diameter.

At one week new trabecular bone grew into spaces between HA particles from the surrounding bone and reached the outermost layer of HA particles. At three weeks, new bone tissues reached the sixth and seventh layers while at the same time enclosing HA particles to a depth of 1000 μm. At six weeks, spaces less than 20m at initial implantation were almost completely filled with new bone tissues. On the other hand, spaces larger than 100 μm had no new bone tissues growing from surrounding bone (Figure 3).

(ii) Bioglass[R], particle size, 100 μm in diameter

At two days, the periphery of Bioglass[R] in the outermost layer became silica-rich, and to which in some areas new bone had formed. At five days, new bone penetrated most of the first two layers. Bioglass bound directly to bone. At twelve days, new bone entered and surrounded most surfaces of Bioglass particles as far as the eighth and tenth outer layers. At six weeks, all particles were enveloped with thick new trabecular bone and very few spaces remained unfilled. In summation, the speed of bone growth around Bioglass particles was much faster and the new bone was much denser than bone growth associated with HA [2,3,4] (Fig. 3).

(iii) A-W glass ceramics.

The grade of the speed and the density of bone growth in to A-W-GC was higher than that of HA and lower than that of Bioglass.

(4) *Resorbable Bioactive Ceramics*

(i) TetCP, DCPD, DCPA, granules size, 100-300 μm in diameter.

TetCP, DCPD and DCPA showed almost the same reactions. At three weeks, new laminar bone formed from the bone base. Ca-P in the vicinity of this new bone began to be slowly replaced by more new bone from the periphery. At the edge of these Ca-P crystals, new bone was slowly taking the place of the Ca-P from three weeks, and the configuration of some crystals was unclear, while others were hardly distinguishable from the new surrounding bone after twelve weeks [5] (Figs. 3,4).

(ii) α-TCP and ß-TCP, granules size, 100-300 μm in diameter.

α-TCP and ß-TCP showed almost the same reactions. At three weeks, laminar new bone tissue of 100-200 μm in width formed from the bone. The density of distribution of the travecular bone was high. At six weeks, over half the mass of the α-, ß-TCP granules was absorbed, and a density of the distribution of the trabecular bone became lower. The interface between α-, ß-TCP granules and bone was rather distinct, which was different from the changes of TetCP (Figs. 3,4).

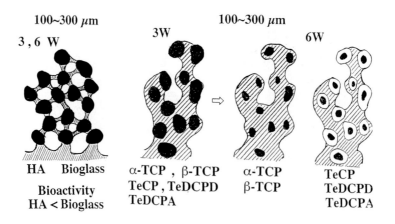

Fig. 3: Bioactive ceramics (100-300 μm), 3, 6 weeks.

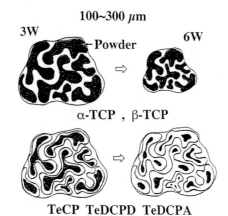

Fig. 4: Bioactive ceramics (100-300 μm), 3, 6 weeks.

(iii) TetCP, α-TCP, ß-TCP, DCPD and DCPA, granules of 10 μ diameter.
TetCP, α-TCP, ß-TCP, DCPD and DCPA of 10 μ diameter, showed similar reactions. At three weeks, few bone growth into the spaces of the Ca-P granules was seen around the Ca-P masses. At six weeks, bone growth into the spaces of Ca-P granules was seen only around Ca-P mass, however, new bone surrounding Ca-P mass increased. However, TetCP DCPD and DCPA showed behavior little different from α-TCP and ß-TCP. TetCP, DCPD and DCPA powders of 10 μm diameter were being taken into the trabecular bone little by little, surrounding Ca-P mass, and being replaced by new trabecular bone (Fig. 5).

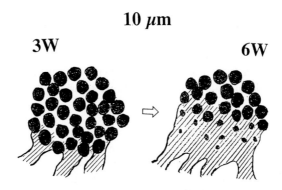

Fig. 5: Bioactive ceramics (10 μm), 3, 6 weeks.

(iv) Low crystalline HA and OCP, granules of 10 μm diameter.
Low crystaline HA and OCP granules of 10 μm diameter showed the similar behavior. At three weeks, laminar new bone tissue of 50-150 μm in width had started to form. The travecular new bone were being developed with these Ca-P granules. At six weeks, the new bone developed with these Ca-P granules to the center of the hole, Ca-P granules were being replaced by the new bone from the peripheries of the granules, and the number granules diminished (Fig. 6).

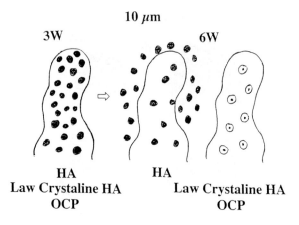

Fig. 6: Bioactive ceramics (10 μm), 3, 6 weeks.

CONCLUSION

HA replaces α-TCP and attaches to the bone at the periphery of SBAB cement. IBBC binds the bone cement to the bone physicochemically by interposing HA. In surface bioactive ceramics, Bioglass was more bioactive than HA. In resorbanle bioactive ceramics, the observed order of greater bioactivity of probability of greater resorbability, were as follows: low crystaline HA and OCP > TetCP, DCPD, and DCPA > α-TCP and ß-TCP. In terms of biocompatibility, α-TCP was more bioacompatible than ß-TCP.

REFERENCES

1.   Oonishi, H.: *The Bone Biomaterial Interface.* Davies JE (ed), University of Toronto Press 1991, 321-333

2.   Oonishi, H., Tsuji, E., Mizukoshi, T., Kushitani, S., Aono, M., Minami, K., Watanabe, A., Ogino, A. and Fujisawa, N.: *Bioceramics Vol.4*, Butterworth-Heinman Ltd., 1991, 191-197.

3.   Oonishi, H., Tsuji, E., Kushitani, S., Aono, M., Minami, K. and Hidaka, T.: *Bioceramics Vol 5*, 1992, 149-153.

4.   Wilson, J. and Low, S. J. : Appl. Biom. 1992, 123-129.

5.   Wilson, J., Beatle, B. S. : Bioceramics Vol. 5, Kobunshi Kankokai, Japan, 1992, 139-146.

6.   Oonishi, H., Kushitani, S., Murata, N., Saito, M., Maruoka, A., Yasukawa E., Tsuji, E. and Sugihara, F. : Bioceramics-6, Butterworth-Heinman Ltd., 1993, 159-161.

7.   Oonishi, H., Kushitani, S., Yasukawa, E., Nakata, A., Koh, S., Hench, L. L., Wilson, J., Tsuji, E. and Sugihara, T, : Bioceramics-7, Butterworth-Heinman Ltd., 1994, 139-144.

II. BIOCERAMICS: PRESENT AND FUTURE

Bioceramics Volume 11, edited by R. Z. LeGeros and J.P. LeGeros
(Proceedings of the 11th International Symposium on Ceramics in Medicine)
New York, NY, USA, November 1998

BIOACTIVE GLASSES: PRESENT AND FUTURE

L. L Hench and J. Wilson

Department of Materials, imperial College of Science. Technology and Medicine Prince Consort Rd., London SW 7 2BP

ABSTRACT

Bioactive implants currently in clinical use as bulk devices or coatings, include dental, orthopedic, maxillo-facial-cranial, and ENT applications. Bioactive glasses, as particulates, are now widely used in repair of bone defects resulting from periodontal disease. The bioactive glass particles lead to rapid proliferation of new bone through a process termed osteoproduction. Use of this osteogenic behavior of bioactive glasses is the basis of a new direction in biomaterials research: the regeneration of tissues. Addition of a rapidly resorbable saccharide-based polymer (dextran) to the bioactive particles makes it possible to control rheology for use in injectable systems for minimally invasive surgery or as a moldable material for filling large defects in bone. Evidence that the bioactive glass particles do not migrate either locally or distantly from defect sites is reviewed. Use of sol-gel processing of bioactive gel-glasses makes it possible to control texture and surface chemistry for use as a resorbable material in tissue regeneration.

KEYWORDS : 45S5 Bioactive glass, regeneration. osteoproduction, migration

INTRODUCTION: THE PRESENT

During the last 25 years the understanding of the mechanisms of bonding of bone and soft connective tissues to bioactive glasses have increased greatly[1,2]. Differences in the mechanism and rate of bone bonding have led to a distinction between bioactive materials with high levels of bioactivity that bond to both bone and soft tissues, Class A bioactive materials.[1,2] and materials with intermediate to low levels of bioactivity which bond only to bone Class B bioactive materials (Table 1)[1,2]. This understanding has expanded use of these materials in numerous clinical applications, which have been discussed in the proceedings of the previous four Bioceramics conferences.

Clinical applications of Class A, bulk 45S5 bioactive glass devices include [3,4]:

    Middle ear prostheses for replacement of ossicles
    Endosseous ridge maintenance implants for augmentation of the alveolar ridge for denture wearers

The statistical survivability of Class A bioactive implants is substantially greater than Class B bioactive implants in the same application, almost entirely because of the importance of maintaining a stable soft tissue interface in these prostheses [3,4].

Clinical applications of 45S5 bioactive glass in the form of a particulate include[1-4]:

    Repair of bone defects associated with periodontal disease
    Repair of bone defects associated with oral and maxillo-facial surgery
    Augmentation of the alveolar ridge for use with dental implants
    Augmentation and repair of bone in orthopedic revision surgery
    Fusion of bone in spinal surgery
    Replacement of bone in iliac crest donor sites

A recent development, presented by Thompson et. al. in this volume, is use of a rapidly resorbable saccharide polymer. dextran, as a vehicle for controlling the rheology of the bioactive glass particulate. Small concentrations of dextram solution added to 45S5 bioactive particles produces a coherent mass which has the handling characteristics of P in the dough state, i.e. a moldable putty. The moldable material has a viscosity sufficiently high that it maintains its shape in a large pleomorphic bone defect. This paper reports that the dextran phase resorbs rapidly and does not affect the rate of bone proliferation which is the same as that of autogeneous bone, 45S5 alone, or a mixture of 45S5 particulate and autogeneous bone. The new moldable material exhibits Class A bioactivity (Table 1).

Wilson et al.[5] showed that a lower molecular weight range of dextran can be used to keep the bioactive glass particles in suspension and maintain them as separate particles while being injected into soft tissue, through a needle. The bioactive glass particles injected into a rabbit ear established a strong bond to the soft connective tissue and the dextran resorbed without any inflammatory response. The augmented soft tissue site was maintained at 80% during the one-year experiment whereas substantial amounts of collagen were resorbed within three months.

An important finding during the histological analyses of bone response to particles of 45S5 bioactive glass was the discovery of the phenomenon of osteoproduction.[6] Osteoproduction involves a rapid colonization of the surface of Class A bioactive particles by osteogenic stem cells. The cells rapidly proliferate and differentiate into osteoblasts which leads to rapid growth of new bone in the defect. The rate of bone growth is nearly three times that of bone growth in the presence of Class B synthetic HA particles.[7] The amount of newly formed bone in the presence of Class A bioactive glass particulate is more than twice that produced in the presence of HA particles.[7]

Table 1 summarizes the range of bioactive materials now available for clinical use, their relative values of bioactivity (determined as IB=100/time to develop a 50% bone-bonded interface), class of bioactivity and type of cellular response in a bone defect.

TABLE I

Material	IB	Class	Cellular Response	
45S5 Bioglass®	12.5	A	Bone and Soft Tissue	Osteoproductive Osteoconductive
Moldable Bioglass® Putty or Injectable	12.5	A	Bone and Soft Tissue	Osteoproductive Osteoconductive
Bioactive Gel-glass	.14	A	Bone and Soft Tissue	Osteoproductive Osteoconductive
A/W Bioactive glass-ceramic	6	B	Bone	Osteoconductive
Ceravital®	5	B	Bone	Osteoconductive
Hydroxyapatite ceramic	3	B	Bone	Osteoconductive
Alumina	0	None	None	Non-adherent capsule

TESTING OF MATERIALS FOR PARTICLE MIGRATION.

The expanded use of particulate bioactive glass, both with and without a resorbable polymer carrier, makes it increasingly important to have confidence that the particles will remain where they are placed during the time of tissue repair. In the past we concentrated on wear particles in bone. since we assumed that the first clinical application would be to provide non-cemented fixation for artificial hips. The complications, which arise as a result of the generation of particles in the artificial hip, are well documented. thus the first tests on bioactive glass particulates were done to investigate the tissue response to potential wear debris. The potential for migration in the lymphatic system of injected particulate must also be addressed.

If particles are present in tissues, effects may occur locally, as happens when metal or polymeric material is trapped around the stem of an artificial hip, or distally if the particle is ingested by a macrophage and transported in the lymphatic circulation until it becomes trapped in a lymph node or elsewhere.[8] The effect of the ingested particle on the macrophage is important, especially when the particle is of a man-made material. as are most biomaterials.

Materials may be classified by their effect on the macrophage, once ingested., as follows:
Class 1: If the material is relatively inert, as are some polymers and metals, it may be carried through the tissues without damaging them until eliminated from the lymphatic system by normal routes, that is by being swallowed or exhaled.

Class 2: If the material is toxic to the cell, as are quartz crystals and asbestos fibers, the consequences are severe since the toxic material is repeatedly ingested by successive waves of macrophages and progressive fibrosis, known as silicosis or asbestosis follows[9].

Class 3: If the material can be digested without harm to the cell, as with tissue debris or bone dust, the macrophage may complete the process locally with little involvement of the lymphatic system.

When considering potential migration, two factors must be considered:
1.   Are wear particles generated?
2.   If they are, do they provoke an adverse tissue response either locally or distantly?

It is now clear that wear particles are not produced by bioactive glasses, since the rapid development of the silica-rich gel layer produces a surface on the glass which covers any surface roughness with a compliant reaction layer, to which collagen is rapidly attached, eliminating relative movement which is the cause of wear.[1,2] This is the first step in the reaction of bioactive materials that distinguishes them from all others.

In an *in-vitro* test[10], primary cultures of rat peritoneal macrophages were exposed to 45S5 Bioglass ® particulates. In this test model, those materials in class 2 above kill more than 50% of the macrophages within 72 hours, and those in class 1, kill 10-20%. When Bioglass ® was tested the figure was 2-5%, the lowest of all materials tested[10]. Electron microscopy of macrophages from this test confirmed the presence of Bioglass® particles[10] (see figure 2 ref.10). In an *in- vivo* test a suspension in saline of the less than 40 μm Bioglass® particles, (of 45S5 and fluoride compositions), were injected into the peritoneal cavities of-rats[10]. After 1 and 2 weeks there was no peritonitis nor adhesions and all major organs were normal. Previous work had shown that the preferred route of excretion of particulate from the peritoneal cavity is via the subserous lymphatics of the diaphragm to the right lymphatic duct and the sternal lymph nodes." These lymph nodes were carefully examined and occasional macrophages containing eosinophil material were found. This may have represented fragments of the silica-gel reaction layer, which can stain in this way. There was no associated fibrosis. In a similar test particulate quartz produced marked lymph node fibrosis. [10]

In a test model designed to evaluate biomaterials by injection into the circulation, so that particles embolise in the lung where their intrinsic effects can be separated from those produced by the implantation procedure[12], Bioglass® particles could be seen, 6 weeks after implantation within a capillary without hindering the circulation (see figure 6 in ref. 10). In addition to these published studies Bioglass® particulate was implanted intramuscularly in rats and the drainage lymph nodes examined. Quartz of comparable size was used as a positive control. The drainage lymph nodes in the test animals were rarely identified correctly and those which were invariably normal. In the quartz group the lymph nodes were always enlarged and fibrotic. As a result of these tests we concluded that there was no hazard associated with bioactive glass particles, that they were treated by macrophages in the same way as the natural materials in class 3, above.

Migration of particles was never a consideration during the development and clinical testing of the bioactive glass devices, which are currently, available. Both solid implants (middle ear prostheses and endosseous ridge maintenance implants) and particulate Perioglas® were designed to be implanted in bone. When the migration problems of Polytef®, used for treatment of urinary incontinence and Proplast® became known, we tried to identify ways in which we could show that Bioglass® particles would not cause such problems, so included histological examination of the drainage lymph nodes, (when we could find them at autopsy) , sections of the major internal organs and the choroid plexus and also chemical digestion and analysis of these organs, for raised silicon levels. No evidence of Bioglass® particles, other than at the injection sites was ever found[13]. This has been confirmed by other workers using the same material.[14]

It is appropriate to consider the mechanism by which troublesome materials such as Polytef® and Proplast® have produced their effects and how they differ from bioactive materials. Both have been used to produce soft tissue augmentation and were successfully marketed for many years. The augmentation was achieved by the production of a granuloma in which the material was surrounded by a mass of phagocytic cells and fibrous tissue."" Such granulomas are inherently unstable and can break down and release the components. Both materials incorporated PTFE, which has, as its most notable property, an inability to adhere to anything. In Polytef® the particles of PTFE were so small, around 5 µm, that they could be immediately transported into the lymphatic system, as described above for class 1 materials. Although these effects were seen in animals, we are not aware of harmful effects in clinical use. The migration of the components of Proplast®, a composite material made from PTFE and carbon was the result of the breakdown of the material itself because of inappropriate use in load-bearing applications, notably as a temporo-mandibular joint replacement. The migration of the scraps of material was into the local soft tissues since they were too large to be transported effectively by macrophages. This material was withdrawn after serious clinical problems were found. The breakdown and local migration were clearly seen in some of our comparative studies in which it was used. [16.17]

These are, as far as we are aware, the two most visible cases of a biomaterial which had migration problems and in both cases the material was inert and did not adhere to surrounding tissue. The particle size is important since only those particles, which can be contained in a macrophage, can be transported into the lymphatics. This size limitation is around 15µm. Bioglass® particulates presently in clinical use for bone augmentation range from 90-710 µm and those particles, which do not become incorporated in bone, disappear from the site during the immediate post-implantation period. This is achieved by a combination of dissolution and removal by phagocytes of those smallest particles, which convert entirely to the gel-layer before they become surrounded by collagen and are thus protected. The excretion of the silica gel produced by these processes has been followed in metabolic studies and has been shown to be removed through the kidneys at levels which never exceed physiological.[14]

The following conclusions regarding migration of bioactive particles can be made from the published data:
1)Long-term clinical use of solid implants in bone, now up to 14 years, has produced no evidence of wear particles nor associated migration. (2) Long-term clinical use of a particulate with a size distribution of 90-710µm in bone has produced no evidence of migration of the smaller particles. Because osteoblasts require silicon, calcium and phosphorus to produce new bone, the particulate is incorporated in the repair and eventually is used up. Experimental studies on this size-range suggest that the smallest particles are converted to the silica-gel layer in the immediate post-implantation period, fragments may be ingested by macrophages and digested without effect as are tissue fragments also during the same period.[6] Bioglass® particles in bone do not migrate, they are incorporated into new bone. (3) In soft tissue, particles at the lower end of this range, 125-355 µm, persists for at least one year since the particulate is not incorporated into connective tissue but produces an effect by its physical presence.[5,13] Although it is possible that not all of the material is retained, any which is removed must be by the mechanisms described above, since no evidence of

migration has been detected. (4) Bioglass® particles in soft tissue are too large to be ingested and transported by macrophages. The only material, which may be ingested, is the reaction (silica-gel) layer, which is digested without harm to the cell. (5) The inherent bioactivity of Bioglass® actively prevents migration both locally and systemically.

The finding that bioactive glasses can be implanted as particle . s where they remain without migration. progressively resorb and lead to rapid proliferation of new bone offers an exciting new direction for the field of biomaterials: the potential for regeneration of tissues.

THE FUTURE

We propose that the emphasis of biomaterials research for the next millenium should focus on use of material that behaves in an implant site in a manner equivalent to an autograft; i.e., a regenerative allograft. Advances in developmental biology, genetic engineering, cellular and tissue engineering, imaging and quantitative *in-situ* diagnostics, provide information that can be used to tailor regenerative bioactive materials. Molecular level control of the texture of hierarchical materials is now possible, using sol-gel processing over a dimensional scale from manometers to millimeters.[1,18] The biological responses to chemical extracts of bioactive glasses and gel-glasses from the $CaO-P_2O_5-SiO_2$ system pro-vide evidence that tissue regeneration is feasible, especially in bone. Recent reviews summarize these findings and discuss possible cellular mechanisms responsible for the rapid bone proliferation.[1,18] The hypothesis is that bioactive glasses provide both an intracellular stimulus to the cells, to enhance osteoblast stem cell proliferation differentiation[1,2,19] and an extracellular environment that is compatible with adsorption and desorption of biologically active enzymes and growth factors. [18,20] Two recent studies by Xynos et al. 21,21 provide evidence that this hypothesis is valid. The response of primary human osteoblasts to Class A 45S5 bioactive glass and 58S bioactive gel-glasses were compared with four different Class B hydroxyapatite-tricalcium phosphate composites of various Ca/P ratios, and two bioinert materials, borosilicate glass and zirconia. Of the materials tested 58S bioactive gel-glass provided the strongest and most rapid cell attachment for the osteoblasts in addition to an ability to stimulate cell membrane activity. The results suggest increased osteoblast chemotaxis. In the second study, they showed that growth of primary human osteoblasts exposed to 45S5 bioactive glass was enhanced and differentiation of cells to the osteoblast phenotype, was stimulated by the Class A bioactive material. There was a clear shift in the cultures from the diploid, resting phase (G) to the premitotic (S) and the apoptotic (sub-GI) phase as a result of 24 hr stimulation. Another recent study by Maroothymaden et al., in this proceedings, has shown that mouse fetal femurs grown on Class A bioactive glasses exhibit greatly enhanced rates of mineralization during four days of growth *in-vitro*. The study also shows that enhanced bone mineralization also occurs when the bone organ cultures are exposed only to the *soluble extracts* of the bioactive glasses. This result confirms the hypothesis that high levels of bioactivity and bone regeneration result. at least in part from intracellular as well as extracellular effects. Further understanding of these molecular, biological consequences of exposure of osteogenic cells to bioactive materials and extracts should provide the information needed to tailor at a biomolecular level, materials that can serve as regenerative allografts.

REFERENCES

1. Hench, LL and West, JK, (1996) Life Chemistry Reports . 13, 187
2. Hench LL. in *Bioceramics 7 (Andersson, Happonen and Yli-Urpo* Oxford: Butterworth-Heinemann, 1990: 241.
3. Hench LL and Wilson June, (1993) *Introduction to Bioceramics,* World Scientific Publications, Singapore
4. Hench LL and Wilson June (I 996), *Clinical Perfor7nance of skeletal Prostheses,* Chapman and Hall, London
5. Wilson, June, Proctor, DC. Elsberg, Laura and Brownlee RE (I 996) *Trans. 5th World Biomaterials Congress.* 1:4 and II: 67 1.
6. Wilson., June and Low. SB (I 992) *J. Applied Biom. 3:* 123 -129.

7.   Fujishiro Y, Hench LL, Oonishi H (I 997) *J Mat Sci. Mat in Med.* 8, 649
8.   Malizia, A A et al (1984) *J.A.M-A.* 251: 3277
9.   Heppleston, A G and Styles, J A (1966 *) Nature* 214: 521-522.
10.   Wilson, June. Pigott, G H, Schoen, F J and Hench, L.L. (1981.) *J.B.MR.. 15:* 805-817.
11.   Jubb, KVF and Kennedy, PC (1963) *Pathology of Domestic Animals,* Academic Press, New York, Vol.12:240
12.   Schoen, F J, Hood, C 1, Coleman, Sylvia, and Robinson, M (1980) *Am.Rev.Resp.Disease.* 121 (4, part 2) 257.
13.   Walker, RD. Wilson, June and Clark, A E (1 992) *J. Urology* 148:145-14
14.   Lai, W. Garino, JP and Ducheyne, P (1998) *Trans. Society for Biomaterials.- XXI.,431*
15.   Mischke, R E. Hyams, V. Shea JJ. et al. (1977 *) Arch. Otolaryngol. 103:* 489-492.
16.   MerwinGE. Atkins, J.Wilson, June and Hench L.L. (1982) *Otolaryngology Head and Neck Surgery* 1290: 461-469
17.   Wilson June and Merwin,GE (1988), Applied Biomat 22 [A2] 159-177
18.   Hench.LL (1 *997) Current Opinion in Solid State and Material Science,* 2: 604-610
19.   Keeting et al.(1992). *J Bone and Mineral Res.;* 7(11): 1281-1289
20.   Lobel KD, Hench LL (1998).JB.M.R 39,575-579.
21.   Xynos ID, et al (1 *998) Transactions of the First Meeting of British Tissue Engineering Society,* June 10, 1998, London, England, p 117
22.   Xynos ID, et al (1998) *Ibid,* p 116

Bioceramics Volume 11, edited by R. Z. LeGeros and J.P. LeGeros
(Proceedings of the 11th International Symposium on Ceramics in Medicine)
New York, NY, USA, November 1998
© 1998 by World Scientific Publishing Co. Pte. Ltd.

COMPOSITE BIOMATERIALS: PRESENT AND FUTURE

W. Bonfield

IRC in Biomedical Materials, Queen Mary and Westfield College, Mile End Road, London E1 4NS, UK

ABSTRACT
Bone consists predominately of a ceramic phase, approximating to hydroxyapatite and an organic phase, collagen, which, through interfacial interaction, constitute a composite material, i.e. the resultant mechanical properties are a combination of those of the individual constituents. This definition of the biological template has lead to the innovation of ceramic reinforced polymer composites, notably of hydroxyapatite-reinforced polyethylene (designated as HAPEX™), as bone substitutes for skeletal implants, which combine mechanical compatibility with a favourable bioactive response. The progression of HAPEX™ from laboratory concept to major clinical application as ossicular replacement prostheses is reviewed and the prospects for future advance considered.

INTRODUCTION
Nature does not design with monolithic materials. All tissues in the body are assemblies of different materials, which produce the range of mechanical properties required for different physiological functions. The functional demands on the skeleton, and hence on bone, the major skeletal tissue, are particularly demanding, with the requirements to: enable upright stance, allow locomotion through muscular action and provide protection for internal organs. It is well established that bone is a natural composite, in which there is an effective transfer of stress between a matrix phase, collagen, and a reinforcing phase, hydroxyapatite in the form of nanoscale, acicular or rod-like, mainly-crystalline aggregates. An early model by Bonfield and Li (1, 2, 3) demonstrated that the deformation of cortical bone as represented by the Youngs modulus could be predicted by a linear rule of mixtures equation based on a uniform strain assumption, as:

$$E_b = E_h V_h + E_c V_c \quad - (1)$$

where E_b, E_h, E_c are the Youngs modulus of bone, hydroxyapatite and collagen, respectively, and V_h and V_c are the volume fractions of hydroxyapatite and collagen, respectively. At that time, the Youngs modulus of hydroxyapatite was not known and was calculated as 63.5 GPa, a value not unreasonable when compared to later measured values for E for sintered hydroxyapatite of ~80 GPa. This model was extended by Katz (4), who demonstrated that it represented an upper bound prediction and presented a two-level composite model i.e. hydroxyapatite reinforced collagen osteon units in a hexagonal array. The essential experimental data underpinned by such models are that cortical bone has a Youngs modulus of 7-25GPa depending on location, is anisotropic by ~2 depending on orientation and is slightly viscoelastic. Such deformation behaviour is as expected from the combination of a linear elastic ceramic, with relatively high Youngs modulus, in a viscoelastic relatively low Youngs modulus polymer-like matrix.

Given the relative disparaties between E_h and E_c in equation (1) (~80:1), then the Youngs modulus of bone depends critically on the volume fraction of hydroxyapatite (V_h), which for adult human cortical support bones is ~0.45. This relatively high volume fraction, results in the maximum stiffness consistent with not producing an associated catastrophic brittle fracture during normal physiological loading. However human cortical bone is a brittle material, with a fracture toughness conditioned by microcrack formation and critical stress intensity (K_c) values from 1.6-2.5MNm$^{-3/2}$(5, 6). Hence while ultimate strength values of bone are significant (e.g. ~50-150 MPa for ultimate tensile strength), it should be emphasised that the combination of stress and critical crack geometry implicit in fracture toughness is the most relevant measure of fracture behaviour when considering bone substitutes.

In summary, the literature on cortical bone would define ideal analogous mechanical behaviour of a bone substitute as a matched Youngs modulus between 7-25GPa, some viscoelasticity (defined in (7)), anisotropy of up to 2 and a fracture toughness of ~2 x 2.5MNm$^{-3/2}$. Some of these properties can be achieved by monolithic bioactive ceramics, glasses and glass ceramics. Indeed the pioneering work on hydroxyapatite (8, 9) Bioglass®(10) and A-W glass ceramic (11) has offered outstanding opportunities for a range of clinical applications. Equally the opportunity exists to deliver the same materials as a reinforcement in a polymer matrix, so as to produce a range of distinctive and different properties. In this paper, the progression of hydroxyapatite reinforced polyethylene composite (HAPEX™) from concept to major clinical application is reviewed and the prospects for alternative reinforcements and matrixenhancement considered.

INNOVATION OF HYDROXYAPATITE REINFORCED POLYETHYLENE (HAPEX™)
Feasibility phase (1979-81)
The project concept was to innovate a bone-analogue material based on the hydroxyapatite-polyethylene system, which, in comparison to cortical bone, was modulus matching, had superior fracture toughness and produced bone bonding. Proof of concept was demonstrated by an experiment in which different volume fractions of particulate hydroxyapatite (HA), ranging from 0.1 to 0.6, were incorporated in a high density polyethylene (PE) matrix (12, 13). Measurement of the associated mechanical properties indicated an increase in Young's modulus from ~1 to ~8 GPa with volume fraction, i.e. demonstrating that there was stress transfer between the two phases and hence that a composite, rather than a mixture, had been produced.

From concept to laboratory prototype (1982-88)
The initial feasibility results required consolidation with a comprehensive range of structural mechanical and biological testing (summarised in a recent review(14)). The key mechanical property result was to establish the appropriate conjunction of the increase in Youngs modulus with HA volume fraction, with the associated decrease in ductility. It was demonstrated that, to retain a fracture toughness greater than that of cortical bone, the useable upper limit of HA volume fraction was 0.4. In parallel, *in vivo* biological assessment indicated that the composite behaved like PE (i.e. formed fibrous capsule) at HA volume fractions ≤0.2 and like HA (i.e. produced bone apposition) at greater volume fractions. Hence the range for both mechanical and biological compatibility was established as a HA volume fraction between 0.2 and 0.4.

The mechanical properties of HA-PE composite were also influenced by variations in both HA and PE. From the ceramic perspective, the instructive finding was that the physical variables affecting sintering of HA powders, i.e. particle size and distribution, as well as surface area and morphology, were key factors in obtaining an effective HA-PE composite. Indeed with a d_{50} value of ~4µm and a convoluted surface, it proved possible to obtain effective filler-matrix bonding by mechanical coupling alone. (Hence chemical coupling, established later (15) as an alternative method for filler-matrix coupling, was not needed). Processing of the HA-PE system remains a complex technology and the use of a twin screw co-rotating extruder was essential to achieve a homogenous HA particle distribution. By the end of this period, it was possible to produce laboratory scale batches of HA-PE composite, with known mechanical and biological properties and potential for application as a minor load bearing skeletal implant.

From clinical trial to pilot scale (1989-93)

Approval was obtained in 1989 for a UK clinical trial of HA-PE composite (at 0.4 HA volume fraction) for suborbital floor reconstruction, with Mr. R N Downes at the RAF Hospital. This trial demonstrated the important advantage of HA-PE composite to be trimmed during surgery with a scapel, so as to obtain good fit of the skeletal defect. The HA-PE composite was inserted without cement and became bonded to the adjacent bone. Clinical follow up of 50 patients has demonstrated a very good outcome (16, 17). With this clinical success, and made possible by the start of the IRC, a pilot scale clean processing facility was established in 1991, so as to be able to produce kilogramme quantities of HA-PE composite.

Licensing and regulations (1994-95)

The HA-PE composite technology was licensed by Smith and Nephew plc in 1994 for clinical application as a bone substitute, with particular focus on ENT applications. Subsequently, the technology was submitted to the Food and Drug Administration in the USA and regulatory approval was granted in 1995.

Commercialisation (1995 -)

HA-PE composite, now designated as HAPEX™, was launched at the American Academy of Otolaryngology as a trimmable shaft in the Goldenburg and Richards middle ear prostheses, designed for both total and partial replacement of the ossicles. Subsequent clinical take-up was rapid, as the trimmable shaft required only one size of implant to match the variable space in the middle ear, allowing the surgeon to achieve good fit. As a consequence, HAPEX™ has now been incorporated in 22 different middle ear prostheses and is available globally. Several thousand patients have received HAPEX™ middle ear implants and initial patient follow up indicates a very satisfactory clinical outcome.

THE FUTURE - DERIVATIVES AND ALTERNATIVES

With clinical success as a middle ear implant, extensions of HAPEX™ are planned for a range of minor load bearing implants in maxillo-, cranial- and reconstructive surgery. The ability to process HAPEX™ to near-nett shape forms is a key attribute under development, so as to reduce production costs, with a final finish machining operation to expose HA particles at the surface.

A major load bearing version of HAPEX™ is also being developed, in collaboration with the IRC in Polymer Science and Technology, by hydrostatic extrusion of the compounded precursor composite. This procedure imposes an oriented molecular structure on the PE matrix with associated anisotropy, and promising enhanced mechanical properties (longitudinal Youngs modulus of ~9 GPa and ultimate tensile strength of ~90 MPa) have been achieved (18).

A key objective is the development of an "instant" bone bonding composite, i.e. producing more rapid osseointegration than the ~1 month current time scale. There is considerable appeal in the utilisation of substituted hydroxyapatites as fillers. In addition the technology of reactive fillers, such as Bioglass® and A-W glass ceramic in PE has been investigated (19, 20). In both cases, it has been demonstrated that a composite effect is achieved, i.e. the Youngs modulus increased with volume fraction. Further work is required to optimise the particle size and distribution, as well as matrix coupling, but a range of mechanical and biological performance would offer the potential for a variety of hard and soft tissue replacements.

ACKNOWLEDGEMENTS

The contributions from colleagues in the IRC and support for the IRC core programme from the Engineering and Physical Sciences Research Council are gratefully acknowledged.

REFERENCES

1   Bonfield W., Li CH. *J. Appl. Phys.* 1966; **37**: 869-875
2   Bonfield W., Li CH. *J. Appl. Phys.* 1967; **38**: 2450-2455
3   Bonfield W., Li CH. *J. Biomechanics* 1968; **1**: 323-329
4   Katz JL. *J. Biomechanics* 1971; **4**: 455-465
5   Bonfield W. *J. Biomechanics* 1987; **20**: 1071-1081
6   Vashishth D., Behiri JC., Bonfield W. *J. Biomechanics* 1997; **30**: 763-769
7   Bonfield W., O'Conner P. *J. Mater. Sci.* 1978; **13**: 202-207
8   De Groot K. *Bioceramics of calcium phosphate* 1983; CRC Press, BocuRaton FL
9   Aoki H. *Science and medical applications of hydroxyapatite* 1991; JAAS , Japan
10 Hench LL., Ethridge EC. *Adv. Biomed. Eng.* 1975; **5**: 35-45
11 Kokubo T., Ito S., Sakka S., Yamamuro T. *J Mater. Sci.* 1985; **20**: 200-208
12 Bonfield W., Grynpas MD., Tully AE., Bowman J., Abram J. *Biomaterials* 1981; **2**: 185-186
13 Bonfield W., Grynpas MD., Bowman J. *UK Patent* 1984; GB2085461B
14 Bonfield W., Wang M., Tanner KE. *Acta mater* 1998; **46**: 2509-2518
15 Deb S., Wang M., Tanner KE., Bonfield W. *J. Mater Sci. Med.* 1996; **7**: 191-197
16 Downes RN., Vardy S., Tanner KE., Bonfield W. *Bioceramics Volume 4* eds Bonfield W, Hastings GW, Tanner KE, 1991; 239-244 Butterworth Heinmann
17 Tanner KE., Downes RN., Bonfield W. *Br. Ceram. Trans.* 1994; **93**: 104-10
18 Ladizesky NH., Wang M., Miettinen EM., Tanner KE., Ward IM., Bonfield W. *Proc Fifth World Biomaterials Congress* 1996: 442
19 Wang M., Bonfield W., Hench LL. *Bioceramics* Volume 8 eds Hench LL, Wilson J, 1995 :383-387
20 Wang M., Bonfield W., Kokubo T. *Bioceramics* Volume 9 eds Kokubo T, Nakamura T, Miyaji F, 1996; 387-391

Bioceramics Volume 11, edited by R. Z. LeGeros and J.P. LeGeros
(Proceedings of the 11th International Symposium on Ceramics in Medicine)
New York, NY, USA, November 1998

CALCIUM PHOSPHATE COATINGS: ALTERNATIVES TO PLASMA SPRAY

K. de Groot

Department of Biomaterials, Leiden University, Prof. Bronkhorstlaan 10, 3723 MB. BILTHOVEN, The Netherlands

ABSTRACT

Calcium phosphate materials have been clinically applied in many areas of dentistry and orthopaedics. Bulk material, available in dense and porous forms is used for alveolar ridge augmentation, immediate tooth root replacement and maxillofacial reconstruction (Aoki 1977; Nery 1978; Metsger 1982; de Groot 1983). However, because calcium phosphate bulk materials are mechanically weak, they cannot be subjected to physiological loads as encountered in the skeleton. Therefore, calcium phosphate coatings on metallic substrates have been developed, which are currently used in loaded situations, like total joint replacements and dental root implants[1,2].

Keywords: calcium phosphate, bioceramics, coatings

INTRODUCTION

The currently most used method to apply a calcium phosphate (Ca-P) coating is the well known plasma spray technique in which a DC electric arc is struck between two electrodes. The arc turns the gases which are being passed through this arc into a plasma (ionized mixture) of high temperature and speed. The Ca-P powder is injected into this high-speed plasma with the result that these powder particles partially melt and are, as such, deposited onto a substrate. Disadvantages of the plasma spray method are: (1) unpredictable phase changes into the Ca-P powder particles; (2) it is a not possible to include temperature sensitive biomolecules (BMP, growth hormones) into such a coating; (3) it is a line-of-sight method. Therefore, new coating techniques have been developed or are in development stage. This overview is limited to wet ambient temperature techniques, allowing inclusion of biomolecules (at room or body temperature). Thus, high temperature techniques, such as various magnetron-sputtering methods, although of great relevance, are not covered in this review.

ELECTROPHORETIC DEPOSITION

Electrophoretic deposition has been used to achieve uniform Ca-P coatings on metallic substrates. This approach is especially useful for porous metal structures such as orderly oriented wire mesh (OOWM). To create the coatings, calcium phosphate powders are electrophoretically deposited from a 3% suspension of powders in isopropanol or other suitable liquid onto titanium. The coating thickness can be varied by changing the electrical field strength and the time of deposition. However, in order to obtain sufficient strength, the deposited powders must be sintered in high vacuum (10^{-6} to 10^{-7} Torr) at 850 to 950°C. The resulting coating consists of a number of Ca-P phases. Further, heating at 850-950°C results in the following: at the coating-substrate interface a Ti-P compound is formed due to P diffusion into the Ti substrate. Because of the densification during sintering, shrinkage and cracking of the coating can occur.

Also thermal stresses induced by the differences in thermal expansion coefficients between the metal and the ceramic film during sintering and cooling can lead to cracking [3, 4]. This means, that, currently, electrophoretic deposition as such is not yet a reliable method, not even with heat treatments and certainly not without heat treatments.

ELECTROCHEMICAL DEPOSITION

In electrochemical deposition, an aqueous electrolyte containing Ca and P ions is decomposed. As a result, calcium phosphate crystals nucleate on a titanium electrode at E=-1600 mV (V_s SCE). Sometimes, the HA coating obtained is heat treated in steam at 125°C for 4hr and then calcined in vacuum at 425°C for 6 hr to densify the film and to improve its bonding to the substrate. The thickness of electrochemically deposited HA coatings is approximately 80 microns and the deposition rate 60 mu/hr.

HA coatings obtained by the electrochemical method have a more uniform structure since the coating is formed gradually through a nucleation and growth process at a low temperature. XRD indicates that the coating is mainly composed of small crystals. The crystallite dimension (D_{002}) is 100nm [5, 6]. Without heat treatments (prohibiting inclusion of temperature sensitive biomolecules), electro-deposited coatings are too weak and easily loosened from the substrate.

SOL-GEL DEPOSITION

The solution-sol-gel route is considered as a method, which results in ceramic coatings with an exact chemical and microstructural composition. The approach can be considered as a wet chemistry approach in which reagents, consisting of the desired components for the coating, are mixed in solution either as a colloidal suspension of inorganic particles, as metal alkoxides or other organic precursors. The coatings are prepared at low reaction temperature, but still need firing at temperatures in the range of 400 to 1000°C. The resulting coatings can be extremely dense and can adhere strongly to the underlying substrate [7].

BIOMIMETIC DEPOSITION

Biomimetic deposition is a method whereby a biologically active bone-like apatite layer is formed on a substrate surface by immersion in a Hank's Balanced Salt Solution or Simulated Body Fluid at 37°C for several days. Prior to the deposition process, the titanium specimens are ground and polished with SiC paper, followed by ultrasonic cleaning and drying. The thickness of this calcium phosphate coatings varies from 1-5 μm and most of the samples have an amorphous or amorphous-crystalline, with a preferred (00*l*) crystallographic orientation [8, 9, 10].

DISCUSSION

Although a number of potential techniques has been described that allow depostion of a Ca-P layer in a wet environment at ambient temperatures, the electrochemical, electrophoretic and sol-gel depositions still need post heat treatments, leaving only the biomimetic deposition as a "true" wet, ambient temperature technique. Nevertheless, since the other methods have the potential of being upgraded into true wet ambient temperature techniques, we have included them in this review.

Wet, ambient temperature Ca-P coatings have advantages as compared to plasma-sprayed ones: phase compositions are more thermodynamically stable and have a more predictable and reproducible composition; the coating process is not line-of sight and is more appropriate for complex geometries and/or porosities; and – probably most importantly – controlled release of incorporated biological molecules, especially members of the BMP family and other growth factors, is quite possible by co-precipitating them from simulated body fluids [11].

REFERENCES:
1. De Groot, K., Geesink, R.G.T., Klein, C.P.A.T., Serekian, P., *J. Biomed. Mater. Res.* 1987; 21: 1375-1381.
2. Cook, S.D., Thomas, K.A., Kay, J.F., Jarcho, M., *Clin, Orthop. Rel. Res.* 1988; 232: 225-243.
3. Ducheyne, P., van Raemsdonck, W., Heughebaert, J.C., Heughebaert, M., *Biomaterials* 1986; 7: 97.103.
4. Ducheyne, P., van Raemsdonck, W., Heughebaert, J.C., Heughebaert, M., *Biomaterials* 1990; 11: 244-254.
5. Shirkanzadah, M., *Biomaterials* 1992; 14: 27-30.
6. Ban, S., Maruno, S., Arimoto, N., Harada, A., Matsuura, M., Hasegawa, J., *Bioceramics* 1994; 7: 261-266.
7. Ducheyne, P., Hench, L.L., Kagan II, A., Martens, M., Bursens, A., Mulier, J.C., *J. Biomed. Mater. Res.* 1980; 14: 225-237.
8. Hanawa, T., Ota, M., *Appl. Surf. Sci.* 1992; 55: 269-276.
9. Kokubo, T., In: Bone-Bonding Biomaterials, eds Ducheyne, P., Kokubo, T., van Blitterswijk, C.A., Publ: Reed Healthcare Communications, Leiderdorp, Netherlands, 1992: 31-41.
10. Leitao, E., Barbosa, M.A., de Groot, K., *J. Mater. Sci: Mat. in Med.*, 1995; 6: 849-852.
11. Wen, H.B., de Wijn, J.R., Li, S.H., Cui, F.Z., de Bruijn, J.D., van Blitterswijk, C.A., de Groot, K., accepted (1998), *J. Biomed. Mat. Res.*

Bioceramics Volume 11, edited by R. Z. LeGeros and J.P. LeGeros
(Proceedings of the 11th International Symposium on Ceramics in Medicine)
New York, NY, USA, November 1998
© 1998 by World Scientific Publishing Co. Pte. Ltd.

CALCIUM PHOSPHATE CEMENTS: Chemistry and Applications

L.C. Chow
American Dental Association Health Foundation Paffenbarger Research Center
National Institute of Standards and Technology, Gaithersburg, MD 20899, U.S.A.

INTRODUCTION

The concept of calcium phosphates as possible dental restorative materials was first presented to the research community in 1982 [LeGeros et al.]. Since the development in 1987 [Brown and Chow] of the first self-hardening calcium phosphate cement (CPC) consisting of tetracalcium phosphate (TTCP) and dicalcium phosphate anhydrous (DCPA) or dicalcium phosphate dihydrate (DCPD), this class of materials have been a subject of considerable interest in biomaterials research. A recent survey of the literature [Chow et al., 1998] shows that there are more than 130 scientific publications and an even greater number of published abstracts on CPC's and closely related systems.

A large number of different combinations of calcium and phosphate-containing compounds have been investigated as potential CPC materials. Besides calcium phosphates, several non-phosphate-containing calcium compounds have also been used as cement components. Many of these cements form HA as the end product while others do not. Some cements develop high strengths but they harden only with the use of an organic acid as the cement liquid. The results of the studies reported in the literature showed that cementation can occur in several distinctly different cement systems that contain calcium phosphates as the major components. These systems may be divided into the following categories: (1) Cements that comprise of calcium phosphate compounds, and water, or a calcium- or phosphate-containing solution is used as the liquid. Hardening of the cement is a result of formation of one or more calcium phosphate compounds in the cement; (2) Cements that consist of essentially calcium phosphates as the solid components, but an organic acid is used as the liquid. Hardening of the cement is the result of complex formation of calcium and the organic acid; (3) These cements are similar to those in (2) above except that the cement liquid is a polymer solution. Hardening of the cement is the result of either formation of HA or complex formation of calcium and the polymer solution; (4) Cements that are composites of calcium phosphates and polymers. The calcium phosphates present in these materials act as fillers and do not play a significant role in the mechanism of cement hardening. Polymerization of the monomers is primarily responsible for the setting of the cement. These materials are more closely related to resin/filler composites than to calcium phosphate cements.

Although each of the above four types of cements has important potential for biomedical applications, the length of this paper limits the discussion only to type 1 cements. Most cements in this category form apatite (HA, calcium-deficient apatite, or carbonated apatite) as the major product while some form DCPD as the major product. The cements consist of one or more of the following calcium phosphates (in the order of decreasing Ca/P ratio): TTCP, α-tricalcium phosphate (α-TCP), β-tricalcium phosphate (β-TCP), amorphous calcium phosphate (ACP), octacalcium phosphate (OCP), DCPA, DCPD, and monocalcium phosphate monohydrate (MCPM). Besides calcium phosphate salts, several nonphosphate-containing calcium compounds have also been used as cement components. These include calcium carbonate (mostly in the crystalline form of calcite), calcium oxide, and calcium hydroxide. The cements are described below in the order of decreasing Ca/P of the reactive component.

TTCP + DCPA and TTCP + DCPD Cements.

These cements were developed in 1983 and approximately 70 publications have reported the chemistry of cement setting reactions, the physicochemical properties, and in vivo characteristics of the cements. In these cements, no acidic or basic byproducts are produced by the setting reaction. The reaction proceeds under a relatively constant-composition condition defined by the "singular point" of the two cement components. The pHs of these cements are in the range of 7.5 to 8.5. With water as the cement liquid, the hardening time, measured by the Gillmore needle method was about 30 minutes and cement developed a compressive strength of 60 MPa in 24 hours [Chow et al., 1991].

Fulmar and Brown [1993] reported that in an aqueous slurry, reaction of 1 mole of TTCP with 2 moles of DCPA formed a calcium-deficient apatite with a Ca/P ratio of 1.5 as the product. Chow et al. [1994] confirmed that this reaction also occurs in the cement with a TTCP/DCPA ratio of ½. They also reported that cements with TTCP/DCPA ratios in a wide range, i.e., from ¼ to 2/1, hardened normally, forming HA with residual amounts of the excess component also present in the product. In this study, the cement that formed stoichiometric HA (from cement with TTCP/DCPA = 1) had the highest strength.

Although a cement hardening time of 30 minutes is satisfactory for some applications, a more rapid hardening is desirable for many other applications. Results from a study [Chow et al., 1994] on the effect of phosphate concentration on HA formation in the TTCP + DCPA cement showed that the rate of HA formation increased significantly by sodium phosphate present in the cement liquid at a concentration of 0.25 mol/L and above. Forty to sixty percent of the CPC powder had converted to HA by 0.5 h, in contrast to about five to ten percent conversion in the absence of phosphate. The rapid HA formation in these cements caused a much more rapid hardening of the cements (5 min) compared to the conventional CPC (30 min) [Ishikawa et al., 1995]. A recent study [Cherng et al., 1995] showed that by adding a small amount (2 wt%) of hydroxypropyl methylcellulose or other gelling agents in water as the cement liquid, the cement paste became significantly more cohesive and a highly washout resistant paste was developed immediately after mixing. This paste remained intact and hardened when immersed in water. The addition of a gelling agent caused a slight increase in hardening time in some cases, but this is remedied by the use of a phosphate solution as the cement liquid. Addition of sodium alginate also improves cement washout resistance [Ishikawa et al., 1995], but because alginate delays the cement setting time it should only be used with a phosphate solution as the cement liquid. Shorter hardening times, greater washout resistance, and other improvements in the handling properties have made the cement significantly easier to use clinically.

In addition to high biocompatibility and self-hardening, the usefulness of these CPCs for repairing bone defects arises from their unique in vivo properties: slow resorption and replacement by new bone formation with no loss in volume. Set CPC consists of tightly packed microcrystalline HA that has a large surface area. Because HA is formed in an aqueous environment and has a relatively low crystallinity, it is similar to biological apatite. These properties are believed to be responsible for CPC's in vivo resorption characteristics.

The TTCP + DCPA cement, which proved to be efficacious in numerous animal studies, was evaluated in several medical centers for cranial defect repair in human subjects [Kamerer et al., 1994; Kveton et al., 1995;1995a; 1996; Weissman et al., 1996].

α-TCP + HA and α-TCP + β-TCP + HA Cements

Ginebra *et al.* [1997] investigated the hardening mechanisms of an α-TCP based cement containing β-TCP (17 %) and HA (2 %) that was mixed with a 2.5 % Na_2HPO_4 solution (P/L = 3.1 g/mL). After 24 h at 37 °C, 80% of the α-TCP converted to HA, while the β-TCP did not react. Fernandez *et al.* [1996] tested the effects of different amounts of HA (2 %, 4 %, or 6 %) added as nucleators to the α-TCP powder, and of different concentrations of Na_2HPO_4 (0, 2 %, 3 %, or 4 %) in the cement liquid on the swelling properties of the cement (i.e., the disintegration upon premature contact with blood or other body fluids). In general, the use of the phosphate solutions was a prerequisite for reducing the swelling period to less than 15 min (to coincided with HT) whereas different amounts of HA did not have any effect. A cement comprised of α-TCP, β-TCP (15 %), and HA (2 %) mixed with a phosphate solution was used to fill the holes in tibia of goats *in vivo* [Jansen et al., 1995]. 3 months and 6 months after implantation, the composition of the hardened cement was $\sim$ 85 % HA and $\sim$ 15 % β-TCP. Histological evaluation revealed that the cement stimulated bone ingrowth. Active resorption by osteoclasts, and well-organized bone characterized by the presence of mature secondary osteons, were observed after 6 months. No inflammatory or foreign body reactions were observed.

α-TCP + DCPA + HA Cements

The properties of cements containing 63.2 % α-TCP, 27.7 % DCPA, and 9.1 % HA mixed with distilled water (P/L = 3.3 g/mL) were investigated [Ferandez et al., 1996a]. It was found that the α-TCP converted to a calcium deficient HA (CD-HA), whereas the DCPA did not react significantly. The extent of the conversion and the CS increased in a strongly correlated manner with time. After 12 days, when conversion was $\sim$ 100 %, the CS was $\sim$ 40 MPa.

α-TCP + CaCO$_3$ Cements

The product of α-TCP and CaCO$_3$ reacting with 1 mol/L phosphate solution as the cement liquid (P/L of 3 g/mL) was a poorly crystalline type-B carbonated apatite [Markovic et al., 1996]. Sugawara *et al.* [Sugawara et al., 1995] evaluated the biocompatibility of a α-TCP + CaCO$_3$ cement mixed with a 0.25 mol/L phosphate solution (pH = 7.4) and implanted subcutaneously in rats. Histopathological observations, performed 2 to 4 weeks after implantation, showed only very slight inflammatory reactions in tissue that were in contact with the implants. Particles of the cement were surrounded by fibrous connective tissue with a small number of lymphocytes and plasma cells. Several foreign body giant cells were observed in the connective tissue adjacent to the particles. The results indicated that the cement is highly compatible in subcutaneous tissues and may be useful in bone grafting and root canal filling applications.

α-TCP + CaCO$_3$ + MCPM Cements

Morgan *et al.* [1997] determined the mechanical properties of the carbonated apatite that formed in the reaction of a α-TCP + CaCO$_3$ + MCPM cement and a phosphate-buffered solution. DTS and CS after 24 h of preparation were 2.1 MPa and 55 MPa, respectively. The average flexural strength measured in three and four point bending was $\sim$ 0.47 MPa. The fracture toughness was $\sim$ 0.14 MPa m$^{1/2}$. The fatigue crack-growth rates and fatigue threshold value were determined and compared to other brittle materials. Stankewich *et al.* [1998] showed that α-TCP + CaCO$_3$ + MCPM cement, added in the injectable form, provided an initial beneficial augmentation (strength and stiffness) to the fixation of femoral neck fractures *in situ*. An α-TCP + CaCO$_3$ + MCPM cement was used as a bone-fracture repair material in humans [Cohen and Whitman 1997]. For patients in the experimental group, the cement was injected into the metaphyseal region of distal radial fractures and patients began mobilizing their wrist within two weeks using a removable splint. For patients in the control group, distal radial fractures were immobilized by casts or external fixators for six to eight weeks. This trial is in progress and, to date, during the first several months after the injury the patients in the experimental group appear to have a greater arc of motion and function in their injured wrist. Final results of this study have to await the completion of the clinical evaluation of the first 150 treated patients and a careful analysis of the data.

β-TCP + MCPM Cements

Different sulfate-containing additives dissolved in water were used to evaluate the effects of sulfate ions on the *in vitro* properties of β-TCP + MCPM cements [Bohner et al., 1995]. At sulfate concentrations < 0.1 mol/L, the HT was significantly prolonged, indicating an inhibitory effect of sulfate ions on the growth of DCPD. At sulfate concentrations > 0.1 mol/L, a sharp decrease in HT as well as in the DCPD crystal size were observed, concomitantly with an increase in the DTS. When this cement, containing calcium sulfate dihydrate, was implanted into rabbit femora, the complete resorption and replacement with new bone was observed after 8 weeks. A β-TCP + MCPM + $CaSO_4 \cdot 0.5H_2O$ cement with and without β-TCP granules, when implanted (as hard cylinders) into surgical defects in rabbit femoral condyles *in vivo*, was surrounded with new bone after 4 weeks. After 8 weeks both cements, but not the β-TCP granules, were almost completely resorbed and replaced by bone tissue. The cement with the nonresorbable β-TCP granules maintained bone formation for a longer time [Ohura et al., 1996].

REFERENCES

1. M. Bohner, J. Lemaitre, K. Ohura, and P. Hardouin, "Effects of sulfate ions on the in vitro properties of β-TCP - MCPM - water mixtures. Preliminary in vivo results," *Ceram. Trans.* **48** 245-59 (1995).
2. W.E. Brown and L.C. Chow, "A new calcium phosphate, water-setting cement," *Cements Research Progress 1986*, ed. P.W. Brown, pp.352-379, Westerville, OH; The Am. Ceram. Soc. (1987).
3. M. Cherng, S. Takagi, and LC Chow, "Effects of Gelling Agents on Calcium Phosphate Cements," *IADR Abstr.* 1845 *J. Dent. Res.* **74** 242 (1995).
4. L.C. Chow, S. Takagi S, P.D. Costantino, and C.D. Friedman. "Self-setting Calcium Phosphate Cements" *Matl. Res. Symp. Proc.* **179**, 3-24 (1991).
5. L.C. Chow, S. Takagi, and K. Ishikawa, "Formation of Hydroxyapatite in Cement Systems." In: *Hydroxyapatite and Related Materials*, Brown PW and B. Constantz, Eds. (CRC Press, Boca Raton, 1994), pp. 127-137.
6. L. C. Chow, M. Markovic and S. Takagi, "Calcium phosphate cements," *Cements Research Progress*, ed. L. J. Struble, Westerville, OH; The Am. Ceram. Soc. (in press).
7. M. S. Cohen and K. Whitman, "Calcium phosphate bone cement--the Norian skeletal repair system in orthopedic surgery," *AORN J.* **65**(5) 958-962 (1997).
8. M. P. Ginebra, E. Fernandez, E. A. P. De Maeyer, R. M. H. Verbeeck, M. G. Boltong, J. Ginebra, F. C. M. Driessens, and J. A. Planell, "Setting reaction and hardening of an apatitic calcium phosphate cement," *J. Dent. Res.* **76**(4) 905-912 (1997).
9. E. Fernandez, M. G. Boltong, M. P. Ginebra, F. C. M. Driessens, O. Bermudez, and J. A. Planell, "Development of a method to measure the period of swelling of calcium phosphate cements," *J. Mater. Sci. Lett.* **15**(11) 1004-1005 (1996).
10. E. Fernandez, J. A. Planell, R. M. Verbeeck, E. A. De Maeyer, J. Ginebra, F. C. M. Driessens, M. G. Boltong, and M. P. Ginebra, "Kinetic study of the setting reaction of a calcium phosphate bone cement," *J. Biomed. Mater. Res.* **32**(3) 367-374 (1996a).
11. M.T. Flumer and P.W. Brown, "Effects of Na_2HPO_4 and NaH_2PO_4 on hydroxyapatite formation," *J. Biomed. mater. Res.* **27** 1095-1098 (1993).
12. K. Ishikawa, Y. Miyamoto, M. Kon, M. Nagayama, and K. Asaoka, "Non-decay type fast-setting calcium phosphate cement: composite with sodium alginate," *Biomaterials* **16**(7) 527-32 (1995).
13. J. A. Jansen, J. E. De Ruijter, H. G. SChaeken, J. P. C. M. Van Der Waerden, J. A. Planell, and F. C. M. Driessens, "Evaluation of tricalcium phosphate/hydroxyapatite cement for tooth replacement: An experimental animal study," *J. Mater. Sci.: Mater. Med.* **6**(11) 653-657 (1995).
14. D. B. Kamerer, C. D. Friedman, P. Costantino, C. H. Snyderman, and B. E. Hirsch, "Hydroxyapatite cement: a new method for achieving watertight closure in transtemporal surgery," *Am. J. Otol.* **15**(1) 47-49 (1994).

15. J. F. Kveton, C. D. Friedman, J. M. Piepmeier, and P. D. Constantino, "Reconstruction of suboccipital craniectomy defects with hydroxyapatite cement: A preliminary report," *Laryngoscope* **105**(2) 156-159 (1995).

16. J. F. Kveton, C. D. Friedman, and P. D. Constantino, "Indications for hydroxyapatite cement reconstruction in lateral skull base surgery," *Am. J. Otol.* **16**(4) 465-469 (1995a).

17. J. F. Kveton, "Obliteration of the eustachain tube using hydroxyapatite cement: A permanent technique," *Laryngoscope* **106**(10) 1241-1243 (1996).

18. R. Z. LeGeros, A. Chohayeb, and A. Shulman, "Apatitic calcium phosphates: Possible restorative materials," *J. Dent. Res.* **61**(Spec. Issue) Abstr. No. 1482, 343 (1982).

19. M. Markovic, S. Takagi and L. C. Chow, "Calcium phosphate cements with incorporated carbonate ions," *J. Dent. Res.* **75**(Special Issue) Abstr. No. 59, 25 (1996).

20. E. F. Morgan, D. N. Yetkinler, B. R. Constantz, and R. H. Dauskardt, "Mechanical properties of carbonated apatite bone mineral substitute: strength, fracture and fatigue behaviour," *J. Mater. Sci.: Mater. in Med.* **8** 559-570 (1997).

21. K. Ohura, B. Flautre, G. Pasquier, and J. Lemaitre, "Resorption of, and bone formation from, new beta-tricalcium phosphate-monocalcium phosphate cements: an in vivo study," *J. Biomed. Mater. Res.* **30**(2) 193-200 (1996).

22. C. J. Stankewich, R. D. Poser, D. N. Yetkinler, A. F. Tencer, and M. F. Swiontkowski, "Augmentation of femoral neck fracture fixation with an injectable calcium-phosphate bone mineral cement," *J. Orthop. Res.* **14**(5) 786-793 (1996).

23. Sugawara, K. Kusama, N. Nishimura, S. Iwanari, M. Nishiyama, I. Moro, and I Kudo, "Histopathological Reactions of A New Calcium Phosphate cement," *J. Dent. Res.* **74**(Special Issue) Abstr. No. 1434, 191 (1995).

24. J. L. Weissman, C. H. Snyderman, and B. E. Hirsch, "Hydroxyapatite cement to repair skull base defects: Radiologic appearance," *Am. J. Neuroradiol.* **17**(8) 1569-1574 (1996)

Bioceramics Volume 11, edited by R. Z. LeGeros and J.P. LeGeros
(Proceedings of the 11th International Symposium on Ceramics in Medicine)
New York, NY, USA, November 1998
© 1998 by World Scientific Publishing Co. Pte. Ltd.

BIOMIMETICS APPLIED TO BIOCERAMICS

T. Kokubo

Department of Material Chemistry, Faculty of Engineering, Kyoto University
Kyoto 606-8501, Japan

ABSTRACT

Any material could form a bonelike apatite on its surface in a simulated body fluid (SBF) with ion concentrations nearly equal to those of human blood plasma, if its surface is modified so that a functional group effective for the apatite nucleation is formed on its surface and/or a component of the apatite is released from the surface. For example, metals including pure titanium, titanium alloys and pure tantalum form the bonelike apatite on their surfaces in SBF, when their surfaces are modified so that Ti-OH or Ta-OH groups are formed on their surfaces and Na^+ ion is released from the surfaces. Organic polymers including polyethyleneterephthalate and polyethylene form the apatite on their surfaces in SBF or 1.5SBF, when their surfaces are modified so that Si-OH groups are formed on their surfaces. Thus obtained apatite-metal and apatite-polymer composites might be useful as bone substitutes, since they exhibit mechanical properties in a wide range as well as high bioactivity.

KEYWORDS: Biomimetiocs, Bioactivity, Simulated body fluid (SBF), Apatite
Apatite-metal composite, Apatite-polymer composite

INTRODUCTION

Bone is a composite in which apatite crystallites are integrated with collagen fibers in a three dimensional structure. It is formed by selective deposition of the apatite crystallites on collagen fibers. This selective deposition is triggered by a catalytic effect of some substance for the apatite nucleation and/or local enrichment of the apatite component in a metastable body fluid which is supersaturated with respect to the apatite.

When similar situations are provided, even an artificial material can form the bonelike apatite on its surface in the living body. For example, when CaO, SiO_2-based ceramics such as Bioglass® and glass-ceramic A-W are implanted into a bone defect, they release Ca^{2+} ion through exchanging with H_3O^+ ion in the body fluid, to form Si-OH groups on their surfaces. Thus formed Si-OH groups induce the apatite nucleation[1] and the released Ca^{2+} ion accelerates the apatite nucleation by increasing the concentration of a component, Ca^{2+} ion, of the apatite in the surrounding body fluid.[2] Once the apatite nuclei are formed, they grow spontaneously by consuming the calcium and phosphate ion from the surrounding body fluid to form a dense and homogeneous bonelike apatite layer. As a result, they can bond to living bone through thus formed bonelike apatite layer.[3,4]

The apatite formation on their surfaces can be reproduced even in an acellular simulated body fluid (SBF) with ion concentrations nearly equal to those of human blood plasma.[3] This indicates that the bonelike apatite layer could be formed in SBF as well as in the living body on various materials including metals and organic polymers, if their surfaces are modified so that the functional groups effective for the apatite nucleation is formed on their surfaces and a component of the apatite can be released from their surfaces. It is expected that various kind of apatite-metal or -organic polymer composites could be formed by this kind of biomimetic process, and might be useful as bone substitutes, since they can exhibit mechanical properties in a wide range, as well as high bioactivity. Some examples of composites of apatite-metal or -polymer composites which are prepared by the biomimetic process are shown in the followings.

APATITE-METAL COMPOSITES

Pure titanium metal is generally covered with a TiO_2 passive layer and hence chemically durable. Even this TiO_2 layer reacts with NaOH solution to form a sodium titanate hydrogel layer as shown in Fig. 1 (A),[5] for example when the titanium metal is soaked in 5M-NaOH solution at 60°C for 24 h.[6] This gel layer is stabilized as an amorphous sodium titanate layer as shown in Fig. 1 (B), for example when the NaOH-treated metal is heat-treated at 600°C for 1 h.[7] It should be noted here that the sodium titanate layer forms a graded structures in which Na and O concentrations gradually decrease towards the interior while Ti increases.[5]

When thus treated metal is soaked in SBF, Na^+ ion in the surface sodium titanate layer is released through exchange with H_3O^+ ion in SBF to form Ti-OH groups on its surface. Thus formed Ti-OH groups first combine with the calcium ion in SBF and later with the phosphate ion to form the apatite, as shown in a separate paper presented in this volume.[8] In this process, the released Na^+ ion accelerates the apatite formation by increasing OH concentration in the surrounding SBF. Once the apatite is formed, it is spontaneously grow by consuming the calcium and phosphate ions in SBF to form a dense and homogeneous layer of the bonelike apatite, as shown in Fig. 2.[9] It should be noted here again that the apatite layer also forms a graded structure in which Ca, P and O gradually decrease towards the interior while Ti increases, as shown in Fig. 1 (C).[5] Because of this graded structure, the apatite layer is tightly bonded to the metal substrate.[10]

The NaOH- and heat-treated Ti metal forms the apatite layer not only in SBF, but also in the living body, and bond to living bone through the apatite layer.[11]

Similar NaOH- and heat-treatments are also effective for titanium alloys including Ti-6Al-4V, Ti-6Al-2Nb-Ta and Ti-15Mo-5Zr-3Al,[9,12] and pure tantalum metal[13,14] in including their apatite-forming abilities in SBF as well in the living body. Thus formed apatite-metal composites are believe to be useful as bone substitute even under load-bearing conditions, since they exhibit high fracture toughness as well as high bioactivity.

APATITE-POLYMER COMPOSITES

Being subjected to O_2 plasma treatment, organic polymers such as polyethyleneterephthalate form oxidized polar groups such as C=O, C-OH and COOH on their surfaces.[15] When thus treated polymers are placed on granular particles of a CaO, SiO_2-based glass in SBF, silicate ions released from the glass particles are trapped by the polar groups on the organic polymers to induce the apatite nucleation. According to TEM-EDX observation, the silicate ions first combine with the calcium ion and later with the phosphate ion to form the apatite,[16] as shown in Fig. 3, similar to the Ti-OH groups described above. The calcium ion released from the glass particles accelerates the apatite nucleation by increasing the Ca^{2+} ion concentration in the surrounding SBF.

When thus treated organic polymers are soaked in another solution supersaturated with respect to the apatite, the apatite nuclei spontaneously grow *in situ* on the organic polymers by consuming the calcium and phosphate ions from the surrounding fluid to form a dense and uniform apatite layer even on fibers constituting of fabric, as shown in Fig. 4.[17] If a solution in which concentration of all the ions including HCO_3^- ion are equal to those of human blood plasma used as the medium for the apatite growth, the apatite identical to the bone mineral in its composition and structure can be formed.[18] The thickness of the apatite layer increases linearly with increasing soaking time in the solution.[19]

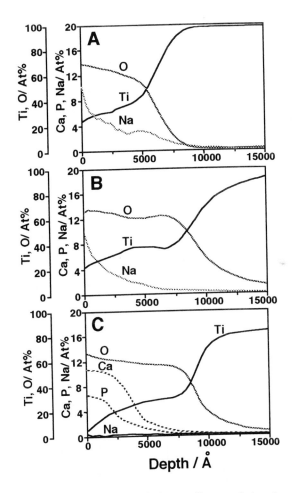

Figure 1. Auger electron depth profiles of the surfaces of titanium metal treated with 5.0M-NaOH solution at 60°C for 24 h (A), subsequently heat-treated at 600°C for 1 h (B) and then soaked in SBF for 3 days (C).

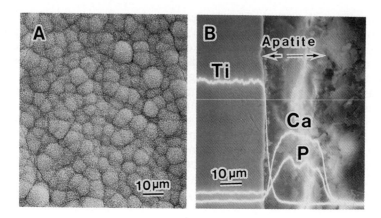

Figure 2. SEM pictures of the surface (A) and the cross-section (B) of the apatite layer formed on pure titanium metal.

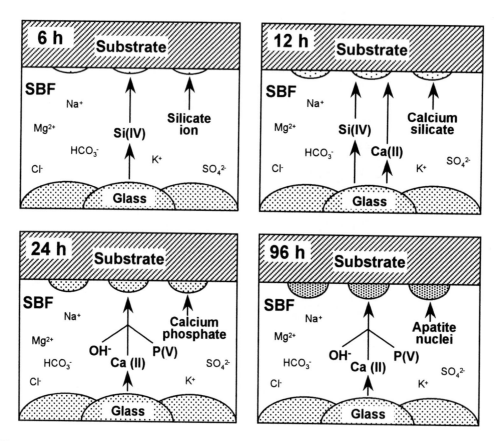

Figure 3. Process of apatite formation by silicate ion attached on an organic polymer.

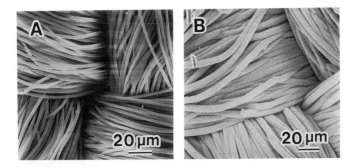

Figure 4. Polyethyleneterephthalate fine fibers constituting a fabric before (A) and after (B) the apatite formation on its surface.

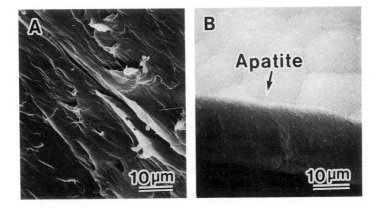

Figure 5. SEM pictures of the surfaces of polyethylene susbtrate modified with Si-OH group on its surface before (A) and after (B) soaking in 1.5SBF for 21 days.

Adhesive strength of thus formed apatite layer to organic polymers reaches 10 MPa.[15]

By this technique, however, the apatite layer can be formed on only the surfaces of the organic polymers faced to the glass particles. In order to form the apatite layer on whole the surface of organic polymers, the Si-OH groups must be formed on them in a liquid or vapor phase without using glass particles. As on of such attempts, the present author recently photografted vinyltrimethoxysilane in vapor phase to polyethylene by using benzophenone as the polymerization initiator and then hydrolyzed the methoxysilane groups into silanol groups with the HCl solution. Although thus treated polyethylene did not form the apatite in SBF, it formed a dense and uniform apatite layer on its surface in a solution (1.5SBF) with ion concentrations 1.5 times those of SBF, as shown in Fig. 5. If the density of the silanol groups further increased and/or the calcium ion is incorporated into the surface layer, apatite could be formed even in SBF. Thus formed apatite-polymer composites in a three dimensional structure analogous to the natural bone might be useful as bone substitutes, since they exhibit mechanical properties analogous to those of the natural bone, as well as high bioactivity.

CONCLUSIONS

Various kinds of apatite-metal and apatite-polymer composite can be prepared by a method mimicking the biomineralization. The characteristics of the products by this method are mechanical properties in a wide range as well as high bioactivity. They could find wide applications as bone-repairing materials.

REFERENCES

1. Li P, Ohtsuki C, Kokubo T, Nakanishi K, Soga N, Nakamura T, Yamamuro T. *J. Am.. Ceram. Soc.*, 1992; **75**: 2094-2097.
2. Ohtsuki C, Kokubo T, Yamamuro T. *J. Non-Cryst. Solids*, 1992; **143**: 84-92.
3. Kokubo T, Ito S, Huanh ZT, Hayashi T, Sakka S, Kitsugi T, Yamamuro T. *J. Biomed. Mater. Res.*, 1990; 24: 331-343.
4. Kokubo T. Biomaterials, 1991; **12**: 155-163.
5. Kim HM, Miyaji F, Kokubo T, Suzuki T, Ito F, Nishiguchi S, Nakamura T. In: Sedel L, Ray C, ed. Bioceramics Vol. 10. Oxford: Elsevier, 1997: 215-218.
6. Kim HM, Miyaji F, Kokubo T, Nakamura T. *J. Ceram. Soc. Japan*, 1997; **15**: 111-116.
7. Kim HM, Miyaji F, Kokubo T, Nakamura T. *J. Mater. Sci. Mater. Med.*, 1997; **8**: 341-347
8. Takadama H, Kim HM, Miyaji F, Kokubo T, Nakamura T. In: LeGeros RZ, LeGeros JP, ed. Bioceramics Vol. 11. Singapore: World Scientific, 1998.
9. Kim HM, Miyaji F, Kokubo T, Nakamura T, *J. Biomed. Mater. Res.*, 1996; **32**: 409-417.
10. Kim HM, Miyaji F, Kokubo T, Nakamura T. *J. Biomed. Mater. Res. :Appl. Biomater.*, 1997; **38**: 121-127
11. Yan WQ, Nakamura T, Kobayashi M, Kim HM, Miyaji F, Kokubo T. *J. Biomed. Mater. Res.*, 1997; **37**: 267-275.
12. Kim HM, Takadama H, Miyaji F, Kokubo T, Nishiguchi S, Nakamura T. In: LeGeros RZ, LeGeros JP, ed. Bioceramics Vol. 11. Singapore: World Scientific, 1998.
13. Miyazaki T, Kim HM, Miyaji F, Kokubo T, Nakamura T. In: Kokubo T, Nakamura T, Miyaji F, ed. Bioceramics Vol. 9. Oxford: Elsevier, 1996: 317-320.
14. Miyazaki T, Kim HM, Miyaji F, Kokubo T, Nakamura T. In: Sedel L, Ray C, ed. Bioceramics Vol. 10. Oxford: Elsevier, 1997: 11-14.
15. Tanahashi M, Yao T, Kokubo T, Minoda M, Miyamoto T, Nakamura T, Yamamuro T. *J. Biomed. Mater. Res.*, 1995; **29**: 349-357.
16. Takadama H, Miyaji F, Kokubo T, Nakamura T. In: Sedel L, Ray C, ed. Bioceramics Vol. 10. Oxford: Elsevier, 1997: 257-260.
17. Tanahashi M, Yao T, Kokubo T, Minoda M, Miyamoto T, Nakamura T, Yamamuro T. *J. Am. Ceram. Soc.*, 1994; **77**: 2805-2808.
18. Kokubo T, Miyaji F, Kishimoto K, Nakumura T. Trans. 5th World Biomater. Cong., 1996; 264.
19. Hata K, Kokubo T, Nakamura T, Yamamuro T, *J. Am. Ceram. Soc.*, 1995; **78**: 1049-1053.

Bioceramics Volume 11, edited by R. Z. LeGeros and J.P. LeGeros
(Proceedings of the 11th International Symposium on Ceramics in Medicine)
New York, NY, USA, November 1998
© 1998 by World Scientific Publishing Co. Pte. Ltd.

PRINCIPLES OF TISSUE ENGINEERING GOVERNING OSTEOGENIC DEVICES

John H. Brekke, D.D.S.,[1] Jeffrey M. Toth, Ph.D.,[2] Esther Vögelin, M.D.[3] and Neil F. Jones, M.D.[4]

[1] THM Biomedical, Inc.,Waterfront Plaza – Suite #608, 325 Lake Ave. South, Duluth, Minnesota;
[2] Medical College of Wisconsin, Department of Orthopaedic Surgery, 9200 West Wisconsin Avenue, Milwaukee, Wisconsin 53226; [3] Abteilung Handchirurgie, Inselspital, CH-3010 Bern, Switzerland;
[4] Department of Plastic and Reconstructive Surgery, Department of Orthopaedic Surgery, School of Medicine, University of California at Los Angeles, Los Angeles, California 90095-6907

Abstract

The essential characteristics of appliances intended to generate controlled, programmable osteogenesis are dictated by the disparate demands placed upon them by wound circumstances, by the cells occupying them and by the surgeons who implant them. This paper illustrates certain principles of design and engineering for these devices by describing metal and ceramic constructs customized for application to the interbody spinal fusion wound model. Other design principles are elucidated by joining conventional plastic surgery procedures with three dimensional, bioresorbable devices to advance processes of osteogenesis.

Keywords: bone morphogenetic protein, osteoinduction, ceramic, polylactic acid, hyaluronan, collagen, tissue engineered device, bone autograft, bone allograft

Introduction

Between 1990 and 1997, incidence of bone graft procedures in the United States increased from 200,000 to 275,000 annually.[6,3] In 1997, spinal fusion operations accounted for 244,000 of these while treatment of maxillofacial, hand and long bone skeletal defects accounted for the remaining 31,000 bone graft surgeries. Autograft and human allograft are the two principle materials used for bone graft procedures.[3]

Successful use of autograft in the spine varies considerably with the surgical site and the amount of graft material required. The use of autograft for anterior *cervical interbody* fusion at a single level produces successful outcomes in about 90% of operations. In contrast, production of successful fusion masses by use of autograft for *posterolateral lumbar* spine fusion is near 70%. Complications associated with the use of autograft for anterior *lumbar interbody* fusion include those associated with autograft harvest, graft collapse, graft subsidence, and pseudoarthrosis. In addition, one study reported that 25% of patients from whom iliac crest grafts had been taken for lumbar spine surgery reported substantial pain at the donor side at an average of five years postoperatively.[11]

Tissue Engineering Principles Governing Design of Osteogenic Devices

Availability of highly pure, recombinant human osteoinductive proteins makes it possible to consider fabrication of synthetic, osteoinductive, bone graft substitute devices. Many investigators have described the physical properties and performance capabilities of an ideal "delivery system" for these morphogens. Their comments have been collected, collated and reduced to a set of six principles governing design and engineering of osteoinductive devices (Table 1).[4,5]

Though biologic performance is the central design consideration for these constructs, other factors are also important. These include: (i) mechanical characteristic requirements for support of induced tissues as well as adjacent host anatomy, (ii) optimum three dimensional architecture, (iii) quantity, quality and

Table 1. Principles of Tissue Engineering Governing Osteogenic Devices

Principle	Description
I. Biocompatibility	Must be non-immunogenic, free of transmittable diseases, and must not elicit chronic foreign body and / or chronic inflammatory reactions. If biodegradable, must completely degrade, in register with bone induction, to physiologic products removed via normal metabolic processes.
II. Gross Architectural Qualities	Must possess an anatomically specific, internal 3-D architecture. Gross size & shape must be readily customized at surgery to conform to individual wound circumstances. Must maintain size, shape and internal 3-D architecture after saturation with morphogen solution / wound fluids long enough to secure its space for occupancy by induced bone.
III. Osteoconduction	Must support bone ingrowth from margins of host bone in the absence of exogenous osteoinductive morphogens.
IV. Chemotaxis	Must afford chemotaxis for mesenchymal and osteoprogenitor cells and must provide a substratum for their attachment.
V. Angiogenesis and Vascularization	Must promote angiogenesis and rapid vascularization within the boundaries of the in vivo cell culture system.
VI. Transport / Controlled Deployment of Morphogens	Must acquire, transport and deliver osteoinductive morphogen without damaging its tertiary conformation, and without irreversibly preventing its interaction with host cells. Must retain the morphogen and all induced biologic activity within the boundaries of macrostructure.
VII. Administrative Issues	Must be fabricated of materials already approved by the U.S. FDA. Must be cost effective over autograft procedures. Must be amenable to sterilization by verifiable processes.

sources of surviving collateral circulation, (iv) provision for initial extracellular matrix, (v) initial host tissue reaction to the implant, and (vi) for biodegradable devices, optimum rates of biodegradation and ability of host tissues to deal with degradation products.

Devices designed to generate programmable osteogenesis may be thought of as three dimensional (3-D), *in vivo* cell culture systems whose components derive from three distinct material classes.[5] The first component, the **macrostructure**, embodies the first three governing principles and is responsible for establishing the unit's gross size and shape, its anatomically specific architecture and mechanical characteristics. The macrostructure is the material foundation - the substratum - of the 3-D, *in vivo* cell culture system. Principles IV and V are manifest in the second component, the **microstructure**, which is responsible for establishing the initial extracellular matrix within the device and for inaugurating chemotaxis and angiogenesis. Additionally, the microstructure is the medium responsible for executing Principle VI; transport and controlled deployment of **soluble morphogens and growth factors**, the third material class critical to osteoinductive *in vivo* cell culture systems. Finally, the *in vivo* cell culture device is responsible for confining all biologic activity within the unit's boundaries and for restricting the morphogen's plieotropic capacity, and mesenchymal cells' pleuripotent nature, to the single task of generating healthy enduring bone of (i) prescribed size and shape, (ii) at prescribed anatomic locations and (iii) possessing site specific mechanical characteristics.

Application of Tissue Engineering to Interbody Spine Fusion

Calcium Phosphate Ceramics +/- rhBMP-2 Calcium phosphates have excellent biocompatibility but are limited in their medical applications by their poor mechanical properties. Evaluation of calcium phosphates for interbody fusion in the canine and caprine cervical spine has shown that graft extrusion, fracture, and incorporation depend on whether the materials are porous or dense. Porous ceramics have the potential for bone ingrowth, but may fracture.

In two caprine studies, we augmented the biphasic ceramic and Biocoral™ with bone morphogenetic proteins (rhBMP-2 and Ne-Osteo) to increase graft incorporation and promote cervical interbody fusion.[1,12] We also used either a titanium cage or an anterior cervical plate to prevent fracture of the porous HA/β-TCP ceramics.[12] In these studies, radiographic fusion scores for all treatment groups were higher than those previously reported for autograft. Despite the presence of an anterior plate or titanium cage, ceramic fractures occurred at the same rate. Graft intrusion/extrusion did not occur in groups with a titanium cage, but did occur with an anterior plate. Groups with bone morphogenetic protein(s) (BMP) did not reveal more peri-implant bone, bone in the anterior or posterior margins, or bone in the pores of the ceramic compared to identical groups without BMPs.[1,12] Thus ceramics may not be effective carriers for BMPs if they change the conformation of the protein. Secondly, the caprine cervical interbody model is more mobile compared to other models, producing a fusion rate of 30-50% with autograft compared to 90% with autograft in humans.

Allograft +/- rhBMP-2 Femoral ring allograft cylinders are currently being used for lumbar interbody fusions. In a primate study, allograft rings were filled with autograft in one group (3 animals) and rhBMP-2 on a collagen sponge in another group (3 animals). These grafts were used for anterior interbody fusion at L7-S1. The autograft + allograft ring group showed partial fusions with an immune response in some animals. The allograft ring with rhBMP-2 group showed: 1) solid fusions at L7-S1, 2) no immune response, and 3) nearly complete allograft resorption with extensive *de novo* bone.[7] This construct complied with the basic tissue engineering principles by providing a mechanically competent macrostructure of allograft ring, a collagen (type I) microstructure and an osteoinductive morphogen (rhBMP-2).

Porous Tantalum +/- rhBMP-2 Since graft collapse and subsidence are complications associated with the use of autograft for anterior lumbar interbody fusion, tissue engineering research has focused on development of metallic macrostructures with a high degree of interconnecting porosity which: 1) simulate the architecture of cancellous bone, 2) have mechanical properties similar to bone, and 3) can induce spinal fusion and obviate the need for autograft harvest. Hedrocel™ (Implex Corp.) is primarily composed of the metal tantalum, which has excellent corrosion resistance, good mechanical properties, and excellent biocompatibility. It is fabricated by chemical vapor deposition of tantalum onto a highly porous reticulated carbon skeleton. The resulting implant has a porosity of 75-80% with interconnecting pores in the range of 500-600μm. With this porosity, a compressive strength of 42.3 MPa and a Young's Modulus of 1.57 GPa (similar to cancellous bone) is obtained.[2] Porous, threaded tantalum cylinders were implanted into 12 sheep for interbody fusion at L4-L5 or L5-L6. Six sheep received a tantalum cylinder implant only. Another 6 sheep received the same cylinder augmented with 1 ml of rhBMP-2 at a concentration of .43mg/ml (43μg/100μL). All sheep were sacrificed at 6 months.

In the tantalum only group, histological analysis showed that 1/6 animals had a certain fusion, 4/6 animals had partial/incomplete fusions and 1/6 animals had a certain non-fusion. Also in this group, there were few fusions in the anterior or posterior margins. Histologically, all 6 animals in the rhBMP-2 group showed solid unions through the device as well as fusions in the anterior and posterior margins. Augmentation with rhBMP-2: 1) produced unions through the device (90% with versus 28% without), 2) induced fusions in the anterior and posterior margins, and 3) eliminated peri-implant pseudoarthroses. All porous tantalum cylinders maintained intervertebral distraction and did not subside.

Titanium Spinal Fusion Cages   Since graft collapse and subsidence are complications associated with the use of autograft for anterior lumbar interbody fusion, titanium spinal fusion cages have been developed. These cages are stronger than autograft and can be implanted via laparoscopic or open anterior and posterior interbody approaches. The titanium cage functions as a macrostructure and satisfies several stipulations of categories I and II of Table 1. It is customary to load the cages with autograft. However, by employing collagen type I as a microstructure, and rhBMP-2 as an osteoinductive morphogen, a bioactive response over and above that of autograft can be anticipated. In an ovine model, titanium cages were inserted via a left anterior retroperitoneal approach. Six animals received a cage packed with rhBMP-2 on a collagen sponge, while 8 animals received a cage packed with iliac crest autograft.

Although radiographs did not reveal non-fusions, histological analysis revealed the presence of thin pseudoarthroses surrounding the cages packed with autograft in 5/8 cases (fusion rate = 37.5%). When the cage was packed with rhBMP-2 on a collagen sponge, a 100% fusion rate was obtained. In addition, quantitative histomorphometry on microradiographs revealed 50% *de novo* bone formation in the rhBMP-2 augmented cages. In this model, augmentation with rhBMP-2 significantly increased the fusion rate of titanium cages compared to the same implant with autograft.

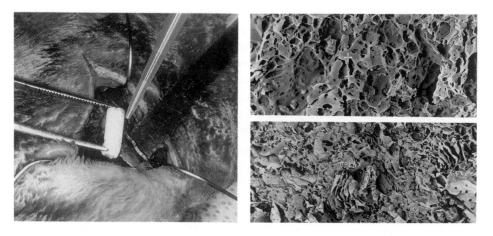

Figure 1a. Charging OPLA / HY with rhBMP-2 Figure 1b. SEM: OPLA macrostructure (above) and OPLA with HY microstructure (below)

A Three Dimensional In Vivo Cell Culture System

We hypothesized that a concert of surgical technique and device design/engineering might be achieved by joining a pedicled periosteal flap (PFL) to a bioresorbable scaffold in the architecture of cancellous bone.[8-10] By investing the scaffolding with biologic attributes critical to the biology of early wound healing and osteogenesis, we might be able to prefabricate a vascularized bone graft applicable to a variety of clinically important wound models. Data from the first pilot study are reported below.

Figure 1a depicts a bioresorbable cylinder designed and fabricated according to the principles of Table 1. It consists of a D,D-L,L-polylactic acid **macrostructure** (OPLA) invested with a **microstructure** of hyaluronic acid (HY); the composite unit is designated OPLA / HY. This cylinder is being charged with a solution of **osteoinductive morphogen (rhBMP-2)**. In the study reported here, these devices were wrapped in a pedicled periosteal flap and implanted into the groin to prefabricate a vascularized bone graft. Once charged with morphogen, this device embodies all six design principles set forth in Table 1. Although osteoconduction (formation of *de novo* bone in the absence of exogenous BMP) was not observed in this model, OPLA macrostructure has demonstrated osteoconductive capacity in other studies.[5]   Figure 1b demonstrates the relationship between the OPLA macrostructure and the dry hyaluronan microstructure prior to investment of the BMP solution.

Materials and Methods   Periosteal flaps (PFL), pedicled on the saphenous artery and vein, were dissected off the medial surface of the tibia of three month old male Lewis rats (360g +/- 19.6g). Each flap measured 3cm X 1cm and consisted of three layers; periosteum, muscle and fascia. After harvesting, the flap was tubed on itself to form a water tight chamber 1cm X 1cm. Vascularized periosteal flaps were constructed in twenty -one animals using both hind limbs (42 flaps); the animals were divided into six groups as follows: Group 1 - empty periosteal chamber; Group 2 - consisted of the periosteal flap and 0.100 ml of rhBMP-2 @ 20μg / 100μL; Group 3 - was identical to Group 2 but the vascular pedicle was ligated proximally; Group 4 - the flap was harvested without the periosteal layer and was turned "inside out"; Group 5 - consisted of the periosteal flap and polylactic acid / hyaluronan matrix (OPLA/HY); Group 6 - was identical to Group 5 but with 0.100ml rhBMP-2 @ 20μg / 100μL invested in the OPLA / HY matrix. (Table 2)

After prefabrication, each periosteal chamber was transferred on its vascular pedicle into the groin. Animals in groups 1-4 were sacrificed at intervals of 4 and 8 weeks after surgery (24 limbs / 12 animals). Animals in groups 5 and 6 were sacrificed at intervals of 2, 4 and 8 weeks after surgery (18 limbs / 9 animals).

Table 2 - Experimental Groups

Group No.	Flaps	Matrices	rhBMP-2	Time Points	Limbs
1	Periosteal Flap	----------	----------	4, 8 weeks	6
2	Periosteal Flap	----------	20μg rhBMP-2	4, 8 weeks	6
3	Avascular Periosteal Flap	----------	20μg rhBMP-2	4, 8 weeks	6
4	Fascial Flap	----------	20μg rhBMP-2	4, 8 weeks	6
5	Periosteal Flap	OPLA / HY	--------------	2, 4, 8 weeks	9
6	Periosteal Flap	OPLA / HY	20μg rhBMP-2	2, 4, 8 weeks	9

Figure 2 - Presence and radiographic density of new bone formation at 2,4, and 8 weeks

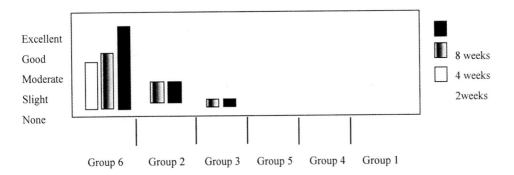

The presence and density of new bone formation in the groin was evaluated radiologically at each time period. The increase in radiodensity was scored using 5 grades (none, slight, moderate, good and excellent) in each group and over time. After sacrifice the chambers were explanted, fixed in formalin and processed for histology. Three transverse sections were taken through the center of each periosteal chamber and stained with hematoxylin and eosin.

Results   All animals survived and gained 21.5% weight over the 8 week period. Radiographically, Group 1 (PFL alone), Group 4 (fascial flap-BMP) and Group 5 (PFL + OPLA / HY) specimens demonstrated no bone formation over the 8 week incubation period. Very little mineralization was observed in some Group 3 specimens (avascular periosteal flaps). Slight radiodensity was observed in Group 2 animals (PFL + BMP). Excellent bone formation was produced in Group 6 specimens (PFL + OPLA / HY + BMP). (Figure 2)

Histology of tissues from Groups 1, 3, 4 and 5 revealed no bone formation. Foci of intermembranous ossification were seen in Group 2 sections (PFL + BMP). Group 6 (PFL + OPLA / HY + BMP) histology showed a progression of structures initiated by fibrous connective tissue which was gradually replaced by intermembranous ossification producing woven bone predominantly at the 4 week observation period, marrow tissue and mixed woven and lamellar bone and marrow tissues at the 8 week period. The osteogenic capacity of periosteum with OPLA / HY was mainly effective in combination with BMP (Group 6). Increased bone formation in Group 6 tissues could be demonstrated quantitatively by increased radiodensity and qualitatively by histologic evidence. Group 5 specimens exhibited a fibrovascular tissue characterized by mild to moderate foreign body and chronic inflammatory reactions. Angiogenesis was seen in Group 5 tissues within the boundaries of the OPLA macrostructure as well as in remnant flap tissue adjacent to the macrostructure's exterior surfaces.

Conclusions

Principles of Table 1 can be employed to produce osteoinductive devices from a variety of different materials. This choice of materials allows the tissue engineer flexibility to customize these constructs according to mechanical and biologic demands of individual wound models. By joining a synthetic device, fabricated according the principles of Table 1, to a pedicled vascular periosteal flap, the therapeutic boundaries of both may be extended to prefabrication of a vascularized bone **autograft,** of prescribed size and shape, that is applicable to a wide variety of orthopaedic reconstructive procedures.

References

1.   An HS, Toth JM, et al. Proceedings, 12th NASS, New York, NY, pp. 313-314, 1997.
2.   Boyd LM, Estes BT. Proceedings, 3rd IMAST, Munich, Germany, 1996.
3.   Brekke, JH. Personal communication. Frost & Sullivan, 1998.
4.   Brekke, J.H.: A rationale for delivery of osteoinductive proteins. Tissue Eng., 2(2): 97-114, 1996.
5.   Brekke, J.H. and Toth, J.M.: Principles of Tissue Engineering Applied to Programmable Osteogenesis. J.   Biomed. Mat. Res. (Applied Biomat.), Special Issue 1, 1998. In Press.
6.   Damien CJ, Parsons JR. *Journal of Applied Biomaterials* 1991;2(3):187-208.
7.   Hecht BP, Fischgrund JS, et al. Proceedings, 12th NASS, New York, NY, p.280, 1997.
8.   Hitoshi I, Susumu T, Hiroshi Y, et al. *Plast Reconstr Surg* 1996;97:512.
9.   Ichiro O, Hironori G, Kazuyoshi S, et al. *Plast Reconstr Surg* 1995;95:1265.
10.   Kostopoulos L, Karring T. *J Clin Periodontol*, 1995;22:247.
11.   Summers BN, Eisenstein SM. *J Bone Jt Surg* 1989;71-B(4):667-680.
12.   Toth JM, Lim TH, et al. Transactions, 43rd ORS, San Francisco, CA, p. 188, 1997.

III. BIOCERAMICS: PREPARATION AND PROPERTIES

Bioceramics Volume 11, edited by R. Z. LeGeros and J.P. LeGeros
(Proceedings of the 11th International Symposium on Ceramics in Medicine)
New York, NY, USA, November 1998
© 1998 by World Scientific Publishing Co. Pte. Ltd.

SINTERED BIOACTIVE COATING OF DENSE ALUMINA

J. Cavalheiro, M.Brás
INEB - Instituto de Engenharia Biomédica
R. Campo Alegre, 823- 4150 Porto Portugal
FEUP - Faculdade de Engenharia da Universidade do Porto

ABSTRACT

Alumina is one of the strongest ceramics. It has been applied in some biomedical applications, namely in the orthopaedic field. Bone bonding to this material is very poor, therefore it is considered as a bioinert ceramic. The objective of this work is to improve the surface properties of alumina using a hot coating technique. The use of sodium silicate solutions provides a bioactive glazing that was evaluated mechanically and submitted to immersion tests in simulated body fluid.

KEYWORDS: alumina, coating, bioactive ceramics.

INTRODUCTION

Alumina is a well-known inert biomaterial. In recent years some of its mechanical properties have been improved and consequently it was largely used in substitute hip joint, particularly for the ball.

The production of wear debris has largely been considered one of the main reasons for the aseptically loosening of those prosthesis(1). To avoid the production of debris some authors attempted to use also ceramic acetabulum. For such type of ceramic/ceramic devices, alumina is considered to be one of the best solutions, because of the low wear rate of the system (2,3).

However, poor adjustment between the socket and bone is a major problem, which induces the migration of the socket and acetabular cup loosening (4,5).

The objective of this work is to change the surface of alumina providing a bioactive surface to this inert biomaterial.

MATERIALS AND METHODS

Samples of pure and dense alumina (Degussa), were immersed in a 25% and 50%(v/v) commercial sodium silicate solution. The samples were dried at 90°C after having removed the excess of solution on the surface with an absorbent paper, and heat-treated at 1000°C (reference S). Another group (SI), after sintering was immersed in the same sodium silicate solution and dried after having removed the excess solution on the surface with absorbent paper.

The structure and chemical composition of the coating was studied using SEM (JEOL 6301 F) and EDS microanalysis (NORAN VOYAGER).

To evaluate the mechanical behaviour of the coatings, a microhardness device (Shimadzu) was used to make Vickers indentation with a 200g load.

The adhesion of the coatings and the possibility of coating peeling-off were also evaluated by the immersion in liquid nitrogen and scratching the surface with a sharp knife.

The surfaces of samples S were covered with 100 µl of de-ionised water (pH 7); two minutes later the pH was measured with strips of indicator paper. Another group of coated samples S, were immersed for 24 h in de-ionised water and the chemical composition of the surface was compared with control samples.

The two groups of samples (S and SI) were immersed in simulated body fluid (SBF) (NaCl 58.5, NaHCO$_3$ 84.0, KCl 74.5, K$_2$HPO$_4$.3H$_2$O 228.0, MgCl$_2$.6H$_2$O 203.3, Na$_2$SO$_4$ 142.1, CaCl$_2$ 111.1 g/ mol) during four days, and half of the samples of group S were re-immersed, now in a solution with 1.5 times the normal concentration of the inorganic solution of human plasma (1.5 SBF), during other four days. The samples surfaces were observed and analysed.

RESULTS AND DISCUSSION

Coatings adhesion

The samples treated with the 50% silicate solution presented a large number of surface cracks. The same problem was observed when the solution of 25% was used without removing the excess of the liquid after immersion.

The observation of the samples in the scanning microscope after scratching or immersion in liquid nitrogen and Vickers indentation indicated that the coating thickness on the sintered conditions used, shouldn't exceed 5-7 μm. If the concentration of the silicate solution is too high (50%), or the excess of the liquid film after immersion in the weaker solution (25%), is not removed, the coating will crack when submitted to mechanical stresses.

In Figure 1a coating peeling may be observed after mechanical damage.

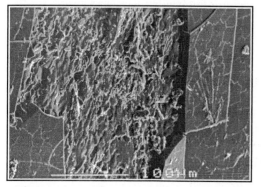 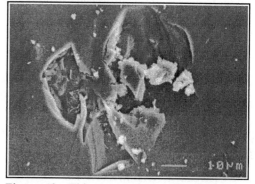

Figure 1a. After mechanical damage, S coatings with a thickness exceeding 5- 7 μm presented cracks.

Figure 1b. Thinner coatings after Vickers indentation exhibit limited destruction of surface.

When the preparation conditions were adjusted, a continuous and sound coating was obtained.

When submitted to the Vickers test, the coating showed only small damages on the areas of contact with the diamond penetrator. The cracks don't propagate around the defect, as it may be observed on Figure 1b.

The analysis of damaged portions of the coating gives information of the type of bonding. It was observed that some Si and Na were combined with the bottom of alumina substrate, after having removed the coating (Figure.2). The presence of alumina on detached layers indicates that the heat-treatment had induced some diffusion from the substrate to the coating layer.

On the SI group samples, damaged coating strips exhibit a net separation between two layers, normally joined together, but separated by a narrow line.

In some exceptional situations the two layers appear to be completely split apart, as can be seen on Figure 3a.

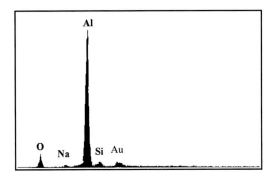

Figure 2. Diffused Si and Na on alumina substrate after sintering of samples S.

The chemical composition of the layer S (Na_2O 7.7, SiO_2 24.3, Al_2O_3 58.8, P_2O_5 2.2, CaO 7.1 Wt%) and I layer (Na_2O 30.0, SiO_2 56.5, Al_2O_3 10.9, Wt%) is a clear indication that the calcium phosphate precipitates were formed under the I layer, that consequently, was not completely attached to the sintered layer.

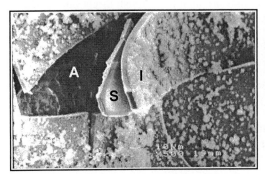

Figure 3 a. Double layer of SI samples. A-alumina base; S-sintered layer; I-layer formed after immersion in silicate solution.

Figure 3 b. Sample S: calcium phosphate precipitates after immersion in SBF and 1.5 SBF.

The layer S is a glass sintered on the alumina substrate, and the I layer is a dried precipitate of a sodium silicate solution. The layer S is chemically bonded to alumina as opposed to the SI, which seems to be only physically bonded to the melted silicate S.

Immersion tests

After two minutes of contact with 100 μL of water, the pH increased to 8.5. The initial solution was removed and another test in the same conditions again raised pH above 8. The alkaline reaction of the coating may explain its ability to induce calcium phosphate precipitation from solution. The selective ion exchange of Na^+ for H_3O^+ can explain the fast increase in pH.

Comparing the surface composition of the coating S, analysed at 22 KeV using EDS, (Al_2O_3 39.4, SiO_2 39.6, Na_2O 20.8 Wt %), with the composition after 24 hours of immersion in water (Al_2O_3 64,5, SiO_2 25.2, Na_2O 10.18 Wt %), we may assume that the large increase of the Al_2O_3

may derive from the alumina substrate influence, that is much stronger after immersion because some dissolution of the coating may cause the coating thickness to be reduced. The relationship between SiO_2/Na_2O changes from 1.9 on the control to 2.48 after immersion. This appears to be the result of a greater loss of sodium to the medium, which will indicate that after immersion, a silica rich layer will remain on the surface.

These results indicate similarities with the accepted dissolution mechanism of the bioactive glass (6).

The immersion in SBF yields different results for the samples S and SI. Four days of immersion were enough to cover SI samples with a thick layer of calcium phosphate precipitates. Samples S needed to remain for longer periods in solution (4 + 4 days), but after immersion for four more days in a higher concentration solution (1.5x SBF), they could achieve a completely covered surface, similar to the SI group.

As it may be observed in Figure 3b, after 4 days of immersion in SBF plus four days in 1.5 SBF, the samples of the S group were totally covered with calcium phosphate precipitates.

The samples of the SI group were more active than the S samples, i.e., they are faster covered with calcium phosphate precipitates, but the layer prepared by simple immersion at room temperature, the I layer, seems to have a weaker bond to the S coating, when compared to the chemical bond between silicate and alumina of the S layer.

As it is generally accepted, the materials that exhibit a fast reaction of calcium phosphate precipitation when immersed in SBF solutions are able to establish direct bone bonding (7); so, we can speculate that the bioactive glazing of alumina could be useful, providing an improved surface to this strong but inert ceramic.

CONCLUSIONS

The hot-treatment of alumina with a sodium silicate solution, allowed the formation of a continuous and thin film of glaze, sintered to the substrate. This coating provides an active surface that is expected to be a useful way of changing the bioinert behaviour of alumina.

REFERENCES

1. Hailey JL et al. Proc. of the 5th World Biomaterials Congress, Toronto, Canada 1996; 550.
2. Sedel L et al. Clin Orthop 1994; **298**: 175-183.
3. Fruth HJ et al. Biomaterials 1997; **18**: 873-876.
4. Winter M et al. Clin. Orthop 1992; **282**: 73-80.
5. H. Plank, Salzer M., In: A. Ravaglioli ed. New York: Elsevier Ap. Science, 1992: 17-25.
6. L. Hench, et al. *Classes of Materials Used in Medicine*. In Biomaterials Science ed. Buddy D. Ratner at al, Academic Press, 1996:73-83.
7. Panjian L., Kazuki N., Klaas de Groot, et al. Biomaterials 1993; **14**: 963-968.

Bioceramics Volume 11, edited by R. Z. LeGeros and J.P. LeGeros
(Proceedings of the 11th International Symposium on Ceramics in Medicine)
New York, NY, USA, November 1998
© 1998 by World Scientific Publishing Co. Pte. Ltd.

CERAMIC FEMORAL COMPONENT OF KNEE PROSTHESIS

J. Cihlár[1], M.Trunec[1] and V. Šída[2]

[1]Technical University of Brno, Technická 2, 616 69 Brno, Czech Republic; [2]Dias Company, P epe ská 1302 , 511 20 Turnov, Czech Republic

ABSTRACT

The technology of powder injection moulding of ceramic femoral components of a knee prosthesis has been developed. The mould for injection moulding designed by CAD was made of surface-hardened stainless tool steel. The feedstocks prepared from alumina, ZTA and zirconia powders and thermoplastic binders were high-pressure-injection moulded and the moulded components were fired in an air atmosphere. Physical and mechanical properties of the ceramic femoral components were evaluated according to EC standards.

It was found that the ceramic femoral components have properties that are sufficient to allow consideration of their use as a replacement of metallic components. The potential application of the powder injection moulding process that has been developed is in the large-scale production of ceramic femoral components and bioceramic parts of intricate shapes.

KEYWORDS: knee prosthesis, injection moulding, alumina, ZTA, zirconia

INTRODUCTION

Current knee prostheses have the femoral component made of metal and the tibial component of polyethylene (UHMWPE). The results obtained for hip prostheses have demonstrated that in terms of abrasive wear the combination of metal and PE exhibits negative properties so that the prostheses have to be ussualy replaced within 10 years. A considerable reduction in abrasive wear of the polyethylene occurs when the metallic femoral component of the hip joint was replaced by a ceramic component [1-4]. Clinical tests conducted by Japanese authors on knee prostheses with ceramic femoral component have also yielded positive results [5,6].

The femoral component of the knee joint is larger and of more intricate shape than that of the hip joint. Its production is therefore much more complicated . There are grounds to believe that ceramic powder injection moulding might be an appropriate method for its fabrication. An advantage of this method lies in the possibility of shaping ceramic components of intricate shapes with high productivity and low costs, and with low demands on finishing operations. A disadvantage of the method can be seen in the complexity of the technological process and the lack of basic information about its individual steps [7]. Problems of injection moulding of ceramic components of ca 100 cm^3 in volume are still the subject of fundamental research.

Falling under this size category   is also injection moulding of the femoral component of knee prosthesis made of bioceramics on the base of alumina, zirconia and ZTA, which is the subject of the present work.

MATERIALS AND METHODS

Used for the preparation of ceramic components of the knee prosthesis were alumina (RC-HP DBH, Malakoff Ind., USA), zirconia (TZ-3YS, Tosoh Corp., Japan) and zirconia- toughened alumina (ZTA-85, Daiichi Kigenso, Japan) and thermoplastic polymeric binder [8]. A flowchart of the preparation of ceramic knee components can be seen in Fig. 1.

The polymer-ceramic melt was injection moulded in a metal mould shown in Fig. 2.

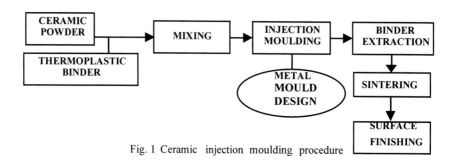

Fig. 1 Ceramic injection moulding procedure

Fig. 2 The mould for injection moulding made of surface-hardened stainless tool steel

The optimum shape of the mould was obtained by the CAD method. The binder in the moulded components was subjected to thermal extraction and the components were subsequently sintered at temperatures from 1500 °C to 1530 °C for a period of 2 hours. The relative density of ceramic specimens was determined by the Archimedes method. Linear shrinkage was established by measuring the dimensions prior and subsequent to sintering. Flexural strength was determined by the three-point method [9] and fracture toughness by the indentation method. The relation for the calculation of fracture toughness from the crack length is given in [10].

RESULTS AND DISCUSSION

The ceramic components after binder extraction are shown in Fig. 3. All three types of ceramic material (A - alumina, B - ZTA, C - zirconia) have a good surface quality without any apparent surface or volume defects. The sintered femoral components are shown in Fig. 4.

All the three types were of good surface quality without visible defects. In all the three cases, e.i. alumina, zirconia and ZTA , the dimensional proportionality of components remained unchanged after sintering. Linear shrinkage of the ceramics after sintering was 16% (alumina, ZTA) or 18.2% (zirconia) (see Table 1). The highest relative density was found in the components made of alumina (99.9%), the lowest in the components made of zirconia (98.9%).

Injection moulded ceramic materials exhibited flexural strength properties comparable with the same values of materials prepared by other methods [9]. The flexural strength values were 530

MPa for alumina components, 650 MPa for ZTA components, and 890 MPa for zirconia components.

The fracture toughness value for alumina and ZTA was 4.3 MPa.m$^{1/2}$, for zirconia the value was twice as high (8.6 MPa.m$^{1/2}$). The Young modulus was decreasing in the following order: alumina > ZTA > zirconia.

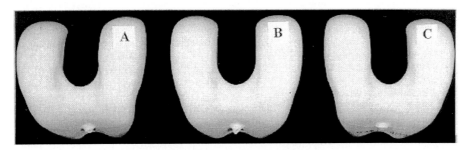

Fig. 3 Ceramic components of the knee prosthesis after binder extraction
(A - alumina, B - ZTA, C - zirconia)

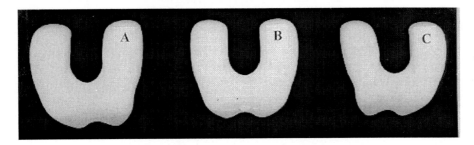

Fig. 4 Ceramic components of the knee prosthesis after sintering
(A - alumina, B - ZTA, C - zirconia)

Table 1 Mechanical and physical properties of bioceramics used for injection moulding of ceramic component of knee prosthesis

Ceramics	MOR [MPa]	Weibull modulus [-]	K_{IC} [MPa·m$^{1/2}$]	E [GPa]	Relative density [% t.d.]	Linear shrinkage [%]
Al$_2$O$_3$	530	7.9	4.3	364	99.9	16.0
ZTA	650	9.1	4.3	326	99.1	16.0
TZP	890	8.8	8.6	200	98.9	18.2

CONCLUSIONS

The shaping of femoral components of knee prostheses made of ceramic materials based on alumina, ZTA and zirconia by injection moulding is feasible. The quality of injection moulded femoral components and the physical and mechanical properties of the ceramics used are comparable with products prepared by other methods.

Continued development of the method of injection moulding will in the near future provide for a comparatively inexpensive production of the majority of intricate bioceramic components.

ACKNOWLEDGEMENT

This study was supported by EC grant CIPA-CT94-0233 and CR grants VS96121.

REFERENCES

1. Willmann G. In: Fischman G, Clare A, Hench LL, ed. *Bioceramics: Materials and Applications, Ceramic Transactions, vol.48*, Westerville: American Ceramic Society, 1994: 83-89.

2. Oonishi H, Igaki H, Takayama Y. In: Oonishi H, Aoki H, Sawai K, eds. *Proceedings of 1st International Symposium on Ceramics in Medicine*, Ishiyaku EuroAmer. Inc., 1988 : 272-277.

3. Ohashi T, Inoue S, Kajikawa K, Ibaragi K, Tada T, Oguchi M, Arai T, Kondo. In: Oonishi H, Aoki H, Sawai K, eds. *Proceedings of 1st International Symposium on Ceramics in Medicine*, Ishiyaku EuroAmer. Inc., 1988: 278-283.

4. Okumura, Yamamuro T, Kumar T, Nakamura T, Oka M. In: Oonishi H, Aoki H, Sawai K, eds. *Proceedings of 1st International Symposium on Ceramics in Medicine*, Ishiyaku EuroAmer. Inc., 1988: 284-289.

5. Oonishi H, Okabe A, Hamagchi T, Nabeshima T. *Orthop. Ceramic Implants* 1982; **1**: 157-160.

6. Inoue H, Yokoyama Y, Tanabe G. In: Oonishi H, Aoki H, Sawai K, eds. *Proceedings of 1st International Symposium on Ceramics in Medicine*, Ishiyaku EuroAmer. Inc., 1988: 301-307.

7. German RM. *Powder Injection Molding*. New Jersey: Metal Powder Industries Federation, 1990: 17-18.

8. Trunec M, Cihlar J, *J. Eur. Ceram. Soc.* 1997; **17**: 203-209.

9. European Standard EN 843-1.

10. Japan Standard JIS R 1607.

Bioceramics Volume 11, edited by R. Z. LeGeros and J.P. LeGeros
(Proceedings of the 11th International Symposium on Ceramics in Medicine)
New York, NY, USA, November 1998
© 1998 by World Scientific Publishing Co. Pte. Ltd.

CERAMIC-CERAMIC BEARING SYSTEMS FOR THP WITH ZIRCONIA HEADS

F. Villermaux, L. Blaise, J.M. Drouin, B. Calès
Norton Desmarquest Fine Ceramics, ZI n°1, 27025 Evreux cedex, France

ABSTRACT

Ceramic-Ceramic (C-C) hip systems are an alternative to Metal-Polyethylene (M-PE) or Ceramic-Polyethylene (C-PE) systems to avoid PE debris and their consecutive adverse body reactions. The development of a ceramic insert was conducted in order to reach high level of tribological and mechanical reliability. Disk-on-disk and 3-point bending tests determined zirconia-alumina as the most appropriate from both wear and mechanical aspects. In this paper, hip joint simulator tests in three different lubricants and Finite Element Analyses (FEA) were conducted to confirm the preliminary results on the head-cup systems. Zirconia-alumina definitively presented a lower wear rate compared to M-PE and C-PE. FEA attested maximum stresses are located in head, justifying use of zirconia for the head rather than for the cup. Decrease of the head-cup clearance reduced the cup stresses so that radial clearance smaller than 45μm should be advised. Decrease of cup thickness induced an increase of the cup stresses which means a thickness lower than 4mm should not be advised.

KEYWORDS: Ceramic-ceramic system, zirconia, alumina, wear, mechanical resistance

INTRODUCTION

Total Hip Prostheses (THP) require low wear rate and high fracture resistant bearing systems. Zirconia ceramic heads facing polyethylene cups have already been successfully implanted for 12 years. Such clinical performances are attributed to the extremely low surface roughness[1,2] and the outstanding mechanical properties of these zirconia heads. As polyethylene became a great concern in terms of debris-induced osteolysis, next generations of bearing systems involve hard-hard pairings. In developing a new C-C bearing system, two aspects have been studied: the tribological performance and the mechanical resistance of the bearing components. In a preliminary study, disk-on-disk tests evaluated zirconia-alumina or alumina-zirconia as the most wear resistant ceramic-ceramic combination.[3-4] Besides, 3-point bending tests on zirconia and alumina rods revealed a bending resistance higher than 1800 MPa for zirconia and about 600 MPa for alumina. As literature on ceramic-ceramic shows fractures preferably located in the head, it seemed the head is more sensitive in C-C systems.[5] This is the reason why, preference has been given to the more mechanical resistant zirconia for the head and the more brittle alumina for the cup.

In this paper, zirconia-alumina head-cup systems were studied on a hip joint simulator with different lubricants and by FEA to study tribological performance and determine safe geometric parameters of the new C-C head-cup systems.

MATERIALS AND METHODS

The ceramics studied were zirconia (Prozyr®, Norton Desmarquest, France) and alumina (Norton Desmarquest, France). All materials were hot isostically pressed after sintering in order to reach full density. Mean grain size is 0.5 and 2 μm for zirconia and alumina respectively.

28 mm ceramic heads and cups were tested on a hip joint simulator (MTS) in an antianatomical position using Paul's curve loading (max load peak at 2.6 kN) at 1Hz up to 5

million cycles (Mc), in comparison with commercially available M-PE and zirconia-PE systems. The tests have been carried out in three different lubricants: Plasmion®, bovine serum diluted at 30% in distilled water, albumin and globulin mixture diluted in distilled water. EDTA has been added in the two last lubricants. The total protein content of the three lubricants was abound 20-30 g/l, as advised by Polineni et al.[6] Weight loss of the cups has been evaluated by a gravimetric method with a balance whose accuracy was 1 mg, and then, volume loss of the cup has been calculated using a density of 3.98 for alumina and 0.93 for PE. Optical interferometer completed the analysis of surface roughness.

Finite Element Analysis of the complete system (stem taper - zirconia head - alumina cup - titanium metal back - bone block) has been carried out on ANSYS 5.3 software (Fig. 1). A 2D axisymmetric model simulated an axial loading to evaluate the stress intensities and distribution for taper-locked cup design along the variations of some geometrical parameters of the cup (thickness, clearance). The mechanical characteristics of the different components are described in Table 1. Some non-linear contact elements have been introduced at the taper-head interface with a friction coefficient of 0.15, at the head-cup interface with a friction coefficient of 0 and at the cup-metal back interface with a friction coefficient of 0.15. The top of the bone block has been constrained to no displacement in Y direction and the base of the stem taper has been constrained to displacement in Y direction until a resultant force of 10 kN.

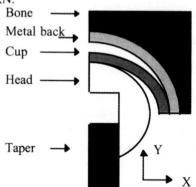

Table 1:. Mechanical Characteristics of Components

	Young modulus	Poisson's ratio
Metallic taper	115 GPa	0.31
Zirconia head	220 GPa	0.29
Alumina cup	330 GPa	0.29
Metal back	115 GPa	0.31
Bone block	20 GPa	0.42

Fig.1: Scheme of the FEA model

RESULTS

Hip joint simulator results

Fig. 2 presents the wear results obtained for the M-PE, zirconia-PE and zirconia-alumina head-cup systems in the three lubricants. For each combination, Plasmion® lubricant induced less volume loss of the cups than the diluted bovine serum and the highest wear rate is obtained with the mixture of albumin and globulin, even for zirconia-alumina as observed by optical interferometer. In the three lubricants, the M-PE produced more wear than the zirconia-PE. The zirconia-alumina systems presented lowest volume loss (lower 1 mm³ after 5 Mc) in the three lubricants.

M-PE data in literature[7] indicate some wear between 46 and 170 mm³/year. Then, considering that one million cycles are equivalent to one year, the most representative lubricant, in term of *in vivo* wear rate, is the diluted bovine serum (54 mm³/Mc) and eventually the mixture of albumin and globulin for the high wear level (104 mm³/Mc).

Decrease of the wear rate from M-PE to zirconia-PE is mainly due to the smaller roughness of the zirconia head (Ra=3 nm) compared to the metallic head (Ra=20 nm).[1,2] Improvement observed with C-C system would be explained by a full fluid lubrication compared to a mixed or boundary lubrication for M-PE and zirconia-PE systems as estimated by calculation.[8]

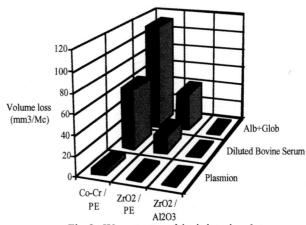

Fig.2: Wear test on hip joint simulator

FEA results

Fig.3 presents the areas of high stress distribution in the complete system as described in Fig. 1 (σ_1 for ceramics and $\sigma_{Von\ Mises}$ for metal and bone). In this case, the zirconia head has a neck length of 0 and the cup has the thickness of 5 mm, a taper angle of 6° and a radial clearance of 45μm. Areas of high tensile stress level in ceramic components are:

a)   in the head: the taper-head interface (hoop stresses) and the top of the bore

b)   in the cup: the outer top and an inner ring around the contact surface with the head.

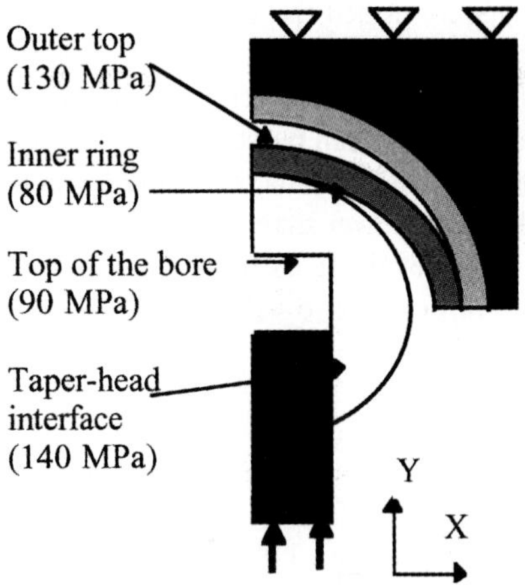

This analysis confirmed the fact that generally the most solicited ceramic component is the head. The studied zirconia presents high mechanical properties and, in particular, a threshold value of the stress

Outer top
(130 MPa)

Inner ring
(80 MPa)

Top of the bore
(90 MPa)

Taper-head
interface
(140 MPa)

Fig.3: σ_1 in ceramic components

intensity factor K_{10} of about 3 MPa√m below which no crack propagation would appear.[9] This stress intensity factor allows to determine a "critical" value of about 900 MPa in fatigue loading. The tensile stress intensities observed here by FEA are much more lower than the "critical" value for the zirconia.

The variation of the stresses in the alumina cup versus the thickness is shown in Fig.4 (for a clearance of 45μm) and versus the clearance in Fig.5 (for a thickness of 5mm). The decrease of the thickness from 7 mm to 3 mm mainly induced a stress increase at the inner surface of the cup from 40 MPa to 250 MPa. Besides, a decrease of the radial clearance from 75 μm to 15 μm mainly induced a stress decrease at the outer top of the cup surface from 200 MPa to 70 MPa. This might be correlated to the increase of the cup-head contact area. The good mechanical properties and the fine microstructure of this alumina lead us to consider a safety coefficient of 0.5 applied to its static bending resistance to determine a fatigue "critical" value of 300 MPa.[10] Then, a thickness lower than 4 mm should not be advised and efforts should be done to reduce the radial clearance down to 45 μm.

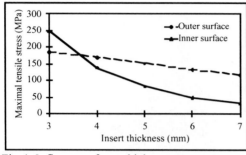
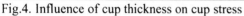

Fig.4. Influence of cup thickness on cup stress

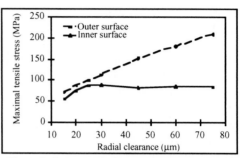

Fig.5. Influence of clearance on cup stress

CONCLUSIONS

Preliminary study allowed to identify zirconia-alumina system as the most wear resistance C-C combination. Because of the higher stresses in the head and the better fracture resistance of the zirconia, preference has been given to a zirconia head facing an alumina cup. Hip joint simulator tests confirmed the clear decrease of wear rate compared to commercially available M-PE or zirconia-PE systems. In this zirconia-alumina systems, FEA attested that higher stresses are located in head rather than in cup. The stresses reached in the zirconia head are always much more lower than burst stress. In contrast, for some extreme geometries of taper-locked cup design, stresses in alumina cup could reach "critical" values leading to high fracture risk. Then, a thickness lower than 4mm should not be advised. Of course, each design should be studied by FEA to evaluate its particular stress distribution and safe geometric parameters. Mechanical tests are in progress to validate the FEA results.

REFERENCES

1. Besong AA, Hailey JL, Ingham E, Stone M, Wroblewski BM, Fisher J. *Bio-Med Mater Eng.* 1997; **7**: 59-65.
2. Derbyshire B, Fisher J, Dowson D, Hardaker C, Brummitt K. *Med Eng Phys* 1994; **16**: 229-235.
3. Chevalier J, Cales B, Drouin JM, Stefani Y. In Sedel L, Rey C, ed. *Bioceramics Volume 10.* Paris:Elsevier Science Ltd:1997; 271-274.
4. Cales B, Chevalier J. In Jacobs JJ, Craig TL, eds, *ASTM STP 1346.* American Society for Testing and Materials, 1998: to be printed.
5. Polineni VK, Wang A, Essener A, Stark C, Dumbleton JH. *23rd Annual Meeting of the Soc for Biomat.* 1997: 154.
6. Toni A, Sudanese A, Busanelli L, Zappoli FA, Brizio L, Giunti A In Sedel L, Cabanela ME, eds. *Hip Sur., Mater. and Dev.,* 1st ed. London: Martin Dunitz Ldt: 1998;267-276.
7. Sawer WL, Anthony ME. In Jacobs JJ, Craig TL, eds, *ASTM STP 1346.* American Society for Testing and Materials, 1998: to be printed.
8. Jin ZM, Dowson D, Fisher J. *Proc Instn Mech Engrs.* 1997; **221H**: 247-256.
9. Calès B, Stefani Y, Olagnon C. Fantozzi G. In Ducheyne P, Christiansen D, eds. *Bioceramics 6*; Oxford: Buiterworth Heinemann: 1993;
10. Guim F, Reere J, Vaughan DAJ. *J Mater Sci.* 1991; **26**: 3275-3286.

Bioceramics Volume 11, edited by R. Z. LeGeros and J.P. LeGeros
(Proceedings of the 11th International Symposium on Ceramics in Medicine)
New York, NY, USA, November 1998

APATITE-FORMING ABILITY OF ZIRCONIA GEL IN MODIFIED SBF SOLUTIONS

M. Uchida,[1] H.-M. Kim,[1] F. Miyaji,[1] T. Kokubo[1] and T. Nakamura[2]

[1]Department of Material Chemistry, Faculty of Engineering, Kyoto University, Kyoto 606-8501, Japan; [2]Department of Orthopedic Surgery, Faculty of Medicine, Kyoto University, Kyoto 606-8507, Japan

ABSTRACT

Apatite-forming ability of zirconia gel was examined in a simulated body fluid (SBF) with ion concentrations nearly equal to those of human blood plasma and those a little increased in its pH, or concentration of calcium or phosphate ion. It was found that the zirconia gel forms the apatite on its surface even in the original SBF and that its apatite-forming ability significantly increases by an increase in pH or concentration of calcium or phosphate ion in SBF. This indicate that zirconia ceramics could exhibit bioactivity when their surfaces are modified so that alkali, calcium or phosphate ion is released from the surface to form a lot of Zr-OH groups on their surfaces in body environment.

KEYWORDS: Sol-gel method, Zirconia gel, Simulated body fluid (SBF), Apatite Bioactivity

INTRODUCTION

Zirconia ceramics have higher fracture toughness, higher flexural strength and lower elastic modulus than alumina ceramics. If they become bioactive, they could find wide applications as bone-repairing materials. It was shown recently that titanium metal and its alloys can become bioactive when they are subjected to NaOH and heat treatments. This is because an amorphous sodium titanate layer is formed on the surfaces of metals by these treatments.[1] The Na^+ ion in the surface layer exchanges with H_3O^+ ion in body environment. The Ti-OH group thus-formed on the surface induces the apatite nucleation, and the released Na^+ accelerates this apatite nucleation by increasing OH^- concentration in the surrounding body environment.

The purpose of the present study is to examine possibility for providing bioactivity to the zirconia ceramics by such surface treatments. A zirconia gel abundant in Zr-OH groups on its surface was prepared as a model substance of the surface layer of the zirconia ceramics, and its apatite-forming ability was examined in a simulated body fluid (SBF) with ion concentrations almost equal to those of the human blood plasma. In order to investigated the effect of ion released from the zirconia ceramics on their apatite-forming abilities, apatite-forming ability of the zirconia gel was also examined in SBFs a little increased in pH, or concentration of calcium or phosphate ion.

MATERIALS AND METHODS

Reagents of $Zr(O\text{-}nPr)_4$, H_2O, C_3H_7OH and HNO_3 were mixed with molar ratio of 1: 34.5: 1: 0.1. A high purity silica glass plate $10 \times 10 \times 1$ mm^3 in size was dipped into the solution and withdrawn at a rate of 1 cm/min by 10 times, and then kept at 40°C for 24 h to obtain a zirconia gel film on its surface.[2]

Simulated body fluid (SBF) and its modified ones, pH values and ion concentrations of which are shown in Table 1, were prepared by dissolving reagent grade chemicals of $CaCl_2$, $K_2HPO_4 \cdot H_2O$, KCl, NaCl, $MgCl_2 \cdot 6H_2O$, $NaHCO_3$ and Na_2SO_4 into distilled water. Each fluids were buffered at the target pH with tris-hydroxymethyl-aminomethane $((CH_2OH)_3CNH_2)$ and HCl at 36.5°C, i.e. at pH 7.50 and pH 7.60 for pH7.50SBF and pH7.60SBF and at 7.40 for all other fluids.

The specimens were soaked in 30 mL of these fluids at 36.5°C for various periods. Surfaces of the specimens after the soaking were examined by thin-film X-ray diffraction (TF-XRD; RINT-1400, Rigaku Co., Japan) and scanning electron microscopy (SEM: S2500CX, Hitachi Co., Japan).

RESULTS AND DISCUSSION

Figure 1 shows the SEM photographs of the surfaces of specimens soaked in the SBF and its modified fluids for 14 days. Island-like spherulites are observed on all the specimens. They were revealed to be crystalline apatite by TF-XRD. It can be seen from Fig. 1 that the density of apatite spherulites fairly increased by increase in pH, calcium or phosphate ion concentration. Figure 2 shows the induction period for the apatite formation on the zirconia gel, which was determined by SEM observation, in the SBF and its modified fluids. It can be seen from Fig. 2 that the induction period for the apatite formation on the zirconia gel decreases significantly with the increase in any of pH, calcium or phosphate ion concentration of the SBF.

It is apparent from these results that zirconia hydrogel forms the apatite on its surface even in the original SBF, and that its apatite-forming ability increases by increase in pH or concentration of the calcium or phosphate ion in SBF. This indicates that Zr-OH groups also can induce the apatite nucleation in SBF similar to Si-OH and Ti-OH groups,[3]

Table 1. The pH and ion concentrations of the human blood plasma and those of the SBF and its modified fluids.

				Ion Concentration / mM					
	pH	Ca^{2+}	HPO$_4{}^{2-}$	K$^+$	Na$^+$	Mg^{2+}	Cl$^-$	HCO^{3-}	SO$_4{}^{2-}$
Blood plasma	7.40	2.50	1.00	5.00	142	1.50	103.0	27.0	0.50
SBF	7.40	2.50	1.00	5.00	142	1.50	147.8	4.20	0.50
pH7.50SBF	7.50	2.50	1.00	5.00	142	1.50	147.8	4.20	0.50
pH7.60SBF	7.60	2.50	1.00	5.00	142	1.50	147.8	4.20	0.50
Ca1.25SBF	7.40	3.13	1.00	5.00	142	1.50	149.1	4.20	0.50
Ca1.50SBF	7.40	3.75	1.00	5.00	142	1.50	150.3	4.20	0.50
P1.25SBF	7.40	2.50	1.25	5.50	142	1.50	147.8	4.20	0.50
P1.50SBF	7.40	2.50	1.50	6.00	142	1.50	147.8	4.20	0.50

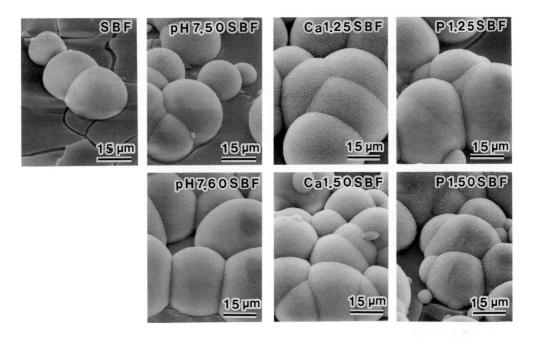

Figure 1. SEM photographs of the surfaces of specimens soaked in SBF and its modified fluids for 14 days.

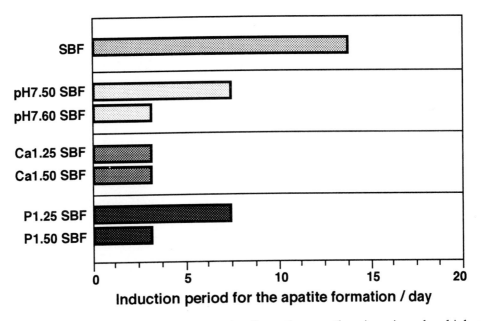

Figure 2. Induction period for the apatite formation on the zirconia gel, which was determined by SEM observation, in the SBF and its modified fluids.

and its apatite nucleation can be accelerated when concentration of OH^-, Ca^{2+} or HPO_4^{2-} ion in the surrounding fluid increased by some reason, since the ionic activity product of the apatite in the surrounding fluid increases. Once the apatite nuclei formed, they grow spontaneously by consuming the calcium and phosphate ions from the surrounding fluid, since the SBF is already highly supersaturated with respect to apatite.[1] When the ionic activity product of the apatite in the surrounding fluid increased, the growth of the apatite is also accelerated. Such a situation could be allowed when zirconia ceramics release alkali, calcium or phosphate ion into the SBF. This indicates that zirconia ceramics also could exhibit bioactivity if their surfaces are modified so that alkali, calcium or phosphate ion is released from their surfaces into the body environment to form a large number of Zr-OH groups on their surfaces.

CONCLUSIONS

Zirconia gel was found to form the apatite on its surface even in the original SBF, indicating that Zr-OH groups are able to induce an apatite nucleation. The apatite formation could be significantly accelerated by a small increase in pH, calcium or phosphate ion concentration in the SBF. These results suggest that zirconia ceramics also could exhibit bioactivity if their surfaces are modified so that alkali, calcium or phosphate ion is released from their surfaces to form a lot of Zr-OH groups on their surfaces in body environment.

ACKNOWLEDGMENT

This study was supported by Grant-in-Aid for Scientific Research, the Ministry of Education, Science, Sports, and Culture, Japan.

REFERENCES

1. Kim H.M, Miyaji F, Kokubo T, Nakamura T, *J. Biomed. Mater. Res.*, 1996; 32: 409-417.
2. Kamiya K, Yoko T, Tanaka K, Itoh H. *Yogyo-Kyoukai-Shi*, 1987; 95: 1157-1163.
3. Li P, Ohtsuki C, Kokubo T, Nakanishi K, Soga N, Nakamura T, Yamamuro T, de Groot K. *J. Biomed. Mater. Res.*, 1994; 28: 7-15.

Bioceramics Volume 11, edited by R. Z. LeGeros and J.P. LeGeros
(Proceedings of the 11th International Symposium on Ceramics in Medicine)
New York, NY, USA, November 1998
© 1998 by World Scientific Publishing Co. Pte. Ltd.

STABILITY OF HYDROXYAPATITE AT PHYSIOLOGIC TEMPERATURE

Paul W. Brown

Room 136 Materials Research Laboratory, Penn State University, University Park, PA 16802

ABSTRACT

Factors controlling the crystallization and dissolution of hydroxyapatite (HAp) are of significant importance with regard to its use as a bioceramic. Of particular interest in this respect is the *in vivo* formation of HAp monoliths by cement-like reactions of calcium phosphate precursors. Depending on the intended application, it is highly desirable that the reactions leading to HAp formation reach nominal completion in clinically relevant periods of time. Also depending on the intended application of a cement preparation, it may be desirable to exercise control over the rate at which the HAp monolith can resorb. Rates of resorption are anticipated to be sensitive to the composition of the HAp formed and to its microstructure.

It is well accepted that non-stoichiometric HAp compositions can be produced at physiologic temperature. However, non-stoichiometric compositions are sometimes regarded as non-equilibrium solids. The stability relationships among HAp compositions having Ca/P ratio extending from 1.5 to 1.67 are discussed. This is done by employing concepts permitting the representation of the relevant phase equilibria in the CaO-P_2O_5-H_2O ternary system. The compositional relationships involving HAp, solution, and acidic calcium phosphates are considered. Establishing these relationships permits the mechanistic paths taken during HAp crystallization to be described. Using this background, parameters influencing the kinetics of HAp formation from calcium phosphate precursors and the likely variations in the aqueous phase during HAp formation are discussed.

KEYWORDS: hydroxyapatite, physiologic, kinetics

INTRODUCTION

Recently there has been much interest in producing hydroxyapatite in monolithic form at physicologic temperature. The genesis of the forming HAp in this way is the work carried out by Brown and Chow at the ADA Fellowship at NBS[1]. Among the reactions by which HAp monoliths can be produced, the following have been studied in detail by the Penn State group[2-4]:

$$2CaHPO_4(\cdot 2H_2O) + 2Ca_4(PO_4)_2O \Rightarrow Ca_{10}(PO_4)_6(OH)_2 \; (+ 4H_2O) \qquad \text{EQ. 1}$$

Calcium-deficient HAp forms according to the following reaction:

$$6CaHPO_4(\cdot 2H_2O) + 3Ca_4(PO_4)_2O \Rightarrow 2Ca_9(HPO_4)(PO_4)_5OH \; (+ nH_2O) \qquad \text{EQ. 2}$$
where n = 1 or 13.

Another example is the formation of calcium-deficient HAp using monocalcium phosphate monohydrate (MCPM)[5]:

$$2Ca(H_2PO_4)_2 \cdot H_2O + 4Ca_4(PO_4)_2O \Rightarrow 2Ca_9(HPO_4)(PO_4)_5OH + 2H_2O \qquad \text{EQ. 3}$$

However in this instance, reaction proceeds in two steps. In the first MCPM reacts with TetCP to rapidly form $CaHPO_4 \cdot 2H_2O$. This, in turn, reacts with the remaining TetCP to form HAp according to EQ 2.

In addition, single-phase HAp forms from a single solid precursor[6]:

$$3\alpha Ca_3(PO_4)_2O + H_2O \Rightarrow Ca_9(HPO_4)(PO_4)_5OH \qquad \text{EQ. 4.}$$

These equations serve to illustrate that HAp of two compositions, $Ca_9(HPO4)(PO4)_5OH$ and $Ca_{10}(PO_4)_6(OH)_2$, can be formed by reactions of calcium phosphate precursors at low temperature. However, it is not universally accepted that calcium-deficient HAp is a thermodynamically stable phase.

ANALYSIS

Our prior work has demonstrated calcium-deficient HAp will form in preference to stoichiometric HAp when the bulk Ca/P ratio is 1.5^{2-5}. For example, $CaHPO_4$ reacts with $Ca_4(PO_4)_2O$ to form non-stoichiometric HAp in the following sequence:

$$12CaHPO_4 + 6Ca_4(PO_4)_2O \Rightarrow 3Ca_{10}(PO_4)_6(OH)_2 + 6CaHPO_4 \qquad \text{EQ 5}$$

Then $$3Ca_{10}(PO_4)_6(OH)_2 + 6CaHPO_4 \Rightarrow 4Ca_9HPO_4(PO_4)_5OH. \qquad \text{EQ 6}$$

If non-stoichiometric HAp were metastable, the principle of free energy minimization would preclude its formation and the final assemblage of solids would be $CaHPO_4$ and $3Ca_{10}(PO_4)_6(OH)_2$, both of which are stable solids. Thus, calcium-deficient HAp formation is not the consequence of the formation of a metastable phase being kinetically favored. Although it solubility will be higher than that of stoichiometric HAp, calcium-deficient HAp is an equilibrium solid. The practical consequence of this is that it is possible to form a range of HAp compositions which will exhibit a range of *in vivo* responses. Calcium-deficient HAp should be anticipated to exhibit greater bioactivity than stoichiometric HAp

A number of implications arise if calcium-deficient HAp is a stable solid. It must exhibit a true solubility. It must co-exist in equilibrium with other solids. Importantly, it is not stoichiometric HAp which exists in equilibrium with the more acidic calcium phosphate $CaHPO_4$; it is $\sim Ca_9HPO_4(PO_4)_5OH$. Because of this, the stability relationships involving HAp and other compounds must be consistent with these consequences. Establishing these provides a means to elucidate the mechanistic path taken in HAp formation.

Figure 1[after 7] illustrates the relationships between HAp, $CaHPO_4$, $Ca(H_2PO_4)_2 \cdot H_2O$, and $Ca(OH)_2$. This figure plots the compositional points and the solubility isotherms for these compounds using the method of plotting the 5th roots of the compositions of solutions and solids[8] expressed in terms of CaO and P_2O_5. In particular this figure permits the compositional variability of HAp to be illustrated. The nose-shaped solubility isotherm for HAp extends from point B to point C. A solubility minimum can be observed. Although $CaHPO_4$,

$Ca(H_2PO_4)_2 \cdot H_2O$, and $Ca(OH)_2$ are compounds of fixed composition, HAp is not. HAp is a compound of variable composition with the range: $Ca_{(10-x)}(HPO_4)_x(PO_4)_{(6-x)}(OH)_{(2-x)}$. If this figure x ranges from 0 to 1, however the limit on x is not critical to the concept that $Ca(OH)_2$ and $CaHPO_4$ exist in equilibrium with hydroxyapatites having different compositions. Thus $Ca(OH)_2$ is in equilibrium with stoichiometric HAp while $CaHPO_4$ is in equilibrium with $\sim Ca_9HPO_4(PO_4)_5OH$. This illustrates the reason why hydroxyapatites having different compositions (Ca/P ratios) can be produced by varying the proportions of the same precursors as illustrated in EQ. 1 and EQ. 2.

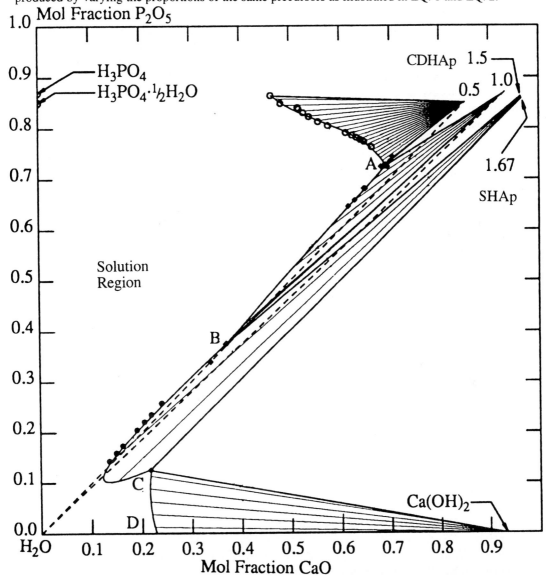

Figure 1. Ternary diagram[after 7] showing the solubility isotherms and compositional points for various calcium phosphates. HAp with Ca/P = 1.5 is CDHAp, stoichiometric HAp is SHAp. Tie lines connect compositions of solutions and solids in equilibrium. The dashed line connecting the water origin with the compositional point for $CaHPO_4$ (not a tie line) intersects the HAp solubility isotherm.

In some instances the rate of conversion of $CaHPO_4$ and $Ca_4(PO_4)_2O$ to HAp can be sluggish. Rapid reaction is desirable to ensure that physical property development is sufficient for wound closure in orthopedic applications or for monolith integrity in dental applications. Figure 1 also provides a basis for establishing the mechanistic path taken when particles of $CaHPO_4$ and $Ca_4(PO_4)_2O$ are intermixed and reacted with water. Prior work[9] showed that the pH values of such reacting assemblages can range from about 10.5 to about 11.5 as the $CaHPO_4$-to-$Ca_4(PO_4)_2O$ ratio increases from 2:1 to 1:1. These pH values were maintained until the reactions reached completion. However, regardless of this ratio, pH values in this range are significantly higher than that theoretically predicted[1]. This is indicative of the dissolution of the acidic reactant, $CaHPO_4$, being the rate limiting step. The basis for slow dissolution of $CaHPO_4$ is shown in Figure 1. When a crystallite of $CaHPO_4$ is placed in water, its dissolution will cause calcium and total phosphate (regardless of the speciation) to enter solution in a molar ratio of 1-to-1. The compositional path taken in this process is established by striking a line between the water origin and the compositional point for $CaHPO_4$. As the solution is enriched with calcium and phosphate, the compositional changes will follow that line. Eventually sufficient dissolution will have occurred that the solution composition will intersect that of a solubility isotherm. If the solution composition intersected the solubility isotherm for $CaHPO_4$, a saturated solution would have been achieved and further dissolution of $CaHPO_4$ would stop. However, Figure 1 shows that $CaHPO_4$ dissolution results in the intersection with the solubility isotherm for HAp, not for $CaHPO_4$. Thus, $CaHPO_4$ dissolution results in a solution saturated in HAp, but not in $CaHPO_4$. Because of this, $CaHPO_4$ dissolution continues causing the solution to become supersaturated with respect to HAp. The greatest driving force for HAp precipitation is near the surfaces of the dissolving $CaHPO_4$ crystallites where the concentrations of calcium and phosphate are the highest. Thus, the incongruent dissolution of $CaHPO_4$ results in its overgrowth by HAp with the consequence that the area of the $CaHPO_4$-solution interfacial region is reduced. Commensurate with this reduction is that further reaction becomes increasingly dependent on diffusionally controlled transport. A similar mechanistic argument can be made in the analysis of HAp formation from $CaHPO_4 \cdot 2H_2O$ and $Ca_4(PO_4)_2O$. Thus, the stability characteristics of HAp in relationship to those of calcium phosphates with which it can exist in equilibrium at physiologic temperature influences the rate at which it may be formed by cement-like reactions.

ACKNOWLEDGMENT

The author gratefully acknowledges the support of NIH Grant DE 09421.

REFERENCES

1. Brown WE, Chow LC. CRP-1986, Westerville: Am Ceram Soc, 1987; 351-79.
2. Martin RI, Brown PW. *J Biomed Mater Res* 1997; **35**: 299-308.
3. TenHuisen KS, Brown PW. *Mater in Med* 1996; **7**: 309-16.
4. TenHuisen KS, Brown PW. *J Biomed Mater Res* 1997 **36**: 233-241.
5. Fulmer MT, Martin RI, Brown PW. *Mater in Med* 1992; **3**: 299-305.
6. TenHuisen KS, Brown PW. *Biomaterials*, in press.
7. Martin RI, Brown PW. *J Am Ceram Soc* 1997; **80**, 1263-66.
8. Brown PW. *J Am Cer Soc* 1992; **75**: 17-22.
9. Brown PW, Hocker N, Hoyle S. *J Am Ceram Soc* 1991; **74**: 1848-55.

Bioceramics Volume 11, edited by R. Z. LeGeros and J.P. LeGeros
(Proceedings of the 11th International Symposium on Ceramics in Medicine)
New York, NY, USA, November 1998

CO₃-APATITE PREPARATIONS WITH SOLUBILITY GRADIENT: POTENTIAL DEGRADABLE BIOMATERIALS

M. Okazaki[1], T. Matsumoto[1], M. Taira[1], J. Takahashi[1] and R.Z. LeGeros[2]

[1]Department of Dental Materials Science and Technology, Osaka University Faculty of Dentistry, Suita, Osaka 565-0871, Japan, and [2]New York University Dental Center, New York, NY 10010, USA.

ABSTRACT

The purpose of this study was to prepare and characterize CO_3 apatite material, which will have a degradable outer layer and a relatively stable core to provide potential biomaterials with solubility gradient. The materials were synthesized at $80 \pm 1°C$ and pH 7.4 ± 0.2, by simultaneously feeding Solution I and Solution II into mechanically stirred 1.3 mol/L acetate buffer solution. Solution I consisted I of 0.5 L of 100 mmol/L $Ca(CH_3COO)_2$; Solution II consisted of 0.5 L of 60 mmol/L $NH_4H_2PO_4$ solution into which a constant concentration of 95 mmol/L $(NH_4)_2CO_3$ was fed. The preparations were characterized using x-ray diffraction (XRD), scanning electron microscopy (SEM) and electron spectroscopy.

X-ray diffraction analysis showed a typically apatitic XRD pattern, although the (300) reflection peak shifted to the higher direction (indicating a CO_3-for-PO_4 substitution) and was broader (indicating lower crystallinity) than that of CO_3-free apatite. SEM analysis showed small congregated crystals. Electron spectroscopy for chemical analyses of pelletized specimen showed a gradient of carbonate concentration, decreasing with depth. The apparent solubility in 0.5 mol/L acetate buffer solution (37°C, pH 4.0) was much higher than that of CO_3-free hydroxyapatite. These results suggested that apatite with carbonate concentration gradient, and subsequently, solubility gradient, can be formed by this process. CO_3-apatite prepared in the manner described in this study may be used as biodegradable materials with solubility gradient.

Keywords: carbonate apatite; functionally graded; solubility; ESCA

INTRODUCTION

Biological apatites (i.e., mineral phases of enamel, dentin, bone, cementum) are not pure calcium hydroxyapatite but carbonate-containing apatite, with coupled substitution of CO_3-for-PO_4 and Na-for-Ca [1]. Synthetic CO_3-apatite with crystallinity and carbonate similar to that of bone apatite can be prepared [2-4]. CO_3-apatite as a possible biomaterial is the subject of several investigations. A composite of CO_3-apatite and collagen prepared previously by Okazaki et al, was shown to have good biocompatibility for both soft and hard tissues in rats [5]. The composite was successfully replaced by new bone. However, bone density and mechanical strength did not seem to recover completely.

Recently, functionally graded materials (FGM) have been developed for use in engineering fields [6]. In the case of apatite, we speculated that each apatite crystal can have an ionic distribution even at the crystal level. Studies on heterogenous apatite formation led to the development of a two-step supply system to prepare apatite whose core and outside or surface composition can be controlled: for example, HAp(*core*)/F-Ap(*surface*) or F-Ap/HAp [7]; CO_3-Ap/$MgCO_3$-Ap or $MgCO_3$-Ap/CO_3-Ap [8].

CO_3 incorporation in the apatite has been shown to affect lattice parameters, cause a reduction in crystallinity (crystal size) and increase in extent of dissolution [3,4,9,10]. In this study, we designed a continuous gradient carbonate supply to investigate the preparation of carbonate-containing apatite with a relatively soluble surface and stable core. A comparatively stable hydroxyapatite covered with metabolic apatite is expected to yield a relatively strong but bioactive material.

MATERIALS and METHODS

Functionally graded carbonate-containing hydroxyapatite, GC03Ap, was synthesized at $80 \pm 1°C$ and pH 7.4 ± 0.2 using a gradient carbonate supply system. Briefly, 0.5 L of 100 mmol/]L $Ca(CH_3COO)_2$ solution (Solution 1) and 0.5 L of 60 mmol/L $NH_4H_2PO_4$ solution (Solution II), into which 0.5 L of 60 mmol/L $NH_4H_2PO_4$ solution containing a constant concentration of 95 mmol/L $(NH_4)_2CO_3$ was continuously supplied, were fed into mechanically stirred 1.3 mol/L acetate buffer solution. Carbonate was supplied in a time-dependent manner according to the following equation.

$$y = C_t/C_o = 1^{(-v}{}_oV_o)^t$$

where V_o: Solution II volume (liter, L) = constant;
C_t: carbonate concentration (mmol/L), time dependent;
v_o: flow rate (L/hr);
C_o: initial carbonate concentration (mmol/L)

Since we wished to obtain $C_{t=2}$ =60 mmol/L (equivalent to the carbonate concentration of bone apatite) when supply flow rate and period are v_o = 0.25 L/hr and 2 hr, we estimated the initial carbonate concentration, C_o = 95 mmol/L, from equation, y = 0.629.

X-ray diffraction (XRD) was used to characterize the precipitates and estimate crystallinity. Measurements were made on a Rigaku Denki X-ray Diffractometer, Utima$^+$ with graphite-monochromatized CuKα radiation at 40 kV, 30 mA. Scanning electron micrographs (SEM) of crystals were obtained with a Hitachi 9000. ESCA analysis with a Shimadzu Axis-HS was carried out on pellets pressed at 25 MPa and annealed at 500°C for lhr. The depth profile of the carbonate peak (Cl_s binding energy: 284-291 eV) was analyzed using the Ar etching technique for 30 min from the surface towards the center of the pellet. Calcium concentrations were determined using atomic absorption spectrophotometer (Shimadzu AA-6400). Total phosphate concentrations were determined by the UV spectrophotometric method [11]. Carbonate concentrations were determined using Conway's titration method [12].

Samples were incubated in 0.5 mol/L acetate buffer solution (37°C, pH 4.0) for one month. Calcium concentration in the solution was adopted as a m arker of apparent solubi lity.

RESULTS and DISCUSSION

Chemical compositions of the precipitate synthesized heterogeneously, $GC0_3Ap$, were Ca 9.18 $\pm$ 0.10 mmol/g, P = 5.11 $\pm$ 0.12 mmol/g and CO_3 = 0.84 $\pm$ 0.09mmol/g. The precipitates gave typically apatitic XRD patterns, although its crystallinity was lower than that of homogeneous hydroxyapatite, HAp. The expanded (300) reflection peak of $GC0_3Ap$ showed an upward shift, indicating a CO_3-for-PO_4 substitution in the apatite [3,4,9]. Line-broadening, $\beta_{1/2}$, of the (300) reflection was much lower than that of homogeneous HAp indicating a reduction in crystallite size [2-4,9]. The phosphate content decreased, reflecting the substitution of CO_3^{2-} ions, when compared with that of HAp. Calcium content also showed a slight decrease due to substitution and consequent lattice imperfection.

Scanning electron micrographs showed coagulated round crystals (Fig.1), which still developed along the c-axis, differing from the plate-like shape of homogeneous CO_3-apatite with similar CO_3 concentrations [4,9,13]. The length along the c-axis was shorter than those of hydroxyapatite and fluorapatite. The shape of GCO_3Ap crystals are probably reflected by the shape of the core HAp but cannot maintain the original sharp hexagonal shape because of the deformation caused by the substitution of CO_3^{2-} ions. FCO_3Ap/CO_3Ap synthesized by a two-step fluoride supply system in the presence of CO_3^{2-} appeared as large hexagonal crystals covered with many small crystals [8,13]. The marked differences in crystal shape between FCO_3-Ap and small CO_3-apatite probably prevented epitaxial crystal formation. On the contrary, in this study, epitaxial formation was observed.

ESCA analysis clearly showed a negative gradient distribution in Cls intensity (atomic concentration) of carbonate from the crystal surface toward the inner core (Fig. 2). Ar etching was performed for 30 min (= 1800 sec). This depth can estimate approximately 90 nm because 1 min Ar etching is equivalent to about 3 nm for SiO_2 as a standard. However, it must be noted that these data are average values not for a single crystal but for multiple crystals arranged at the smooth flat surface of the pellet. With the results of ESCA, we can speculate on the graded carbonate concentration in the apatite crystals. The carbonate concentration at the surface of the crystal may be much higher than that of the inner core. Furthermore, previous results obtained in two-layer crystals also suggested this gradient of carbonate concentration [7].

Apparent solubility of GCO_3-Ap was increased markedly compared to homogeneous HAp, and was slightly lower than that of homogeneous CO_3-Ap (Ca = 43.6 $\pm$ 0.7 mmol/L). The apparent solubility in one month was not markedly different from that following incubation for one day (Ca = 40.5 $\pm$ 0.3 mmol/L). After a 1-hr short incubation, the (300) reflection peak was split and showed a slight downward shift, i.e. approached the position of hydroxyapatite. SEM observation of the residual powder sample showed slim needle-like crystals.

The apparent solubility was much higher than that of HAp and similar to that of homogeneous CO_3-Ap. This may have been due to the control of the solubility of the soluble surface layer which contained higher levels of CO_3, since CO_3 substitution in apatite has been shown to cause an increase in its solubility [10]. This gradation is desirable for biodegradable CO_3-Ap with a soluble surface and relatively stable core for use as a biomaterial.

This study demonstrates a method for the preparation of functionally graded CO_3-Ap.

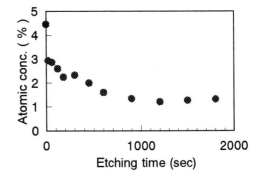

Fig. 1: SEM micrograph of functionally graded CO_3-apatite (GCO_3Ap).

Fig. 2: Cls depth profile of electron spectroscopy (ESCA) of CO_3 concentration of GCO_3Ap.

ACKNOWLEDGMENTS

The valuable technical assistance of Drs.M.Inoue (Institute of Scientific and Industrial Research, Osaka University) and Mr. Y. Yoshida (Shimadzu Co. Ltd). in SEM and ESCA analyses is gratefully acknowledged. This work was supported in part by Research Grants No. 08672233, 09558119 and 10123218 from the Ministry of Education of Japan.

REFERENCES

1.   LeGeros RZ. *Prog Cryst Growth Charact* **4**: 1-45, 1981
2.   Okazaki M, Moriwaki Y, Aoba T, Doi Y, Takahashi J. *Caries Res* **15**: 477-483, 1981.
3.   LeGeros RZ, Trautz, OR, LeGeros JP, Klein E. *Bull Soc Chim (Fr)*, pp. 1712-1723, 1968.
4.   LeGeros RZ. Calcium Phosphates in Oral Biology and Medicine. Vol. 15. Myers H (Ed). In: Monographs in Oral Sciences, Basel: Karger, 1991.
5.   Okazaki M, Ohmae H, Hino T. *Biomaterials* **10**:564-568, 1989.
6.   Hirai, T. *Materials Science and Technology* Vol. 17B Weinheim: VCH Verlagsgesellshaft MBH 1996, pp.295-341.
7.   Okazaki M. Biomaterials **13**: 749-754, 1992.
8.   Okazaki M, LeGeros RZ. Adv Dent Res **10**: 252-259, 1996.
9.   LeGeros RZ, Trautz OR, LeGeros JP, K]ein E, Shirra WP. *Science* **155**:1409-1411, 1967.
10. LeGeros RZ, Tung M. *Caries Res* **17**: 419-429, 1983.
11. Eastoe JE. *Method for the Determination of Phosphate, Calcium, and Protein in Small Portions of Mineralized Tissues* (PhD Thesis). Liege: Universite de Liege, 1965.
12. Conway EJ. *Microdiffusion Analysis and Volumetric Error.* 3rd ed, Van Nostrand, New York, 1950.
13. Okazaki M. *J Dent Res* **72**: 1285- 1290, 1993.

Bioceramics Volume 11, edited by R. Z. LeGeros and J.P. LeGeros
(Proceedings of the 11th International Symposium on Ceramics in Medicine)
New York, NY, USA, November 1998
© 1998 by World Scientific Publishing Co. Pte. Ltd.

PROCESSING OF POROUS HYDROXYAPATITE BY STARCH CONSOLIDATION

L.M. Rodríguez-Lorenzo[1], J.M.F. Ferreira[2], M. Vallet-Regí[1]

[1]Departamento de Química Inorgánica y Bioinorgánica, Facultad de Farmacia, Universidad Complutense, E-28040 Madrid, Spain; [2]Departamento de Engenharia Cerámica e do Vidro, Universidade de Aveiro, 3810-Aveiro, Portugal.

ABSTRACT

A new consolidation method for forming porous ceramic called "starch consolidation" has recently been developed. The procedure is based on the gelling ability of starch in water, belongs to the group of direct consolidation methods and allows a good homogeneity of the consolidated bodies. In this work, porous hydroxyapatite materials have been manufactured using starch, both as consolidator/binder and as a pore former. Slurries with a 50 % of solid load were prepared and moulded in plastic moulds. After drying, burning out the starch and sintering, materials with porosities between 45 and 69 % were obtained with the overall pore structure dominated by the large spherical shaped pores of about 80 μm left by the starch particles and smaller pores due to the contact areas of larger pores. Flexural strength of the materials was measured in four points bending test. The strength of the prepared materials decreases linearly with the total porosity.

KEYWORDS: Porous hydroxyapatite, starch consolidation, ceramic processing

INTRODUCTION

There are different techniques to obtain porous ceramics such as the polymeric sponge method[1] or foaming processes[2], but, a general problem is how to control the processing and the ultimate material properties in terms of pore structure and component dimensions. Recently a new method called "starch consolidation" has been developed[3]. The procedure is based on the gelling ability of starch in water, belongs to the group of direct consolidation methods and allows a good homogeneity of the consolidated bodies. In this work, porous hydroxyapatite (OHAp) materials have been manufactured using starch, both as consolidator/binder and as a pore former..

MATERIALS AND METHODS

OHAp was obtained by a coprecipitation method[4]. The powder was calcined at 900°C for one hour, and the particles were deagglomerated by ball milling in an agate container with silicon nitride balls of 15 mm of diameter as grinding media. Commercial starch Trecomex AET1 with a particle average size of 55 μm was chosen like pore former. 40 cm^3 of suspension was obtained using an ammoniun policarbonate, Targon 1128, as dispersant.

The suspensions were prepared firstly by mixing water and dispersant with a mechanical stirrer, then OHAp was added in the desired percentage and finally starch until 50 % volume of solid was reached. The slips were poured into plastic moulds of 120 mm x 50 mm x 5 mm and were dried at 80 °C for one hour. After drying, the starch was burned out at 500 °C and the blocks sintered at 1100°C for 2h.

The particle size distribution of OHAp was obtained in a Sedigraph 5100. Density of the samples was measured using Archimedes principle by immersion in mercury. The pore structure formed by the starch particles of sintered materials was studied by scanning electron microscopy (SEM) in a Hitachi S-4100. Total porosity and pore size distribution were determined in a Micromeritics Autopore III from 0.47 psi to 6 x 10^4 psi and the mechanical properties were performed in four points bending up to fracture in a machine equipped with a 1 KN capacity load cell and working at a cross head speed of 0.5 mm/min.

RESULTS AND DISCUSSION

OHAp was calcined to achieve an appropriate specific surface area of about 10 m^2/g for colloidal processing[5]. Larger specific surface areas tends to agglomerate i.e. form uncontrolled lumps and clusters. Agglomerates contain random-size pores that can seriously interfere with sintering. In addition, high surface area can raise the viscosity of the slip requiring more liquid to bring the viscosity down to workable level, more liquid means less powder, lower green density and inferior mechanical behaviour[6] A median particle diameter of 0.55 μm with the size distribution displays in figure 1 was obtained after 20 hours of ball milling. This particle distribution turned out to be the most adequate for processing by viscosity measurements of suspensions with 50% volume of solid.

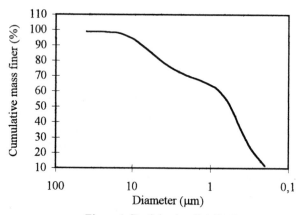

Figure 1. Particle size distribution

Suspensions with different ratios OHAp/starch were prepared in order to obtain materials with different final porosity. Gelling ability of starch in water was employed to consolidate the suspensions into ceramic bodies. Increasing the temperature to 80 °C, starch granules swell by absorbing water, the OHAp particles are compressed by the draining of water forcing the particles closer to each other and causing a flocculation process which may assist the consolidation of the entire particulate suspension into a rigid body. Blocks of 120 mm x 50 mm x 5 mm have been consolidated in this way. After drying and demoulding, burning out the starch and sintering were performed in an integrated process, it was necessary to use a rate as low as 0.5°/min up to 500 °C to burn out the starch without causing any cracking, doing in this way, the weight loss per minute is minimum avoiding the cracking even in the materials with higher percentage of starch, then a sintering rate of 5°/min was employed up to 1100 °C followed by a plateau of 2 hours and free cooling inside the furnace until room temperature was reached.

Materials with different percentage of porosity were obtained. Figure 2 depicts the porosity measured from different techniques. The slope of the trend line drawn is close to 1 suggesting that the total pore volume can be fully characterized by the porosimeter indicating an open pore network. SEM micrograph shows the large spherical shaped pores of about 80 μm left by the starch particles dominating the overall porosity (figure 3), while Hg porosimetry shows smaller pores corresponding to the contact areas between larger pores. Pore curves distribution (figure 4) are independent of the percentage of porosity achieved showing that it is possible to design materials with a controlled percentage of porosity and pore distribution.

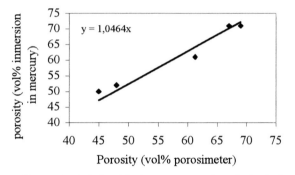

Figure 2. Relationship between porosity obtained from inmersion in mercury and from porosimeter

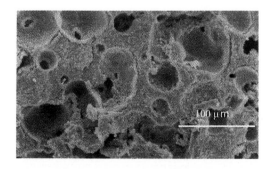

Figure 3. SEM micrograph of the surface of fracture of the specimen with 44% of porosity

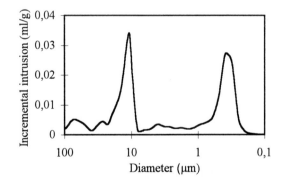

Figure 4. Pore distribution

Specimens of 50 mm x 3 mm x 5 mm were cut from the obtained blocks and used in four point bending tests. Porous materials are weaker than the equivalent bulk form in proportion to the percentage of porosity[7], so that as the porosity increased, the strength of the material decreased linearly as shown in figure 4. Flexural strength of the materials with 45 and 48 % of porosity are within the range of the values obtained for cancellous bone[8] but when porous materials are thought to be use as biomaterials, much surface area will be exposed to the effects of the environment so the ageing of the ceramic, with their subsequent decrease in strength should be studied and related to the rate of bone ingrowth needed to stabilize the implant. Ageing studies of these materials and the modifiers that have to be added to achieve higher sizes of pores are in progress.

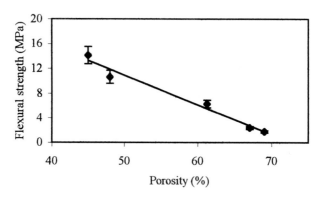

Figure 4 influence of porosity on flexural strength

The main advantages of this method are the simplicity of the process, the possibility of forming complex shapes with different percentage and size of pores and the low-cost processing equipment/materials needed.

ACKNOWLEDGMENTS

Financial support of CICYT (Spain) through research project MAT96-0919 is acknowledged

REFERENCES

1.- Saggio-Woyanski j, Scott C. Am Ceram Soc Bull 1992; **71**: 1674-1682.

2.- Minnear WP. In: Cima M.J., ed *Ceramic Transations, Vol 26* Westerville, The American Ceramic Society, 1995: 150-56.

3.- Lyckfeld O, Ferreira JMF. J of the Eur Ceram Soc 1998;**18(2)**: 131-140

4.- Vallet-Regí M, Rodríguez-Lorenzo LM, Salinas AJ. Solid State Ionics 1997;**101-103**: 1279-1285.

5.- Shanefield DJ. *Organic Additives and Ceramic Processing*. Boston: Kluwer Academic Publishers, 1996 : 91-115.

6.- Lange FL. J Am ceram Soc 1989; **72(1):** 3-15.

7.- Hench LL. In Ratner BD, Hoffman, Schoen FJ, Lemons JA eds. *Biomaterials Science*. San Diego: Academic press 1996: 73-84.

8.- Hench LL, Wilson J. In Hench LL, Wilson J. eds. *An Introduction to Bioceramics*. Singapore: World Scientific, 1993 : 1-24.

Bioceramics Volume 11, edited by R. Z. LeGeros and J.P. LeGeros
(Proceedings of the 11th International Symposium on Ceramics in Medicine)
New York, NY, USA, November 1998
© 1998 by World Scientific Publishing Co. Pte. Ltd.

CRYSTAL GROWTH AND STRUCTURE ANALYSES OF CARBONATE HYDROXYAPATITE

Y. Suetsugu, M. Kikuchi, K. Sato and J. Tanaka

National Institute for Research in Inorganic Materials. 1-1 Namiki, Tsukuba, Ibaraki 305-0044, Japan.

ABSTRACT
Single crystals of carbonate apatite, $Ca_{10-x/2}(PO_4)_{6-x}(CO_3)_xCO_3$ (CAp), and carbonate hydroxyapatite, $Ca_{10-x/2}(PO_4)_{6-x}(CO_3)_x(OH)_{2-2y}(CO_3)_y$ (CHAp) were grown by a $CaCO_3$-$Ca(OH)_2$ flux method. The crystals obtained were hexagonal prismatic elongated along the c-axis. The largest crystal was 1 mm in diameter and 10 mm in length. The concentration of CO_3 ions in the crystal could be controlled (y=0 to 1 for the A-site, and x=0 to 0.5 for the B-site, respectively) by changing the composition of the flux. The a-axis parameter changed from 0.942 (HAp) to 0.948 nm (CAp) with increase of the concentration of A-site CO_3 while c-axis parameter remained unchanged at 0.689 regardless of the substitution of carbonate ions. X-ray structure analysis supported by the angular dependence of polarized IR spectra indicated that the triangular plane of CO_3 ion in the A-site could take six equivalent locations around the six-fold axis of rotatory inversion parallel to the c-axis so that one C-O bond was located on that axis and those six configurations are randomly occupied.

Keywords: Carbonate hydroxyapatite, single crystal, flux method, X-ray structure analysis

INTRODUCTION
Carbonate ions can replace both OH (A-site) and PO_4 (B-site) in hydroxyapatite, $Ca_{10}(PO_4)_6(OH)_2$ (HAp) structure[1]. Because biological HAp microcrystal almost always include substantial amounts of CO_3 ions, it is important to understand the substitution of CO_3 ions in HAp and the structure of CAp or CHAp i order to have a fundamental understanding of the inorganic component in biological hard tissue and for the development of new artificial bone materials. However, mainly because of the lack of sufficiently large enough single crystals, the detailed structure and crystallochemical properties of CAp and CHAp have been unknown. In this paper, single crystals of CAp and CHAp were grown by a flux method controlling the concentration of CO_3 ions and the structure of CAp was investigated.

MATERIALS and METHODS
Mixed dry powder of calcium carbonate ($CaCO_3$,CC), calcium hydroxide ($Ca(OH)_2$,CH) and tricalcium phosphate ($Ca_3(PO_4)_2$) were sealed in a platinum capsule. The compositions of starting materials of main samples are listed in Table 1. The capsules were heated up to 1400°C under Ar gas pressure of 50MPa, and the growth of single crystals was performed by lowering the temperature by 5°C/hour. Residual flux was eliminated by immersing the aggregated samples in 10 wt% EDTA-Na_2 aqueous solution.

Table 1. Starting materials and formulae of crystals.

Sample	Starting materials			Formula of crystals
	TCP mol%	CC mol%	CH mol%	
1	25	75	0	$Ca_{9.75}[(PO_4)_{5.5}(CO_3)_{0.5}](CO_3)_{1.0}$
2	35	60	5	$Ca_{9.85}[(PO_4)_{5.7}(CO_3)_{0.3}][(OH)_{0.9}(CO_3)_{0.55}]$
3	30	60	10	$Ca_{9.9}[(PO_4)_{5.8}(CO_3)_{0.2}][(OH)_{1.4}(CO_3)_{0.3}]$
4	16	16	68	$Ca_{9.97}[(PO_4)_{5.94}(CO_3)_{0.06}](OH)_{2.0}$
5	25	0	75	$Ca_{10.0}(PO_4)_{6.0}(OH)_{2.0}$

The chemical compositions of the crystals obtained were analyzed by an electron probe microanalyzer (JEOL JXA-8600MX) and a carbon analyzer (Leco CS-444LS) which was equipped with an IR detector for the quantitative analysis of CO_2 gas desorbed from samples. X-ray data for crystals were measured using an Rigaku AFC-5R four-circle diffractometer and HOPG monochromated $AgK\alpha$ (rotating anode, 40kV, 180mA) radiation. Unit-cell parameters were refined (no symmetry constraints) using diffraction angles from 20 to 25 automatically centered reflections. X-ray diffraction data for the structure analysis of CAp were collected for all reciprocal space to $40°$ 2θ using a 2θ-ω scan technique. Structure calculations were undertaken using the Xtal set of programs[2].

RESULTS AND DISCUSSION
Crystal growth and control of CO3 concentration

The crystals obtained were hexagonal prismatic and elongated along the c-axis. Figure 1 shows the crystals of sample No.1 and No.5. The size of crystals increased with CH content in the starting materials. The largest crystal was 1mm in diameter and 10mm in length. The chemical composition of the crystals varied with the composition of their starting materials. Sample No.1 whose flux was enirely CC and contained no CH had the formula of $Ca_{9.75}[(PO_4)_{5.5}(CO_3)_{0.5}](CO_3)_{1.0}$ in which A-sites were completely occupied and 1/12 of B-sites

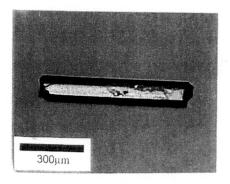
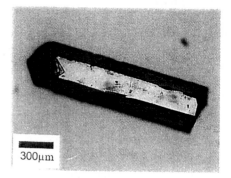

Figure 1. Crystals of CAp (sample No.1, left), and HAp (sample No.5, right).

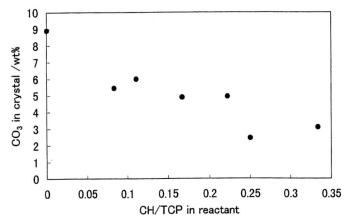

Figure 2.   Control of CO_3 content of CHAp by varying CH/TCP of starting materials.

were substituted by CO_3 ions.   The flux of only CH produced stoichiometric HAp (sample No.5). When the flux contained both CC and CH, composition of the crystals varies according to the composition of the starting materials.   When CC was the major component of the flux and the mole ratio of CH/CC ranged from 0 to 1/6 like samples No.2 and 3, CO_3 content depended on CH/TCP as shown in Fig.2.   Conversely, the flux of dominant CH with a small amount of CC (CC/CH ranged from 0 to 1/4) produced CHAp crystals in which only the B-site was substituted by CO_3 ions.   In this case the concentration of CO_3 ion depended on CC content in the flux, but it was very limited (x=0.06 at most).

the cell parameters for sample No.1 was a=0.948nm and a=0.942nm for sample No.5.   The a-axis parameter increased with the concentration of carbonate ion in principle but did not simply follow Vegard's law.   However, the c-axis parameters was 0.689nm in all cases.

Structure analysis of CAp

From the preliminary study of the X-ray diffraction, it was concluded that the space group of the crystal of sample No.1 was $P\bar{6}$ and the results of the polarized IR measurement indicated that the CO_3 triangular plane was parallel to the c-axis for the A-site and perpendicular to the c-axis for the

Table 2.   Crystal data and crystal-structure refinements for sample No.1.

Space group	$P\bar{6}$
Unit-cell dimensions	
Least squares	
a /nm	0.9483
b /nm	0.9485
c /nm	0.6897
α /°	89.98
β /°	89.97
γ /°	119.99
Structure refinement	
a	0.9489
c	0.6897
R_w	0.027

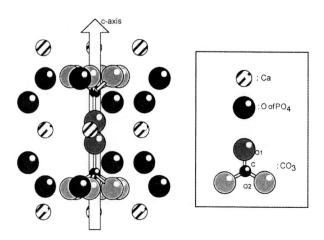

Figure 3.   Configuration of CO_3 ion substituting A-site in CAp.

B-site[3].   Using this information the crystal structure calculation was undertaken for a crystal of sample No.1.   Taking into consideration that the B-site substitution was small enough not to influence the structure factor, the calculation was performed for the chemical formula $Ca_{10}(PO)_6CO_3$.   To calculate the configuration of CO_3 in the A-site, C was fixed on the six-fold axis of rotatory inversion.

Table 2 contains crystal data and results of crystal-structure refinements for sample No.1. Figure 3 shows the configuration of CO_3 ion substituting the A-site.   the CO_3 ion in the A-site could take three equivalent configurations around the six-fold axis of rotatory inversion so that one C-O bond was on that axis.   Further, the mirror plane located perpendicular to the c-axis at z=0, 1/2 required three more equivalent positions.   Therefore there were six equivalent positions for CO_3 ion in one unit cell.   These six equivalent positions were occupied randomly, such disordered distribution of CO_3 ions caused the symmetries of the space group $P\bar{6}$.

SUMMARY

CAp and CHAp single crystals were grown by a CC-CH flux method. the concentration of carbonate ions in the crystals could be controlled by changing the composition of the flux.   X-ray structure analysis indicated that the triangular plane of CO_3 ion in the A-site could take six equivalent locations around the six-fold axis of rotatory inversion parallel to the c-axis so that one C-O bond was located on that axis and the six configurations are randomly occupied.

ACKNOWLEDGEMENT

The authors would like to thank Dr. D Walsh of NIRIM for critical reading of the manuscript.

REFERENCES

1   Bonel G, Montel G, Comp. Rend. Acad. Sci. (Paris), 1964; **258**: 923-926.
2   Hall SR, King GSD, Stewart JM, Xtal 3.4 User's manual, 1995; University of Western Australia.
3   Suetsugu Y, Shimoya I, Tanaka J, *J Am Ceram Soc* 1998; **81** [3]: 746-748.

Bioceramics Volume 11, edited by R. Z. LeGeros and J.P. LeGeros
(Proceedings of the 11th International Symposium on Ceramics in Medicine)
New York, NY, USA, November 1998
© 1998 by World Scientific Publishing Co. Pte. Ltd.

EFFECTS OF CARBONATE SUBSTITUTION ON THE STRENGTH OF SINGLE CRYSTAL HYDROXYAPATITE

A. Ito[1], K. Teraoka[2], K. Maekawa[2], K. Onuma[1] and T. Tateishi[1]

[1]National Institute for Advanced Interdisciplinary Research, 1-1-4 Higashi, Tsukuba-shi, Ibaraki 305, Japan; [2]Institute of Earth Science, School of Education, Waseda University, 1-6-1 Nishiwaseda, Shinjuku-ku, Tokyo 169-50 Japan.

ABSTRACT

Bending strength and solubility of single crystal hydroxyapatite and OH-carbonated hydroxyapatite were investigated. In air, average strengths of these single crystals were from 450 to 513 MPa and were nearly constant up to a carbonate content of 0.62 CO_2 wt%. The strength of these single crystals is comparable to that of dense alumina ceramics. However, the carbonate incorporation increased stress corrosion susceptibility: the average strength in water decreased significantly by 23 to 43 % with an increase in carbonate contents although no significant decrease in average strength was found for the hydroxyapatite single crystals in water.

Negative logarithm of solubility product for OH-carbonated hydroxyapatite decreased linearly with an increase in carbonate contents, with values of 117.1 and 115.2 for hydroxyapatite and the OH-carbonated hydroxyapatite with 0.62 CO_2 wt%, respectively. This means that the OH-carbonated hydroxyapatite single crystals with 0.62 CO_2 wt% dissolve 1.31 times faster, hence contributing to the increased susceptibility to stress corrosion, than the hydroxyapatite single crystals in water.

Therefore, hydroxyapatite single crystals are superior to OH-carbonated hydroxyapatite single crystals as a component of composite used for a load-bearing purpose.

KEYWORDS: Single crystal hydroxyapatite, carbonate content, bending strength, solubility.

INTRODUCTION

Single crystal hydroxyapatite (HAP) has a value of bending strength 2.5 times higher than that of dense HAP ceramic in air. [1,2] This indicates that it is possible to develop a new type of load-bearing and bioactive implants using these single crystals as a monolithic phase or a component of composite.

These single crystals have been grown hydrothermally by the hydrolysis of CaHPO4 by agradually-heating technique with a temperature gradient applied to a vessel.[3] The preparation of

OH-carbonated hydroxyapatite (CHAP) single crystals is less difficult with a high degree of reproducibility than HAP single crystals, as far as we have experienced. However, the effects of carbonate incorporation on the mechanical properties of the single crystals are less clear. In the present study, three-point bending strength of HAP and CHAP single crystals with various carbonate contents were measured, and the relation between the bending strength and solubility was described.

MATERIALS AND METHODS

HAP single crystals were prepared from 6g of calcium hydrogen phosphate and 600 ml of water placed in a glass tube (45 mm I. D. x 560mm) in a pressure vessel (50 mm I. D. x 586mm: Taiatsu Co., Ltd., Tokyo, Japan).[3] Sintered hydroxyapatite disks were used as seeds (10 mmφ x 4 mm). The top and bottom part of the glass tube were quickly heated at 180 and 150 °C, respectively. Then the top part was heated up to 310 °C at a heating rate of 0.005 °C/min. The pressure vessel was opened 6 days after reaching the desired temperature. OH-carbonated hydroxyapatite single crystals were prepared in the same manner as HAP single crystals but with the starting materials supplemented with dry ice.

The crystals selected for three-point bending tests have neither cracks nor fluid inclusions and show uniform extinction polarization-microscopically. Before the bending test, one of the (100) faces was marked with bonding a 17 μmφ steel wire to identify the bending direction after fracture. The bending tests were performed in air and in water. The bending strength was measured by using a modified ultra-microhardness tester (DUH-50, Shimazu) with a span of 380 μm, a loading rate of 5.0×10^{-4} N/sec and a bending direction being perpendicular to the c-axis of apatite. Values about crystal dimensions required for the calculation of bending strength were obtained by an image analysis technique.

OH-carbonated hydroxyapatite powders prepared by heating a hydroxyapatite powder at 800 - 1000 °C at a CO_2 gas pressure ranging from 0 to 2.5 MPa were immersed in a 0.1M KCl solution and equilibrated at 25± 3 °C in glass vials. The vial stopper had a hole (4 mmφ) and was joined to a syringe filter with a pore size of 0.22 μm to introduce air into the vials to maintain a constant partial pressure of CO_2 gas ($P_{CO2} = 10^{-3.52}$ atm) in each vial. Solubility product of OH-carbonated hydroxyapatite (Ksp) was calculated according to a method described elsewhere.[4]

RESULTS AND DISCUSSION

The average strengths of the crystals in air were from 450 to 513 MPa and were nearly constant up to a carbonate content of 0.62 CO_2 wt% (Fig. 1). The strengths of the crystals in air were 2.5 times higher than that of dense HAP ceramic, and comparable to that of dense alumina ceramic.[5-9] No significant decrease in average strength was found for HAP single crystals in water. However, the average strengths of CHAP single crystals decreased significantly by 23 to 43 % in water in proportion to the carbonate content. Therefore, the carbonate incorporation increased stress corrosion susceptibility of the single crystals.

The increase in stress corrosion susceptibility is due to an increase in solubility of apatite. The solubility of OH-carbonated hydroxyapatite increased with an increase in the carbonate content. The negative logarithm of solubility product (pKsp) for pure hydroxyapatite and OH-carbonated hydroxyapatite powders decreased linearly with an increase in the carbonate content (Fig. 2). The relation between the pKsp values and the carbonate contents was expressed as:

$$pKsp = 117.1 - 2.9981 \times (CO_2 \ wt\%). \qquad (1)$$

The pKsp values for the single crystals of HAP and the CHAP with 0.62 CO_2 wt% were calculated from Eq. (1) as 117.1 and 115.2, respectively.

From the pKsp values, a dissolution rate can be obtained for the single crystals of HAP and CHAP with 0.62 CO_2 wt%. Dissolution at a crack tip is an important factor of stress corrosion, enhancing crack opening and propagation. An initial dissolution rate, J, defined as the flux of total phosphate in a liquid diffusion layer on the surface of hydroxyapatite is expressed as:

$$J = A(Ksp)^{1/16} \qquad (2)$$

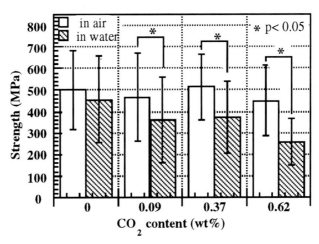

Figure 1. Average strength of single crystals as a function of carbonate contents.

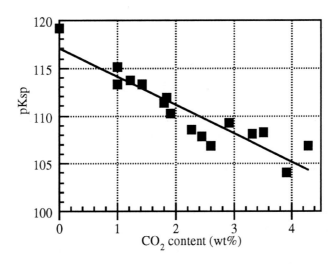

Figure 2. pKsp values of the OH-carbonated hydroxyapatite as a function of carbonate contents.

where A is a constant.[10] The J is expressed as moles of total phosphate transported per unit area of the surface of apatite at the initial stage of dissolution where calcium and phosphate concentrations in water are regarded as zero. A ratio of J_{CHAP}/J_{HAP} was calculated as 1.31 for the CHAP single crystals with 0.62 CO_2 wt%. This means that the CHAP single crystals with 0.62 CO_2 wt% dissolve 1.31 times faster than the HAP single crystals when they are subjected to the three-points bending tests in water. The increase in dissolution rate could be the reason of the increase in stress corrosion susceptibility.

Therefore, HAP single crystals are superior to CHAP single crystals as a monolithic phase or a component of composite used for a load-bearing purpose although the preparation of HAP single crystals are more difficult than that of CHAP single crystals.

CONCLUSIONS

In air, the average strengths of single crystals of hydroxyapatite and OH-carbonated hydroxyapatite were from 450 to 513 MPa and were nearly constant up to a carbonate content of 0.62 CO_2 wt%. The strength of these single crystals is comparable to that of dense alumina ceramic. However, the average strength of OH-carbonated hydroxyapatite single crystals decreased significantly by 23 to 43 % in water due to stress corrosion. On the contrary, no significant decrease in average strength was found for hydroxyapatite single crystals in water.

Therefore, hydroxyapatite single crystals are superior to OH-carbonated hydroxyapatite single crystals as a component of composite used for a load-bearing purpose although the preparation of hydroxyapatite single crystals are more difficult.

REFERENCES

1.   Teraoka K, Ito A, Tateishi T, Tsutsumi S. *J Biomed Mater Res* 1997; **34**: 269-272.
2.   Ito A, Teraoka K, Tsutsumi S, Tateishi T. In: Kokubo T, Nakamura T, Miyaji F, eds. *Bioceramics* Vol.9. Oxford UK: Elsevier, 1996: 189-192.
3.   Ito A, Nakamura S, Aoki H, Akao M, Teraoka K, Tsutsumi S, Onuma K, Tetsuya T. *J. Crystal Growth* 1996; 163: 311-317.
4.   Ito A, Maekawa K, Tsutsumi S, Ikazaki F, Tateishi T. *J Biomed Mater Res* 1997; **36**: 522-528.
5.   Jarcho M, Boren CH, Thomas MB, Bobick J, Kay JF, Doremus RH. *J. Mater. Sci.* 1976; **11**: 2027-2035.
6.   Thomas MB, Doremus RH, Jarcho M, Salsbury RL. *J. Mater. Sci.* 1980; **15**: 891-894.
7.   Akao M, Aoki H, Kato K. *J. Mater. Sci.* 1981; **16**: 809-812.
8.   De With G, Van Dijik HJA, Hattu N, Prijs K. *J. Mater. Sci.* 1981; **16**: 1592-1598.
9.   Halouani R, Bernache-Assolant D, Champion E, Ababou A. *J. Mater. Sci. Materr in Med.* 1994; **5**: 563-568.
10. Dedhiya MG, Young F, Higuchi WI. *J Dent Res* 1973; **52**: 1097-1109.

Bioceramics Volume 11, edited by R. Z. LeGeros and J.P. LeGeros
(Proceedings of the 11th International Symposium on Ceramics in Medicine)
New York, NY, USA, November 1998
© 1998 by World Scientific Publishing Co. Pte. Ltd.

CHEMISTRY AND CRITICAL AGEING OF HYDROXYAPATITE SOL-GEL SOLUTIONS

C.S. Chai[1], K.A. Gross[1], K. Kannagara[1], B. Ben-Nissan[1], L. Hanley[2] and P. Layrolle[3]

[1]Department of Chemistry, Materials and Forensic Science, University of Technology, Sydney, PO Box 123, Broadway, NSW 2007, Australia.
[2]Department of Chemistry, University of Illinois at Chicago, IL 60607-7061, USA.
[3]IsoTis, Prof. Bronkhorstlaan 10, 3723 MB Bilthoven, The Netherlands.

ABSTRACT

In previous work we have demonstrated that production of hydroxyapatite coatings using an alkoxide based sol-gel route requires control of solution ageing time and heating schedule. [31]P nuclear magnetic resonance spectroscopy was used to investigate the changes during ageing of the sol and thermal gravimetric analysis employed to study the behaviour of the gels as a function of temperature. Results from ^{31}P nuclear magnetic resonance spectroscopy and thermal analysis revealed that sols must be aged for at least 24 hours to complete the interaction of the two precursors. Deposition of the sol for coating production will then yield monophasic hydroxyapatite. ^{31}P NMR revealed that P-O-C bonds present in the precursor material are gradually replaced by P-O-Ca bonds with an accompanying change in oxidation state from P(III) to P(V). Thermal analysis was used to examine hydrolysed gels and showed that sols aged less than 24 hours contain unreacted calcium diethoxide which decomposes to CaO upon heating. Prefiring is necessary to remove most of the residual organic materials. Final heating up to 800 °C produces crystallization at 550 °C and removal of the remaining organic constituents for formation of a thin hydroxyapatite layer.

KEYWORDS: Hydroxyapatite, sol-gel, alkoxide, ageing, nuclear magnetic resonance, chemistry

INTRODUCTION

The sol-gel process has been used successfully in the preparation of various inorganic coatings (i.e., SiO_2, Al_2O_3, ZrO_2, TiO_2). In this soft chemistry route, metal alkoxides $M(OR)_n$ convert to amorphous polymeric gels of metal oxides through controlled hydrolysis and condensation reactions. Thin and uniform metal oxide films, with desired chemical and phase compositions, can be easily processed by dipping the substrates into viscous sols, drying and firing them at relatively low temperatures. Although the sol-gel processing of glasses and oxides is well documented, only few attempts have been reported on the sol-gel synthesis of HAp material.

Previous studies[1,2] have shown that the phase purity of HAp was related to critical ageing time of alkoxide gels. In the present work, the course of the reaction between reagents was followed with liquid ^{31}P nuclear magnetic resonance spectroscopy to determine the chemical transformations taking place during the maturation of gels.

MATERIALS AND METHODS

The method by which hydroxyapatite sols were prepared and the subsequent deposition onto substrates including single crystal magnesia, alumina, partially stabilised zirconia and titanium has been described in detail elsewhere[2,3].

Differential thermal analysis (DTA) and thermogravimetric analysis (TGA) were carried out using a SDT 2960 simultaneous thermal analyser (TA Instruments, Newcastle, USA). The powder was heated at 10°C/min to 500°C, held for 15 minutes at that temperature then heated to 1200 C at 3.33 C/min in a stagnant air atmosphere. This heating schedule was chosen to replicate conditions used for coating production.

X-ray diffraction technique with a grazing incidence geometry (Siemens D5000, Karslruhe, Germany) was used to examine coatings due to the small coating thickness. This technique minimised the signal generated by the underlying substrate. Coatings were examined using CuKα radiation at 40kV and 30mA, with X-ray incident angle of 1 , from 29-40 , with step size 0.02 and step time of 5 seconds.

Nuclear magnetic resonance (NMR) spectra were obtained on a 300 DRX Bruker (Bruker-Spectrospin, Sällanden, Switzerland) spectrometer operating at 121.495 MHz for ^{31}P using a 60606 Hz sweep width and a 90° (8.1 ms) pulse. Data was collected in 16K points using 16 scans. Pulse delay was 2 seconds with an acquisition time of 0.135 seconds. All ^{31}P spectra were taken with proton decoupling and data acquired at 300K. Orthophosphoric acid (85 vol.%) was chosen as an external reference. Both the triethyl phosphite (contains $\leq$ 1% of triethyl phosphate $[(C_2H_5O)_3P(O)]$ and $\leq$ 1% diethyl phosphite $[(C_2H_5O)_2P(O)H]$) and the hydroxyapatite sol were examined by ^{31}P NMR.

RESULTS AND DISCUSSION

Differential thermal analysis (DTA) of the aged samples show an endotherm followed by three exotherms positioned at 220, 400 and 550°C (Fig. 1). The endothermic reaction at low temperature is believed to be related to the desorption of alcohols and adsorbed water. The first two exotherms correspond to polycondensation and the release of organics thus requiring a prefiring temperature of 500°C. There is a steady and gradual weight loss corresponding to 8wt.% over this temperature range. Coatings fired to temperatures between 500 and 900°C and analyzed by X-ray diffraction indicate that crystallization occurs between 500 and 600°C. Samples aged for 0 and 2 hours maintain constant weight in the temperature range 400 C to 650 C. As ageing times increase up to 24 hours, the rate of weight loss in the temperature range increases slowly.

The TGA of the gels aged for different times showed a decrease in the overall weight loss with increased ageing. After 24 hours of ageing, the total weight loss at temperatures greater than 800°C equates to a value of 28-30 wt.%. Previous work has shown that this is the critical time for ageing of the solution to obtain a product consisting only of hydroxyapatite.[3] Gels produced from sols aged for less than 24 hours also display a exothermic response at approximately 290 C, which could be attributed to the thermal behaviour of unreacted calcium diethoxide. Between 550 C and 740 C, gels aged for less than 24 hours lose weight rapidly, with a weight loss inversely proportional to ageing time. Thermal analysis and X-ray diffraction performed on hydrolysed calcium diethoxide have shown that this weight loss between 550 C and 740 C is due to the presence of unreacted calcium diethoxide at the solution stage. DTA and thermogravimetric analysis (TGA) curves for samples aged between 1 and 7 days are indistinguishable from one another. This would tend to indicate that the reactions taking place during the ageing period have gone to completion, such that when deposited, monophasic hydroxyapatite films can be produced.

X-ray diffraction revealed that coatings produced from sols aged for period less than 4 hours contain hydroxyapatite (JCPDS 9-432) in combination with calcium oxide (JCPDS 4-777), and another unidentified phase characterised by a peak at 31.2 (Fig. 2). As ageing time progresses, the proportion of calcium oxide relative to hydroxyapatite was observed to decrease. For coatings prepared from sols aged between 1 and 7 days, hydroxyapatite was the only phase detected.

It was observed that uncombined calcium diethoxide hydrolyses to form calcium hydroxide (JCPDS 4-733), which further transforms to calcium carbonate (JCPDS 5-586) at approximately 300 C. The calcium carbonate then decomposes beginning at 540 C to leave calcium oxide, as identified by x-ray diffraction. It is this endothermic reaction which is characteristic of gels produced from sols aged for less than 24 hours.

^{31}P NMR spectroscopy is a useful tool for following the ageing behaviour of the sol. Spectra for diluted triethyl phosphite and hydroxyapatite sol immediately after preparation are essentially identical. They consist of lines at +139 ppm, indicating that while the various species have been mixed in the preparation of the sol, they have not yet reacted. Figure 3 displays the ^{31}P NMR spectra of the sol-gel solution as a function of ageing time following initial mixing. The lower spectrum labelled "No age" was recorded within one hour of mixing: it displays a sharp and intense peak at a chemical shift of +139 ppm. The "No age" spectrum is similar to that observed for the unreacted P(OEt)$_3$ blank with the +139 ppm peak in agreement with the literature assignment for this compound.[4] As the solution ages, a broad doublet peak with maxima at -99 and -105 ppm grows in intensity. No further changes in the spectra were observed between 1 and 7 days of ageing. The doublet is assigned to phosphorus in the chemical state [Ca-O-PO$_3$]$_n$, where two of the oxygen atoms in the PO$_3$ are bound to additional P or Ca atoms in the sol.[5] The shift in the primary P peak from +139 to near -100 ppm is consistent with a change in oxidation state from P(III) to P(V). The NMR data indicates that ageing is required by the kinetics of the reaction between the two alkoxide precursors and condensation steps of the sol-gel synthesis.

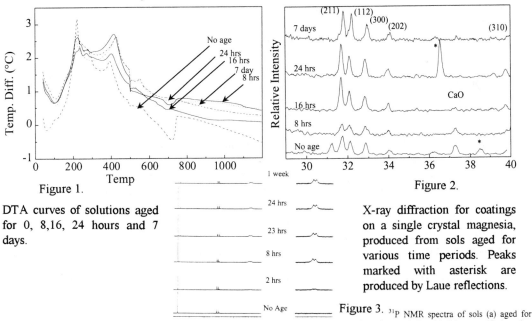

Figure 1.

DTA curves of solutions aged for 0, 8, 16, 24 hours and 7 days.

Figure 2.

X-ray diffraction for coatings on a single crystal magnesia, produced from sols aged for various time periods. Peaks marked with asterisk are produced by Laue reflections.

Figure 3. ^{31}P NMR spectra of sols (a) aged for various time periods, with (b) a magnified section showing the phosphate doublet.

In addition to the doublet forming, another peak consistent with a chemical shift to +135 ppm emerges. It is believed that this peak is generated by the condensation mechanism between calcium and phosphorus alkoxides. During the ageing period, the phosphorus atom may eventually become surrounded by 3 calcium atoms linked by oxy-bridges, which is similar to findings reported previously. This reaction would then form networks or oligomers of varying sizes, which would explain the broad nature of the phosphate doublet. This would indicate that hydrolysis and polycondensation take place in the sol, using free hydroxyl groups rather than moisture absorbed from the atmosphere or supplied by artificial means. In situ ^{31}P NMR studies at temperatures between 27 C and 67 C have shown that the formation of this species is the rate determining step in the ageing process.

The peaks from -1 to +10 ppm correspond to phosphorus impurities in the P(OEt)$_3$ reagent and intermediates in the sol-gel reaction. Previous ^{31}P NMR experiments on titanium phosphate sol-gel reactions attributed peaks in this region to O=P(OEt)$_{3-x}$(OH)$_x$ compounds.[6] These compounds may also exist as intermediates in the synthesis of the calcium phosphate sol-gel. The chemical shifts of these small peaks change upon addition of calcium ethoxide, however, the intensities of the peaks in the region of -1 to $+10$ ppm remain constant over the complete time period and are not believed to participate in the ageing reactions..

The chemical changes taking place in the sol observed by 31P NMR are complete after 24 hours with no further changes observed up to one week after sol preparation. These findings are consistent with thermal analysis and XRD findings.

CONCLUSIONS

The combined use of thermalogravimetric analysis, ^{31}P nuclear magnetic resonance and X-ray diffraction have revealed that that a time of 24 hours is necessary for complete combination of the calcium and phosphorus ethoxides to produce a hydroxyapatite coating. Preparation of a homogeneous coating then requires a prefiring at 500 °C to remove most of the organics followed by a final firing at 800°C. Monophasic hydroxyapatite coatings can be prepared using an alkoxide based sol-gel technique. [31]P nuclear magnetic resonance spectroscopy and X-ray diffraction work indicate that the reaction between the reactants is complete after 24 hours. If sols are used prior to this time, free calcium diethoxide, hydrolyses to calcium hydroxide. Calcium hydroxide reacts with carbon dioxide to form calcium carbonate and finally decomposes to leave calcium oxide after heat treatment at temperatures greater than 540 C.

REFERENCES

1. Chai CS, Ben-Nissan B, Pyke S, Evans L. In: *Surface Modification Technologies, 7.* 1993: 509-523.
2. Ben-Nissan B, Chai CS. In: Kossowsky R. and Kossovsky N, eds. *Advances in Materials Science and Implant Orthopaedic Surgery*, Netherlands: Kluwer Academic Publishers, 1995: 265-273.
3. Ben-Nissan B, Chai CS, Gross KA. In: Sedel L and Rey C, eds. *Bioceramics Vol. 10,.* Paris: Elsevier Science, 1997:175-178.
4. Dixon KR. In: Mason J, ed. *Multinuclear NMR*, New York: Plenum Press, 1987: 369.
5. Layrolle P and Lebugle A., *Chem. Mater.* 1996; **8**: 134 -144.
6. Livage J, Barboux P, Vanderborre MT, Schmutz C, F. Taulelle F. *J. Non-Crys Solids* 1992; **147/148**: 18-23

Bioceramics Volume 11, edited by R. Z. LeGeros and J.P. LeGeros
(Proceedings of the 11th International Symposium on Ceramics in Medicine)
New York, NY, USA, November 1998
© 1998 by World Scientific Publishing Co. Pte. Ltd.

EFFECT OF SILICON CONTENT ON THE CHEMICAL AND PHASE COMPOSITION OF NOVEL SILICON-SUBSTITUTED HYDROXYAPATITES.

I.R. Gibson[1], L.J. Jha[1,2], J.D. Santos[2], S.M. Best[1] and W. Bonfield[1]

[1] IRC in Biomedical Materials, Queen Mary and Westfield College, Mile End Road, London, E1 4NS, UK; [2] National Institute of Biomedical Engineering, Praca do Coronel Pacheco, No.1, 4050 Porto, Portugal

ABSTRACT

A range of novel silicon-substituted hydroxyapatites (Si-HA), containing 0.2, 0.4 and 0.8 wt% silicon, have been prepared by an aqueous precipitation method. The different compositions were calculated so that the Ca/(P+Si) ratio was constant at 1.67. X-ray Fluorescence (XRF) and X-ray Diffraction (XRD) were used to characterise the chemical and phase compositions of the different as-precipitated and sintered Si-HA compositions, respectively. Chemical analysis by XRF indicated that the Ca/(P+Si) ratio of all compositions remained constant at 1.67±0.01. Phase analysis of sintered samples by XRD showed that a single phase was obtained for all compositions which matched closely the standard diffraction pattern of HA. Measurement of the lattice parameters showed a decrease in the a axes and an increase in the c axis with increasing silicon content. These results indicated that a substitution of silicon for phosphorus (or silicate for phosphate) occurred for all compositions, but this did not affect the phase stability of the material.

KEYWORDS: silicon, hydroxyapatite, substitution, bioceramic

INTRODUCTION

The number of biomedical applications of hydroxyapatite (HA) ceramics will be increased if the associated bioactivity is improved. A potential method of improving the bioactivity of hydroxyapatite is the incorporation of silicon (or silicate groups) into the hydroxyapatite lattice[1], as it is considered that small levels of silicon are important for healthy bone metabolism[2]. *In vitro* and *in vivo* studies by Carlisle[2,3] have indicated the importance of silicon to bone formation and calcification. In particular, electron microprobe studies showed that silicon levels of up to 0.5 wt% were observed in active growth areas, such as the osteoid, of the young bone of rats[2]. The aim of this study was to prepare and characterise a range of compositions of a new hydroxyapatite-based material by a simple aqueous precipitation reaction, which contained small levels of silicon, but still retained the HA structure on sintering.

MATERIALS AND METHODS

A stoichiometric HA was prepared by a precipitation reaction[4] between calcium hydroxide, $Ca(OH)_2$ and orthophosphoric acid, H_3PO_4; the molar amounts are listed in Table 1. A series of silicon-substituted hydroxyapatites, containing 0.2, 0.4 and 0.8 wt% silicon, were prepared[1]. The quantities of reactants were calculated by assuming that silicon would substitute for phosphorus in the HA lattice. Therefore, the number of moles of H_3PO_4 in stoichiometric HA was the same as the number of moles of (H_3PO_4 + SiAcetate) in the Si-HA, Table 1. The precipitation reaction was carried out at room temperature at a pH of 10.5 After mixing the reactants, the suspension was aged and the resulting precipitate was filtered, dried, and then ground to a fine powder.

Powder compacts and portions of the powders (2g) were sintered at 1200°C for 2 hours. The Ca, P and Si contents of the samples were determined by XRF spectroscopy (Philips PW1606 spectrometer) and the CO_3 contents were measured by C-H-N analysis (Medac Ltd., UK). The phase composition of the as-prepared and heat-treated samples was determined by X-Ray Diffraction (XRD) using a Siemens D5000 diffractometer with Cu K_α radiation. The effect of silicon substitution on the structural parameters of HA and Si-HA was determined by Rietveld refinement of the X-ray diffraction data collected for heat-treated powders.

RESULTS

The results of the chemical analysis by XRF of the stoichiometric hydroxyapatite (HA) and silicon-substituted hydroxyapatite (Si-HA) powders are represented in Figures 1 and 2. The measured silicon content (wt%) of the different samples is compared with the expected values in Figure 1. The plot is linear and the measured vales are very comparable to the expected values. Figure 2 shows the effect of silicon content on the measured Ca/P and Ca/(P+Si) molar ratios. The former molar ratio increases steadily with increasing silicon substitution, whereas the latter remains unchanged. All of the as-prepared samples contained small levels of carbonate, as measured by C-H-N analysis, but no carbonate was detected in samples after sintering at 1200°C.

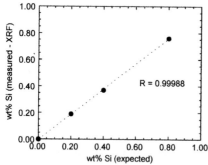 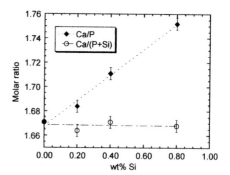

Figure 1. The measured (XRF) silicon contents vs. the expected silicon contents of Si- HA.

Figure 2. The effect of silicon substitution on the measured Ca/P and Ca/(P+Si) ratios of Si-HA.

Table 1. Quantities of reactants used and the expected Ca/P and Ca/(P+Si) molar ratios

Sample	No. of moles $Ca(OH)_2$	No. of moles H_3PO_4	No. of moles $Si(CH_3COO)_4$	Ca/P ratio (expected)	Ca/(P+Si) ratio (expected)
Stoich. HA	0.500	0.297	0	1.68	1.68
0.2 wt%Si-HA	0.500	0.293	0.004	1.71	1.68
0.4 wt%Si-HA	0.500	0.289	0.008	1.73	1.68
0.8 wt%Si-HA	0.500	0.281	0.160	1.78	1.68

X-ray diffraction patterns of as-prepared HA and Si-HA samples are shown in Figure 3. The broad diffraction peaks suggest that the material is composed of very small apatite crystals[5]. The silicon substitution does not appear to affect the diffraction pattern of as-prepared hydroxyapatite. Diffraction patterns were obtained for HA and Si-HA samples which had been heat-treated at 1200°C for 2 hours, Figure 4. The patterns appear to be identical, with no secondary phases such as TCP or CaO detected. All the diffraction peaks matched the standard for HA[6]. The incorporation of 0.2-0.8 wt% silicon into the HA lattice appears to have no direct effect on the phase composition.

The changes in the lattice parameters of HA with increasing silicon substitution are shown in Figure 5, and the change in occupancy of the OH site and the distortion index, D_{index}, in Figure 6. Silicon substitution resulted in a decrease in the a-axes and an increase in the c-axis of the unit cell of HA. The number of OH groups in the unit cell of hydroxyapatite decreased when silicon is incorporated into the structure. The effect of an ionic substitution on the structure of HA could be illustrated by calculating the distortion index, which indicated the distortion of the PO4 tetrahedra in the HA lattice. No distortion of the PO4 tetrahedra would result in a D_{index} of zero, as all the O-P-O bond angles would be 109.47°. The silicon substitution caused a substantial increase in the D_{index} of stoichiometric HA of more than 50%.

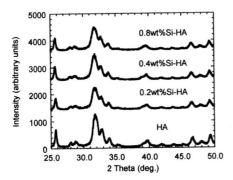

Figure 3. XRD patterns of as-prepared HA and HA-Si samples.

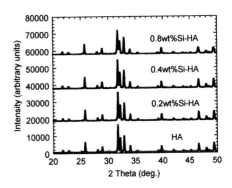

Figure 4. XRD patterns of heat-treated (1200°C) HA and Si-HA samples; no secondary phases such as $Ca_3(PO_4)_2$ or CaO were detected.

DISCUSSION

In this study, a range of compositions of silicon-substituted hydroxyapatite were prepared that contained between 0 and 0.8wt% silicon. A reaction mechanism that replaced some of the phosphate ions required to make stoichiometric HA with silicate ions was devised[1], as proposed in Eq. 1. To compensate for the extra negative charge of the silicate groups, some of the OH groups will be lost, thus retaining charge balance.

$$10Ca^{2+} + (6-x)PO_4^{3-} + xSiO_4^{4-} + (2-x)OH^- \rightarrow Ca_{10}(PO_4)_{6-x}(SiO_4)_x(OH)_{2-x} \qquad (1)$$

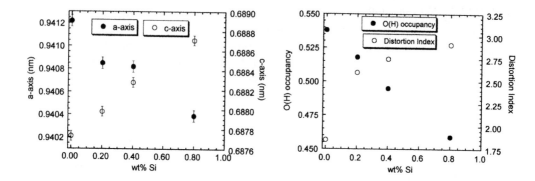

Figure 5. Effect of Si substitution on the lattice parameters of HA.

Figure 6. Change in OH site occupancy and D_{index} of HA with increasing Si substitution.

This substitution mechanism results in an increase in the Ca/P molar ratio with increasing levels of Si substitution, but the correct ratio of Ca/(P+Si) remains constant at 1.67(1). This indicates that all of the Si was incorporated into the HA lattice where it occupied a 'P' site, as described in equation 1. Furthermore, changes in the structural parameters such as the cell parameters, the decrease in the number of OH groups and the increase in the distortion index was indicative of a larger Si ion substituting for a smaller P ion in the HA structure. Further evidence of the incorporation of Si into the HA lattice is the X-ray diffraction patterns, Figure 4, in which no additional phases were observed for any of the heat-treated Si-HA samples.

CONCLUSIONS

Various amounts of silicon can be substituted for phosphorus in hydroxyapatite, but at the same time the hydroxyapatite structure is maintained. From the results of chemical analysis, a substitution mechanism has been devised which describes the incorporation of a silicon (or silicate) at the expense of a phosphorus (or phosphate) and a hydroxide ion. The Si-HA is stable upon sintering and only small structural changes are observed due to the silicon substitution.

ACKNOWLEDGEMENTS
The support of the Engineering and Physical Sciences Research Council for funding of the IRC in Biomedical Materials is gratefully acknowledged.

REFERENCES
[1] Best SM, Bonfield W, Gibson IR, Jha LJ and Santos JD, "Silicon-Substituted Apatites and Process for the Preparation Thereof," International Patent Appl. No. PCT/GB97/02325
[2] Carlisle EM, *Science*, 1970; **167**; 179-280
[3] Carlisle EM, *Calc. Tiss. Int.*, **33**, 27-34 (1981)
[4] Akao M, Aoki H and Kato K, *J. Mat. Sci.*, 1981; **16**; 809-812
[5] Osaka A, Miura Y, Takeuchi K, Asada M and Takahashi K, *J. Mat. Sci. Mater. in Med.*, 1991; **2**; 51-55
[6] PDF Card no. 9-432, ICDD, Newton Square, Pennsylvania, U.S.A.

Bioceramics Volume 11, edited by R. Z. LeGeros and J.P. LeGeros
(Proceedings of the 11th International Symposium on Ceramics in Medicine)
New York, NY, USA, November 1998
© 1998 by World Scientific Publishing Co. Pte. Ltd.

SYNTHESIS, SINTERING AND MECHANICAL CHARACTERISTICS OF NON-STOICHIOMETRIC APATITE CERAMICS

S. Raynaud, E. Champion, D. Bernache-Assollant

Laboratoire de Matériaux Céramiques et Traitements de Surface, ESA CNRS 6015,
123, avenue Albert Thomas, 87060 Limoges, France.

ABSTRACT

The effect of Ca/P atomic ratio on the thermal behavior and mechanical characteristics of HAP based ceramics was investigated. Ca-deficient HAP powders with Ca/P ratio ranging from 1.6667 to 1.6315 were prepared by a precipitation method. The synthesized powders were single phased, of apatitic structure : $Ca_{10-x}(PO_4)_{6-x}(HPO_4)_x(OH)_{2-x}$. During calcination, the specific surface area of powders started to decrease at 400°C and the surface reduction rate increases with the decrease of Ca/P ratio. The decomposition of the initial apatitic phase in a biphasic compound (stoichiometric HAP and TCP $Ca_3(PO_4)_2$) occurred from 700°C. The sintering, studied from dilatometry using powders calcined at a temperature below dissociation, showed that a decrease of Ca/P ratio of the initial phase decreased the densification rate during the first stage of sintering. This indicated that HPO_4^{2-} groups influenced the diffusion mechanisms. Nearly fully dense biphasic (HAP+TCP) materials were produced by hot pressing. The highest mechanical properties were obtained for Ca-deficient HAP ceramics having an atomic ratio Ca/P close to 1.65 ($\sigma_f \approx 150$ MPa; $K_{IC} \approx 1$ MPa.m$^{1/2}$). Conversely, stoichiometric HAP had the lowest fracture strength and toughness.

KEYWORDS : Hydroxyapatite, Stoichiometry, Synthesis, Strength, Toughness.

INTRODUCTION

Some studies concerning the mechanical characteristics of non-stoichiometric hydroxyapatite ceramics have been reported during the last decade.[1-6] But, most of them only give some data of fracture strength or toughness for a too wide range of variation of Ca/P ratio. Moreover, because several physical parameters (grain size, residual porosity) also influence the sintering behavior and modify the mechanical properties, the effect of powder stoichiometry is not clearly understood, yet.

From this basis, the objective of this work was to investigate the contribution of the Ca/P atomic ratio on the thermal behavior and mechanical characteristics of HAP based ceramics of interest for biological applications.

MATERIALS AND METHODS

The started powders were prepared by an aqueous precipitation from the addition of a diammonium phosphate $(NH_4)_2HPO_4$ solution to a calcium nitrate $Ca(NO_3)_2$ solution maintained at a constant temperature. The pH was regulated by addition of an ammoniac solution. Then, the suspensions were filtered. The Ca/P ratio of the resulting powders was determined from X-ray diffraction patterns (Siemens D5000 apparatus) according to the AFNOR S 94-066 standard. The specific surface area was measured by BET method (Surface analyzer Micromeritics ASAP-2010. N_2; 8 points) on powders heat treated between 400°C and 800°C.

For the sintering analysis, powders calcined down the same specific surface area of 30 m^2g^{-1}, were pressed under a 100 MPa compressive stress. The linear shrinkage was determined by dilatometry (Setaram TMA 92) in air at 1250°C for 30 min at the heating rate of 5°Cmin^{-1}. Samples were also hot pressed under a compressive stress of 20 MPa at 1100°C for 30 min.

The relative density of sintered materials was measured by the Archimedean method in water. Flexural strength was determined by 3-point bending on 20×3×3 mm^3 polished (diamond paste 3 μm) samples with a 16 mm span at a cross-head speed of 0.2 mm.min^{-1}. Fracture toughness was measured by Vickers indentation technique under a 19.6 N applied load. K_{IC} values were calculated using the equation proposed by Evans.[7]

RESULTS AND DISCUSSION

Characterization and sintering of powders

The synthesis conditions (pH, temperature) and the mean characteristics of powders are summarized in Table1.

Table 1. Preparation conditions and characteristics of powders.

pH	T (°C)	Ca/P	So at 400°C (m^2g^{-1})	β-TCP (wt% at 1000°C)
9	95	1.6667	57.9	0
7.5	85	1.6630	---	2
7	85	1.6576	62.5	5
7	70	1.6430	62.2	13
7	60	1.6315	67.7	20

In order to produce Ca-deficient hydroxyapatite with decreasing Ca/P atomic ratios both pH and temperature of synthesis must be decreased simultaneously. X-ray diffraction patterns showed that the as synthesized powders were single phased, of apatitic structure : $Ca_{10-x}(PO_4)_{6-x}(HPO_4)x(OH)_{2-x}$. In agreement with the literature data,[8] this phase remains stable up to about 700°C. Then, at higher temperature it is decomposed into stoichiometric HAP $Ca_{10}(PO_4)_6(OH)_2$ and β-tricalcium phosphate $Ca_3(PO_4)_2$; TCP.

During thermal treatment of calcination, independent from the Ca/P atomic ratio, the specific surface area of powders begins to decrease from 400°C. The highest rates are registered between 600°C and 700°C (Fig. 1). As no shrinkage was noticed below 700°C (Fig. 2), densification mechanisms do not occur up to that temperature. This means that the surface reduction of powders during calcination may be attributed to particle coalescence. As described in the case of pure HAP,[9] this grain growth should result from superficial diffusion. The rate of surface reduction increases with a decrease of Ca/P ratio, indicating an influence of HPO_4^{2-} ions (the powders being single phased below 700°C).

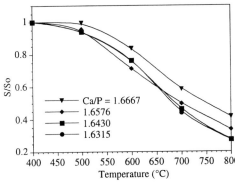
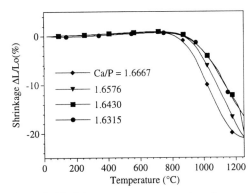

Figure 1. Evolution of specific surface area of powders versus calcination temperature.

Figure 2. Shrinkage versus temperature for powders initially precalcined down to 30 m^2g^{-1}.

From 700°C, the densification begins to occur (Fig 2). Whereas a decrease of Ca/P ratio favored surface reduction below 700°C, it decreases the densification rate. This can be explained by the decomposition of the initial apatitic compound into HAP and TCP between 700°C and 800°C. Thus, the presence of TCP as second phase (Tab. 1) which exhibits a lower sinterability than HAP,[3] decreases slightly the sintering rate.

Though natural sintering might have been used, hot pressing was chosen to produce dense materials with limited grain growth. Indeed, hot pressing allows to obtain materials with a higher relative density and an average grain size of about 5 times smaller than that obtained after natural sintering (Table 2).

Table 2. Elaboration conditions and typical characteristics of resulting materials.

Elaboration	relative density (% of d_{th})	average grain size (μm)
Hot pressing 1100°C-20 MPa-30 min	> 99	0.2 - 0.5
Natural sintering 1250°C-30 min	90 - 93	1 - 2

Strength and toughness of hot pressed materials

The mechanical characteristics were investigated on dense hot pressed materials. Bending strength and toughness are given in Figures 3 and 4, respectively. They show that there is no evidence for distinct changes of toughness values whereas the ultimate strength depends strongly on the composition. The lowest strength and toughness are obtained for stoichiometric HAP ($\sigma_f \approx 70$ MPa; $K_{1C} \approx 0.85$ MPa.$m^{1/2}$). Ca-deficient HAP with a Ca/P close to 1.65 (i.e. about 8% TCP)

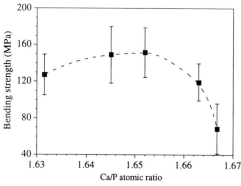

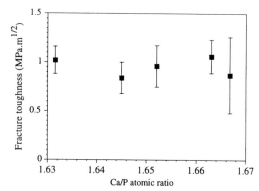

Figure 3. Fracture strength of hot pressed materials versus initial Ca/P atomic ratio.

Figure 4. Toughness of dense materials versus initial Ca/P atomic ratio.

presents the highest values ($\sigma_f \approx 150$ MPa; $K_{1C} \approx 1$ MPa.m$^{1/2}$). This result can be compared with those found in two other studies which also indicated a lower strength for stoichiometric HAP.[1,3] These variations cannot be attributed to a change of residual porosity or to a modification of the average grain size which remain quite constant for all these materials. A more detailed analysis of the microstructure appears necessary to explain these results.

CONCLUSION

The stoichiometry of the initial apatitic calcium phosphate powders appears to be an important parameter for the elaboration of HAP based materials. The presence of a small amount of TCP after densification (i.e. Ca-deficient hydroxyapatite powder) greatly increases the strength of the material without important modification of the sintering. A more detailed analysis of the microstructural design of materials having a Ca/P ratio close to the stoichiometric value is under investigation for a better understanding of such variations of the mechanical reliability.

REFERENCES

1. Toriyama M, Kawamura S, Shiba S. *Yogyo Kyokai Shi* 1987; **95**: 456-458.
2. Asada M, Oukami K, Nakamura S, Takahashi K. *J Ceram Jpn Inter Ed* 1988; **96**: 583-586.
3. Royer A, Viguie JC, Heughebaert M, Heughebaert JC. *J Mat Sci Mater Med* 1993; **4**: 76-82.
4. Slosarczyk A, Stobierska E, Paszkiewicz Z, Gawlicki M. *J Am Ceram Soc* 1996; **79**: 2539-44.
5. Toriyama M, Ravaglioli A, Krajewski A, Celotti G, Piancastelli A. *J Eur Ceram Soc* 1996; **16**: 429-436.
6. Slosarczyk A, Bialoskorski J. *J Mat Sci Mater Med* 1998; **9**: 103-108.
7. Evans AG, Charles EA. *J Am Ceram Soc* 1976; **59**: 371-372.
8. Mortier A, Lemaitre J, Rouxhet PG. *Thermochimica Acta* 1989; **143**: 265-282.
9. Ababou A, Bernache-Assollant D, Heughebaert M. *Ann Chim Fr* 1994; **19**: 165-175.

Bioceramics Volume 11, edited by R. Z. LeGeros and J.P. LeGeros
(Proceedings of the 11th International Symposium on Ceramics in Medicine)
New York, NY, USA, November 1998
© 1998 by World Scientific Publishing Co. Pte. Ltd.

FORMATION OF FLUORIDATED HYDROXYAPATITE FROM TRICALCIUM PHOSPHATE (TCP) IN ORGANIC MEDIA

K. Sakamoto[1], Y. Tsunawaki[1], S. Yamaguchi[2], J. Ichihara[2], A. Nakahira[3], M. Okazaki[4]

[1]Osaka Sangyo University, Nakagaito, Daito, Osaka 574-0013, Japan; [2] ISIR, Osaka University, Mihogaoka, Ibaraki, Osaka 567-0047, Japan ; [3] Kyoto Institute of Technology, Goshokaidocho, Matsugasaki, Sakyo-ku, Kyoto, 606-0962, Japan; [4]Osaka University Faculty of Dentistry, Yamadaoka, Suita, Osaka 565-0871, Japan

ABSTRACT

Solvothermal reactions of α-tricalcium phosphate (α-TCP) with NH_4F were investigated in water-organic solvent system. In the system using a series of aliphatic alcohols the formation of fluoridated hydroxyapatite $[Ca_{10}(PO_4)_6(OH)_{2-x}F_x]$ (FHAp) was confirmed. The formation rate of FHAp from α-TCP and the shape and size of FHAp were influenced by the hydrophobicity of aliphatic alcohols similarly to the formation of HAp from α-TCP. The product obtained in water-1-octanol biphasic system was a mixture of needle-like particles (~0.5 x 1~4 μm) with ultrafine particles (~0.1 μm), whereas the product in water (in the absence of organic solvent) consisted of fine particles less than 1 μm. The formation rate showed unusual dependence on the concentration of fluoride ion and on the reaction temperature.

   We found that this biphasic reaction system was applicable to the reaction of β-TCP to afford FHAp in a uniform shape. This is the first example of synthesis of FHAp from β-TCP as long as we know.

KEYWORDS: fluoridated hydroxyapatite; α-tricalcium phosphate; β - tricalcium phosphate;

INTRODUCTION

   There has been considerable interest in transformation of α-tricalcium phosphate (α-TCP) to hydroxyapatite (HAp) and its derivatives due to the control of crystal formation.[1] In the previous work[2], we reported that hydrolysis of α-TCP in water-aliphatic alcohol system was enhanced with increasing hydrophobicity of alcohol. It was found that in biphasic system using hydrophobic alcohol such as 1-octanol needle-shaped HAp was obtained uniformly in contrast to that in the absence of alcohol. As well as HAp fluoridated hydroxyapatite (FHAp) is a potent biomaterial.[3,4] We investigated the formation of FHAp by use of this solvothermal reaction of α-TCP in the presence of fluoride ion in organic media and also tried to the formation of FHAp from β-TCP. We now report these results.

EXPERIMENTAL PROCEDURE

α-TCP and β-TCP were provided by Taihei Chemical Industrial Co. Ltd. A reaction of α-TCP powder (2 mmol) with various concentration of aqueous ammonium fluoride solution (0.35, 0.70, or 1.4 mmol of NH_4F in 18 ml of water) was carried out in organic solvent [ethanol, 1-butanol, or 1-octanol] (25 ml) under stirring. The initial pH value was kept to about 6.0 without any other agent. After the reaction for 2-120 hours at various temperatures, the products were collected by filtration, washed with ethanol and distilled water, and dried in air for 5 hours at 40 °C. The obtained products were identified by X-ray diffractometry (XRD; Rigaku Geigerflex RAD IA) and their chemical compositions were also analyzed. The shape and size of products were observed by scanning electron microscope (SEM; Hitachi FESEM H800) and transmission electron microscope (TEM; Hitachi H8000, 200 kV).

RESULTS AND DISCUSSION

Incorporation of F ions in the HAp formation process starting from α-TCP was attempted with aqueous NH_4F solution in the addition of a series of aliphatic alcohols. The hydrolysis rate of α-TCP with F$^-$ was influenced by the hydrophobicity of the aliphatic alcohols in a similar direction to the hydrolysis of α-TCP to HAp.[2] In each case the formation of fluoridated hydroxyapatite $[Ca_{10}(PO_4)_6(OH)_{2-x}F_x]$ (FHAp) was confirmed by chemical composition analysis and powder X-ray diffractometry.[5] Figure 1 (a and b) shows the TEM photographs of FHAp prepared with 0.70 molar ratio of NH_4F/TCP in water-1-octanol biphase and in water (in the absence of organic solvent). The product in water-1-octanol biphasic system was a mixture of needle-like particles (length : about 1~4 μm, width : ~0.5 μm) with ultrafine particles (~0.1 μm), whereas the product in water consisted of fine particles less than 1 μm. Contribution of 1-octanol to the process of FHAp crystal growth was at least recognized, although the operating mechanism is not elucidated.

When the molar ratio of NH_4F to α-TCP was varied to 0.17, 0.35, or 0.70, the corresponding amount of fluoride ion was incorporated to the product finally. In our cases the X-ray diffraction angle (2θ) of (300) shifted to higher angle with increasing the amount of incorporated F$^-$, as described by E.C. Moreno[5]. This indicates the replacement of OH$^-$ with F$^-$ and reduction of the unit length of a-axis of the crystal.

The formation rate of FHAp in water-1-octanol system unusually depended on the reaction temperature and the concentration of F$^-$. Figure 2 shows the conversion ratios after the reaction with variation of F$^-$ concentration at various temperature for 4 h, which were estimated by relative intensity of α-TCP to FHAp in XRD patterns. In low F$^-$ concentration, increasing the reaction temperature, the formation rate increased. In high F$^-$ concentration, inversely, the formation rate decreased. It was found that the transformation of α-TCP to FHAp showed the highest reactivity when 0.17 molar ratio of NH_4F/TCP was used at 70 °C.

We found that the water-1-octanol-biphasic reaction system was applicable to the reaction of β-TCP to FHAp. Increasing the reaction temperature and F$^-$ concentration, the formation rates increased in contrast to that of α-TCP. Furthermore the obtained FHAp was uniform particles. TEM photographs of FHAp prepared with 0.35 and 0.70 molar ratio of NH_4F/TCP at 70 °C are also shown in Figure 1c-f. The shapes and sizes of FHAp were varied by the incorporated fluoride amount. A favored crystal growth was observed in octanol biphasic system (the left) than in water system (the right). This is the first example of synthesis of FHAp from β-TCP as long as we know.

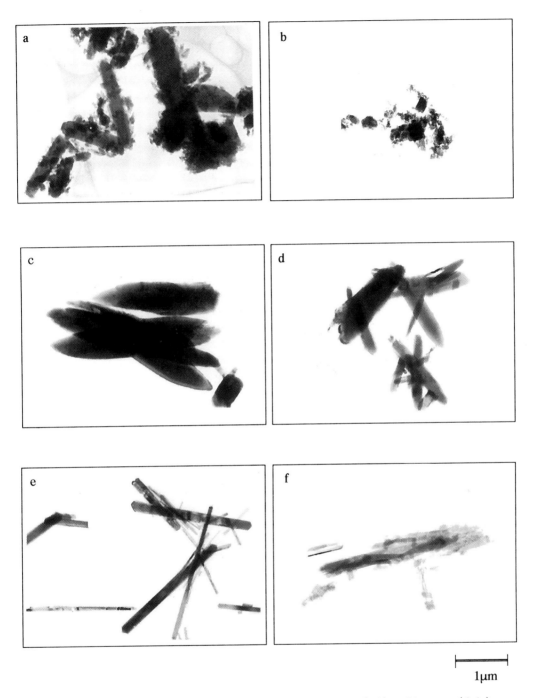

Figure 1. The TEM photographs of FHAp prepared in 1-octanol (left) and in water (right).
0.70 molar ratio of NH$_4$F/α-TCP (a-d), 0.35 molar ratio of NH$_4$F/β-TCP (e, f)

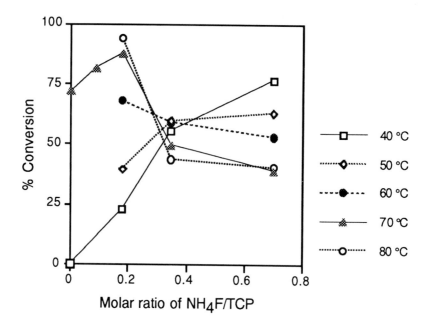

Figure 2. Transformation of α-TCP to FHAp in water-1-octanol biphase

CONCLUSION

Shape-controlled fluoridated hydroxyapatite $[Ca_{10}(PO_4)_6(OH)_{2-x}F_x]$ (FHAp) was effectively prepared by hydrolyses of α-TCP and β-TCP with NH_4F in water-hydrophobic alcohol biphasic system. In both reactions of α-TCP and β-TCP there were differences in the rates of hydrolysis with fluoride incorporation and the processes of FHAp crystal growth. Hydrophobic alcohol biphasic system is considered to control the latter process.

ACKNOWLEDGMENT

The authors thank Taihei Chemical Industrial Co. Ltd. for providing α- and β-TCP. This research was partly supported by Grants-in Aid for Scientific Research from the Ministry of Education, Science and Culture of Japan (No.09558119 and 10680795).

REFERENCES

1. Yoshimura M, Suda H, Okamoto K, Ioku K, *J. Mater. Sci.*, 1994; **2 9**: 3399.
2. Sakamoto K, Yamaguchi S, Nakahira A, Kijima K, Okazaki M, *Proc. Bioceramics*, 1997; **1 0**: 241-244.
3. Hench L, *J. Mater. Ceram. Soc.*, 1991; **7 4**: 1487.
4. Monma H, Ueno S, *Gypsum&Lime*, 1979; **1 6 3**: 226-232.
5. Moreno EC, *Nature*, 1974; **2 4 7**: 64.

Bioceramics Volume 11, edited by R. Z. LeGeros and J.P. LeGeros
(Proceedings of the 11th International Symposium on Ceramics in Medicine)
New York, NY, USA, November 1998
© 1998 by World Scientific Publishing Co. Pte. Ltd.

CHEMICAL TRANSFORMATIONS OF BIOLOGICALLY RELEVANT CALCIUM PHOSPHATES IN AQUEOUS MEDIA DURING A STEAM STERILIZATION

S.V. Dorozhkin, M. Schmitt, J.M. Bouler, G. Daculsi

Centre de Recherche sur les Matériaux d'Intérêt Biologique, UPRES EA 2159, Faculté de Chirurgie Dentaire, BP 84215, 44042 Nantes Cedex 1, France. Fax : +33 (0)2 40 08 37 12

ABSTRACT

This presentation is devoted to investigations on a steam sterilization to transformation of different calcium phosphates in aqueous media. Suspensions of $CaHPO_4 \cdot 2H_2O$ (DCPD), calcium deficient apatite (CDA) and biphasic calcium phosphate (BCP) were prepared by mixing of 0.2 g of the each powder with 5.0 ml of deionized water, followed by a steam sterilization (20 min at 121°C) in an autoclave. After being sterilized, the suspensions were filtered followed by investigations on the solids obtained with scanning electron microscopy, IR-spectroscopy and X-ray diffraction; as well as solution pH and calcium concentrations were determined in the liquid phases. Similar measurements were made with the same samples, but without the sterilization. The sterilization procedure was found to result in dehydration of DCPD and fast hydration of calcium oxide incorporated into the crystal structure of BCP with simultaneous changing in solution pH from 7.3 to 5.5 for the solutions in equilibrium with DCPD, and from 8.5 to 10.6 for those in equilibrium with BCP. No changes in solid and minor changes in solution pH were found to happen during sterilization of CDA. Thus, a steam sterilization may have a different influence on calcium phosphates suspensions: it can result in dehydration (DCPD), fast hydration (CaO in BCP) or have no great influence (CDA).

KEYWORDS: Calcium phosphates, steam sterilization, chemical transformations.

INTRODUCTION

Different calcium phosphates and items covered with them are widely used in medicine because they have an excellent biocompatibility both with hard and soft tissues of human body.[1,2] But prior to the clinical use, all the materials must be sterilized. Different cleaning and sterilization procedures (e.g. gamma and laser irradiation, plasma cleaning, steam sterilization, ethylene oxide and chemical detergents) are commonly used for this purpose in medicine.[3-7]

In spite of a wide application of calcium phosphates in medicine, surprisingly there are only few publications devoted to an influence of the sterilization conditions on chemical properties of inorganic calcium phosphates. Surface of pure stoichiometric hydroxyapatite (HA) was found to remain unchanged after a steam sterilization in an autoclave, but a sterilization with gamma irradiation resulted in driving off the weakly bonded surface water and distortion of surface phosphate complexes.[8] Steam sterilization of dental gypsum at 132°C and 121°C was found to result in its dehydration.[9] This presentation is devoted to study on a steam sterilization procedure in an autoclave to chemical transformations of some calcium phosphates in aqueous media.

MATERIALS AND METHODS

Three different calcium phosphates: $CaHPO_4 \cdot 2H_2O$ (DCPD), calcium deficient apatite (CDA) and biphasic calcium phosphate (BCP - it consists of 60% of hydroxyapatite and 40% of β-$Ca_3(PO_4)_2$) were chosen for the sterilization experiments. The choice has been made, because BCP is widely used in surgery[2,9,10] and it is produced from CDA by heating the latter at 1050°C during 5h,[9,10] while CDA is prepared from DCPD by chemical interaction of the latter with NaOH (2670 g of solid DCPD and 480 g of solid NaOH are added into 17 l of de-ionized water) at 100°C during 4 h followed by filtration of the CDA obtained, its washing with water and drying at 70°C.[9,10] Initial chemicals used (DCPD and NaOH) were purchased from Merck.

Water suspensions of the above calcium phosphates (0.2 g of the solid and 5 ml of water) were steam sterilized in an autoclave according to the standard procedure used in dentistry (20 min at 121°C).[11] Solution pH were measured both before and after the sterilization. After being sterilized, suspensions were filtered, followed by calcium determination in the liquid phase by a calcium selective electrode (Model 97-20 ionplus, Orion Research Inc.), while chemical and structural compositions of the solids were studied with FTIR (Magna-IR 550, Nicolet), X-ray diffraction (XRD) (Diffract 5000, Siemens) and scanning electron microscopy (JSM 6300, JEOL). Similar measurements were also performed with the same non-sterilized suspensions.

RESULTS

The results obtained for the solutions equilibrated with the calcium phosphates investigated are summarized in the Table 1. Index "s" after some abbreviations means the sterilized samples.

Table 1. Chemical composition of the solutions equilibrated with calcium phosphates.

	sol. pH, initial	sol. pH 30.09	sol. pH 01.10	sol. pH 02.10	sol. pH 03.10	sol. pH 04.10	sol. pH 10.10	sol. pH 13.10	Ca^{2+} mol/l**
DCPD	7.29	7.22	7.20	7.20	7.19	7.17	7.11	7.14	$4 \cdot 10^{-4}$
DCPD$_s$	7.29*	5.52	5.56	5.53	5.59	5.61	5.58	5.61	$5 \cdot 10^{-3}$
CDA	8.78	8.64	8.61	8.57	8.60	8.59	8.58	8.61	$4 \cdot 10^{-5}$
CDA$_s$	8.78*	8.20	8.18	8.13	8.09	8.06	8.02	8.01	$5 \cdot 10^{-5}$
BCP	8.51	9.80	10.18	10.46	10.59	10.63	10.57	10.56	$<10^{-5}$
BCP$_s$	8.51*	10.60	10.59	10.58	10.56	10.53	10.51	10.56	$<10^{-5}$

*measurements were made before the sterilization
**measurements were made on the 13.10.97

No changes within sensitivity of the methods employed were found to happen both with CDA and BCP during the sterilization procedure, while the results of FTIR and XRD pointed out to the complete transformation of DCPD into its anhydrous form ($CaHPO_4$). No admixtures of other calcium phosphates were found to be present in the anhydrous form of $CaHPO_4$.

DISCUSSION

Two points should be emphasized in the results of Table 1. First, solution pH in equilibrium with all calcium phosphates studied has been changed immediately after the sterilization and except that for BCP, remained more or less constant within next 2 weeks. Second, there is an essential difference between BCP and other calcium phosphates (DCPD and CDA): solution pH for the sterilized (BCP_s) and non-sterilized (BCP) samples became equal after 4 days after the sterilization procedure and later remained unchanged, while both for DCPD and CDA solution pH for the sterilized and non-sterilized samples were always different. The latter points out that the steam sterilization results in changes of the BCP hydrolysis kinetics only, but it is not the truth for DCPD and CDA. Some irreversible changes have happened during their sterilization.

In the case of DCPD, both FTIR and XRD pointed out to formation of anhydrous $CaHPO_4$ as a result of the steam sterilization. Thus, dehydration of DCPD occurs during the sterilization:

$$CaHPO_4 \cdot 2H_2O = CaHPO_4 + 2H_2O \qquad (1)$$

Both $CaHPO_4 \cdot 2H_2O$ and $CaHPO_4$ are known to be in equilibrium with water solutions at different temperatures: the former at t < 50°C, while the latter at t > 60°C.[2] That is why, dehydration of DCPD according to reaction (1) is in a good agreement with the references. On the other hand, according to the solubility phase diagram for the system $Ca(OH)_2 - H_3PO_4 - H_2O$ at 25°C, solubility of anhydrous form is always a little bit less than that for DCPD within pH range of 4 – 8.[12] The latter should always result in DCPD dehydration in water media at room temperatures. A small shift in solution pH (from 7.22 till 7.14 during 2 weeks) can not be seriously considered as a confirmation of the DCPD dehydration at room temperature (it may be attributed to a drift of an electrode potential), but it goes in the direction of pH decreasing, as happened after sterilization.

Here there is another point to be discussed. According to reaction (1) no pH changes should happen during the DCPD dehydration, while in reality solution pH decreased from 7.2 till 5.6. The latter is responsible for calcium concentration increasing in the solution (last column in the Table 1). Indeed, according to the solubility diagram, solubility of any calcium phosphate increases with pH decreasing.[12] But why has the solution pH been changed? According to the calculations made by Dr. Lemaitre, solubility differences between DCPD and its anhydrous form may cause the pH drop for 0.2 pH units only.[13] On the other hand, if one assumes that during the sterilization 0.064% of DCPD transforms into HA and phosphoric acid (hydrolysis of DCPD):

$$5CaHPO_4 \cdot 2H_2O = Ca_5(PO_4)_3OH + 2H_3PO_4 + 9H_2O \qquad (2)$$

solution pH will be as low as 5.4.[13] The latter is very close to the experimentally found values of 5.5 - 5.6 (see Table 1). This assumption is also in a good agreement with the solubility diagram of calcium phosphates: HA is less soluble if compared both with DCPD and its anhydrous form under solution pH > 4.5.[12] Such small value of HA obtained (0.064% in the solid phase) can be detected neither by FTIR nor by XRD.

Next point to be discussed is a difference between pH of solutions in equilibrium with CDA (pH within 8.0 - 8.6) and BCP (pH ≈ 10.6) (see Table 1). According to the results obtained, some chemical changes should happen during preparation of BCP from CDA at 1050°C. In order to elucidate this question, a thermo-gravimetric analysis (TGA) was made for BCP preparation.

According to the results obtained, transformation of CDA into BCP results in total mass decreasing of 8.7%. Most part of the mass decreasing (8.15%) happens at temperatures below 350°C and the rest part of it (0.55%) happens at 650 - 700°C. The former is due to elimination of traces of water and the latter is due to carbonate.[14,15] In spite of the fact that neither FTIR nor XRD have been able to detect carbonate in the CDA, its presence appears to be very possible. According to the specifications for initial chemicals given by Merck, an amount of carbonate is not standardized in DCPD and there is up to 1% of Na_2CO_3 in solid NaOH. So, the results of TGA are reasonable and differences in solution pH between CDA and BCP may be explained by presence of 0.7% CaO in BCP. This conclusion is in agreement with the references, because no chemical changes were found to happen during the steam sterilization of pure HA.[8]

Finally, an influence of the steam sterilization to CDA should be discussed. As mentioned above, a small drop in solution pH (from 8.6 till 8.0-8.2) is the only difference found between the sterilized and non-sterilized samples of CDA (Table 1). This pH drop may be explained either by presence of traces of DCPD and their hydrolysis according to reaction (2) or by partial re-crystallization of CDA into less soluble HA[12] according to an approximate chemical reaction:

$$10Ca_9HPO_4(PO_4)_5OH + 8H_2O = 9Ca_{10}(PO_4)_6(OH)_2 + 6H_3PO_4 \qquad (3)$$

Both ways result in pH decreasing. A slow but permanent pH decreasing from 8.2 to 8.0 during next 2 weeks in the sterilized sample of CDA (Table 1) seems to be in favor of reaction (3).

REFERENCES

1. de Groot K, ed. *Bioceramics of Calcium Phosphate*. CRC Press, Boca Raton, FL, 1983: 146 p.
2. LeGeros, RZ. *Calcium Phosphates in Oral Biology and Medicine*. Monographs in Oral Science. Vol. 15. Basel: S. Karger AG, 1991: 201 p.
3. Zislis T, Martin SA, Cerbas E, Heath JR, Mansfield JL, Hollinger JO. *J Oral Implantol* 1989; **15**: 41-46.
4. Smith DC, Pilliar RM, Chernecky R. *J Biomed Mater Res* 1991; **25**: 1045-1068.
5. Block CM, Mayo JA, Evans GH. *Int J Oral Maxillofac Implants* 1992; 7: 441-449.
6. Kawahara D, Ong JL, Raikar GN, Lucas LC, Lemons JE, Nakamura M. *Int J Oral Maxillofac Implants* 1996; **11**: 435-442.
7. Suwanprateeb J, Tanner KE, Turner S, Bonfield W. *J Biomed Mater Res* 1998; **39**: 16-22.
8. Marquis PM, Wilson J, Fayolle M, Shelton RM. In: Yamamuro T. et al. ed. *Bioceramics 5*. Kobunshi Kankokai, 1992: 309-316.
9. LeGeros RZ. *J Dent Res* 1986; **65**, 292.
10. Bouler JM, Trécant M, Delécrin J, Royer J, Passuti N, Daculsi G. *J Biomed Mater Res* 1996, **32**, 603 - 609.
11. Whyte MP, Brockhurst PJ. *Australian Dental J* 1996; **41**, 128-133.
12. Brown WE, Chow LC. *J Cryst Growth* 1981; **53**, 31-41.
13. Lemaitre J. Private communication. See also: Vereecke G, Lemaitre J. *J Cryst Growth* 1990; **104**, 820-832.
14. Rey C, Frèche M, Heughebaert M, Heughebaert JC, Lacout JL, Lebugle A, Szilagyi J, Vignoles M. In: Bonfield W. et al. ed. *Bioceramics 4*. Butterworth-Hainemann Ltd., 1991: 57-64.
15. Tampieri A, Celotti G, Szontagh F, Landi E. *J Mater Sci Mater Med* 1997; **8**, 29-37.

Bioceramics Volume 11, edited by R. Z. LeGeros and J.P. LeGeros
(Proceedings of the 11th International Symposium on Ceramics in Medicine)
New York, NY, USA, November 1998
© 1998 by World Scientific Publishing Co. Pte. Ltd.

SOLUBILITY TESTS OF COMMERCIAL APATITE PRODUCTS

G. Berger, R. Gildenhaar, U. Ploska

Federal Institute for Materials Research and Testing, Unter den Eichen 87, D-12200 Berlin, Germany

ABSTRACT

Five commercial apatite products for surgical implantation manufactured from several raw materials and by different methods were investigated by X-ray diffraction analysis (XRD), thermal gravimetrical analysis (TGA), chemical analysis, and in two different types of solubility tests. The products could be distinguished clearly by the thermal analysis and the solubility tests, but not by the XRD method. The two solubility tests showed the influence of chemical composition and the behavior of the products in an application situation. It is proposed by the authors that the introduction of a "standard bone defect" – i. e. a constant volume filled with granulated material (bulk density) to a definite solvent volume – would approximate the application better than the use of a constant ratio of mass (or surface area) to solvent volume.

KEYWORDS

commercial apatites, solubility test, thermogravimetric analysis

INTRODUCTION

Apatite is currently the most widely applied inorganic nonmetallic bone substitution material. It is used as granules or shaped materials as well as in the form of a powder for coating metal implants. There are more than 10 commercial products in the form of granules for filling bone defects, all called hydroxyapatite or biological apatite. These products are known to be manufactured from different raw materials and by different methods. These factors have a major influence on the purity and morphology of the products themselves and, thus on certain qualities like strength, chemical durability etc.

The present paper deals with the investigation of these correlations. Five well known commercial products available for application in human beings were examined by common investigation methods, such as XRD, TGA, chemical analysis, and additionally by means of a solubility test. The solubility behavior is a characteristic material feature reflecting very sensitively variations in chemical compositions as well as in morphology. A special investigation method demonstrated the influence of both and showed clear differences between the products.

MATERIALS AND METHODS

Five commercial apatite products obtained from several manufacturers and labeled as bone fill materials were investigated in this study.

The BET surface of the original granules was established with an ASAP 2000 surface area measuring apparatus from Micromeritics Inc., USA, with Kr or N_2 as adsorbing gas. XRD spectra of powdered materials were obtained using a D5000 diffractometer manufactured by Siemens, Germany. A STA 409 thermoanalyzer (Netzsch Gerätebau GmbH, Germany) was employed for recording mass loss (heating rate 10 Kmin⁻¹).

For the chemical analysis, the phosphate samples were dissolved in a 15 % HCl solution. The ion concentration was measured by using the Optima 3000 ICP-OES apparatus, Perkin Elmer Inc., USA.

The solubility behavior was investigated by leaching the granulated materials with 0.2 M TRIS HCl buffer solution ($pH_{37 \cdot c}$ = 7.4 ± 0.2) for 120 hours. The tests were carried out once applying a constant ratio of mass to solvent volume using 200 mg of granules and 200 ml of the buffer solution (test 1), and a second time realizing a constant ratio of the surface area to solvent volume of 5 cm⁻¹ (test 2). In the latter case the materials mass corresponding to a surface area of 0.1 ± 0.01 m² was leached with 200 ml of the buffer solution. The concentration of the leached ions in the eluates was measured by using the Optima 3000 ICP-OES apparatus, Perkin Elmer, USA.

RESULTS AND DISCUSSION

All commercial bone fill materials investigated in these trials are labeled as "hydroxyapatite" or in one case as "biological apatite", but it is known that three of them are so-called "biological apatites" [1 – 3]. In other words, they are produced from biological materials such as bone, corals and algae, respectively. They are a carbonate apatite rather than a hydroxyapatite and contain other impurities.

There are, however, only slight differences in XRD patterns between the materials (see Fig. 1). The results showed small additions of whitelockite in the pattern of SA1 and an apatite of low crystallinity in the pattern of SA 4.

Table 1 shows that the materials do not exhibit noticeable differences in their chemical composition. All products show similiar Ca to P ratios, but they differ in the mass of compounds that are not determined, such as OH^-, CO_3^{2-}, adsorbed water, and lattice water. Differences in mass loss were also determined thermogravimetrically (Fig. 2). The "synthetic apatites" (SA2, SA3) show only a slight mass loss at about 1100 °C which is caused by the OH groups. In contrast, the mass loss of the "biological apatites" started at lower temperatures due to adsorbed and lattice water and because of the carbonate groups.

The solubility behavior determined by tests 1 and 2 can be seen in Figures 4 and 3, respectively. There are considerable differences between the results of both tests. If the ratio of material surface area to solvent volume is kept constantly (test 2), the surface area of the material has no influence on the solubility. In this case, the following order is obtained (see Fig.3):

$$SA4 \leq SA5 < SA1 < SA2 \ll SA3$$

This order of solubility reflects the influence of the minor components (H_2O, CO_3^{2-}, OH^-). There is a remarkable correlation between material specific solubility and mass loss measured by

Table 1: Chemical composition of different commercial apatite products

Code	Main compounds [mass %]		Minor compounds [mass %]				Residue (OH⁻ CO_3^{2-} H_2O) [mass %]	Ratio of Ca:P	Surface area [m²/g]
	Ca	PO₄	Mg	K	Na	Si			
SA1	37.01	53.36	0.11	0.03	0.03	0.07	9.35	1.64	2.97
SA2	38.76	54.99	<0.01	<0.01	0.01	<0.01	6.21	1.67	0.18
SA3	39.00	54.99	0.25	<0.01	0.12	0.03	5.6	1.68	0.51
SA4	36.16	50.07	0.52	<0.01	0.57	<0.01	13.17	1.71	96.65
SA5	33.44	48.36	2.51	<0.01	0.14	0.37	15.17	1.64	8.10

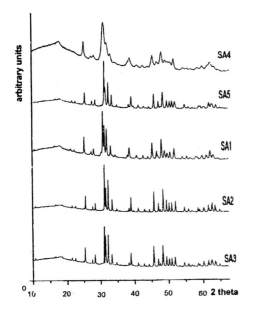

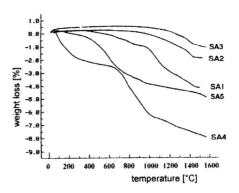

Fig. 2: TG curves of apatite samples

thermogravimetric analysis. SA4 shows the highest mass loss due to the volatilization of water, carbonate, and hydroxyl groups. For SA5 and SA1 the mass loss is smaller and starts at higher temperatures. SA3

Fig. 1: X-ray diffraction pattern of apatite samples

shows the lowest and latest mass loss and the highest solubility. If the weight difference of sample SA3 was correlated with loss of the stochiometric amount of water released by thermal decomposition of hydroxyapatite, the value would have to be equal to that of SA2. Because of the lower value, it is believed that SA3 partially consists of oxyapatite. Assuming this, solubility in 0.2 M TRIS HCl buffer solution decreases in the order of oxyapatite, hydroxyapatite, and carbonate apatite.

In practice, the influence of the surface area dominates the effect of the chemical constitution, as seen from the results of test 1 (Fig. 4). Excluding SA3, the order of solubility is then opposite because for the same amounts of the various materials the resulting surface area is necessarily different. These solubility values reflect the sequence given in the literature with regard to carbonate apatite and hydroxyapatite.

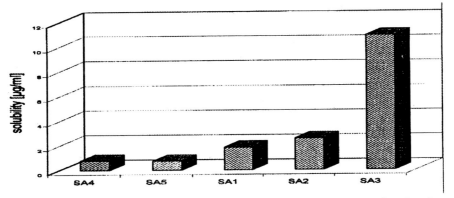

Fig.3: Solubility behavior of different apatite samples with a constant ratio of surface area to solvent volume

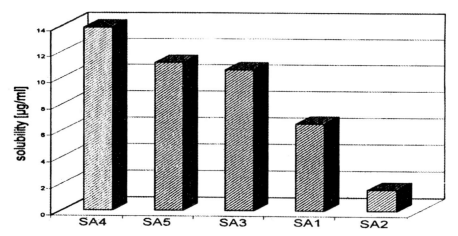

Fig. 4: Solubility behavior of different apatite samples with a constant ratio of mass
to solvent volume

The differences of the results of tests 1 and 2 indicate the much discussed layer formation due to the heterogeneous solution process of the hydroxyapatite [4-5]. It is also obvious that the results of the two tests are not comparable because the test conditions strongly affect the values. The conditions of test 1 seem to approximate the clinical application of granules closer than those of test 2.

CONCLUSIONS

The results of this study demonstrate that commercial hydroxyapatite products for surgical implantation do not show great differences in their XRD pattern or in their chemical composition (Ca to P ratio) but that they are indeed distinct in therms of their thermogravimetrical behavior and solubility.

Two solubility tests were used. The first test was carried out applying a constant mass to solvent volume ratio (test 1) and the second realizing a constant ratio of surface area to solvent volume (test 2). Both tests show very different results and describe the chemical solubility in a special manner, as is normally done in the literature. Consequently, the authors propose that the introduction of a "standard bone defect" – e.g. a constant volume filled with granulated material (bulk density) - would approximate the application better than the use of a constant ratio of mass (or surface area) to solvent volume.

This seems to be the best way to compare different granulated materials that are used for filling bone defects.

References

1. LeGeros, R. L., Baustita, C., Styner, D., LeGeros, J. P., Vijiayaraghavan, T. V., Retino, M. and Vledencanas, A., *Bioceramics* Volume 8, Pergamon, Oxford 1995, 81-87
2. LeGeros, R.L., Zheng, R., Kijkowska, R., Fan, D. and LeGeros, J.P, *Characterization and Performance of Calcium Phosphate Coatings for Implants*, ed. Horowitz/Paar, STP 1196 ASTM,43-53
3. Ruyter, I.E., *Advances in Biomaterials* Volume 10, Biomaterial Tissue Interfaces, 495-501
4. La Mer, V., *J. Phys. Chem.* 66, (1962), 973-978
5. Thomann, J. M., Voegel, J. C., Gramain, Ph., *Colloids and Surfaces*, 54 (1991) 145-159

Bioceramics Volume 11, edited by R. Z. LeGeros and J.P. LeGeros
(Proceedings of the 11th International Symposium on Ceramics in Medicine)
New York, NY, USA, November 1998
© 1998 by World Scientific Publishing Co. Pte. Ltd.

RELATIONSHIP BETWEEN BIOACTIVITY AND TEXTURAL PARAMETERS IN GLASSES

F. Balas, J. Pérez-Pariente and M. Vallet-Regí

Departamento de Química Inorgánica y Bioinorgánica, Facultad de Farmacia, Universidad Complutense, E-28040 Madrid, Spain.

ABSTRACT

Four different glasses in the system $SiO_2 \cdot P_2O_5 \cdot CaO \cdot MgO$ with different silica and magnesium contents have been prepared by a sol-gel route. The glasses were calcined at 600°C and characterised by chemical analysis, surface area (BET method), porosity and XPS. The *in vitro* bioactivity of the calcined samples was determined by immersion in a SBF solution. Surface area and porosity increases with the silica and magnesium content, while a strong inhibitory effect of magnesium on the hydroxyapatite (HA) growth rate is observed. XPS showed strong differences in the chemical composition of the bulk and surface of the glass. The relevance of this chemical heterogeneity and textural properties for the bioactivity behaviour of the glass is discussed.

KEYWORDS: Bioactive glasses, sol-gel, textural properties.

INTRODUCTION

The formation of a calcium phosphate layer on bioactive materials when they are immersed in a simulated body fluid (SBF)[1,2] is a complex surface phenomenon which, in a first instance, can be thought to be dependent on both chemical and textural parameters.

In this paper, we elaborate on the relationship between the growth rate of HA layer and surface area, pore size and volume and chemical composition of glasses obtained by a sol-gel route. Four different glasses have been prepared in the system SiO_2-P_2O_5-CaO-MgO, with different silica contents, following the method early described[3,4]. MgO was added from $Mg(NO_3)_2 \cdot 6H_2O$. Chemical composition of these materials is given in Table 1.

Table 1. Chemical composition of glasses (mol%).

	SiO_2	P_2O_5	CaO	MgO
65S	65	4	31	0
65SM	65	4	25	6
75S	75	4	21	0
75SM	75	4	17	4

MATERIALS AND METHODS

For the study, discs obtained from the dried sol-gel powders were calcined in air at 600°C for 3 hours. After thermal treatment, pieces of glass with a high surface area and porosity were obtained (Table 2). Both properties, as well as the average pore diameter in the macropore region

($d_p > 50$ nm), increase when around 20% of calcium is replaced by magnesium. Besides this, a narrow pore size distribution in the mesopore range ($2 < d_p < 50$ nm) is also obtained (Figure 1).

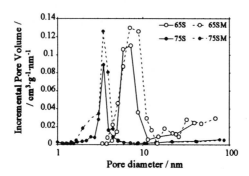

Figure 1. Pore diameter distribution for sol-gel glasses.(BJH method for pores from 1.7 to 300 nm).

Table 2. Textural parameters for glasses.

	N₂ adsorption			Hg porosimetry	
	S_{BET} / m²·g⁻¹	V_{BJH} / cm³·g⁻¹	d_p / nm	Porosity / %	d_p / μm
65S	125.5	0.32	7.2	41.5	0.1
65SM	218.0	0.40	7.1	49.7	1.0
75S	178.8	0.21	3.5	61.7	0.7
75SM	302.5	0.22	3.4	71.3	11.0

RESULTS AND DISCUSSION

When soaked in the SBF solution, the growth rate of the HA layer can be monitored by XRD as a function of time. This is illustrated in Figure 2 for the sample 65S. Hydroxyapatite is detected after 1 day, and after two weeks aggregates of needle-shaped HA crystals cover the substrate surface (Figure 3). However, strong differences are observed in the growth rate of the apatite layer, as it is shown in Figure 4, where the area of the (211) reflection of HA has been plotted as a function of time for the four samples. The highest rate of formation takes place on the materials which do not contain magnesium, but the one with the highest porosity (75S) apparently can accommodate more calcium phosphate than the other (65S). Partial replacement of calcium by magnesium provokes a strong reduction of the initial crystal growth rate, but nevertheless a steady increase of the apatite as a function of time is observed in both cases. Then the amount of apatite formed under prolonged soaking in the SBF could be related with the porosity of the glass and the apatite would grow into the pores following a pattern which could be described as a "sponge" filling model. On the other hand, a detailed analysis of the initial rate of apatite formation should take into account factors dependent on the liquid phase composition but also on the surface of the glass. The level of Ca^{2+} ion in the solution stabilises after 5 days around 270 and 230 ppm for the samples with 65 and 75 mol% of SiO_2, respectively.

It is worth to notice that no influence of magnesium content in the glass on the Ca^{2+} concentration in solution is observed, despite of the strong inhibitory effect that this element has on the HA formation. Clearly, the crystallisation rate of apatite in this case should be strongly influenced by the nature of the glass surface. The growth of the HA layer onto the glass could, in a first instance, be controlled by the surface area of the substrate. According to Table 2, the surface area increases with the SiO_2 and MgO content of the glass, but both affect in a negative manner the growth of HA. Therefore, this behaviour suggests that not all the glass surface might be equally active in nucleating the HA crystals.

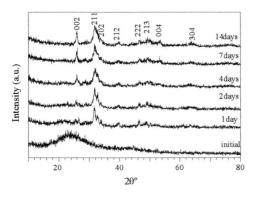

Figure 2. XRD pattern of 65S glass after several soaking times in SBF. The reflections corresponding to crystalline HA are indicated.

Figure 4. Variation of area under (211) HA reflection *vs.* soaking time in SBF solution.

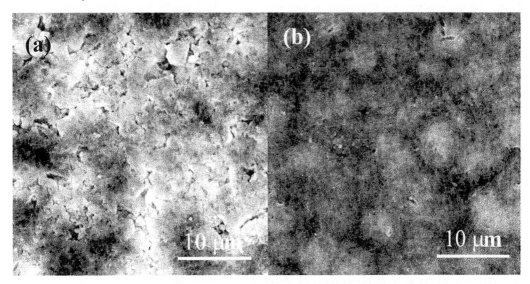

Figure 3. SEM image of glass 65S (a) before soaking and (b) after 2 weeks in SBF.

The XPS analysis of the glass reveals strong differences in the chemical composition between the bulk and the glass surface (Table 3), which is poorer in calcium than the bulk, but contains a higher phosphorus content (except for sample 75S). The addition of magnesium to the glass results in a strong increase of phosphorus at the surface, and a high level of magnesium is also detected. Indeed, the sample with the highest concentration of magnesium in the surface (65SM) has the lowest activity in HA growth.

The high phosphorus and calcium concentration in the surface and the reluctance of phosphorus to form Si-O-P bonds[5,6] makes possible the existence of calcium phosphate domains into the silica matrix, whose presence in the glass might be relevant in their *in vitro* bioactivity. In this context, the role of magnesium can also be understood, as it has been reported, to have an inhibitory effect on the formation and growth of HA and other crystalline calcium phosphates[7-10].

Table 3. XPS surface chemical composition (at%).

	Si	P	Ca	Mg
65S	70.1	11.7	18.1	0
65SM	61.2	14.9	12.5	11.3
75S	88.8	3.9	7.3	0
75SM	76.9	10.2	9.3	3.5

CONCLUSIONS

An increase in surface area an porosity of glasses is obtained by rising the amount of silica and magnesium into the solid. The high porosity of the magnesium-free samples with the highest SiO_2 content might explain its ability to accommodate a larger amount of HA. However, neither the calcium concentration in the solution , which changes very little for one sample to another, nor the surface area can explain the strong inhibitory effect of the magnesium present in the glass on the crystallisation growth rate of HA.

XPS shows that the glass surface is richer in phosphorus and poorer in calcium than the bulk, and the magnesium, if present, is also abundant. These results would be consistent with a highly heterogeneous surface where microdomains of calcium phosphate could be present and serve as nucleation centres for HA crystallisation.

ACKNOWLEDGEMENTS

The authors wish to thank to CICYT financial support through research project MAT96-0919.

REFERENCES

1. Kokubo T, Kushitani H, Sakka S, Kitsugi T, Yamamuro T. *J Biomed Mater Res* 1990; **24**, 721-734.
2. Ohtsuki C, Kokubo T, Yamamuro T. *J Non-Cryst Solids* 1992; **143**: 84-92.
3. Li R, Clark AE, Hench LL. *J Appl Biomater* 1991; **2**: 231-239.
4. Pereira MM, Clark AE, Hench LL. *J Biomed Mater Res* 1994; **28**: 693-698.
5. Iler RK. *The Chemistry of Silica*. New York: John Wiley & Sons, 1979: 296-297.
6. Mysen BO. *Structure and Properties of Silicate Melts*. Amsterdam: Elsevier, 1988: 201-215.
7. TenHuisen KS, Brown PW. *J Biomed Mater Res* 1997; **36**, 306-314.
8. Amjad Z, Koutsoukos P, Nancollas GH. *J Coll Int Sci* 1984; **101**: 250-257.
9. Brown JL. *Soil Sci Soc Am J* 1981; **45**: 482-486.
10. Nancollas GH, Tomazic B, Tomson M. *Croat Chem Acta* 1976; **48**: 431-438.

Bioceramics Volume 11, edited by R. Z. LeGeros and J.P. LeGeros
(Proceedings of the 11th International Symposium on Ceramics in Medicine)
New York, NY, USA, November 1998
© 1998 by World Scientific Publishing Co. Pte. Ltd.

LONG-TERM REACTIONS IN VITRO WITH BIOACTIVE GLASS S53P4

Peltola M.[1,2], Suonpää J.[1], Aitasalo K.[1], Andersson Ö.[3], Määttänen H.[4] and Yli-Urpo A.[2]

[1] Department of Otorhinolaryngology - Head and Neck Surgery, Turku University Central Hospital, FIN-20520 Turku, Finland, [2] Institute of Dentistry, University of Turku, FIN-20520 Turku, Finland, [4] Department of Radiology, Turku University Central Hospital and [3] Abo Akademi University, Turku, Finland.

ABSTRACT

Bioactive Glass S53P4 (BG) is a glass-ceramic material used in obliterating bony cavities e.g. frontal sinuses. In this *in vitro* study we observed the behaviour of a massive amount of BG (25 g) in simulated body fluid (SBF) . The aim was to study, is it possible to estimate the long-term durability and resorption of BG in the obliterated cavities indirectly with regular computer tomography (CT) monitorings.

The mass of BG tested was equivalent with that used in the obliteration operation. Granules of sizes 0.63 - 0.8 mm and 0.8 - 1.0 mm were incubated up to 6 months in SBF in standard conditions. The BG masses were scanned by computer tomography (CT) and the scans were analyzed by Region of Interest (ROI) selection at 1, 3 and 6 months in the middle of BG masses. At the same area calciumphosphate - (CaP) and silica- (Si) gel - layers were studied by scanning electron microscopy (SEM) and by energy dispersed X - ray analysis (EDXA) at 1, 3 and 6 months. Silicon and phosphate dissolution were detected with current plasma atom emission spectroscopy (DCP-AES) at 1 week and monthly up to 6 months.

In SBF CaP - layers were found on the surface of the upper granules. The thickest CaP - layer was on the uppermost granules. Silicagel-layer occured normally. Both Si-release and pH increased significantly at 1 and 2 months. P-release was highest at 1 week and decreased during CaP - formation. According to these results the loss of chemical components and resorption may be confidently estimated by decrease of the Hounsfield units in ROI-selection.

KEYWORDS : Frontal sinus obliteration with BG, long-term , region of interest , durability

INTRODUCTION

Alloplastic materials have been employed in frontal sinus obliteration to eliminate the second procedure required to obtain an autograft and because failure frequency has in many reports exceeded 25 percent [1]. Failla reported good results in obliterating the traumatized frontal sinus with acrylate [2]. Rosen and Nachtigal[3] used hydroxyapatite and trabecular bone mixture for obliteration of frontal sinuses. They followed - up 24 months four patients and estimated the density of obliterating material by region of interest. These measurements indicated efficient packing with no resorption of hydroxyapatite or bone within or around the obliterated space. Yamagishi et al [4] used hydroxyapatite in frontoethmoidectomy.

Bioactive glass (BG) is a glass - ceramic material. It has been proved to be a safe and biocompactible material [5,6]. A massive amount (25 g) of BG granules have been used as obliteration material in osteoplastic frontal sinus surgery [7,8,9]. Additional experimental information on the long-term stability of large BG-mass is needed to monitor the trustworthiness of the BG as an obliteration material in the frontal sinuses. The conditions particularly for new bone formation in the cortical bone cavity are probably different to those for spongious bone cavities filled with BG granules.

In this study we developed an *in vitro* model to simulate the obliterated frontal sinus and observed reactions to a equivalent BG- amount with that used in the obliteration operation. We estimated the durability and resorption of BG amount indirectly with computer tomography (CT) and with Region of Interest (ROI) - selection. In addition we monitored the loss of chemical components, formation calciumphosphate (CaP) and silicagel-layers of BG at the same time.

MATERIALS

BG S53P4 of the composition SiO_2 53 ; CaO 20.0 ; NaO 23.0 ; P_2O_5 4.0 weight % in two granule sizes was tested. Ten separate BG masses were tested, each of them weighing 25 g. Five of masses were granule size 0.63 - 0.8 mm and the other five were of granule size 0.8 - 1.0 mm. Each BG mass was implanted into a plastic polypropene centrifuge test tube (Kartell ®) .The bottom wall of each test tube was perforated with 500 round holes, 0.5 mm in diameter.The perforated test tubes were cut horizontally into two parts . The upper part of the test tube was wedged in the neck of the container from which the lower part was hung in the middle of the solution by means of four polyamid wires (Figure 1) . With the perforated plastic test tubes it was possible to increase the area of BG granules reacting with surrounding solution . Each BG mass was placed into a plastic polypropene container (Azlon ®), with a volume of 2000 ml . The containers were filled with simulated body fluid (SBF) solution prepared according to Kokubo et al [10] and Yamada et al [11] . To solution, $C_7H_5NaO_2$ (sodiumbentzoate) 0.2 g/l was added to prevent infections during incubation . They were put in an incubator at $37 \pm 0.25\,°C$. Each of above mentioned components and all the instruments were sterilized in ethyleneoxide . SBF solutions were changed every month and it took place in the laboratory in sterile conditions in a laminar cupboard . In the new solutions pH was 7.3 ± 0.05 .

METHODS

The BG masses were studied in the midline of mass at 1, 3 and 6 months with computer tomography (CT Picker PQ 2000) 1.5 and 3.0 mm slice thickness in SBF solution . All the parameters of the CT-scanning (radiation energy and time and position of the BG - mass) were equalized with patients scannings at each scanning session . During each session a teflon disk was also scanned as a reference body of the containers outer wall . In this way it was possible to obtain information to make sure that each scanning session is comparable for each others and show it by known reference material (Figure 1) . At eight separate regions, in the midline of BG mass, the density of the slices was analyzed by Region of Interest (ROI) - selection by the CT - machine (Figure 1) . After scanning the BG - masses were first rinsed with deionized water and then with same volume of 70 % ethanol . Dried masses were embedded in epoxy (Skandiplex ®) and later studied with scanning electron microscope (Stereoscan 360 Cambridge) SEM and energy dispersed X-ray analysis (EDXA) . The cumulative loss of silicon (Si) and phosphate (P) was detected with direct current plasma atom emissiom spectroscopy (DCP - AES) from SBF .

ROI - selection is based on digital absorption coefficients of each pixels in the selected region transformed to Hounsfield units . In the Hounsfield scale air   obtain   strongly negative unit - 1000, water 0 and bone strongly positive unit + 100 - 1000 [12]. The mean unit of saline moistened BG granules is 1182 [7] .

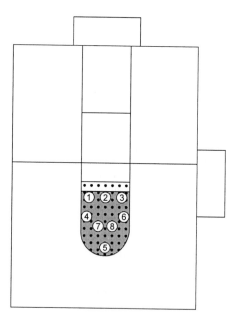

Figure 1 .   In the midline cross sectioned BG - mass in the middle of SBF solution .
Numbered areas analyzed with ROI - selection . On the right outer wall
of container is a reference teflon disk .

RESULTS

Results of the dissolute test are shown in table 1 .

Table 1 . Cumulative loss of Silicon and Phosphate

Granules / Silicon 0.63 - 0.8 mm 0.8 - 1.0 mm	252.16 151.3	496.2 340.5	733.5 523.2
Granules / Phosphate 0.63 - 0.8 mm 0.8 - 1.0 mm	32.91 35.64	38.92 44.2	77.6 96.0
Controls	1 MO	3 MO	6 MO

Dissolution of Si and P was detected with current plasma atom emission spectroscopy (DCP-AES) at each time when SBF solution changed . pH monitored at same time . Cumulative loss of chemical components is given in mg . Both Si and pH increased significantly 1 to 2 months . P - releasing was highest at 1 week and decreased during CaP - formation .

Results of the ROI-selection are presented in table 2 .

Table 2 . Hounsfield units in SBF

0.63 - 0.8 mm Granules	1364.0 ± 68.7 1350.9 ± 63.4	1313.4 ± 59.0 1301.6 ± 58.8	1288.7 ± 87.5 1289.1 ± 72.0	1.5 mm 3 mm
0.8 - 1.0 mm Granules	1437.4± 54.3 1442.5± 52.3	1426.8 ± 49.9 1429.2 ± 45.0	1409.9± 62.2 1393.3±57.3	1.5 mm 3 mm
Reference Teflon Disk	1076.0±10.3 1082.9±12.6	1081.3±16.7 1087.0±15.5	1085.8± 17.6 1086.7± 15.2	1.5 mm 3 mm
Controls	1 MO	3 MO	6 MO	Thickness of slices

Mean Hounsfield units and standard deviations of each CT slice . Scanning parametrs 130 kV and 150 mA/2.0 sec were equalized at each scanning session . In the uppermost part of CT slice Hounsfield units were some higher than central or near the test tube wall . In the uppermost granules there was CaP - layer determined with SEM and EDXA, but in the other parts of BG mass there was no CaP - layer . Silica gel layer was on each BG granule .

CONCLUSIONS AND DISCUSSION

The loss of chemical components and resorption was shown to decrease the Hounsfield units in ROI - selection . From 1 to 6 months granules 0.63 - 0.8 mm and 1.5 mm CT slice decrease Hounsfield units and density of BG - masses was 5.5 % and with 3 mm CT slice 4.6 % . At the same period with granules 0.8 - 1.0 mm and 1.5 mm CT slice the decrease was 2.0 % and with 3 mm CT slice 3.4 %. The reference values meaned with teflon disk stayed at the same level from 1 to 6 months . BG granules 0.63 - 0. 8 mm loose its chemical components and weight during test 3.2 % and respectively 0.8 - 1.0 mm granules 2.5 % .

It has been difficult to find trustworth, biocompactible and safe material to obliterate frontal sinuses . BG seems to be stable, durable and trustworth material . Its behaviour can be estimated confidently by indirect measurements like CT and ROI - selection . In this *in vitro* study simulated the conditions in the obliterated frontal sinus after operation.The model was developed for clinical purposes to estimate and monitor obliterated frontal sinuses . However in the human conditions of frontal sinuses there are wide variety of other parameters, which could not be simulated in this *in vitro* model .

REFERENCES

1. Schenck NL Laryngoscope 1975 ; **85** 76-92
2. Failla A Laryngoscope 1980 ; **90** 47-52
3. Rosen G, Nachtigal D Laryngoscope 1995 ; **105** 553-555
4. Yamagishi M, Ishizuka Y, Nakano Y Am. J Rhinology 1993 ; **7** 267-271
5. Nagasae M, Abe Y, Chikira M, Udagawa E Biomaterials 1992 ; Vol **13** 172-175
6. Wilson J, Pigott GH, Schoen FJ, Hench LL Journal of Biomedical Materials Research 1981 ; **15** 805 - 817
7. Aitasalo K, Peltola M, Suonpää J, Yli - Urpo A, Andersson Ö, Varpula M, Happonen R-P Bioceramics 1994 ; Vol. **7** 409-414
8. Aitasalo K, Suonpää J, Peltola M, Yli-Urpo A Bioceramics 1997 ; Vol. **10** 429-432
9. Peltola M, Suonpää J, Aitasalo K, Varpula M, Yli-Urpo A, Happonen R-P Head and Neck 1998 ; **20** 315 - 319
10. Kokubo T, Kushitani H, Sakka S, Kitsugi T, Yamamuro T Journal of Biomedical Materials Research 1990 ; **24** 721-734
11. Yamada S, Nakamuro T, Tanahashi M, Kokubo T, Oka M, Yamamuro T Bioceramics 1994 ; Vol. **7** 299-303
12. Wegener OH Whole computerized tomography 1983 Schering AG West Germany

Bioceramics Volume 11, edited by R. Z. LeGeros and J.P. LeGeros
(Proceedings of the 11th International Symposium on Ceramics in Medicine)
New York, NY, USA, November 1998
© 1998 by World Scientific Publishing Co. Pte. Ltd.

CHEMICAL REACTIVITY OF EXPERIMENTAL BIOACTIVE GLASSES

A. S. Rizkalla, D. W. Jones, T. Routledge, G. C. Hall and M. Langman

Div. Biomaterials, Dalhousie University, 5981 University Av., Halifax, N. S., Canada. B3H 3J5

ABSTRACT

This study quantifies calcium, phosphorus and sodium deposited on resin substrates stored in static and dynamic 1.5 SBF solutions for 14 days @ 37°C, in the presence of two experimental glasses (Mean particle size 14.14 ± 0.34 µm) in the system (SiO_2-CaO-Na_2O-P_2O_5). The control material was 100% silica glass. The material reactivity for silane and non-silane treated conditions were evaluated using a Kokubo biomimetic method. Deposits of Ca and Na on substrates were analyzed using AAS and for P by 'Heteropoly Blue'. Significantly higher weights of Ca and P were deposited on substrates for non-silane treated Glass#1, compared to Glass#2 and Silica control ($p<0.0001$). The weaker network of Glass#1 may be responsible for higher Ca and P deposits. Silane treatment appears to produce a barrier to ionic release. Significant proportions of deposition came from the SBF solution. In terms of ionic release, static tests appear to be significantly more sensitive to glass compositions and silane treatment than dynamic tests ($p<0.0001$). The Kokubo method is a valuable tool in evaluation of candidate bioactive glass fillers for orthopedic bone cement formulations.

KEYWORDS Chemical Reactivity, Bioactive Glass, Biomimetic, Simulated Body Fluid

INTRODUCTION

The aim of our current research is to determine mechanisms and optimize methods involved in wet-chemical synthesis leading to development of glass-ceramic biomaterials with improved properties.[3-5, 11-12] The research will attempt to develop formulations with optimal bioactivity and improved mechanical properties. These materials may find application in various forms including resin/ceramic bioactive composite bone cement materials. The work of Hench[1, 2] and Kokubo[6-7] has shown that the surface of $CaO \cdot SiO_2$-based glasses provide favourable sites for apatite nucleation. A silica hydrogel layer is formed on the surface of the glass that induces heterogeneous nucleation of apatite by complexation of phosphate when placed in simulated body fluid (SBF). Kokubo[6-7] has further indicated that a continuous and uniform layer of an apatite similar to bone mineral can be formed on the surface of materials including organic polymers. The development of glass-ceramic filled bone cements demonstrating controlled surface activity with direct bonding to bone offers potential for long-term stabilization of orthopedic implants.

The surface of a hydrated composite containing a bioactive glass has the potential to form apatite and stimulate osteogenesis. The human body fluid is supersaturated with respect to apatite under normal conditions, once apatite nuclei are formed, they can spontaneously grow. The release of calcium ions from bioactive glass or glass-ceramic into simulated body fluids can promote apatite nucleation on the surface of the glass or glass-ceramic. The development of glass formulations with optimal bioactivity incorporated as constituents within a resin matrix to produce a composite system may have application as a bone cement material.

Wet chemical methods can be used to produce glass and ceramic materials with a wide range of physical and chemical properties. Such materials can be made to have varying degrees of degradation and ionic release. In previous work we have synthesized a range of different glass materials using wet chemical methods.[3-5, 9-10] Studies have also been conducted relating physical properties and structure to the bulk chemical composition of the glass and ceramic.[9-10]

OBJECTIVE

To utilize the *in vitro* Kokubo biomimetic method,[6-7] to determine the amount of calcium, phosphorus and sodium compounds deposited on a resin substrate when stored in simulated body fluid (SBF) with glass particulate materials of varying composition.

METHODS AND MATERIALS

Experimental glass materials were synthesized by wet chemistry. Three glass materials (Glass #1, Glass #2 and Silica) were produced.   Glass #1 had a CaO/P_2O_5 ratio of 9.00 and a $SiO_2/CaO+Na_2O$ ratio of 0.90. 'Glass #2 had a $SiO_2/CaO+Na_2O$ ratio of 1.00. The Silica material was 100% amorphous SiO_2. The synthesized glass materials were ground to a mean particle size of 14.14 ± 0.34 μm. Half of the glass particles were surface coated with a coupling agent 3-(methoxlyoxypropyl)-trimethoxysilane. The silane was stirred in deionized water buffered (3.0-3.3 pH) at 23-30°C for one hour. Particles were blended in solution and further stirred for 4 hours. Treated particles were dried for 4 hours at 60°C, and crushed gently to separate any agglomeration.   The other half of the glass particles were not silane coated.

The reactivity of the three glass materials in both silane and non-silane treated conditions were evaluated (n =3) using the Kokubo biomimetic method. A mass of 0.5g of each the six particulate glass materials were immersed in 1.0 SBF and 25 X 1.1 mm resin disc substrates placed above each sample and stored for one week to evaluate their ability to form deposits of Ca, P and Na (or apatite nuclei) on the resin substrate. Following this, half of the resin substrates were soaked in a static solution of 1.5 SBF at 37°C for 14 days. The other half of the substrates were soaked in a dynamic storage solution of 1.5 SBF for the same period of time. The dynamic storage solution was changed every 2 days. Blanks (n =3) were used as a control for each of the SBF conditions (i.e., no particulate glass material, only resin substrate surface). Deposits on the surface of the substrates were chemically analyzed for Ca and Na using AAS and for P by the 'Heteropoly Blue' method (n = 3).

RESULTS AND DISCUSSION

The weight of Ca, Na and P deposited on the substrate surfaces in SBF using static and dynamic sampling methods are shown in Table 1. Data for both silane and non-silane treated surfaces are shown. Comparisons between the static deposits for Ca and P with silane and non-silane coating are illustrated in the bar diagrams Figures 1 and 2. The static sampling tests for the Glass #1 with silane coating resulted in a very significantly lower Ca deposition. This indicates that the Ca tends to be contributed from the glass rather than the SBF during static sampling. The weaker more ion leachable glass network in the Glass #1 may have been responsible for the higher Ca and P deposits in the case of the non-silane treated samples. The static sampling tests seem to support the view that silane treatment may be producing a limiting barrier to Ca and P release in the case of Glass #1. In contrast, the dynamic sampling tests did not show a significant difference in Ca deposits between the silane and non-silane treated glass. Non-linear regression analysis showed an excellent correlation between Ca deposited in static and dynamic SBF solutions (P<0.01). No correlation was obtained for the P and Na deposits. Significantly higher levels of Ca, P and Na deposits were obtained from the dynamic SBF tests compared to the static tests (P< 0.0001). Considerable amounts of P were deposited during the dynamic sampling for the blank and silica particles, confirming that P is predominately deposited from the SBF and was independent of the chemistry of any particulate composition present. The results of this study indicate that significant proportions of the Ca and P deposited on resin substrates, in the presence of bioactive and non-bioactive glasses can come from SBF solutions.

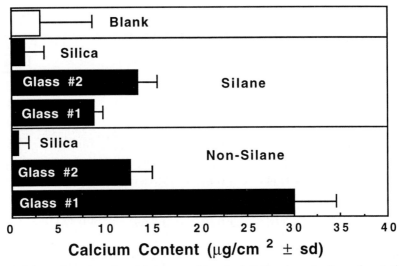

Figure 1. Calcium deposits after 14 days soaking in 1.5 X concentration of a static solution of simulated body fluid at 37°C.

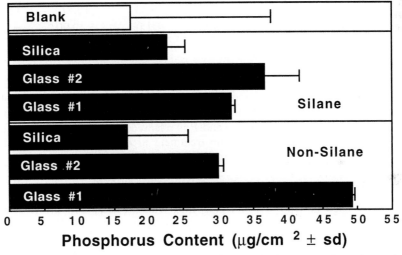

Figure 2. Phosphorus deposits after 14 days soaking in 1.5 X concentration of a static solution of simulated body fluid at 37°C.

This study also demonstrates the compositional effect of the glass in providing ionic constituents for deposition which can result in nucleation of apatite by complexation of phosphate when placed in SBF for subsequent crystalline growth. The presence of a silane coating and a glass composition which has a much higher percentage of non-bridging oxygen both appear to influence the ionic release and precipitation mechanisms. Results indicate the significant contribution of P deposition from the SBF which is independent of the composition of the glass particulate materials. These results support *in vivo* data of Ohura et al.,[8] which indicated that a P_2O_5-free $CaO.SiO_2$ glass formed a Ca, P-rich layer and bonded with bone.

Table 1. Weight/unit area ($\mu g/cm^2$) of Ca, Na and P deposited on the substrate surface

Glass Material	Calcium Static	Calcium Dynamic	Sodium Static	Sodium Dynamic	Phosphorus Static	Phosphorus Dynamic
Glass #1 (non-silane)	29.93 ± 4.62	179.13 ± 21.35	1.80 ± 1.20	20.04 ± 6.39	49.22 ± 0.44	259.56 ± 3.10
Glass #2 (non-silane)	12.57 ± 2.35	168.76 ± 26.59	0.64 ± 0.10	18.62 ± 2.86	30.01 ± 0.73	269.57 ± 3.10
Silica (non-silane)	0.69 ± 1.20	88.83 ± 31.62	0.80 ± 0.10	12.29 ± 0.84	16.83 ± 8.80	180.00 ± 55.92
Glass #1 (silane)	8.61 ± 1.02	192.96 ± 3.05	0.60 ± 0.10	20.65 ± 2.59	31.81 ± 0.53	278.49 ± 4.74
Glass #2 (silane)	13.47 ± 2.12	156.46 ± 20.50	0.64 ± 0.20	17.50 ± 0.88	36.79 ± 5.04	260.44 ± 11.83
Silica (silane)	1.42 ± 2.01	130.33 ± 8.65	1.04 ± 0.88	17.42 ± 2.54	22.62 ± 2.69	255.97 ± 17.69
Blank	3.12 ± 5.41	73.93 ± 3.05	0.93 ± 0.10	9.43 ± 1.00	17.57 ± 19.90	113.49 ± 4.74

CONCLUSIONS

The biomimetic test method may prove to be a valuable tool in the evaluation of candidate bioactive glass fillers for orthopedic bone cement formulations. The weaker network of Glass #1 may be responsible for higher Ca and P deposits. The use of a silane versus non-silane treated surface test, demonstrated that significant Ca and P is released from the non-silane treated glass. The static tests appear to indicate that silane treatment produces a barrier to ionic release. Significant proportions of deposition came from the SBF solution as well as the glass.

ACKNOWLEDGEMENTS

The authors acknowledge the support from DePuy Inc., Warsaw, Indiana for this research project.

REFERENCES

1) Hench LL, Wilson J. *Science* 1984; **226**:630-636.
2) Hench LL. *Ann N Y Acad Sci* 1988; **523**(1):54-71.
3) Jones DW, Sutow EJ, King HW, Rizkalla AS, Hall GC. *J. Can. Ceram. Soc*. 1986; **55**:42-49.
4) Jones DW, Rizkalla AS, Johnson JA, Sutow EJ. *J. Mater. Sci.* 1991; **26**:6501-6506.
5) Jones DW, Rizkalla AS, In: Rusin RP, Fischman GS, eds., *Ceram.Trans* 1995; **63**: 87-91.
6) Kokubo T, Ito S, Huang ZT, *et al.*, *J. Biomed. Mater. Res.* 1990; **24**: 331-343.
7) Kokubo T, In: Hench L, Wilson J. eds. *Advanced Series in Ceramics*, World Scientific, 1993: **1**: 75-88.
8) Ohura K, Nakamura T, Yamamuro T, *et al.*, *J. Biomed. Mater. Res.* 1990; **25**: 357-365.
9) Rizkalla AS, Jones DW, Hall GC, Sutow EJ. *Br. Ceram. Trans. J.* 1992; **91**:41-44.
10) Rizkalla AS, Jones DW, Sutow EJ. *Br. Ceram. Trans. J.* 1992; **91**:12-15.
11) Rizkalla AS, Jones DW, Clarke DB, Hall GC. *J. Biomed. Mater. Res.* 1996; **32**: 119-124.
12) Rizkalla AS, Jones DW, Hall GC. *Brit. Ceram. Trans.* 1997; **96**: 16-20.

Bioceramics Volume 11, edited by R. Z. LeGeros and J.P. LeGeros
(Proceedings of the 11th International Symposium on Ceramics in Medicine)
New York, NY, USA, November 1998
© 1998 by World Scientific Publishing Co. Pte. Ltd.

STUDY OF THE SOL-GEL PROCESSING OF GLASS-CERAMIC POWDERS IN THE SiO_2-Al_2O_3-CaO-CaF_2 SYSTEM. PART 2: MICROSTRUCTURE EVALUATION

M.S. Zolotar [1], C.A.C. Zavaglia [1], L.P. Cardoso [2] & J.A. Fraymann [2]

[1] DEMA/FEM, Caixa Postal 6168; [2] IFGW, Caixa Postal 6165, Universidade Estadual de Campinas, Campinas, SP, 13083-970, Brazil.

ABSTRACT

As an effort to develop high purity, homogeneous glasses and glass-ceramic powders in the SiO_2 - Al_2O_3 - CaO - CaF_2 system with controlled microstructures, the present work aimed at the microstructure evaluation of such powders obtained by the sol-gel technique through X-ray diffraction analysis and differential thermal analysis. According to the fluorine/calcium ratio, it was possible to obtain glass-ceramics with one or more of the following phases: fluorite, anorthite, t-mullite and a mixture of calcium fluorosilicates. Changes in the aluminium and silicon contents resulted in glass-ceramics with varying degrees of crystallinity.

KEYWORDS: Biomaterials, glass ionomer cements, sol-gel, microstructure evaluation.

INTRODUCTION

Glass ionomer cements (GIC's) exhibit low fracture toughness, despite their ability to chemically bond to bone, dentine and tooth enamel and to release fluorine ions, which could make them ideal substitutes for the amalgam as a posterior filling material, as well as bone substitutes and bone cements in joint replacement surgery[1,2].

Also, both variation in the final glass composition due to fluorine loss during melting, together with uncontrolled changes in its microstructure due to necessary correcting heat treatments during the commercial manufacture of the GIC's as an attempt to reduce and control their performance, make it even more difficult to produce a cement with desirable mechanical properties[1,2].

As an effort to develop high purity, homogeneous glasses and glass-ceramics in the SiO_2 - Al_2O_3 - CaO - CaF_2 system with controlled microstructures, the present work aimed at the microstructure evaluation of such powders obtained by the sol-gel technique.

EXPERIMENTAL PROCEDURE

Glass powders with 12 different calcium, silicon, aluminium and fluorine contents were synthesised from $Ca(NO_3)_2.4H_2O)$, TEOS, $Al(NO_3)_3.9H_2O$ and H_2SiF_6 in an aqueous acidic medium[3]. The chemical compositions of these powders, shown in Table 1, were chosen from a 21-points design generated through the mixture design technique, following the procedure described in detail elsewhere[3].

Table 1: Chemical compositions for the 12 experimental glass powders[*]

Compositions	SiO_2	Al_2O_3	CaO	H_2SiF_6	Compositions	SiO_2	Al_2O_3	CaO	H_2SiF_6
1	0.25	0.30	0.42	0.03	7	0.35	0.42	0.08	0.15
2	0.25	0.47	0.25	0.03	8	0.25	0.58	0.08	0.09
3	0.33	0.39	0.25	0.03	9	0.25	0.52	0.08	0.15
4	0.40	0.49	0.08	0.03	10	0.25	0.64	0.08	0.03
5	0.30	0.47	0.08	0.15	11	0.25	0.41	0.19	0.15
6	0.38	0.45	0.08	0.09	12	0.25	0.30	0.36	0.09

* Compositions given in mol% of SiO_2, Al_2O_3, CaO and H_2SiF_6.

The as-dried powders (120°C/24h) were heat-treated at 450°C/5-6h, after which their microstructure evaluation was carried out, through x-ray diffraction (XRD) analysis (tube anode, Cu; tension, 40kV; current, 30mA; start angle, 10°; end angle, 70°; step size, 0.020°; time per step, 1-2s) and differential thermal (DTA) analysis (Ar athmosphere; heating rate, 10°C/min; 20 to 1350°C; α- Al_2O_3 as reference).

The XRD analysis was performed for the as-dried and heat-treated powders, as well as for the glass ceramic powders obtained after heat treating at the temperatures corresponding to important endothermic/exothermic reactions observed in the DTA curves.

RESULTS AND DISCUSSION

It was possible to identify four distinct typical patterns for the 12 compositions studied on what concerns their DTA curves and crystalline phase formation relative to their different calcium, aluminium, silicon and fluorine contents.

For the low fluorine, medium to high calcium compositions (1, 2 and 3), the typical DTA curve (Figure 1) showed two weak and broad exotherms at 750-770°C and at 980-990°C, corresponding respectively to the crystallization of fluorite (CaF_2) and that of a mixture of anorthite ($CaAl_2Si_2O_8$) and several calcium fluorosilicates [$Ca_5(SiO_4)_2F_2$, $Ca_5Si_2O_8F_2$, $Ca_{10}Si_3O_{15}F_2$ and $Ca_{6-0.5x}Si_2O_{10-x}F_x$), as seen in Figure 2.

The second typical pattern was observed for the low fluorine, low calcium compositions (4 and 10). These powders showed only amorphous scattering with a maximum in the 20-30° region, even after heat treatment at temperatures as high as 950°C, as seen in Figure 2. No significant DTA peaks were observed for these powders (Figure 1). A similar behaviour was observed in a previous work for silica-alumina sol-gel glasses[5], suggesting the need of minimum calcium and fluorine contents in order to obtain any crystalline phase after heat treatment for glasses of the compositions studied.

For the medium and high fluorine, low calcium compositions (5,6,7,8 and 9) a completely different behaviour was observed, as seen in Figures 1 and 3. The presence of CaF_2, topaz [$Al_2SiO_4(F,OH)_2$] and a poorly crystalline tetragonal mullite ($3Al_2O_3.2SiO_2$), together with an amorphous scattering maximum in the 20-30° region after heat treatment at 755°C/2h, followed by further crystallization of t-mullite and anorthite after heat treatment at 960°C were accounted for as follows.

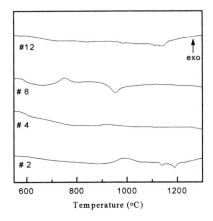

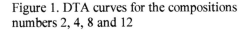

Figure 1. DTA curves for the compositions numbers 2, 4, 8 and 12

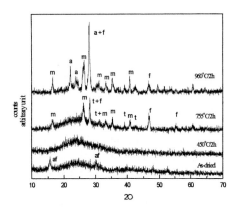

Figure 3: XRD patterns for composition 8. af-$Al(OH,F)_3$.$0.375H_2O$; a-anorthite; f- fluorite; m-mullite

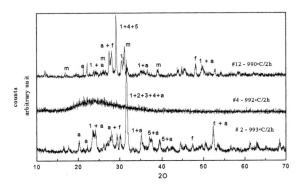

Figure 2. XRD patterns for compositions 2, 4 and 12.
a-anorthite; f-fluorite; m-mullite; 1-$Ca_5(SiO_4)_2F_2$; 2-$Ca_5Si_2O_8F_2$; 3-$Ca_{10}Si_3O_{15}F_2$; 4-$Ca_{6-0.5x}Si_2O_{10-x}F_x$

The as-dried powders showed the presence of residual $Al(OH,F)_3$.$0.375H_2O$ as the only poorly crystalline phase, together with an amorphous scattering maximum in the 20-30° region. This could correspond to the presence of amorphous hydrated kaolinite [$Al_2Si_2O_5(OH)_4$], as well as some aluminium fluoride, resulting from incomplete dehydration of $Al(OH,F)_3$.$0.375H_2O$ during drying. The dehydration of the remaining $Al(OH,F)_3$.$0.375H_2O$ after heat treatment at 450°C/5-6h, resulting in amorphous aluminium fluoride, explains the extinction of the lines present in the x-ray pattern of the as-dried powders.

Subsequent dehydration of kaolinite and its reaction with aluminium fluoride, accompanied by a sharp endothermic reaction at 664.7°C, was then followed by the formation of topaz and t-mullite[6]. The latter should have been accompanied by a medium endothermic peak at 750°C but, on the other hand, only a sharp exotherm at 751.4°C was observed[6]. As this temperature also corresponds to the crystallization of fluorite[1,2], whose main lines are present in the XRD pattern of the heat-treated powder at 755°C, it was concluded that both effects were added, resulting in the observed exotherm.

The small endotherm at 812.8 °C, corresponding to the onset of the decomposition of topaz, together with the sharp endotherm at 954.2°C, which represents the further decomposition of topaz with the formation of t-mullite, account for the observed XRD pattern for the powders heat treated at 960°C, but for the presence, in the latter, of anorthite. The lack of the exothermic peak corresponding to the crystallization of anorthite, which usually follows crystallization of fluorite in this type of glasses[1,2], could have been offset by the strong endotherm associated with the decomposition of topaz.

As the silicon content was increased and the aluminium content decreased, the degree of crystallinity of the heat-treated glasses decreased, with amorphous scattering present even at temperatures as high as 1000°C.

For those powders with intermediate compositions, i.e., medium to high fluorine and medium to high calcium contents (11 and 12), a behaviour corresponding to both the first and second patterns was observed, with the formation of fluorite and anorthite, as well as t-mullite and a mixture of calcium fluorosilicates, as seen in Figure 2.

CONCLUSIONS

The sol-gel glass powders with 12 different calcium, silicon, aluminium and fluorine contents studied in the present work exhibited four distinct typical patterns on what concerns their differential thermal analysis curves and crystalline phase formation. According to the fluorine/calcium ratio, it was possible to obtain glass-ceramics with one or more of the following phases: fluorite, anorthite, t-mullite and a mixture of calcium fluorosilicates. Changes in the aluminium and silicon contents resulted in glass-ceramics with varying degrees of crystallinity, including glasses which remained amorphous even at high temperatures. Thus, by employing the sol-gel processing technique, it was possible to obtain glass-ceramic powders with controlled microstructures.

ACKNOWLEDGEMENTS

The authors would like to acknowledge the financial support of CNPq and FINEP/PRONEX.

REFERENCES

1. Hill RG, Goat C, Wood D. *J Amer Ceram Soc* 1992; **75**:778-785.
2. Hill RG, Wood D. *Biomaterials* 1991; **12**:164-170.
3. Zolotar MS, Zavaglia CAC. *J Non-Cryst Sol* 1998 (in print).
4. Wilson AD, McLean JW. *Glass-ionomer Cement*. Chicago: Quintessence Books, 1988: 27.
5. Zolotar MS, Bavaresco VP, Zavaglia CAC. (unpublished work).
6. Abdel-Rehim AM. *J Thermal Analysis* 1997; 48: 177-202.

Bioceramics Volume 11, edited by R. Z. LeGeros and J.P. LeGeros
(Proceedings of the 11th International Symposium on Ceramics in Medicine)
New York, NY, USA, November 1998

INFLUENCE OF THE CHEMICAL COMPOSITION ON THE MECHANICAL PROPERTIES AND *IN VITRO* SOLUBILITY OF PHOSPHATE GLASSES IN THE SYSTEM P_2O_5-CaO-Na_2O

J.Clément[1], L.Ekeberg[1], S.Martinez[2], M.P.Ginebra[1], F.J.Gil[1] and J.A.Planell[1]

1 CREB, Dpt. Ciència dels Materials i Enginyeria Metal.lúrgica. ETSEIB. Universitat Politècnica de Catalunya. Diagonal 647, E-08028, Barcelona, Spain; [2]Dpt. Cristal.lografia, Mineralogia i Recursos Minerals. Universitat Barcelona. Marti i Franqués s/n. E-08028, Barcelona, Spain.

ABSTRACT

Phosphate glasses could be of a great interest as bone substitution materials, due to their chemistry close to that of bone and their property of being completely soluble. The aim of this study is to evaluate the influence of the chemical composition on the mechanical properties and the solubility of a range of phosphate glasses in the system P_2O_5-CaO-Na_2O. The Young Modulus (E), Vickers hardness (HV) and fracture toughness (K_{IC}) were evaluated by Vickers and Knoop indentation tests, and the solubility *In Vitro* was evaluated by mass loss per unit time measurements. Solubility tests were carried out in simulated body fluid (SBF) at 37°C. Superficial changes during soaking were observed by Optical and Environmental Scanning Electron Microscopy.

The Young Modulus of the glasses studied increased with the CaO content, showing values between 68,61 and 116,54 GPa, while the fracture toughness seemed to correlate with the P_2O_5 content, obtaining values ranging from 0,645 to 0,957. The solubility appeared to be dependent on the Na_2O content, as the mass loss per unit time highly increased as the mol.% of sodium in the glass increased.

KEYWORDS: Phosphate glasses, mechanical properties, solubility.

INTRODUCTION

In the last decades, the development of ceramic materials for the repair and reconstruction of bone has been of a great interest. Bioactive ceramics, glasses, and glass-ceramics have been intensively studied and have opened up new possibilities in implantology, due to their capacity to form on their surface an active hydroxycarbonate apatite (HCA) layer identical to the mineral phase of bone[1,2]. As a result of the study of the dissolution mechanisms of glasses in water, phosphate based glasses in the system P_2O_5-CaO-Na_2O have appeared as potential materials for use as biomaterials due to their property of being completely soluble and their chemical composition similar to that of the inorganic phase of bone[3]. These glasses consist of a polymeric tetrahedral structure based on $[PO_4]^{3-}$ groups, which can be attached to a maximum of three neighbouring tetrahedra as in crystalline P_2O_5. The addition of modifiers such as CaO or Na_2O breaks the continuity of the glass. The ratio CaO/Na_2O will control the dissolution rate of the glass, leading to dissolution times ranging between a few days to several months.

Given the structural function, at least in the initial stages, that a bone substitute should perform in service, its mechanical properties are of major importance. In a previous study[4,5], it has been demonstrated that the use of indentation tests is a simple and suitable method for the evaluation of the mechanical properties of phosphate based glasses, due to the simplicity of the specimen preparation and the large quantity of data points that can be generated rapidly. The aim of the present work is to provide a better understanding of the influence of the chemical composition on the mechanical properties, the kinetics of solubility and the dissolution mechanisms of a range of phosphate based glasses.

MATERIALS AND METHODS

Different glasses in the system P_2O_5-CaO-Na_2O have been prepared using $NH_4H_2PO_4$, Na_2CO_3 and $CaCO_3$ as raw materials. The glasses were obtained by melting on a platinum crucible at temperatures ranging between 1200 to 1350°C and by quenching on a metallic plate pre-heated at 300°C. the materials were finally annealed during 30 minutes at a temperature corresponding to their glass transition temperature and then left for 8 hours under gradual cooling conditions. The glasses prepared contained between 5 to 15 mol.% Na_2O in order to obtain relatively low dissolution rates. Glass formation could be observed in compositions possessing more than 35 mol.% P_2O_5, in accordance to a study by Vogel et al.[6], as lower phosphate containing glasses crystallised spontaneously . Figure 1 shows the phase diagram of the ternary glass system with the molar composition of the different glasses prepared.

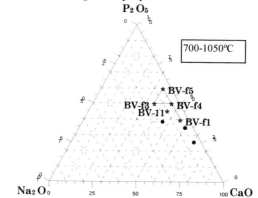

Figure 1. Ternary phase diagrams of the glass system studied.
(*: glass compositions prepared, •: glass compositions that crystallised spontaneously)

The mechanical properties of the glasses were assessed by Vickers and Knoop indentation tests. 2 samples of each glass were embedded in a polyester resin at room temperature and polished by means of 0,05 μm diameter alumina particles. Indentations were introduced using a microhardness testing machine, with an indentation load of 300 g applied during 30 seconds for Vickers measurements, and a load of 100 g applied during 30 seconds for the Knoop indentations. A minimum of 20 indentations were carried out in each case for each material.

The fracture toughness of the glasses was evaluated, according to a previous study[5], using the model of Blendell[7] described in equation (1), corresponding to a radial-median crack system.

$$K_{IC} = 0,0303(HVa^{1/2})(\frac{E}{HV})^{2/5} \log(8,4\frac{a}{c}) \qquad (1)$$

where c represents the crack length (mm), a the Vickers indent length (mm), HV the Vickers hardness (GPa), and E the Young's modulus of the material (GPa).

The Young's modulus was evaluated by measurements of the elastic recovery observing the relative contraction of the surface diagonals of Knoop impressions[8] according to equation (2).

$$\frac{b'}{a'} = \frac{b}{a} - \alpha \frac{HV}{E}$$

(2

where $b/a = 1/7$ is the nominal ratio of short to long half-diagonal, b'/a' is the corresponding value of the recovery, and α is a constant calibrated experimentally to a value of $0,52$[9].

The dissolution of the glasses was monitored by measuring the mass loss per unit time of 3 pieces of each composition studied during soaking in Simulated Body Fluid (SBF) at 37°C, prepared according to Kokubo et al.[2]. The solution volume was 50 ml, and the mean initial surface area of the samples was 400 mm². At different times, the glasses were removed from the SBF, washed in distilled water and in pure acetone and allowed to dry for 24 hours. Samples were weighted and surface changes were observed by Optical and Environmental Scanning Electron microscopy. Finally, the glasses were replaced in SBF.

RESULTS AND DISCUSSION

The results obtained for the mechanical properties of the glasses studied are represented in table 1. It can be noticed that the Vickers hardness ranged between 326,32 and 363,44 Kg/mm² and the Young's modulus between 68 and 116 GPa. The values obtained for the fracture toughness ranged between 0,645 and 0,957 MPa.m$^{1/2}$

Table 1. Mechanical properties of the glasses studied (Value ± Standard deviation)

Glass Type	HV (Kg/mm²)	E (GPa)	K_{IC} (MPa.m$^{1/2}$)
BV-f3	326,32 ± 6,73	68,61 ± 8,69	0,82 ± 0,023
BV-f5	328,62 ± 7,88	72,70 ± 9,22	0,957 ± 0,012
BV-f4	352,36 ± 0,98	106,04 ± 12,73	0,77 ± 0,025
BV-f1	363,44 ± 5,46	116,54 ± 10,26	0,645 ± 0,017
BV-11	357,28 ± 8,24	92,82 ± 5,26	0,79 ± 0,03

In order to understand better the influence of the glass composition on the mechanical properties of the glasses, figure 2 shows the evolution of the mechanical properties in function of the ratio CaO/P_2O_5 for glasses with a constant Na_2O content of 5 mol.% (BV-f1, BV-f4 and BV-f5). It can be clearly seen that the Young's modulus increased about 60% when the ratio CaO/P_2O_5 increased from 0,6 to 1,4. In opposition the fracture toughness decreased about 67%, from which the K_{IC} seems to correlate with the phosphate content. The present results can be explained by considering the structure of the phosphate glasses. The addition of modifiers in the phosphate network disrupts bonds and creates non-bridging oxygen atoms in the glass. However, these added cations can provide ionic cross-linking between non bridging oxygen atoms of two different chains. Thus, increasing the bond strength of this ionic link, the glass structure can be strengthened and, consequently the mechanical properties increased. This means that, with increasing the divalent Ca^{2+} content, strong reticulations are formed and the glass becomes stiffer. On the other hand, by increasing the phosphate content of the glass larger polymeric chains may be obtained and the number of ionic cross-link between two different chains would decrease. This may explain why the fracture toughness highly increases with the phosphate content.

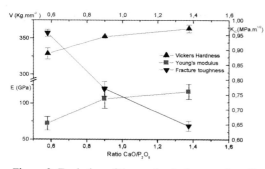

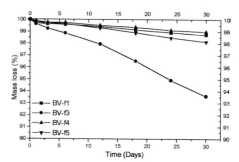

Figure 2. Evolution of the mechanical properties of phosphate glasses in function of the ratio CaO/P$_2$O$_5$

Figure 3. Sample weight loss versus soaking time in SBF at 37°C for the different glasses studied

The results of the mass loss of the different glasses in function of the soaking time in SBF at 37°C are shown in figure 3. It can be observed that, after a couple of days, the dissolution seem to stabilise and the kinetics of solubility appears to be linear with time. On the other hand, it can be noticed from these curves that the dissolution rate of phosphate glasses depends mainly on the Na$_2$O content of the glass. Indeed, the glasses with the same sodium content showed a similar weight loss with time, whereas the glass with the highest sodium content showed a dissolution rate about one order of magnitude higher.

Microscopic analysis of the superficial changes during the dissolution in SBF of the phosphate glasses studied showed that the dissolution mechanisms consist in the formation of cracks at the surface of the samples in a first stage. With increasing dissolution time, the microcracking increases, leading to the leaching of glass particles. The same process could be observed for each glass composition, showing the fastest crack formation for the glass with the higher sodium content. It does not seem that an HCA layer appear on the glass surface as observed in SiO$_2$ containing bioactive glasses[1,2].

AKNOWLEDGEMENTS

The authors are grateful to the CICYT for providing financial support through project MAT96-0981 and the European Commission for the TMR grant ERBFMBICT972152.

REFERENCES

1. Hench L.L. *J Am Ceram Soc* 1991; **74[7]**: 1487-510.
2. Kokubo T. *J of Non-Cryst. Solids* 1990; **120**: 138-151.
3. Burnie J, Gilchrist T, in: Vicenzini P. (ed) *Ceramics in Surgery*, Elsevier, The Netherlands, 1983: 169-176.
4. Gil F.J *et al*., In: Sedel L, Rey C (eds). *Bioceramics10*, Elsevier Science Ltd., 1997: 553-556.
5. Clement J *et al*. . *J Mat. Sci., Mat. in Medicine* 1998; publication pending.
6. Vogel J, Wange P, Hartmann P. *Glastech. Ber. Glass Sci. Technol.* 1997; **70[7]**: 220-223.
7. Blendell J, Ph.D. Thesis, 1979, MIT Press, Cambridge, MA.
8. Marshall D.B, Noma T, Evans A.G. *J Am Ceram Soc.* 1982; **65**: C175-C176.
9. Ontañon M *et al*, In:Doherty P (ed) *Biomaterials-Tissue interfaces*, Elsevier, Amsterdam, 1992.

Bioceramics Volume 11, edited by R. Z. LeGeros and J.P. LeGeros
(Proceedings of the 11th International Symposium on Ceramics in Medicine)
New York, NY, USA, November 1998

NOVEL POLY LACTIC ACID COMPOSITES CONTAINING ß-Ca(PO$_3$)$_2$ FIBERS

Toshihiro Kasuga[1], Haruhiko Fujikawa[1], Yoshio Ota[2], Masayuki Nogami[1] and Yoshihiro Abe[1]

[1]Department of Materials Science and Engineering, Nagoya Institute of Technology, Nagoya 466-8555, Japan; [2]Yabashi Industries Co. Ltd., Ogaki 503-2213, Japan.

ABSTRACT

A new type of biomaterial for bone repair with modulus of elasticity close to that of natural bone was prepared using bioresorbable poly lactic acid (PLA) and high-strength ß-Ca(PO$_3$)$_2$ fibers treated with dilute NaOH solution. A mixture consisting of PLA dissolved by using methylene chloride and the fibers was dried at ambient temperature, and subsequently it was hot-pressed uniaxially at 180 °C, resulting in fabrication of a PLA-composite containing ß-Ca(PO$_3$)$_2$ fibers. Almost no degradation in the bending strength was observed even when a large amount of the fibers (*e.g.,* 60 wt%) was introduced, and the modulus of elasticity was increased effectively with increasing the fiber content. The bending test of the composites showed that very high energy is consumed for their fracture and that the fracture proceeds step by step, even beyond the maximum stress.

KEYWORDS: Calcium metaphosphate fiber, poly lactic acid, composite, Young's modulus.

INTRODUCTION

Modulus of elasticity of dense bioceramics for bone repair, in general, is much higher than that of natural bone. Materials with the high modulus induces a problem of stress shielding which leads to bone resorption.[1] In our earlier work, high-strength ß-Ca(PO$_3$)$_2$ fibers with low modulus of elasticity were reported to be extracted successfully from the crystallized products of calcium ultraphosphate glasses.[2] The inorganic fibers show good biological compatibility[3] and safety.[4] New types of bioceramics have been synthesized using the ß-Ca(PO$_3$)$_2$ fibers.[5,6]

Since the stress shielding is apt to occur due to use of rigid materials such as conventional metals or ceramics, materials with modulus of elasticity which is similar to that of natural bone (5 ~ 15 GPa) are requisite for some applications. Poly lactic acid[7] (PLA) is one of the polymers showing good biocompatibility and bioresorbability. The resorption rate is controllable by degree of polymerization or copolymerizing. The modulus of elasticity of PLA, however, is much lower (2 ~ 3 GPa) than that of natural bone. Some efforts have been carried out for preparation of composites consisting of PLA and calcium phosphate particles such as hydroxyapatite or ß-tricalcium phosphate with osteoconductivity.[8,9] For meeting the requirements on the modulus, however, a large amount of the particles of ~80 wt% should be introduced into PLA or its copolymer as a matrix phase.[8] Such materials show catastrophic fracture typically. We anticipated that novel artificial bones with ductility and modulus of elasticity close to that of natural bone can be prepared by hybridizing PLA with the ß-Ca(PO$_3$)$_2$ fibers. This paper describes the preparation of the composites.

MODIFICATION OF ß-Ca(PO$_3$)$_2$ FIBERS

The preparation procedures of ß-Ca(PO$_3$)$_2$ fibers were described in our previous papers.[2,5] The obtained fibers were 2 ~ 10 µm in diameter with aspect ratios of 20 ~ 100. Almost no bond between PLA and the fibers is formed. Kikuchi *et al.* suggested[10] that C=O in ester group in PLA forms weak bonds with calcium ions in the orthophosphates. In the present work, surface of the fibers has been successfully converted into the orthophosphate phase by chemical treatment: the fibers were soaked in 0.2-M NaOH aqueous solution for 5 h at 70 °C. Although only ß-Ca(PO$_3$)$_2$ was identified as a crystalline phase in an x-ray diffraction pattern of the fibers after the treatment, new particle-shaped products of several tens nanometer in size were seen densely on their surface. Raman bands due to PO$_4$ group[11] were observed with strong those due to PO$_3$ group in the spectrum of the fibers after the treatment. It is suggested that the fibers have a calcium orthophosphate layer around the surface. The modified fibers (denoted by CPF, hereafter) were used for preparation of the PLA-composites.

PREPARATION OF PLA-COMPOSITES CONTAINING ß-Ca(PO$_3$)$_2$ FIBERS

Poly-L-lactic acid produced by Shimadzu Corp. (LACTY #2012; mean molecular weight of ~160,000) was used for preparation of the composites. The 10 g of PLA was soaked in 100 mL of methylene chloride at room temperature. After PLA was dissolved completely, CPF was put into the PLA-solution and then the mixture was stirred well. The mixture was cast into a stainless die of 38-mm diameter and was dried for 8 h at room temperature. Raman spectrum showed that there exists no methylene chloride in the dried product. The product was hot-pressed in the die uniaxially for 0.25 h at 180 °C under a pressure of 40 MPa.

Figure 1 shows bending strengths and Young's moduli of the composites as a function of CPF content. The tensile surface was perpendicular to the hot-pressing axis. The strengths of the composites were almost independent of the content. The materials showed bending strengths of 50 ~ 60 MPa, although they were slightly lower than that (60 ~ 70 MPa) of PLA without CPF. Since a large amount of CPF is apt to be agglomerated in the matrix phase of PLA, it is not easy to prepare the composite containing the fibers over 60 wt% using the procedure in the present work. The Young's modulus of the composite increased almost monotonously with increasing CPF content. CPF would form a chemical bond with PLA: the bond may play an important role in improvement of the mechanical properties. It is supposed that, during the mixing of CPF with PLA dissolved by methylene chloride, they are linked together, resulting in development of the PLA-composite without the serious agglomeration of the fibers. In the present work, the materials with modulus of elasticity of >5 GPa was obtained by preparation of the PLA-composite containing CPF more than 35 wt%.

Figure 2 shows a typical pattern of stress-strain curve measured by three-point bending test for the composite containing 35 wt% CPF. The material is not broken catastrophically: its fracture proceeds step by step even beyond the maximum stress of ~60 MPa. The maximum strain of the composite is an order of magnitude larger (~2 x 10^{-2}) than that[6] of a hydroxyapatite ceramic (~1 x 10^{-3}). That is, the fracture surface energy of the composite in the present work was estimated as more than 20 times higher than that of the ceramic. The material is ductile and tough.

Figure 3 shows an SEM photo of the fracture faces of the composite containing 35 % CPF after the bending test. Numerous traces of the fiber pull-out can be seen. Very high energy is believed to be consumed for the fracture of the composite by the pull-out of the fibers and the crack deflection. These mechanical properties are expected to meet the biomechanical requirements of some applications such as bone plates or temporary internal fixation of bones broken or damaged.

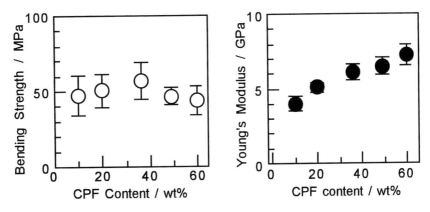

Figure 1. Three-point bending strength and Young's modulus as a function of CPF content.

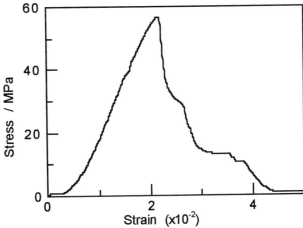

Figure 2. Typical stress-strain curve of the PLA-composite containing 35 wt% CPF.

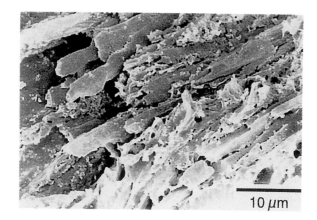

Figure 3.   SEM photo of fracture face of the PLA-composite containing 35 % CPF.

ACKNOWLEDGMENT

This work was supported by Grant-in-Aid for Scientific Research (No. 09680851) from the Ministry of Education, Science, and Culture of Japan, and also in part by Nippon Sheet Glass Foundation for Materials Science and Engineering.

REFERENCES

1. Hench LL. In: Hench LL, Wilson J, ed. *An Introduction to Bioceramics.* Singapore: World Scientific, 1993: 365-374.
2. Kasuga T, Ichino A, Abe Y. *J Ceram Soc Japan,* 1992; **100** 1088-1089.
3. Niimi, A *et al; Private Communication.*
4. Ota Y, *et al; to be submitted.*
5. Kasuga T, Tsuji K, Ota Y, Abe Y, Niimi A, Ueda M. In: Wilson J, Hench LL, Greenspan D, ed. *Proc 8th Inter Symp Ceramics in Medicine,* NY: Pergamon, 1995: 415-420.
6. Kasuga T, Ota Y, Tsuji K, Abe Y. *J Am Ceram Soc* 1996; **79** 1821-1824.
7. (a) Reed AM, Gilding DK. *Polymer* 1981; **22** 494-498; (b) Ikada Y. *Byotai-Seiri* 1988; 7 309-315.
8. Kikuchi M, Suetsugu Y, Tanaka J, Akao M. *J Mater Sci: Mater in Med* 1997; **8** 361-364.
9. Hyon S-H, Jamshidi K, Ikada Y, Higashi S, Kakutani Y, Yamamuro T. *Koubunshi Ronbunshu* 1985; **42** 771-776.
10. Kikuchi M, Cho S-B, Tanaka J, Koyama Y, Kobayashi T, Takuda K, Akao M. *J Jpn Soc Powder and Powder Metallurgy* 1998; **45**: 36-40.
11. Blakeslee KC, Condrate RA. *J Am Ceram Soc* 1971; **54** 559-563.

Bioceramics Volume 11, edited by R. Z. LeGeros and J.P. LeGeros
(Proceedings of the 11th International Symposium on Ceramics in Medicine)
New York, NY, USA, November 1998

ELASTIC PROPERTIES OF EXPERIMENTAL BIOACTIVE GLASS COMPOSITES

D. W. Jones, A. S. Rizkalla, T. Routledge and G. C. Hall.

Div. Biomaterials, Dalhousie University, 5981 University Av., Halifax, N. S., Canada. B3H 3J5

ABSTRACT

Dynamic elastic moduli were determined for experimental composites containing bioactive glass filler (SiO_2-CaO-P_2O_5-Na_2O) synthesized by wet chemistry. The two matrix resins used contained 2-dimethyl-aminoethyl methacrylate and camphorquinone ('A' 50% BISGMA and 50% TEGDMA, and 'B' 15% low molecular weight hydrophilic monomer, 42.5% BISGMA and 42.5% TEGDMA). Filler particles with and without silane treatment were blended with resin 'A' and 'B' to produce composite materials (25-75% filler loading). The moduli for unfilled resins 'A' and 'B' were also determined. Specimens were stored in SBF @ 37°C for 4, 8, 14 and 60 days, and in water for 60 days. Composites with matrix 'B' exhibited lower modulus for non-silane versus silane treated condition for all periods of storage in SBF and water ($P < 0.05$). Composite 'B' (no-silane treatment) had a higher modulus following storage in water compared to SBF for 60 days ($P = 0.0005$). Composite 'B' with silane treated filler exhibited a reduction in modulus following 4 to 60 days in SBF ($P = 0.0001$). Results show that it is important to evaluate mechanical properties of bioactive glass/resin composites following storage in SBF rather than water.

KEYWORDS   Bioactive, Composite, Elastic Modulus, Silane

INTRODUCTION

Wet chemical methods produce glass and ceramic materials that are more homogeneous at the atomic level than those produced by conventional glass making methods. When synthetic materials are used as substitutes for natural tissues, they may be required to: a) fill a space, b) physiologically interact with body fluids, c) stimulate osteogenesis, d) restore function of surrounding tissue and e) provide permanent stress bearing skeletal repair. Skeletal stress bearing repair is by far the most difficult problem that must be faced when attempting to use artificial materials to replace natural tissues. One method of overcoming the inherent limitations of mechanical properties of artificial materials is in the use of composite systems. Ceramics are the most biologically acceptable of materials and have been used in a wide range of applications as biomaterials. Certain ceramic and glass compositions can bond to bone and induce osteogenesis. Such materials can be made to have varying degrees of degradation and ionic release. The aim of our current research is to optimize wet chemical methods for synthesizing filler particles as an aid in the development of bioactive glass/ceramic fillers for a composite bone cement.[1, 5, 6] Using feedback from the Kokubo method[3, 4] to indicate the potential bioactivity of the glasses in simulated body fluid the bone cement composite formulations of glass/ceramic-dimethacrylate matrix resin will be optimized to be both bioactive and to have a specific modulus of elasticity. We believe that improved biomedical composite bone cement systems can be developed using bioactive glass-ceramic filler particles synthesized by wet chemical methods. It is also possible that a dimethacrylate matrix resin composite material will result in a more biocompatible material than conventional methacrylate bone cement.

Bone cement compositions can be formulated using a matrix resin with a lower polymerization exotherm and polymerization shrinkage than mono(methyl methacrylate) in combination with a bioactive glass/ceramic filler having potential for encouraging tissue ingrowth at the cement bone interface. In the past, existing materials have been adopted for use as biomaterials; today it is possible for biomaterials to be customized and designed to have specific properties. This is particularly true for wet chemical synthesis of ceramic fillers for composite biomaterials that can be produced having unique properties. We are producing glasses having structures and compositions not attainable by conventional manufacturing methods. The wet chemical synthesis methods allow for variations in formulation to be easily made with good control of composition and high chemical purity. The surface of a hydrated composite containing a bioactive glass has the potential to form apatite and stimulate osteogenesis. The development of glass formulations with optimal bioactivity incorporated as constituents within a resin matrix to produce a composite system may have application as an improved bone cement material.

Composite systems have the advantage that they can readily be produced with modulus of elasticity closely matching natural tissues. The modulus of elasticity of bone cement materials is considered important in terms of the level of stress transfer and the resistance to fracture during function. This paper reports on the influence of silane treatment of bioactive glass filler particles on the modulus of elasticity of experimental composite systems.

OBJECTIVE

The aim of this project was to study the effect of surface silane treatment of the filler particles on the elastic moduli for experimental bioactive glass/resin composites. In addition, two different resin matrix systems were also evaluated.

METHODS AND MATERIALS

An experimental bioactive/glass material was synthesized by wet chemistry, with the following weight percent composition SiO_2 45.65 ± 0.11, CaO 44.67 ± 0.21, P_2O_5 4.93 ± 0.16, Na_2O 4.76 ± 0.18. A series of bone cement composite materials were produced from the experimental bioactive glass or bioactive glass-ceramics synthesized by wet chemistry combined with dimethacrylate resin matrix polymers. Composite bone cements containing different filler loadings of the bioactive glass or glass-ceramic (25, 50, 70 and 75% by weight) were produced. Some compositions were also evaluated with and without silane coupling on the surface of the glass or glass-ceramic filler. These compositions were evaluated for elastic modulus and compared with traditional commercial methacrylate bone cement. Composite materials were stored at 37°C for 14 or 60 days in distilled water or from 4, 8, 14, and 60 days in simulated body fluid prior to testing. Two types of resin systems were used as the matrix phase. One (Matrix 'A') consisted of a 50% BISGMA and 50% TEGDMA monomers, combined with 2-dimethylaminoethyl methacrylate and camphorquinone. The second resin matrix material (Matrix 'B') contained 15% of a lower molecular weight hydrophilic monomer in combination with 42.5% BISGMA and 42.5% TEGDMA monomers. Half of the glass particles were untreated, the other half had the surface coated with a silane coupling agent 3-(methoxlyoxypropyl)-trimethoxysilane. The silane was stirred in deionized water buffered (3.0-3.3 pH) at 23-30°C for one hour. Particles were blended in solution and further stirred for 4 hours. Treated particles were dried for 4 hours at 60°C, and crushed gently to separate any agglomeration prior to blending with the monomers, and 2-dimethylaminoethyl methacrylate and camphorquinone.

The glass fillers with and without silane treatment were blended with the dimethacrylate monomer system to produce a combination of 4 different composite materials with 25-75% filler loading. Two additional groups of specimen were produced from the unfilled resin matrix monomers (Matrix 'A' and 'B'). Specimens were stored in a 1.5 concentration of a static solution of simulated body fluid (SBF) @ 37°C for periods of 4, 8, 14 and 60 days, as well as in water 60 days prior to testing. Dynamic moduli of elasticity (Young's, shear and bulk) and Poisson's ratio (n=3) were obtained. These dynamic tests were conducted at room temperature (23 ± 2°C) in air using both longitudinal and shear wave lithium niobate crystals and an ultrasonic wave technique.[2] Moduli and Poisson's ratio were calculated from shear and transverse sound velocity values and from density measurements. Dynamic modulus values were obtained for disc specimens of the glass filler, the unfilled matrix resin as well as for the various combinations of filler loading in the composite materials.

RESULTS AND DISCUSSION

The dynamic Young's modulus values obtained for the 4 glass/resin composites with 70% filler loading and the unfilled resin systems are shown in Tables 1 and 2 below. The mean dynamic Young's modulus for the two resin matrix materials (Table 2) ranged from 4.69 ± 0.04 to 5.41 ± 0.14 GPa, depending upon the composition, age and storage conditions. The dynamic Young's modulus of the glass filler was 94.20 ± 0.63 GPa; the shear modulus was 37.35 ± 0.18 GPa; and the bulk modulus was 65.77 ± 1.14 GPa; the Poisson's ratio for the glass was 0.261 ± 0.003 and the specific gravity was 2.87 ± 0.01.

Table 1. Bioactive Glass Composites, Young's Modulus (GPa ± sd)

Time Days		Matrix 'A' Non-Silane	Matrix 'A' Silane	Matrix 'B' Non-Silane	Matrix 'B' Silane
4	(SBF)	12.9 ± 0.1	15.7 ± 0.3	13.0 ± 0.7	15.1 ± 0.1
8	(SBF)	13.0 ± 0.2	14.0 ± 0.5	12.3 ± 0.3	14.1 ± 0.2
14	(SBF)	13.2 ± 0.4	12.7 ± 0.2	12.5 ± 0.2	13.8 ± 0.3
60	(SBF)	12.8 ± 0.2	13.9 ± 0.1	12.1 ± 0.1	13.3 ± 0.0
60	(Water)	13.7 ± 0.1	13.8 ± 0.1	13.1 ± 0.1	13.3 ± 0.1

Table 2. Unfilled Matrix Resin Systems, Young's Modulus (GPa ± sd)

Time Days		Polymer 'A'	Polymer 'B'
4	(SBF)	5.41 ± 0.14	5.07 ± 0.12
8	(SBF)	5.07 ± 0.13	5.00 ± 0.09
14	(SBF)	4.97 ± 0.04	4.99 ± 0.04
60	(SBF)	5.33 ± 0.08	4.97 ± 0.08
60	(Water)	4.96 ± 0.06	4.69 ± 0.04

Composites with matrix 'B' exhibited a lower modulus for the non-silanized versus silanized materials for all periods of storage in SBF and 60 days in water (P< 0.05). The non-silane treated composite 'B' stored in water for 60 days had a significantly higher modulus compared to storage in SBF for 60 days (P= 0.0005). The silane treated composite 'B' exhibited a very significant reduction in elastic modulus from 4 days to 60 days in SBF (P= 0.0001).

Comparisons of the dynamic Young's modulus for experimental bioactive glass/resin composite formulations containing 25, 50 and 75% by weight of filler are illustrated in the bar diagram in Figure 1. This data illustrates the effect of silane treatment on the Young's modulus and compares the experimental materials with two commercial products. The silane treatment significantly increased the modulus of the composite system by improving the stress transfer between the matrix resin and filler. In contrast to conventional methacrylate bone cement, the range of dynamic moduli values for the experimental composite systems were significantly higher and within the typical range of values for cortical bone.

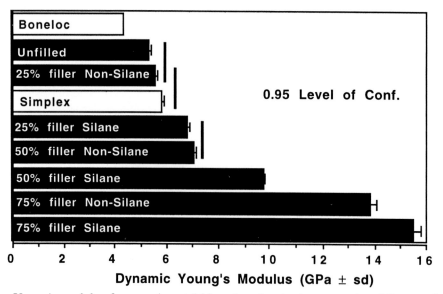

Figure 1. Young's modulus for experimental bioactive glass/resin composites (silane and non-silane treated). Filler loadings 25, 50, and 75% by weight. Commercial bone cement materials shown for comparison. [Boneloc orthopedic cement, BioMet Inc., Warsaw, Indiana, 46581, USA.; Simplex orthopedic cement, Howmedica Inc., Rutherford, NJ. USA.].

Linear and non-linear regression analysis of filler (weight %) versus Young's, shear and bulk elastic moduli gave excellent correlations ($P < 0.001$). The Poisson's ratio for the experimental bioactive glass/resin composites with the silane treated filler consistently exhibited a lower Poisson's ratio for all filler loadings compared to the non-silane treated filler.

CONCLUSIONS

The data provide useful information which may allow the development of more effective bioactive composite materials with appropriate mechanical properties. The data for modulus of elasticity demonstrates that it is important to evaluate bioactive glass/resin composite systems following storage in SBF rather than water.

ACKNOWLEDGEMENTS

The authors acknowledge the support from DePuy Inc., Warsaw, Indiana for this research project.

REFERENCES

1)   Jones DW, Rizkalla AS, In: Rusin RP, Fischman GS, eds. Bioceramics: Materials and Applications II, *Ceram. Trans*. 1995; **63**: 87-91.
2)   Jones DW, Rizkalla AS. *J. Biomed. Mater. Res. (Applied Biomaterials)*;1996; **33**: 89-100.
3)   Kokubo T, Ito S, Huang ZT, Hayashi T, Sakka S, Kitsugi T, Yamamuro T. *J Biomed. Mater. Res.* 1990; **24**: 331-343.
4)   Kokubo T, Hata K, Nakamura T, Yamamuro T. In: Bonfield W, Hastings GW, Tannes KE. eds. *Bioceramics,* Butterworth-Heinemann, 1991;**4**: 113-120.
5)   Rizkalla AS, Jones DW, Hall GC. *Brit. Ceram. Trans.* 1997; **96**: 16-20.
6)   Rizkalla AS, Jones DW, Clarke DB, Hall GC. *J. Biomed. Mater. Res.* 1996; **32**: 119-124.

Bioceramics Volume 11, edited by R. Z. LeGeros and J.P. LeGeros
(Proceedings of the 11th International Symposium on Ceramics in Medicine)
New York, NY, USA, November 1998
© 1998 by World Scientific Publishing Co. Pte. Ltd.

Changes in Mechanical Properties and GBR Application of TCP/CPLA Composite

Masanori Kikuchi[1], Kimiyasu Sato[1], Yasushi Suetsugu[1], Junzo Tanaka[1]
Yoshihisa Koyama[2] and Kazuo Takakuda[2]

[1]National Institute for Research in Inorganic Materials, 1-1 Namiki, Tsukuba, Ibaraki 305, Japan.
[2]Division of Inorganic Materials, Institute for Medical and Dental Engineering, Tokyo Medical and Dental University, 2-3-10 Kanda-Surugadai, Chiyoda-ku, Tokyo 101, Japan.

ABSTRACT

Mechanical strength changes *in vitro* and *in vivo*, and guided-bone-regeneration (GBR) applications of β-tricalcium phosphate (TCP) / co-polymerized poly-L-lactide (CPLA) composite were examined using physiological saline solution and in vivo studies conducted using beagles. Mechanical strength of composites soaked in physiological saline decreased and reached plataue after 4 weeks. Conversely, the CPLA decreased greately in strength afgter 4 weeks' soaking. In beagles' subcutaneous tissue, no changes in mechanical properties of the composites and CPLA were observed after 8 weeks. A GBR test using beagles' mandibles and tibias showed excellent regeneration of bone up to $20 \times 10 \times 10$ mm^3 for mandibles' and 20 mm in length for tibias' bone defects. These results suggested that the composites keep sufficient mechanical properties *in vivo* and are applicable as a GBR membrane.

KEYWORDS

β-tricalcium phosphate, co-polymerized poly-L-lactide, composite, mechanical properties change, guided tissue regeneration, guided bone regeneration

INTRODUCTION

β-tricalcium phosphate (TCP) is well known as a bioactive ceramic and is used in medical and dental fields as bone fillers and bone substitutes. The ceramic, when implanted into a bone, can be substituted by bone; however, this ceramic is brittle and the substitution process requires muchh time. However, some kinds of polyester are known to be biodegradable biomaterials, though such polymers have no osteoconductivity. In a previous study[1,2], the authors reported the preparation, mechanical properties and biocompatibility of TCP/CPLA(co-polymerized poly-L-lactide)[3] composites which had good properties for artificial bone substitute materials. In this study, mechanical strength changes *in vitro* and *in vivo*, and guided-bone-regeneration (GBR) applications of the TCP/CPLA composite were examined.

MATERIALS AND METHODS

TCP was prepared by a wet method using Ca(OH)$_2$ and H$_3$PO$_4$ as starting materials and heated at 1073 and 1373K for 3 hours. CPLA was prepared by the co-polymerization of L-lactide and poly(ethylenesebacate-co-hexamethylenesebacate). Hard (CPLA-H) and soft (CPLA-S) types of CPLAs, which have a mean molecular weight of 150,000 for CPLA-H and 70,000 for CPLA-S, were used in this study. TCP and CPLA were mixed by a thermal kneading method using a LABO PLASTOMILL® (Toyo Seiki). CPLA was fused in the plastomill at 453K for 1 minute, and TCP powder preheated at 453K was added and mixed with the CPLA melt for 10 minutes at 50 rpm for CPLA-S and at 10 rpm for CPLA-H. Then, the composites obtained were formed into a plate and a sheet by a heat press at 453K and kept at 293K for 30 minutes to crystallize CPLA.

For mechanical property tests, the plate was cut into test pieces, 20×5×3 mm³ in size. Test periods were 1-24 weeks for the *in vitro* test and 1-12 weeks for the *in vivo* test. Five test pieces were used in each period. The test pieces were soaked in physiological saline (100 cm³ for 1-12 weeks and 300 cm³ for 24 weeks) and kept in 310K incubator and were implanted into beagles' back subcutaneous tissues. Mechanical properties were measured by the three-point bending strength test with a universal testing machine of 15 mm in span and at 500μm/min crosshead speed. The molecular weight change of CPLA after the thermal treatment was evaluated with gel permeation chromatography. Changes in Ca and P concentration in physiological saline were measured by ICP spectroscopy, and also pH changes were measured by a pH meter. Changes in chemical interaction between TCP and CPLA were measured by FT-IR method. Surface structure changes of the composites were observed by SEM.

The composite sheets were implanted as guided bone regeneration(GBR) membranes after shaping during surgical operation and implanted into artificial bone defect of beagles' mandibles and tibias. The maximum sizes of the defects were 20×10×10 mm³ for mandibles and 20mm in length for tibias. Röntogenographic observation was carried out every one week. The tissue around implants was extracted at 4, 8 and 12 weeks after implantation and observed histologically.

RESULTS AND DISCUSSION

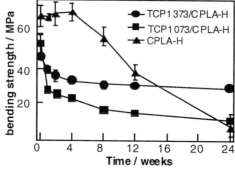

Figure 1. Changes in bending strength in phiysiological saline solution.

Figure 2. Changes in Young's modulus in phiysiological saline solution.

The three-point bending strength and Young's modulus of the composites as a function of soaking time in physiological saline are shown in Figs. 1 and 2. Both bending strength and Young's modulus decreased rapidly in the first 4 weeks, however, both reached plateau after 4 or more weeks' soaking. Conversely, those of CPLA decreased drastically after 4 weeks postsoaking. Molecular weight changes

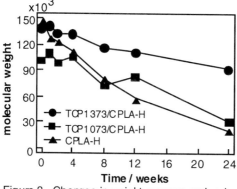

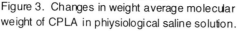

Figure 3. Changes in weight average molecular weight of CPLA in phiysiological saline solution.

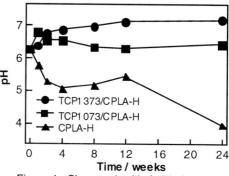

Figure 4. Changes in pH of phiysiological saline solution.

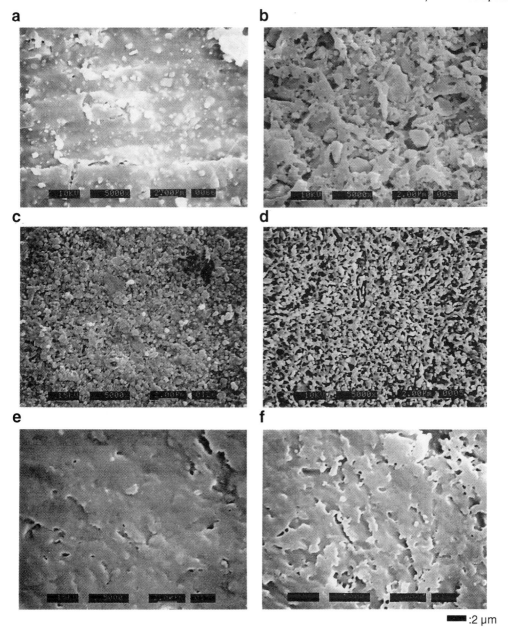

Figure 5. SEM observation of TCP/CPLA composites and CPLA surface, a: TCP1373/CPLA-H before soaking, b: 12 weeks' after soaking, c: TCP1073/CPLA-H before soaking, d: 12 weeks' after soaking, e: CPLA-H before soaking and f: 12 weeks' after soaking.

as a function of soaking time are shown in Fig.3. The molecular weight of CPLA decreased just after soaking, however that of the composites decreased very slowly. Generally, the hydrolysis reaction of polyester is promoted by an acid or basic catalyst. pH measurements (Fig. 4) show that the pH remained neutral when the composites were soaked due to neutralization of TCP and L-lactic acid produced by the hydrolysis reaction of CPLA. Therefore, self-catalytic hydrolysis reaction of CPLA can be inhibited.

Figure 5 shows SEM observation of the composite surfaces before and after soaking in physiological saline. TCP particles were dissolved clearly from the surface of the composites after 12 weeks' soaking. Increasing of Ca concentration of the physiological saline also supported TCP dissolution.   In the beagles' back subcutaneous tissue, no obvious changes in mechanical properties of the composites were observed up to 8 weeks, because subcutaneous tissue has a poor supply of body fluid.

Röntgenographic and histological observation of GBR experiments at each period showed rapid and perfect bone regeneration of mandible defects up to $20 \times 10 \times 10$ mm^3 in size and tibia defects up to 20 mm in length.   The composite membrane was disappear during 4-8 weeks' after operation. This rapid and perfect regeneration was not observed in CPLA membranes.

These *in vitro* and *in vivo* investigations show that TCP powder could plausibly enhance cell differentiation by releasing Ca and PO$_4$ ions as well as adjust pH of surrounding body fluid.   These results indicate that the TCP/CPLA composite is utilizable as a GTR and/or GBR membrane.

CONCLUSION

Good values for the mecahnical properties of TCP/CPLA composites were maintained in the use of GBR membranes, also the pH of the surrounding solution remained unchanged.   The composite membranes enhanced bone regeneration for a mandible's and tibia's defect, probably due to the dissolution of TCP.   The composites will be utilizable as a GBR membrane for a relatively large bone defect.

ACKNOWLEDGMENT

The CPLA plastics were provided by Dainippon Ink Chemicals, Inc.   The authors are grateful to Mr. Yutaka Tashiro and Dr. Toshiro Ariga at Dainippon Ink Chemicals, Inc. for supplying CPLA and for measuring its molecular weight

REFERENCES

1 Masanori Kikuchi, Yasushi Suetsugu, Junzo Tanaka and Masaru Akao, *Journal of Material Science: Materials in Medicine*, 1997, **8[6]**, 361-364.
2 Masanori Kikuchi, Junzo Tanaka, Yoshihisa Koyama and Kazuo Takakuda, *Journal of Applied Biomaterials*, in print.
3 Kakizawa, Y., *Kagaku to Kogyo*, 1995, **48 [9]**, 1070-1072.

Bioceramics Volume 11, edited by R. Z. LeGeros and J.P. LeGeros
(Proceedings of the 11th International Symposium on Ceramics in Medicine)
New York, NY, USA, November 1998

MECHANICAL STRENGTH AND DYNAMIC YOUNG'S MODULUS OF GLASS REINFORCED HYDROXYAPATITE BIOCOMPOSITES

M. A. Lopes[1,2]; F. J. Monteiro[1,2]; R. F. Silva[3] and J. D. Santos[1,2]

[1]INEB – Instituto de Engenharia Biomédica, Rua do Campo Alegre, 823, 4150 Porto, Portugal Fax +351 2 2087310
[2]Department of Metallurgy and Materials, FEUP, University of Porto, Portugal
[3]Department of Glass and Ceramics, UIMC, Aveiro University, 3810 Aveiro, Portugal.

ABSTRACT

The effect of $CaO-P_2O_5-MgO$ glass system in promoting microstructural changes of hydroxyapatite-glass composites and its relation with mechanical properties were investigated. Composites were characterized by X-ray powder diffraction and quantitative phase analysis performed by the Rietveld method using General Structure Analysis Software. Density measurements were performed in mercury using the Archimedes principle. Flexural bending strength was determined from concentric ring-on-ring testing and statistical variations in strength analyzed by applying Weibull distribution. Dynamic Young's modulus was assessed by impulse excitation of vibration (ASTM C 1259-96). Composites showed a significant improvement in biaxial bending strength when compared to hydroxyapatite. The presence of tricalcium phosphate (TCP) appeared to be the major responsible for this enhancement, besides the high densification obtained for the composites. These secondary phases presence induced a decrease in Young's modulus for the composites when compared to HA.

KEYWORDS: Hydroxyapatite glass composites, microstructure, tricalcium phosphate, mechanical strength, Young's modulus

INTRODUCTION

Hydroxyapatite (HA) has been widely used in both orthopedic surgery and dentistry. However, because of problems related to bone replacement in load bearing applications in the skeleton, several attempts have been made in order to approximate its mechanical properties to those of bone. Mechanical properties of a material, besides its biocompatibility, provide a decisive criterion in its selection for some specific biomedical purposes. The effect of $CaO-P_2O_5-MgO$ glass system in promoting microstructural changes of HA-glass composites and hence affecting the Weibull distribution of biaxial bending strength and Young's modulus was investigated.

MATERIALS AND METHODS

Glass reinforced HA composites were prepared by adding 2.5 and 4.0wt% of a glass (50.0%mol P_2O_5, 16.5%molCaO, 33.5%mol MgO) to commercial HA (P120 batch, Plasma Biotal, UK). A detailed procedure for the preparation of the glass and composites has been reported previously[1]. For assessing the flexural bending strength and the Young' modulus,

paralelipipedic shaped samples, respectively. Hydroxyapatite and composite samples were then liquid phase sintered at 1200, 1250, 1300 and 1350°C. For X-ray diffraction analysis, a Siemens D5000 diffractometer, equipped with a scintillation counter and a graphite diffracted beam monochromator was used. Quantitative phase analyses were performed by the Rietveld method using General Structure Analysis Software (GSAS, Los Alamos National Laboratory). Structure refinement details were previously described[2]. Triple density measurements were performed, in mercury, using the Archimedes principle. Scanning electron microscopy (SEM) was used to analyze the microstructure of the composites after polishing to 1μm finish with diamond paste, and chemical etching with 10wt% citric acid solution for 3-4 min at room temperature. Grain size measurements were carried out on SEM photomicrographs, using a planimetric procedure according to ASTM E 112-88. A minimum of three fields was counted to ensure reasonable average. Flexural bending strength was determined from concentric ring-on-ring testing in a concentric jig with 20 mm supporting span and 10 mm loading span at a cross head speed of 5 mm/min. The rupture modulus was calculated using the equation proposed by Soltesz[3]. For each material, 12 test specimens were used. Dynamic Young's modulus was assessed, in triplicate, at room temperature by Impulse Excitation of Vibration according to ASTM C 1259-96.

RESULTS AND DISCUSSION

After chemical etching, SEM examination showed pores homogeneously distributed and mainly located at grain boundaries which are typical of a liquid phase sintering process. Table 1 shows the phase quantification results, obtained from the XRD diffractograms, using the Rietveld method. At the sintering temperature range studied, a secondary phase, β-TCP, was detected in the glass reinforced hydroxyapatite composites. At 1350°C, composites presented of another secondary phase, α-TCP, resulting from β-TCP conversion. With 4.0 wt% glass addition, higher transformation ratio of HA into both β-TCP and α-TCP occurred as compared to 2.5 wt% glass addition. Porosity values are also shown in Table 1.

Table 1. Phase quantification and porosity results (%)

	1200 °C				1250 °C				1300 °C				1350 °C			
	HA	β-TCP	α-TCP	P (%)	HA	β-TCP	α-TCP	P (%)	HA	β-TCP	α-TCP	P (%)	HA	β-TCP	α-TCP	P (%)
HA	100	0	0	11.7	100	0	0	6.9	100	0	0	5.0	100	0	0	6.1
2.5wt%D1-HA	66.0	34.0	0	7.9	67.0	33.0	0	3.8	67.2	32.8	0	3.2	65.2	24.3	10.5	4.1
4.0wt%D1-HA	50.2	49.8	0	15.9	46.6	53.4	0	3.8	49.2	50.8	0	3.2	44.3	42.9	12.8	3.4

A decrease in porosity was observed with increasing sintering temperature. Glass addition has contributed to reduce composites porosity by acting as a sintering aid. From Figure 1 a steady increase in grain size, G, of the HA matrix may be seen with increasing sintering temperature for all materials. At 1200 °C sintering temperature it was not feasible to measure matrix grain size because of the high porosity present in the composite materials after chemical etching. Composites showed larger grain size than HA. No differences in grain size, G, were seen based on glass level additions during the sintering process. Flexural bending strength (FBS) of glass-reinforced HA composites was found to be about twice or three times higher than that of unreinforced HA, as it is exemplified in Figure 2.

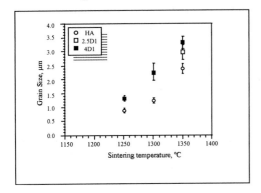

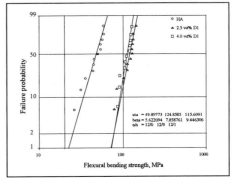

Fig. 1. Grain size (μm) vs. sintering temperature (°C)   Fig. 2. Weibull statistics analysis

The increase in flexural bending strength (FBS) observed for all materials, from 1200 to 1250 °C, is mainly due to the reduction in porosity, since no significant changes in calcium secondary phases formation were detected (see Tab. 1 and Fig. 3).

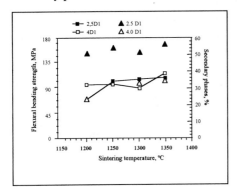

Table 2. Weibull moduli for HA and glass reinforced HA composites

	1200 °C	1250 °C	1300 °C	1350 °C
HA	5.8	5.2	3.0	5.0
2.5wt%D1-HA	10.8	6.3	7.4	7.9
4.0wt%D1-HA	5.8	7.3	19.7	9.5

Fig. 3 Bending strength (MPa) vs. TCP phases (%)

Despite the increase in grain size from 1200 to 1250°C, an increase in FBS was observed due to porosity reduction, acting as a predominant factor. At the highest temperature the grain size factor became predominant causing a slight reduction in strength, since no further increase in density was observed. The presence of a glassy phase in the sintering process of the composites has caused the transformation of HA into β-TCP, which is known to have higher strength than HA. The higher FBS found for the glass-reinforced HA composites compared to HA should be caused by a combined effect of porosity reduction and presence of secondary phases, being the latter the main factor. The improvement in strength associated with the presence of small quantities of secondary phases (β and α-TCP) should derive from inhibition of crack propagation and internal stresses from phase transformations. Dispersion of mechanical bending strength values was assessed by applying the maximum likelihood method to the well-known statistical distribution of Weibull. From Table 2 it can be seen that higher moduli were obtained for the composites as compared to HA, reflecting the better uniformity of composite microstructures. Figure 4 plots the Young's modulus (E) versus sintering temperature. A steady increase of E is observed with the sintering temperature from 1200 to 1300°C. HA showed, at all temperatures, higher E modulus values than glass reinforced composites, whereas lower E values were found for the 4.0 wt% glass addition composites than for 2.5wt% ones.

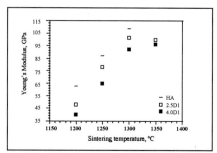

Fig. 4 Youngs Modulus (GPa) vs. sintering temperature (°C)

Young's modulus seems to depend more on porosity rather than on secondary phases presence since its variation with sintering temperature followed a similar trend for HA and HA-glass composites. Indeed, the strong increase observed with the sintering temperature is associated with a reduction in porosity for all materials. However, the lower Young's modulus values found for composites compared to HA are mainly attributed to the presence of secondary phases. In fact, at temperatures above 1200 °C, similar porosity levels were obtained for the 4.0 and 2.5wt% glass addition, and therefore the lower E values found for 4.0 wt% compared to 2.5wt% glass addition is a direct consequence of the presence of β-TCP. For 1350 °C sintering temperature, Young's modulus of HA and HA-glass composites became closer, probably as a consequence of the opposite effect of the presence of secondary phases and porosity reduction.

ACKNOWLEDGEMENTS

Authors wish to acknowledge the financial support of PBICT/CTM/1890/95 research project and FMRH/BD/1355/94 grant financed by Fundação para a Ciência e Tecnologia.

REFERENCES

1.   J. D. Santos, J. C. Knowles, R. L. Reis, F. J. Monteiro, G. W. Hastings " Microstructural Characterisation of Glass Reinforced Hydroxyapatite Composites" Biomaterials, 15(1):5-10; 1994.
2.   M. A. Lopes, J. D. Santos, F. J. Monteiro, J. C. Knowles "Glass Reinforced Hydroxyapatite: A Comprehensive Study of the Effect of Glass Composition on the Crystallography of the Composite" J. Biomed. Mater. Res., 39(2):244-251; 1998.
3.   Soltesz, U; Ritcher, H.; Kienzler, R. "The concentric-ring test and its applications for determine the surface strength of ceramics", High Tech. Ceram., Elsevier Sci. Publ., B. V., Netherlands, 1987:149-159

Bioceramics Volume 11, edited by R. Z. LeGeros and J.P. LeGeros
(Proceedings of the 11th International Symposium on Ceramics in Medicine)
New York, NY, USA, November 1998
© 1998 by World Scientific Publishing Co. Pte. Ltd.

THE FORMATION OF HYDROXYAPATITE AND HYDROXYAPATITE-BASED COMPOSITES

Paul W. Brown, Caner Durucan and Yaser Greish
The Pennsylvania State University, University Park, PA 16802

ABSTRACT

This overview discusses formation of hydroxyapatite (HAp) and HAp-based composites by chemical processes. The only solid capable of forming phase-pure HAp in monolithic form at low temperatures is α–tricalcium phosphate (α-TCP). Its reaction forms calcium-deficient HAp; this is of interest because it is significantly more bioactive than stoichiometric HAp. Although prior studies of α-TCP hydrolysis have shown it to be sluggish, our work has now demonstrated that HAp can be rapidly formed from α-TCP at physiological temperature. The kinetics of HAp formation by direct hydrolysis of α-TCP will be discussed.

Like α-TCP, tetracalcium phosphate (TetCP) will hydrolyze to form HAp. Because TetCP has a Ca/P ratio > 1.67, its hydrolysis also forms $Ca(OH)_2$. Advantage can be taken of $Ca(OH)_2$ formation by hydrolyzing TetCP in the presence of acidic polymers. The overall reactions leading to HAp-polymer composites will be described. In composite formation Ca ions neutralize interact with the carboxyl sites on these polyelectrolytes. This interaction can lead to the formation of Ca salt bridges between adjacent polymer chains and can result in the formation of composites exhibiting high strengths.

KEY WORDS: TCP hydrolysis, hot pressing, HAp-polymer composites

INTRODUCTION

α-Tricalcium Phosphate Hydrolysis to Hydroxyapatite The low temperature formation of hydroxyapatite (HAp) by cement-type reactions has been identified.[1-3] They typically involve acid-base reactions between particulate calcium phosphate precursors and direct hydrolysis of a solid calcium phosphate. However a single solid capable of forming phase-pure HAp in monolithic form at low temperature is α-tricalcium phosphate (α-TCP).[4] The reaction is particularly attractive because it forms calcium-deficient HAp, which is more soluble than stoichiometric HAp, and therefore may be incorporated into bone more readily. Also due to nature of its hydrolysis reaction, α-TCP can be used as moldable cement to repair bone defects by placement into the site of a defect prior to hardening. This paper describes the variations in hydrolysis kinetics for HAp formation at and near physiologic temperature for particulate and preformed pellets of α-TCP.

Hydrolysis of Tetracalcium Phosphate in Presence of a Poly(alkenoic) Acid Like TCP tetracalcium phosphate ($Ca_4(PO_4)_2O$, TetCP) will also hydrolyze to HAp. This is of interest because TetCP is the only calcium phosphate more basic than HAp and is the base used in many aqueous processes forming HAp.[5] Complete TetCP hydration produces HAp and calcium hydroxide according to:

$$3Ca_4(PO_4)_2O + 3H_2O \longrightarrow Ca_{10}(PO_4)_6(OH)_2 + 2Ca(OH)_2$$

The addition of a poly(alkenoic acid) that contains carboxylic acid (-COOH) groups to the system can thus result in an acid-base reaction between the $Ca(OH)_2$ and the acid, forming a crosslinked structure in which HAp crystals are embedded. It is well known that acid-base reactions usually take place in aqueous media. However, the current aim is to study the reaction of TetCP in presence of a poly(alkenoic acid) in the solid state using a hot pressing technique. This technique resembles those used in metallurgy and was first used on powder mixtures of metal oxides and poly(acrylic acid).[6-8]

EXPERIMENTAL PROCEDURE

The formation of calcium deficient HAp was accomplished by following hydrolysis reaction:

$$3\alpha Ca_3(PO_4)_2 + H_2O \rightarrow Ca_9(HPO_4)(PO_4)_5OH$$

α-TCP was prepared by a solid sate reaction between reagent grade calcium carbonate ($CaCO_3$) and calcium pyrophosphate ($Ca_2P_2O_7$). The volume average particle size was 3.3 μm.

The formation kinetics of HAp from α-TCP were monitored by isothermal calorimetry at 37°C, 45°C, 56°C. Calorimetric experiments were performed both on powders and pellets of α-TCP typically using a 1:1 liquid-to-solid ratio. The details of the isothermal calorimeter system can be found elsewhere.[9] Total heat evolution was determined by integrating the rate data, and plots of heat evolved are presented in kJ/mol of HAp formed.

The poly(alkenoic acid) used was an acrylic-itaconic copolymer. TetCP was prepared from $CaCO_3$ and $Ca(H_2PO_4)_2.H_2O$ by firing at 1310°C for 2 hours. TetCP and the copolymer powders were mixed together then hot-pressed at different temperatures, pressures and times. The composites formed were analyzed by X-ray diffraction (XRD), infrared (FT-IR) techniques and by SEM.

RESULTS

α-Tricalcium Phosphate Hydrolysis to Hydroxyapatite Figure 1 shows the heats of reaction in kJ/mol of HAp formed. A typical heat curve reaches plateau at complete reaction after which no further heat is produced. A reaction heat of 133 kJ/mol is indicative of complete reaction.[10] The extent of heat evolution when α-TCP was hydrolyzed in pellet form was lower than when hydrolysis was carried out in powder form. This is valid for all temperatures. The total heat liberated is around 133 kJ/mol for particulate samples indicating that hydrolysis reaches completion at each temperature. The time for complete reaction decreased to 6 hours from 18 hours by the increase in hydrolysis temperature from 37°C to 56°C. This is around 11 h. for hydrolysis at 45°C. The reaction has not proceeded to completion for pressed samples even at the highest temperature after 20 hours. The total heat output for pressed samples is in the range of 70-95 kJ/mol after 20 h of reaction. Extent of HAp formation at different reaction temperatures was also confirmed with companion XRD analyses.

Such behavior may be due hydrolysis kinetics being strongly controlled by the ability of water to reach the reactant α-TCP. This was also reflected by the total porosity of the resultant HAp structures. The total porosity is 55-70% for the HAp formed from particulate α-TCP. This value is 35-45% for the pressed pellets, where water penetration is limited. Better defined and narrower characteristic peaks for HAp formed at higher temperatures suggest bigger HAp crystallite size. This is consistent with the SEM microstructure, which shows finer HAp morphology at the lowest hydrolysis temperature. The HAp formed at higher temperature appears in flake like form rather than thin needles indicating microstructural coarsening above physiologic temperature.

Hydrolysis of Tetracalcium Phosphate in Presence of a Poly(alkenoic) Acid Samples pressed at 200°C & 20 kpsi for 10 min. did not produce HAp. Raising the temperature to 300°C at constant pressure of 40 kpsi for 10 min., led to an increased extent of reaction between TetCP and copolymer and consequently the extent of conversion was found to increase.

When samples were hot-pressed at 300°C and 40 kpsi for time periods up to 30 min., the conversion of TetCP to HAp was found to increase dramatically giving > 90 % yield of well-crystallized HAp as can be observed in Figure 2. At these conditions, there was a large increase in intensity of the IR band characteristic of the carboxylate group which confirms the results that a high proportion of HAp was formed in a matrix of Ca salt of the copolymer. $Ca(OH)_2$ was not observed.

Preliminary determination of the mechanical properties of these composites gave a value of 145 kg/mm^2 for the hardness of a sample hot-pressed at 300°C & 40 kpsi for 30 min. This high value can thus be explained in terms of the cross linking of the copolymer by the salt formation together with the action of the formed HAp as a filler. These results suggest that composites prepared by this method can be used as a biomaterial for a variety of applications.

SUMMARY

The hydrolysis of α-TCP to HAp at and near physiological temperature was established. This cement type reaction produced approximately 55-70 % dense Ca-deficient HAp. Setting times for hydrolysis reaction and morphologies of resultant HAp were found to be strongly dependent on reaction temperature. During the formation of HAp from particulate α-TCP at 37°C nucleation can be observed at around 2 hours and completion takes about 18 hours. The times and duration of nucleation and growth periods shifted to shorter times with increasing temperature. Transformation advances without formation of any other calcium phosphate phase but only phase pure HAp. Porosity contributes the transformation of preformed shapes of α-TCP.

Preparation of a bioactive composite by hot pressing of a powder mixture of TetCP and copolymer was described. Variables affecting the conversion of TetCP to HAp were considered. The composites were found to consist of HAp in a matrix of a Ca salt of copolymer. XRD and FT-IR results showed the extent of HAp formed as a result of the reaction between TetCP and copolymer increased with temperature, pressure and/or time. Over 90% HAp was formed at 40,000 psi and 300°C when hot pressed for 30 min. At these conditions, a composite with a T_g > 300°C and a hardness of 145 kg/mm^2 was produced. These findings suggst that a new class of biomaterials with promising characteristics can be prepared using the hot pressing technique.

ACKNOWLEDGMENT

The authors gratefully acknowledge NSF grant DMR 9510272.

REFERENCES

1. Brown WE, Chow LC. *CRP-1986*, Westerville: Am Ceram Soc, 1987; 351-79.
2. Fulmer MT, Brown PW. *J. Am. Ceram. Soc.* 1991; **74**: 934-40
3. Brown PW, Hocker N, Hoyle S. *J Am Ceram Soc* 1991; **74**: 1848-55.
4. Monma H, Kanazawa T, *Yogio-Kyoki Shi* 1976; **84**, 209-215.
5. Martin RI, Brown PW. *Adv Cement Res* 1993; **5**, 119-125.
6. Fitzgerald WE, Nielsen LE. *Proc Roy Soc (London)* 1964; **A282**: 137-146.
7. Fields JE. Nielsen LE. *J Appl Polym Sci* 1968; **12**: 1041-1051.
8. Nielsen LE. *Polym Eng Sci* 1969; **9**: 356-359.
9. TenHuisen KS, Brown PW. *Mater in Med* 1996; **7**: 309-16.
10. Leamy P, Brown PW, TenHuisen KS, Randall CR. *J Biomed Mater Res*, submitted.

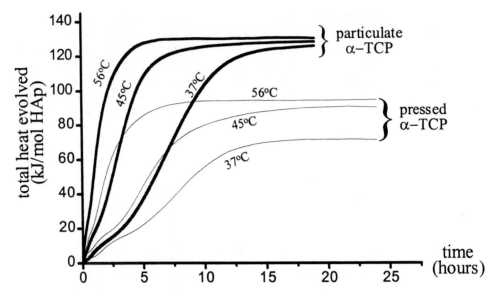

Figure 1 Total heat evolution during HAp formation from particulate and pressed pellets of α-TCP at diffrent temperatures

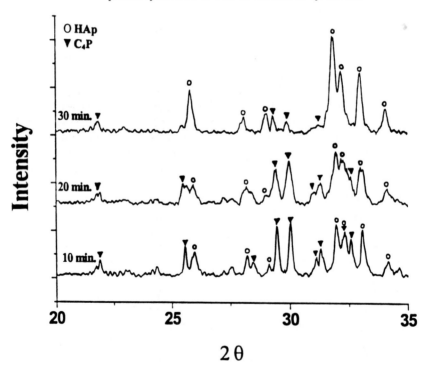

Figure 2 X-ray diffraction patterns for composites hot-pressed at 40 kpsi and 300°C for different time periods

Bioceramics Volume 11, edited by R. Z. LeGeros and J.P. LeGeros
(Proceedings of the 11th International Symposium on Ceramics in Medicine)
New York, NY, USA, November 1998
© 1998 by World Scientific Publishing Co. Pte. Ltd.

EVALUATION OF BIOGLASS®- AND HYDROXYAPATITE-REINFORCED POLYETHYLENE COMPOSITES AFTER AGEING IN SIMULATED BODY FLUID

J. Huang, M. Wang, S. Best, K.E. Tanner and W. Bonfield

IRC in Biomedical Materials, Queen Mary and Westfield College, Mile End Road, London E1 4NS, UK

ABSTRACT

The effect of ageing in simulated body fluid (SBF) on the mechanical performance of Bioglass®- and hydroxyapatite- (HA) reinforced high density polyethylene (HDPE) composites (Bioglass®/HDPE and HAPEX™, respectively) was studied. A weight increase of 6 to 9% occurred for the Bioglass®/HDPE composites after 6 months in SBF, but in contrast, the weight increase for HAPEX™ was less than 1%. As a result of the high reactivity of Bioglass®/HDPE composites, their tensile strength and Young's modulus decreased after 6 months in SBF, while the fracture strain increased. The reduction in the modulus of Bioglass®/HDPE was less than 2% for Vp = 30%, but 25% for Vp = 40%, for which severe degradation of Bioglass® particles was observed. In comparison, there was no decrease in the tensile strength, Young's modulus or fracture strain for HAPEX™ samples.

KEYWORDS

Bioglass®, hydroxyapatite, composite, ageing, mechanical properties and SEM

INTRODUCTION

The development of a hydroxyapatite (HA) reinforced high density polyethylene (HDPE) composite (HAPEX™) as a bone analogue material has been reported previously[1], and the composite has achieved clinical success as an orbital floor prosthesis [2,3] and middle ear implant. By incorporating highly bioactive Bioglass® 45S5 particles into the HDPE matrix, a new Bioglass®/HDPE composite has been produced [4], which retains *in vitro* bioactivity and biocompatibility [5,6,7]. As an implant material, the composite is in contact with physiological fluid throughout its service life and therefore the performance of the composite under wet conditions needs to be evaluated. In this study, the changes in the mechanical properties of both composites have been investigated after immersion in physiological solution for 6 months.

MATERIALS AND METHODS

Bioglass®/HDPE and HAPEX™ composites with particle volume percentages (Vp) of 20, 30 and 40 were produced by incorporation of Bioglass® particles (45S5, US Biomaterials) or HA (P88,

Plasma Biotal) into HDPE (Rigidex, BP) matrix through twin-screw extrusion and compression moulding [4,8]. The density of the composites was measured according to Archimedes' principle , the microstructure has been characterised by X-ray diffraction, Fourier transform infrared spectroscopy and scanning electron microscopy.

Simulated body fluid (SBF K9) was used to immerse the specimens, as it closely resembles the ion concentrations in blood plasma[9]. SBF K9 was prepared by dissolving reagent-grade chemicals[7] and buffered to pH 7.25 at 37°C with tris-(hydroxymethyl) aminomethane and hydrochloric acid. Dumbbell shape tensile specimens (ISO 527) of both composites and unfilled PE were machined from plaques, and the specimens were immersed in SBF at 37°C for 6 months. The weight changes (Δwt%) of the composites produced by immersion were measured. Tensile testing of the composites (before and after immersion in SBF) was conducted on an Instron 6025 mechanical testing machine at a crosshead speed of 0.5 mm min^{-1} at ambient temperature with an extensometer to measure strain, 5 specimens of each group were tested. The tensile strength, Young's modulus and strain at failure were determined. The fracture surfaces of the composites were examined using a JEOL 6300 scanning electron microscope (SEM).

RESULTS AND DISCUSSION

The density of both Bioglass®/HDPE and HAPEX™ composites increased with the volume percentage (Vp) of the fillers, as did the Young's modulus of the composites. The tensile strength of HAPEX™ increased with increasing Vp of HA, while that of Bioglass®/HDPE decreased. The strain to failure of both composites decreased with increasing Vp.

After 6 months in SBF, a weight increase of 6 to 9% occurred for all the Bioglass®/HDPE composites, while the weight increase for HAPEX™ was less than 1%. The tensile strength and Young's modulus of Bioglass®/HDPE composites decreased, while the fracture strain increased, as shown in Figure 1. The reduction in the modulus of Bioglass®/HDPE was less than 2% for Vp = 30%, but 25% for Vp = 40%. The decrease in tensile strength of Bioglass®/HDPE occurred at all Vp tested, but was accompanied by an increase in ductility. When the fracture surfaces were examined, severe degradation of Bioglass® particles was observed, particularly at Vp = 40% (Figure 2), which contributed to the reduction in Young's modulus and tensile strength and increased ductility through the associated decoupling, increase in porosity and reduction in fill content. In comparison, there were no changes in the tensile strength, Young's modulus or fracture strain for HAPEX™ samples.

As has been reported previously[10], no degradation of HAPEX™ occurred after ageing for 3 months and this study confirms that tensile properties remain unchanged for up to 6 months. The stability of HAPEX™ was attributed to the insoluble HA particles, while Bioglass® 45S5 is known to react with physiological solution to form a surface apatite layer, which plays an important role for the formation of direct bonding with host tissue *in vivo* [11]. This bioactivity was retained in the Bioglass®/HDPE composite[5], and the *in vitro* bioactivity and biocompatibility of Bioglass®/HDPE composite were proportional to the Vp of Bioglass® [7]. However, this study shows that the modulus of Bioglass®/HDPE composite at Vp = 40% decreased dramatically after ageing in SBF as a result of its high reactivity. Therefore, the ageing performance of Bioglass®/HDPE needs to be considered in selection of an optimal composition.

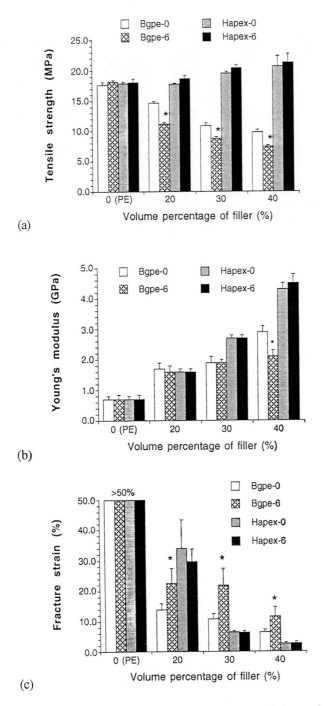

Figure 1. Changes of (a) tensile strength (b) Young's modulus and (c) fracture strain of Bioglass®/HDPE (Bgpe) and HAPEX™(Hapex) before(-0) and after 6 months (-6) immersion in SBF. * indicates a statistically significant difference from that of 0 month (p<0.05).

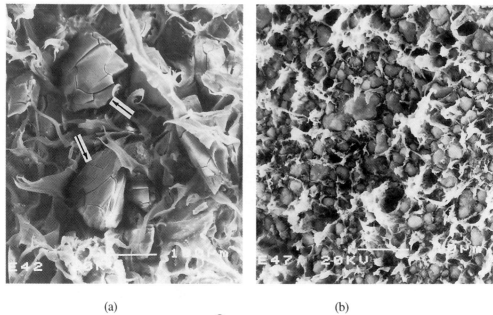

(a)   (b)

Figure 2. Fracture surfaces of (a) Bioglass®/HDPE and (b) HAPEX™ after 6 months immersion in SBF, arrows show the partial dissolution of Bioglass® particles.

CONCLUSIONS

These results demonstrate that HAPEX™ exhibits no significant change after ageing in SBF up to 6 months. For Bioglass®/HDPE composite, the mechanical properties are reduced with time in SBF, with the magnitude of the reduction related to the volume fraction of Bioglass®.

ACKNOWLEDGEMENTS
The financial support from US Biomaterials for this project and the continuing support of EPSRC for the IRC core programme are gratefully acknowledged.

REFERENCE
1. Bonfield W, *J Biomed Eng* 1988; **10**: 522-536.
2. Downes RN, Vardy S, Tanner KE, and Bonfield W, 1991; *Bioceramics* **4**: 239-246.
3. Tanner KE, Downes RN, Bonfield W, *Brit Ceram Trans* 1994; **93**: 104-107.
4. Wang M, Bonfield W, Hench L L, 1995;*Bioceramics* **8**: 383-388.
5. Huang J, Wang M, Rehman I, Knowles J, Bonfield W, 1995; *Bioceramics* **8**: 389-395.
6. Huang J, Wang M, Rehman I, Bonfield W, 1996, *Bioceramics* **9**: 431-434.
7. Huang J, DiSilvio L, Wang M, Rehman I, Ohtsuki C, Bonfield W, *J Mater Sci Mater Med* 1997; **8**: 809-813.
8. Wang W, Porter D, Bonfield W, *Brit Ceram Trans* 1994; **93**: 91-95.
9. Kokubo T, Kushitani H, Sakka S, Kitsugi T, Yamamuro T, *J Biomed Mater Res* 1990); **24**: 721-734.
10. Huang J, DiSilvio L, Wang M, Tanner KE, and Bonfield W, *J Mater Sci Mater Med*, 1997, **8**, 775-779.
11. Hench L L, *J Am Ceram Soc,* 1991; **74**: 1487-1510.

Bioceramics Volume 11, edited by R. Z. LeGeros and J.P. LeGeros
(Proceedings of the 11th International Symposium on Ceramics in Medicine)
New York, NY, USA, November 1998
© 1998 by World Scientific Publishing Co. Pte. Ltd.

STIFF AND BIOACTIVE COMPOSITES BASED ON STARCH, POLYETHYLENE AND SiO$_2$ - CaO·P$_2$O$_5$ - MgO GLASSES AND GLASS-CERAMICS

R. L. Reis[1,2], I. B. Leonor[1,3], M. T. Rego[1], A. M. Cunha[3], M. H. Fernandes[4], R. N. Correia[4]

[1] INEB - Institute for Biomedical Engineering, Biomaterials Laboratory, Rua do Campo Alegre, 823, 4150 Porto, Portugal; [2] Dept. of Metallurgical and Materials Science Eng., Fac. Eng. U. Porto, Rua dos Bragas, 4099 Porto Codex, Portugal; [3] Dept. of Polymer Eng., U. Minho, Campus de Azurém, 4800 Guimarães, Portugal; [4] Dept. of Ceramics and Glass Eng., U. Aveiro, Campus de Santiago, 3800 Aveiro, Portugal

ABSTRACT

This study evaluated the possibility of creating new stiff and bioactive composites based on both: (i) novel biodegradable starch based polymers (starch/ethylene-vinyl alcohol blends - SEVA-C), and (ii) high molecular weight polyethylene (HMWPE), for temporary and permanent applications respectively. Both polymers were reinforced with bioactive glasses (BGE1) and glass-ceramics (BGE1C), with 90% of the particles below 10 μm in the SiO$_2$-3CaO·P$_2$O$_5$-MgO system. These fillers were incorporated, in weight fractions up to 40% wt. into both types of matrixes. The composites were compounded by twin-screw extrusion (TSE) and then injection moulded. The mechanical properties of the composites were evaluated in tensile tests, and their bioactivity was assessed by analysing the respective surfaces (SEM/EDS) after different immersion periods in a simulated body fluid (SBF). Ca, P, Si and Mg concentrations were followed vs. time by induced-coupling plasma (ICP) spectroscopy, and x-ray diffraction (XRD) was used to identify the crystalline phases present on the films formed at the materials surfaces. The obtained results indicated that the modulus of the composites increased for higher amounts of BGE1 and specially BGE1C, while the strains at break decreased. For the BGE1C filler it was possible to produce composites matching the stiffness of human cortical bone. The bioactivity of SEVA-C composites become relevant for BGE1 amounts of only 20% wt., for immersion periods higher than 30 days. On the contrary, for the HMWPE matrix composites weight fractions of at least 40% wt. were necessary to confer a bioactive character to the composites.

KEYWORDS: bioactive ceramics; composites; polymers: biodegradable; bioactivity; bone replacement.

INTRODUCTION

It is well known that bioactive ceramics can directly bond to living bone via an apatite layer deposited on their surface when they are implanted in the body[1-4]. The major problem of these materials, which inhibits their applications on several types of implants, is their poor mechanical properties[5]. Many experiments have been carried out in the last few years, in order to try to solve this problem. Bonfield and his co-workers[6] introduced the original concept of a bioceramic reinforced polymeric composite. The approach was based on considering cortical bone as the template for a bone replacement material[6]. By combining polymers with bioceramics, researchers hope to overcome the mismatch of mechanical properties that currently exists between implants and natural load bearing tissues, and to obtain simultaneously a bioactive composite[7, 8].

In the present study two types of bioactive ceramics, namely a glass and a glass-ceramic crystallised from it, have been used as fillers of a bioinert polyethylene and a novel starch based biodegradable polymer. The main aims of the present study were to assess the importance of the type of filler (and its original stiffness) used over the mechanical properties improvement, as well as to characterise the bioactivity of the developed composites.

MATERIALS AND METHODS

In this work two different kinds of polymers were studied as composite matrix: (i) high molecular weight polyethylene (HMWPE, Hostalen® GM 9255F, Hoechst, Germany) and (ii) a biodegradable starch/ethylene-vinyl alcohol blend (SEVA-C, Mater-Bi 1128RR, Novamont, Italy). Bioactive glasses (BGE1) and glass-ceramics (BGE1C) in the SiO_2 - $3CaO.P_2O_5$ - MgO system were used as reinforcements of both polymers. The glass-ceramic (BGE1C) was obtained from BGE1 by a single stage heat-treatment (970°C for 1h)[9,10]. The transition and crystallisation temperatures were determined by differential thermal analysis (DTA), and the crystalline phases were identified by X-ray diffraction (XRD)[9,10]. The manufacturing process for both composites consisted of a compounding stage in a twin-screw extruder (TSE) followed by injection moulding in a Klockner-Ferromatik Desma FM20 machine. Before the composites processing, the particle size of the fillers was characterised by a laser granulometry and classified to 90% of the particles below 10μm. The fillers were incorporated in weight fraction up to 40% wt. into both types of matrixes. The tensile samples produced were dumb-bell shaped specimens with a cross-section of 2x4mm. The composites were tensile tested in an Instron 4505 machine, using a resistive extensometer, in order to determine the secant modulus at 1% strain ($E_{1\%}$), the ultimate tensile stress (UTS) and strain at break (ε_r %). The cross-head speed was 5 mm/min until 1% strain and then 50 mm/min until fracture. The fracture surfaces were examined by SEM. The bioactivity of the composites was evaluated by immersing the samples at 37°C in a simulated body fluid (SBF) for different periods up to 30 days. Then, the respective surfaces were analysed by SEM/EDS and thin-film XRD (1° incidence angle). The evolution of the Ca, Mg, Si and P concentrations was determined by induced coupled plasma spectroscopy (ICP).

RESULTS & DISCUSSION

The particles of the fillers (both BGE1, and BGE1C) used in both matrixes, were found to be well dispersed, with a homogenous and uniform distribution, in the polymeric phase after compounding by TSE. Subsequent composite processing (by injection moulding) did not alter these characteristics. Table 1 and 2 present the obtained mechanical properties. For SEVA-C matrix, the reinforcement with BGE1 led to a higher modulus, while UTS and ε_r decreased. The reinforcement of the HMWPE matrix with different concentrations of BGE1C proved to be very efficient. With the increase in the BGE1C weight fractions, the modulus increased significantly (Table 2). It was possible to obtain values of stiffness and strength in the bounds of human cortical bone, associated to a reasonable ductility. For 40%wt. of BGE1C, the composites became more brittle and exhibited a reduced UTS. This result may be associated with the deterioration of the filler/polymer interaction and formation of reinforcement agglomerates.

Table 1 - Results of the tensile tests for SEVA-C matrix injection moulded composites. BGE1 ($\phi < 10$ μm) was used as reinforcement.

Material	$E_{1\%}$ (GPa)	UTS (MPa)	ε_r (%)
SEVA-C	1.83 ± 0.12	38.9 ± 1.5	16.7 ± 4.4
SEVA-C + 10%BGE1	2.32 ± 0.13	37.1 ± 3.5	2.4 ± 0.6
SEVA-C + 20%BGE1	3.85 ± 0.55	32.3 ± 0.9	1.4 ± 0.1
SEVA-C + 30%BGE1	3.73 ± 0.84	28.9 ± 3.2	1.2 ± 0.2

Table 2 - Results of the tensile tests for HMWPE matrix injection moulded composites. Effect of the type of reinforcement (BGE1 or BGE1C – both with a $\phi < 10$ μm)

Material	$E_{1\%}$ (GPa)	UTS (MPa)	ε_r (%)
HMWPE	1.29 ± 0.40	29.0 ± 0.7	35.1 ± 2.8

HMWPE + 10%BGE1	1.59 ± 1.85	39.2 ± 0.9	21.8 ± 6.9
HMWPE + 20%BGE1	1.72 ± 0.18	39.2 ± 1.1	13.3 ± 2.5
HMWPE + 30%BGE1	2.11 ± 0.27	35.5 ± 0.7	11.4 ± 0.8
HMWPE + 40%BGE1	2.69 ± 0.30	35.4 ± 0.3	10.5 ± 1.7
HMWPE + 10%BGE1C	7.29 ± 0.55	131.1 ± 1.2	24.3 ± 4.6
HMWPE + 20%BGE1C	8.17 ± 0.68	123.0 ± 0.2	13.9 ± 1.8
HMWPE + 30%BGE1C	9.89 ± 0.45	127.1 ± 1.6	14.9 ± 3.8
HMWPE + 40%BGE1C	11.22 ± 0.39	116.9 ± 1.9	13.6 ± 4.1

SEM observation of the fracture surfaces of the composites suggested that there was no real bond between the bioactive glass particle and both matrixes, but the use of the TSE and of a smaller particle size of the filler (as compared to previous works[11]) allowed for a final uniform distribution of the filler, as well as for a significant increase in the modulus of the composites.

The bioactivity tests were only performed for HMWPE and SEVA-C matrixes reinforced with BGE1. The formation of an apatite-like layer was observed for SEVA-C composites containing at least 20% of BGE1, after 30 days immersion in a simulated body fluid (SBF). As immersion periods in SBF increase (up to 90 days), the thickness and the density of the apatite layer was enhanced (Fig. 1). Thus, the bioactivity of SEVA-C composites become relevant for BGE1 amounts of only 20% wt., for immersion periods higher than 30 days.

Figure 1. The formation of an apatite layer on the surface of an SEVA-C + 20% BGE1 composite after (a) 0, (b) 30, (c) 60 and 90 (d-surface, e-cross-section) days immersion in SBF.

Thin-film XRD analysis of the surface of the composite, after immersion for different time periods in SBF, evidenced the existence the characteristic main peaks of hydroxylapatite (HA), which were compared with the standard pattern of HA (JCPDS 9-432). The intensity of the apatite peaks increased gradually with greater immersion times, which proved the growth of the apatite layer on the composite (Fig. 2). These results are due to SEVA-C water uptaking capability, which favours the dissolution of the inner bioactive glass particles that leach Mg and Si (confirmed by ICP results) that create sites for the formation of Ca-P nuclei, with consequent precipitation of HA. This results in a decrease on the Ca and P concentration in the solution (Fig. 3).

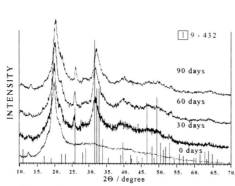

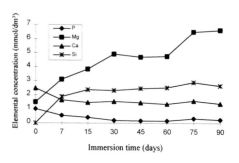

Figure 2. XRD patterns of film formed on SEVA-C+20% BGE1 composite after 0, 30, 60 and 90 days, immersion in SBF at 37°C.

Figure 3 Evolution of Ca, P, Si and Mg elemental concentration (ICP results) in the SBF solution as a function of the immersion time for 20% BGE1 reinforced SEVA-C composites.

On the contrary, for the HMWPE matrix composite, a weight fraction of at least 40% wt. was necessary to confer a bioactive character to the composites. Furthermore, this was true only if a careful polishing (with a 3-4 μm diamond paste) of the composites surface was carried out, prior to immersion, in order to expose the bioactive glass particles.

CONCLUSIONS

Both bioinert and biodegradable matrix composites reinforced with bioactive glasses and glass-ceramics were successfully produced. The mechanical performance of the composites, namely their stiffness and strength, was improved through the use of a stiffer filler (BGE1C). A modulus of 10.5 GPa and a tensile strength of 120 MPa (for HMWPE+40%BGE1C), in the bounds of human cortical bone, could be obtained. The formation of an apatite layer on the surface of both composites confirms that the composite exhibits *in vitro* bioactivity. The kinetics of the apatite film formation depends on the polymeric matrix and on its degradation and water uptaking capability, being faster, and happening for lower BGE1, amounts in SEVA-C based composites. The developed composites may find applications as bone-matching bioactive replacement materials.

REFERENCES

1. Hench LL, Wilson J, *An Introduction to Bioceramics*, World Scientific, Singapore, 1993: 1-24.
2. Hench LL, *J. Am. Ceram. Soc.* 1991; **74**: 1487-510.
3. Hench LL, La Torre GP, In: Yamamuro T, Kokubo T, Nakamura T, ed. *Bioceramics 5*, Japan: Kankokai Inc., 1992: 67-74.
4. Filgueiras MR, La Torre G., Hench LL, *J. Biomed. Mat. Res.* 1993; **27**: 445-453.
5. Cheol YK, Sungmin Kwon, In: Sedel L, Rey C, ed. *Bioceramics 10*. Oxford: Elsevier Science, 1997: 37-40.
6. Bonfield W., In: Kokubo T, Nakamura T, Miyaji F, ed. *Bioceramics 9*, Oxford: Elsevier Science, 1996: 11-13.
7. Reis RL, Cunha AM, Allan PS, Bevis MJ, *J. Polymers for Advanced Technologies* 1997; **16**: 263-277.
8. Reis RL, Cunha AM, Bevis MJ, *Medical Plastics and Biomaterials* 1997; **4**: 46-50.
9. Oliveira JM, Fernandes MH, Correia RN, In: Yamamuro T, Kokubo T, Nakamura T, ed. *Bioceramics 5*, Japan: Kankokai Inc., 1992: 7-14.
10. Oliveira JM, Fernandes MH, Correia RN, *Biomaterials* 1995; 16: 849-854.
11. Reis RL, Cunha AM, Fernandes MH, Correia RN, In: Sedel L, Rey C, ed. *Bioceramics 10*. Oxford: Elsevier Science, 1997: 415-418.

Bioceramics Volume 11, edited by R. Z. LeGeros and J.P. LeGeros
(Proceedings of the 11th International Symposium on Ceramics in Medicine)
New York, NY, USA, November 1998
© 1998 by World Scientific Publishing Co. Pte. Ltd.

PHYSICO-CHEMICAL AND HISTOLOGICAL BEHAVIOURS OF HOMOLOGOUS HYDROXYAPATITE/POLYMER COMPOSITE MEMBRANES

R. Martinetti[1], N. Zaghini[1], L. Dolcini[1], A. Krajewski[2], A. Ravaglioli[2], P. Cerrai[3], G.D. Guerra[3], M. Tricoli[3], A. Piattelli[4], A. Scarano[4].

[1] Fin-Ceramica Faenza S.r.l., via Ravegnana 186, I-48018 Faenza, Italy; [2] IRTEC-CNR, via Granarolo 64, I-48018 Faenza, Italy; [3] CSMPB-CNR, via Diotisalvi 2, I-56126 Pisa, Italy; [4] Scuola di Odontoiatria, Università di Chieti, via Dei Vestini 11, 66013 Chieti Scalo, Italy.

ABSTRACT

Membranes made with polymers are frequently used in the biomedical field for a guided regeneration of tissues. The authors have conceived a new type of membrane based on porous micro-granules of ceramic hydroxyapatite (HA) introduced into a new type of polymeric matrix. HA is useful for its biological behaviour and for modification of physico-chemical behaviour of the polymeric matrix. A comparison of the physico-chemical and histological behaviours between two similar periodontal membranes is the matter of this paper. A substantial difference involves the chemical nature of the polymeric matrix: one is the -poly(ε-caprolactone)-*block*-poly(oxyethylene)-*block*-poly(ε-caprolactone)- copolymer (PCL-POE-PCL); the other is a mechanical mixture of poly(ε-caprolactone) (PCL) and poly(ethylene glycol) (PEG). During resorption all the membranes made with both polymeric systems produce a diffused micro-porosity the dimensional range of which assures intercommunication to liquids and large molecules but does not allow cells of any kind to get through the membrane (at least for 2 months after implantation). In this way the bone guided regeneration is assured for a long time.

KEYWORDS: periodontal membranes; composites (polymer/ceramic); bone guided regeneration; copolymer or mixture.

INTRODUCTION

Studies[1,2] carried out at IRTEC-CNR and Fin-Ceramica Faenza Srl. have produced a new type of periodontal membrane which exhibits good performances in clinical trials. This membrane was particularly studied to serve as guided bone regeneration boundary[5]. The membrane obtained by mixing hydroxyapatite granules with a mechanical mixture of polyethylene glycol (PEG) and polycaprolactone (PCL) was recently proposed in the market. A variation in the preparation of the membrane[3] was to produce a composite with both organic components polymerised and not simply mixed. In this case the matrix component is the -poly(ε-caprolactone)-*block*-poly(oxyethylene)-

block-poly(ε-caprolactone)- copolymer (PCL-POE-PCL). This work concerns a comparison of physical and physico-chemical properties relative to particular properties of the two versions of the organic matrix of the membrane during its dissolution in the time. In particular, some characterisations such as the kinetics of dissolution and the transformation connected with the subjected degradation in simulating body fluid are considered. In this paper we will distinguish the two versions as two different membranes introducing the codes M1 for the membranes made with matrix PCL/PEG mechanical mixture and M2 for the membranes made with matrix PCL-POE-PCL block copolymer. Tests carried out *in vitro* and *in vivo* demonstrated that the composite membrane plays its role with an efficiency higher than the only polymeric membrane.

MATERIALS AND METHODS

The membranes are prepared by mixing in $CHCl_3$ HA granules and the polymeric component. After homogenisation $CHCl_3$ was completely extracted in vacuum. When implanted *in vivo* both types of membrane undergo in the time a complete re-absorption of the polymeric material in about 6 months through natural draining due to the body fluids. To simulate as best as possible the draining that would occur *in vivo*, the same dissolution test utilised in a previous work[3] was adopted. The simulation consists in submitting the samples (γ-ray sterilised) to dissolution rate test *in vitro* which consists in a steady flow rate (0.0032 cm^3 sec^{-1}), at constant temperature of 37°C, of physiological Phosphate Buffered Solution (PBS) (Table 1) and in changing it, with a fresh one, at constant intervals of time. For this tests a frequency of change every 7 days of PBS was chosen[3].

Table 1. Composition of the PBS solution

Chemicals	KCl	NaCl	KH_2PO_4	Na_2HPO_4	$MgCl_2 \cdot 6H_2O$	$CaCl_2 \cdot 2H_2O$
Mg/l	200	8000	200	1150	100	133

The samples, drawn out from the solution at every prefixed expiration date, were washed with distilled water, dried, weighed and examined by SEM (Leica Cambridge Stereoscan), so collecting kinetic dissolution rate data and microphotographs of the micro-morphological rearrangement of the membrane microstructure. The difference between the actual weight of each sample and the one it had at the beginning was calculated, obtaining a value for each sample; the mean value of such differences and the related standard deviation were calculated.

The same membranes were also submitted to examination of behaviour *in vivo*. 8 mm diameter bone defects were made through a borchole-sampling extractor machine in both tibias of 18 New Zeland rabbits previously anaesthetised with Ketalar and locally infiltrated with mepivacaine 3%. A screw implant was inserted in every defect and the implant was covered with a membrane: M1 on the left leg of the animal and M2 on the right one. Histological examination of the samples were carried out at different times (1-2-3-4-8-12 weeks) after sacrifice of three rabbits each time (6 samples). The samples were fixed and dehydrated in steps of immersions in a series of alcoholic solutions with increasing concentration, ranging from 70% to 100%. Each step went on for 24 hours. The dried samples were therefore infiltrated with monomer and polymerised with Technovit 7200 VLC resin (Kulzer, Wehrheim, Germany). The obtained solid blocks were sliced by the disc cutting system "Precise 1" (Assying, Rome, Italy) to obtain 70 μm thick samples.

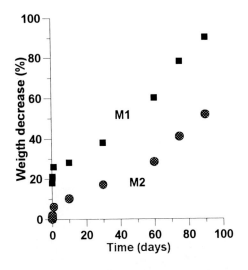

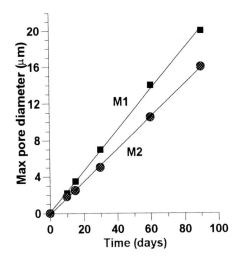

Figure 1 – Dissolution trend in PBS.   Figure 2 – Porosity evolution in PBS.

RESULTS AND CONCLUSIONS

In contact with the solution M1 membrane exhibits a very quick dissolution in a first step, followed by a rate dissolution only slightly greater than the one of M2 membrane (Figure 1). Therefore M1 membrane shows to dissolve *in vitro* faster than M2 one. This is attributed to the initial fast dissolution of PEG, very soluble in water, and to a consequent more developed surface of contact for the slower dissolution of PCL. The same test shows that both types of membrane produce a homogeneous diffused random distribution of elongated micro-pores the maximum size of which is deducible from Figure 2. Also the development of the porosity is slightly faster for M1 than for M2 as a consequence of the dissolution trend. In the chosen operative condition, some pores reach a maximum size of 20 μm after 90 days, but at that time the membrane is so thin to be evanescent (practically insubstantial or disappeared). This range of micro-porosity allows intercommunication to liquids and large molecules, but prevents every kind of cell from crossing the membrane for at least 2 months after implantation. So a correct progress of the guided bone regeneration process is assured for a long time. This behaviour in particular is useful in dentistry.

The same membranes were also tested *in vivo*. Histological examinations on the taken bioptic samples have shown a faster bone maturation in the presence of the M1 membrane. A difference of dissolution rate from one side to another of this membrane was evinced, attributed to inhomogeneous distribution of both components of the matrix (probably due to PEG residuals). Histological sections of M2 samples exhibit instead the presence of some poly-nucleated cells with a resorption faster than M1 one. The only possible explanation is the need to obtain an ester-hydrolysis process with H^+ capture by copolymer; this process probably interferes with the normal activity of macrophages and induces them to try to phagocytize the long copolymer molecule or the ester-hydrolysis products. Both types of membrane show however a general good course and are well tolerated by tissues up to a final complete dissolution of the polymeric matrix, with integration, remodelling and partial dissolution of the HA grains. Despite the *in vitro* tests, M1 shows to dissolve *in vivo* a bit slower than M2 (Figures 3 and 4). This may be due to the presence of phagic cells in the M2 membrane which metabolise faster the polymeric matrix.

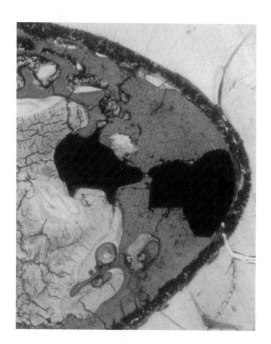 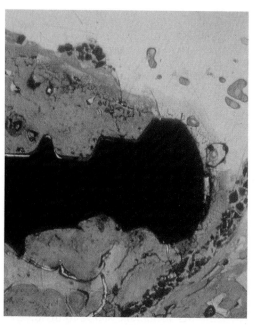

Figure 3 – M1 membrane 4 weeks after implantation. The integrity of the membrane and its adaptation to newformed bone is visible. No interface gaps are present. (12×).

Figure 4 – M2 membrane 4 weeks after implantation. A loss of membrane integrity is visible. New formed bone is present into the membrane volume. (15×).

The results o *in vivo* implants on rabbits show a complete re-adsorption in about 12 weeks, while in humans (periodontal implant) it is greater than 6 months. During the first times of *in vivo* test, only with M2 membrane some macrophages were detected.

REFERENCES

1. R. Martinetti, A. Ravaglioli, A. Krajewski, C. Mangano; Biomateriali 9 (1/2) (1995) 43-49.
2. C. Mangano, R. Martinetti, A. Ravaglioli; Fourth Euro-Ceramics, Vol. 8, Bioceramics, Edited by A. Ravaglioli (Faenza Editrice, 1995) 243-248.
3. R. Martinetti, L. Dolcini, A. Krajewski, A. Ravaglioli, P. Cerrai, G.D. Guerra; Proc. of 9th International Conference on Modern Materials & Technologies (CIMTEC '98, Florence, June 1998), SXI-5; L07, Edited by P. Vincenzini (*in press*).

Bioceramics Volume 11, edited by R. Z. LeGeros and J.P. LeGeros
(Proceedings of the 11th International Symposium on Ceramics in Medicine)
New York, NY, USA, November 1998
© 1998 by World Scientific Publishing Co. Pte. Ltd.

IDENTIFICATION OF THE AMORPHOUS PHASE IN PLASMA SPRAYED APATITE COATINGS

K. A. Gross[1,2], M. Phillips[2], B. Ben-Nissan[3], C. C. Berndt[4]

[1]Department of Materials Engineering, Monash University, Clayton 3168, Australia. [2]Microstructural Analysis Unit, University of Technology, Sydney, Australia; [3]Department of Chemistry, Materials and Forensic Sciences, University of Technology, Sydney, Australia; [4]Department of Materials Science and Engineering, SUNY at Stony Brook, USA.

ABSTRACT

Most hydroxyapatite coated implants produced by plasma spraying contain the amorphous phase which affects the longevity of the coatings. It is thus necessary to measure, locate and quantify this in the microstructure for quality control and analysis of retrieved implants. Several methods are available both for micro-characterization and analysis on the calcium phosphate coatings. These techniques include microscopy (optical, secondary electron and cathodoluminescence), spectroscopy (infra-red and Raman), thermal analysis and X-ray diffraction. The amorphous phase produces peak broadening in infra-red, however the interpretation is complex due to the contribution of residual stresses. Raman spectroscopy yields an individual peak located at 950 cm^{-1}. Crystallization events in thermal analysis indicate that the chemical composition of the amorphous phase may be hydroxyl rich or hydroxyl depleted. The most useful of these techniques is microscopy where the location, distribution, size and quantity of these regions can be readily ascertained. The information from these techniques will be discussed to reveal the nature and facilitate identification of the amorphous phase.

KEYWORDS: amorphous, characterization, microstructure, hydroxyapatite, plasma spraying

INTRODUCTION

Crystallinity is an important parameter to measure insofar that it influences the degradation of hydroxyapatite coatings and hence the stabilization of dental and orthopaedic biomedical devices. In the past, crystallinity has been defined as a measure of crystal size and/or lattice perfection in reference to chemically synthesized homogeneous powders or the inorganic fraction of bone.[1] The measurement was mainly performed with X-ray diffraction and supplemented with infra-red spectroscopy. A lower crystallinity material was described by a lower diffraction peak intensity with respect to the background in X-ray diffraction patterns or a loss of resolution of the various vibrational modes in the PO_4 bands in infra-red spectra.[2]

Crystallinity in reference to coatings, produced by plasma spraying hydroxyapatite, includes both the lower crystal perfection caused by cooling from high temperatures and an amorphous phase, which like a glass, has no long range order. The adopted definition of crystallinity in plasma sprayed coatings refers to the amount of amorphous phase present in the coatings. Characteristics of the amorphous and the crystalline phase will be identified to enable macro or micro characterization of the coatings.

METHODS

Coatings used for analysis include those produced at The Thermal Spray Laboratory, State University of New York at Stony Brook and a commercially available coating.

Powder was prepared for thermal analysis, infra-red spectroscopy, and X-ray diffraction by crushing in a mortar and pestle. The coating otherwise was polished to a surface finish of 0.05µm for identification of amorphous regions with Raman spectroscopy or microscopy.

X-ray diffraction was conducted with Cu Kα radiation over a two theta range of 20 to 40 degrees using a step size of 0.02 degrees and an acquisition time of 4 seconds per step.

Tranparent tablets were produced by compressing a homogeneous mixture of the prepared powder with 1 wt.% KBr. This tablet was then subjected to infra-red spectroscopy analysis set to a resolution of 4 cm^{-1}.

Heat exchange was monitored upon heating at a rate of 10°C/min with differential thermal analysis in a stagnant air atmosphere.

Laser-Raman microanalyses were conducted using the argon green line at 514.5 nm, with a laser power of 20 mW; exciting wavelength of 514.532 nm. A spectral slit width of 3.12 cm^{-1} was selected. Spectra from the irradiated area, using a spot diameter of 1 µm^2, were recorded within the range of 800 and 1200 cm^{-1} with an acquisition time of 200 seconds.

Cathodoluminescence (CL) microanalysis was performed using an Oxford Instruments MonoCL2 CL system attached to a JEOL 35C SEM equipped with a Microspec Wavelength Dispersive X-ray Spectrometer. Panchromatic CL images were collected using a Link ISIS digital image capture system at 1024 x 800 pixels with a 100 µsec dwell time per pixel.

RESULTS AND DISCUSSION

X-ray diffraction of a plasma sprayed coatings with a medium crystallinity exhibited a decrease in diffraction peak intensity (Fig. 1). Hydroxyapatite is identified by the main peak intensity at 31.8° whereas the amorphous phase is detected by a broad peak centred at 30-31°.

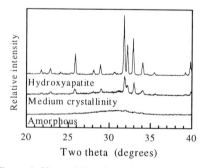

Figure 1. X-ray diffraction of an amorphous phase, medium crystallinity coating and hydroxyapatite.

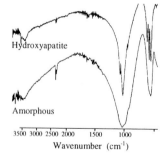

Figure 2. Infra-red spectra of an amorphous phase and hydroxyapatite.

This broad emission has been detected in other synthetic amorphous calcium phosphates with different compositions[3] and is representative of a short range repetitive unit such as the bond length between the oxygen and the phosphorus in the phosphate groups. Similarly, infra-red spectra of the amorphous phase contains broad emission bands representing a wide variation of vibrations possible in the more unrestricted volume within the amorphous phase (Fig. 2). The broad emission represents contribution both from the stressed lattice and the amorphous phase.

While it is possible to distinguish different calcium phosphate phases with X-ray diffraction in their crystalline form, the differences in the short range order are very minimal. Energy X-ray absorption fine structure experiments conducted on acidic and basic calcium phosphates in the amorphous state have revealed very similar spectra.[4]

Raman microprobe on the crystalline and the amorphous areas within the coating produced peaks centred at 958 cm^{-1} and 950 cm^{-1} respectively (Fig. 3). This is in agreement with previously conducted work.[7] The shift in the Raman band and the high intensity signal suggests that the components of residual stress and amorphous phase content would be easier to differentiate. Since tricalcium phosphate also exhibits a peak at 950 cm^{-1}, X-ray diffraction must be used in conjunction with Raman spectroscopy.

Differential thermal analysis (DTA) of hydroxyapatite (HAp) and the amorphous phase are similar except for a crystallization peak at 500 and 700 °C (Fig. 4). These peaks suggest that the amorphous phase does not represent fine crystallites but a random positioning of the phosphate groups and calcium ions which after a rearrangement are able to form a stable hydroxyapatite. The two exothermic peaks are indicative of crystallization of a hydroxyl rich amorphous phase to hydroxyapatite at about 500 °C and crystallization of a hydroxyl deficient amorphous phase to oxyapatite (OAp) at 720 °C.[5] Plasma sprayed coatings containing the amorphous phase can thus contain localized areas with different hydroxyl ion concentrations.

Plasma sprayed coatings involve heat transfer through the coating which can promote the formation of small crystals. Identification of the amorphous phase by microscopy can lead to different interpretations of an amorphous phase. At the light microscopy magnification level, it is possible to distinguish the two areas based on the higher reflected light intensity from the crystalline phase (Fig. 5a). The amorphous phase (darker grey) is nonuniformly distributed within the coating and located around crystalline areas and adjacent to the substrate.[6]

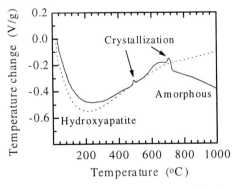
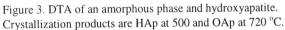
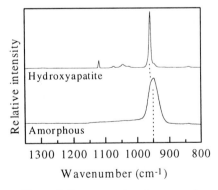

Figure 3. DTA of an amorphous phase and hydroxyapatite. Crystallization products are HAp at 500 and OAp at 720 °C.

Figure 4. Raman spectra of an amorphous phase exhibits a broad phosphate band.

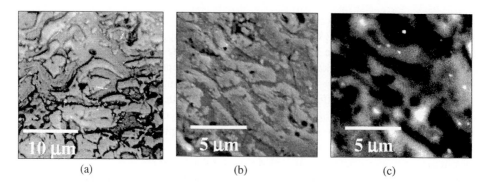

(a)   (b)   (c)

Figure 5. Microstructures of hydroxyapatite coatings in cross section as observed by (a) optical microscopy, (b) scanning electron microscopy and (c) cathodoluminescence microscopy. The lighter areas in (a) and (b) represent the crystalline phase and in (c) represent the amorphous regions. Field of view in (a) is 25 x 25 μm and in (b) and (c) is 12 x 12 μm.

Crystalline regions in a secondary electron image also appear lighter (Fig. 5b). The difference in intensity between the crystalline and the amorphous phase is lower than in light microscopy. The coating microstructure clearly shows long crystalline lamellae surrounded by the amorphous phase in a 70 wt.% crystallinity coating.

Cathodoluminescence microscopy uses the different light emission of the two phases during exposure to an electron beam. The light response from the amorphous phase is significantly higher that the crystalline phase. This allows a map to be made of the amorphous regions (Fig. 5c). Since the light is also emitted by subsurface amorphous areas, the cathodoluminescence image may not correspond exactly with the secondary electron image.

Cathodoluminescence microscopy can be perfomed on an unprepared flat surface like a histological section. This tool offers a means of detecting the amorphous phase not possible previously.

CONCLUSION

To completely identify the amorphous phase it is important to use several techniques. It is recommended that differential thermal analysis be used in conjunction with X-ray diffraction and light spectroscopy (either infra-red or Raman). Microscopy can then be used to identify the location of the amorphous phase within the microstructure of the coating.

ACKNOWLEDGEMENT
One of the authors (CCB) acknowledges support from NSF-MRSEC DMR9632570.

REFERENCES
1. Le Geros RZ. *Prog Crystal Growth Charact* 1981; **4**:1-45.
2. Le Geros RZ, Shirra WP, Miravite MA, Le Geros JP. *Coll Int CNRS* 1973, **230**:105-115.
3. Posner AS, Betts F. *Accts Chem Res* 1975, **8**:273-281.
4. Nelson LS, Holt C, Harries JE, Hukins DWL. *Physica B*, 1989, **158(1-3)**: 105-6.
5. Gross KA, Gross V, Berndt CC. *J Amer Cer Soc* 1998, **81(1)**:106-12.
6. Gross KA, Berndt CC *et al. Int J Oral Maxillofac Implants*, 1997, **12**:589-597.
7. Weinlaender M, Beumer J, Kenney EB *et al. J Mater Sci: Mater in Med* 1992, **3**:397-401.

Bioceramics Volume 11, edited by R. Z. LeGeros and J.P. LeGeros
(Proceedings of the 11th International Symposium on Ceramics in Medicine)
New York, NY, USA, November 1998
© 1998 by World Scientific Publishing Co. Pte. Ltd.

HA/ACP RATIOS IN CALCIUM PHOSPHATE COATINGS ON DENTAL AND ORTHOPEDIC IMPLANTS: EFFECT ON PROPERTIES

R. Z. LeGeros, Y. E. Kim, R. Kijkowska, V. Zurita, C. Bleiwas, P.-Y. Huang,
B. Edwards*, F. Dimaano**, J. P. LeGeros

New York University College of Dentistry, 345 East 24th Street, New York, NY
*Howmedica R&D, New Jersey; **Osteonics, Inc., New Jersey

ABSTRACT

Plasma-sprayed 'HA' coatings on dental and orthopedic implants as well as coatings deposited on metal substrates by other methods were characterized using x-ray diffraction (XRD), infrared (IR) spectroscopy and scanning electron microscopy. Dissolution properties were investigated in acidic buffer (0.1M KAc, pH 6, 37°C). Differences in HA/ACP ratios were observed between: (1) coatings deposited on coupons compared to those deposited on cylindrical dental implants; (2) between inner and outer coating layers; (3) among coatings on dental and orthopedic implants. ACP component affects the characteristics of the XRD patterns and IR spectra and greatly affect the extent of dissolution of the coating. Significant change on surface morphology before and after exposure to acid solution were shown by SEM. The stability of implant coating (and ultimately, of the implant) *in vivo* may be dependent on the HA/ACP ratio.

Keywords: hydroxyapatite, amorphous calcium phosphate, coating, implant

INTRODUCTION

Calcium phosphate ceramics, in spite of their desirable properties (biocompatibility, osteoconductivity, bioactivity, forms direct attachment to bone [3,7,11,17]) lack the strength necessary for load-bearing areas [7]. Calcium phosphate coated implants is believed to combine the bioactivity of the ceramic and the strength of the metal. Methods of depositing coatings on metal substrates include: ion-sputtering, electrochemical deposition, plasma-spray [5,6,9,18,19]. Plasma-spraying with hydroxyapatite (HA) ceramic as the source, is the method used to coat commercial dental and orthopedic implants.

Many studies have demonstrated that 'HA'-coated implants had a higher degree of bone attachment, higher interfacial strength and accelerated fixation [2,3,6,7]. In addition, the coating minimize the leakage of potentially harmful metal ions [4]. However, a small number of studies observed implant failure attributed to the resorption of the coating [1,8]. Unfortunately, analysis of coating composition for either 'successful' or 'failed' coated implants were not available. In addition, reported analyses of coatings have not been quantitative [6,16]. The purpose of our on-going studies on coatings [9-15] is to determine their quantitative composition and determine the effect of the ACP component (or HA/ACP ratio) on the properties of the coating.

MATERIALS and METHODS

Coatings on coupons were analyzed directly with x-ray diffraction (Philips APD 3520). Coatings on dental implants were analyzed using the in situ (i.e., without scraping) method developed by LeGeros JP [12,13]. IR absorption analyses were made on pellets prepared by mixing about 1 mg of powdered coating and 300 mg KBr (IR grade) pressed at 12,000 psi. Standard hydroxyapatite (HA), TetCP, α-TCP, ß-TCP were prepared as described previously [9]. Amorphous calcium phosphate, ACP, was prepared by adjusting the plasma-spraying parameters using HA ceramic as source material (Fig. 1). HA/ACP mixtures were prepared by intimately mixing HA ceramic and ACP (plasma-sprayed) in the ratios: 100/0, 70/30, 50/50, 30/70, 1/100. These mixtures were also analyzed similarly as the coatings. Dissolution properties were investigated in acidic buffer (0.1M KAc, pH 6, 37°C) by monitoring the calcium ions released into the buffer with time, using an ion-selective electrode. Coated dental and orthopedic implants were purchased from manufacturers.

RESULTS and DISCUSSION

Coatings on dental and orthopedic implants were shown to consist crystalline (principally of HA, with small amounts of TetCP, α-TCP, ß-TCP, and sometime CaO) and non-crystalline (amorphous calcium phosphate, ACP) phases. For the coatings on the dental implants, the HA/ACP ratios varied from 28/72 to 66/34 (Table 1).

The HA component was about 95% of the crystalline phases, regardless of the HA/ACP ratio. This figure is sometimes misleading used to describe a coating as 95% HA (when actually this means 95% of the crystalline phase is HA, the coating may have more than 50% ACP phase).

Table 1: Coating Composition of Dental Implants

Implant #	% Crystalline phases (mean)	%ACP (mean)	Composition of Crystalline Phases
A	48	52	*HA + TetCP + CaO
B	66	34	*HA
C	30	70	*HA + TetCP + α-, ß-TCP
D	28	72	*HA + TetCP
E	42	58	*HA + TetCP
F	57	43	*HA + TetCP + α-, ß-TCP + CaO
G	50	50	*HA + TetCP + α-, ß-TCP + CaO
H	37	63	*HA + TetCP + α-, ß-TCP + CaO

*ACP - amorphous calcium phosphate; *HA: 95% ± 2% of the crystalline phases.*

This variability may be largely due to the difference in plasma-spraying parameters since the manufacturer use HA ceramic source of similar composition and crystallinity.

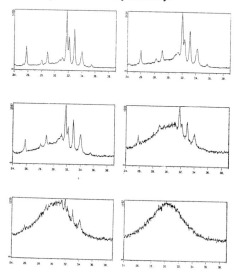

Fig. 1: XRD patterns of coatings showing effect of plasma-spray parameters on coating composition.

Composition of coatings depended on the method used for depositing the coating. Coating composition by ion-sputtering (by laser or radio frequency): ACP; by electrodeposition, ACP, DCPD (dicalcium phosphate dihydrate), OCP (octacalcium phosphate), AP (calcium deficient apatite), depending on the pH and temperature of the reaction; by plasma-spray: HA + ACP + TetCP + α-TCP + ß-TCP and sometimes CaO (Table 1).

A composition gradient was also observed: the HA/ACP ratio was lower in the inner layer (layer closest to the metal substrate) compared to the outer layer (furthest away from the substrate). This difference maybe due to the temperature difference between the metal substrate and the coating.

The coating on a coupon (presumably plasma sprayed under similar conditions as the dental implants) had a higher HA/ACP compared to the actual coating on the cylindrical implant. This difference maybe due to the difference in geometry between the coupon and the implant.

The HA component of the coating has lower crystallinity, shown by broader diffraction peaks (Figs. 2A,2B,2C), compared to the HA ceramic source (Fig. 3A). The broadening observed is not due to the presence of ACP; as can be seen from the HA/ACP mixture (Fig. 3B) and the HA on coating (Fig.2).

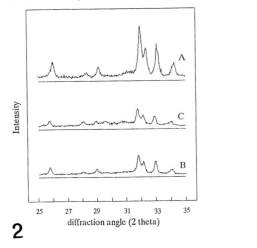

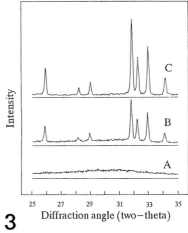

Fig. 2: X-ray diffraction patterns of plasma-sprayed 'HA' coatings on different orthopedic implants.
Fig. 3: X-ray diffraction patterns of amorphous calcium phosphate, ACP (A); 50/50 mixture of HA ceramic and ACP (B) and HA ceramic (C)

The dissolution properties of the coating depended on the HA/ACP ratio, the higher the ratio, the lower the extent of dissolution, whether from coating (Fig. 4) or the mechanical mixtures of HA and ACP (Fig.5).

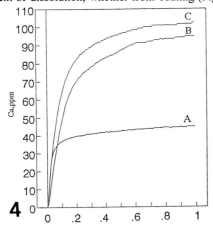

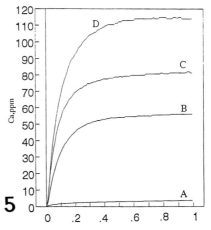

Fig. 4: Comparative dissolution (ppm Ca with time, hrs) of coatings on orthopedic implants in acidic buffer.
Fig. 5: Comparative dissolution of HA ceramic (A); HA/ACP mixture, 50/50 (B) and 30/70 (C); ACP (D).

X-ray diffraction analyses of the coating composition before and after exposure to the acidic buffer show the preferential dissolution of the more soluble calcium phosphate phases: ACP, α-TCP and ß-TCP (Fig. 6). SEM analyses showed marked changes in surface morphology before (Fig. 7A) and after acid exposure (Fig. 7B). After acid exposure, wide canals were observed. It is logical to assume that the canals were formerly occupied by the more soluble calcium phosphate phases (principally ACP). Therefore, coatings with very low HA/ACP ratio are more susceptible to lamination or 'lifting off' of the coating, which may eventually lead to implant failure.

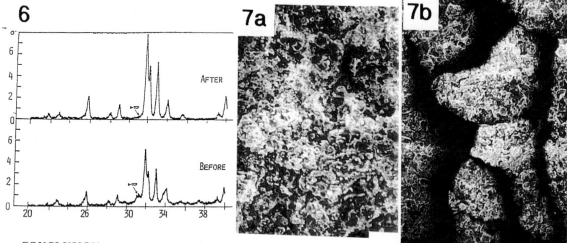

CONCLUSION

The ACP (i.e., HA/ACP ratio) component of the implant coating has a significant effect on the properties of the coating (affects broadening of the XRD peaks and resolution of the IR spectra). More importantly, it increases the extent of dissolution. Instability of the plasma-sprayed 'HA' coating is related to the ACP component: the lower the HA/ACP ratio, the greater the instability.

Acknowledgements

The technical collaboration of Drs. D. Mijares and M. Retino are gratefully acknowledged.

REFERENCES

1. Bloebaum RD, Dupont JA. *J Arthop* **8**: 97-102, 1993.
2. Cook SD, Thomas KA, Dalton JE, Volkman RK, Whitecloud TS, Kay JE. *J Biomed Mater Res* **26**: 989-1001, 1992.
3. Daculsi G, LeGeros RZ, Deudon C. Scan Micros **4**:309-314, 1990.
4. Ducheyne P, Healy KE. *J Biomed Mater Res* **22**: 1127-1163, 1988.
5. Ducheyne P, Van Raemdonck W, Heughebaert JC, Heughebaert M. *Biomaterials* **7**: 97-103, 1986.
6. Koch B, wolke JGC, deGroot K. *J Biomed Mater Res* **24**: 665-667, 1990.
7. Jarcho M. Lin Orthopaed **157**: 259-278, 1981.
8. Johnson BW. *CDA J* **20**: 33-41, 1992.
9. LeGeros RZ. Calcium Phosphates in Oral Biology and Medicine. Monographs in Oral Sciences. Vol. 15. Myers H (ed). S. Karger, Basel 1991.
10. LeGeros RZ. Clin Mat **14**: 65-88, 1993.
11. LeGeros RZ, Daculsi G. In: Handbook of Bioactive Ceramics. Vol. 2. Yamamuro N, Hench L, Wilson-Hench J (eds). CRC Press, pp. 17-28, 1990.
12. LeGeros, JP, LeGeros RZ, Burgess A, Edwards B., Zitelli J. In: *Characterization and Performance of Calcium Phosphate Coatings for Implants.* ASTM STP 1196. Horowitz E, Parr JE (Eds), American Society for Testing Materials, Philadephia, pp. 33-42, 1994.
13. LeGeros RZ, LeGeros JP, Kim Y, Kijkowska R, Zheng R, Bautista C. *Bioceramics: Mat and Appl* **48**: 173-189, 1995.
14. LeGeros JP, LeGeros RZ. *17th Annual Meeting of the Society for Biomaterials,* abstr 192, 1991.
15. LeGeros RZ, Kijkowska R, Zheng R. *19th Annual Meeting of the Society of Biomaterials,* abstr. 221, 1993.
16. Maxian SH, Zawadsky JP, Dunn MG. *J Biomed Mater Res* **27**: 111-117, 1993.
17. Osborn JF, Newesely H. *Biomaterials* **1**: 108-111, 1980.
18. Redepenning J, Schlessinger T, Burnham S, Lippiello L, Miyano J. J Biomed Mat Res **30**:287-294, 1996.
19. Serekian P. In: Hydroxylapatite Coatings in Orthopedic Surgery. Geesink RGT, Manley MT (eds). Raven Press, pp. 81-87, 1993.

Bioceramics Volume 11, edited by R. Z. LeGeros and J.P. LeGeros
(Proceedings of the 11th International Symposium on Ceramics in Medicine)
New York, NY, USA, November 1998
© 1998 by World Scientific Publishing Co. Pte. Ltd.

THE GENERATION OF A DENSE (Mg^{2+}, CO_3^{2-})-CONTAINING APATITE FILM CHEMICALLY BONDED TO TITANIUM DIRECTLY FROM AQUEOUS SOLUTIONS

Panjian Li and Frank Matthews

Applied Research, Johnson & Johnson Professional Inc., 325 Paramount Drive
Raynham, MA 02767, USA

ABSTRACT

The previous studies have demonstrated that a large number of TiOH groups present in a titanium oxide prepared by a sol-gel process can initiate the formation of apatite in both simulated and true body fluids[1,2]. The finding is the basis of the chemical treatment of titanium to achieve surface bioactivity by creating TiOH groups. It has been reported that the treatment of titanium in 5-10 M NaOH can convert the surface to a sodium titanate. The sodium titanate changes to a hydrated titanium oxide in the simulated and true physiological solutions which then stimulates the formation of apatite [3,4]. We report in this paper an alternative for growing an apatite film on titanium. The novel process combines the creation of TiOH groups and the formation of apatite in a single metastable solution that is exposed to an artificial atmosphere consisting of CO_2 and O_2. The reactions among these three components (titanium, solution and artificial atmosphere) result in the transformation of titanium surface into the apatite that has important features of bone mineral.

KEYWORDS: titanium implants, apatite coating, bioactive surface, simulated body fluid.

Introduction

Commercially-pure titanium and the alloy Ti6Al4V have demonstrated superior biocompatibility. However, they are not bioactive; namely they can neither conduct bone formation nor form a chemical bond to bone. The use of plasma-sprayed hydroxyapatite (HA) coating has proven to be an effective way to add bioactivity to titanium implants so that they can acquire better bone apposition and stronger fixation. However, concern about de-bonding of the plasma-sprayed HA coating and the potential of producing ceramic particles has impeded wider acceptance of this coating. Efforts have been made to develop alternative methods for producing high quality HA coating on titanium. The methods based on metastable aqueous solutions, or biomimetic methods, are beginning to show considerable promise because they are much simpler and easier to control than high temperature plasma spraying [5,6]. More importantly, these low temperature solution methods can produce superior HA coatings and they can be very efficient for generating HA on those implants with intricate surfaces such as bead-coated porous surfaces. All biomimetic methods reported so far require a pretreatment of titanium in order for HA to be formed. In this work, a novel method is reported for generating a dense (Mg^{2+}, CO_3^{2-})-containing apatite film on titanium directly from an aqueous solution without any pretreatment.

Materials and Methods

Ti6Al4V disks 14.6 mm diameter and 2.0 mm thick were gradually ground and polished down to 1.0 μm surface finish by diamond powders. The samples were cleaned and rinsed with de-ionized water. They were dried at 60 °C for 1 hour before being soaked in an aqueous solution. The solution was 0.15 M NaCl supplemented with other electrolytes present in the body. These electrolytes include 2.8 mM $CaCl_2$, 1.75 mM K_2HPO_4, 1.88 mM $MgCl_2$ and 27.0 mM $NaHCO_3$. The solution was buffered at pH 7.2 using tris and 1.0 N HCl. After reacting with the solution at 37 °C under a controlled environment in a glass reactor for 2 and 4 days, the Ti6Al4V specimens were removed from the solution, rinsed with de-ionized water and dried at 60 °C. The samples were analyzed using various techniques that include diffuse deflectance infrared Fourier transform spectroscopy (DRIFTS), scanning electron microscopy-energy dispersive X-ray (SEM-EDX), thin-film x-ray diffraction (TF-XRD), Auger emission spectroscopy (ASE) and X-ray photo electron spectroscopy (XPS). A tensile detachment test was also conducted to measure adhesion between the apatite film and the titanium substrate.

Results and Discussion

Figure 1 includes a SEM micrograph of the surface of a Ti6Al4V disk that reacted with the solution for 4 days. The presence of a calcium phosphate film was confirmed by EDX analysis, indicating successful conversion of the titanium surface to calcium phosphate. Both EDX and AES analyses suggested incorporation of Mg^{2+} in the calcium phosphate. The thickness of the calcium phosphate film was estimated to be about 0.5 μm by SEM examination on a cross-section of the sample. The calcium phosphate was identified to be in an amorphous form by TF-XRD. DRIFTS analysis showed that the amorphous calcium phosphate was apatitic and contained carbonate groups (Fig.1-bottom). There were two types of carbonate groups distinguished by their location in apatite. One was located in the sites for phosphate groups while another substituted for OH groups. Thus, the apatite formed on titanium had important characteristics of bone mineral. The AES compositional profile of a Ti6Al4V sample after being soaked in the solution for 2 days revealed a transitional zone between the apatite and titanium oxide. The continuity in composition indicated a chemical bonding of the apatite to the titanium oxide. Both XPS and AES analyses demonstrate that the solution-titanium reactions leading to the formation of apatite film included the incorporation of phosphate into the titanium oxyhydroxide (TiOOH) developed on the titanium surface. Adhesion strength between the apatite film and the substrate was measured to be in excess of 30 MPa in a tensile detachment. Failure generally occurred at the apatite-glue interface.

Conclusion

A dense amorphous (Mg^{2+}, CO_3^{2-})-containing apatite film can be formed on titanium surface at 37 °C in 4 days directly from an aqueous solution similar to body fluids. The apatite formation does not require any pretreatment of titanium. The bonding between the apatite and titanium is chemical in nature.

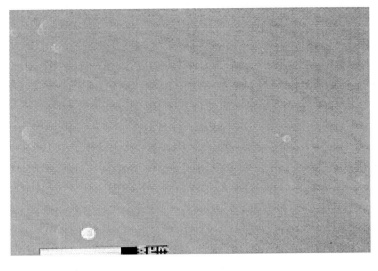

(bar = 5 μ m)

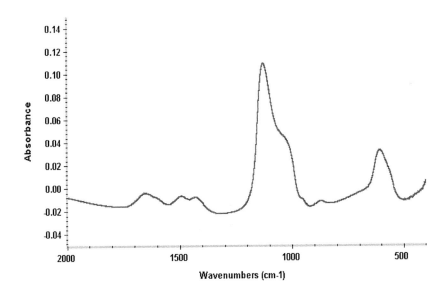

Figure 1. A SEM micrograph (top) and DRIFTS spectrum for the surface of a Ti6Al4V sample after being soaked in the solution for 4 days.

REFERENCES

1. Li P, de Groot K. *J Biomed Mater Res* 1993; 27:1495-1500.
2. Li P, de Groot K, Kokubo T. *J Am Ceram Soc* 1994; 77:1307-1315.
3. Hata K, Kokubo T, Nakamura T, Yamamuro T. *J Am Ceram Soc* 1995; 78:1049-1053.
4. Yan WQ, Nakamura T, Kobayashi M, Kokubo T, Kim HM, Miyaji F. *Bioceramics* 1996; 9:305-308.
5. Kokubo T, Miyaji F, Kim HM, Nakamura T. *J Am Ceram Soc* 1996; 79:1127-1129.
6. Campbell AA, Fryxell GE, Linehan JC and Graff GL. *J Biomed Mater* 1996; 32:111-118.

Bioceramics Volume 11, edited by R. Z. LeGeros and J.P. LeGeros
(Proceedings of the 11th International Symposium on Ceramics in Medicine)
New York, NY, USA, November 1998
© 1998 by World Scientific Publishing Co. Pte. Ltd.

SUPERPLASTIC Ti-ALLOY TOUGHENED HYDROXYAPATITE

Toru Nonami, Hiroshi Taoda, Akira Kamiya, Katsuyoshi Naganuma, Tsutomu Sonoda,
Tetsuya Kameyama

National Industrial Research Institute of Nagoya, 1-1 Hirate-cho, Kita-ku, Nagoya 462, Japan

ABSTRACT

In this study, we attempted to implant hydroxyapatite granules into the superplastic Ti-4.5Al-3V-2Fe-2Mo substrate. In order to improve the biocompatibility of the alloy, pure titanium film was coated on the surface by reactive DC sputtering method in advance. The coated film was approximately 3 μm in thickness. Hydroxyapatite granules in 32-38 μm diameter were spread over the substrate and pressed to implant the granules into the substrate. This was achieved at 750 °C or 800 °C, 17 MPa for 10 min.

Considerable cracks were observed at the surface of the substrate which had been implanted granules at 750 °C. It was supporsed that the film was deformed locally by implanting granules, and it tore. However, at 800 °C, no cracks were found and the granules were implanted satisfactory. The ductility of pure titanium at 800 °C is higher than at 750 °C, the film was expanded equally. The only tops of the granules remained exposed and they were firmly stuck in the substrate. The hydroxyapatite implanted Ti-alloy composite are expected to be useful for biomaterials, such as artificial bones and dental roots.

KEY WORDS: Hydroxyapatite, granule, implant, superplastic, Ti-alloy, sputtering

INTRODUCTION

As artificial hip joints and artificial roots need intensities, metals such as stainless and titanium are mainly used as their materials. However, metals do not have satisfactory affinities for living bodies.

Having biological affinity, hydroxyapatite (hereafter named HAp) is suitable for biological hard tissues[1]. However, because of its poor mechanical properties, particularly low fracture toughness, it cannot be used under a heavy load and its application is limited. If HAp can be coated onto a metallic material, such a composite may be a good biomaterial in terms of its affinity for a living body and high mechanical strength[2,3]. Recently, by utilizing a special characteristic of superplastic Ti-4.5Al-3V-2Fe-2Mo-alloy that it is transformative, we have developed the method to implant HAp granules into the surface of Ti-alloy[4,5].

However, Ti-alloy contains aluminium and vanadium etc., which are potentially harmful to human bodies. On the other hand, pure titanium has been utilized as a biomaterial. In a previous study[6], we developed a method of coating the alloy surface with pure titanium film by DC sputtering in argon atmosphere, in order to improve the dental applicability of the alloy. In this study, we tried to implant HAp granules into the pure titanium coated Ti-alloy substrate.

EXPERIMENTS

Reactive DC suputtering

A planar magnetron sputtering system (ANELVA Corp. type SPE-210H) with a stainless steel chamber 200 mm in diameter and 130 mm in height was used. The planar target used for this study was a 99.99 mass% pure titanium disk 100 mm in diameter. Ti-4.5Al-3V-2Fe-2Mo substrate[7] (NKK, SP-700, hereafter named Ti-alloy) of size 0.49 mm x 20 mm x 20 mm cleaned with organic solvent was mounted on a water-cooled substrate holder.

The argon gas was introduced into the chamber which was evacuated to 1×10^{2} Pa or loss in advance. The pre-sputtering between the target and the shutter in the atmosphere of pure argon was carried out to clean the target surface. Titanium film was coated by reactive DC sputtering for 18min. Discharge voltage and current were at 400V and 1A, respectively. (hereafter named Ti-Ti-alloy)

Implantation

HAp was granulated with the spray-dryer. And the granules were heated for 3 hours at 1200 °C, and were sifted 32-38 μm. The specimens were coated with grease and granules adhered to its surface.

By using a hot press, HAp granules were implanted into the Ti-alloy substrates. Specimens were set in the hot press, and pressed under a pressure of 17 MPa for 10 min at 750 °C or 800 °C. Diameter of granules (b) were measured using an optical microscope. The height of projected part of granules (a) were measured using surface analyzer. The implantation ratio (%) of granules were calculated by the following Eq. (1) . 30 granules were measured to get an average of data points.

$$\text{Implantation ratio (\%)} = (b - a) \ / \ b \times 100 \tag{1}$$

RESULTS AND DISCUSSIONS

Appearance and surface Morphology of Ti-Ti-alloy

The film appeared to be uniform and adhesive. The surface of the Ti-Ti-alloy showed a metallic gloss, and observed to consist of uniformly accumulated submicron-sized particles. Upon more detailed observation of the topography of the accumulated deposit, pits and bumps on the order of several microns were found. These might reflect pits and bumps existing originally on the substrate surface. The film might be deposited on the alloy substrate with high topographic fidelity to the substrate surface. The thickness of the film was approximately 3 μm.

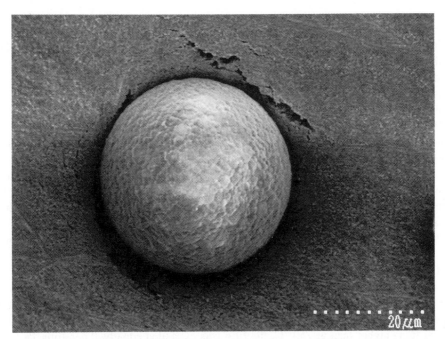

Figure 1. SEM micrograph of Ti-Ti-alloy. HAp granules were implanted at 750 °C for 10 min with 17 MPa.

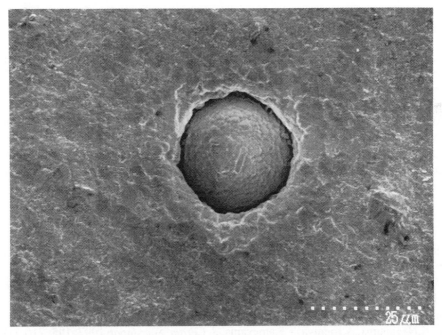

Figure 2. SEM micrograph of Ti-Ti-alloy. HAp granules were implanted at 800 °C for 10 min with 17 MPa.

Implantation

After implanting, aluminium, iron and titanium were detected at the surface of Ti-alloy by EDS spectra. On the other hand, only titanium was present at the surface of Ti-Ti-alloy. Granules were not deformed at a uniform implantation of every specimen. The surface of specimen showed a metallic gloss, and a reaction wasn't observed with shape.

The implantation ratio of HAp granules in Ti-alloy surface was 100 % at 750 °C, but that of Ti-Ti-alloy was 35 %. As the ductility of pure titanium is lower than that of Ti-alloy, transformative resistance of pure titanium is high. Therefore it is considered that those granules were prevented from being implanted.

Figure 1 presents SEM micrograph of the surface of HAp implanted Ti-Ti-alloy. Considerable cracks were found around the implanted granules, the part where is hollowed by implanting the granules. In side of the cracks, aluminium and titanium were detected by EDS. It is clear that Ti-alloy is exposed on the surface.

It is considered that the cracks are generated only on the film of pure titanium. This is judged by the cracks thickness. Therefore it is supposed that the film was deformed locally by implanting granules, and then it tore.

On the other hand, at 800 °C, there were entirely no cracks, and the implantation ratio of granules was 100 % as shown in Figure 2. Generally, pure titanium is deformed super-plastically under high temperature, which is more than approximately 800 °C. Thus, the ductility of pure titanium at 800 °C is higher than at 750 °C, the film was expanded equally. Therefore the local deformation of the film was avoided. Consequently, it is supposed that no cracks were generated on the film. As the mentioned above, HAp granules could be implanted suitably into the Ti-Ti-alloy at 800 °C.

CONCLUSIONS

In this study, pure titanium film was coated on the surface of Ti-4.5Al-3V-2Fe-2Mo by reactive DC sputtering in Ar gas, and implantation of HAp granules was examined.

(1) Deposited titanium film was approximately 3 μm in thickness, and the film might be deposited on the alloy substrate with high topographic fidelity to the surface .

(2) After HAp granules having been implanted, the surface of the titanium coated alloy showed metallic gloss. Only titanium was detected by EDX.

(3) On the surface of substrate, considerable cracks were observed around the granules which had been implanted at 750 °C. However, at 800 °C, no cracks were found and the granules were implanted suitably.

REFERENCES

1. S.L.Hulbert, L.L. Hench, D. Forbers and L.S. Bowman, *Ceram. Inter* 1982; **8**: 131-140.
2. T.Nonami, *Mat.Res.Soc.Symp.Proc* 1989; **175**: 71-74.
3. P. Li, C. Ohtsuki, T. Kokubo, K. Nakanishi, N. Soga and K. de Groot, *J. Biomed. Mater. Res* 1994; **28**: 7-15.
4. T.Nonami, A.Kamiya, K.Nagunuma, T.Kameyama, *J. Mater. Sci. Med* 1998; **9**: 203-206.
5. T.Nonami, K.Nagunuma, A.Kamiya, T.Kameyama, *J. Ceram. Soc. Japan* 1997; **105:** 710-712.
6. T.Sonoda and M. Kato, *Materials Research Bulletin*, 1997; **32**: 1419-1426.
7. C.Ouchi, K.Minakawa, K. Takahashi and A. Ogawa, *NKK Gihou* 1992; **138**: 17-23.

Bioceramics Volume 11, edited by R. Z. LeGeros and J.P. LeGeros
(Proceedings of the 11th International Symposium on Ceramics in Medicine)
New York, NY, USA, November 1998
© 1998 by World Scientific Publishing Co. Pte. Ltd.

IN VITRO PERFORMANCE OF VACUUM PLASMA SPRAYED COATINGS ON CARBON FIBER REINFORCED POLY(ETHERETHERKETONE)

S.-W. Ha[1], K. L. Eckert[1], F. Birchler[1], A. Gisep[1], H. Gruner[2], E. Wintermantel[1]

[1] Chair of Biocompatible Materials Science and Engineering, Department of Materials,
ETH Zürich, Wagistr. 23, CH-8952 Schlieren
[2] Medicoat AG, Gewerbe Nord, CH-5506 Mägenwil

ABSTRACT

In the present study, short-term *in vitro* stability of VPS-HA coatings on CF/PEEK was investigated. VPS-coating stability tests were performed in two simulated physiological solutions to study the *in vitro* dissolution behavior of the HA-coatings. Further, extraction tests were carried out to study whether certain products which were formed during the VPS process might leach out or dissolve during *in vitro* extraction and adversely affect cell-performance of MC3T3E1 osteoblastic cell-line. Stability testing of VPS-HA coated CF/PEEK substrates in two simulated physiological solutions, SBF and Ringer solution, at 37°C for up to 28 days showed a complex transformation reaction, including dissolution of mainly TCP and precipitation of calcium phosphate occurred within the first day. Coating thickness determination showed that no significant reduction of coating thickness was observed within the experimental time scale. It is therefore concluded that coating thickness and integrity was not affected within 28 days of immersion. Further, it was shown that mitochondrial and lysosomal activity was not affected by the extract solutions at any concentration and treatment period tested. It is therefore concluded that no products which affect basic cell functions were extracted during the immersion time interval considered in this study.

KEYWORDS

Vacuum plasma spraying, carbon fiber reinforced PEEK, hydroxyapatite, *in vitro* performance

INTRODUCTION

The high thermal resistance of PEEK compared to most thermoplastic polymers makes it suitable for high temperature applications. PEEK is normally processed at temperatures around 400°C and exhibits good thermal stability in this temperature range [1]. Thermal decomposition of PEEK has been studied by Hay et al. [2] and the volatile degradation products have been analyzed by chromatography and mass spectroscopy after condensation in liquid-nitrogen traps. The authors showed that volatiles such as phenol, dibenzofuran and various oligomers containing the furan unit were produced between 400 and 550°C. It was shown in a previous study that vacuum-plasma-spraying is a suitable technique for obtaining titanium and hydroxyapatite coatings on carbon fiber reinforced PEEK [3]. It is assumed that such coatings will enable long-term fixation of the anisotropic composite material in bone tissue. To investigate the short-term *in vitro* stability of the VPS-Ti and VPS-HA coatings on CF/PEEK immersion in two different simulated physiological solutions was performed. Coating morphology and coating thickness after immersion testing were investigated with SEM and ground section analysis. Ca and P concentrations in the immersion solution were analysed with ICP-AES. Extraction tests were performed to study whether certain products which were formed during the VPS process might leach out or dissolve during *in vitro* extraction.

MATERIALS AND METHODS

Extruded CF/PEEK disks with a diameter of 10 mm and a height of 4 mm were prepared and coated with HA as described in elsewhere [3]. Immersion tests were performed in simulated body fluid (SBF) [4] and Ringer solution (Braun, Switzerland) at 37°C, with pH of 7.1. Soaking was carried out in a laboratory shaker (Infors HT) with a rotation speed of 70 rpm, for 1, 3, 7, 14 and 28 days. After immersion, the samples were dried at 100°C for 3 hours and at 180°C for 3 hours. Coating thickness determination and cross-section analysis was performed by using scanning electron microscopy (SEM, Hitachi S-2500C). Ion concentrations in the solutions were measured using inductively coupled plasma atomic emission spectroscopy (ICP-AES) with an 3580B ICP-AES "Minitorch" spectrometer (Applied Research Laboratories). Concentrations of Ca, P and Ti were analysed. At each time step three samples were tested.

Extraction tests were performed with VPS-Ti coated CF/PEEK specimens. The samples were put into a reagents tube and 5 ml of sterile, deionized water as extraction fluid was added. The material was shaken in a laboratory shaker at 37°C at 70 rpm for 3, 5 and 9 days. After immersion, the extraction fluids were diluted with the corresponding control water extract solution. The diluted extract solutions were mixed with cell culture medium as follows: 80% extract, 10% of 10 fold concentrated α-MEM cell culture medium, 5% sodium bicarbonate solution (7.5 g/100 ml in deionized H_2O) and 5% heat inactivated fetal bovine serum (FBS). Therefore, the resulting extract fluid concentrations were: 80%, 40%, 20%, 10% and 5%. MC3T3E1 osteoblastic cell-line was used for the extraction tests. 4500 cells per well were seeded in 96 well microtiter plates and incubated at 37°C, 5% CO_2 and 95% relative humidity in α-MEM cell culture medium, containing 10% FBS and 0.3% gentamycin. After 24 hours the medium was completely removed and 100 μl/well of the extracts in the above described concentrations were added to the cells and incubated for 7 days. Mitochondrial and lysosomal activity was taken as an index for cell functionality.

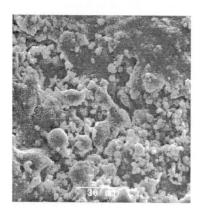 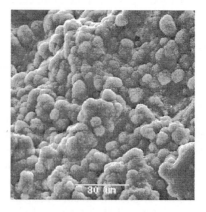

Figure 1   Scanning electron micrographs of a sample surface immersed in Ringer solution (left) and in SBF (right) at 37°C for 28 days.

RESULTS AND DISCUSSION

After immersion in Ringer solution, slight morphological modifications were observed with SEM. The VPS-HA coating contained areas with a glassy morphology and areas where the morphology seemed unchanged (fig. 1 left). Ion concentration in the Ringer solution showed a remarkable increase of both Ca and P during the first day of immersion (fig. 3). Between the first day and 28 days of immersion in Ringer solution Ca and P concentration continuously decreased, indicating the continuous precipitation of calcium phosphate. No dissolution of Ti was observed during immersion in Ringer solution within the detection limit of Ti < 0.01 mg/l. After 1 day of immersion in SBF, the melt-like structure of VPS-HA coatings changed to spherulitic shapes with a dimension of 1-5 µm (fig. 1 right). During the first day, an increase of Ca concentration in the SBF solution of 0.4-0.8 mM from the initial concentration was measured (fig. 3). P concentration showed no increase in the immersion solution, indicating the precipitation of calcium phosphate on the coating surface. These results indicate that dissolution of Ca and P and precipitation of calcium phosphate occurred concurrently during the first day of immersion in SBF. Between the first and 28th day of immersion a continuous reduction of Ca and P was measured indicating the precipitation of calcium phosphate. No dissolution of Ti was observed during immersion in SBF within the detection limit of Ti < 0.01 mg/l. Cross-section analysis of the VPS-HA coatings revealed that HA coating thickness did not significantly change during immersion in SBF and Ringer solution at 37°C (fig. 2). Further, SEM micrographs of the cross-sections revealed no alteration of coating integrity after 28 days of immersion in both simulated physiological solutions. Figure 4 shows the results of the MTT test and the NR assay. The obtained data are displayed relative to the control value. It can be seen that mitochondrial and lysosomal activity was not affected by the extract solutions at any concentration and treatment period tested (fig. 4). From these results it is suggested that no products which affect basic cell functions were extracted during the immersion time interval considered in this study.

REFERENCES

[1] McGrail P.T., *Polymer International*, 41(2), 1996, p. 103-121.

[2] Hay J.N., Kemmish D.J., *Polymer*, 28, 1987, p. 2047-2051.

[3] Ha S.-W., Gisep A., Gruner H., Mayer J., Wintermantel E., Bioceramics, Vol. 10, p. 203-206.

[4] Kokubo T., Hata K., Nakamura T., Yamamuro T., Bioceramics, Vol. 4, p. 113-120.

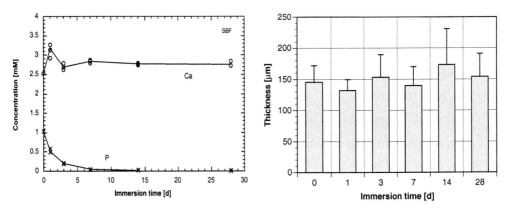

Figure 2   Coating thickness values of VPS-HA coatings after immersion in Ringer solution (left) and in SBF (right) at 37°C, showing no significant changes within the studied soaking period (n=9). Coating thickness value determination was performed at different sites of the cross-sections.

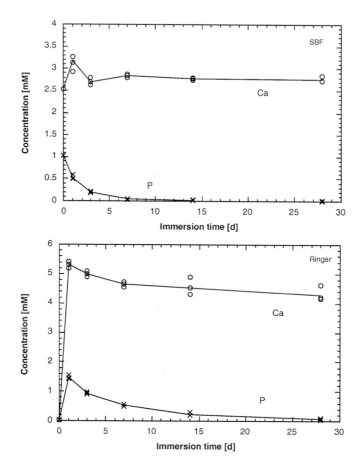

Figure 3   Molar concentrations of Ca and P in SBF and Ringer solution (n=3).

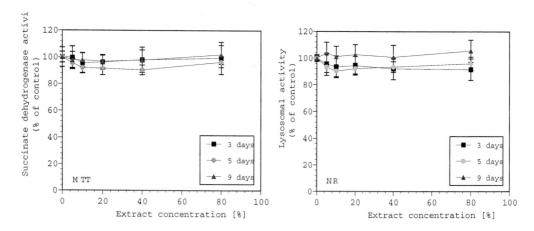

Figure 4   The results of the MTT- (left) and NR-assay (right) show that cell vitality remained constant over the entire concentration range during 3, 5 and 9 days of extraction in water (n=21).

Bioceramics Volume 11, edited by R. Z. LeGeros and J.P. LeGeros
(Proceedings of the 11th International Symposium on Ceramics in Medicine)
New York, NY, USA, November 1998
© 1998 by World Scientific Publishing Co. Pte. Ltd.

HYDROXYAPATITE - ZIRCONIA COMPOSITE COATINGS via PLASMA SPRAYING PROCESS

V.J.P. Lim, K.A. Khor[†], L. Fu, P. Cheang*

School of Mechanical and Production Engineering
*School of Applied Science
Nanyang Technological University
Nanyang Avenue, Singapore 639798
Singapore

ABSTRACT

In this study, HA and Yttria-Stabilized Zirconia (Y-ZrO_2) powders were ball-milled and then sprayed onto Ti-6Al-4V alloy substrates. The effect of spraying current on the phase composition was investigated. The amount of decomposition of HA increases with the increase of spraying current from 600A to 1000A. The impurities, as a result of the decomposition were α-TCP and CaO, though a small amount of TTCP was also detected. The influence of ZrO_2 on the decomposition of HA was also studied. The results show that ZrO_2 reacts with CaO in HA to form $CaZrO_3$. As a result of this reaction, it caused an increase in the decomposition of the CaO-poor HA.

Keywords: *Hydroxyapatite, Zirconia, Plasma Spraying, Composite, Reinforcement*

INTRODUCTION

One major application of Hydroxyapatite (HA), $Ca_{10}(PO4)_6(OH)_2$ coating is to serve as a covering material for titanium or other metals used in implants. In these cases, the biocompatibility is assured by HA while the mechanical aspects of it are provided by the metal. One alternative to the implant material would be a bioceramic composite, formed by a bioactive ceramic like HA and a bioinert phase such as zirconia (ZrO_2) and alumina (Al_2O_3). Zirconia is mechanically stronger than alumina ceramic and has a good biocompatibility [1]. Moreover, it has also been shown that a stress-induced phase transformation of zirconia from tetragonal to monoclinic phase has resulted in the increase in its strength and fracture toughness [2].

Thermal spray technique (plasma spray and high velocity oxy-fuel) is employed to produce HA-ZrO_2 composite coatings because of their high thermal efficiency and relative economy [4]. However due to the high temperature of thermal spray technique, HA tends to degrade and loose some of its bioactive properties. It is reported that HA starts to degrade into oxyapatite and tricalcium phosphate at temperatures above 1220^0C [3]. Furthermore, interaction between the different powder should also be considered in the composite material.

This paper presents HA-ZrO_2 coatings produce via the plasma spraying. The effect of spraying current was investigated together with the influence of ZrO_2 on the phase stability of HA. The cross-section microstructures of the coatings were also studied to evaluate the distribution of ZrO_2 in the coating.

EXPERIMENTAL METHODS AND MATERIALS

Mechanical Alloying of HA and Y-ZrO_2 Powders

HA and yttria-stabilized ZrO_2 powders were obtained commercially with an average particle size range of 34 µm and 30 µm respectively. The HA particles were spherical in shape while ZrO_2 is angular. Both powders have a purity of 99% and are 100% crystallinity. The powders were mechanically ball milled together for 3 hrs in 3 different weight proportions, namely 50, 30 10% wt. ZrO_2 (Sample A, B and C respectively)

Plasma Spraying of HA-ZrO$_2$ powders

The substrates used for the coatings were Ti-6Al-4V. They were sand blasted using SiC grits and ultrasonically cleaned. A 100 kW net energy computerized plasma control system coupled with a robot unit (Praxair Surface Technologies) was used. 3 different spraying currents were used (600A, 800A and 1000A) to study the effects of spraying current.

Results and Discussions

Figures 1 and 2 shows the BSE photos of polished cross sections of Sample B1 and B3 respectively. The coatings appear to be dense and relatively homogeneous with even distribution of unmelted ZrO_2 particles. Good interfacial contact is evident by the absence of pores. Lamella orientation is closely parallel to the substrate, generating a thoroughly uniform coating with good structure integrity. Basically, the HA particles are completely melted, but it can also be noted that there are unmelted ZrO_2 particles, as indicated by the white spherical balls embedded into the HA matrix. It can be noted that there were more unmelted ZrO_2 particles in the coating for Figure 1 than compared with that of Figure 2. This difference was the result of a lower spraying current.

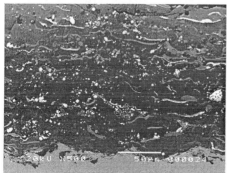 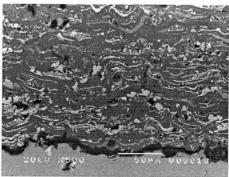

Figure 1: Polished Cross-section of Sample B (Spraying Current of 600A) Figure 2: Polished Cross-section of Sample B (Spraying Current of 1000A)

Plasma sprayed HA are known to contain other bioresorble phases such as α-TCP, β-TCP, TTCP, amorphous calcium phosphate (ACP) and CaO [5][6]. These impurities come from the decomposition of the apatite induced by the plasma spraying process and it increases with the increase in spraying current (Table 1). Referring to Table 1, the ratio of CaO/HA increases with an increase in spraying current. However, it is noted that the ratio of CaO reduced significantly after heat treatment at 900°C for 3 hrs.

Table 1: Ratio of CaO/ HA

Sample	As-Sprayed	Heat Treated
B (600A)	0.16	0.06
B (800A)	0.32	0.08
B (1000A)	1.05	0.16

The phase decomposition probably proceeds in several steps: at high temperature, possibly above 1450 °C, there is decomposition of HA to form α-TCP and TTCP. Being an unstable phase at room temperature, α-TCP naturally transforms to β-TCP (stable phase at room temperature) at about 1100 °C [7]. As for the TTCP phase, under the high heat content, it would further decompose to form HA and CaO [8]. Previous work done by Locardi et al. [9] has also confirmed that at temperature over 1300 °C, the following process takes place,

$$Ca_{10}(OH)_2(PO_4)_6 \, [HA] \rightarrow 2Ca_3(PO_4)_2 \, [TCP] + Ca_4P_2O_9 \, [TTCP] + H_2O \tag{1}$$

followed by,

$$Ca_4P_2O_9 \rightarrow Ca_3(PO_4)_2 + CaO \tag{2}$$

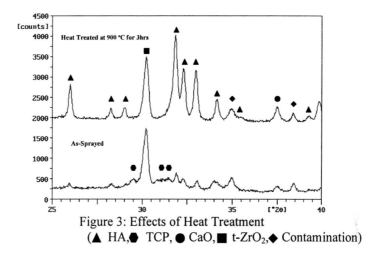

Figure 3: Effects of Heat Treatment
(▲ HA, ◆ TCP, ● CaO, ■ t-ZrO_2, ◆ Contamination)

Referring to Figure 3, there were only traces of α-TCP (as-sprayed XRD pattern) instead of β-TCP which contradicts to the above mentioned whereby α-TCP transforms into β-TCP at room temperature. A proposed following explanation is such that when a HA particle strikes the substrate, its temperature falls steeply, during the process, α-TCP and TTCP have formed in the drop. The decrease in temperature causes it to go below that of the phase stability temperature. This rapid temperature decrease is much faster than that of α-TCP could transform to a lower temperature phase (β-TCP). Hence at temperature below the phase stability of α-TCP, the initially formed calcium phosphate (α-TCP) would still remains [10]. The amorphous present in the as-sprayed coating is a metastable phase and tends to recrystallize. Upon heat treatment in air, the transformation of unstable amorphous phase into stable HA occurs. Two possible reactions can occur as a result of moisture in the air[11],

$$Ca_4P_2O_9 + 2Ca_3(PO_4)_2 + H_2O \rightarrow 2Ca_5(PO_4)_3(OH) \tag{3}$$
$$3Ca_3(PO_4)_2 + H_2O + CaO \rightarrow 2Ca_5(PO_4)_3(OH) \tag{4}$$

The occurrence of phase transformation from tetragonal to monoclinic ZrO_2 during plasma spraying has played a significant role in the strengthening effect of the HA-ZrO_2 coating. It is known that during the phase transformation there would be a volumetric increase of ZrO_2 and it generates a compressive stress state to strengthen or retard crack growth.

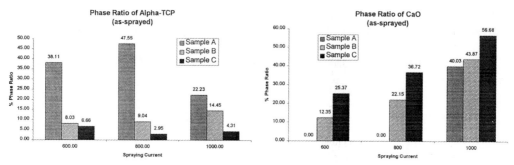

Figure 4: α-TCP Phase Ratio   Figure 5: CaO Phase Ratio

XRD patterns have indicated the influence of ZrO_2 on the impurities phases. Results from Figures 4 and 5 have shown that the addition of ZrO_2 results in an increase in α-TCP phase and a decrease in CaO phase. A small amount of $CaZrO_3$ was also present. One possible explanation is that the CaO in HA have diffused with ZrO_2 to form $CaZrO_3$ due the high temperature of the plasma flame. In past works done by Chang et al. [2], the proposed reaction was as follows:

$$ZrO_2 + Ca_{10}(PO_4)_6(OH)_2 \rightarrow CaZrO_3 + Ca_3(PO_4)_2 + H_2O \qquad (5)$$

With the reactions of ZrO_2 and CaO, there would be a reduction of CaO in HA. As a result, the decomposition of CaO-poor HA into α-TCP phase will be accelerated and increased. Equation 5 infers that α-TCP and $CaZrO_3$ would have been produced in equal quantity, yet the reaction product of $CaZrO_3$ is scarce. This is because although the temperature of the plasma jet was high, the time for the molten HA to react with ZrO_2 was limited, and hence the quantity of reaction product was small. This reaction might help to bond ZrO_2 to HA.

Conclusions

Composite coating of HA-ZrO_2 was prepared using the plasma spraying process. Homogenous HA-ZrO_2 coatings were obtained with unmelted ZrO_2 particles distributed uniformly in the HA matrix. Lamella structures of possible $CaZrO_3$ was closely parallel to the substrate, indicating good structure integrity. The degradation of HA was much affected by the spraying current. Phase transformation of ZrO_2 was also observed which would contribute to the toughening of the composite coating. CaO in HA may have reacted with ZrO_2 to form $CaZrO_3$ and as a result, it accelerates the decomposition of HA.

References

[1] T. Nakamura, Bioceramics vol.9 (1996): 31-34.
[2] E. Chang, W.J. Chang, B.C. Wang, C.Y. Yang, *J. of Mat. Sci.: Mat. in Med.* 8 (1997): 193-200.
[3] J. Li, H. Liao, L. Hermansson, *Biomaterials 17* (1996): 1787-1790.
[4] C.S. Yip, K.A. Khor, N.L. Loh, P. Cheang, *J. Mat. Processing Tech.* 65 (1997): 73-79.
[5] K.A. Khor, P. Cheang and Y. Wang, *JOM*, vol.49, 2 (1997): 51-57.
[6] W.D. Tong, J.Y. Chen and X.D. Zhang, *Biomaterials*, vol.16, 11, (1995): 829-832.
[7] H.X. Ji and P.M. Marquis, *Biomaterials*, vol.14, 1 (1993): 64-68.
[8] C.Y. Yang, B.C. Wang, E. Chang, J.D. Wu,, *J. of Mat. Sci.: Mat. in Med.*, 6 (1995): 249-257.
[9] B. Lorcardi, U.E. Pazzaglia, C. Gabbi and B. Profilo, *Biomaterials*, vol.14, 6 (1993): 437-441.
[10] Z. Zyman, Y. Cao and X. Zhang, *Biomaterials*, vol.14, 15 (1993): 1140-1144.
[11] Y. Cao, J. Weng, J.Y. Chen, J.M. Feng, Z.J. Yang and X.D. Zhang, Biomat., vol.17, 4 (1996): 419-424.

Bioceramics Volume 11, edited by R. Z. LeGeros and J.P. LeGeros
(Proceedings of the 11th International Symposium on Ceramics in Medicine)
New York, NY, USA, November 1998
© 1998 by World Scientific Publishing Co. Pte. Ltd.

SYNTHESIS OF TRICALCIUM PHOSPHATE COATINGS USING PLASMA-ENHANCED METALORGANIC CHEMICAL VAPOR DEPOSITION

Y. Gao and Allison A. Campbell

Pacific Northwest National Laboratory, P.O. Box 999, MS K8-93, Richland, WA 99352, USA.

ABSTRACT

Crystalline α-tricalcium phosphate coatings were synthesized by plasma-enhanced metalorganic chemical vapor deposition (MOCVD). Structure, composition, and surface morphology of the coatings were characterized by x-ray diffraction, x-ray photoelectron spectroscopy, and scanning electron microscopy, respectively. All coatings were very dense and mirror-like. X-ray diffraction showed that the as-grown coatings with the Ca/P ratio ranged from 1.45 to 1.55 were crystalline, whereas the coatings with the Ca/P ratio greater than 1.55 or less than 1.45 were amorphous. The crystalline α-TCP coatings exhibited strong growth texture. The textured orientations varied at different growth temperatures. The microstructure of the TCP coatings strongly depended on the growth temperatures. The grain size of the coatings increased as increasing the growth temperature.

KEYWORDS: Tricalcium phosphate, coatings, MOCVD

INTRODUCTION

Use of prosthetic implants has been increased rapidly. The implants are commonly made of titanium alloy. However, Ti alloys do not form a direct bond with bone. There is now considerable evidence to demonstrate that calcium phosphate (CP) coatings can enhance bone apposition to endosseous implants. One rationale underlying the use of calcium phosphates is the belief that they permit bone to bond to their surface and thus enhance implant fixation. Hydroxyapatite (HA) and tricalcium phosphate (TCP) are particularly attractive materials for hard tissue implants in plastic surgery because their capability of directly integrating to bone tissues by their resorption (e.g. TCP) or by allowing the intergrowth of new bones into their porous structure (e.g. HA). There are several methods to make such coatings, among which plasma spraying is the most frequently used technique to produce HA coatings[1-3]. However, studies of TCP coatings are very limited. This paper reports our recent results of thin TCP coatings. Since TCP has relatively high solubility in body fluid, a release of TCP could help facilitate bone formation. In addition, coated implants can be put into a solution with proteins, antibiotic or growth factors that can be adsorbed before surgery. Once implanted, the release of TCP will also release these agents to improve growth of new bones and to prevent infection.

We have used plasma-enhanced metalorganic chemical vapor deposition (MOCVD) to produce TCP coatings with excellent crystal quality, and controlled surface characteristics. Though MOCVD has not been applied for synthesis of bioceramic coatings, it has been developed for deposition of other ceramic coatings such as oxides and nitrides with superior quality for semiconductor applications. In the MOCVD process, a gaseous stream of metalorganic precursors containing the reactive constituents for the desired coating material is directed at heated substrate, where a reaction takes place to form a solid film. Reaction byproducts are pumped out. The process is terminated when a desired thickness is reached. MOCVD is known to be capable to produce uniform coatings on complex-shape substrates. In the present study, we demonstrate, for the first time, that MOCVD is a useful growth technique for bioceramic coatings. The results on MOCVD synthesis of TCP coatings and structural characterization are reported in this paper.

EXPERIMENTAL

The MOCVD system used in this study is based on Emcore's Discovery 75 Oxide System, modified to incorporate a 1.5 kW downstream microwave source for oxygen plasma, and two *in-situ* monitoring probes: Fourier transform IR spectrometer and multi-wavelength spectroscopic ellipsometer. The Discovery 75 design uses a cold-wall, vertical stainless steel reactor with substrates mounted on a high speed rotating disk. The substrates are heated by a molybdum filament and the maximum temperature is about 1000 °C. The MOCVD system has a direct liquid-source injection system with two source reservoirs. The liquid injection delivery system is particularly suitable for multicomponent coatings. A detailed description of the system has been given elsewhere[4].

Commercially available $Ca(C_{11}H_{19}O_2)_2$ (bis (tetramethl,heptanedionato)Calcium) and $(C_2H_5O)_3PO$ (trimethylphosphate) were used as the precursors for Ca and P, respectively. Individual precursors in a desired molar composition were initially dissolved and diluted in a common solvent at room temperature. These two solutions at a selected ratio were delivered to a vaporizer heated at 230 °C by a precision pump. The composition of calcium phosphate coatings was controlled by selecting flow rates of each solution. The TCP coatings were deposited at temperatures from 500 °C to 650 °C at 10 Torr. Growth rate and coating thickness were monitored in real time by spectroscopic ellipsometry. The growth rate was about 15 nm/min, and the thickness ranged from 0.1 μm to 1 μm. The substrate temperature and flow rates of carrier gas were varied to control the film structure, composition, and thickness uniformity. Silicon (100) wafers (1" or 2" diameter) were used as substrates. A thin TiO_2 layer (200 Å) was first grown on Si wafers before depositing TCP coatings. The purpose for depositing the TiO_2 layer was to obtain a substrate surface similar to that of Ti alloy implants since all Ti alloy implants consist of a thin native oxide layer of Ti.

Crystal structure determination of TCP coatings was carried out by X-ray diffraction using a Philips MPD X'pert powder diffractometer using Cu Kα radiation. The Ca/P ratio of the coatings and oxidation state of Ca and P were analyzed by means of X-ray photoelectron spectroscopy (XPS) using PHI Quantum 2000. XPS spectra were excited by monochromatized Al Kα radiation. Surface morphology of the coatings was characterized by scanning electron microscopy (SEM) using field-emission LEO 982.

RESULTS AND DISCUSSION

All coatings were very smooth and mirror-like. Spectroscopic ellipsometry revealed that coatings were transparent, suggesting high crystal quality. This is consistent with the observation of color change as a function of coating thickness. SEM observations showed that no cracks were present in the coatings.

X-ray diffraction (XRD) showed that as-deposited coatings were crystalline, pure α-TCP. No post-deposition annealing was needed to form crystaline phases. Fig. 1 shows XRD patterns of TCP coatings deposited at three different temperatures. All peaks can be indexed by the Joint Committee on Powder Diffraction Standard (No. 9-348) for α-TCP. The flat defined baseline of the spectra is indicative of a crystalline material with little or no amorphous content. The most notable difference between these spectra is related to the structural texture of the coatings. These preferred growth orientations strongly depend on the growth temperature. The relative intensities of the peaks for the α-TCP coating deposited at 650 °C are similar to those for powder samples, suggesting that the α-TCP coating is randomly oriented. Strong peaks at 2θ=22.2° and 34.6° are observed for the coating deposited at 575 °C, indicating that the coating is (150) and (080) oriented. Further decrease of the growth temperature to 500 °C leaded to a (060) texture, corresponding to the peak at 2θ=25.8°. The results suggested that homogeneous nucleation and growth occurred at 650 °C, and the deposition was dominated thermodynamically. In contrast, the deposition was controlled by growth kinetics at lower growth temperatures. Different crystallographic orientations dominated grain growth at different temperatures, resulting in different texture.

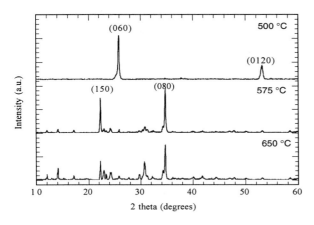

Fig. 1 X-ray diffraction patterns from TCP coatings deposited at 650 °C, 575 °C and 500 °C, showing different growth texture.

The surface morphology of the coatings was very different and was strongly dependent of the growth temperatures as shown in Fig. 2. The grain size of the coatings decreased as decreasing the growth temperature. The grain size of the TCP coating deposited at 650 °C is almost ten times larger than that at 575 °C, whereas the grain size was not resolved for the coating deposited at 500 °C. The results suggested that grain growth was much faster at higher temperatures. In addition, all three surfaces were very dense and homogenous in appearance. It was noted that the thickness of the coatings was similar for a given period of growth time at the three temperatures, indicating that the nucleation rate was higher at low temperatures as compared to that at high temperature, resulting in a similar thickness. Thus, the high nucleation rate and low grain growth at low temperatures resulted in dense, fine-grain microstructure, whereas the low nucleation rate and high grain growth at high temperatures leaded to dense, course-grain microstructure. Such a temperature dependence of the coating microstructure makes it possible to deposit TCP coatings with controlled surface characteristics.

The composition of the TCP coatings was determined from Ca 3p and P 2p core-level intensities in XPS. The Ca/P ratio was calculated from the measured Ca $3p_{3/2}$ and P 2p peak areas in the same spectrum after correction for photoemission sensitivity factors. XPS revealed that the composition was very uniform across the substrates with a variation of less than 5%. Fig. 3 shows a typical XPS spectrum of the TCP coatings. The Ca/P ratio in the present study varied from 1.35 to 1.65 by controlling the flow rates of the Ca and P solutions. It was found that the coatings with the Ca/P ratio from 1.45 to 1.55 were crystalline, α-TCP. However, the TCP coatings contained a notable amount of amorphous phase for the Ca/P ratio close to 1.45 or 1.55. In contrast, the coatings with the Ca/P ratio higher than 1.55 or less than 1.45 were complete amorphous phase.

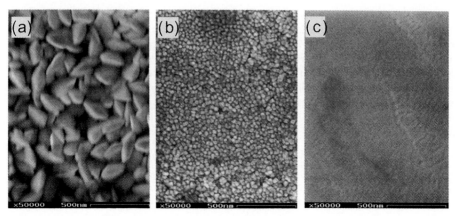

Fig. 2 Scanning electron micrographs of the a-TCP coatings deposited at 650 °C (a), 575 °C (b), and 500 °C (c).

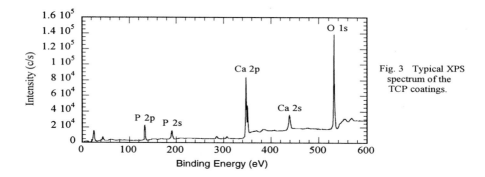

Fig. 3 Typical XPS spectrum of the TCP coatings.

CONCLUSIONS

Highly textured α-TCP coatings with controlled surface characteristics were synthesized by plasma-enhanced MOCVD. The as-grown coatings with the ca/p ratio ranged from 1.45 to 1.55 were crystalline, whereas the coatings with the ca/p ratio greater than 1.55 or less than 1.45 were amorphous. The grain size of the coatings increased as increasing the growth temperature. The results showed that MOCVD is a useful deposition technique for synthesis of α-TCP coatings with high crystal quality and controlled surface characteristics.

ACKNOWLEDGMENTS

This work was partially supported by the U.S. Department of Energy, Office of Energy Research. Battelle operates the Pacific Northwest National Laboratory for the U.S. Department of Energy under contract DE-ACO6-76RLO1830.

REFERENCES

1.   Thomas, KA, Orthopedics 1994; **17**: 267-278.

2.   Campbell AA., Journal of Biomedical Materials Research, 1996, **32**: 111-118.

3.   Cui, FZ, Luo, ZS, Feng, QL, J Mater. Sci.: Mater. In Medicine 1997; **8**: 403-405.

4.   Gao, Y, submitted to Thin Solid Films.

Bioceramics Volume 11, edited by R. Z. LeGeros and J.P. LeGeros
(Proceedings of the 11th International Symposium on Ceramics in Medicine)
New York, NY, USA, November 1998
© 1998 by World Scientific Publishing Co. Pte. Ltd.

HYDROXYAPATITE COATING BY A SOL-GEL PROCESS CONTAINING AN INTERMEDIATE GLASS LAYER

Changkook You and Sukyoung Kim

School of Metallurgical and Materials Engineering
Yeungnam University, Kyungsan, Kyungbuk 712-749, KOREA

ABSTRACT

A transparent HA sol was prepared and coated on Ti6Al4V substrates by a spin-coating technique. The crystallization of the HA coated on the metallic substrates could be done at relatively low firing temperatures as low as 600℃. In order to increase the adherence of the HA coating layer to the Ti-alloy substrates, an intermediate glass sol was coated onto the substrate. It have been found that the number of cracks in the coating layers of both HA and glass was considerably decreased with dimethyl formamide (DMF) addition, and the morphology of the HA surface containing glass layer was smooth with fine grain structure. The smoothness of the HA coated layer was affected with the roughness of the grit-blasted substrate. The HA coating layer on the substrate grit-blasted with below 20 μm-alumina powder showed the smoother and more uniform than that with 50 μm powder.

INTRODUCTION

Hydroxyapatite (HA) coatings on metallic implants have been attracted to induce new bone in-growth and subsequently increase fixation stability by improving the bond between the implant and bone tissue[1]. Various techniques for HA coating on metallic implants have been developed including plasma-spraying which is currently being used. However, it was found to undergo changes in phase composition, crystallinity and morphology of metallic substrates due to the elevated temperature process[2]. In contrast, sol-gel derived HA coating can be done at relatively low firing temperatures as low as 900℃, which is below the decomposition temperature of HA and the transformation temperature of Ti-alloy. In order to utilize the bioactivity of HA and enhance the bonding strength between a HA coating layer and a substrate, the functionally gradient coating containing glass layer by dip coating method has been attempted in recent years[3,4].

In the present study, we prepared a HA sol by sol-gel process and coated on Ti6Al4V substrates using spin coating method. In an attempt to increase the adherence of the HA coating layer to the substrate, the glass sol was coated on the substrate. It was expected that the small difference of the thermal expansion coefficient between glass (7.8×10^{-6}/℃) and Ti-alloy substrate (9.4×10^{-6}/℃)[5] decreases the thermal stress at the interface of the glass and substrate. And then HA (13.3×10^{-6}/℃) was coated on an intermediate glass layer. Their coating characteristics were compared with that of HA coated only.

MTERIALS AND METHOD

The precursor HA sol was prepared by the reaction of $Ca(NO_3)_2 4H_2O$ (Aldrich 99%, USA) with $(OC_2H_5)_3P$ (Fluka 97%, Japan) in methyl alcohol using correct amounts to obtain the stoichiometric Ca/P ratio of 1.67, followed by the addition of 0.03mol HCl and various amounts of NN-dimethyl formamide (DMF) as a Drying Control Chemical Additive. The mixed solution was aged at 80°C for 12 hours, thereafter, filtrated through 0.2 μm-syringe filter. Glass sol (CaO-P$_2$O$_5$-SiO$_2$-B$_2$O$_3$ system) was prepared using Ca(NO$_3$)$_2$4H$_2$O, (OC$_2$H$_5$)$_3$PO, Si(OC$_2$H$_5$)$_4$ and H$_3$BO$_3$ in ethyl alcohol[6], and aged at 50°C for 12 hours and also gone through filtration.

The deposition of HA and glass layer was performed onto Ti6Al4V substrate by a spin coating at 3500 rpm for 50 seconds, where the substrates were grit-blasted with 20 μm and 50 μm alumina powder respectively. The specimens of glass sol coated were immediately baked and dried at 150°C, and then heat-treated at 600°C for 1hour. HA coating on the glass layer was then conducted and heat-treated at 600°C. The functionally gradient HA-G-Ti composite was formed. The powders and coated samples were characterized using TG/DTA and XRD, and the surface morphology of HA and glass layers was studied using SEM.

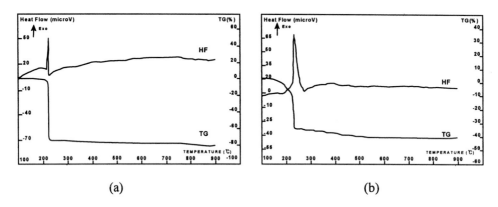

Fig. 1. TG/DTA curves of (a) HA and (b) glass gels dried at 150°C

RESULTS AND DISCUSSIONS

DTA results from HA and glass gels dried at 150°C indicate exothermic reactions at about 220°C and 240°C respectively (Figure 1). It may be concluded the exothermic peaks were due to the combustion of the residual ethanol and dimethyl formamide in specimens, from the abrupt weight loss in TG curve at the temperatures. After that, the curves have no obvious changes. The XRD patterns of the dried gels calcined at 600°C for 1 hour are shown in Figure 2. In the sample of HA coated on a glass layer, a broad amorphous hump and low crystalline peaks are shown, where the crystalline phase corresponds to HA peaks. It is considered that higher firing temperatures are needed to obtain a HA with higher crystallinity.

Figure 3 shows an SEM micrograph of HA and glass layers coated onto 50 μm grit-blasted substrates with and without the addition of DMF after heat-treating at 600°C. The HA surface coated without DMF was rough and porous resulting from rapid elimination of organic materials. In contrast, the HA layers coated with 0.05 mol and 0.1 mol of DMF were relatively smooth and dense (Fig. 3b and 4a), which is considered that the addition of DMF effectively retards drying rate and elimination of organic groups. And the number of cracks in glass layers is also considerably decreased with the addition of DMF. This may be due to the pores among the polymeric network after evaporation of solvent filled by DMF.

Figure 4 represents the HA and glass layers coated onto 20 μm grit-blasted substrates. Both surfaces are fairly homogeneous and smooth and show few cracks, compared to the surface on substrates grit-blasted with 50 μm powder (Fig. 3d and 4b). The rougher surface with deep valley in 50 μm grit-blasted substrates is due to the larger volume of coating layer, which may causes to have more cracks due to their high shrinkage during drying and firing.

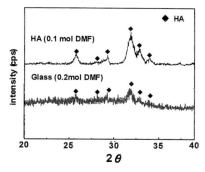

Fig. 2. XRD patterns of HA and glass gel dried at 150℃ (heat-treated at 600℃)

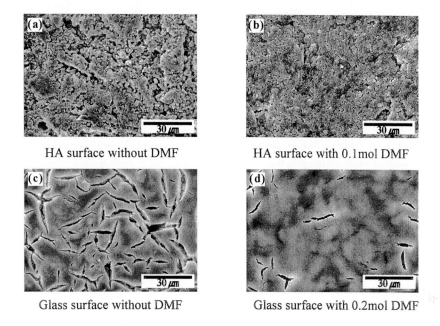

HA surface without DMF   HA surface with 0.1mol DMF

Glass surface without DMF   Glass surface with 0.2mol DMF

Fig. 3. SEM of HA and glass layers coated on 50 μm-blasted substrate with and without the addition of DMF (heat-treated at 600℃)

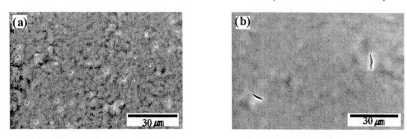

HA surface with 0.1mol DMF   Glass surface with 0.2mol DMF

Fig. 4. SEM of (a) HA and (b) glass layers coated on 20 μm-blasted substrate. (heat-treated at 600℃)

The surface morphology of the HA layers coated on a glass layer pre-coated onto 20 μm and 50 μm grit-blasted substrate is shown in figure 5. Both HA coated surfaces show uniform and fine grain structure. However, large cracks are still appeared in the HA layer coated on 50 μm grit-blasted substrate (Fig. 5a).

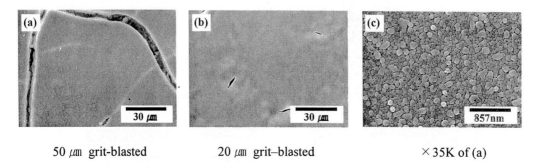

| 50 μm grit-blasted | 20 μm grit-blasted | $\times$35K of (a) |

Fig. 5.   SEM of HA coatings on glass layer pre-deposited by spin coating

CONCLUSIONS

1. HA surface coated without DMF was rough and porous resulting from rapid elimination of organic materials. In contrast, the layers coated with DMF were relatively smooth and dense.
2. HA surface coated onto 20 μm grit-blasted substrate was fairly homogeneous and smooth and show few cracks, compared to the results on the substrate grit-blasted with 50 μm powder.
3. The surface morphology of the HA layers coated on a glass layer pre-coated onto 20 μm and 50 μm grit-blasted substrates showed uniform and fine grain structure, however, large cracks was observed in the HA layer coated on 50 μm grit-blasted substrates.

REFERENCES

1. Liu DM, Chou HM and Wu JD., J. *Mater. Sci.: Mater. Med.* 1994; **5**: 147-153.
2. Yang CY, Wang BC, Chang E and Wu JD., J. Mater. Sci.: Mater. Med. 1995; **6**: 249-257.
3. Maruno S, Ban S, Wang YF, Iwata H, and Itoh H., *J. Ceram. Soc. Japan* 1992; **100, 4**: 362-367.
4. Chern Lin JH, Liu ML and Ju CP., *J. Mater. Sci.: Mater. Med.* 1994; **5**: 279-283.
5. Maruno S, Hayashi K, Sumi Y, Wang YF and Iwata H., *CRC Handbook of Bioactive Ceramcis,* Vol II. Ed. Yamamuro T, Hench LL and Wilson J. CRC Press 1991; 187-193.
6. Aizawa M, Itatani K, Howell FS, Kinoshita M and Kishioka A., *J. Ceram. Soc. Japan Int.* Ed. 1992; **103**: 544-547.

Bioceramics Volume 11, edited by R. Z. LeGeros and J.P. LeGeros
(Proceedings of the 11th International Symposium on Ceramics in Medicine)
New York, NY, USA, November 1998
© 1998 by World Scientific Publishing Co. Pte. Ltd.

HYDROXYL INCORPORATION IN APATITE COATINGS PRODUCED BY PULSED LASER DEPOSITION

M.B. Mayor, J.L. Arias, F.J. García-Sanz, S. Chiussi, J. Pou, B. León, M. Pérez-Amor
Dpto. de Física Aplicada, Universidade de Vigo, Lagoas-Marcosende, E-36200 Vigo, Spain, fax no. +34-86-812201

ABSTRACT

Pulsed laser deposition was used to produce apatite thin films on silicon substrates. Using a hydroxylapatite (HA) target and an ArF laser, layers were deposited in a trace atmosphere of D_2O, instead of H_2O, in order to study the incorporation of hydroxyl (OH) groups in the coatings. The influence of the deuterium oxide pressure (0.3-0.8 mbar) and the substrate temperature (450-525 °C) on the films parameters was studied. The percentages of OD incorporated in the film from the atmosphere and the OH incorporated from the target in the crystalline apatite structure was determined by measuring the area under the stretching bands of the OH (3571 cm^{-1}) and OD (2636 cm^{-1}) groups in the FT-IR spectra of these coatings. A minimum pressure of 0.30 mbar of water vapor (deuterium oxide vapor) was required to obtain crystalline coatings. Above this pressure, there were no great differences in the percentage of OD (amounting around 50%) incorporated in the coatings, with regard to OH.

KEYWORDS: Calcium phosphate coatings, pulsed laser deposition, hydroxyl incorporation

INTRODUCTION

Among several calcium phosphate ceramics proposed, hydroxylapatite (HA) has received particular attention because its composition and structure are similar to those of the mineral part of natural bone. As far as load bearing implants are concerned, good results have been obtained using HA coated titanium implants. Among different coating methods producing such calcium phosphate films, the Plasma Spray technique is currently the only commercial method producing them onto implant devices, but presenting some problems such as poor coating-substrate adherence, and poor cristallinity[1]. Recently, Pulsed Laser Deposition (PLD) appears to be the most promising coating technique in order to achieve coatings with suitable properties for medical applications.

As reported earlier[2-4], the most important parameters controlling the composition and the properties of films grown by PLD from HA targets are the substrate temperature, the type of gas and its pressure during the deposition process, where water vapour has produced the best results with regard to crystallinity and OH content.

With the aim to investigate the origin of different hydroxyl groups in such HA coatings, heavy water atmosphere has been used in order to determine, which kind of hydroxyl incorporation can be attributed to the HA-target, which one to the surrounding atmosphere and how the atmosphere pressure (P_a) and the substrate temperature (T_s) can affect the formation and modification of these groups.

MATERIAL AND METHODS

Targets were produced from commercial powder of HA supplied by Plasma Biotal Ltd., Derbyshire, U.K.. The raw powder was pressed and sintered to obtain targets with a density of at least 95% of the theoretical density of HA. The used PLD system, described in detail previously[5], consists basically of a vacuum chamber, which can be evacuated to a total base pressure of $\sim 10^{-6}$ mbar by a turbomolecular pump, and then the atmosphere of deuterium oxide vapour (D_2O) was supplied to the chamber from a tank. The films were analysed by Fourier Transform Infrared spectroscopy (FT-IR) collected with a Bomem MB-100 Fourier spectrometer in the range of 410-4000 cm^{-1} with a spectral resolution of 4 cm^{-1}.

RESULTS

The obtained FT-IR spectra of the carbonated HA films deposited by PLD in D_2O vapour atmosphere show a new band around 2636 cm^{-1} as compared to experiments performed in H_2O vapour. Calculations based on the reduced masses, lead to the conclusion that this band can be assigned to OD groups equivalent to the typical OH groups in HA (3573 cm^{-1}).

Figure 1 shows the FT-IR spectra, in the range of the OH and OD groups of the coatings deposited at different conditions. Both, the stretching band of OH groups incorporated in the apatite lattice and the band corresponding to OD groups (3573 cm^{-1} and 2636 cm^{-1} respectively) are detected for all deposition conditions, thus meaning that the OH incorporated in the films has its sources both in the target as well as in the chamber atmosphere.

An additional OD band is observed at 2686 cm^{-1}, which can be attributed to the equivalent to the 3643 cm^{-1} OH band[6]. These two bands might be assigned to several species located on the external surfaces of the apatite crystals[7], belonging to a $Ca(OH)_2$ phase, to POH groups of biphosphate ions or to OH groups located at the end of the hydroxyl columns in the crystal faces. The OH band at 3643 cm^{-1} was only observed in the samples deposited at 0.3 mbar of total pressure (T_s= 485°C) and in the samples deposited at 525 °C of substrate temperature (P_a=0.45 mbar), figure 1 (a) and (i) respectively. The corresponding OD band at 2686 cm^{-1} shows its highest values at the highest T_s and at lowest P_a. As shown in our previous work[5,8], at 0.8 mbar and 445 °C of these two series in water vapor atmosphere, the coating becomes amorphous, and therefore cannot incorporate much OH and OD.

The total concentration of the OH and OD in the apatite lattice, calculated from FT-IR areas of the OH and OD bands[7], increases as both temperature and pressure are increased (Table 1). Only for the coatings obtained at 0.8 mbar these total concentration decreases according to its dramatic change in crystallinity. The OD concentration increases as both T_s and P_a are increased. Nevertheless, the OH concentration remains practically constant as P_a is increased and increases as T_s is raised, excepting at the highest T_s.

The fraction of the OH replaced by OD in the apatite lattice coming from the atmosphere can be evaluated from the ratio of the OD concentration to the total concentration of OH and OD. This OD percentage increases as both processing parameters, T_s and P_a, are increased (Table 1).

Table 1 also shows the Full Width at Half Maximum (FWHM) from the OD band at 2636 cm^{-1} for each deposition condition. Since it is an indicator of the degree of disorder of the hydroxyl ions with respect to their exact sites in which the hydroxyl ions should be, its narrowing at low temperatures and at high pressures denotes a higher order of the hydroxyl groups in the apatite lattice, along the channel formed by the Ca(2)[9], with the exception of the 445 ºC sample that becomes amorphous at such temperatures.

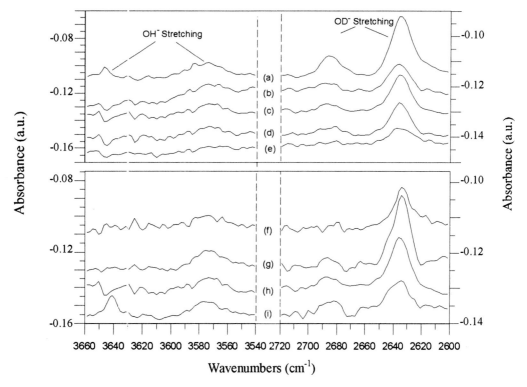

Figure 1: FT-IR spectra in the OH⁻ and OD⁻ range from the coatings produced by PLD at 0.45 mbar of D_2O vapor pressure and at substrate temperatures of (a) 525 ºC (b) 505 ºC (c) 485 ºC (d) 470 ºC (e) 450 ºC and from the coatings deposited at 485 ºC of substrate temperature, with (f) 0.8 mbar (g) 0.6 mbar (h) 0.45 mbar (i) 0.3 mbar of D_2O vapor pressure.

The absorption peaks at 1465 y 1419 cm⁻¹, in all deposition conditions, indicate the existence of the carbonate ions in the films. These absorption bands are characteristic of CO_3^{2-} substitution for PO_4^{3-} in the apatite lattice[10]. The intensity of the v_3 CO_3^{2-} band at 1419 cm⁻¹ increases slightly as T_s rises and diminishes as the pressures increases. Arends and Davison[11] found a linear relation between the extinction coefficient of carbonate band at 1419 cm⁻¹ and the carbonate content for different carbonated apatites. Table 1 also summarizes the carbonate calculated content for the coatings, using this method.

DISCUSSION

Considering that carbonate is the main substitutional group in the apatite lattice and that the positions of the v_3 carbonate bands, as measured in our films, are characteristic for an environment involving substitution of CO_3^{2-} for PO_4^{3-}, the model of Labarthe can be assumed for our films[10], should also be valid using D⁺ instead of H⁺, and corroborating this model the increase of the OH and its corresponding OD content in the apatite lattice is accompanied by a decrease of CO_3^{2-} with increasing total pressure, as already demonstrated in our group[8].

Table 1. Concentration of the OH and OD and CO_3^{2-} content in the apatite lattice, calculated from FT-IR spectra, of the coatings at the different deposition conditions.

P (mbar)	$[OD_{2636}+OH_{3571}]$ μM	[OD] μM	[OH] μM	$\%[OD_{2636}]$	FWHM OD_{2636}	$\%[CO_3]$
0.80	1700±500	800±300	900±200	50±30	13.5	1.90±0.04
0.60	2300±500	1300±300	1000±200	60±30	13.5	3.40±0.10
0.45	1500±400	800±200	700±100	50±30	17.3	4.80±0.10
0.30	1600±400	700±300	900±200	40±20	19.2	7.00±0.10
T (°C)	$[OD_{2636}+OH_{3571}]$ μM	[OD] μM	[OH] μM	$\%OD_{2636}$	FWHM OD_{2636}	$\%[CO_3]$
525	1700±400	1200±300	500±100	70±30	19.3	6.10±0.50
505	1500±300	700±200	800±200	50±20	19.2	5.80±0.10
485	1500±300	800±200	700±200	50±20	17.3	4.80±0.10
465	1400±300	700±200	600±100	50±20	17.3	4.90±0.15
445	700±200	400±100	300±100	50±30	21.2	5.1±0.10

From this model it is clear that the OH content should be lower when the CO_3^{2-} concentration increases. Contradicting this general behaviour, the simultaneous increasing of both the OH and the carbonate content in the coatings, as the substrate temperature is raised, could be explained if one considers that by increasing the T_s a greater number or/and size of the apatite crystals in the coatings is obtained. This effect is corroborated by the OD FWHM widening at higher substrate temperatures, exhibiting a loss of the degree of ordering of the OD ions within the channels. Such lost of ordering tends to show the presence of the OH vacancies and of vacancies in the Ca(2) sites forming the walls of the channel[9].

The OD stretching band at 2686 cm^{-1}, which is attributed to a $Ca(OD)_2$ phase[7,9], increases at lower P_a and at higher T_s. The peak area for the OH- band corresponding to $Ca(OH)_2$ is only detectable at 0.3 mbar. This effect can be explained by a higher presence of calcium outside of the apatite lattice, according to the model proposed by Labarthe[10]. These Ca^{2+} ions would react mostly with the D_2O of the atmosphere than with the OH of the target forming more stable species such as $Ca(OD)_2$ than $Ca(OH)_2$.

The increase of the %OD in the coatings as the D_2O vapor pressure is increased indicates the essential role of a OD ions rich atmosphere providing the necessary ions to form the apatite structure. The slightly increase of the %OD when T_s is varied, accompanied by a less presence of the OH ions transported from the target to the substrate by the plasma plume, can be explained by the increase of the dissociation velocity of the D_2O molecule as the substrate temperature is increased, together with a higher D_2O convection flux to the surface producing a higher circulation of the OD atmosphere near to the substrate.

CONCLUSION

In conclusion, the water vapor atmosphere plays a more essential role in the OH- content of the coatings as compared to the target OH. It was demonstrated that the OH content of the coatings can be improved either by increasing the water vapor pressure, but affecting also the crystallinity of the coatings, or by the increasing the substrate temperature. In this case a $Ca(OH)_2$ phase is also incorporated. Therefore, in order to tailor crystallinity and composition of pulsed laser deposited carbonated apatite, an effective incorporation of OH primarily from the atmosphere must be guaranteed.

ACKNOWLEDGMENTS

This work was partially supported by C.I.C.Y.T. (MAT93-0271), U.E. CRAFT (BRE2.CT94.1533), MINER (PATI 665/95), Xunta de Galicia (INFRA94-58) and Universidade de Vigo.

REFERENCES

1. Yang CY, Wang BC, Chang E, Wu JD. *J Mater Sci: Mater Med* 1995; **6**: 258-265.
2. Cotell CM, Chrisey DB, Grabowski KS, Spregue JA. *J Appl Biomat* 1992; **3**: 87-93.
3. Sardin G, Varela M, Morenza JL. In: Brown PW and Constanz B, ed. *Hydroxyapatite and related materials*, Boca Raton: CRC Press, 1994; 225-230.
4. Arias JL, Mayor MB, García-Sanz FJ, Pou J, León B, Pérez-Amor M, Knowles JC. *J Mater Sci: Mater Med.*1997; **8**: 873-876.
5. Mayor B, Arias J, Chiussi S, García F, Pou J, León B, Pérez-Amor M. *Thin Solid films* 1997; **317**: 363-366.
6. Angell CL, Schaffer PC. *J Phys Chem* 1965; **69**: 3463-3470.
7. Cant NW, Bett JAS, Wilson GR, Hall WK. *Spectrochim Act* 1971; **27A**: 425-439.
8. Arias JL, García-Sanz FJ, Mayor MB, Chiussi S, Pou J, León B, Pérez-Amor M. *Biomaterials* 1998, in press.
9. Young RA, Holcomb DW. *Calcif Tiss Int* 1982; **34**: S17-S32.
10. Labarthe JC, Bonel G, Montel G. *Ann Chim* 1973; **8**: 289-301.
11. Arends J, Davidson CL. *Calcif Tiss Res* 1975; **18**: 65-79.

Bioceramics Volume 11, edited by R. Z. LeGeros and J.P. LeGeros
(Proceedings of the 11th International Symposium on Ceramics in Medicine)
New York, NY, USA, November 1998
© 1998 by World Scientific Publishing Co. Pte. Ltd.

CRYSTALLINITY, ROUGHNESS AND POROSITY ANALYSIS OF HYDROXYAPATITE COATINGS OBTAINED BY PLASMA SPRAY PROCESSING

Sidney N. Silva[1] , José Roberto T. Branco[2] and Marivalda M. Pereira[1]

[1] Dep. de Engenharia Metalúrgica e Materiais, UFMG, Rua Espirito Santo n° 35, Centro, 30160.030 - Belo Horizonte-MG, [2] Fundação Centro Tecnológico de Minas Gerais, Av. José Cândido da Silveira, 2000, Belo Horizonte-MG, BRAZIL.

ABSTRACT

Plasma spray processing parameters greatly affect the structural characteristics of the coatings since operation conditions change the enthalpy of the torch, causing substantial melting of the particles and also affecting the cooling and solidification processes. In this work, the effect of the main process parameters - arc current, proportion of primary/secondary gases and distance torch-substrate - on the crystallinity, roughness and porosity of hydroxyapatite coatings were evaluated. The experiments were carried out using the factorial statistical planning, with three parameters in two levels. The hydroxyapatite powder used was from Calcitek-USA. The crystallinity index was determined based on a quantitative procedure using the x-ray diffraction spectra. The roughness was measured by perfilometry and the porosity was estimated based on the weight of the coatings. The crystallinity index measured varied from 20-68%, the porosity from 3-25% and the roughness from 3,5-4,5 µm, for the different coating conditions. The process parameter which had the major effect on all the characteristics evaluated was the distance torch-substrate. Heat treatment of the coatings increased the crystallinity index to 99%.

KEYWORDS: Coatings, Hydroxyapatite, Plasma spray, Structure

INTRODUCTION

The plasma spray process parameters (PSP) affect the structure of the coatings, specially with respect to crystallinity, porosity, adhesion and cohesion. It is possible with some operation conditions to obtain very high enthalpy in the flame causing substantial fusion of the particles. The structure of the coatings will also depend on the time of permanence of the particles in the flame and on the solidification and cooling conditions. The high temperature of the plasma and the high cooling rates can promote the formation of amorphous phases, as it has been observed for hydroxyapatite coatings[1-3]. During the interaction particle-substrate the solidification and the liquid flow on the substrate occur simultaneously. The individual particles deform into shapes called splats[4]. The shape and size of the splats depend on the starting powder and on operation conditions and will affect the structure of the coating.

It is limited the number of papers that treat the relation between the process parameters and the structure of hydroxyapatite coatings in a systematic way. In this work an experiment matrix was set by the factorial statistical planning, with three parameters in two levels, to evaluate the effect of three main process parameters - arc current, distance torch-substrate and proportion of primary/secondary gases - on the crystallinity, porosity, and roughness of the coatings.

EXPERIMENTAL PROCEDURE

The substrate used for the coatings was the titanium alloy Ti6Al4V. Rectangular samples (22x22x1.5mm) were previously grit blasted and cleaned. The HA powder used was from CALCITEK, with particle size in the range 40-150μm ($P_{50} = 89$μm). The equipment used was METCO 3MBII.

The experiments were carried out using the statistical factorial planning, with three variables in two levels (high and low), as specified below:

    1 - proportion of primary/secondary gas: (primary gas=argon,   secondary gas=hydrogen)

        high (+) = 100/10 psi   low (-) = 100/5 psi

    2 - distance torch-substrate

        high (+) =150 mm   low (-) = 50 mm

    3 - arc current

        high (+) = 400 A   low (-) = 300 A

The factorial planning resulted in a matrix with 8 experiments, with replica, as shown in Table 1. The powder feed was 4g/min. The coating was done with a fixed number of steps.

Table 1. Statistical Factorial Planning Matrix

Sample	Proportion of gases	Distance torch-substrate	Current
AAA	(+)	(+)	(+)
AAB	(+)	(+)	(-)
ABA	(+)	(-)	(+)
BAA	(-)	(+)	(+)
ABB	(+)	(-)	(-)
BBB	(-)	(-)	(-)
BAB	(-)	(+)	(-)
BBA	(-)	(-)	(+)

In the evaluation of the crystallinity of the coating the X-ray diffraction analysis was used. A relative crystallinity index was defined as[5]:

$$CI = (A_c/A_0)100\% \qquad (1)$$

where A_c is the area below the XRD crystalline peaks from 25-35° for the coating and A_0 is the area the peaks in the same region for the HA powder. To calculate the areas, the XRD curves were deconvoluted in amorphous and crystalline components using spectral functions

Gaussian: $a_o \exp[-0{,}5\ (x - a_1/a_2)^2]$ amorphous phase   (2)

Lorentzian: $a_o/\{1+[(x - a_1)/a_2]^2\}$ crystalline phase   (3)

where a_0 is the amplitude , a_1 is the center and a_2 is the width. Figure 1 illustrates the fitting of this functions to the powder, considered 100% crystalline, and to a coated sample with a calculated crystallinity index of 45%.

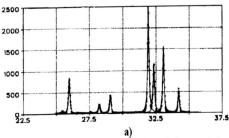 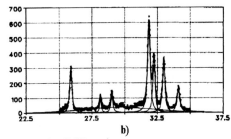

Figura 1. Deconvolution of DRX peaks. a) HA powder, b) HA coating

The roughness was measured with a Taylor Robson perfilometer, model Surtronic 3. Five measurements were done near the center of each sample. The bulk density of the coatings was calculated based on coatings weight and thickness measurements, and the porosity than calculated according to the equation:

$$\text{Porosity} = 1 - (\rho_{bulk}/\rho_{true}) \qquad (4)$$

where ρ_{bulk} is the calculated density and ρ_{true} is the density of HA (3,2 g/cm^3).

RESULTS

The results for all coatings are presented in Table 2. The crystallinity index varied from 40 to 60%, the porosity from 3 to 26% and the roughness from 3.5 to 4.5 μm. The statistical significance and the effect of the process parameters was evaluated using the statistical program MINITAB. Table 3 shows the effect of each variable and interactions among them on crystallinity, roughness and porosity.

Table 2. Roughness, Porosity and Crystallinity Index of Coatings

Sample	Crystallinity	Roughness (Ra)	Porosity (%)
BBB(S_1/S_2)	58.00/55.90	3.67 ± 0.23/3.47 ± 0.12	9.4
ABB(S_1/S_2)	60.50/59.10	3.65 ± 0.30/3.67 ± 0.12	15.6
BAB(S_1/S_2)	42.80/43.50	3.85 ± 0.19/3.87 ± 0.12	25.9
AAB(S_1/S_2)	48.60/50.10	4.47 ± 0.31/4.40 ± 0.40	6.3
BBA(S_1/S_2)	56.90/55.50	4.00 ± 0.43/4.05 ± 0.44	3.1
ABA(S_1/S_2)	55.50/54.20	4.13 ± 0.12/3.67 ± 0.12	6.3
BAA(S_1/S_2)	40.10/40.20	4.53 ± 0.31/4.13 ± 0.23	12.5
AAA(S_1/S_2)	40.05.40.10	4.33 ± 0.23/4.13 ± 0.23	4.7

Table 3. Effect off Plasma Spray Process Parameters (PSP) on the Structure of the Coatings

PSP (Interactions)	Crystallinity	Roughness	Porosity
Gas	1,91	0,11	46,56
Distance	-13,77	0,43	-44,44
Current	-4,49	0,24	-20,91
Gas-distance	1,16	0,13	- 4,51
Gas-current	-2,62	-0,22	-27,34
Distance-current	-1,64	-0,11	-19,49
Gas-distance-current	-0,52	-0,12	-7,46

The PSP distance, current and the interactions gas-current and distance-current had a significant effect of decrease on the CI. An increase in these parameters from the low level (-) to the high level (+) leads to a decrease in the CI. The proportion of gases and the interaction gas-distance present a significant effect of increase. The distance torch-substrate was the parameter that most affected the CI. The PSP proportion of gases presented a significant effect of increase on the porosity. Increasing this variable from the low level to the high level increased the porosity. All the other variables and interactions present an effect of decrease on the porosity. With respect to roughness, the PSP distance, gas, current and interaction gas-distance present a significant effect of increase.

The effect of the process parameters on the CI were also studied beyond the range set in the planning presented before. The modifications presented in Table 4 were carried out. A decrease in the values of CI was observed when distance and current were increased. Forced cooling of the substrate, by use of compressed air, decreased the CI to 20%, the lowest obtained in this work. Decreasing the proportion of hydrogen increased the CI to 68%. A decrease in the distance below 50 mm resulted in accentuated heating and oxidation of the substrate, destroying the adherence of the coating. Coating was not possible when the proportion of gases was decreased below 100/3.

A heat treatment of the coating was also carried out. Samples with initial CI of 40 % were heated at 600°C during 5 to 20 minutes. The CI increased to 99% in about 20 minutes.

Table 4. Modifications in the PSP

Sample	Gas (psi)	Distance (mm)	Current (A)	Crystallinity (%)
1	100/10	180	400	37,1
2	100/15	150	450	21,5 (*)
3	100/14	150	450	45,5
4	100/10	180	450	31,3
5	100/3	150	300	38,7
6	100/3	50	300	68,6

(*) substrate cooled with compressed air.

CONCLUSIONS

All three process parameters studied (current, distance and proportion of gases) had significant effect on the crystallinity, roughness and porosity of HA coatings. The distance torch-substrate was the parameter which presented the major effect. The CI was varied from 30 to 70% with variation in the PSP. Samples with forced cooling presented an CI of 20%. The heat treatment increased the CI to 99%. The roughness and porosity varied from 3,5-4,5μm and 3-25%, respectively, with variation in the PSP.

REFERENCES

1. Sampath, S. *Ph.D. Thesis*, SUNY at Stony Brook, USA, 1989
2. Yankee, SJ, Pletka, BJ. Proc. International Thermal Spray Conference, 1992, 453-457.
3. Gross, KA, Berndt, CC. *Bioceramic* 1995, **8**: 361-366
4. Herman, H. *Scientific American* 1988, 112-117.
5. Prevey, P S, Rotthwell, RJ. *Characterization and Perfomance of Calcium Phosphate Coatings for Implants, ASTM SPT 1196*, Philadelphia, 1994, 63-79.

Bioceramics Volume 11, edited by R. Z. LeGeros and J.P. LeGeros
(Proceedings of the 11th International Symposium on Ceramics in Medicine)
New York, NY, USA, November 1998
© 1998 by World Scientific Publishing Co. Pte. Ltd.

INFLUENCE OF CRYSTAL GROWTH ON SPUTTERED FILMS OF HYDROXYAPATITE ONTO TITANIUM

Jun-ichi Hamagami[1], Daisuke Kokubu[1], Takao Umegaki[1], and Kimihiro Yamashita[2]

[1]Department of Applied Chemistry, Graduate School of Engineering, Tokyo Metropolitan University, 1-1 Minami-Osawa, Hachioji, Tokyo 192-0397, Japan; [2]Institute for Medical and Dental Engineering, Tokyo Medical and Dental University, 2-3-10 Kanda-Surugadai, Chiyoda, Tokyo 101-0062, Japan

ABSTRACT

This report demonstrates the poling effects on the crystal growth of the sputtered hydroxyapatite (HAp) films using the simulated body fluid as *in vitro* testing medium. HAp thin films with 2 μm thickness were prepared onto titanium plate from the $CaHPO_4$ powder target by r.f. magnetron sputtering, followed by the annealing at 200℃ for 24 hr under a high water vapor pressure using an autoclave. The specimens were polarized in a dc field of 25 kV/cm at 300℃ for 1 hr, and then soaked in the SBF for the prescribed time. SEM observation showed that, compared with nonpolarized HAp specimens, polarized HAp accelerated or decelerated crystal growth, depending on the polarity; while the negatively charged surface was accelerated, the positively surface was decelerated. The HAp coatings polarized in negatively charged surface could be more useful in the fields of dental and medical application.

KEYWORDS: Hydroxyapatite, Sputtered thin film, Titanium metal, Poling treatment, Simulated body fluid, Crystal growth

INTRODUCTION

Radio frequency magnetron sputtering combined with post-annealing is one of the practical coating methods of hydroxyapatite ($Ca_{10}(PO_4)_6(OH)_2$, HAp) for clinical implant use [1-8]. The most advantage of this sputtering method is strong adhesion between coating and substrate. The biocompatibility of the sputtered coating implants was confirmed by the *in vivo* experiment using rabbits [7]. We have succeeded in preparation of HAp single-phase film onto titanium metal, which was obtained from calcium-phosphate glass used as sputtering target and low temperature annealing method. There are two key points; one is the sputtering target of calcium phosphate glass with Ca/P ratio of 0.75, which value is much lower than that of a stoichiometric HAp (Ca/P=1.67) [2]; the another one is the annealing at temperatures at least as high as 140℃ under high water vapor pressure using an autoclave [6].

HAp ceramics show dielectric properties below ~500℃. From a result of the thermally stimulated currents methods, HAp ceramics can be polarized above 212℃ which corresponds the monoclinic-to-hexagonal phase transition temperature caused by the reorientation of the OH⁻ ions along the c-axis in the HAp crystal structure [9]. We have recently discovered the acceleration and deceleration of bone-like crystal growth by *in vitro* experiment using the simulated body fluid (SBF[10]) on electrically poled bulk HAp [11,12]. The crystal growth depends on the electric polarization conditions. Beside HAp ceramics, the electrically poled barium titanate ($BaTiO_3$)

ceramics shows the same results on the apatitic crystal growth[12,13].

This paper first demonstrates the electrically poled HAp sputtered thin films onto titanium has an influence on the crystal growth in the *in vitro* experiments on apatitic crystal growth in the SBF.

MATERIALS AND METHODS

The precursor films were prepared by the r.f. magnetron sputtering apparatus (SPK-301, Tokki Co.).   The target for sputtering was calcium monohydrogen phosphate ($CaHPO_4$, DCP) powder (Taihei Chemical Industrial Co., Ltd.).   The substrate was 99.5% pure titanium metal plate (30 $\times$ 10 $\times$ 0.5 mm, Niraco Co.), which was mounted on a holder with cooling by water flow.   The r.f. power was 2.5 W/cm^2 operating at 13.56 MHz.   The sputtering was carried out in an argon atmosphere of 0.67 Pa.   The as-sputtered films were about 2 μm thickness.

These as-sputtered films were crystallized by post-annealing.   The method used for obtaining HAp crystal structure was as previously described [6].   The annealing was conducted at 200℃ for 24 hr under the saturated water vapor pressure using an autoclave.   As-sputtered and post-annealed specimens were characterized by X-ray diffraction (XRD), FT infrared (FT-IR) analyses.

Electrically poling of the post-annealed films was performed the electrode configuration illustrated in Figure 1.   The specimens were polarized sandwich between two metal electrodes; one is the titanium substrate, the other was a platinum foil contacted physically to the film surface. After the external dc electric field of 25 kV/cm was applied, the specimens was heated to 300℃ for 1 hr, and thereafter cooled to the room temperature under applying dc voltage.   In the poling treatment of the HAp films, negative and positive charged surfaces were denoted as N- and P-surface, respectively.   The specimens without poling treatment were abbreviated as 0-surface.

These specimens were soaked in 1.5 SBF, which contains the 1.5 times concentration of inorganic ions in the human body, with pH=7.25 at 36.5℃ for 1 to 3 days.   After soaking, the specimens were washed and dried, and then subjected to scanning electron microscopy (SEM).

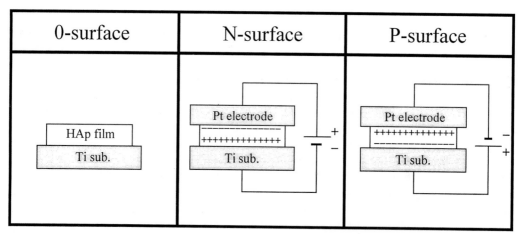

Figure 1.   Schematic illustration of the electrode configurations for the electrically poling treatment of the post-annealed films onto titanium and their abbreviations used.   The specimens were polarized in 25 kV/cm at 300℃ for 1hr.

RESULTS AND DISCUSSION

The post-annealed film was confirmed as single phase HAp from the XRD pattern.   The film was also confirmed by FT-IR to contain phosphate ions but hydroxyl ion did not detected.   These analytical results indicate the present film was assumed to be nonstoichiometric oxyhydroxyapatite.

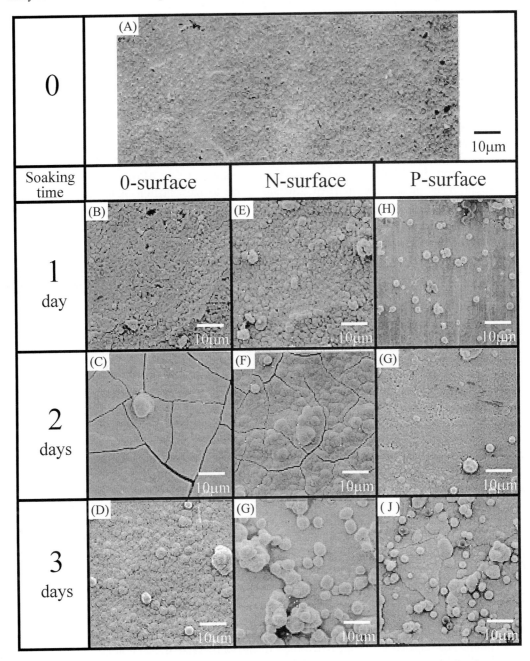

Figure 2. The scanning electron micrographs of the surfaces before (A) and after (B-J) soaking in the simulated body fluid (SBF) at 36.5℃. The photographs (B-J) were the surfaces of non-polarized films (B, C, D), negative-polarized films (E, F, G), and positive-polarized films (H, I, J) after immersion in SBF for 1, 2, 3 days.

Figure 2 shows the scanning electron micrographs of the film surfaces before (A) and after (B-F) immersion in 1.5 SBF. Before immersion (A), it shows the HAp film surface onto titanium. HAp coating was homogeneously covered with titanium substrate. After soaking in SBF, all the specimens with or without poling treatment occurs more or less the crystal growth. Good bioactivity of the coatings is validated by *in vitro* tests of the bone-like crystal growth in SBF. The amount of the grown crystals or layers increases with soaking time. Comparison of crystal growth rate of non-poled and poled specimens reveals different each other. Furthermore the rates depend on the polarity of the films; the rate of the N-surface is faster than that of the P-surface. These results are in good agreement with previous experimental data for HAp bulk ceramics and the model of changes in the crystal growth was reported [12]. The grown crystal rate compares also the 0-surface with the N-surface; the growth speed of the N-surface is higher than that of the 0-surface. These differences between 0- and N-surface are not clearly for HAp bulk ceramics [12]. This discrepancy is probably caused by varying the amount of the OH^- ions in the HAp lattice. The origin of the polarization of HAp structure is due to reorientation of the dipole moments between O^{2-} and H^+ of lattice OH^- ions [9].

SUMMARY

The poling effect on the crystal growth in simulated body fluid for the HAp sputtered thin films (2 μm thick) onto titanium substrates was phenomenologically investigated with a scanning electron microscope. The crystal growth is promoted in the negative charged surface and it is restrained in the positive one.

ACKNOWLEDGMENTS

This present research was financially supported by the Grants-in-Aid for both Scientific Research (A)(2) (Nos. 08405057, 10305047) and Encouragement of Young Scientists (No. 10750499) from the Ministry of Education, Science, Sports and Culture. One of the authors (K. Y.) is also indebted to The Sumitomo Foundation for undertaking his research project. We thank Taihei Chemical Co. Ltd. for providing the $CaHPO_4$ powder used as the sputtering target in this work.

REFERENCES

1. Arashi T, Yamashita K, Kanazawa T, Umegaki T. *Phos Res Bull* 1991; **1**: 221-226.
2. Yamashita K, Arashi T, Kitagaki K, Yamada S, Umegaki T. *J Am Ceram Soc* 1994; **77**: 2401-2407.
3. Yamashita K, Yagi T, Umegaki T. *J Am Ceram Soc* 1996; **79**: 3313-3316.
4. Yamashita K, Yagi T, Nakamura K, Umegaki T. *Phos Res Bull* 1996; **6**: 123-126.
5. Yamashita K, Yagi T, Hamagami J, Umegaki T. *Bioceramics* 1996; **9**: 337-340.
6. Hamagami J, Nakamura K, Sekine Y, Yamashita K, Umegaki T. *Bioceramics* 1997; **10**: 207-210.
7. Hulshoff JED, van Dijk K, van der Waerden JPCM, Wolke JGC, Kalk W, Jansen JA. *J Biomed Mat Res* 1996; **31**: 329-337.
8. Wolke JGC, de Groot K, Jansen JA. *J Biomed Mat Res* 1998; **39**: 524-530.
9. Hitmi N, La Cabanne C, Young RA. *J Phys Chem Solids* 1986; **47**: 533-546.
10. Tanahashi M, Kokubo T, Nakamura T, Yamamoto T. *J. Am Ceram Soc* 1995; **78**: 1049-1053.
11. Yamashita K, Oikawa N, Umegaki T. *Proc. 2nd Pac Rim Cont. Ceramics* 1996; (in press).
12. Yamashita K, Oikawa N, Umegaki T. *Chem Mater* 1996; **8**: 2697-2700.
13. Yonehara E, Yamashita K, Umegaki T. *Phos Res Bull* 1996; **6**: 301-304.

Bioceramics Volume 11, edited by R. Z. LeGeros and J.P. LeGeros
(Proceedings of the 11th International Symposium on Ceramics in Medicine)
New York, NY, USA, November 1998
© 1998 by World Scientific Publishing Co. Pte. Ltd.

CONVERSION OF ELECTROLYTICALLY DEPOSITED MONETITE TO HYDROXYAPATITE

M. H. Prado da Silva [1,2], G. D. A. Soares [2], C. N. Elias [3], I. R.Gibson [1], S. M. Best [1] and W. Bonfield [1]

[1] IRC in Biomedical Materials, Queen Mary and Westfield College, Mile End Road, London, E1 4NS, U.K., [2] COPPE/UFRJ; P.O.Box 68505; RJ - 21945-970; RJ., Brazil, [3] E.E.I.M.V.R. / UFF. Av dos Trabalhadores 420; RJ - Brazil

ABSTRACT

A highly crystalline and homogeneous HA coating was produced on pure titanium dental implants. The process involves electrolytic deposition of monetite and further conversion into pure HA by hydrothermal treatment. XRD analysis showed that the electrolytic coating consisted of high crystallinity monetite, while SEM analysis revealed crystals with a plate-like morphology. After hydrothermal treatment in NaOH, XRD analysis confirmed that the monetite was totally converted to high crystallinity HA. Observation of the specimens using SEM revealed that the plate-like monetite crystals were transformed to needle-shaped hydroxyapatite crystals. This finding is in contrast with previous studies on the transformation of brushite to hydroxyapatite which showed no morphological change.

KEYWORDS: Monetite, hydroxyapatite, titanium, coating, osseointegration

INTRODUCTION

Osseointegration of dental implants implies a direct, structural and functional connection between ordered living bone and the surface of a load-carrying implant. [1]

The normal procedure for dental implant surgeries involves two steps: first, the implant is inserted and allowed to osseointegrate unloaded. After integration has been presumed to occur, the prosthesis (tooth) is screwed on the implant, allowing load transmission. In order to reduce time between surgeries, dental implants coated with bioactive materials have been commercially produced. The aim of these bioactive materials being the promotion of a biological and thus strong bond with the forming bone. Hydroxyapatite (HA) is the most commonly used bioceramic coating on titanium implants, however, commercial coatings produced via plasma-spray deposition show the presence of cracks, formation of other phases and poor adhesion with the substrate. Other techniques such as electrolysis [2] and sol-gel processes [3] are alternatives to the plasma-spray process.

In this study, a technique was developed to produce a coating of pure and crystalline hydroxyapatite. This result was achieved by the transformation of pure monetite, electrolytically deposited on titanium, to hydroxyapatite.

MATERIALS AND METHODS

A cylindrical titanium implant 7mm in length by 2.2 mm in diameter was used as a cathode for the electrolytic deposition. A pure platinum plate bent to the shape of a cylinder was used as an anode. The electrodes were placed concentric to each other with the implant in the centre, and a distance of 10mm between the anode and the cathode. Implants were coated using 0.5M $Ca(OH)_2$, 0.3M H_3PO_4 and 1M CH_3CHCO_2HOH (lactic acid) as the electrolyte. Electrolysis was performed at a constant DC voltage of 2V for 50 minutes, at 80°C. The coating thus produced was then soaked in a solution of 0.1M NaOH at 60°C for 48h. The specimen was then thoroughly washed in distilled water and air dried. Phase composition was characterised by X-ray diffraction (XRD). Coating morphology was assessed by scanning electron microscopy (SEM).

RESULTS AND DISCUSSION

The coating presented a plate-like microstructure, as can be seen by Figure 1. It can be observed that the coating is fairly homogeneous in terms of crystal size and surface coverage. The titanium substrate was completely covered.

XRD analysis indicated that the coating consisted of high crystallinity monetite, as shown in Figure 2. No peaks associated with titanium were detection the pattern. This result confirms the homogeneity observed by SEM.

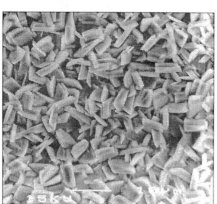

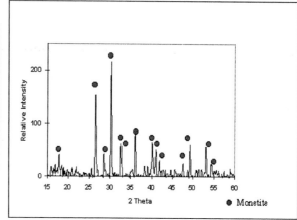

Figure 1 - SEM picture of the implant coated with monetite (1000X).

Figure 2 - XRD pattern showing the presence of monetite.

After hydrothermal treatment in NaOH at 60°C, the specimen was observed by SEM. The microstructure consisted of very fine shaped crystallites. At low magnification, a needle-like structure was observed growing from the surface of the previous monetite crystals (Figure 3). At higher magnification (figure 4), it can be clearly seen that the monetite microstructure has been completely transformed into a very fine, multi-needle microsctrucuture. This result is in contrast with previous studies on the transformation of brushite to hydroxyapatite without a change in morphology [4].

The XRD spectrum of the implant treated with NaOH confirmed that monetite was transformed to pure and crystalline hydroxyapatite (figure 5).

 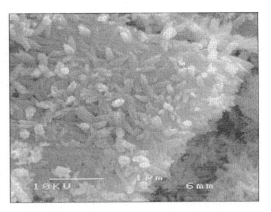

Figure 3 - Hydroxyapatite microstructure after treatment with NaOH at 60°C (3000X).

Figure 4 - Hydroxyapatite microstructure at high magnification (20000X) after treatment with NaOH.

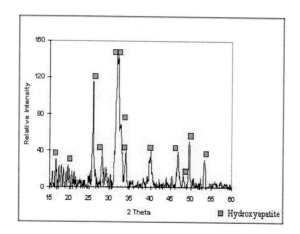

Figure 5 - XRD pattern showing the conversion of monetite to hydroxyapatite.

CONCLUSIONS

The final microstructure consisted of very fine needle-shaped crystals of hydroxyapatite. These crystallites grew from the surface to the monetite crystals. At high magnification, it was possible to observe that each monetite crystal gives rise to a multitude of hydroxyapatite needles. The needle-like microstructure is expected to provide bioactivity, as the hydroxyapatite crystals found in bone are also very fine. There was a substantial change in the morphology of the microstructure after the conversion from monetite to hydroxyapatite. Further *in vitro* tests are necessary to confirm the bioactivity of this coating.

ACNOWLEDGEMENTS

The support of the EPSRC for the IRC grant; CAPES, from the Brazilian government, for the support and Conexao Ltda. for having provided the implants for this study.

REFERENCES:

1 - A - Brånemark, P.-I., "Introduction to Osseointegration", Tissue-Integrated Prostheses - Osseointegration in Clinical Dentistry, Br©nemark, P.-I., Zarb, G., A., and Albrektsson, T., 1985, pp. 11 - 76;
2 - Asaoka, N., Best, S., and Bonfield, W., Bioceramics Volume 10, Elsevier Science Ltd., Paris, 1997, 447-450;
3 - Deputa, A., Lada, W., Olczak, T., LeGeros, R.Z., and LeGeros, J.P., Bioceramics Volume 9, Elsevier Science Ltd., Oxford, 1996, 313-316;
4 - Redepenning, J., Schlessinger, T., Burnham, S., Lippiello, L., and Miyano, J., Journal of Biomedical Materials Research, Volume 30, John Wiley & Sons Inc., 1996, 287-294.

Bioceramics Volume 11, edited by R. Z. LeGeros and J.P. LeGeros
(Proceedings of the 11th International Symposium on Ceramics in Medicine)
New York, NY, USA, November 1998

MECHANICAL AND STRUCTURAL CHARACTERISATION OF BIOACTIVE COATINGS

X.Y.Yang, M.Wang, K.A.Khor and Y.Wang

School of Mechanical and Production Engineering, Nanyang Technological University, Nanyang Avenue, Singapore 639798

ABSTRACT

Hydroxyapatite powders were made by reacting orthophosphoric acid with calcium hydroxide and dense bioactive coatings were subsequently produced by the plasma spraying technique. Three types of flame spheroidised hydroxyapatite monolayer coatings and two types of functionally graded coatings were manufactured. Precursor powders and bioactive coatings were characterised using various techniques. Micro-indentation was employed to assess mechanical properties of coatings. The crack propagation behaviour was also investigated. It was found that anisotropy of mechanical properties of as-sprayed coatings existed, which was related to the lamellar structure produced by the plasma spray technology. Average microhardness values of monolayer coatings decreased as the indentation load increased. The relationship between indentation load and indent diagonal observed Meyer's law. It was revealed that microhardness was affected by characteristics of precursor powders used for plasma spraying. The indentation fracture toughness of as-sprayed coatings was in general agreement with data found in the literature.

KEYWORDS: *hydroxyapatite, tricalcium phosphate, functionally graded coating, properties*

INTRODUCTION

Hydroxyapatite (HA) is widely used in various forms in the medical field. Being osteoconductive, one of its applications is to form a coating on metallic implants to serve as an interfacial bioactive phase between the implant and surrounding tissue after implantation [1, 2]. Apart from its bioactivity, a satisfactory HA coating must be tough and adherent for clinical uses.

Some tough but bioinert ceramics such as TiO_2, Al_2O_3 and ZrO_2 were used to form bioactive ceramic composites [3-5]. Other calcium phosphates such as tricalcium phosphate (α-TCP) can also be considered for toughening HA. Additionally, due to its resorbability, α-TCP in the HA-based composites can gradually dissolve after implantation so as to promote enhanced osseointegration.

One method to improve properties of coatings and the bonding strength between the coating and the substrate is to employ a coating with a novel structure. A functionally graded material, which has a compositional gradient from the surface to the interior of the material, can be used for such purposes [6]. In our investigation, functionally graded coatings (FGCs) were designed according to the adhesive strength and bio-resorbability of various components in the coatings. This paper presents some preliminary results on monolayer HA coatings and bioactive FGCs.

EXPERIMENTAL PROCEDURE

HA powders were produced using the precipitation method. Two solutions, orthophosphoric acid (H_3PO_4) and calcium hydroxide ($Ca(OH)_2$) with a concentration of 1M, were used for the reaction:

$$10Ca(OH)_2 + 6H_3PO_4 \longrightarrow Ca_{10}(PO_4)_6(OH)_2 + 18H_2O \qquad (1)$$

The reaction temperature was carefully controlled at 40°C. The precipitated HA powder was spray dried at 200°C. The sprayed dried powder was then flame sprayed into distilled water and finally oven dried to change particle characteristics. A vibratory sieving system was used to separate the flame spheroidised HA into three particle size ranges (R_p): 20~45µm, 45~75µm and 75~125µm.

The flame spheroidised HA (SHA) powders were sprayed onto Ti-6Al-4V plates to form bioactive coatings by using a 40 kW plasma spray system (SG-100, Miller Thermal Inc., USA). Argon was used as the main plasma forming gas and helium the auxiliary gas. The feeding rate of powders was about 20g/min and the spraying distance was 8~10cm.

Two types of FGCs were obtained by using (a) SHA powders with different R_p and (b) mixtures of SHA and spherical α-TCP powders. Table 1 shows the composition of FGCs. The thickness was around 400µm for each monolayer SHA coating and approximately 130µm for each sub-layer in FGCs.

Table 1   Composition of functionally graded coatings

Designation	The First Layer*	The Second Layer	The Third Layer
FGC 1	SHA (R_P: 20~45µm)	SHA (R_P: 45~75µm)	SHA (R_P: 75~125µm)
FGC 2	SHA (R_P: 20~45µm)	50wt% SHA, 50wt% α-TCP	α-TCP

* The first layer refers to the layer next to the Ti-6Al-4V substrate.

Phases of powders and bioactive coatings were analysed by using a Philips MPD 1880 X-ray diffractometer (XRD), while chemical components were detected by using energy dispersive X-ray spectroscopy (EDX). Cross-sections of coatings were prepared following an established procedure [6]. Microhardness tests were then performed on these cross-sections using Shimadzu HMV-2000 and HSV-20 hardness testers. Vickers diamond indenters were used. Indentation loads were 0.1, 0.2, 1.0, 2.0 and 2.5kgf and the holding time remained 15 seconds for all tests. A Cambridge Stereoscan 360 scanning electron microscope (SEM) was used to examine the microstructure of bioactive coatings and the morphology of Vickers indents. The indentation crack length was measured for obtaining the fracture toughness of various coatings.

RESULTS AND DISCUSSION

EDX spectra of spray dried HA powder showed that the main elements of the powder were calcium and phosphate. The Ca/P ratio was approximately 10:6, which is the stoichiometric value for pure hydroxyapatite.

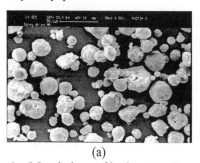   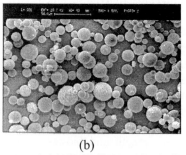

(a)   (b)

Fig.1   Morphology of hydroxyapatite powder: (a) sprayed dried, (b) flame spheriodised

Morphologies of spray dried and flame spheroidised HA powders are shown in Fig.1. The mean particle size of spray dried HA powder was within 50µm. Some pores could be found on the surface of these particles, indicating that the density of particles was lower than that of bulk HA. After flame spheroidisation, the shape of HA particles became spherical and the mean particle size decreased.

XRD patterns of spray dried and flame spheroidised powders were compared with the standard pattern for HA. It was demonstrated that the powders were chemically pure HA. Because the peak/background ratio was low while the width of peaks was wide, the amount of amorphous phase in the spray dried powders was thought to be high. It was noted that the relative crystallinity of HA increased and that no decomposition of HA was encountered through flame spheroidisation.

It was found that SHA significantly improved HA processability during plasma spraying. SEM examination of cross-sections of as-sprayed SHA coatings revealed that these coatings were dense and that the microstructure was composed of several randomly stacked lamellae. Some micropores and microcracks can be seen at the intersection of these lamellae. Therefore, the cracks induced by micro-indentation can propagate along the inter-lamellae defects.

Fig.2 shows a Vickers indent in the centre of an SHA coating. It was found that indentation cracks could not be produced when the indentation load was below 1.0kgf, but the four edges of Vickers indents were distinct under such loads. When the indentation load was above 1.0kgf, the length of induced microcracks became longer as the indentation load increased. Such phenomenon was observed in all three types of monolayer SHA coatings. The initiation site of microcracks induced was not the exact tip of the indent diagonal but near inter-lamellae defects.

The microhardness test results of SHA coatings are shown in Table 2. It was evident that microhardness of as-sprayed SHA coatings was affected by characteristics of feedstock powders. With a relatively small R_p, a much denser HA coating could be obtained and mechanical properties of the coating would be consequently better.

Table 2   Microhardness of monolayer SHA coatings

Indentation Load	Microhardness (VHN)		
(kgf)	R_p: 20~45μm	R_p: 45~75μm	R_p: 75~125μm
0.1	330	302	270
0.2	291	274	242
1.0	267	251	221
2.0	256	234	209
2.5	247	228	199

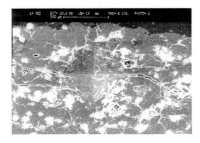

Fig.2   A Vickers indent and induced microcracks in the SHA coating (L=2kgf)

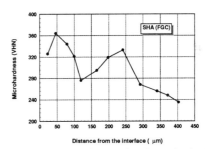

Fig.3   Variation of microhardness in the SHA functionally graded coating

Fig.3 exhibits the variation of microhardness in the SHA FGC (L=0.1kgf). It shows that the sub-layer with a large R_p possessed low microhardness. It was found that indentation load (L) and indent diagonal length (d) observed Meyer's law:

$$L = a \times d^{n} \tag{2}$$

where a is a material-related constant and n the Meyer parameter. In the current investigation, n is lower than 2 for plasma-sprayed SHA coatings. Microhardness (H) can be expressed by the following equation:

$$H = A \times L^{1-2/n} \tag{3}$$

where A is a constant. Because n is lower than 2, the microhardness value decreases as the indentation load increases. Results obtained from other ceramic materials show a similar trend [7].

The indentation fracture toughness (K_{IC}) can be calculated using the following equation [8]:

$$K_{IC} = 0.016 \ (E/H)^{1/2} \ (L/C^{3/2}) \tag{4}$$

where E is Young's modulus of the coating and C the crack length. Assuming Young's modulus of HA was 100GPa [6], fracture toughness values of SHA coatings and sub-layers of FGCs were obtained (Table 3). It was noted that K_{IC} decreased as the feedstock particle size increased. K_{IC} was around 1MPa·m$^{-1/2}$ when the particle size was below 45μm. It decreased dramatically to less than 0.55MPa·m$^{-1/2}$ when the particle size was above 45μm. Results for three sub-layers of FGC 1 were similar to those of respective monolayer SHA coatings with the same R_p. K_{IC} values of FGC 2 showed that the fracture toughness of α-TCP was about 1.41MPa·m$^{-1/2}$, which was higher than that of SHA. Moreover, K_{IC} of the second layer of FGC 2 remained at 1.28MPa·m$^{-1/2}$, while K_{IC} of the first layer of FGC 2 (i.e. the HA layer) decreased to 1.05MPa·m$^{-1/2}$. It could be inferred that the addition of tougher ceramics would improve the fracture toughness of pure HA coatings. The fracture toughness of SHA coatings was in general agreement with other investigations [5]. Therefore, methods such as post-spray treatment or introducing a toughening phase should be considered for improving the toughness of HA coatings.

Table 3   Fracture toughness of monolayer SHA coatings and sub-layers of FGCs

Designation of Coatings	SHA (20~45μm)	SHA (45~75μm)	SHA (75~125μm)	FGC 1 (1st layer)	FGC 1 (2nd layer)	FGC 1 (3rd layer)
K_{IC} (MPa·m$^{-1/2}$)	0.948	0.547	0.455	1.045	0.569	0.469

CONCLUSIONS

1. Dense HA coatings and bioactive FGCs can be produced by using flame spheroidised HA powders and spherical α-TCP powder. Microhardness of coatings is affected by characteristics of feedstock powders.
2. The average microhardness value of SHA coatings decreases as the indentation load increases. The relationship between indentation load and indent diagonal observed Meyer's law, with the Meyer parameter being lower than 2.
3. The propagation of induced microcracks demonstrates anisotropy of the coatings, which is related to the lamellar structure produced by the plasma spray method.
4. The fracture toughness (K_{IC}) of SHA coatings decreases as the particle size range increases. Methods such as post-spray treatment or introducing a toughening phase need to be used to improve their fracture toughness.

ACKNOWLEDGEMENTS

Two co-authors (XYY and YW) thank Nanyang Technological University for providing research scholarships. The technical assistance provided by Ms. Yong Mei Yoke is gratefully acknowledged.

REFERENCES

1. Lin JHC, Liu ML, Ju CP, *J. Mater. Sci. Mat. Med.*, (1994), **5**, 279-283
2. Radin SR, Ducheyne P, *J. Mater. Sci. Mat. Med.*, (1992), **3**, 33-42
3. Salomoni A, Tucci A, Esposito L, Stamenkovic I, *J. Mater. Sci. Mat. Med.*, (1994), **5**, 651-653
4. Silva VV, Domingues RZ, *J. Mater. Sci. Mat. Med.*, (1997), **8**, 907-910
5. Slosarczyk A, Bialoskorski J, *J. Mater. Sci. Mat. Med.*, (1998), **9**, 103-108
6. Khor KA, Cheang P, Wang Y, *J. Minerals, Metals & Materials Society*, (1997), **49**, 51-57
7. Bull SJ, Page TF, Yoffe EH, *Phil. Mag. Lett.*, (1989), **59**, 281-288
8. Beshish GK, Florey CW, Worzala FJ, Lenling WJ, *J. Thermal Spray Technol.*, (1993), **2**, 35-38

Bioceramics Volume 11, edited by R. Z. LeGeros and J.P. LeGeros
(Proceedings of the 11th International Symposium on Ceramics in Medicine)
New York, NY, USA, November 1998
© 1998 by World Scientific Publishing Co. Pte. Ltd.

COMPARATIVE STUDY OF SOME EXPERIMENTAL OR COMMERCIAL CALCIUM PHOSPHATE BONE CEMENTS

F.C.M. Driessens[1], M.G. Boltong[1], E.A.P. De Maeyer[1], C.W.J. Vercruysse[1],
R. Wenz[2] and R.M.H. Verbeeck[1]

[1]Department of Dental Materials Science, Dental School, Institute for Biomedical Technologies,
University of Gent, De Pintelaan 185 (P8), B-9000 Gent, Belgium
[2]Merck Biomaterial, D-64271 Darmstadt, Germany

ABSTRACT

Five experimental or commercial calcium phosphate bone cements were collected. X-ray diffraction of the cement powders was carried out to determine their phase composition. The recommended liquid/powder ratio's were derived from the instructions for use. The injectability of the cement pastes was determined right after mixing. The initial and the final setting time were determined at 20°C and 37°C with Gilmore needles. The compressive strength was determined after immersion for 1 day in Ringer's solution. The results show that Biocement D is superior, Norian SRS is average and Cementek is inferior in various respects. These cements are osteotransductive, i.e. upon implantation in bone they are transformed into new bone at a rate determined by the local remodelling process.

KEYWORDS: calcium phosphate cements, bone cements, injectability, setting time, compressive strength, phase composition, osteotransductivity.

INTRODUCTION

Brown and Chow[1] described the first calcium phosphate bone cement CPBC. Such a material consists of a liquid and a powder which can be mixed into a paste which sets spontaneously at room or body temperature whereby a precipitate is formed which contains one or more calcium phosphates. CPBC's are known in which the calcium phosphate precipitate is either brushite $CaHPO_4.2H_2O$ or calcium hydroxyapatite $Ca_{10}(PO_4)_6(OH)_2$ or calcium deficient hydroxyapatite $Ca_9(HPO_4)(PO_4)_5$ OH or amorphous calcium phosphate ACP or carbonated apatite of a variable composition[2,3]. These materials are being commercialized right now or are already on the market. For the present comparative study the products mentioned in Table 1 were collected.

Table 1. Calcium phosphate bone cements collected for this study.

Name of the product	L/P	Manufacturer or Distributor
Norian SRS,	0.46	Norian Corporation, Cupertino, CA, USA
Cementek, Ref. 815123, Lot SP 2/9607	0.43	Teknimed S.A., Vic en Bigorre, France
Biocement D	0.30	Merck Biomaterial, Darmstadt, Germany
Experimental 1	0.75	not known to the investigators
Experimental 2	0.33	not known to the investigators

METHODS OF INVESTIGATION

The calcium phosphate bone cements were stored at room temperature in their containers until use. X-ray diffraction was used to determine the qualitative phase composition of the cement powders and of the completely hardened cements. Fourier-transform infrared spectroscopy was used to analyze qualitatively for OH^- and CO_3^{2-} groups, both in the initial cement powders and in the final hardened cements.

Cement pastes were obtained by mixing the cement powder and the cement liquid according to the manufacturers instructions. The injectability I% of these cement pastes was determined 2 min after starting the mixing by extrusion from a 20 ml disposable syringe of Millipore (Bedford, Massachusetts) Catalogue Number XX 1102012. They have an opening of 2 mm. Amounts of about 3 g of cement paste were taken and the "injectability" was taken as the percentage by weight of that paste of this amount of paste which could be extruded from the syringe by hand.

The initial setting time t_I and the final setting time t_F were determined both at 20°C in air and at 37°C while the sample was immersed in Ringer's solution, as published elsewhere[4]. The compressive strength C of the cements was determined 1 day after immersion of the samples in Ringer's solution with a Lloyd's Mechanical Testing Machine at a cross-head speed of 1 mm min^{-1}. For that purpose cylindrical samples were made with a height of 12 mm and a diameter of 6 mm in a teflon mold. They were ground parallel on emory paper and demolded just prior to testing[5].

Quantitative chemical testing of the initial cement powders and of the hardened cements 1 day after immersion in Ringer's solution was done on the Ca content by Atomic Absorption Spectrometry and on P content by UV-VIS spectroscopy on the phospho-molybdate complex. The molar Ca/P ratio's were calculated from these results.

RESULTS

The qualitative phase composition of the initial cement powders and of the hardened cements are given in Table 2. Ap stands for apatite, α-TCP for α-tertiary calcium phosphate, TTCP for tetracalcium phosphate, DCP for dicalcium phosphate and DCPD for dicalcium phosphate dihydrate. The sequence of phases is given in decreasing order. According to FTIR the products Norian SRS and Biocement D contained B-type CO_3^2. after setting. All products except Experimental 1 contained OH^- groups after reaction.

Table 2.   Qualitative phase composition of the cement powders and of the hardened cements.

Product	Cement powder	Hardened cement
Norian SRS	α-TCP, $CaCO_3$	Ap, $CaCO_3$
Cementek	TTCP, α-TCP	Ap
Biocement D	α-TCP, DCP, $CaCO_3$, Ap	Ap, DCP, $CaCO_3$
Experimental 1	ACP, DCPD	ACP, DCPD
Experimental 2	α-TCP, TTCP, DCP	Ap, DCP

Table 3.   Injectability I%, initial setting time $t_I^{(min)}$, final setting time $t_F^{(min)}$ and compressive strength C (MPa) of the calcium phosphate bone cements.

Product	I	t_I (20°C)	t_I (37°C)	t_F (20°C)	t_F (37°C)	C
Norian SRS	83 (1)*	22 (1)	6½ (½)	37 (1)	8½ (½)	33 (5)
Cementek	81 (1)	36 (1)	9½ (½)	64 (2)	17 (1)	8 (2)
Biocement D	94 (1)	9½ (½)	2 ¾ (¼)	19 (1)	7½ (½)	48 (3)
Experimental 1	96 (1)	70 (5)	11 (1)	> 200	19 (1)	4 (1)
Experimental 2	92 (1)	90 (15)	9 (1)	180 (30)	24 (1)	15 (5)

*Standard deviations between brackets.

The working properties I%, t_I and t_F as well as the compressive strength C are shown in Table 3. The injectability of Norian SRS and Cementek are on the low side. It can have some advantage, if t_I (20°C) and t_F (20°C) are relatively long, but certainly t_I (37°C) and t_F (37°C) must be as short as possible. That applies to Norian SRS and Biocement D. As far as strength is concerned, for load bearing applications the hardened cement must be as strong as human trabecular bone (which is maximum 30 MPa). This applies marginally to Norian SRS and more than sufficiently to Biocement D. Further, the values of t_I and t_F can be adjusted for Biocement D over a wide range by varying[6] the accelerator concentrations % Na_2HPO_4 in the cement liquid. The values for Biocement D in Table 3 apply to 4% accelerator. This means that as far as handling and mechanical properties are concerned Norian SRS is average and Biocement D is superior, whereas Cementek and Experimental 1 are the least suitable and certainly not for load bearing applications neither is Experimental 2.

The first four materials were analyzed for Ca and P content. See Table 4. Especially Cementek looses calcium upon storage during 1 day in Ringer's solution, Norian SRS and Biocement D loose less calcium and Experimental 1 seems to be practically stable during the first day of immersion.

Table 4.   Analyses of some cement powders and of their cements after 1 day immersion in Ringer's solution.

Product	Cement powders			Cements after immersion		
	% Ca	% P	Ca/P	% Ca	% P	Ca/P
Norian SRS	38.17	17.30	1.705	35.64	16.47	1.672
Cementek	35.92	15.90	1.746	34.68	16.58	1.616
Biocement D	36.15	18.47	1.513	34.80	18.16	1.481
Experimental 1	31.38	18.02	1.346	31.73	18.24	1.344

DISCUSSION

At this moment it becomes clear that several calcium phosphate bone cements are going to compete on the market for bone substituting materials. Terms like osteoconductive, osteoinductive and osteogenic are of wide spread use nowadays, but they are not suitable to describe the actual in vivo behaviour of CPBC's upon implantation. In fact, their in vivo behaviour resembles most that op B-TCP ceramics, i.e. they are resorbed by osteoclastic activity whereas on the interface new bone is deposited by osteoblasts. So these materials do not substitute permanently for bone, they are slowly replaced by new bone. Such a behaviour has been called osteotransductivity[7], i.e. biodegradation and at the same time replacement by new bone occurs. In this respect, many clinicians demand from the manufacturers that they indicate how rapid this transformation into new bone proceeds. This demand, however, is not realistic because, first of all, the local remodelling rate at the site of the implant will control this process and thus the outcome will depend on species, age and site. And, secondly, it is expected that the type of CPBC, i.e. the nature of the calcium phosphate precipitate as mentioned in the introduction, plays only a minor role in the control of the rate of osteotransduction. This is due to the fact that most of the CPBC's are already apatitic, whereas the other CPBC's of the brushite and the APC type pass into an apatitic stage upon some weeks long contact with body fluids. Further animal experiments are necessary to investigate whether there will be a difference in the rate of osteotransduction between CPBC's at all.

The outcome of this comparative study is that Biocement D is superior compared to the known competing calcium phosphate cements. It should be noted that in addition to the good properties of injectability, setting times and compressive strength it also has a suitable dough time, a short cohesion time, no shrinkage or expansion during setting, no rise or decrease in temperature during setting, no cytotoxicity during and after setting and a pH between 7 and 8.5 during setting and of about 7.5 after setting[7,10]. These properties make this CPBC biocompatible in any respect.

REFERENCES

1. Brown WE and Chow LE. In : PW Brown (Ed.) Cements Research Progress, Am. Ceram. Soc. Westerville OH 1986; 351-379.
2. Driessens FCM. Fourth Euro Ceramics 1995; **8**:77-83.
3. Driessens FCM, Planell JA, Gil FJ. In : Wise DL, Trantolo DJ, Altobelli DE, Yaszemski MJ, Gesser JD, Schwarz ER (Eds.) Encyclopedic Handbook of Biomaterials and Bioengineering, Post B : applications, Vol. 2, New York, Marcel Dekker Inc. 1995; 855-877.
4. Driessens FCM, Boltong MG, Bermudez A, Planell JA. J. Mater. Sci. Mat. Med. 1993; **4**:503-508.
5. Bermudez O, Boltong MG, Driessens FCM, Planell JA. J. Mater. Sci. Mat. Med. 1993; **4**:389-393.
6. Fernandez E, Boltong MG, Ginebra MP, Bermudez A, Driessens FCM, Planell JA. Clinical Materials 1994; **16**:99-103.
7. Driessens FCM, Khairoun I, Boltong MG, Planell JA. Bioceramics 1997; **10**:279-282.
8. Driessens FCM, De Maeyer EAP, Fernandez E, Boltong MG, Berger G, Verbeeck RMH, Ginebra MP, Planell JA. Bioceramics 1996; **9**:231-234.
9. Constantz BR, Barr BM, Quinoit J, Ison IC, Baker JT, McKinney L, Goodman SB, Sumner DR, Gunasekaran S. Fourth World Biomaterials Congress, Berlin, 1992; p 56.
10. Ginebra MP, Fernandez E, Boltong MG, Planell JA, Bermudez O, Driessens FCM, Bioceramics 1994; **7**:273-278.

Bioceramics Volume 11, edited by R. Z. LeGeros and J.P. LeGeros
(Proceedings of the 11th International Symposium on Ceramics in Medicine)
New York, NY, USA, November 1998
© 1998 by World Scientific Publishing Co. Pte. Ltd.

SETTING CONTRACTION OF VLC COMPOSITE RESINS AND GLASS-IONOMER CEMENTS

V.Fano, W.Y.Ma, I.Ortalli, K.Pozela

Istituto Scienze Fisiche dell'Università
Istituto Nazionale Fisica della Materia
Via Volturno, 39, 43100 Parma, Italy
FAX +39.0521.903712

ABSTRACT

The contraction kinetics of VLC composite resins and GIC was experimentally analyzed by scanning laser beam method. The length of the samples was 2-4 mm and the accuracy of the length measurements was ±1 µm. The comparison of the experimental data with the analytical expression of the contraction in VLC materials required all the various steps (initiation, propagation and termination) of the polymerization process to be clearly distinguished. The experimental expression we used for the best fit included a time constant (0.12 min $\geq \tau \geq 0.50$ min) and a corrective factor ($0.25 \geq \beta \geq 0.75$). For GIC maerials, the best fit of the theoretical expression of the contraction with the experimental values showed an additional exponential term, which characterized the evaporation process.

KEYWORDS: Composite resins, glass-ionomer cements, dimensional variation, restorative materials.

INTRODUCTION

The contraction of visible light cured (VLC) composite resins and glass-ionomer cements, which are dental restorative materials, is affected by some factors [1-5] related to the polymerization of the resin (degree of conversion, concentration of methacrylate groups, volume fraction of the resin). Other factors are dependent on the filler (type, size and coating) and concentration of the photosensitizer-photoreducer system, which affects the ultimate structure and density of the polymer network. For glass-ionomer materials, containing volatile substances (water), the contraction is affected significantly by the evaporation of the acqueous component too. Consequently some informations concerning these phenomena, particularly the plymerization and evaporation, can be obtained by the study of the contraction as a function of time and by comparison with the numerical model.

In this work, we show that the details of the polymerization (the initiation period and the start of propagation step) of VLC composite resins are well highlighted by the behavior of the contraction as a function of time. The kinetics of the contraction, due to the propagation of the polymeric chains has been compared with the theoretical behavior based on the chemical reaction.

The contraction of a glass-ionomer cement has been analyzed too. In this case the contraction is due both to the polymerization reaction and to evaporation of the volatile component. By the best fit of these two expression with the experimental curve, the kinetics of both polymerization and evaporation has been assessed quantitatively.

MODELING

Polymerization Contraction

The contraction induced by the polymerization process can be assumed dependent on the concentration of reacted monomers. The reaction of VLC monomer involves three principal steps: photosensitization and initiation (1° step), propagation of the polymeric chains (2° step), termination of the reaction (3° step). The concentration of monomers, involved in the initiation step, is relatively small and can be neglected. For VLC polymerization, the propagation step rapidly achieves steady state conditions. In these conditions, contraction (contraction$_{pol}$) is assumed to be proportional to the degree of conversion (DC) of the monomers, $(M_o-M)/M_o$, where M_o is the initial concentration, M is the concentration at time t, i.e.

$$\text{contraction}_{pol} \propto \text{DC} = \frac{M_o - M}{M_o} = \frac{d[M]}{dt} \tag{1}$$

The integration of equation (1) gives an exponential function of time:

$$\text{contraction} \propto 1 - \exp - (t/\tau_1), \tag{2}$$

where τ_1 is a time constant - the time for the contraction to attain 1-exp(-1) value, i.e. 0.632 of its final value, a_1 The resins of composite materials are highly cross-linked glassy materials. In this case

$$\text{contraction}_{pol} \propto 1-\exp-(t/\tau_1)^\beta, \tag{3}$$

where $0 \le \beta \le 1$.

Evaporation Contraction

Glass polyalkenoate cements consist of ion-leachable glass powder and a polyalkenoic acid. Owing to the evaporation of water of the acid part, the contraction expression of these materials must show an additional term (contraction$_{ev}$). Assuming this term proportional to the water concentration on the surface, C, the total contraction (contraction$_{tot}$) can be expressed by the equation

$$- \text{contraction}_{tot} = - (\text{contraction}_{pol} + \text{contraction}_{ev}) =$$

$$= \Delta L_o + a_1 \left[\exp - \left(\frac{t-t_o}{\tau_1} \right)^\beta - 1 \right] + a_2 \left[\exp - \left(\frac{t-t_o}{\tau_2} \right) - 1 \right] \tag{4}$$

where ΔL_o and t_o are the change of the length and the time at the beginning of the propagation reaction, a_1 and a_2 are the final dimensional change due to the polymerization and evaporation respectively.

EXPERIMENTAL

Commercially available materials (Silux plus, 3M, and Fuji II LC, GC) were handled following the instructions of manufacturer. The specimens (1.5 mm width, 2-4 mm length) were polymerized by blue light irradiation for 1 minute (mini-halogen light Heliolux II Vivadent, 1 min irradiation).

The linear dimensional change was measured by laser beam scanning in accordance with the method described in.[8] The signals from the laser apparatus were recorded continuously (two or more automatic measurements per second) by a computer system. The zero-time of the graphs corresponded to the start of the irradiation. Accuracy of measurements: ±1 μm.

RESULTS AND DISCUSSION

Composite Resins

The expression (3) show that the shrinkage kinetics of composite resins is characterized by τ and ß parameters and supposes that the starting time of the propagation step is known. Owing to the exponential behavior, the accuracy in the measurement of the starting time can affect significantly the fit of the equation (3). Our method of measurement allowed to examine the details of the transition from the initiation step to the propagation one. Fig. 1 is an example of a composite resin in the early stage of the polymerization. The experimental points were recorded two times per second. Usually, materials of different manufacturers were nearly constant in length during 2-4 seconds immediately after the start of irradiation; an exponential decrease followed this step.

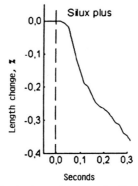

Figure 1. Contraction of Silux plus in the early stage of polimerization. Zero-time is the start of irradiation.

The validity of the equation (3), related to a composite resin, was tested by comparing the kinetics of the experimental contraction with the calculated curves. Fig. 2 shows an example. The continuous curve is the theoretical one; the points are recorded experimentally, τ and ß values of different materials were: $0.12 \geq \tau \geq 0.50$ min, $0.25 \geq ß \geq 0.75$.

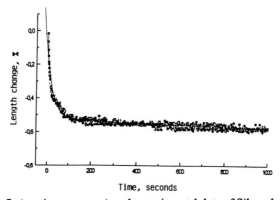

Figure 2. The best fit (continuous curve) and experimental data of Silux plus contraction. τ=0.3, β=0.5.

Glass-ionomer Materials

The validity of the equation (4) was tested by comparing the kinetics of the experimental contraction of a glass-ionomer cement with the calculated curves. Fig. 3 shows the experimental data (curve 1) and the best fit (curve 2) related to Fuji II CL specimen. The curve 2 is a sum of two functions, which are expressions of the setting reaction (τ and β are similar to the values of the composite resins) and the evaporation process.

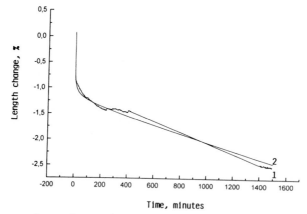

Figure 3. The experimental curve (curve 1) and the best fit (curve 2) of a Fuji II LC specimen. For the fit, the expression (4) has been used ($\tau = 0.3$, $\beta = 0.3$, $a_1 = 1.2$)

The preliminary results, related to other materials, show that the contribution, due to the setting reaction, is half of the total contraction on average. A more detailed study is in progress.

CONCLUSIONS

The behavior of the contraction as a function of time gives quantitative informations about the polymerization mechanism and the evaporation process.
The best fit of the theoretical expression with the experimental data suggests that the short test of contraction can substitute the long experimental tests in order to determine the final contraction.

ACKNOWLEDGEMENTS

This work has been supported in part by M.S.T.A. II Project of C.N.R..

REFERENCES

1. Asmussen E, Scand J Dent Res 1982;90:484-489.
2. Munksgaard EC, Hansen EK, Kato H. Scand J Dent Res 1987;95:526-531.
3. Feilzer AJ, De Gee AJ, Davidson CL. Prosthet Dent 1988;59:297-300.
4. Bausch JR, de Lange K, Davidson CL, Peters A, de Gee AJ. J Prosthet Dent 1982;48:59-67.
5. Bowen RL, Rapson JE, Dickson G. J Dent Res 1982;61:654-658.
6. Braem M, Lambrichts P, Vanherle G, Davidson CL. J Dent Res 1987;66:1713-1716.
7. Cook WD, Beech DR, Tyes MJ. Biomaterials 1985;6:362-368.
8. Fano V, Ma WY, Ortalli I, Pozela K. Biomaterials, in press.

Bioceramics Volume 11, edited by R. Z. LeGeros and J.P. LeGeros
(Proceedings of the 11th International Symposium on Ceramics in Medicine)
New York, NY, USA, November 1998
© 1998 by World Scientific Publishing Co. Pte. Ltd.

INFLUENCE OF REACTION KINETICS ON THE SETTING AND HARDENING PROPERTIES OF DCP-α-TCP BONE CEMENTS

E. Fernández,[1,2] S.M. Best,[1] F.J. Gil,[2] M.P. Ginebra,[2] F.C.M. Driessens,[2] J.A. Planell[2] and W. Bonfield[1]

[1]IRC in Biomedical Materials, Queen Mary and Westfield College, Mile End Road, London E1 4NS, UK; [2]Dept. of Materials Science and Metallurgy, Universitat Politècnica de Catalunya, Av. Diagonal 647, 08028-Barcelona, Spain.

ABSTRACT

Calcium phosphate cements (CPC) are of considerable interest in medicine and dentistry due to their excellent biocompatibility and bone-repair properties. The aim of this study was to identify the chemical reactions responsible for the setting and hardening of $CaHPO_4$-α-$Ca_3(PO_4)_2$ (DCP-α-TCP) cements and to determine how calcium carbonate (CC) influences kinetics and mechanical properties.

DCP and α-TCP mixtures containing 10 wt% CC were adjusted to Calcium/Phosphorus (Ca/P) ratios in the range 1.30 to 1.50. X-ray Diffraction (XRD) was used to record the evolution of dissolving and precipitating phases. Compressive strength measurements were performed in an Instron testing machine.

XRD showed: a) strong correlation between the reactivity of the different phases and the Ca/P ratio of the mixture; b) hydration of α-TCP into a calcium deficient hydroxyapatite (CDHA) was responsible for setting and for a further increase in compressive strength and c) 5 wt% CC combined with CDHA to give a mineral phase more similar to bone. Compressive strength showed a retardation in its evolution rate against the CC addition. However, at saturation and for the optimum mixture, compressive strength reached values up to 40% higher than CC-free samples.

KEYWORDS: Calcium phosphate cements, carbonate apatites, X-ray diffraction

INTRODUCTION

Calcium deficient hydroxyapatite (CDHA; $Ca_9(HPO_4)(PO_4)_5OH$) is the final product of the setting reaction in several α-TCP based cement systems.[1,2] CDHA crystallites are nucleated on the surface of α-TCP particles from the calcium phosphate supersaturated solution which surrounds the particles after their initial dissolution. Further dissolution of α-TCP particles and growth of CDHA crystals is controlled by a diffusion process through the initial shell of CDHA crystallites. The initial setting and final hardening properties of the cement material depend on the formation of the framework of entangled crystals trough this diffusion process.

To improve the biocompatibility of these cements, the CDHA structure has been modified into a calcium carbonate deficient apatite (CCDA), which is more similar to bone mineral than stoichiometric hydroxyapatite,[3] by adding $CaCO_3$ (CC) to the initial powder mixture. However, the presence of carbonate ions in a supersaturated solution of calcium phosphates affects the crystallisation of the apatite and limits the size and morphology of the forming CCDA crystallites.[4-6] The objective of this study was to investigate how CC affects the setting and hardening properties of cements formed mainly by mixtures of DCP and α-TCP. Smaller and more spheroidal crystallites are expected to affect the formation of the crystallite-shells and as a consequence the network of entangled crystals responsible for the mechanical properties.

MATERIALS AND METHODS

Powder cement samples

DCP and α-TCP mixtures were prepared so as to obtain Ca/P ratios from 1.30 to 1.50 and were coded as series A, A130 to A150, respectively. The same samples were prepared with an addition of 10 wt% of CC and were coded as series B, B130 to B150, respectively.

XRD and FTIR analysis

The cement pastes, prepared at a water to powder ratio (W/P) of 0.35 ml/g, were placed in Teflon moulds and immersed in Ringer's solution at 37°C for 120 hours. After that time, cement pastes were removed from the moulds, quenched in acetone, dried for several days and powdered for study by XRD and Infra-red Spectroscopy (IR). Diffraction peaks were indexed with the appropriate Joint Committee Powder Diffraction Standards (JCPDS) files. IR was performed on pressed discs made of a mixture of cesium bromide with 0.3 wt% powder samples.

Compressive strength

The cement samples (6 mm in diameter and 12 mm in height) were polished and unmolded after soaking for different time intervals up to a maximum time of 120 hours. The compressive strength was measured using an Instron testing machine at 1 mm/min crosshead speed at ambient temperature and hardening curves were obtained for each Ca/P ratio sample.

RESULTS AND DISCUSSION

XRD and FTIR analysis

Fig. 1 shows that, after 5 days of ageing, series A can be evaluated as a two-phase system by XRD.[7] Eqs. 1 and 2 quantify the weight fraction of DCP (w_{DCP}) and/or CDHA (w_{CDHA}) by measuring the ratio of the intensity of a certain diffraction peak in the mixture (I_{DCP} or I_{CDHA}) over the same intensity peak in a pure sample (I_{DCP}^P or I_{CDHA}^P). The mass absorption coefficients of DCP and CDHA, in cm²/g, are M_{DCP}=73.27 and M_{CDHA}=84.97, respectively. Experimental points in Fig. 1 were obtained measuring the most intense diffraction peaks of DCP (hkl=1$\underline{1}$2; $2\theta°$=30.20) and CDHA (hkl=211; $2\theta°$=31.82). w_{DCP} and w_{CDHA} were calculated assuming that both, DCP did not react and α-TCP fully converted into CDHA according to its molar relation.

$$\frac{I_{DCP}}{I_{DCP}^P} = \frac{M_{DCP} \cdot w_{DCP}}{M_{CDHA} + \left(M_{DCP} - M_{CDHA}\right) \cdot w_{DCP}} = \frac{73.27 \cdot w_{DCP}}{84.97 - 11.7 \cdot w_{DCP}} \quad (1)$$

$$\frac{I_{CDHA}}{I_{CDHA}^P} = \frac{M_{CDHA} \cdot w_{CDHA}}{M_{DCP} - \left(M_{DCP} - M_{CDHA}\right) \cdot w_{CDHA}} = \frac{84.97 \cdot w_{CDHA}}{73.27 + 11.7 \cdot w_{CDHA}} \quad (2)$$

Series B was composed after the same period of setting by DCP, α-TCP, CDHA and CC. In order to reduce mathematical calculations that system was reduced to a three-phase system, where the average <α-TCP-CDHA> phase has a mass absorption coefficient, <M>=85.7 cm²/g, equal to the average value of the phases themselves ($M_{\alpha\text{-TCP}}$=86.43; M_{CDHA}=84.97). Eq. 3 gives the ratio of the intensity of the CC phase in the three-phase system (I_{CC}) with respect to a pure phase of CC (I_{CC}^P), as a function of the weight fractions of unreacted CC (w_{CC}) and DCP (w_{DCP}). Experimental values of I_{CC}/I_{CC}^P were obtained from XRD patterns for the most intense peak of CC (hkl=104; (2θ)=29.40°). With the result from series A that DCP did not react, w_{DCP} was approximated to the weight fraction of DCP into the original mixtures and an approximate value of w_{CC}=0.038 ± 0.003 was obtained for a mathematical fit of Eq. 3 at a 95% confidence level (see Fig. 2), which indicates that nearly 4 wt% of the original CC was still present as a separate phase.

$$\frac{I_{cc}}{I_{cc}^P} = \frac{M_{cc} \cdot w_{cc}}{\langle M \rangle + w_{cc} \cdot \left(M_{cc} - \langle M \rangle\right) + \left(M_{DCP} - \langle M \rangle\right) \cdot w_{DCP}} = \frac{74.36 \cdot w_{cc}}{85.7 - 11.34 \cdot w_{cc} - 12.43 \cdot w_{DCP}} \quad (3)$$

Experimental points for I_{DCP}/I_{DCP}^P and $\langle I_{\alpha\text{-TCP}}/I_{\alpha\text{-TCP}}^P + I_{CDHA}/I_{CDHA}^P \rangle$ were measured as above and strong correlations were obtained (see Fig. 2) when these points were represented against w_{DCP} (calculated with the hypothesis of DCP non reactivity) and the mathematical expressions of a two-phase model (see Eqs. 1 and 2) of DCP and an average phase of $\langle\alpha\text{-TCP-CDHA}\rangle$, which means that 4 wt% of unreacted CC did not greatly influence the intensity of the other phases.

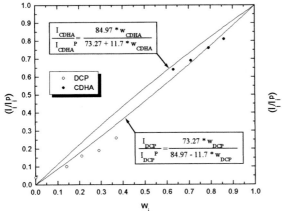 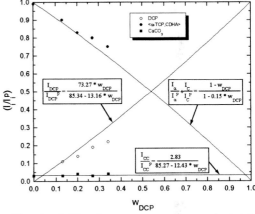

Fig. 1. Calibration curves and experimental measurements of I_{DCP}/I_{DCP}^P versus w_{DCP} and I_{CDHA}/I_{CDHA}^P versus w_{CDHA}.

Fig. 2. Calibration curves and experimental measurements of I_{DCP}/I_{DCP}^P, $\langle I_\alpha/I_\alpha^P + I_C/I_C^P \rangle$ and I_{CC}/I_{CC}^P versus w_{DCP}.

The analysis of the IR spectra showed characteristic substitutions of PO_4^{3-} groups by CO_3^{2-} ions at ~872 cm^{-1} and ~1415 cm^{-1} and between 1464 cm^{-1} and 1480 cm^{-1} confirming that CDHA was partially transformed into CCDA.

Compressive strength

Figs. 3 and 4 show that the addition of CC resulted in a retardation with time of the development of the compressive strength, C(MPa), of the cement mixtures, which is an indication of the different crystalline networks which are evolving during the setting and hardening of the cement samples. Lower values of the compressive strength at the initial stages of the setting reaction, as a result of CC addition, are compatible with a finer crystalline microstructure and with a reduced interfacial strength of the contact points developed between crystals.

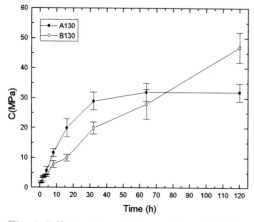
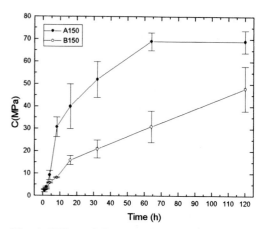

Fig. 3. Effect of the addition of 10 wt% CC in a cement sample with Ca/P=1.30 on the hardening curve.

Fig. 4. Effect of the addition of 10 wt% CC in a cement sample with Ca/P=1.50 on the hardening curve.

CONCLUSIONS

It has been observed that DCP phase did not react when α-TCP fully transformed into CDHA, as α-TCP is the responsible phase for the setting and hardening characteristics of the cements. When cement mixtures were modified with CC, carbonate ions disturb the dissolution of α-TCP, not only retarding the process, but also influencing the precipitation of the original CDHA crystallites into CCDA crystallites, which are more similar to the mineral phase of bone. This retarding effect was demonstrated to affect the resultant compressive strength of the cements.

ACKNOWLEDGEMENTS

This work was supported by an European Grant TMR # ERBFMBICT972733. The authors thank the CICYT (Spain) for funding this work through project MAT94-0911. EPSRC is also gratefully acknowledged for the core grant for the IRC in Biomedical Materials.

REFERENCES

1. Ginebra MP, Fernández E, De Maeyer EAP, Verbeeck RMH, Boltong MG, Ginebra J, Driessens FCM, Planell JA. *J. Dent. Res.* 1997; **76, 4**: 905-912.
2. Fernández E, Ginebra MP, Boltong MG, Driessens FCM, Ginebra J, De Maeyer EAP, Verbeeck RMH, Planell JA. *J. Biomed. Mater. Res.* 1996; **32**: 367-374.
3. Legeros RZ, Legeros JP, Daculsi G, Kijkowska R. In: Wise DL et al. eds. *Encyclopedic handbook of biomaterials and bioengineering*, New York: Marcel Dekker, 1995: 1429-1463.
4. Legeros RZ, Trautz OR, Legeros JP, Klein E. *Bull. Soc. Chim.* 1968; **sp. No.**: 1712-1718.
5. Legeros RZ, Legeros JP, Shirra WP, Trautz OR. *Adv. X-ray Anal.* 1971; **14**: 57-66.
6. Legeros RZ, Shirra WP, Miravite MA, Legeros JP. *Coll. Intern. CNRS.* 1973; **230**: 105-115.
7. Cullity BD. In: *Elements of X-ray diffraction.* 2nd. Ed. Addison-Wesley, Inc. (1978).

Bioceramics Volume 11, edited by R. Z. LeGeros and J.P. LeGeros
(Proceedings of the 11th International Symposium on Ceramics in Medicine)
New York, NY, USA, November 1998

THE EFFECT OF Na2HPO4 ADDITION ON THE SETTING REACTION KINETICS OF AN α-TCP CEMENT

M.P. Ginebra[1] , E. Fernández[1] , F.C.M. Driessens[2] , J.A. Planell[1]

[1] CREB. Dept of Materials Science and Metallurgical Engineering, Universitat Politècnica de Catalunya, Av. Diagonal 647, 08028 Barcelona, Spain; [2] Dept. of Dental Materials Science, University Hospital, De Pintelaan 185, B-9000Gent, Belgium.

ABSTRACT

Recent studies have pointed out the possibility to obtain a bone cement based on the hydrolysis of α-$Ca_3(PO_4)_2$ (α-TCP) to a calcium deficient hydroxyapatite (CDHA) at body temperature. However, when plain α-TCP is used, the hardening of the cement is too slow for clinical requirements. One possible way of accelerating it is the addition of Na_2HPO_4. The aim of this study is to investigate the mechanisms responsible for this accelerating effect. Two different cement formulations were prepared, the powder phase being α-TCP and the liquid phase being either distilled water or a Na_2HPO_4 aqueous solution. The hardening rate of the cement was determined and the progress of the hydrolysis reaction was evaluated by means of x-ray diffraction (XRD) and scanning electron microscopy (SEM).

In contrast to the water prepared cement, the use of the phosphate solution produced a continuous strength acquisition starting from the mixing of the cement. The saturation value obtained was 40% higher than that obtained with the water prepared cement. A good correlation was observed between the strength acquisition of the cement and CDHA formation. XRD and SEM showed that the addition of Na_2HPO_4 strongly influenced the hydrolysis kinetics of α-TCP, by eliminating the induction period of the reaction.

KEYWORDS: Calcium phosphate cements, calcium deficient hydroxyapatite

INTRODUCTION

The possibility to obtain an apatitic material in a monolithic form at room or body temperature by means of a cementitious reaction was an important breakthrough in the field of bioceramics research[1], since it supplied with a material which was moldable, and therefore could adapt to the bone cavity, presenting a good fixation and an optimum tissue-biomaterial contact, necessary for stimulating the bone ingrowth on it.

Recently a bone cement has been described which is based in the hydrolysis of α-TCP (α-$Ca_3(PO_4)_2$ to a calcium deficient hydroxyapatite (CDHA)[2]. The hydrolysis reaction, however, is slow in water, and it should be accelerated in order to comply with the clinical requirements. The use of a phosphate solution as the cement liquid has resulted in an acceleration of the setting reaction of different phosphate cement formulations[3-8]. This effect is analogous to the common ion effect which takes place in gypsum hydration[9].

The aim of this study is to evaluate the influence of the use of a phosphate solution in the kinetics of the α-TCP hydration and their consequences in the hardening characteristics of the cement.

MATERIALS AND METHODS

The cement solid phase consisted of α-$Ca_3(PO_4)_2$, which was milled in a ball agate mill, the final powder having a specific surface of (1.0 ± 0.03) m^2/g. Two cement formulations were prepared, one of them employing as a liquid phase distilled water and the other one a 2.5 wt% Na_2HPO_4 solution in water . The liquid/powder used was 0.32 mL/g.

Powder and liquid were mixed in a mortar for about 1 min. Cylindrical samples of the cement were prepared (6mm diameter and 12 mm height) in Teflon molds. After 15 min they were immersed in Ringer's solution at 37°C for either 1, 2, 4, 8, 16, 32, 64 or 360 h from the mixing of the powder and the liquid. For each period 8 samples were prepared. After immersion the samples were polished and tested under compression at a cross-head speed of 1mm/min with an Universal Testing Machine. Immediately after they had been tested, they were quenched in acetone and dried to stop the reaction. Two samples were investigated with scanning electron microscopy, and the other ones were crushed in order to perform x-ray diffraction studies.

RESULTS AND DISCUSSION

The hardening process of the two cement formulations can be appreciated in Figure 1, where the compressive strength as a function of time is represented.

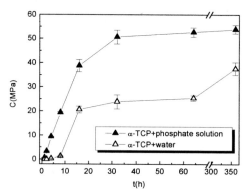

Figure 1. Compressive strength evolution of the two cements
studied as a function of the reaction time

The cement prepared with water exhibited an initial period of about 8h, during which no hardening was observed. After this interval, the compressive strength increased, reaching a saturation value of 38 MPa. In contrast, when a phosphate containing solution was used, the strengthening of the cement took place from the moment when the powder and the liquid were mixed. The phosphate solution had an accelerating effect on the hardening of the cement. In particular, it appeared that the induction period was eliminated. This can be relevant for some clinical applications where an early strength acquisition is necessary. It must be noted that, for instance, when water was substituted by the phosphate solution as the cement liquid, the compressive strength reached after 8 h increased from 1.3 MPa to 20 MPa. Furthermore, the final strength was also increased in a 40%.

The x-ray diffraction patterns shown in Figure 2 were helpful to identify the underlying mechanisms responsible for this behavior. Specifically, they contribute to elucidate whether this accelerating effect in the cement hardening can be attributed to an acceleration of the hydrolysis reaction. As it can be observed in Fig. 2, when the α-TCP was hydrolyzed in plain water the intensity of the α-TCP peaks did not decrease appreciably after 8 h of reaction, and the apatitic phase was hardly detected. In contrast, when phosphate ions were present in solution a reduction in the α-TCP peak intensities and the presence of a apatitic phase was noticeable already after 2 h of reaction. After 360 h both cements had transformed into a poorly crystalline apatitic phase. However, whilst in the phosphate solution the transformation seemed to have reached completion, in the water prepared cement some α-TCP is still detected.

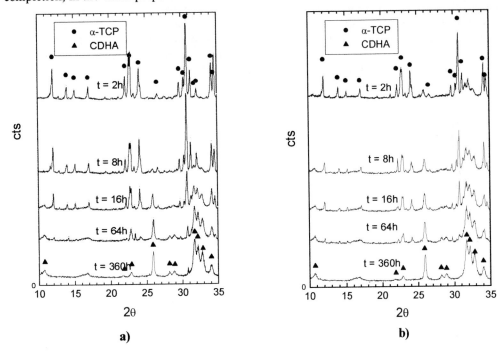

Figure 2. Diffraction patterns of the two cements after immersion in Ringer's solution at 37°C during different periods of time. A) cement prepared with α-TCP and distilled water ; b) cement prepared with α-TCP and the phosphate containing solution

The microstructural observations carried out by SEM gave complementary information about the transformations occurring during the hardening of the cements. The mechanism of cement hardening, which consists of the α-TCP dissolution and the precipitation of CDHA crystallites from the supersaturated solution is clearly accelerated when the liquid phase contains phosphate ions. As it can be seen in Figure 3, whereas in the cement prepared with water no precipitated crystals are appreciable around the α-TCP particles after 2 h of reaction, they can be clearly observed in the cement prepared with the Na_2HPO_4 solution. After 8 h of reaction, the size of the precipitated crystals is much larger when the phosphate solution has been used. This evolution is coincident with the XRD results and can explain the induction period observed in the strength acquisition of the cement.

Figure 3. SEM pictures after different times of reaction of the cements consisting of a) α-TCP with water after 2 h; b) α-TCP with phosphate solution after 2 h; c) α-TCP with water after 8 h; d) α-TCP with phosphate solution after 8 h

Therefore, it can be stated that the acceleration of the cement hardening when the phosphate containing solution is used is directly related to the acceleration of the precipitation of the apatitic phase, with the suppression of the induction period of the reaction.

ACKNOWLEDGEMENTS

The authors thank the CICYT for funding this work through project MAT94-0911

REFERENCES

1. Brown WE, Chow LC, *J. Dent. Res.* **62** (1983), 672.
2. Ginebra MP *et al., J. Dent. Res.* **76** (1997) 905-912.
3. Fulmer MT, Brown PW, *J. Biomed. Mater. Res.* **27** (1993), 1095-1102.
4.Fernández E. *et al., Clinical Materials* **16** (1994), 99-103.
5.Chow LC, Takagi S, Ishikawa K, in: P.W. Brown (Ed.), "Hydroxyapatite and related materials", CRC Press, Florida (1994), 127.
6.Ishikawa K *et al., J. Mater. Sci. Mater. Med.* **6** (1995), 528-533.
7.Miyamoto Y *et al.* , *Biomaterials* **16** (1995), 855-860.
8. Brown PW, Fulmer MT, *J. Biomed. Mater. Res.* **31** (1996) 395-400.
9. Jorgensen KD, Posner AS, *J. Dent. Res.* **38** (1959), 491- 499.

Bioceramics Volume 11, edited by R. Z. LeGeros and J.P. LeGeros
(Proceedings of the 11th International Symposium on Ceramics in Medicine)
New York, NY, USA, November 1998
© 1998 by World Scientific Publishing Co. Pte. Ltd.

INCORPORATION OF A CONTROLLED-RELEASE GLASS INTO A CALCIUM PHOSPHATE CEMENT

I. Khairoun[1], MP. Ginebra[1], MG Boltong[1*], S. Martinez[2], JA Planell[1] and FCM Driessens[1*].

[1]CREB (Centre de Recerca en Enginyeria Biomèdica), Dept. of Materials Science and Metallurgical Engineering, Universitat Politècnica de Catalunya, Av. Diagonal 647, E-08028, Barcelona, Spain; [2]Department of Crystallography and Mineralogy, Faculty of Geology, Universitat de Barcelona, Spain. *Present Address: Department of dental Materials Science, Dental Clinic, University Hospital, De Pintelaan 185, B-9000 Gent, Belgium.

ABSTRACT

In this study a controlled release phosphate glass in the system $CaO-Na_2O-P_2O_5$ is used for trying to make a calcium phosphate cement macroporous. A sieve fraction of this glass ranging between 105 and 400 μm was incorporated in a calcium phosphate cement, where the powder contained $\alpha-Ca_3(PO_4)_2$ (α-TCP), $CaHPO_4$ (DCP) and precipitated hydroxyapatite (HA). The glass content of the cement was 10 wt %. The setting times were determined with Gillmore needles. Soaking was carried out during 4 days, 2 and 5 weeks in Ringer's solution and 0.5% $CaCl_2$ at 37 °C prior to determination of the compressive strength. Scanning electron microscopy (SEM) was used for microstructural analysis and X-ray diffraction to analyse the reaction.

The glass retarded slightly the cement setting and reduced significantly the compressive strength. SEM pictures and XRD patterns of the samples after 5 weeks of ageing showed that the glass was not dissolved but that large brushite crystals were formed. Ageing in $CaCl_2$ solutions resulted in more brushite formation than ageing in NaCl solutions. In conclusion, the incorporation of controlled-release glasses into this calcium phosphate cement and their subsequent ageing in aqueous solutions did not result in the formation of macropores in the cement structure.

KEYWORDS: Calcium phosphate cement, biodegradable glass, compressive strength, setting time, brushite formation.

INTRODUCTION

In the early *in vivo* evaluation of calcium phosphate ceramics it was not clear which role in their resorption was played by their composition and crystal structure on one hand and which importance their density and, hence, their porosity had on the other hand[1]. Soon it became clear that in bone histology studies β-TCP is resorbed and replaced by new bone but that hydroxyapatite ceramic HA is not resorbed but incorporated in the bone[2,3]. When HA was made macroporous and covered with bone marrow cells, bone tissue growed into the pores, even when the ceramic was implanted subcutaneously[4]. Nowadays, manufacturers have a preference for making their products macroporous in order to speed up their osteointegration[5].

In this study a phosphate glass occurring in the system $CaO-Na_2O-P_2O_5$ is used for the purpose of obtaining a macroporous calcium phosphate cement. In contact with aqueous solutions like body fluids this glass dissolves slowly, and Ca^{2++}, Na^+ and phosphate ions are released[6]. The effect of the glass incorporation on the evolution of the mechanical properties of the cement is also investigated, inorder to elucidate if this glass could be used as a reinforcing phase.

MATERIALS AND METHODS

The phosphate glass was made of a mixture of $NH_4H_2PO_4$, Na_2CO_3 and. It was melted in a platinum crucible at a temperature of 1100 °C and quenched on a metallic plate preheated at 350 °C and subsequently annealed. The chemical composition of the glass was P_2O_5 61.5 %, Na_2O 7.7 %, CaO 30.8 % in terms of molar ratio. A sieved fraction of this glass was selected with diameters ranging from 105 to 400 μm. The calcium phosphate cement called Biocement F consisted of 63.2 wt % α-$Ca_3(PO_4)_2$ (α-TCP), 27.7 wt % $CaHPO_4$ (DCP) and 9.1 wt % of precipitated hydroxyapatite (PHA) and was prepared as described in a previous paper[7]. The glass content of the cement was 10 wt %. The samples were prepared at a liquid/powder ratio (L/P = 0.32 ml/g) and the liquid concentration was a 2.5 wt % solution of in water. The initial and final setting times initial and final (t_I and t_F respectively) were determined with Gillmore needles. Teflon molds were used to prepare cement cylinders with a height of 12 mm and a diameter of 6 mm and soaking was carried out during 4 days, 2 and 5 weeks in Ringer's solution and 0.5 % $CaCl_2$ at 37 °C (the solutions were refreshed every 3 days) prior to determination of the compressive strength using an Universal Testing Machine INSTRON-4507 at 1 mm/min cross-head speed. Scanning electron microscopy (SEM) was used for microstructural analysis and X-ray diffraction to analyse the reaction.

RESULTS

The initial setting time (t_I)and the final setting time (t_F) of Biocement F alone and containing 10 % of the glass are given in Table 1. The addition of the glass retarded the setting of the cement somewhat. The data for the compressive strength (CS) after 4 days, 2 weeks and 5 weeks of ageing in solutions of NaCl or $CaCl_2$ which were refreshed every 3 days are also given in Table 1. For Biocement F it did not make any difference whether ageing was done in $CaCl_2$ or NaCl solutions. As far as the compressive strength is considered, the glass incorporation resulted in a considerable decrease of the strength right after complete setting (4 days) and the strength did not change upon subsequent immersion for 2 or 5 weeks in NaCl or $CaCl_2$ solutions.

Fig.1 shows the XRD pattern of the Biocement F-Glass combination after 4 days, 2 weeks and 5 weeks of ageing in 0.5 % $CaCl_2$ solution. After 5 weeks the peaks of brushite are superimposed on the apatite pattern of the Biocement F.

Table 1. Initial setting time (t_I), final setting time (t_F) and compressive strength (CS) after 4 days, 2 weeks and 5 weeks of ageing in solutions of NaCl or CaCl$_2$ which were refreshed every 3 days of Biocement F alone and containing 10 % of the glass.

Cement	t_I (min)	t_F (min)	CS-4d (MPa)	CS-2w (MPa)	CS-5w (MPa)
F (NaCl or CaCl$_2$)	6-6.5	10.5	36 (5)[*]	33 (4)	32 (4)
F-Glass (NaCl)	7-7.5	11.5	19 (3)	19 (3)	22 (3)
F-Glass (CaCl$_2$)	7-7.5	11.5	23 (3)	19 (3)	19 (3)

* Standard deviation between brackets (n = 8)

Fig.2 shows the XRD pattern of Biocement F and the Biocement F-Glass combination after 5 weeks of ageing in 0.9 % NaCl solution. Both curves show the apatite pattern of Biocement F. However, the upper curve has the brushite pattern superimposed, although less intense than the upper curve of Fig.1.

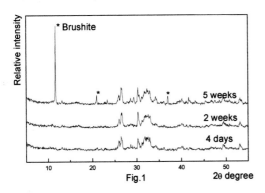

Figure 1. XRD of the Biocement-Glass combination after different periods of time aging in a 0.5% CaCl$_2$ solution

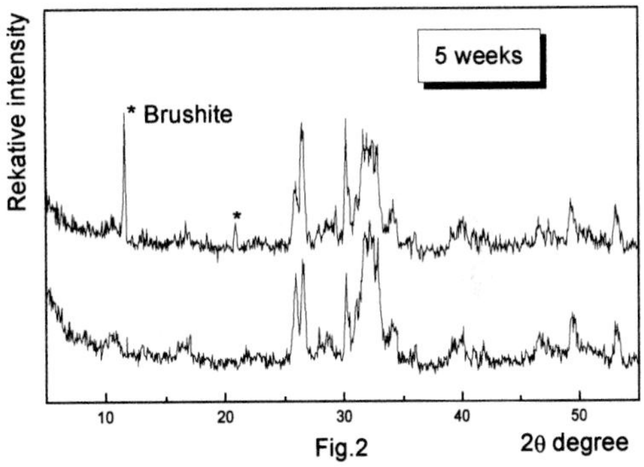

Figure 2. XRD of Biocement F (lower curve) and Biocement-glass combination (upper curve) after 5 weeks of ageing in Ringer's solution

SEM pictures of the Biocement F-Glass combination showed that the structure of the glass was amorphous after 4 days or even after 2 weeks of ageing. However, after 5 weeks the vitreous particles were not observed any more and some crystals could be appreciated with different morphology from the apatitic phase which had been formed as a result of the cement reaction.

DISCUSSION AND CONCLUSION

According to Figs.1 and 2 both in 0.9 % NaCl solution and in 0.5 % CaCl$_2$ solution the glass particles addition did not hinder the setting of the cement, since the presence of an apatitic phase, which is the reaction product of the cementing reaction[6] was clearly detected already after 4 days. However, during ageing the glass particles gave rise to brushite formation. Probably, simultaneously to this transformation some sodium, phosphate and calcium ions were released to the soaking solution.

Implantation studies have shown that under *in vivo* conditions the biodegradable controlled-release glass is completely resorbed within 3 months, after implantation in bone as well as in soft tissue[6]. In bone the glass seemed to shrink first and simultaneously there was ongrowth of new bone. In these implantation studies it is quite possible that before degradation first a transformation of the glass into brushite has occurred, similar to the brushite formation of the present experiment. But implantation of brushite on itself also results in complete resorption[8], also because the solubility of brushite in body fluids is higher than the actual concentration of calcium and phosphate

The behaviour of Biocement F upon implantation is quite different. After subcutaneous implantation under exclusion of direct cellular contact, but open contact with body fluids the material remained stable[9] meaning that the calcium deficient hydroxyapatite which has formed after the setting in Biocement F is in physico-chemical equilibrium with the body fluids. However, implantation in bone resulted in resorption of the cement and formation of new bone[10]. It is presumable that after implantation of the Biocement F-Glass combination into bone the glass particles will also be transformed first into brushite. As this brushite will have a higher solubility than the calcium and phosphate concentration in the bone extracellular fluid, the brushite particles will keep dissolving,. It is expected that after some time the structure of the implanted Biocement F-Glass combination will show up some macropores.

On the other hand, the present study has shown that the glass particles do not act as a reinforcing phase in the cement, but on the contrary they reduce its compressive strength.

ACKNOWLEDGEMENTS

The authors would like to thank the CICYT for funding this work through project MAT 96-0981.

REFERENCES

1. Winter *M et al*., *Biomaterials* **2** (1981) 159-160
2. Osborn JF and Donath K, *Dtsch. Zahnartzl. Z.* **39** (1984) 970-976
3. Klein CPAT, Patka P and Der Hollander W, *Biomaterials* **10** (1989) 59-62
4. Ohugushi M et al., *J.Biomed.Mater.Res.***26** (1992) 885-895
5. Eggli PS, Muller W and Shenk RK, in: Pizzoferato et al (Eds) Advances in Biomaterials, Elsevier, 1987, p. 53-56
6. Burnie J and Gilchrist T in:P.Vincenzini (Ed) Ceramics in Surgery, Elsevier,1983, 169-176.
7. Fernandez E *et al*., *J.Biomed. Mater. Res.* **32** (1996) 367-374.
8. Constantz BR *et al*., Fourth World Biomaterials Congress, Berlin, 1992, p.56
9. Driessens FCM *et al*., *J.Mater.Sci.Mater.Med.* **6** (1995) 272-278
10. Jansen, JE *et al*., *J.Mater.Sci.Mater.Med.* **6** (1995) 653-657

Bioceramics Volume 11, edited by R. Z. LeGeros and J.P. LeGeros
(Proceedings of the 11th International Symposium on Ceramics in Medicine)
New York, NY, USA, November 1998
© 1998 by World Scientific Publishing Co. Pte. Ltd.

NEW HYDROXYAPATITE COMPOSITE RESIN AS A BIOACTIVE BONE CEMENT: IMPROVEMENT OF HANDLING AND MECHANICAL PROPERTIES

Takaaki Shibuya[1], Masanobu Saito[2], Kazuyoshi Kawagoe[1], Kenichi Hino[3], Toshihide Nakashima[3], Atsushi Murakami[4] and Takahiro Ochi[1]

[1]Department of Orthopaedic Surgery, Osaka University Medical School
2-2 Yamada-oka, Suita 565-0871, Osaka, Japan
[2]Department of Orthopaedic Surgery, Osaka-Minami National Hospital
2-1 Kidohigashi-machi, Kawachinagano 586-8521, Osaka, Japan
[3]R&D Department of Medical and Dental Products, Kuraray Co., Ltd
1621 Sakazu, Kurashiki 710-8622, Okayama, Japan
[4]Department of Chemical Engineering, Himeji Institute of Technology
2167 Shosya, Himeji 671-2201, Hyogo, Japan

ABSTRACT

We developed hydroxyapatite composite resin (CAP) which was composed of 80% w/w hydroxyapatite granules (mean particle size: 2 μ m) and 20% w/w methacrylic monomers. We previously reported CAP (old CAP) as a moldable and self-hardening material similar to polymethylmethacrylate (PMMA) cement, which had superior mechanical strength and osteoconductive properties. However, it was difficult to remove air bubbles from old CAP pastes and to use a cement gun with it, since the viscosity of old CAP was relatively high. In this study, new CAP with lower viscosity was prepared by changing the formulation of the monomers of CAP. This new CAP allowed removal of air bubbles from the pastes during paste manufacture and improvement of the mixing and delivery system. Fatigue properties of the new CAP were much better than those of PMMA cement. Thus, new CAP has been successfully developed, and is a promising bioactive cement which can be used in practical surgical sites.

KEYWORDS: Bone cement, Bioactive cement, Hydroxyapatite

INTRODUCTION

Polymethylmethacrylate (PMMA) cement which yields the secure initial fixation of the implants, has been successfully used in total joint arthroplasty. Although PMMA cement remains the common standard of fixation, loosening of the cemented components over time is a major concern. One of the mechanical and biological factors of this failure results from the character of PMMA cement. PMMA cement has some disadvantages, including growth of fibrous tissue at the cement-bone interface,[1] thermal damage to the surrounding bone during polymerization,[2] and cement fracture[3]. To overcome these disadvantages, we developed hydroxyapatite composite resin (CAP) (Kuraray Co. Ltd., Kurashiki, Japan) as a new type of bioactive cement.

We showed that CAP (old CAP) which was polymerized by mixing of two pastes was a moldable and self-hardening material similar to PMMA cement, and that it had superior mechanical strength and the biological property of achieving direct contact with bone.[4] Although this cement is useful for fixation of implants, it required certain improvement. Mixing of the old CAP was performed in an open bowl, and no delivery system was used. Therefore, we aimed to introduce easy-to-use devices for mixing and delivery, and to reduce air bubbles in the cement mantle. However, it was difficult to use a cement gun and to remove air bubbles from the old CAP, because its viscosity was relatively high.

In this study, new CAP with lower viscosity was developed by changing the formulation of the monomers included in CAP pastes. New CAP permitted the use of mixing and a delivery system. The mechanical properties of new CAP were measured.

MATERIALS and METHODS

Preparation of new CAP

CAP is composed of 80% w/w hydroxyapatite (HA) granules with a mean particle size of 2 μm and 20% w/w methacrylic monomers. The HA granules are sintered at 1200°C and treated with silane. The methacrylic monomers consist of bis-phenol-A glycidyl methacrylate (BIS-GMA), 2,2-bis-(4-methacryloyloxyethoxyphenyl) propane (BIS-MEPP) and triethyleneglycol dimethacrylate (TEG-DMA). Polymerization is begun by mixing approximately equal volumes of two pastes, one of which includes the HA granules treated with silane, the methacrylic monomers and benzoyl peroxide as a initiator, and the other of which includes HA granules, the monomers and diethanol-p-toluidine as an accelerator. To decrease the viscosity of CAP and to maintain bioactive properties, only the formulation of the monomers was changed, and the amount of HA was not changed. The proportions of the three monomers of the new CAP were changed to 30:20:50 in weight ratio, from 35:35:30 for the old CAP.

Mixing and delivery system

The two pastes of the new CAP were stored in a divided cylinder (Fig. 1). The double syringe container can be fitted onto a cement gun (MIXPAC SYSTEMS, Rotkreuz, Switzerland) (Fig. 2). Approximately equal volumes of the two pastes are automatically mixed through a static mixing tip put on the cement gun (Fig. 2).

Setting time and peak curing temperature

The setting time of the new CAP and the peak curing temperature were measured. To monitor the time-temperature profile, a thermocouple was placed on the outer wall of a cylinder, which was wrapped in aluminum foil. The new CAP was injected into the cylinder. The peak curing temperature was obtained directly from the recordings. The setting time was defined as the period between the start of mixing and the time when a temperature midway between the ambient and peak temperature was reached. PMMA cement (Zimmer LVC, Zimmer, Warsaw, IN, USA) was studied in the same way.

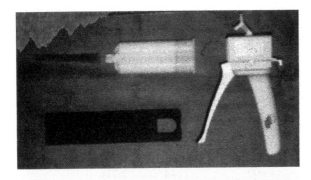

Fig. 1. Cement gun for new CAP

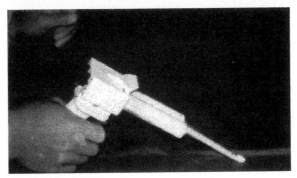

Fig. 2. Injection of new CAP

Mechanical testing

To examine the fatigue properties of new CAP, three-point bending testing was performed using rectangular beams (30 x 2 x 2 mm) on an Instron 1175 universal material testing machine at a cross head speed of 1mm/minute. After conditioning in 37°C water for 24 hours, fifteen specimens were tested sinusoidally at 10 Hz in a water bath at a temperature of 37°C. Fatigue testing of PMMA cement was performed in the same fashion for comparison.

RESULTS

Mixing and delivery system

New CAP could be used with the cement gun. It was difficult to push out the old CAP using the cement gun, while the new CAP could easily be pushed out (Fig. 3).

Setting time and peak curing temperature

The setting time of the new CAP was approximately five minutes, when the peak curing temperature was 46°C. These values was the same as for the old CAP. PMMA cement had corresponding values of 7.7 minutes and 76.3°C.

Mechanical testing

Fatigue testing revealed a longer fatigue life for new CAP than for PMMA cement (Table 1).

Table 1. Fatigue properties of new CAP and PMMA cement

No.	New CAP		PMMA cement	
	Cycle	Stress (Kgf/mm2)	Cycle	Stress (Kgf/mm2)
1	94	3.870	135	3.150
2	110	4.050	165	2.700
3	157	3.870	169	3.150
4	168	4.050	198	2.790
5	561	3.600	428	2.700
6	621	3.870	849	2.430
7	1996	3.600	1144	2.250
8	3011	3.600	1898	2.250
9	3406	3.150	2184	2.250
10	5853	3.150	3906	1.800
11	14255	3.150	4958	1.800
12	21303	2.700	20452	1.440
13	22881	2.700	66254	1.350
14	44995	2.700	479446	0.900
15	1000000	2.250*		

*no break

DISCUSSION

Vacuum mixing for PMMA cement improved the mechanical properties of the cement by reducing porosity.[5] In addition, the use of cement guns produced uniformity of cement around implants and improved the quality of the cement mantle. Old CAP had no mixing and delivery system, since it was not suitable for vacuum mixing or use of cement guns due to its relatively high viscosity. Therefore, efforts to reduce the viscosity of CAP without loss of its mechanical and biological properties and to introduce use of a mixing and delivery system for CAP were required for practical surgical application of CAP.

In this study, we prepared new CAP with lower viscosity by changing the formulation of the monomers included in the pastes. To preserve the biological properties of old CAP, the amount of HA included was not changed. Two pastes of the new CAP could be manufactured under vacuum conditions, before packing into a double syringe container. New CAP could be injected using the cement gun. In this process, air was rarely entrapped in the cement.

Fatigue testing, which reflects actual repetitive weight-bearing more closely than static tests revealed that new CAP had a better fatigue life than PMMA cement.

We have successfully developed new CAP. Improvements in mixing and delivery technology and reduction of porosity have thus produced a promising bioactive cement which can be used in practical surgical sites such as those of total joint arthroplasties.

REFERENCES

1. Freeman MAR, Bradly GW, Revell PA. *J Bone Joint Surg* 1982; **64B**: 489-493.
2. Homsy CA, Tullos HS, Anderson MS, DiferranteNM, King JW. *Clin Orthop* 1972; **83**: 317-328.
3. Jasty M, Maloney WJ, Bragdon CR, Haire T, Harris WH. *J Bone Joint Surg* 1990; **72A**: 1220-1229.
4. Saito M, Maruoka A, Mori T, Sugano N, Hino K. *Biomaterials* 1994; **15**: 156-160.
5. Wixson RL, Lautenschlager EP, Novak MA. *J Arthroplasty* 1987; **2**: 141-149.

Bioceramics Volume 11, edited by R. Z. LeGeros and J.P. LeGeros
(Proceedings of the 11th International Symposium on Ceramics in Medicine)
New York, NY, USA, November 1998
© 1998 by World Scientific Publishing Co. Pte. Ltd.

INFLUENCE OF POLYSACCHARIDES ON BRUSHITE CEMENT PROPERTIES

P. Van Landuyt, G. Pouchkine and J. Lemaître

Laboratory of Powder Technology, Surface Chemistry and Biomaterials Group,
Swiss Federal School of Technology, MX-Ecublens, CH-1015 Lausanne, Switzerland.

ABSTRACT

The aim of this study is to improve brushite cement injectability by adding hydrosoluble polysaccharides and to assess the influence of these polymers on mechanical properties and setting time.

Hydroxypropylmethylcelluloses (HPMC) of two different molecular weights were used for comparison. HPMC solutions exhibit a shear-thinning and non-thixotropic behavior, which is favorable for injection through a syringe nozzle. The presence of the setting retardors H_2SO_4 and $Na_2H_2P_2O_7$ does not influence the rheological properties of HPMC solutions but decreases slightly the viscosity of the β-TCP suspensions investigated. A temperature increase from 25 °C to 40 °C induces a slight viscosity decrease. Qualitative injection tests show that good injectability is obtained by adjusting the solid/liquid ratio and the polymer concentration. The influence of HPMC on setting time and mechanical properties has been assessed for various suspension viscosities, HPMC molecular weights and solid/liquid ratios. Shorter setting times occur at higher solid/liquid ratios or in the presence of polymer. Diametral tensile strength increases at higher solid/liquid ratio, which is related to porosity decrease. The addition of HPMC, in the range of concentration necessary for injectability, does not influence mechanical resistance and porosity.

In conclusion, small additions of HPMC to the mixing liquid improve injectability. At such low polymer concentrations, no effect has been observed on mechanical properties. However, polymer concentration has to be minimized in order to keep acceptable setting times.

KEYWORDS : cement, rheology, polymer, mechanical properties, setting time.

INTRODUCTION

Nowadays, various bioceramics present very good in-vivo behavior in terms of biocompatibility and/or resorbability. Most of them are commercialized as sintered granules or blocks which are not easy to use. Calcium phosphate cements harden in situ and the possibility to inject them through a syringe should be a major advantage for this type of material. Injectability includes two conditions. First, cement rheology has to allow injection through a syringe nozzle and second, the cement paste should not disperse upon contact with physiological liquids.

Brushite cements are prepared by mixing tricalcium phosphate (β-TCP) and monocalcium phosphate monohydrate (MCPM) powders with water. The optimal quality of the β-TCP powder, the setting retardors (H_2SO_4 and $Na_2H_2P_2O_7$) concentrations and the mechanical properties have been determined in previous studies [1, 2]. In-vivo experiments show that the cement is biocompatible and resorbs within 3 months in a distal femoral site of rabbit [3]. The aim of this work is to improve cement injectability by adding small amounts of hydrosoluble polymer. Hydroxypropylmethylcellulose (HPMC) was chosen because modified celluloses present high solubility in water and are available with well controlled quality. First, the rheological behavior of HPMC solutions and β-TCP suspensions were measured. Then, the minimal HPMC concentration necessary to obtain good injectability was determined qualitatively by carrying out injection tests in water. Finally, the influence of cement compacity, polymer concentration and molecular weight on setting time and diametral tensile strength were assessed.

MATERIALS AND METHODS

Sample preparation. The following raw materials were used : β-TCP prepared by thermal treatment of DCP (Merck, ref. 2144) and HAP (Bioland, ref. 202/93/106) mixture, MCPM (Albright & Wilson, IBEX), $Na_2H_2P_2O_7$ (Fluka, ref. 71501), H_2SO_4 (Merck, ref. 731), HPMC3000 and HPMC20000 (Aqualon-Hercules, Culminal, ref. VK-2445 and VK-2135, respectively). Molecular weights given by the supplier are 76000 and 552000 g/mol for HPMC3000 and HPMC20000, respectively. The polymeric solutions were prepared by progressively adding HPMC powder in water while stirring to avoid the formation of lumps. Then the solutions were stirred overnight in order to achieve complete polymer dissolution. The cement samples were prepared by adding 1.2 g β-TCP and 0.8 g MPCM to a mixing liquid composed of 0.1 M H_2SO_4, 0.1 M $Na_2H_2P_2O_7$ and x wt% HPMC (x is the weight fraction of polymer which is adjusted in function of the molecular weight and the cement compacity). After setting, this cement has a theoretical composition of 90 wt% brushite and 10 wt% of residual β-TCP.

Characterization techniques. The rheological behavior of polymeric solutions and β-TCP suspensions was measured on a coaxial cylinder system (Mettler, Rheomat RM180) for shear rate ranging from 6.5 to 1291 sec^{-1}. The setting times measurements were performed using the Vicat needle method [4]. Diametral tensile strengths were determined on cylindrical specimens (Ø : 8.7 mm ; H : 6.5 to 8 mm) aged for 24 hours at 20 °C in 100% relative humidity. Adamel Lhomargy DY31 testing machine was used with a strain rate of 1 mm/min. The open porosity of hardened cements was measured by the Archimede's method, using isopropanol as the immersion liquid.

Statistics. The effects of solid/liquid ratio, polymer concentration and molecular weight were studied systematically using a 2^3 factorial statistical design described in Table I. The different mixing liquid viscosities correspond to a shear rate of 841/s and are obtained as follows : 10 mPa.s solutions contain 0.47 wt% HPMC3000 or 0.27 wt% HPMC20000 and 30 mPa.s solutions contain 0.78 wt% HPMC3000 or 0.50 wt% HPMC20000. Mechanical tests were performed in triplicate. The results were analyzed using the ANOVA technique [5].

Table I. Experimental design of the study of injectability, setting time and diametral tensile strength of brushite cements.

Factors	Levels	
	Low	High
Solid/liquid ratio	2.0 g/ml	2.5 g/ml
Polymer	HPMC3000	HPMC20000
Mixing liquid viscosity (841/s)	10 mPa.s	30 mPa.s

RESULTS AND DISCUSSION

Rheological behavior. Rheological measurements show that the HPMC solutions are shear-thinning and non-thixotropic irrespective of molecular weight (figure 1(a)). As expected, higher polymer concentration and molecular weight increase the viscosity. Shear-thinning behavior of polymeric solution appears when the randomly organized polymeric chains align with the flow. Shear-thinning solutions exhibit a constant viscosity value at high shear rate. During injection through a syringe nozzle, shear rates around 1000/sec are reached. For this reason, the viscosities at a shear rate of 841/s have been used to compare different HPMC solutions.

The effect of temperature and setting retardors concentration on polymer solutions viscosity has been assessed. A temperature increase from 25 to 40 °C lowers the viscosity. For example, a 25 % viscosity decrease is measured when a 23 mPa.s HPMC3000 solution is heated from 25 °C to 40 °C. Increasing setting retardors concentration from 0.05 M up to 0.1 M has no effect on solutions viscosity.

Figure 1(b) shows that β-TCP suspensions are shear-thinning and thixotropic. Moreover higher β-TCP contents increase thixotropy. In the presence of setting retardors, lower suspension viscosities are measured. This is probably due to partial β-TCP dissolution in acidic solution.

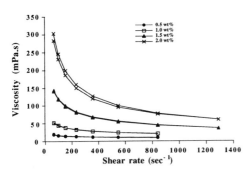

Figure 1. Rheological behavior of HPMC3000 solutions.

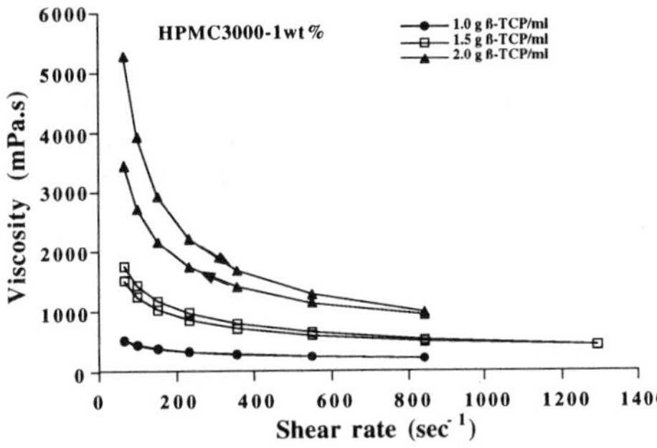

Figure 2. Rheological behavior of β-TCP suspension .

Injectability. The minimal polymer content necessary to obtain good injectability was determined qualitatively by injection tests in water. Higher solid/liquid ratio increases cement viscosity and lowers the polymer concentration needed. Cements with 2.0 and 2.5 g/mL solid/liquid ratios were investigated. Without polymer addition, the cement pastes disintegrate upon contact with water for both solid/liquid ratios, which hamper cement hardening. Injection tests have shown that 10 mPa.s solutions allow good injectability for 2.5 g/mL cements, whereas 30 mPa.s solutions are necessary to obtain injectability for 2.0 g/mL cements. On the basis of injection tests, 8 cement compositions described in table I were chosen for setting time and diametral tensile strength measurements.

Setting time. Figure 3 compares the experimental setting times of HPMC containing cements with a control without polymer. The most significant factors are the solid/liquid ratio and the presence of polymer. Setting times decrease when solid/liquid ratio is higher, which is due to a lower retardor quantity. Shorter setting times are obtained for HPMC-containing cements, irrespective of molecular weight. This effect is stronger at higher solid/liquid ratio.

Diametral tensile strength and porosity. Figures 4 and 5 show that diametral tensile strength is not sensitive to HPMC, but depends mainly on cement porosity. 2.0 and 2.5 g/mL cements show mean diametral strengths of 1.7 and 3.0 MPa, respectively. Lower polymer concentration in the mixing liquid does not affect significantly diametral tensile strength and porosity. However, we have noticed that higher polymer concentrations in the mixing liquid promote bubble formation, and therefore increase the number of defects in the hardened cements.

CONCLUSION

HPMC's are promising rheological additives for improving brushite cement injectability. Their shear-thinning behavior favors injection through a syringe. Injection tests in water have shown that the viscosity of the mixing liquid has to be adapted to the solid/liquid ratio of the cement. Adequate injectabilities are obtained with polymer concentrations in the mixing liquid lower than 1 wt%. Shorter setting times are obtained in the presence of polymers, which are still acceptable for practical use. HPMC has no effect on diametral tensile strength and porosity.

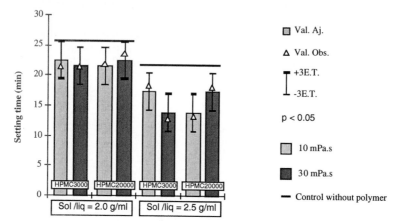

Figure 3. Setting times of cement samples.

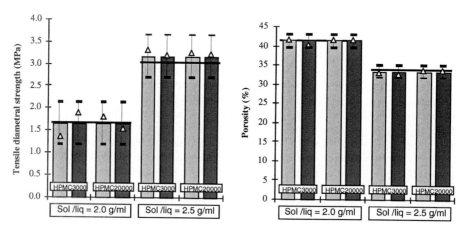

Figure 4. Diametral tensile strength of cement samples.

Figure 5. Open porosity of cement samples.

ACKNOWLEDGEMENTS

This work has been supported by the Board of the Swiss Federal Schools of Technology (PPM project n°4.2.D). The support of the Robert Mathys Foundation and Stratec Medical is gratefully acknowledged.

REFERENCES

[1]   P. Van Landuyt & J. Lemaître. Bioceramics, vol.9, 1996, 205-208.
[2]   P. Van Landuyt, C. Lowe & J. Lemaître. Bioceramics, vol.10, 1997, 477-480.
[3]   Ohura K., Bohner M., Hardouin P., Lemaître J., Pasquier G. & Flautre B. J. Biomed. Mater. Res. 30 (1996) 193-200.
[4]   Bohner M., Lemaître J. & Ring T.A. J. Amer. Ceram. Soc. 79 (1996) 1427-1434.
[5]   Montgomery D.C., Design and analysis of experiments. (3rd Ed.) Wiley & Sons New York, 1991.

IV. CELLS AND BIOCERAMICS INTERACTIONS *IN VIVO*

Bioceramics Volume 11, edited by R. Z. LeGeros and J.P. LeGeros
(Proceedings of the 11th International Symposium on Ceramics in Medicine)
New York, NY, USA, November 1998
© 1998 by World Scientific Publishing Co. Pte. Ltd.

Al_2O_3 CONTAINING AW GLASS CERAMIC STIMULATES *IN VITRO* BONE FORMATION

H. Ohgushi[1], T. Yoshikawa[1,2], H. Nakajima[1,2], S. Tamai[1], S. Tabata[3], Y. Dohi[4] and K. Okunaga[5]

Departments of Orthopedics[1], First Department of Pathology[2], Chemistry[3] and Public Health[4], Nara Medical Univ., Nara, Japan. Nippon Electric Glass Co.[5], Shiga, Japan.

ABSTRACT

Fresh marrow cells were obtained from femora of Fischer rats and cultured in a medium containing 15% fetal calf serum (FCS) until confluence. After trypsinization, cells were subcultured at a cell density of 100×10^3/35mm well in the presence of FCS, β-glycerophosphate, ascorbic acid phosphate and dexamethasone on four different culture substrata. The period of subculture was 2 weeks and the substrata used were culture dish, apatite-wollastonite containing glass ceramics (AW) having two different surface roughnesses, and Al_2O_3 containing AW (Al/AW). The glass matrix of AW contained MgO, CaO, P_2O_5 and SiO_2, whereas Al/AW contained Al_2O_3 in addition to these components. The subculture on all substrata showed many alkaline phosphatase (ALP) positive nodules. Though the DNA contents of the cells on these substrata were not significantly different, the number of nodules, ALP activity and bone Gla protein (BGP) mRNA level of the cells on Al/AW was the highest among these substrata. These results indicate that Al_2O_3 containing AW glass ceramic stimulates the osteoblastic differentiation of marrow stromal stem cells and therefore, the ceramic is useful material for the bone reconstruction surgery.

KEYWORDS: Glass ceramics, bone marrow, tissue culture

INTRODUCTION

Apatite wollastonite containing glass ceramic (AW)[1,2] can show bone bonding property and thus the ceramic is bioactive, however when the ceramic contains Al_2O_3, the ceramic (Al/AW) loses the bioactivity.[3,4] Though the Al/AW is not bioactive, effect of the ceramic on osteoblastic differentiation is not clear. It is well known that there are two types of stem cells in marrow cell population, one is hematopoietic stem cells and the other is stromal stem cells which can differentiate into osteogenic cells of osteoblast and chondrocyte.[5,6] The differentiation of the stromal stem cells can be seen in a culture condition when the culture medium contains dexamethasone and β-glycerophosphate.[7] In this tissue culture condition, active osteoblasts together with mineralized nodules appear on a culture dish, and we reported[8] that the mineralized nodule is not simple calcification but the nodule is *in vitro* counterpart of bone formed *in vivo*. Therefore, we investigated the osteoblastic phenotype expression of cultured rat marrow stromal stem cells on various culture substrata (culture dish, AW glass ceramics having two different surface roughnesses and Al/AW).

MATERIALS AND METHODS

Fabrication of glass ceramics:

AW and Al/AW glass ceramics were synthesized by the method previously described.[3, 9,10] The chemical composition of the AW and Al/AW ceramics is described in Table 1. Glass powders of the composition were compacted and sintered at $1050^{\circ}C$ and $1030^{\circ}C$ for AW and Al/AW, respectively. They each contained crystalline phases of about 35-wt% of apatite and about 40% of ß-wollastonite ($CaSiO_3$). The apatite in AW was oxyfluoroapatite ($Ca_{10}(PO_4)_6$, (O,F_2))and that in Al/AW was oxyapatite ($Ca_{10}(PO_4)_6$, (O)). The glass matrix of AW contained MgO, CaO, P_2O_5 and SiO_2, whereas Al/AW contained Al_2O_3 in addition to these components.   The ceramic was disk shaped, 34 mm in diameter and 2mm in thickness.   The surface roughness of both AW and Al/AW was about 0.22µm. AW ceramics having the roughness of 0.78µm was also used in this study.   The AW ceramics having surface roughness of 0.22µm and 0.78µm were designated as AW0.2 and AW0.8, respectively.[11]

Marrow cell culture:

The culture condition was essentially the same as reported by Maniatopoulos [7] with minor modifications.[8, 11] Briefly, primary culture was done using marrow cells from the bone shaft of rat femora to leach confluent in Y-75 flasks (Costar Co., Cambridge, Ma).   The medium consisted of Eagle-Minimal Essential Medium (MEM) and 15% fetal calf serum (FCS).   The confluent cultured cells were trypsinized and seeded at 100×10^3 cells/ 35mm on Falcon tissue culture plates (Nippon Becton Dickinson Co., Tokyo, Japan) with and without ceramics for subculture.   Just before the cell seeding, AW and Al/AW glass ceramic disks were placed in the wells.   The subculture was done with 2 ml of the medium supplemented with 10 mM Na beta-glycerophosphate, 82 µg/ml vitamin C phosphate and 10nM Dexamethasone.   The culture medium was renewed three times a week. After 2 weeks of subculture, the cultured cells were stained for alkaline phosphatase and analyzed biochemically (DNA contents, alkaline phosphatase activity and Northern blot against bone Gla protein cDNA) as described previously.[8,11-13]

Table   1, Composition of glass ceramics

ceramics	Composition (wt %)					
	MgO	CaO	SiO_2	P_2O_5	CaF_2	Al_2O_3
AW	4.6	44.7	34.0	16.2	0.5	0
Al/AW	3.6	40.4	33.2	16.5	0	6.3

RESULTS AND DISCUSSION

As shown in the Fig. 1, Al/AW ceramic showed the most extensive alkaline phosphatase (ALP) stain. The ALP stain indicates that marrow stromal stem cell can easily differentiate into osteoblast on the surface of Al/AW ceramic and the extensive ALP stain on the Al/AP was confirmed by quantitative analysis.   As shown in the Fig. 2, the DNA contents of the marrow cells on all substrata were not significantly different.   In contrast, the ALP activity of the cells on Al/AW was about 2 times more than that on control culture dish.   The results of the DNA contents that represent the cell number implied that cell proliferation was not affected by any of the culture substrata.   The highest ALP activity of the cells was found on the Al/AW and the lowest activity was found on the culture dish. These biochemical analyses confirmed that glass ceramics especially Al/AW ceramic promotes the osteoblastic differentiation of marrow stromal stem cells.   Another fact we should consider is that not only the composition of the materials' surfaces but also the surface roughness may affect the adhesion and function of the cells in tissue culture experiments.   In fact, Gomi and Davies observed the different bone forming capability of rat marrow cells on different surface roughness of polystyrene culture dish substrata[14] and Schwartz and Boyan reported the importance of materials surface roughness and topography on mesenchymal cell response.[15] However as shown in Fig. 1 and 2, AW 0.2 and AW 0.8 did not show significant differences concerning the ALP stain and ALP activities and thus the surface roughness of this range (0.2 - 0.8um) did not affect the cell activity.

Though the high ALP activity is found in the cell membrane of bone forming osteoblasts, ALP is not specific for bone tissue and many other tissues express ALP activity. To further prove the osteoblastic differentiation, demonstration of a more specific marker for osteoblasts is necessary. In this regard, bone Gla protein (BGP, osteocalcin) is the most reliable marker, as other tissues do not show obvious amounts of BGP.   Northern blot analysis showed that mRNA of the housekeeping gene, β-actin, was evenly seen in the cells on all culture substrata, whereas expression of BGP mRNA was varied.   The highest and lowest expression was seen in the cell cultured on Al/AW and on culture dish, respectively.

All the results presented here showed that Al/AW enhances the osteogenic differentiation of marrow stromal cells in the presence of dexamethasone, which is essential for the *in vitro* osteoblastic differentiation of marrow stromal cells. Without dexamethasone, only fibroblastic cells appeared on a tissue culture dish and parameters of osteoblastic phenotype expression such as high activity ALP and BGP were extremely low in the marrow cell culture.   However, to our surprise, recent data evidenced that Al/AW not AW can show *in vitro* osteoblastic differentiation even without dexamethasone.[16] Therefore, the Al/AW ceramic has strong osteogenic property compared to other ceramics.

The data of protein expression represented by ALP stain and activity (Fig 1 and 2) and the gene expression determined by Northern blot of BGP mRNA confirmed that the surface of Al/AW ceramic promotes the osteoblastic differentiation of marrow stromal stem cells.   Together with our previous report that cultured marrow in porous ceramics can show immediate *de novo* bone forming capability when implanted *in vivo* [17], present results obtained by marrow cell culture on the Al/AW clearly demonstrate the usefulness of Al/AW ceramic for the bone reconstruction surgery.

Alkaline phosphatase stain

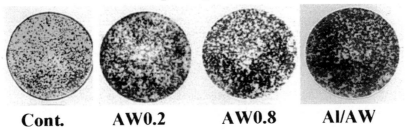

| Cont. | AW0.2 | AW0.8 | Al/AW |

Figure 1. ALP stain of marrow cell culture after 2 weeks.
Cont: Control culture dish, AW 0.2:AW having surface roughness of 0.22μm, AW 0.8: AW having surface roughness of 0.78μm, Al/AW: Al₂O₃ containing AW having surface roughness of 0.22μm.

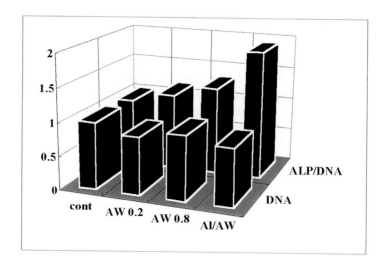

Figure 2. DNA and ALP activity of marrow cell culture after 2 weeks.
Cont: Control culture dish, AW 0.2:AW having surface roughness of 0.22μm, AW 0.8: AW having surface roughness of 0.78μm, Al/AW: Al_2O_3 containing AW having surface roughness of 0.22μm. DNA content and ALP/DNA (ALP activity divided by the DNA content) of the cells on control culture dish are set as 1.

REFERENCES

1. Kokubo T, Ito S, Sakka S, Yamamuro T. *J Mater Sci* 1986; **21**:536-540.
2. Nakamura T, Yamamuro T, Higashi S, Kokubo T, Ito S. *J Biomed Mater Res* 1985;**19**:685-698.
3. Kitugi T, Nakamura T, Yamamuro T, Kokubo T, Shibuya T, Takagi M. *J Biomed Mater Res* 1987; **21**:1255-1271.
4. Kitsugi T, Yamamuro T, Nakamura T, Kokubo T. *Internat Orthop (SICOT)* **1989;13**:199-206.
5. Owen M, In: Peck WA ed. *Bone and Mineral Research* Vol. 3, Elsevier Science Publisher B.V.1985:1-25.
6. Ohgushi H, Goldberg VM, Caplan AI, J Orthop Res 1989;**7**: 568-578.
7. Maniatopoulos C, Sodek J, Melcher AH, *Cell Tissue Res.* 1988; **254**:317-330.
8. Ohgushi H, Dohi Y, Katuda T, Tamai S, Tabata S, Suwa Y. J Biomed Mat Res 1996;**32**:333-340
9. Kokubo T, Ito S, Huang T, Hayashi T, Sakka S, Kitugi S, Yamamura T. *J Biomed Mater Res* 1990;24:331-343.
10. Kokubo T, Kushitani H, Sakka S, Kitugi T, Yamamuro T. *J Biomed Mater Res* 1990;**24**:721-734.
11. Ohgushi H, Dohi Y, Yoshikawa T, Tamai S, Tabata S, Okunaga K, Shibuya T. *J Biomed Mat Res* 1996; **32**:341-348
12. Ohgushi H, Dohi Y, Tamai S, Tabata S. *J Biomed Mat Res* 1996; **27**:1401-1407.
13. Yoshikawa T, Ohgushi H, Okumura M, Tamai S, Dohi Y, Moriyama T. *Calcified Tissue International* 1992; **50**: 184-188.
14. Gomi K, Davies JE *J Biomed Mat Res* 1993; **27**: 429-431.
15. Schwartz Z, Boyan BD. *J Celluar Biochem* 1994; **56**: 340-347
16. Ohgushi H, Yoshikawa T, Nakajima H, Tamai S, Dohi Y, Okunaga K. Submitted to *J Biomed Mat Res*
17. Yoshikawa T, Ohgushi H, Tamai S. *J Biomed Mat Res* 1996;**32**:481-492

Bioceramics Volume 11, edited by R. Z. LeGeros and J.P. LeGeros
(Proceedings of the 11th International Symposium on Ceramics in Medicine)
New York, NY, USA, November 1998
© 1998 by World Scientific Publishing Co. Pte. Ltd.

ATOMIC AND MOLECULAR MECHANISMS UNDERLYING THE OSTEOGENIC EFFECTS OF BIOGLASS® MATERIALS

L. Chou, S. Al-Bazie, D. Cottrell, R. Giodano, D. Nathason

Molecular Biocompatibility Laboratory, Goldman School of Dental Medicine, Boston University, 100 East Newton Street, Boston, MA 02118, USA.

ABSTRACT

The aim of this *in vivo* study was to determine the atomic and molecular mechanisms underlying the osteogenic effects of Bioglass® materials. Sol-gel Bioglass®, PerioGlas®, and hydroxyapatite (HA) were implanted endosteally in bilateral proximal tibial condyles of twenty-four rabbits for two and eight weeks. Surgical trauma at the same location without implant materials was included as a control. New bone formation was evaluated histomorphometrically. Expressions of two bone formation markers, osteocalcin (OC) and alkaline phosphatase (AKP), were measured immunohistochemically. Distributions of material elements at the interfaces were identified with EDAX on nondecalcified tissue sections. The results showed that at 2 weeks, higher silica-containing sol-gel Bioglass® generated the greatest amount of woven bone and cartilage which was replaced by dense compact bone at 8 weeks. PerioGlas® yielded a higher level of intramembranous bone than HA and surgery alone. OC expression was significantly up-regulated by sol-gel Bioglass® ($p<0.01$) and PerioGlas® ($p<0.05$). AKP expression was essentially at the same level among the groups tested. EDAX analysis indicated that sol-gel Bioglass® quickly released a high level of Si which then distributed to the areas of surrounding tissue, followed by an increased concentration of Ca and P indicating an early bone formation. High S reading at sol-gel Bioglass® interfaces also indicated a higher activity of endochondral bone formation which was consistent with histological findings at 2 weeks. The results suggested that sol-gel Bioglass® may have an early and significant osteogenic effect by releasing a higher level of Si and stimulating OC synthesis, resulted in a greater amount of new bone formation.

KEYWORDS: bioglass, hydroxyapatite, osteocalcin, alkaline phosphatase

MATERIALS AND METHODS:

Materials and Animal Models: Twenty-four adult male New Zealand rabbits each weighing approximately 4 Kg were used in this study. Three different materials: sol-gel Bioglass®, PerioGlas® (USBiomaterials Co., FL), and hydroxyapatite (HA, Calcitek Co., CA) particulates, were tested. Particle size and chemistry of these materials are described in Tables 1 and 2.

Methods: For surgical implantation on the animal models, a profusely irrigated trephine bur was used to make a 5 x 10 cm hole through the medial cortex of the tibia while leaving the lateral cortex of the tibia intact. The sterilized implant particulates were placed in the bone using special syringes that were adapted to the level of bone cortex. Six implantation sites were assigned

Table 1. Particle Size of the Materials

sol-gel Bioglass®	PerioGlas®	Hydroxyapatite
300 ~ 700 µm	90 ~ 700 µm	100 ~ 700 µm

Table 2. Chemical Composition of the Materials by EDAX *(atomic %)*

	sol-gel Bioglass	PerioGlas	Hydroxyapatite
Si	60.19	43.98	39.56
Ca	20.25	13.07	52.55
P	10.06	8.55	6.97
Na	0.36	33.04	0.37
Mg	0.04	1.22	0.21
K	0.25	0.13	0.34
Total	100.00	100.00	100.00

for each of the materials being tested, as well as for the surgery alone without any material as a control. Animals were sacrificed at 2 weeks or 8 weeks to harvest the block specimens of the tibia containing implanted materials.

Samples were immediately fixed with 4% paraformaldehyde. Three of six samples from each material groups and time intervals were decalcified in ethylenediaminetetraacetate (EDTA) for 6 weeks, followed by paraffin embedding. The paraffin tissue sections were used for H&E staining for histomorphological examination, and for immunohistochemical staining for bone morphogenic protein evaluation. Other three samples from each groups were subjected to plastic-embedding using epoxy resin (Buehler, Lake Bluff, IL) without decalcification. Hardened specimens were sectioned and ground into the sections of ~40 µm thickness. Half of the undecalcified sections were stained with H & E for morphological evaluation; other half of the sections were used for EDAX analysis.

In histomorphometric analysis, the amounts of woven bone formation around implant interfaces, and new bone formation into interparticulate spaces were measured using a video micrometer (Javelin Systems, Torrance, CA) which was connected to a light microscope. Implanted particulates remaining in undecalcified sections of different time intervals were also examined to access the biosolubility of different materials.

In immunohistochemical analysis, decalcified sections were labeled with osteocalcin monoclonal antibody or with alkaline phosphatase monoclonal antibody, followed by biotinylated IgG secondary antibody and avidin biotin complex. The labels were visualized by DAB system and enhanced by gold chloride. Three representative areas of each section were examined under a light microscope. The signals of gold chloride/DAB granules for osteocalcin and alkaline phosphatase were counted within selected 0.01 mm^2 views of the interfaces using a micrometer attached to a microscope. The means were then normalized on a per mm^2 basis.

RESULTS:

Biosolubility of the materials was evaluated on H&E stained nondecalcified plastic sections. PerioGlas® degraded significantly at 2 weeks and completely at 8 weeks. The rate of degradation for sol-gel Bioglass® was slightly slower than PerioGlas®. The residual particles of sol-gel Bioglass® were observed at 8 weeks. HA remained essentially unchanged at both 2 and 8 weeks.

Histomorphologically, intramembranous bone formation, predominantly immature woven bone, was observed in PerioGlas® and HA implant sites, as well as the surgery control sites, at both 2 and 8 weeks to different extends. Sol-gel Bioglass® sites showed a mixed form of intra-membranous and endochondral bone formations at 2 weeks, but at 8 weeks the cartilage portion was completely replaced by dense compact bone. The amounts of bone formation on either the tissue site or the materials sites (bone growing into interparticulate spaces or replacing material particulates) of implant/tissue interfaces were measured separately and described in Table 3.

Table 3. Bone Growth on Both Sites of Implant Interfaces or Surgical Margin (mm)

	sol-gel Bioglass®		PerioGlas®		HA		Surgery	
	MS*	TS*	MS	TS	MS	TS	MS	TS
2 weeks	1.6	3.1	1.1	2.1	0.5	0.2	0.7	0.5
8 weeks	complete	3.4	complete	1.7	complete	0.2	1.9	0.5

MS = material sites of the interface   TS = tissue sites of the interface

Studies of osteocalcin (Fig.1) and alkaline phosphatase (Fig.2) expressions at the interface regions indicated that sol-gel Bioglass® induced significantly higher level of osteocalcin than

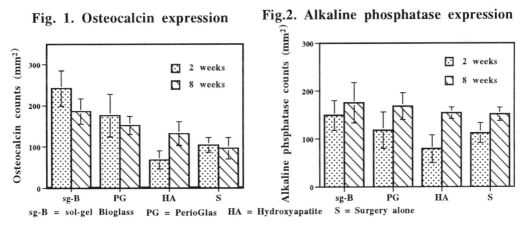

Fig. 1. Osteocalcin expression   **Fig.2. Alkaline phosphatase expression**

sg-B = sol-gel Bioglass   PG = PerioGlas   HA = Hydroxyapatite   S = Surgery alone

PerioGlas® ($p<0.05$), HA ($p<0.01$) and surgery alone ($p<0.01$) at 2 weeks. In comparison with surgery alone, HA seemed to inhibit the expression of osteocalcin at 2 weeks.

Ion distribution at the implantation sites was evaluated by EDAX analysis on nondecalcified plastic sections. The areas on both sides of the interface were measured. The results from sol-gel Bioglass® groups are presented in Table 3. Compared with sol-gel Bioglass®, Si release was significantly less in PerioGlas® gourp ($p<0.05$) and HA group ($p<0.01$) (data not shown).

Table 3. Chemical Distribution at sol-gel Bioglass® Implant Interfaces (atomic %)

2 weeks	+1 mm <---	Material side	*	Tissue side --->	+1 mm	--->	+2 mm
Si	14.78	4.12	I	8.79	13.92		2.09
Ca	28.37	8.70	N	9.01	14.47		9.47
P	7.31	7.88	T	8.47	11.64		18.51
S	7.81	24.26	E	11.88	15.47		31.90
Cl	24.99	0	R	0	37.74		26.21
8 weeks		<-------	F	------->			
Si	12.72	21.22	A	0.41	0.58		0.29
Ca	56.64	37.96	C	64.63	59.93		59.44
P	17.76	34.45	E	32.40	35.95		37.96
S	0	0	*	0	0		0
Cl	0	0		0	0		0

CONCLUSIONS:

Biomaterials tested in this study had about the same particle sizes, but distinguished chemical compositions, described as higher Si/lower Na and Ca sol-gel Bioglass®, lower Si and Ca/higher Na PerioGlas®, and lower Si/lower Na/higher Ca HA. Shortly after implantation, Sol-gel Bioglass® released a significantly higher level of Si which then distributed to the areas of surrounding tissue. This unique Si rich environment might be responsible for stimulating osteogenic cells at the interfaces to generate a significantly higher level of osteocalcin expression at the early stage of implantation, resulting in a remarkably increased intramembranous bone formation and temporal endochondral bone formation which could be replaced by dense compact bone within eight weeks. Moderate solubility of sol-gel Bioglass® might be an additional advantage to this temporal osteogenic event. Further *in vitro* studies are in progress to verify this atomic and molecular basis of Bioglass-induced osteogenesis.

ACKNOWLEDGEMENTS: This study was supported by grants from American Association of Oral and Maxillofacial Surgery and USBiomaterials Co., FL.

Bioceramics Volume 11, edited by R. Z. LeGeros and J.P. LeGeros
(Proceedings of the 11th International Symposium on Ceramics in Medicine)
New York, NY, USA, November 1998
© 1998 by World Scientific Publishing Co. Pte. Ltd.

THE RESPONSE OF HUMAN OSTEOBLAST CELL LINES TO PHOSPHATE-BASED SOLUBLE GLASSES

V. Salih[1], I.J.Jalisi[2], D.Lee[2], K.Franks[1], G. W. Hastings[3], J.C. Knowles[1], I. Olsen[4]

Departments of Biomaterials[1] and Periodontology[4], Eastman Dental Institute, University of London, 256 Gray's Inn Road, London WC1 8LD, U.K.; [2]IRC in Biomedical Materials, Institute of Orthopaedics, Royal National Orthopaedic Hospital, Brockley Hill, Middlesex HA7 4LP, U.K.; [3]Institute of Materials Research & Engineering, The National University of Singapore, Kent Ridge, Singapore 119260.

ABSTRACT

Two human osteoblast cell lines, MG63 and HOS (TE85), were incubated *in vitro* in culture medium containing increasing concentrations of extracts of phosphate-based glasses. The effects of the extracts on the proliferation of the cells were measured using the MTT assay. A cell ELISA assay was used to measure fibronectin (FN), osteonectin (ON) and bone sialoprotein (BSP), antigens which play a fundamental part in connective tissue integrity and function. The results indicated that, over a period of 5 days, the glass extracts did not adversely affect the growth of the cells compared with control cultures. However, the expression of FN and especially ON, but not BSP, was found to be down-regulated, especially when cells were cultured in the presence of the more soluble glass extracts. These findings suggest that these glasses are not cytotoxic and could be effective for use in bone repair systems after their composition is modified to elicit an optimal biological response from the host tissue.

KEYWORDS: soluble glasses, osteoblasts, proliferation, extracellular matrix.

INTRODUCTION

A novel group of glasses has recently been developed that are phosphate-based, the solubility of which is directly related to their chemical composition[1]. Such biomaterials could promote the growth of soft and hard connective tissue cells as occurs, for example, in the repair of periodontal defects and bone[2]. The purpose of this study was to determine the biocompatibility of these soluble glasses by examining certain key features of the cellular response of two human osteoblast-like cell lines *in vitro*.

MATERIALS AND METHODS

Glass Formulations

The glasses were composed of calcium oxide (CaO), sodium oxide (Na_2O) and phosphorous pentoxide (P_2O_5). They were prepared in the form of rods, approximately 70mm long. Individual discs, of total surface area approximately $5cm^2$, were cut from each rod using a diamond rotary saw. All discs had a smooth finish and appeared opaque. The P_2O_5 mol.% weight was kept constant at 45%. The solubility of the glasses is related to the proportion of CaO present, glasses containing lee than approximately 20% CaO being very soluble, whereas those containing more than approximately 20% are much less soluble. The composition of the glasses used in the present experiments is shown in Table 1, which also indicates their solubility.

Preparation of Glass Extracts

Glass discs were sterilised by dry heat at 180°C for 2 h. They were placed into 50 ml Falcon tubes containing 10 ml of cell culture medium. This latter volume was chosen in accordance with BS-EN 30993-5 (1994), which recommends that the ratio between the surface area of the test material and the volume of the extraction vehicle is equal to or greater than $0.5cm^2/ml$. A volume of 5 ml of each extract was collected for each glass, after 1 day and after 5 days of incubation at

37°C, with occasional agitation. Because of precipitation of the more soluble glasses, extracts of all the glasses were passed through a 0.22μm Millipore filter and then stored at –20°C.

Table 1 – Composition and relative solubility of phosphate-glass preparations

Glass No.	Solubility	Composition (mol. %)		
		CaO	Na$_2$O	P$_2$O$_5$
44	+++	8	47	45
47	+++	16	39	45
51	+	28	27	45
54	+	40	15	45

Cell Culture

Two human osteosarcoma cell lines, HOS (TE85) and MG63, were used in this study. Both show osteoblast-like characteristics and are often used as experimental models for investigating aspects of osteoblast function[3]. The cells were cultured at 37°C in a humidified atmosphere of 5% CO$_2$ in air, in flasks containing 10 ml of DMEM supplemented with 10% (v/v) foetal calf serum, 2 mM L-glutamine, 50 IU/ml of penicillin and 50 μg/ml of streptomycin. The culture media were changed twice weekly and for sub-culture the monolayers were rinsed with phosphate-buffered saline (PBS) and incubated with trypsin-EDTA for 5 min at 37°C, prior to reculturing in 96-well microtitre plates. Dilutions of 1:100 (1%) and 1:2 (50%) of the glass extracts were prepared using DMEM culture medium. HOS and MG63 cells were incubated with the 1% and 50% dilutions of the glass extracts in 96-well microtitre plates as described below.

MTT Assay for Cell Proliferation

MTT is a substrate that is converted by a mitochondrial enzyme, which is active in living cells, to yield a dark blue formazan product. The intensity of the colour produced is directly related to the number of viable cells, and thus their proliferation *in vitro*. Cells were plated at a density of 2000 cells/well in replicate 96 well culture plates and allowed to attach overnight at 37°C, after which the media were removed and replaced by the diluted extracts. Cells maintained in normal culture medium were used as controls. The cells were then incubated for a further 5 days. Cell proliferation was measured after 1, 3 and 5 days using the MTT test (Chemicon, Temecula Ca., USA). Absorbance was measured at 560nm using a Titertek Multiskan Spectrophotometer. The results are expressed as the average absorbance of 6 replicate wells.

ELISA for Expression of Tissue-Specific Antigens

The enzyme-linked immunosorbent assay (ELISA) requires few cells and can measure large numbers of samples simultaneously. 2000 cells/well were seeded into 96-well microtitre plates and incubated for 2 days at 37°C, after which the medium was removed and replaced by either 100 μl of fresh DMEM (controls) or the respective diluted extracts. After a further 5 days of incubation the medium was removed and the cells fixed and permeabilised with 3% paraformaldehyde/0.1% saponin in PBS. The cells were then washed with PBS containing 0.05% Tween. Non-specific binding was inhibited by adding 200 μl of PBS-Tween containing 1% milk to each well and incubating for 1 h. After washing, the cells were reacted with rabbit antibodies against FN, ON and BSP (1:1000 dilution) for 1 h. After washing, horseradish peroxidase (HRP)-conjugated goat anti-rabbit antibody (1:5000 dilution) was applied for 30 min. After further washing, the enzyme substrate, o-phenylenediamine dihydrochloride was added for 10 min. The reaction was stopped by adding 25 μl of 2 M H$_2$SO$_4$. The absorbance was measured at 450nm.

RESULTS AND DISCUSSION
Cell proliferation

Fig. 1 shows the proliferation of MG63 cells cultured in the presence of the glasses extracted for 1 day (a, b) and 5 days (c, d).

Fig. 1a - 1 day extract, 1% dilution

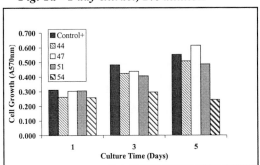

Fig. 1b – 1 day extract, 50% dilution

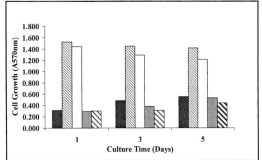

Fig. 1c - 5 day extract, 1% dilution

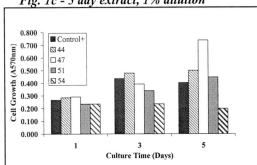

Fig. 1d - 5 day extract, 50% dilution

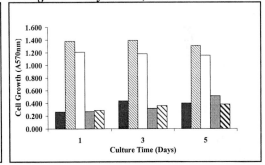

Fig. 1. – The effects of glass extracts on the growth of MG63 cells at 1, 3 and 5 days.

There is a marked difference in the growth of the MG63 cells depending on the concentration and composition of extract used. Extracts obtained after 1 day and diluted 1:100 had little effect on cell proliferation, except for the glass with the highest CaO concentration (No. 54), which resulted in a decrease in cell number (Fig. 1a). In contrast, when higher concentrations (50%) of extracts of the more insoluble glasses (Nos. 51 & 54) were added, they did not affect cell growth compared with the control cells, whereas the low CaO glasses (Nos. 44 & 47) increased the apparent cell numbers (Fig. 1b). Similar results were obtained when the 5-day extracts were added to the cells either dilute (Fig. 1c) or highly concentrated (Fig. 1d). However, the apparent increases in proliferation caused by the very soluble glasses (Nos. 44 & 47; Fig. 1b, 1d) may not have been due to an actual change in cell numbers, but rather to an absorbance effect caused by precipitation of these glasses in solution. This caused turbidity in the media, which interfered with the absorbance measurements and the cells in these cultures were found not to be viable and became detached. The results for HOS cells were very similar (data not shown). These results suggest that at low concentrations (1%) of glass extracts, there are no obvious deleterious effects on the viability and proliferation of MG63 cells even in the presence of the very soluble glass extracts. However, at higher concentrations (50%), the more soluble glasses (CaO content <20%) appeared to inhibit proliferation, even when extracted for only 1 day.

Antigen expression

The expression of FN, ON and BSP was measured by ELISA as described. Table 2 shows the levels of these antigens expressed by MG63 and HOS cells incubated with the concentrated (50%) extracts obtained on days 1 and 5 of a soluble (No. 44) glass and less soluble (No. 54) glass.

Table 2 – Expression of connective tissue antigens in MG63 and HOS cells

Cell Type	Glass No.	Days of Extract	Relative Antigen Expression (% of control)		
			FN	ON	BSP
MG63	44	1	41	31	59
	44	5	51	36	86
	54	1	79	33	131
	54	5	59	34	93
HOS	44	1	44	44	68
	44	5	46	38	62
	54	1	50	41	61
	54	5	61	33	60

The results show that, in the presence of the concentrated extracts, both cell types expressed all three antigens, although at reduced levels compared to the controls. The more soluble glass (No. 44) appeared to inhibit expression of all 3 antigens more than the less soluble glass extract (No. 54), for both cell types. Thus, in MG63 cells, while FN levels were only 41 and 51% of the control in the presence of the more soluble glass, they were 79 and 59% of control with the less soluble glass (day 1 and day 5 extracts respectively). Similar differences were found for HOS cells. ON was the most severely affected antigen being only 31 to 44% of control levels under all conditions. In contrast, while BSP was 59 and 86% of controls in the presence of the soluble glass, this antigen was unaffected by the low solubility glass (131 and 93% of control levels). In HOS cells, however, BSP expression reached only 68% of that in control cells. The apparent down-regulation of expression of some of these proteins by the presence of soluble glass products may be due to direct effects on protein synthesis or to the different turnover rates of the proteins.

CONCLUSION

These studies have shown that human osteoblast cell lines can proliferate and express several antigens even in the presence of highly concentrated (50%) extracts of phosphate-based soluble glasses. However, while the expression of BSP was largely unaffected by the extracts and remained near control levels, particularly in the MG63 cells, the expression of FN and especially ON were considerably reduced compared to controls. Further chemical modification of these glasses is now in progress in order to elicit a more optimal biological response for potential clinical application.

REFERENCES

1. Burnie J. Controlled Release Glass (CRG) – A New Biomaterial (1982) PhD Thesis.
2. Videau JJ & Dupuis V. *Eur. J. Solid State Inorg. Chem.* 1991; **28**: 303-343.
3. Clover J & Gowen M. *Bone* 1994; **15**: 585-591.

Bioceramics Volume 11, edited by R. Z. LeGeros and J.P. LeGeros
(Proceedings of the 11th International Symposium on Ceramics in Medicine)
New York, NY, USA, November 1998

AN *IN VITRO* EVALUATION OF NANOPHASE ALUMINA FOR ORTHOPAEDIC / DENTAL APPLICATIONS

Thomas J. Webster[1], Richard W. Siegel[2], and Rena Bizios[1]
[1]Departments of Biomedical Engineering and [2]Materials Science and Engineering
Rensselaer Polytechnic Institute, Troy, NY 12180-3590

ABSTRACT

Osteoblast adhesion on nanophase alumina (Al_2O_3) was investigated *in vitro*. Osteoblasts in Dulbecco's Modified Eagle Medium (DMEM) did not adhere to alumina in the absence of serum. In the presence of 10% fetal bovine serum in DMEM, however, osteoblast adhesion on nanophase (23 nm grain size) alumina was significantly ($p < 0.05$) greater than on conventional (177 nm grain size) alumina after 1, 2, and 4 hours. The improved mechanical properties of nanomaterials, in addition to the established biocompatibility of nanophase ceramics, constitute characteristics that promise improved orthopaedic / dental implant efficacy.

KEYWORDS: Nanophase alumina, orthopaedic / dental, implant, osteoblast, adhesion

INTRODUCTION

In the course of normal, daily activities, mechanical loads are applied to mammalian bone; for example, jaws sustain 0.25 kN during chewing while hip joints are exposed to 3 – 5 kN during walking [1]. In fact, these physiological force requirements have become the primary criterion for selecting materials (such as commercially pure titanium, Ti-6Al-4V and Co-Cr-Mo alloys) for orthopaedic / dental applications. Conventional single-phase materials which have been developed for various industrial applications (*e.g.*, in aeronautical or space engineering) have been used as orthopaedic / dental implants as long as they were tolerated by the human body and met certain specifications, such as strength requirements under loading [3]. In contrast, ceramics, which have exceptional biocompatibility properties with bone cells and tissues, but are brittle under loading, have experienced limited use in biomedical applications. Unfortunately, the use of conventional metals and metal alloys that meet mechanical requirements for bone replacements under loading have not produced the "ideal" orthopaedic / dental implant material; in fact, under long-term physiological loading, metal material failures (such as initiation and propagation of cracks) have resulted in clinical complications that necessitated surgical removal of failed bone implants [1].

With the advent of nanostructured materials (materials with grain sizes less than 100 nm in at least one dimension)[4], which possess improved mechanical characteristics, it may now be possible to formulate biomaterials with specific mechanical (*i.e.*, comparable to those of bone under loading) and biocompatibility properties. For example, compared to conventional materials, nanophase metals become considerably harder (by a factor of 2 to 7) and nanophase ceramics exhibit enhanced ductility as grain size is reduced [5]. Nanomaterials with enhanced mechanical properties could replace conventional orthopaedic / dental metal implants that fatigue-fail due to crack initiation and propagation during loading. In addition, nanomaterials with enhanced surface properties that promote osteoblast functions (such as adhesion, proliferation, and the formation of mineral deposits) could replace conventional orthopaedic / dental implants that fail to promote osseointegration.

The present study of the mechanical properties and cytocompatibility of nanophase alumina is the first investigation of the potential use of nanophase ceramics for orthopaedic / dental applications.

MATERIALS AND METHODS

Substrates

Circular alumina (γ-Al_2O_3) samples (10 mm in diameter; 2 mm thick) were prepared by compacting nanophase (23 nm grain size) alumina powder (Nanophase Technologies Corp.) in a tool-steel die *via* a uniaxial pressing cycle (0.2 GPa to 1 GPa over a 10 minute period). The nanophase compacts were sintered (in air at 10 °C / minute) from room temperature to a final temperature of either 1,000 °C or 1,100 °C and maintained at either 1,000 °C or 1,100 °C, respectively, for 2 hours to obtain grain sizes less than 100 nm [6]. Conventional alumina samples were sintered (in air at 10 °C / minute) from room temperature to a final temperature of 1,200 °C and maintained at 1,200 °C for 2 hours to obtain grain sizes greater than 100 nm [6]. Alumina grain size was determined by multiple-point BET method.

Prior to cell culture experiments, all samples were degreased, ultrasonically cleaned and sterilized (in a steam autoclave at 120 °C for 30 minutes) according to standard protocols [2]. Borosilicate glass coverslips (reference material) were etched in 1 N NaOH and prepared for cell culture experiments again according to standard protocols [2].

Cell Culture

Osteoblasts were isolated *via* sequential collagenase digestions of neonatal rat calvaria [2] and cultured in Dulbecco's Modified Eagle Medium (DMEM; Gibco), supplemented with 10% fetal bovine serum (Gibco) in a 37 °C, humidified, 5% CO_2 / 95% air environment. These cells were passaged and, as needed, lifted from polystyrene tissue culture flasks using small volumes (*i.e.*, less than 1 mL) of PET, an enzymatic solution, and routine cell culture procedures [2]. The osteoblastic phenotype was determined by morphology, alkaline phosphatase activity and mineral production. Osteoblasts population number 2-4 were used in the experiments.

Cell Adhesion

Osteoblasts (3,500 cells / cm^2) in DMEM (in the presence or absence of 10% fetal bovine serum) were seeded per substrate and allowed to adhere in a 37 °C, humidified, 5% CO_2 / 95% air environment for 0.5, 1, 2, and 4 hours. After the prescribed time period, osteoblasts adherent on opaque alumina substrates were fixed with 4% formaldehyde in sodium phosphate buffer and stained with Hoechst (No. 33342; Sigma); the cell nuclei were, thus, visualized and counted using fluorescence miscroscopy (365 nm excitation; 400 nm emission). Osteoblasts adherent on glass were fixed with 4% formaldehyde in sodium phosphate buffer, stained with Coomassie Blue and counted using a light microscope. Cell density (cells / cm^2) was determined by averaging the number of adherent cells in five random fields per substrate.

Statistical Analysis

The osteoblast adhesion experiments were run in triplicate and repeated at three different times. Numerical data were analyzed statistically using student t-tests; statistical significance was considered at $p < 0.05$.

RESULTS AND DISCUSSION

The average grain size of the alumina compacts sintered at 1,000 °C was 23 nm (*i.e.*, the size of the nanophase alumina powder used in preparing the substrates). In contrast, nanophase alumina grain size increased to 177 nm (a value more in the range of conventional material formulations) when the alumina compacts were sintered (in air at 10 °C / minute) to 1,200 °C. Mechanical properties (specifically, the modulus of elasticity as determined *via* three-point bending tests) of the alumina samples were investigated as a function of alumina grain size; compared to the 177 nm grain size alumina, the modulus of elasticity of the 23 nm alumina grain size decreased by 70 %. Furthermore, porosities of the conventional and nanophase alumina samples were similar. These results provide evidence that the mechanical properties of alumina can be controlled and improved through the use of nanophase formulations.

In addition, *in vitro*, cellular models were utilized to determine the cytocompatability of the nanophase alumina of interest to the present study. Osteoblasts in DMEM did not adhere on alumina in the absence of serum. In the presence of 10% serum, however, osteoblast adhesion on nanophase alumina was significantly ($p < 0.01$) greater than osteoblast adhesion on borosilicate glass (reference substrate) after 1, 2, and 4 hours. More importantly, compared to osteoblast adhesion on conventional (177 nm grain size) alumina, osteoblast adhesion on nanophase (23 nm grain size) alumina was significantly ($p < 0.05$) greater after 1, 2, and 4 hours; in fact, compared to conventional (177 nm grain size) alumina, osteoblast adhesion increased by 46 % on nanophase (23 nm grain size) alumina after 4 hours.

The mechanism(s) of cell interactions with nanophase materials need to be further investigated and elucidated. Biomaterials of the future must elicit responses from osteoblasts that promote the swift deposition of new bone on the surface of implants and support bonding of juxtaposed bone that stabilize prostheses *in situ* and, thus, minimize motion-induced damage to surrounding tissue. Moreover, since for anchorage-dependent cells (like osteoblasts), adhesion is the prerequesite to subsequent cell functions (*e.g.*, proliferation, synthesis of extracellular matrix proteins, formation of mineral deposits, *etc.*) enhanced responses could be expected from cells interacting with nanophase materials. Since proteins mediate cell interactions on substrates, the present data imply that nanophase materials may promote interactions (such as adsorption, configuration, bioactivity, *etc.*) of select serum protein(s) which enhance osteoblast adhesion.

The results of the present study also provide the first evidence of the cytocompatibility of nanophase alumina. Nanostructured ceramics provide as yet unexplored alternatives for biomedical applications; the improved mechanical properties of nanomaterials, in addition to the established biocompatibility of nanophase ceramics, constitute characteristics that promise improved orthopaedic / dental implant efficacy.

REFERENCES

1. Kaplan, F.S., Hayes, W.C., Keaven, T. M., Boskey, A. Einhorn, T. A. and Iannotti, J. P. In Simon, S.R. ed. *Orthopaedic Basic Science*, American Academy of Orthopaedic Surgeons, Columbus, OH, 1994 : 127.
2. Puelo, D.A., Holleran, L.A., Doremus, R.H. and Bizios, R. *Journal of Biomedical Materials and Research* 1991; **25**: 711-723.
3. Ratner, B. *Journal of Biomedical Materials and Research* 1993; **27**: 873-850.
4. Siegel, R.W. *Scientific American* 1996; **275**; 42-47.
5. Siegel, R. W. and Fougere, G.E. *Materials Research Society Symposium* Proceedings, 1995, **362**, 219.
6. Wu, S.J. *Journal of American Ceramic Society* 1996; **79**, 2207-2211.

Bioceramics Volume 11, edited by R. Z. LeGeros and J.P. LeGeros
(Proceedings of the 11th International Symposium on Ceramics in Medicine)
New York, NY, USA, November 1998
© 1998 by World Scientific Publishing Co. Pte. Ltd.

CELL PROLIFERATION AND ANTIGEN EXPRESSION ON HYDROXYAPATITE/CaO-P$_2$O$_5$ MULTILAYERED COATINGS

M. P. Ferraz[1, 3, 4], J. C. Knowles[1], I. Olsen[2], F. J. Monteiro[3, 4], J. D. Santos[3, 4]

Departments of Biomaterials[1] and Periodontology[2] Eastman Dental Institute, London, UK, [3]INEB-Instituto de Engenharia Biomedica, Rua do Campo Alegre, 823 4150 Porto, Portugal, [4]Departmento de Engenharia Metalurgica e Materiais, Porto, Portugal

ABSTRACT

Multilayered coatings composed of mixtures of HA and P$_2$O$_5$-based bioactive glasses offer potential clinical benefit, so double-layer plasma-sprayed coatings were prepared and the biological response was studied.

A human osteosarcoma cell line, HOS, was grown in α-MEM alone and α-MEM to which was added progressively increasing proportions of media which had previously been incubated with the different material coatings for up to 5 days. Analysis of cell proliferation using the MTT assay showed that these materials had no notably deleterious effects on the growth of bone-like cells. However, measurements of the expression of cell-specific antigens by ELISA and Flow Cytometry indicate that there are subtle effects of the materials which could have important clinical consequences.

KEYWORDS: Calcium phosphate coatings, Cell proliferation, Antigen Expression

INTRODUCTION

Hydroxyapatite (HA) has very limited bioactivity, producing only slow osseointegration and requiring prolonged periods of immobilisation for patients. The use of phosphate-based glasses as alternatives is limited because of their high solubility in physiological environments, thus preventing their application as coatings on prostheses. However, multilayered coatings composed of mixtures of HA and P$_2$O$_5$-based bioactive glasses could be of potential clinical benefit, as the glass component would induce an initial fast response after implantation and the more stable HA phase would facilitate longer term integration with regenerating tissue. In the present study double-layer plasma-sprayed coatings were therefore prepared and the biological response was measured with a view to developing a more effective implant material.

A human osteoblast-like cell line, HOS, was grown in α-MEM alone and α-MEM containing increasing proportions of media which had previously been incubated with the different material coatings. Cell proliferation, using the MTT assay, and the expression of cell-specific antigens, using ELISA and flow cytometry (FCM), were carried out in order to assess the potential toxicity of these materials.

MATERIALS AND METHODS

Materials Preparation

Coatings were made on a Ti-6Al-4V alloy substrate and were composed of 60 μm of commercial HA followed by a 60 μm second layer containing HA and 2% or 4% of a P$_2$O$_5$-CaO based glass (HA, HA2 and HA4 respectively). The added glass thus incorporated elements commonly found in bone mineral and had the following composition (mol%): 35% P$_2$O$_5$, 35% CaO, 20% Na$_2$O, 10% K$_2$O. The preparation of these coatings has been previously described[1], and other studies have shown that these composites exhibit higher bioactivity when compared with HA in dense form[2-3].

Preparation of material extracts

Coatings were detached from the Ti-6Al-4V substrate and milled to obtain a particle size of less then 20 µm. The powders were then incubated with α-MEM at a concentration of 0.5g/ml at 37°C in 5% CO_2 in air for a period of 5 days. The suspension was then centrifuged, filtered and stored at –20 °C.

Cell culture and proliferation analysis

The human osteosarcoma cell line, HOS, was cultured at 37°C in a humidified atmosphere of 5% CO_2 in air, in 75 cm^2 flasks containing 10 ml α-MEM, 10% foetal calf serum (FCS), 2 mM L-glutamine, 50 IU/ml of penicilin and 50 µg/ml streptomycin. The media was changed every third day and, for sub-culture, the cell layer was rinsed twice with phosphate-buffered saline (PBS) and incubated with trypsin-EDTA solution for 10 min at 37°C. The trypsin was inactivated by adding an equal volume of complete medium at room temperature, the cells washed twice by centrifugation and resuspended in complete medium for re-seeding and growing in new culture flasks.

The cells were plated at a density of 10^4 cells/ml on 96 well plates and allowed to attach for 6 h at 37°C, after which the medium was removed and replaced by the undiluted extract (U) and by the extracts diluted 1 in 50 (D). In control wells the medium was replaced by fresh α-MEM only. The cells were then incubated for a further 1, 3 and 5 days. Cell proliferation was measured at each of these times using the MTT test (Chemicon, Temecula Ca., USA). The results are shown as the average absorbance, of 6 replicate wells, at 560 nm (A_{560}).

Antigen expression by enzyme-linked immunosorbent assay (ELISA)

ELISA is a highly specific, antibody-based colorimetric assay which measures the presence of a particular antigen in cells or fluid sample. A secondary antibody conjugated to an enzyme is used to detect the binding of the primary antibody to the antigen, a subsequent enzyme-substrate reaction producing a coloured product which is quantified by absorbance readings. In this work, the cell ELISA technique was used to detect the effects of the material extracts on the expression of osteonectin (ON) and fibronectin (FN) by the cells, since these antigens have previously been shown to have a key role in bone development, repair and regeneration.

The cells were plated at 10^4 cells/ml in 96-well plates and allowed to settle for 6 h at 37 °C, after which the medium was removed and replaced by 200 µl of fresh α-MEM and the extracts U and D respectively. After 5 days of incubation the medium was discarded and the cells washed 3 times with PBS. The cells were fixed and permeabilised by adding 200 µl of PBS containing 3% paraformaldehyde and 0.1% saponin to each well. After incubating at 37°C for 15 min, the cells were washed 5 times with PBS-Tween buffer. 200 µl Of PBS-Tween containing 1% milk was then added to each well and incubated at 37°C for 1 h to block non-specific binding by the antibody. The plates were again washed with PBS-Tween 5 times and 50 µl of rabbit polyclonal antibodies against ON and FN (Dako, UK) (diluted 1:1000) were added to 6 replicate wells each. Negative controls received PBS only. The plates were incubated for 1 h at 37°C and washed 5 times with PBS-Tween. Horseradish peroxidase (HRP)-conjugated goat anti-rabbit secondary antibody (Dako, UK) (diluted 1:5000) was added to each well (50 µl) and incubated for 30 min at 37°C. After washing, 75 µl of o-phenylenediamine dihydrochloride (OPD) substrate was added and the plates incubated for 10 min at 37°C. The reaction was stopped by adding 25 µl of 2 M H_2SO_4. The absorbance was measured at 450nm (A_{450}) using a Titertek Multiskan Spectrophotometer.

Antigen expression by flow cytometry (FCM)

The cells were plated at 10^{4}cells/ml and grown in 75 cm^2 flasks in α-MEM alone (control cultures) and with the U and D extracts, as described. The expression of ON and FN were measured after 5 days of culture. The cells were washed twice with PBS and detached using 20 mM EDTA in PBS for 5 min at 37°C. They were centrifuged at 400 g for 7 min and the pellet resuspended and again centrifuged. They were fixed in 1% (w/v) paraformaldehyde in PBS for 30 min, then washed, centrifuged and resuspended in a washing buffer (PBS with 2% FCS and 0.05% sodium azide). Cells were permeabilized for 10 min using washing buffer with 0.1% saponin, then washed, centrifuged and resuspended. Aliquots of 10^5 fixed cells were used to measure the level of each antigen by FCM.

Cells were incubated for 60 min at room temperature with the rabbit polyclonal antibodies against ON and FN (both diluted 1:100). Normal, pre-immune rabbit serum was used as a negative control. Cells were then washed, centrifuged and resuspended in washing buffer containing 0.1% saponin. The secondary antibody, fluorescein isothiocynate (FITC)-conjugated swine anti-rabbit IgG (Dako, UK), (diluted 1:20), was added for 30 min at room temperature. Cells were washed again and resuspended in 0.5ml of washing buffer and analysed using a FACScan Flow Cytometer (Becton Dickinson). Analysis was performed on a total of 10000 cells. Data were collected and analysed with CellQuest Software (Becton Dickinson).

RESULTS AND DISCUSSION

Cell proliferation

The proliferation of HOS cells was evaluated using an MTT test as above. The results in Fig. 1 show that after 1 day of incubation in the presence of the U extracts of HA, HA2 and HA4, proliferation was much lower than in the control cultures (approximately 33, 34 and 30%, respectively). The D cultures also resulted in a decrease in proliferation, although the extent depended on the glass content of the composites. Thus, while HA alone was nearly 91% of control cultures, the diluted HA2 was only 65% and the diluted HA4 had only 40% of the number of control cells. By day 3 however, even the U extracts had little if any effect on proliferation, all being between 85-92% of the control levels. By day 5 the number of cells in the extract cultures were the same as in control (99%-111%). The results in Fig. 1 thus indicate that the main inhibitory effects of the extracts, observed most markedly on day 1, is fully overcome after 5 days of culture, at which time the number of cells equal the control. This suggests the possibility that while there was a delay of cell proliferation which was caused by the high concentration of the extracts, the effects of these materials were not cytotoxic to the osteoblasts, which fully recovered

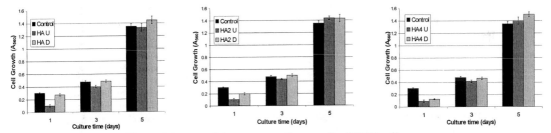

Fig 1. Effects of the material extracts on the growth of HOS cells.

FN and ON expression measured by cell-ELISA

Cell ELISA technique was used to examine the influence of the material extracts on the expression of ON and FN, as described in the Materials and Methods. Table 1 shows the expression of FN and ON by cells incubated with the material extracts. These results indicate that the expression of both ON and FN by HOS cells was unaffected by any of the U or D extracts of HA or any of the composites. Thus, as no statistically significant down-regulation of these antigens was produced by the extracts, there appears to be no evidente adverse effects of any of these materials on the expression of these antigens by HOS cells.

Table 1. ELISA analysis of the effects of material extracts on FN and ON expression.

Material Extracts		Antigen expression (% of control)	
		ON	FN
HA	U	100	102
	D	96	102
HA2	U	100	102
	D	103	97
HA4	U	105	109
	D	101	112

ON and FN expression measured by FCM

The cell ELISA procedure measures only the average of the population of all cells and also only has a relatively low sensitivity in detecting small changes in antigen expression. In contrast, FCM analyses each cell individually, using a much more sensitive fluorescent marker as a measure of the relative level of each antigen. The results in Table 2 show the relative levels of antigen expression by the HOS cells grown on the material extracts. While ON expression was somewhat down-regulated by the U extracts of HA, the U extract of HA2 and HA4 had no effect, whereas the D extracts of these latter 2 materials both substantially decreased antigen expression. Notably, these two D extracts also down-regulated FN expression, in marked contrast to the D extract of HA, which actually up-regulated both ON and FN over the levels expressed by the cultures incubated with the U extracts. Thus, the effects of the material extracts appear to be concentration dependent, suggesting that for each of the materials there is an optimal "biocompatible" concentration of the extract. Moreover, there seems to be an inverse relationship between the effects of the materials on the expression of the two antigens and proliferation, since the D extracts of HA2 and HA4 both reduced relative antigens levels but nevertheless increased the relative proliferation of the cells over that in the U cultures (Fig. 1).

Table 2. FCM analysis of the effects of material extracts on FN and ON expression by HOS cells.

Material Extracts		Antigen expression (% of control)	
		ON	FN
HA	U	86	74
	D	133	87
HA2	U	101	98
	D	63	59
HA4	U	103	83
	D	76	62

CONCLUSION

The results of this study show that the extracts of HA and the HA glass composites appeared to have no major long-term effects on HOS proliferation. However, they modulated the expression of bone antigens. Although the cell ELISA technique was not sufficiently sensitive to detect such changes, FCM showed that there are subtle effects of the materials which could have important clinical consequences. Studies are now in progress using heterogeneous cultures of bone cells to determine cell-specific responses to these materials.

AKNOLEDGMENTS

Authors would like to acknowledge the financial support of JNICT through the project "New plasma-sprayed bioactive coatings" Ref. PBIC C/CTM/1890/95 and PRAXIS grant XXI/BD/9716/96.

REFERENCES

1. Silva PL, Santos JD, Knowles JC, Monteiro FJ, *J. Mai. Sci.: Mat. Med*, 1996, **7**, 187-189.
2. Jha LJ, Santos JD, Knowles JC, *J Biomed Mat Res* 1996; **31**, 481-486.
3. Ferraz MP, Monteiro FJ, Santos JD, *9th International Conference on Biomedical Engineering-Singapore* 1997, 557-559.

Bioceramics Volume 11, edited by R. Z. LeGeros and J.P. LeGeros
(Proceedings of the 11th International Symposium on Ceramics in Medicine)
New York, NY, USA, November 1998
© 1998 by World Scientific Publishing Co. Pte. Ltd.

STUDY OF OSTEOPONTIN INVOLVEMENT IN OSTEOBLAST DIFFERENTIATION FOR ALLOGENIC TRANSPLANTATION OF *in vitro* CULTURED BONE

Atsuko Nemoto[1], Toshimasa Uemura[1], Yin-kun Liu[2], Takafumi Yoshikawa[3], Takashi Ushida[1] and Tetsuya Tateishi[1]

[1]National Institute for Advanced Interdisciplinary Research (NAIR), Tsukuba Research Center, Tsukuba, Ibaraki, 305-8562, Japan; [2]Shanghai Medical University; [3]Nara Medical University

ABSTRACT

Porous hydroxyapatite (HA) is one of good template for transplantation of *in vitro* cultured bone tissues. For obtaining higher efficiency of bone formation *in vitro*, composites of bone matrix proteins and template like porous HA, might be useful tool. In this point of view, we investigated the effect of several bone matrix proteins such as collagen type I, fibronectin, osteocalcin, osteonectin, osteopontin and BSP on osteoblast differentiation. Results of immunofluorescence, mRNA expression and dissociative extraction on osteoblastic primary cells suggested that collagen type I, osteopontin, and BSP might play an important role in osteoblast early differentiation. Moreover study of integrin mediated signal transduction via p125 focal adhesion kinase (FAK) autophosphorylation strongly correlated with alkaline phosphatase (ALP) expression at the transcription level. This means osteopontin might act as a trigger in the early differentiation of osteoblast.

KEYWORDS: osteopontin, FAK, osteoblast, ALP

INTRODUCTION

With respect to the osteoblast differentiation through the remodeling process, it can be said that the adhesion procedure of the pre-osteoblast to the bone surface is one of the major turning points in the differentiation process, at which the pre-osteoblasts become matured osteoblasts with bone formation ability. These associations closely resemble cell substratum relationships of *in vitro* cell culture systems. To construct of this *in vitro* cell culture system, most important factor is extracellular matrix protein (ECM). ECM binds to integrin receptor on cell membrane. The binding of integrins to ECM occurs at specialized sites known as focal adhesions. Within a focal adhesion, the cytoplasmic domain of the integrin is linked to the actin cytoskeleton via a complex array of protein-protein interactions. The binding of integrins to ECM and the activation of inducible p125 focal adhesion kinase (FAK) are subjects of biological significance which require detailed study.

MATERIALS&METHODS

Materials

Anti-FAK rabbit polyclonal antibody and *p*-Tyr (Py20) monoclonal antibody were purchased from Santa Cruz Biotechnology Inc., CA, USA. The fibronectin, vitronectin and collagen type I were from Sigma Co., MO, USA, Cosmo Bio Co., Ltd., Japan and Wako Pure Chemical Industries Ltd., Japan, respectively. Osteopontin was purified from newborn rat calvaria by the normal procedure with modification in our laboratory. Other reagents and chemicals were commercially available with analytical purities.

Cell culture

UMR 106-6 cells were donated by the group headed by Prof. Jaro Sodek at the University of

Toronto. The cells were cultured in α-MEM containing 167 units/ml penicillin G, 10^{-6} M dexamethasone, 50 μg/ml gentamicin and 0.3 μg/ml amphotericin B. The α-MEM was supplemented with 15% fetal bovine serum and 50 μg/ml of freshly prepared ascorbic acid, and cultured at 37°C with 5% CO_2. Six well plates were coated with various ECM. The concentrations of collagen type I (Co I), fibronectin (FN), vitronectin (VN), and osteopontin (OPN) were 500 μg, 50 μg, 25 μg and 25 μg/ml respectively. The coated wells were washed. Then the cells were resuspended, plated on the wells at a density of $1\text{-}3\text{x}10^6$, and incubated.

Immunoprecipitation

The monolayer cells were washed twice with PBS. After the addition of 0.8 ml of lysate buffer, the cell lysate were collected. After preclarification with protein A agarose, 10 μl of antibody and protein A agarose were added and incubated. After centrifuge, SDS-PAGE sample buffer was added. All samples were applied to 7.5% SDS-PAGE gel and detected by silver staining.

Reverse transcription and polymerase chain reaction (RT-PCR)

UMR cells with a density of $4\text{-}6.8\text{x}10^6$ cells were resuspended into dishes (10 cm in diameter) coated with FN, OPN and Co I, respectively. The cells were incubated at 37°C with 5% CO_2. After incubation, total RNA was extracted by TRIzol reagent. The primers for rat alkaline phosphatase (BLKP ALP) were as follows: P1: 5' CTT CCC ACC CAT CTG GG 3'; P2: 5' CTC CCG CCA CGG CGC TC 3'. For β-actin, which was used as an internal standard, the primers were: PF: 5' CTT CCT TCC TGG GCA TGG AG 3'; PR: 5' TGG AGG GGC CGG ACT CGT CA 3'. The length of the PCR products for ALP and β-actin were 129 and 315 bp respectively. Reverse transcription was carried out under the following conditions. The reaction mixtures were incubated at 55°C for 30 min. Then they were heated at 99°C for 5 min, chilled at 5°C for 5 min, and transferred directly to the PCR reaction. The running program was for amplification was pre-heating at 94°C, 2 min. The cycle program for the ALP was 94°C, 45 s; 50°C, 30 s; 72°C, 2 min, for 40 cycles. For the β-actin, the program was 94°C, 1 min; 60°C, 1 min; 72°C, 1 min, and the number of cycles was 34. The PCR products were analyzed on 2% agarose gel and stained with ethidium bromide.

Table 1 Expression of bone proteins in osteoblastic primary cells

Proteins	Extraction[1]	mRNA[2]	Immunofluorescence
collagen type I	G	B	
	(E)	C	
		A	
fibronectin	G	no data	cell-cell adhesion
osteopontin	E	B	
		C	calcification
		A	cell-substratum adhesion
BSP	E	C	calcification
		A	cell-substratum adhesion
osteonectin	G	B	
		C	
		A	
osteocalcin	G	A	no direct contribution to calcification

[1]Extraction; G: guanidine hydrochloride, E: EDTA
[2]Expression of mRNA; B: before, C: during and A: after mineralization

RESULTS
Expression of bone proteins
In the previous study, we investigated on the expression of bone proteins in rat bone marrow derived osteoblastic primary cells. Table 1 summarizes the results obtained from immunofluorescence and AFM observations, along with the results of the mRNA expressions reported by Sodek's group in Toronto and immunodetection results with the dissociative extraction method. The column headed "Extraction" in Table 1 shows where each bone protein expressed, that is, G is the guanidine hydrochloride extract, which means the proteins are weakly bound to the cell surface, and E is the EDTA extract, which means the proteins are found in the secreted bone minerals. The column headed "mRNA" shows when each bone protein expressed in the osteoblastic primary cells. Normally, the cells begin to secrete calcified matrix around 10 days after dissection, defined as the period of initial calcification. In this column, the letters B, C and A mean that the protein expresses before, during and after the period of the initial calcification, respectively. Co I, OPN and BSP were expressed during the period of initial calcification, and found in the secreted bone minerals. These results suggest that Co I, OPN and BSP might play an important role in initial biomineralization.

Production and autophosphorylation of FAK induced by UMR cells attached to extracellular matrix proteins
We compared the production and auto-phosphorylation of FAK induced by UMR cells attached to plastic, VN, OPN and Co I surface. UMR cells with a density of 2.47×10^6/well were placed on the ECM and incubated for 60 min at 37°C. Immunoprecipitation with anti-FAK antibody and p-Tyr antibody were then carried

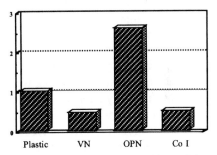

Fig. 1 Relative FAK specific activity in UMR cells cultured on ECM

out to estimate the content and the auto-phospholylation of FAK. The relative FAK specific activity (expressed as the ratio of FAK autophosphorylation to FAK content) in UMR cells cultured on ECM, is shown in Fig. 1. Although there was a high content of FAK in the UMR cells cultured on Co I and VN surfaces, the calculated ratios indicate that OPN and FN had a significantly greater effect on the phosphorylation of FAK on tyrosine than did VN and Co I. This may mean that OPN and FN play an important role in FAK-mediated signal transduction via cell surface integrin-ECM interaction.

Kinetics of FAK and ALP gene expression in UMR cells attached to OPN and Co I surfaces
ALP is known to act as an early differentiation marker in osteoblast differentiation. In this study, RT-PCR was employed in order to detect ALP mRNA expression. Table 2 shows the induction of FAK specific activity and ALP expression in UMR cells placed on OPN and Co I. This indicates that OPN was responsible for the early stage induction of ALP expression, while Co I functioned to

Table 2 Induction of FAK specific activity and ALP expression of UMR cells on OPN and Co I surfaces

	OPN			Co I		
	30 min	60 min	90 min	30 min	60 min	90 min
FAK specific activity	2.02	1.18	1.61	2.71	0.22	0.53
ALP expression	2.34	1.20	0.47	1.33	1.51	1.52

maintain the ALP level within the cell. Further statistical analysis reveals that ALP mRNA expression correlated to FAK activity in the case of OPN induction (r=0.59), but not in that of Co I induction (r=-0.07). In sum, during the early stage of UMR cell differentiation, OPN expression occurred earlier than Co I expression. This indicates that ALP expression may be regulated mainly by OPN.

DISCUSSION

OPN is known as an adhesive protein which appears in bone matrix. As shown in Table 1, we compared the expression of several matrix proteins in rat bone marrow derived osteoblastic primary cells, using the immunofluorescence technique. We found that among these proteins, OPN, BSP, and Co I may play an important role in the early differentiation of the osteoblastic cells. Moreover, cell adhesion and ALP assays of the osteoblastic cells have suggested that pre-osteoblasts by recognizing OPN. However, until now these have been only hypotheses, requiring detailed experiments such as those carried out in this study to investigate the pathway of signal transduction via integrin-ECM binding in osteoblasts.

FAK may be a component of the signal transduction pathway and may be responsible for the transmission of signals from cell surface integrins into the cells. FAK generation and auto-phosphorylation/dephosphorylation are different events within cells. Here, in the case of spreading UMR cells onto ECM surfaces, our results showed that both the production and phosphorylation of FAK were induced, but the degree of ability to induce varied. In order to describe the efficiency of integrin-mediated signal transduction, we examined the specific activity of FAK as expressed by the proportion of phosphorylation to content. FAK may be autophosphorylated on tyrosine residues by various signal molecules such as c-Src, PKC and integrin β subunits, which generally indicated that FAK has been activated. Tyrosine phosphorylation of FAK may regulate FAK activity-mediated signal transduction. FAK, presenting only in cellular focal adhesion, might be responsible for phosphorylating the components of focal adhesion - for example, tenascin, paxilin or talin - and regulating the interaction of integrin with the cytoskeleton and/or the extracellular matrix. In the present study, after plating UMR cells to ECM for 30 min, active FAK was strongly induced by both FN and OPN, but not by VN or Co I.

ALP expression at the transcription level was a biological marker indicating the early differentiation of UMR cells *in vitro*. During the first 30 min, ALP expression induced by OPN was much higher than that induced by Co I and FN. At 30 min, the specific activity of FAK induced by OPN and Co I was at about the same level. However, Co I did not increase the expression of ALP. During 90 min of incubation, ALP mRNA expression only correlated to FAK activity induced by OPN. The explanation for this is that the response of tyrosine phosphorylation of FAK to a distinct signaling pathway implies the possibility of specific phosphorylation at different tyrosine residues, which may in turn lead to different effector functions. The results of the present study suggest that OPN may trigger ALP gene expression via integrin-mediated FAK activation.

The present results not only give strong support to our previous work, indicating that OPN is responsible for early differentiation in osteoblasts; they also indicate a difference between the roles of Co I and OPN in osteoblast differentiation. That is, both OPN and Co I are necessary in osteoblast differentiation, but the former has the role of a trigger and the latter has the role of spontaneous induction.

Bioceramics Volume 11, edited by R. Z. LeGeros and J.P. LeGeros
(Proceedings of the 11th International Symposium on Ceramics in Medicine)
New York, NY, USA, November 1998
© 1998 by World Scientific Publishing Co. Pte. Ltd.

ACTIVITY OF HUMAN OSTEOBLAST-LIKE CELLS ON BIOGLASS®, HYDROXYAPATITE AND FLUORIDE-SUBSTITUTED HYDROXYAPATITE.

A.J.S. Peaker[1], K.-A. Hing[1], I.R. Gibson[1], L. Di-Silvio[2], S.M. Best[1], L.L. Hench[3], W. Bonfield[1]

[1]IRC in Biomedical Materials, Queen Mary and Westfield College, Mile End Road, London;
[2]IRC in Biomedical Materials, Institute of Orthopaedics, Brockley Hill, Stanmore;
[3]Department of Materials, Imperial College, Prince Consort Road, London.

ABSTRACT

This is the first report of a series of comprehensive studies designed to compare and contrast bioactivity of Bioglass® (BG), hydroxyapatite (HA), 0.05wt% and 0.5wt% fluoride-substituted hydroxyapatite (0.05F-HA and 0.5F-HA). The purpose of this study was to investigate the effect of the materials on the activity of a primary human osteoblast-like cell line. Apatite materials were synthesised by an aqueous precipitation method and fully characterised by a combination of methods including X-ray diffraction (XRD), X-ray fluorescence (XRF), and (Scanning Electron Microscopy), SEM. Cells were cultured on sintered (HA, 0.05F-HA and 05F-HA) or cast discs (45S5 Bioglass® - BG) for a period of 14 days. Expression of alkaline phosphatase (AlP) was used as an indicator of osteoblast phenotype whilst an alamarBlue biochemical assay measured metabolic activity of cells in direct with the materials. An MTT ((3-[4,5-dimethylthiazol])-2,5-diphenyl tetrazolium bromide) cell viability assay was used to measure cell activity in response to varying amounts of solute leached into ascorbate-free culture medium by the materials. Peak AlP expression, normalised per μg of DNA, was achieved first, amongst the biomaterials, on the HA discs. The alamarBlue assay indicated that the cells had a similar metabolic activity on all the materials at each time point. Activity of the cells in the MTT assay showed a marked concentration dependence. The medium eluted from BG powder, at a very high surface area/volume ratio, was toxic at full eluate concentration and 50% dilution. At progressively greater dilution the eluate produced a beneficial effect on cell activity. The eluted medium from the BG discs showed the highest cell activity. Fluoride substitution, in the apatites, had a stimulatory effect on cell activity.

INTRODUCTION

Bioglass® and hydroxyapatite are bioactive materials, i.e. they exhibit direct bonding to hard tissues. The rate at which this process occurs differs between the two materials: Bioglass® showing much faster bone bonding than hydroxyapatite[1]. Bone mineral ,which is similar in structure to HA, contains many ionic substituents, including fluoride. By incorporating fluoride into the HA crystal lattice it is anticipated that a new generation of materials with enhanced bioactive properties can be developed[2]. Using a human osteoblast-like cell line, it may be possible to explain the differences between the materials *in vivo* using *in vitro* methods.

MATERIALS AND METHODS

The hydroxyapatite materials were synthesised using a $Ca(OH)_2/H_3PO_4$ aqueous precipitation method. Fluoride was introduced using NH_4F. Synthesised powders were pressed at 200MPa for 2s and heated at 1150°C for 2h to produce sintered discs. 45S5 Bioglass® frit was melted at 1450°C and discs cast. Discs were subsequently annealed at 450°C for 12h.

A human osteoblast-like (HOB) cell line, isolated from trabecular bone chips, was used for the cell cultures. Cells were seeded at a density of 2×10^4 cells ml^{-1} on BG, HA, 0.05F-HA and 0.5F-HA discs for a period of 14 days. Thermanox™ discs were used as a control. The cells were cultured in Dulbecco's Modified Eagle's Medium supplemented with 10% foetal calf serum (DMEM) and maintained at 37°C and an atmosphere of 5% CO_2. Cellular activity was measured at 1, 2, 4, 7 and 14 days using an alamarBlue biochemical assay which measures the reduction in the culture medium due to the cells. Alkaline phosphatase activity was measured using a COBAS-BIO (Roche, UK) centrifugal analyser) at 2, 4, 7 and 14 days as a marker of osteoblast differentiation and normalised per μg of DNA.

Eluates were prepared by placing the materials in discs and powder form on a rotating mixer for 90h in DMEM at 37°C. A surface area to volume ratio (SA/V) of $1cm^2$/ml was used for the discs. The same weight of powder was used, therefore giving a much higher SA/V. Material and medium were filtered and the eluates diluted with DMEM to give 100, 50, 20, 10 and 5% of the original concentration. The eluates were used to culture cells, at a concentration of 6×10^5 cells ml^{-1}, for 1 day at 37°C in an atmosphere of 5% CO_2. MTT was added to the cells. The mitochondrial enzyme succinate dehydrogenase, only present in viable cells, converts the MTT to a blue coloured formazan crystal. The amount of blue colour is proportional to the number of viable cells. Polyvinyl chloride was used as a positive control. Pure DMEM was used as the negative control.

RESULTS

The hydroxyapatites were 100% phase pure as verified by XRD and had a Ca/P ratio of 1.67+/- 0.01 as determined by XRF.

Proliferation, as measured by the alamarBlue assay, showed little difference in the metabolic activity of the cells on the materials over the 14 day culture period (fig 1a).

Peak alkaline phosphatase (AlP) expression (expressed per μg DNA) was reached first on the Thermanox™ control discs. Peak AlP expression was reached at between 4-6 days on the HA discs and at 7 days on the 0.05F-HA, 0.5F-HA and BG discs (fig 1b).

(a)   (b)

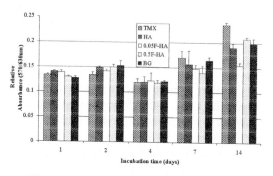 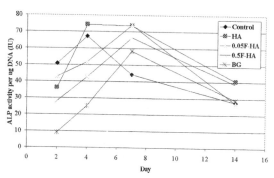

Figure 1 (a) assessment of cellular activity (proliferation) using alamarBlue™ assay and (b) cellular differentiation measuring alkaline phosphastase activity.

The pH of the 100% eluate concentrations measured at 37°C is shown in table 1.

Table 1. pH of 100% eluate concentrations measured at 37°C after 90h rolling.

Sample	pH
DMEM (negative control)	8.29
BG – powder	10.23
HA – powder	7.44
0.05F-HA – powder	7.61
0.5F-HA – powder	7.53
BG -disc	8.71
HA – disc	8.37
0.05F-HA – disc	8.24
0.5F-HA - disc	8.17

The pH of the DMEM at 37°C prior to eluate preparation was 7.53; the rise in pH of the pure DMEM solution during the 90h eluate preparation period should be noted.

The pH of the BG powder is far greater than that of the DMEM whereas that of the apatite powders decreases relative to the DMEM control. pH of the apatite disc eluates is very similar to that of the DMEM while that of the BG discs rises only slightly above that of the DMEM.

The MTT assay results are presented relative to the cellular activity of the negative control (DMEM), i.e. the horizontal line at value 1 on the y-axis, (fig 2) and show that the all the materials in powder form had a detrimental effect on cellular activity at 100% eluate concentration. There is a particularly sharp decrease in cell activity when the BG powder elution concentration is greater than 50%. The cell activity from the apatite powder eluates are very similar.

The disc eluates from all the materials show markedly different results from the powder. The BG disc elution shows the greatest activity with the highest activity being found at 5% elution concentration. The cell activity in the apatite disc eluates shows the same trend - increasing activity with decreasing eluate concentration. The activity of the disc eluates increases in the order HA < 0.05F-HA < 0.5F-HA < BG.

DISCUSSION

This initial study shows that care must be taken in choosing relevant starting conditions for *in vitro* cell culture studies, in order that the results can be compared meaningfully with *in vivo* data. Peak AlP expression is reached first on the HA, then on the BG and the fluoride-substituted apatites, suggesting that HA is the more bioactive material. However, it is known that BG undergoes a very rapid series of well-defined surface chemical changes in aqueous solution[3] resulting in a sharp rise in interfacial pH. The cells are exposed to the rapid change in pH in the static environment of the cell culture model and therefore take more time to adjust to the material surface then they would *in vivo*, where there is a constant flow of blood over the surface. The apatite materials undergo a far slower surface chemical transformation thus subjecting the cells to a less harsh initial environment. The cell activity in the MTT assay appears to be a function of both surface area and ionic substituent. The beneficial or detrimental effects on cell activity appear initially to be due to an optimum pH environment. However, there is also the potential for critical concentrations of soluble species leaching out of the materials, e.g. Ca, P , Na and Si for BG and Ca and P for the apatites. Soluble species of Si have been shown to have a mitogenic effect on bone cells[4].

The BG disc eluate has a pronounced beneficial effect on cell activity even with a relatively high pH at the 100% eluate concentration. Cell activity is also enhanced, albeit to a lesser degree, in the apatite disc eluates, where the 100% eluate pH is much closer to a physiological level. This

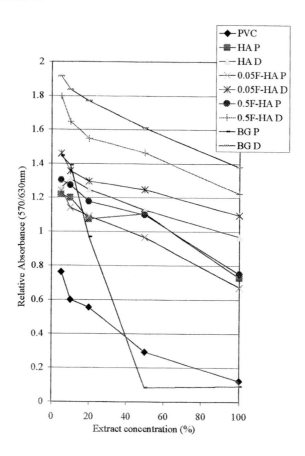

Figure 2. Relative cellular activity from MTT assay.

suggests either that the cells prefer a slightly alkaline environment or, as is more likely, the soluble Si, which is only present in the BG eluates, is having a stimulatory effect on cell activity.

Increasing the fluoride content (0 - 0.05 - 0.5wt%) has a beneficial effect on the cell activity from the disc eluates. Fluoride substitution is known to decrease the solubility of the apatite structure[5] which would give the cells a less chemically volatile environment to deal with.

ACKNOWLEDGEMENTS

The authors wish to acknowledge the financial support of the IRC core grant from the Engineering and Physical Sciences Research Council (UK) and US Biomaterials for supply of the Bioglass frit.

REFERENCES

1. Oonishi H., Kushitani S., Yasikawa E., Iwaki H., Hench L.L., Wilson J., Tsuji E., Suguhara T., *Clinical Orthopaedics and Related Research*; 1997; **334**: 316-325.
2. Hing K.A., Di-Silvio L., Gibson I.R., Ohtsuki C., Jha L., Best S.M., Bonfield W. In: L Sedel, C Rey, ed. *Bioceramics 10*; 1997: 19-22.
3. Hench L.L., *Journal of the American Ceramic Society*; 1991; **74**: 1487-1510.
4. Keeting P.E., Oursler M.J., Wiegand K.E., Bonde S.K., Spelsberg T.C., Riggs B.L., *Journal of Bone and Mineral Research*; 1992; **7**: 1281-1289.
5. LeGeros R.Z., *Prog. Crystal Growth Charact.*; 1981; **4**: 1-45.

Bioceramics Volume 11, edited by R. Z. LeGeros and J.P. LeGeros
(Proceedings of the 11th International Symposium on Ceramics in Medicine)
New York, NY, USA, November 1998
© 1998 by World Scientific Publishing Co. Pte. Ltd.

EFFECT OF BOVINE BONE-DERIVED MATERIALS ON HUMAN OSTEOBLAST-LIKE CELLS *IN VITRO*

C. G. Frondoza[1], R.Z. LeGeros[2], D.S. Hungerford[1]

[1]The Johns Hopkins University, Baltimore, MD and
[2]New York University College of Dentistry, NY

ABSTRACT

Some bovine bone derived materials are used for bone repair. The purpose of this study was to evaluate the effect of such materials on the proliferation of human osteoblasts using an *in vitro* model. Particles of bovine cortical bone were treated to remove the inorganic phase (specimen A); other particles were treated to remove the organic phase (specimen B) then sintered at 950°C (specimen C); other particles without the organic phases were suspended in NaF solution then sintered at 950°C (F-treated, specimen D). The specimens were characterized using x-ray diffraction and infrared absorption spectroscopy. The specimens were washed and irradiated using UV. Human osteoblast-like cells (MG63) which exhibit the phenotype of normal osteoblasts were used as the cell model. Cells were incubated at 10^5cells/ml in the presence of absence of the test materials (20 mg/well/ml) in triplicate wells for 3 d at 37°C, 5% CO_2. The cells were pulsed with 20 Ci ^{3} H-thymidine during the last 24h and DNA synthesis was determined from the TC precipitable radioactivity. <u>Results:</u> Cells propagated in the presence of all samples and appeared morphologically intact. The DNA synthetic rate

Keywords: bone-derived materials, osteoblasts, *in vitro*

INTRODUCTION

Materials of synthetic and natural origins are currently as bone graft materials [1-3]. Among the materials of natural origin are those derived from bovine bone. The physico-chemical properties of these materials are critical for new bone formation capable of regenerating the lost tissue. Depending on the method of preparation, bovine bone-derived materials may be cytotoxic for bone cells or inhibit their metabolism. To clarify this question, we tested the hypothesis that different preparation of bovine bone-derived materials have different effects on bone cell proliferation and metabolism. To test this hypothesis, this study investigated the effect of different bovine bone-derived materials on metabolism of human osteoblast-like MG-63 cell line which exhibits features of normal osteoblasts [4].

MATERIALS AND METHODS

<u>Preparation of bovine-bone derived materials</u>: A large piece of bovine cortical bone was cleaned of all connective tissues, boiled, dried and coarsely ground and sieved. Particles ranging in size from 180 to 250 μm were collected and treated as follows: (1) treated with 0.1M HCl to remove the mineral phase (Specimen A); (2) treated with 6% NaOCl to remove the organic phase (specimen B); (3) removal of organic phase then sintered at 950°C (specimen C): (4) treated with NaF solution then sintered at 950°C (specimen D).

Investigation of cell proliferation and metabolism: Human osteoblast-like MG63 cells were plated at 1 x 10 5/ml onto 24 well plates (Costar Corp., Cambridge MA) in the presence or absence of 20/mg/ml/well of test particles. Control cells in media alone or cells with particles were incubated at 37oC , 5% CO2 for four days. The cells were pulsed with 10uCi of 3H-thymidine (ICN Radiochemicals, Irvine, CA 50 Ci/mmol) during the last 24 hrs. Proliferative capacity was analyzed by measurement of DNA synthesis based on radiolabeled thymidine incorporation.

RESULTS

X-ray diffraction and FTIR analyses of bovine bone-derived materials prepared for this study showed the following: (1) treatment with HCl resulted in the removal of mineral phase leaving the organic phase (collagen); (2) treatment with NaOCl resulted in the removal of the organic phase leaving the mineral phase which is carbonate hydroxyapatite [5]; (3) subsequent sintering at 950°C caused the removal of most of the carbonate in both the untreated and F-treated specimen; (4) F-treatment caused the incorporation of F in the bone apatite, confirming earlier studies [6].

MG63 osteoblast-like cells in the presence of bovine derived materials (specimens A, B, C and D) remained viable during the three-day incubation. Cells incubated with F-treated particles (specimen D) appeared the healthiest (Fig. 1). These cells were confluent and were refractile when viewed with a phase-contrast inverted microscope. Those cells in close proximity to the particles (Fig. 1B) were similar in morphology as the control cells incubated without the particles (Fig. 1A).

Exposure of osteoblast-like cells to the four bovine-bone derived preparations showed that these materials were not cytotoxic. Of the four preparations tested, the F-treated material (specimen D)best stimulated DNA synthesis (Fig. 2). Cells incubated with F-treated particles exhibited 3 to 4-fold increase in their proliferative capacity based on their incorporation of radio-labeled thymidine.

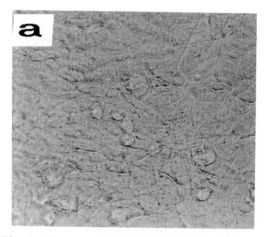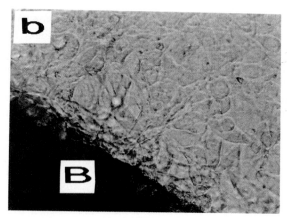

Fig. 1a: Human osteoblast-like cells (MG63) cultured in medium alone
Fig. 1b: Cells cultured with bovine-bone derived particles (B) in the medium
(original magnification, 20X)

³H-thymidine Labeling of Human Osteoblast-like MG-63 Cells After Incubation with Bone Derived Particles

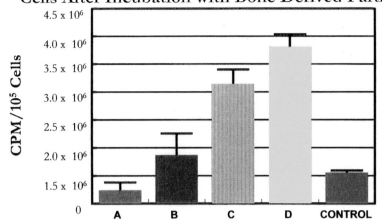

Fig. 2: Cell proliferation on different materials derived from bovine bone (A, B, C, and D) compared to control. (A) bone without mineral phase (i.e., collagen); (B) bone without organic phase (bone apatite or carbonatehydroxyapatite), unsintered; (C) bone apatite sintered; (D) sintered F-treated bone apatite

DISCUSSION and CONCLUSION

The principal finding of this preliminary study is that bovine bone-derived materials can support the proliferation and metabolism of human osteoblast-like cells to a different degree. Cell proliferation was lowest on the bone organic matrix (principally collagen) and the highest on the F-treated bone. This fluoride effect may be related to the observed effects of fluoride on in vitro mineralization [7].

Acknowledgements

This study was supported in part by research grant no. DE12388 from the National Institute for Dental Research of the National Institutes of Health. The technical collaboration of Drs. M. Retino and D. Mijares gratefully acknowledged.

REFERENCES

1. Jarcho M. *1981; Clin Orthop* **157**: 259-278.
2. deGroot K. *Bioceramics of Calcium Phosphates.*1983. CRC Press, Boca Raton.
3. Daculsi G, Passuti N, Martin S, Deudon C, LeGeros R, Raher S. 1990; J Biomed Mater Res **24**: 379-396.
4. Price N, Bendall ST, Frondoza C, Jinnah RH, Hungerford DS. 1997; J Biomed Mater Res **37**: 394-400.
5. LeGeros RZ. Prog Crystal Growth Charact **4**: 1-45.
6. LeGeros RZ, Singer L, Ophaug R, Quirolgico G. In: Osteoporosis. Menzcel J, Robin GC, Makin M (Eds). J Wiley & Sons, New York, pp. 327-341, 1982.
7. Bellows CG, Aubin JE< Heersche JNM. *1993; J Bone Min Res* **10**: 1357-1364.

Bioceramics Volume 11, edited by R. Z. LeGeros and J.P. LeGeros
(Proceedings of the 11th International Symposium on Ceramics in Medicine)
New York, NY, USA, November 1998
© 1998 by World Scientific Publishing Co. Pte. Ltd.

EFFECT OF VARIATION IN CA:P RATIO ON CELLULAR RESPONSE OF PRIMARY HUMAN OSTEOBLAST-LIKE CELLS TO HYDROXYAPATITE-BASED CERAMICS

K.A. Hing[1], I. R. Gibson[1], L. Di-Silvio[2], S.M. Best[1], W. Bonfield[1]

[1] IRC in Biomedical Materials, Queen Mary and Westfield College, Mile End Road, London E1 4NS, UK; [2] IRC in Biomedical Materials, Institute of Orthopaedics, Brockley Hill, Stanmore, HA7 4LP, UK.

ABSTRACT

Three batches of hydroxyapatite-based sintered ceramic discs with Ca:P ratios of 1.70, 1.67 and 1.62, were prepared and designated CaP1, CaP2 and CaP3, respectively. XRD demonstrated that CaP2 discs were composed of phase pure hydroxyapatite, while CaP1 and CaP3 discs contained second phases of calcium-oxide and β-TCP, respectively. Assessment of the cellular response of primary human osteoblast-like (HOB) cells to leachable substances from the three discs demonstrated enhanced activity in those cells exposed to CaP3 discs. Biochemical and morphological assessment of HOBs in direct contact with the disc surfaces demonstrated that all the materials were able to support proliferation and differentiation of the cells. However, the small changes in Ca:P ratio affected the precise nature of the cellular response on the three hydroxyapatite-based ceramics. Enhanced proliferation and rate of differentiation being achieved only in cells incubated on the phase-pure HA.

KEYWORDS
Calcium-Phosphate, Phase-Purity, Hydroxyapatite, Osteoblast.

INTRODUCTION
A previous study[4] has demonstrated the sensitivity of cellular response to the presence of minor amounts (0.3-0.8 wt% fluoride) of additional ionic species substituted within the HA lattice. However, in addition to substitutions in the hydroxyapatite (HA) lattice, the Ca:P ratio of commercial material is often non-stoichiometric, and may vary from 1.62 to 1.72 [1,5,8]. Few studies have been reported on the effect of non-stoichiometry on the bioactivity of fully crystalline materials. Best et al.[2] demonstrated that the presence of tri-calcium phosphate (TCP) in a HA-based substrate contributed to substrate/cell interface degeneration, resulting in reduced viability in osteoblast cells on the ceramic surface. More usually, authors have considered the effects of non-stoichiometry in materials containing an amorphous component[3,7], and these studies tend to report that chemical dissolution occurring in HA with low crystallinity enhances osteoblast cell proliferation, cell attachment and growth. Furthermore, substrates containing more amorphous material have been reported to invite a more intimate association between the extra-cellular matrix and the substrate[3].

The objective of this study was to compare the cellular response of primary human osteoblast-like (HOB) cells to three fully sintered calcium-phosphate (CaP) ceramic substrates with varying Ca:P ratios.

Table 1 - Results of XRF analysis (wt%).

	CaO	P_2O_5	SiO_2	Al_2O_3	MgO	Na_2O	MnO_4
CaP1	53.9	40.1	< 0.02	<0.02	<0.02	<0.03	<0.01
CaP2	53.8	40.9	< 0.02	<0.02	<0.02	<0.03	<0.01
CaP3	53.4	41.7	< 0.02	<0.02	<0.02	<0.03	<0.01

MATERIALS AND METHODS

Powders with differing Ca:P ratios were prepared by precipitation between varying proportions of $Ca(OH)_2$ and H_3PO_4, the precipitate was filtered, dried and milled to pass through a <75 μm sieve. The sieved powders were uniaxially pressed into discs at 40 MPa and sintered at 1200°C for 2 hours to a final diameter of 12 mm. The Ca:P ratio of sintered discs was determined using X-ray fluorescence (XRF) and the phase composition by X-ray diffraction (XRD).

Biological response to the different CaP ceramics was evaluated using human osteoblast-like (HOB) cells, passage 18, isolated from femoral trabecular bone. A MTT (3-[4,5-dimethylthiazol]-2,5-diphenyl tetrazolium bromide) assay was performed to assess cell viability in response to exposure to leachables from the CaP ceramics, where the assay quantifies the reduction of the tetrazolium salt to a formazan product by living cells. The cells were incubated in eluates prepared by placing one CaP disc in 2 ml of Dulbecco's Modified Eagles Medium, supplemented with 10 % foetal calf serum (DMEM), on a rotating mixer for 90 hours. The stock eluates were diluted in DMEM prior to addition to HOBs seeded in 96-well plates at a concentration of 6×10^5 cell.ml^{-1}. Biocompatibility was further assessed by direct culture of HOBs seeded on the CaP discs at a concentration of 1.2×10^5 cell.ml^{-1} and incubated in 1 ml of culture medium for periods of up to 21 days, with fresh culture medium changes, as necessary. As a control, HOBs were also cultured on Thermanox™ discs under identical conditions. Proliferation was assessed by measurement of total DNA[6] and tritiated thymidine ([^{3}H] TdR) uptake on 1, 2 and 14 day cultures. The alamarBlue™ Assay was employed to measure metabolic activity throughout the study and alkaline phosphatase (ALP) activity was assayed as a predictor of osteoblastic differentiation using a COBAS-BIO (Roche, UK) centrifugal analyser. Cellular morphology was studied qualitatively by scanning electron microscopy (SEM).

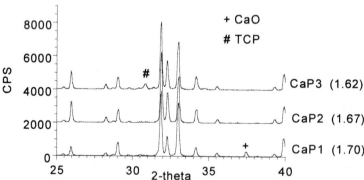

Figure 1 XRD patterns for sintered substrates with Ca:P ratios of 1.70, 1.67 and 1.62.

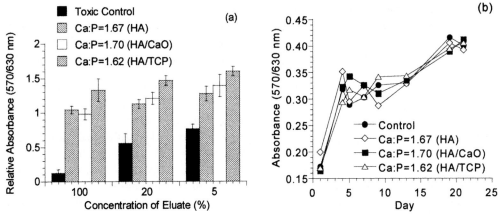

Figure 2 Assessment of cellular metabolic activity using (a) MTT, and (b) alamarBlue™ assays.

RESULTS AND DISCUSSION

Ca:P ratios, as determined by XRF analysis, were 1.70, 1.67 and 1.62 for CaP1, CaP2 and CaP3, respectively. XRD demonstrated CaP2 discs to be phase pure HA, while CaP1 and CaP3 discs contained second phases of calcium-oxide and β-TCP, respectively (Fig.1).

MTT assay results (Fig. 2a) indicated that all samples were non-cytotoxic. Furthermore, the activity of cells incubated in CaP3 eluates was significantly enhanced, indicating that release of both calcium and phosphate ions into the medium had a stimulative effect on HOB cell metabolism, as found by Maxian et al[7]. In contrast, the results of the alamarBlue™ assay (Fig.2b) demonstrated no significant variation between the metabolic activity of the HOBs incubated in direct contact with the different CaP substrates. However, trends such as pulses of activity at 4 and 7 days on CaP2 substrates, compared to reduced HOB activity on CaP3 discs and enhanced HOB activity on CaP1 discs, were observed. These results highlight the responsiveness of HOBs to both topography and local variation in pH at the substrate interface, rather than bulk ionic concentration.

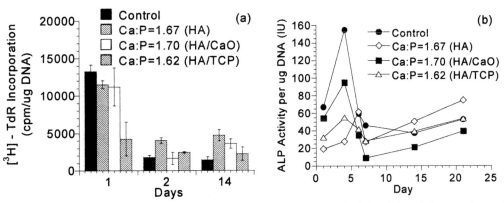

Figure 3 Assement of (a) cellular proliferation by measurement of tritiated thymidine uptake and (b) expression of osteoblastic phenotype by measurement of alkaline phosphatase activity.

In contrast, measurement of the [^{3}H] TdR incorporation of HOBs in direct contact with the various substrates demonstrated enhanced proliferation on phase-pure CaP2 and CaO-containing CaP1 discs (Fig 3a). Furthermore, measurement of ALP activity (Fig.3b) indicated differences in HOB behaviour, with a delay of peak ALP expression on phase-pure HA discs from 4 to 6 days, while the strongest peak was recorded for HOBs cultured on CaP1 discs. However, at later time points (from day 14), the level of ALP activity was highest in HOBs incubated on phase-pure CaP2 substrates, indicating a greater degree of cellular differentiation on these substrates. Scanning electron microscopy of the cultures indicated that initial cellular adhesion was strongly effected by the Ca:P ratio. After day 1 in culture there were marked differences in the cellular morphology. HOBs cultured on CaP2 and CaP3 substrates had a flattened morphology, and showed good cell attachment; in contrast to the HOBs on CaP1 substrates. Examination of 4 day cell cultures demonstrated that proliferation had occurred on all substrates with surfaces being 90-95% occupied by HOBs. However, HOBs on CaP2 appeared to be more active, and morphologically different, having large numbers of long processes. Cells on the other surfaces however, possessed fewer short processes. Furthermore, there was evidence of considerable CaP3 substrate disintegration. After 7 days in culture HOBs were seen to be confluent on all substrate surfaces.

CONCLUSION

These findings demonstrate that, although all materials supported HOB proliferation and differentiation, the small changes in Ca:P ratio affected the precise nature of the cellular response to the three hydroxyapatite based substrates, with both enhanced proliferation and an elevated rate of differentiation being achieved only in cells incubated on the phase pure HA.

ACKNOWLEDGEMENTS

The authors wish to acknowledge the financial support of the IRC core grant from the Engineering and Physical Sciences Research Council (UK), in addition to the assistance of Mr. M. Kayser.

REFERENCES

1   Akao M., Aoki H., Kato K.. *J. Mater. Sci.* 1981; **16**: 809-812.
2   S. Best, B. Sim, M. Kayser, S. Downes, *J. Mater. Sci.: Mater. Med.* 1997; **8**: 97-103.
3   de Bruijn J. *Calcium Phosphate Biomaterials: Bone Bonding and Biodegradation Properties*, PhD. Thesis, Leiden, 1993: 45-62.
4   Hing K.A., Di-Silvio L., Gibson I. R., Ohtsuki C., Jha L. J., Best S.M., Bonfield W. In: L Sedel, C Rey, ed. *Bioceramics 10*; 1997: 19-22.
5   Jarcho M., Bolen C.H., Thomas M.B., Bobick J., Kay J.F., Doremus R.H. *J. Mater. Sci.* 1976; **11**: 2027-2035.
6   Kapuscinski J., Skoczylas B., *Anal. Biochem.*1977; **83**: 252-257.
7   Maxian S.H., Melican M.C., Gross K.A., Berndt C.C., Zawaddsky J.P. In: *Proc. 21st Annual meeting of the Soc. for Biomaterials*, San Francisco, 1995: 200.
8   de With G., van Dijk H.J.A., Hattu N., Prijs K. *J. Mater. Sci.* 1981; **16**: 1592-1598.

Bioceramics Volume 11, edited by R. Z. LeGeros and J.P. LeGeros
(Proceedings of the 11th International Symposium on Ceramics in Medicine)
New York, NY, USA, November 1998
© 1998 by World Scientific Publishing Co. Pte. Ltd.

EFFECTS OF BIOMATERIALS ON OSTEOARTHRITIS AND RHEUMATOID SYNOVIAL CELLS: MODULATION OF EICOSANOID AND PROINFLAMMATORY CYTOKINE PRODUCTION

B. Liagre[1], J. L. Charissoux[2], P. Vergne[3], D. Bernache-Assollant[4], and J. L. Beneytout[1]

[1]Facultés de Médecine et de Pharmacie, 2 rue du Docteur Marcland, 87025 Limoges Cedex, France; [2]Service d'Orthopédie-Traumatologie, [3]Service de Rhumatologie, CHRU de Limoges, Hôpital Dupuytren, 2 avenue Martin Luther King, 87042 Limoges Cedex, France; [4]LMCTS, U.P.R.E.S.A. CNRS 6015, 123 avenue Albert-Thomas, 87060 Limoges Cedex, France.

ABSTRACT

Aseptic loosening is the most common reason for failure of replacement arthroplasties and is thus a major clinical problem. Human fibroblast-like synoviocytes (FLS) are a source of a variety of potential bone-resorbing agents which include prostaglandin E_2 (PGE_2), leukotriene B_4 (LTB_4), interleukin-1 (IL-1) and interleukin-6 (IL-6). Our study explored the *in vitro* response of human osteoarthritis (OA) or rheumatoid arthritis (RA) FLS to large chromium-cobalt-molybdenum (Cr-Co-Mo) alloy, small alumina (Al_2O_3) or small dioxide zirconium (ZrO_2) particles by analysing IL-1α and IL-6 production and arachidonic acid metabolism via lipoxygenase (LOX) and cyclooxygenase (COX) pathways. A portion of opsonized Al_2O_3 or ZrO_2 particles was endocytosed and was found in numerous phagolysosomes in human FLS cytoplasms in contrast to large Cr-Co-Mo alloy particles. The present study demonstrates that Cr-Co-Mo particles increased human FLS proliferation, IL-1α and IL-6 production and the synthesis of LOX and COX products in contrast to Al_2O_3 or ZrO_2 particles which did not modify these phenomena. This study suggests that human OA or RA FLS stimulated with certain particles such as Cr-Co-Mo may play an important role in periprosthetic osteolysis by releasing bone-resorbing proinflammatory mediators.

KEYWORDS: Biomaterials, arthritis; synoviocytes; cytokines; eicosanoids.

INTRODUCTION

Total hip replacement has now become well accepted worldwide as a mean of correcting a variety of hip disorders, including those caused by severe rheumatoid arthritis (RA) and osteoarthritis (OA), severe traumatic arthritis, and congenital dysplasia. The tissue invariably present at this interface has been termed the pseudosynovial membrane due to its histological similarity to synovium. Synovial tissue contains at least two distinct populations of cells: macrophage-like (type A) and fibroblast-like (type B) synoviocytes.[1] Between endosteal bone and implants or cement, the synovium-like membrane contains metal particles, cement or polyethylene, and, moreover, various types of cells such as macrophages. Based on these findings, it is hypothesized that the particulate debris from the bone cement or prosthetic materials may stimulate macrophages and adjacent proinflammatory cells to cause loosening. Local proliferation of type B synoviocytes contributes substantially to synovial hyperplasia.[2] These cells contribute to the inflammatory response, by releasing substances such as prostaglandins, metalloproteinases, and cytokines, which regulate cellular functions within the synovial compartment and cause tissue damage. These processes are regulated by a variety of cytokines and cytokine inhibitors, acting individually, synergistically, or antagonistically. The levels of interleukin-1 (IL-1) and interleukin-6 (IL-6) are elevated in the synovial fluid of RA patients.[3] Arachidonic acid is an ubiquitous fatty acid constituent of phospholipid membranes that can be liberated via the activation of phospholipase A_2. Released arachidonic acid is metabolized via the membrane-associated cyclooxygenase (COX) enzymatic pathway or via various lipoxygenase (LOX) pathways to yield monohydroxyeicosatetraenoic acids (HETEs), leukotriene B_4 (LTB_4), and peptido-leukotrienes (LTC_4, LTD_4, and LTE_4). LTB_4 plays a critical role in the progression of collagen-induced arthritis: this metabolite stimulates osteoclastic bone resorption both in vitro and in vivo[4] and peptido-leukotrienes stimulate isolated avian osteoclast-like cells to form resorption lacunae. Human synoviocytes are able to express 5-LOX,[5] 12-LOX,[6] COX-1 and COX-2.[7] Induction of COX-2 is important for lamellar bone formation elicited by mechanical strain and the main COX-2 metabolite, PGE_2, increased the skeletal response to mechanical loading. IL-1, IL-6 and PGE_2 either alone or synergistically are responsible for inducing the bone resorption in organ culture.

In our work, by comparing the recent results with hydroxyapatite and fluorapatite,[8] we sought to determine if large chromium-cobalt-molybdenum (Cr-Co-Mo) alloy particles, small alumina (Al_2O_3) and dioxide zirconium (ZrO_2) particles were able to increase eicosanoid production. Because cytokines have been implicated in the cellular response seen in arthritis, we examined the synthesis of IL-1α and IL-6 by OA and RA FLS exposed to these biomaterials.

MATERIALS AND METHODS

Cr-Co-Mo powder was supplied by Bioland (Toulouse, France). The mean particle size is about 80 μm. The morphological characteristics of these particles were examined by scanning electron microscopy (SEM). As shown in Figures 1A and 1B, these particles are spherical agglomerates composed of small grains with small nodules located on the surface. Al_2O_3 powder (AP 52) was supplied by Aluminium Pechiney (Gardanne, France). This powder was calcined at 1550°C for 45 minutes. For characterization, a small fraction of the powder was analyzed by SEM. The powder is composed of agglomerates (Fig. 1C) containing small grains (< 2 μm) (Fig. 1D). Medical quality ZrO_2 powder was supplied by Ceramiques Techniques Desmarquet (Evreux, France). Yttrium oxide stabilized ZrO_2 (2.9% molar) was granulated and calcined at 1400°C. For characterization, a small fraction of the powder was analyzed by SEM. The powder is composed of large spherical granulates (Figure 1E) containing small grains (< 2 μm) (Figure 1F). Particles were sterilized and opsonized according to Estensen et al..[9]

OA and RA synoviocytes were isolated from fresh synovial biopsies obtained from OA and RA patients undergoing hip synovectomy. Synovia were minced and digested by enzymatic reaction. Adherent cells were cultured in complete medium and, at confluence, cells were trypsinized and passed. Cells were used between passages 4 and 8 when they morphologically resembled FLS.

Cr-Co-Mo powder was opsonized and incubated at 10^3 particles/10^6 FLS for 48 h, for two weeks or for one month. Al_2O_3 and ZrO_2 powders were opsonized and incubated at 10^6 particles/10^6 FLS for 48 h, for two weeks or for one month. Particles and cells were seeded in the culture flask at the same time. All synoviocyte conditioned media were assayed for IL-1α, IL-6 and PGE_2 by EIA kits. Furthermore, synoviocyte cultures were collected for analysis of exogenous arachidonic acid metabolites by reverse-phase-high pressure liquid chromatography (RP-HPLC) according to Liagre et al..[6]

Cultured FLS observations were realized by transmission electron microscopy (TEM) according to Liagre et al..[8]

RESULTS AND DISCUSSION

In the presence of Al_2O_3 or ZrO_2, synoviocyte proliferation slowed over time. Under our experimental conditions, no cytotoxic effects were observed when these particles were present. Moreover, the presence of Cr-Co-Mo particles increased synovial proliferation over time. At 10^3 Cr-Co-Mo particles/10^6 cells, no cytotoxic effect was observed over time. Cr-Co-Mo particles at the concentration of 10^4 particles/10^6 cells proved to be toxic for FLS (the viability was less than 50% by day 4). After incubation with Al_2O_3 or ZrO_2 particles, FLS endocytosed a portion of these particles that were found in numerous phagolysosomes (Fig. 2A and 2B respectively). However when OA and RA FLS internalized ZrO_2 particles, certain cells formed pseudopods that surrounded the particles before endocytosis (Fig. 2C and 2D respectively). No endocytosis was seen with large Cr-Co-Mo particles (average diameter = 80 μm). Small Al_2O_3 and ZrO_2 particles did not increase IL-1α, IL-6 and eicosanoid production by OA or RA FLS. On the contrary, particulate Cr-Co-Mo alloy increased IL-1 and IL-6 synthesis, PGE_2 and $(12S)$-12-hydroxy-5,8,10-heptadecatrienoic acid (HHT) (another metabolite of the COX pathway) production, and eicosanoid synthesis by LOX pathways. IL-6 synthesis by OA FLS increased by 96% after 2 days, 66% after 15 days and 65% after 30 days. This increase was seen to a lesser extent in RA FLS: 40 % after 2 days, 54% after 15 days and 41% after 30 days. IL-1α production increased greatly over time in OA FLS (79%, 103% and 93% respectively) and in RA FLS (98%, 129% and 93% respectively) but the difference in the increase between the two cell types was less than that seen with IL-6. Curiously, even though RA FLS synthesize more eicosanoids (well established) than OA FLS, activation of eicosanoid synthesis is very close for both cell types when exposed to Cr-Co-Mo particles. This increase varied between 1.2- and 1.9-fold according to the metabolite examined. Since we did not see endocytosis of these particles, a possible explanation may take into account the large particle size or the release of soluble metal ions from the alloy particles.

In conclusion, using our experimental conditions, OA or RA FLS are capable of endocytosing small sized biomaterials (< 2 μm). Al_2O_3 and ZrO_2 did not increase the synthesis of IL-1α, IL-6, PGE_2 and HHT, and also did not increase the production of leukotrienes and HETEs in human OA or RA FLS. Moreover, large Cr-Co-Mo alloy particles (median diameter = 80 μm) adhered to the cells and were not endocytosed but these particles significantly increased the secretion of proinflammatory cytokines (IL-1α and IL-6) and eicosanoid synthesis. As the *in vitro* model on the interactions of macrophages with biomaterial developed by Voronov et al.,[10] we have developed an interesting *in vitro* model to examine the inflammatory response which is secondary to a biomaterial/FLS interaction.

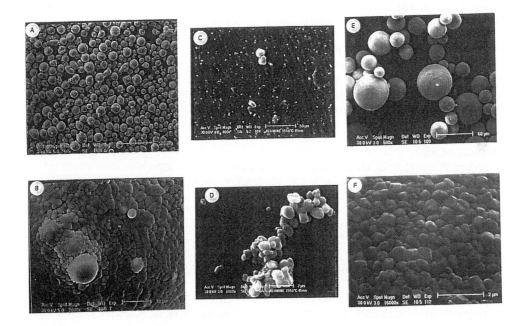

Figure 1: (A) SEM observation of Cr-Co-Mo agglomerates containing small grains **(B)** with small nodules located on the surface; **(C)** SEM observation of Al_2O_3 agglomerate containing small grains **(D)**; **(E)** SEM observation of ZrO_2 granulates containing small grains **(F)**.

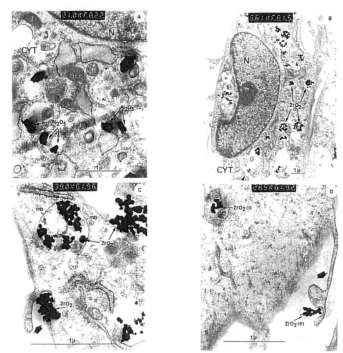

Figure 2: (A) and **(B)** TEM observations of human OA FLS exposed to respectively Al_2O_3 or ZrO_2 particles during 1 month; Black arrows show intracytoplasmic particles; N, nucleus; CYT, cytoplasm. **(C)** TEM observation of human OA FLS cytoplasm exposed to ZrO_2 particles during 1 month; Small black arrows show intracytoplasmic particles in phagolysosomes limited by a simple membrane (mb); Large black arrow shows pseudopod surrounding the particles before endocytosis. **(D)** TEM observation of human RA FLS cytoplasm exposed to ZrO_2 particles during 1 month; ZrO_2(e), extracellular ZrO_2 particles; ZrO_2(i), intracellular ZrO_2 particles in phagolysosome; Large black arrow shows pseudopod surrounding the extracellular particles before endocytosis.

REFERENCES

1. Barland P, Novikoff AB, Hamerman D. *J Cell Biol* 1962; **14:** 207-220.
2. Qu Z, Hernandez Garcia C, O'Rourke LM, Plank SR, Kohli M, Rosenbaum JT. *Arthritis Rheum* 1994; **37:** 212-220.
3. Houssiau FA, Devogelaer JP, van Damme J, Deuxchaisnes CN, van Snick J. *Arthritis Rheum* 1988; **31:** 784-788.
4. Garcia C, Boyce BF, Gilles J, Dallas M, Qiao M, Mundy GR, Bonewald LF. *J Bone Miner Res* 1996; **11:** 1619-1627.
5. Bonnet C, Bertin P, Cook-Moreau J, Chable-Rabinovitch H, Treves R, Rigaud M. *Prostaglandins* 1995; **50:** 127-135.
6. Liagre B, Vergne P, Rigaud M, Beneytout JL. *FEBS Lett* 1997; **414:** 159-164.
7. Vergne P, Liagre B, Bertin P, Cook-Moreau J, Treves R, Beneytout JL, Rigaud M. *J Rheumatol* 1998; **25:** 433-440.
8. Liagre B, Charissoux JL, Leboutet MJ, Bernache-Assollant D, Beneytout JL. *J Biomed Mater Res* 1997; **38:** 243-256.
9. Estensen RD, White JG, Holmes B. *Nature* 1974; **248:** 347-348.
10. Voronov I, Santerre JP, Hinek A, Callahan JW, Sandhu J, Boynton EL. *J Biomed Mater Res* 1998; **39:** 40-51.

Bioceramics Volume 11, edited by R. Z. LeGeros and J.P. LeGeros
(Proceedings of the 11th International Symposium on Ceramics in Medicine)
New York, NY, USA, November 1998
© 1998 by World Scientific Publishing Co. Pte. Ltd.

THE GENE EXPRESSION OF MT1-MMP, CATHEPSIN K, MMP-9 AND TRAP IN HIGHLY ENRICHED RABBIT OSTEOCLASTS INDUCED BY DIFFERENT BONE MATRIX PROTEINS AND IVORY AT THE TRANSCRIPTION LEVEL

H.-Y. Deng[1,2], T. Uemura[1], A. Nemoto[1], Y.-K. Liu[1,3]

[1]Bioinic Design Group, National Institute for Advanced Interdisciplinary Research (NAIR), Tsukuba Research Center, Ibaraki 305-8562, Japan.
[2]Research Center of Geriatric Medicine, [3]Liver Cancer Institute, Shanghai Medical University, Shanghai 20032, P.R. China

INTRODUCTION

Osteoclast marker enzymes, such as membrane-type matrix metalloproteinase (MT1-MMP), matrix metalloproteinase 9 (MMP-9), cathepsin K, and tartrate-resistant acid phosphatase (TRAP), have been implicated in osteoclastic migratory activity and osteoclastic bone resorptive activity. Bone matrix proteins may play important roles in the regulation of the gene expression of these enzymes through cell-matrix interaction. In this study, we attempted to obtain information about the gene expression of MT1-MMP, cathepsin K, MMP-9 and TRAP in pure rabbit osteoclasts induced by ivory and different bone matrix proteins such as collagen type I (Co I), fibronectin (FN), vitronectin (VN) and osteopontin (OPN).

MATERIALS and METHODS

1. Osteoclast isolation and culture:
Highly enriched osteoclasts were isolated from 10-day old rabbits [1]. The long bones of rabbits were minced in α-MEM. The unfractioned bone cells were collected and seeded on collagen gel-coated dishes. After 3-hr incubation, the culture was treated with PBS containing 0.001% pronase and 0.02% EDTA for 15 min at room temperature in order to remove the non-adherent hempoietic cells and loosely attached stromal cells. Then the culture was treated wit 0.01% collagenase for 5 min at room temperature to completely remove the stromal cells. Highly purified osteoclasts were obtained in suspension by a final treatment with 0.1% collagenase.

2. Osteoclast gelatin zymography:
The conditioned medium and the lysates of osteoclasts attached to ivory slices or plastic dishes were subjected to 7.5% SDS-PAGE gels containing 0.2% gelatin. After electrophoresis, the gels were submerged in 2.5% Triton X-100 for 30 min to remove the SDS and then incubated for 16 h at 37°C in a reaction buffer (50 mM Tris-HCl, pH 7.6, 150 mM NaCl, 10 mM $CaCl_2$). After electrophoresis, the gels were submerged in 0.25% coomassie brilliant blue R-205, gelatinolytic activities were observed as clear bands without staining against the stained background. Protein molecular standards from Pharmacia were used for molecular weight determination.

3. Detection of mRNA expression of mRNA expression of osteoclasts marker enzymes by RT-PCR:

(a) Substrate preparation and osteoclast attachment:

The FN, VN, OPN were coated in a neutral coating buffer (20 mM Tris-HCl, pH 7.4, 150 mM NaCl, 1 mM $CaCl_2$ and 1 mM $MgCl_2$) and the concentrations were 50, 25, 25 µg/ml respectively. Co I (500 µg/ml) was coated in an acidic solution (2N HCl, pH 3.0, 0.1 mM $CaCl_2$, 1 mM $MgCl_2$). Round ivory slices (1.45 cm in diameter) were placed in 24-well culture plates.

Highly enriched rabbit osteoclasts were plated on the different substrate described above then cultured for 2h.

(b) RT-PCR

The osteoclast total RNA was isolated by the single-step method (TRIzol reagent kit, Life Technologies). The mRNA expression was detected by RT-PCR. The PCR primers used are as follows:

	PRIMER SEQUENCE	LENGTH OF PCR PRODUCTS(bps)
MT1-MMP	S:5'-CCCCGCTGCGGTGTTCCAGAC-3'	387
	A:5'-CTCCGC GGAGTCAAAGTGGGTGTCCCC-3'	
MMP-9	S:5'-TGGCCGGCCACTGTGCGCCCCTCCGAG-3'	663
	A:5'-CACTAGGTTCACCTCGTTCCGGGTACT-3'	
Cathepsin K	S:5'-AGCTGGGGAGAAAGCTGGGGAAACAAAG-3'	243
	A:5'-AGGCACAAACAAATGGGGAAACCAAACA-3'	
TRAP	S:5'-AAGGAGGACTACGTGCTCGTGGCCGGC-3'	189
	A:5'-TCCACTCAGCACGTAGCCCACGCCGTT-3'	
β-actin	S: 5'-CTTCCTTCCTGGGCATGGAG-3'	315
	A: 5'-TGGAGGGGCCGGACTCGTCA-3'	

The reverse transcription reaction mixture contained 20 U of RNasin, 4 µl of 25 mM $MgSO_4$, 8 µl of 2.5 mM dNTPmix, 4 µl of 5xAMV buffer, 5 U of AMV reverse transcriptase, 20 pmol of oligo-dT, 0.5 µl of RNase-free water and 1 µl (approximately 1 µg) of template RNA. The final volume of this reaction mixture was 20 µl. The reaction mixture was incubated at 48°C for 45 min, heated at 94°C for 2 min, and then chilled at °C followed by PCR reaction.

The PCR reaction mixture contained 4 µl of 2.5 mM dNTP mix, 10 µl of TaKaR 10 x PCR buffer (10 mM Tris-HCl, pH 8.3, 500 mM KCl, 15 mM $MgCl_2$), 2.5 U of TaKaRa rTag enzyme, 79.5 µl of pure water, and 25 pmol of each primer. The final volume of this PCR reaction mixture was 100 µl. The PCR products were analyzed on 2% agarose gels and stained with ethidium bromide. For semi-quantitative analysis of the PCR products, ß-actin was used as the internal standard.

RESULTS

Gelatin zymography

Five negative staining bands indicating gelatinlytic activities were found in the conditioned medium and the lysates of osteoclasts attached to ivory slices and to plastic dishes. The molecular weight of the five bands was 116 KDa, 100KDa, 95 KDa, 78 Kda and 78KDa. The three bands with larger molecular weights seem to be the zymogen and complex zymogen of MMP-9. The two bands with smaller molecular weights seem to be the active forms of MMP-9.

The mRNA expression of the marker enzymes in osteoclasts induced by different matrix proteins and ivory is shown in Table 1.

Table 1. The mRNA expression of MT1-MMP, MMP-9, cathpesin K, and TRAP in osteoclasts induced by different matrix proteins and ivory

	MT1-MMP	MMP-9	cathepsin K	TRAP
fibronectin	0. 294 (0. 39)*	1. 051 (0. 99)*	2. 746 (2. 80) *	2. 017 (2. 13) *
vitronectin	0. 429 (0. 57) *	0. 794 (0. 75) *	1. 500 (1. 53) *	2. 073 (2. 19) *
osteopontin	0. 790 (1. 05) *	1. 648 (1. 55) *	2. 129 (2. 17) *	1. 889 (2. 00) *
collagen type I	0. 759 (1) *	1. 061 (1) *	0. 980 (1) *	0. 945 (1) *
ivory	1. 180 (1. 55) *	1. 271 (1. 20) *	1. 301 (1. 33) *	1. 600 (1. 69) *

All data are expressed as a density ratio of the relevant band to that of the related ß-actin band and obtained as the mean value form at least three individual experiments.
*The mRNA expression of 4 enzymes on FN, VN, OPN compared with their expression on Co 1. The mRNA expression of the osteoclast marker enzymes by the same bone matrix protein or ivory: OPN, an important ligand for osteoblast $\alpha_v\beta_3$ integrin, and ivory had a stronger induction on all the selected osteoclast marker enzymes than Co I, a ligand of engagement of osteoclast $\alpha_2\beta_1$.

The MRNA expression of the same osteoclast marker enzyme induced by different bone matrix proteins is shown in Fig. 1. The induction profiles are as follows: MT1-MMP mRNA expression: ivory > OPN > Co I > VN >FN; MMP-9 mRNA expression: OPN > ivory >Co I > FN > VN; cathepsin K mRNA expression: FN > OPN > VN > ivory > Co I. TRAP mRNA expression: VN > FN > OPN > ivory > Co I.

CONCLUSIONS

Utilizing the RT-PCR method, we have demonstrated that at least at the transcription level, highly enriched osteoclasts express MT1-MMP, MMP-9, cathepsin K and TRAP, and that the mRNA expression of these enzymes is regulated by the interaction of bone matrix proteins with osteoclasts. The results of osteoclasts gelatin zymography indicate that rabbit osteoclasts may express the enzyme protein MMP-9.

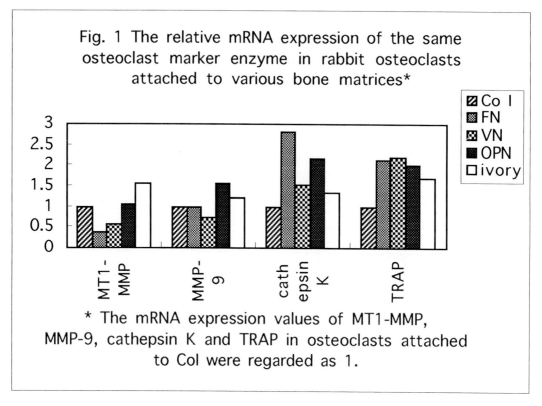

Fig. 1 The relative mRNA expression of the same osteoclast marker enzyme in rabbit osteoclasts attached to various bone matrices*

* The mRNA expression values of MT1-MMP, MMP-9, cathepsin K and TRAP in osteoclasts attached to Col were regarded as 1.

OPN has a stronger induction on the mRNA expression of all the selected osteoclast marker enzymes than Co I. This indicates that integrin $ß_3$ may plat a more important role than $ß_{11}$ in the regulation of the gene expression of these enzymes.

The gene expression profile of the same osteoclast marker enzyme induced by different bone matrix proteins is different. This may be due to the different receptor (integrin and non-integrin receptor) pathways used by the different bone matrix proteins when they interact with osteoclasts as well as the specific molecular conformation of different bone matrix proteins.

REFERENCES

1. Kakudo S, Miyazawa K, Kameda T. *J Bone Miner Metab* **14**:129-136 ,1996

Bioceramics Volume 11, edited by R. Z. LeGeros and J.P. LeGeros
(Proceedings of the 11th International Symposium on Ceramics in Medicine)
New York, NY, USA, November 1998
© 1998 by World Scientific Publishing Co. Pte. Ltd.

SOL-GEL DERIVED TITANIA COATINGS FOR CELL-CULTURE SUBSTRATES

J. Elbel[1], L. Polonchuk[2], K. L. Eckert[1], H. Eppenberger[2], E. Wintermantel[1]

[1] Biocompatible Materials Science and Engineering, Department of Materials, ETH Zurich, Wagistrasse 23, CH-8952 Schlieren, Switzerland.
[2] Institute of Cell Biology, ETH Zürich-Hönggerberg HPM, 8039 Zürich, Switzerland.

ABSTRACT

Titania ceramics, alumina ceramics and glass were coated with sol-gel derived titania films to fabricate cell culture scaffolds for ARC (adult rat heart muscle cells). These coatings mask the differences in surface chemistry of the substrates, thus allowing to evaluate specific cell responses to changes in topography. In order to achieve reproducible coatings, dip-coating was performed by immersing the substrates into a sol and retracting them at a defined rate of 0.5 mm sec^{-1}. Titania scaffolds were seeded with freshly isolated rat cardiomyocytes in M199 medium (Gibco, Scotland) supplemented with 20% fetal calf serum, creatine and penicillin/streptomycin and incubated at 37 °C, 5% CO_2, 95% humidity. The topography of the substrates and the films were characterized by SEM and laser profilometry. The topography in the nanometer range was characterized by AFM. The surface roughness of the uncoated substrates varied from R_a= 0.5 µm (glass) to R_a= 0.9 µm (alumina) to R_a= 1.6 µm (titania). SEM characterization of the coatings showed, that the grain size of the sol-gel derived titania layers was in the range of 20-50 nm. Microscopical characterization of the cell morphology indicated that the sol-gel derived titania coatings prevented cell spreading for a culture period of 9 days.

KEYWORDS: titania ceramics, sol-gel, coatings, scaffolds, cardiomyocytes

INTRODUCTION

The surface of titania ceramics produced by a standard ceramic sintering process was demonstrated to be favorable for the growth of adult rat cardiomyocytes (ARC) in culture (figure 1, 2) [1]. As an alternative to conventional ceramics sol-gel derived titania ceramics are of interest [2]. They are of high chemical purity and can be developed to exhibit a homogeneous microstructure in the nanometer range. In this work, sol-gel derived titania ceramics were developed as coatings on different materials. Glass, alumina and titania were coated with sol-gel derived titania films to fabricate cell culture scaffolds for ARC. The coatings mask the different surfaces allowing the evaluation of specific cell responses to distinct changes of topography without changing surface chemistry. Thus influences of surface topography could be investigated independently of chemical characteristics of the underlying substrate surface.

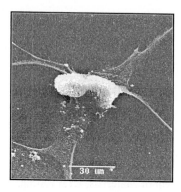

Figure 1: Polymeric cell culture dish; the morphology of the cardiomyocytes has changed after 7 days. Cytoplasm spreads over a wide area.

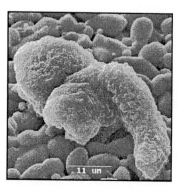

Figure 2: Uncoated titania ceramics. The cardiomyocytes do not spread but maintain their differentiated state for a period of 14 days in culture.

MATERIALS AND METHODS

Sol-gel coating

Glass cover slips, commercially available alumina substrates (CeramTec, Germany) and titania ceramic discs [3] were used as substrates. The sol was prepared by hydrolyzing titaniumisopropoxide (Fluka, Switzerland) in isopropanol (Fluka, Switzerland) in a mixture of H_2O (dest.) and 65% HNO_3 (Fluka, Switzerland). The molar ratio was chosen as $H_2O / Ti^{4+} = 200$; $H^+ / Ti^{4+} = 0.2$. To adjust viscosity and to prevent the coatings from cracking during heat treatment, hydroxyethylcellulose (HEC, Fluka, Switzerland) was added to the sol as a binder. Dip-coating was performed by immersing the substrates into the sol and retracting them at a rate of 0.5 mm sec^{-1}. After 12 h drying in ambient atmosphere the coatings were sintered at 500° C for 1 h.

Cell culturing

Uncoated and sol-gel coated titania ceramics were cleaned with ethanol, autoclaved and placed in 24-well culture dishes. Plastic Petri dishes ("Nunc", Life Technologies AG, Switzerland) were seeded as controls. The scaffolds were seeded with freshly isolated rat cardiomyocytes with a density of $7.5 * 10^5$ viable cells per dish in M199 medium (Gibco, Scotland) supplemented with 20% fetal calf serum, creatine and penicillin/streptomycin and incubated at 37 °C, 5% CO2, 95% humidity. After plating, cells were fixed with glutaraldehyde (Fluka, Switzerland), dehydrated in agraded alcohol series and critically point dried with CO_2.

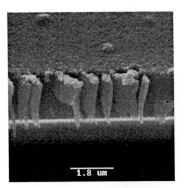

Figure 3 a: glass substrate coated with a sol-gel derived titania layer, (10000 x).

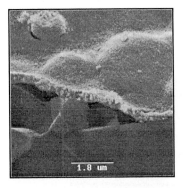

Figure 3 b: alumina substrate coated with a sol-gel derived titania layer, (15000 x).

Figure 3 c: titania substrate coated with a sol-gel derived titania layer, (25000 x).

Characterization

The topography of the substrates and the films were characterized by scanning electron microscopy (SEM, Hitachi S-2500C) and laser profilometry (UBM, Germany). The surface topography in the nanometer range was characterized by AFM (Nanoscope III a). Primary adherence and phenotypic changes of cardiac cells in culture were investigated using SEM.

Results and Discussion

The sol-gel derived titania coatings showed a granular structure with a grain size in the range of 20 to 50 nm (figure 3 a to c). The thickness of the layers depended on the roughness of the substrates (glass<alumina<titania). On glass ($R_a = 0.5$ µm) a monolayer of titania crystallites with a size of approximately 50 nm was observed. On the alumina substrates ($R_a = 0.9$ µm) the sol-gel derived coating had a thickness of 1 µm and on titania ceramics ($R_a = 1.6$ µm) the thickness was 1.5 µm. On the rough substrates occasional crack formation was observed (figure 5 b), which was probably due to increased coating thickness.

AFM characterization demonstrated that the sol-gel derived titania coatings were able to cover the substrate surfaces without changing characteristical features of the substrate topography. However, features in the nanometer size, such as crystal growth steps and sharp edges were smoothed (figure 4 a, b).

SEM characterization of the heart muscle cell morphology (figure 1, 5 a, b) demonstrated an influence of the sol-gel derived coating on the maintenance of the original cardiomyocyte morphology. On polymeric culture dishes heart muscle cells spread over a wide area and cytoplasm protruded out (figure 1). On titania ceramics with a grain size in the range of 10 to 15 µm (figure 5 a), the differentiated shape of the cardiomyocytes was maintained over a period of 9 days in culture. On sol-gel derived titania, cardiomyocytes maintained their cell structure after 9 days in culture and showed the original, rod-shaped morphology of freshly isolated cardiomyocytes (figure 5 b).

Conclusions

Reproducible coatings were achieved by the developed dip-coating procedure. The coating did not change characteristical features of the original topography. Cardiomyocytes cultures investigation demonstrated that the original rod-like cell morphology was best preserved on sol-gel coated titania ceramic substrates.

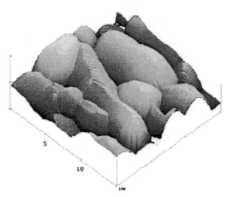

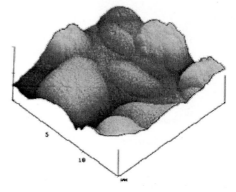

Figure 4 a: AFM surface plot of uncoated titania ceramics. Growth steps can be recognized on the crystallites.

Figure 4 b: AFM surface plot of the sol-gel coated titania ceramics. The original granular structure of the ceramic substrate is preserved. Details like growth steps are smoothed by the coating.

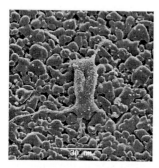

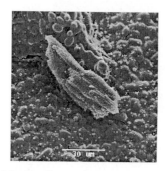

Figure 5 a: Cardiomyocytes, 9 d on uncoated titania ceramics. Slight cell spreading can be observed.

Figure 5 b: Cardiomyocytes, 9 d on sol-gel coated titania ceramics. The original rod-like shape of the cell is maintained.

Literature

[1]   Polonchuk L. O., Blum J., Eckert K.-L., Eppenberger H. M., Wintermantel E., Establishment of Cardiac Tissue-Like Culture Using Biocompatible Scaffolds, 23 rd Annual Meeting of the Society for Biomaterials, New Orleans, 1997.

[2]   Kohl R., Titanoxid- und Titannitridmembranen für die Ultrafiltration, PhD-Thesis, University Erlangen-Nuernberg, 1996.

[3]   Eckert K.-L. B. Stieger, M. Petitmermet, S.-W. Ha, A. Bruinink, F. Birchler, M. Gersbach-Fey, P. Meier-Abt, E. Wintermantel., Porous titania ceramics as substrate for liver cell culture, Göteborg, Sweden, 1997, P90.

Bioceramics Volume 11, edited by R. Z. LeGeros and J.P. LeGeros
(Proceedings of the 11th International Symposium on Ceramics in Medicine)
New York, NY, USA, November 1998

EFFECT OF SILICON NITRIDE CERAMIC ON HUMAN OSTEOBLAST-LIKE CELLS

Sohrabi, A[1]., Kue, R. C[2]., Lin, J[2]., Nagle , D. C[2]., Frondoza, C.G[1]., Hungerford, D.S[1]

[1]The Johns Hopkins University Dept. of Orthopaedic Surgery, Good Samaritan Hospital, 5601 Loch Raven Blvd. G-1 Baltimore, MD 21239; [2]Dept. of Material Science and Engineering, 3400 Charles Streets, Baltimore, MD 21218

ABSTRACT

This study was designed to determine the effect of Si_3N_4 particles on human osteoblast-like MG-63 cells *in vitro*. Two preparations of silicon nitride were used: (1) sintered-reaction bonded 15mm discs polished to a surface roughness of 0.03 µm with diamond discs; and (2) machine generated particles ranging from < 1.00 to 5.00 µm. Both preparations were sterilized by autoclave. The MG-63 cells were plated onto 24 well polystyrene plate containing sintered-reaction bonded silicon nitride discs or control polystyrene surfaces for 48 hours. The DNA synthesis rate for cells growing on the ceramic discs (7000 cpm/10^5/cells) showed similar proliferative capacity to control cells growing on polystyrene surface (4000 cpm/10^5/cells), $P>0.05$. To evaluate the response of cells to ceramic particles, 1, 10, 100 µg/ml or control media alone were incubated with 1×10^5/osteoblast-like cells/ml for 24 hours. Cells incubated with silicon nitride particles did not decrease in DNA synthetic activity. Cells exposed to: (a) 1, (b) 10, (c) 100 µg/ml of Si_3N_4 particles had (a) $12 \pm 1.3 \times 10^4$, (b) $10.5 \pm 1.5 \times 10^4$, and (c) $11.0 \pm 1.7 \times 10^4$ cpm, respectively, compared to the media control $11.6 \pm 2.6 \times 10^4$ cpm, as indicated by uptake of ^{3}H-thymidine. The results of this study suggests that silicon nitride as a molded material or as particulates is biologically inert and does not hinder the growth and metabolic activity of human osteoblast-like MG-63 cells. Further studies need to be carried out to evaluate the possible use of silicon nitride as a ceramic biomaterial for joint prostheses.

KEYWORDS: Silicon Nitride, Bioceramics, Osteoblasts, *in vitro*

INTRODUCTION

Wear particles generated from the articulating surface of prostheses have been implicated as a contributing factor to the aseptic loosening and eventual failure of joint implants. Their suspected role in aseptic loosening has prompted the search for material with greater wear resistance. Silicon nitride is a high performance ceramic characterized by high wear resistance, good fatigue life and fracture toughness, and a low coefficient of friction. It is currently being used in moving load bearing components of automobile engines.[1] The wear resistant property of this ceramic makes Si_3N_4 a potential candidate as articulating surfaces for prosthetic implants. Availability of prosthetic materials capable of greater wear resistance will help minimize generation of wear debris which has been reported to mediate an inflammatory response and subsequent osteolysis.[2-3] These adverse tissue responses have been associated with failure of prostheses. A previous study using a porous Si_3N_4 intramedullary rod inserted into femurs of rabbits had shown marrow stroma differentiation and bone growth into the porous implants. [4] The purpose of this study was to evaluate the response of human bone cells to silicon nitride. Our hypothesis was that silicon nitride promotes proliferation and metabolism of human osteoblasts. To test this hypothesis, we utilized a human osteoblast-like cell line MG-63, which express as characteristics of normal osteoblasts.

MATERIALS AND METHODS

Silicon nitride (Conducting Materials Corp., Columbia, MD) was used as: sintered-reaction-bonded (SRBSN) discs measuring 15 mm in diameter and 3 mm in thickness cut with a diamond-head drill press and polished using a diamond free-lapping technique. The surface roughness was analyzed by profilometry. Machine generated particles ranging from < 1.00 to 5.00 µm were also used. Both preparations were sterilized by steam autoclaving at 270 °C for 20 minutes. Human osteoblast-like cells MG-63 1×10^5/ml isolated from human osteosarcoma (American Type Culture Collection, Rockville, MD) were plated onto 24 well polystyrene plates (Costar Corp., Cambridge, MA) containing the 15 mm ceramic discs. Wells without discs served as controls. To determine the response of cells to ceramic particles, 1, 10, 100 µg/ml or control media alone were incubated with 1×10^5 osteoblast-like cells/ml. Proliferative capacity was analyzed by measurement of DNA synthesis by ^{3}H- thymidine incorporation. Twenty µCi/well of ^{3}H-thymidine (ICN Radiochemicals, Irvine, CA 50Ci/mmol) was added to each well. After 24 hours, the DNA was retrieved by trichloroacetic (TCA) precipitation and ^{3}H-thymidine uptake was measured by liquid scintillation counting (LS 6500, Beckman Instruments, Palo Alto, CA). Some wells were trypsinized and the harvested cells were also cytospun into slides for autoradiography.

STATISTICAL ANALYSIS

The data was expressed as arithmetic mean ± 1 SD. The results were examined by using JumpIn 3.15 with multiple comparison by one way ANOVA. Any differences were considered statistically significant when p-value < 0.05.

RESULTS

Figure 1

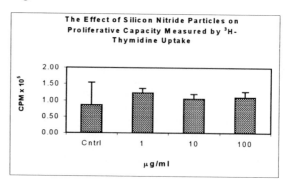

**Figure 1. The Effect of Silicon Nitride Particles on Proliferative Capacity
Measured by ³H-Thymidine Uptake**

Osteoblast-like MG-63 cells following a 48-hour exposure to silicon nitride particles were retrieved and next analyzed for DNA synthetic activity by using ^{3}H-thymidine radiolabeling uptake techniques. Each bar represents the mean of four separate experiments $\pm$ 1 SD.

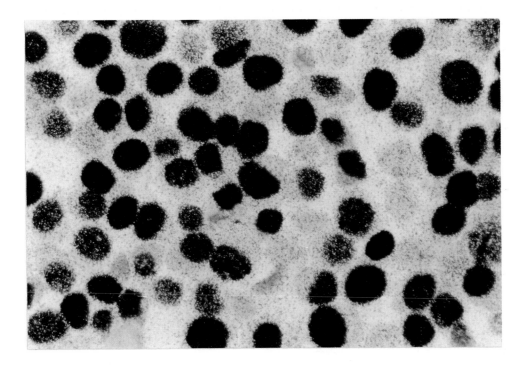

**Figure 2. Incorporation of ^{3}H-thymidine by Osteoblast-like MG-63 Propagated on
Silicon Nitride Discs.**

Mg-63 cells in were incubated with media alone or sintered Si_3N_4 discs at 37^0C, 5% CO_2. Cells were labeled with ^{3}H-thymidine as a measure of DNA synthesis. After 48 hours of labeling, cells were harvested from the discs, cytospun onto slides and were then autoradiographed.

Exposure of human osteoblast-like MG-63 cells to Si_3N_4 particles did not alter their proliferative capacity (Figure 1). Incubation of osteoblast-like cells with 1 to 100 μg/ml of silicon nitride particles did not decrease DNA synthesis activity compared to the media control (91-106% of control cells, P>0.05). The 0steoblast-like MG-63 cells appeared fibroblast-like on the surface of the silicon nitride discs by 48 hours of culture. After 48 hours of incubation, MG-63 cells recovered from the silicon nitride discs excluded trypan blue dye indicating that the retrieval procedure did not impair cell viability (Figure 2). The osteoblast-like MG-63 cells proliferated on the surface of sintered-reaction-bonded silicon nitride. The DNA synthesis rates for cells growing on the ceramic discs (7000 cpm/10^5/cells) were similar to cells growing on control polystyrene surface (4000 cpm/10^5/cells), P>0.05.

DISCUSSION/CONCLUSION

The present study provides the first demonstration that silicon nitride as a bulk material or as particulates is non-cytotoxic and does not impair the proliferation and metabolism of human osteoblast-like MG-63 cells. It is of interest that silicon nitride particles did not have detectable DNA synthetic stimulatory effect unlike particles from other biomaterials used for prosthetic components. Previous studies using human osteoblast-like MG-63 *in vitro* have demonstrated increase in DNA synthesis of human osteoblast-like MG-63 cells following exposure to cobalt, titanium, alloys, and peek. Whether this is an induced response to injury by the particles is not clear. [5-6] The lack of toxicity of this bioceramic is further confirmed by our observations that cells exposed to silicon nitride did not become pyknotic and retained their well defined morphology similar to the cells growing in control media. These findings support the potential utility of silicon nitride as a prosthetic material.

ACKNOWLEDGEMENTS

Supported by the JHU Department of Material Sciences & Engineering, the JHU Orthopaedic-Rheumatology Gift Fund and the Good Samaritan Hospital.

REFERENCES

1. Katz N. *Mater. Res. Soc. Sym.* 1993; **287**: 197-208.
2. Wrobleski B. Revision Surgery in Total Hip Arthroplasty 1989; **Springer-Verlag**: 63-70.
3. Sedel L, Nizard R, Kerboull L, Wivoet J. *Clin. Orthop.* 1994; **298**: 175-183.
4. Howlett C, McCarthey E, and Ching W. *Clin. Orth. Rel. Res. 1989;* **244**: 296-301.
5. Price N, Bendall SP, Frondoza C, Jinnah RH, Hungerford DS. *J.Biomed. Mater. Res.* 1997; **37**: 394-400.
6. Lin TW, Corvelli A A, Frondoza CG, Roberts JC, Hungerford DS. *J.Biomed. Mater. Res.* 1997; **36**: 137-144.

Bioceramics Volume 11, edited by R. Z. LeGeros and J.P. LeGeros
(Proceedings of the 11th International Symposium on Ceramics in Medicine)
New York, NY, USA, November 1998
© 1998 by World Scientific Publishing Co. Pte. Ltd.

FLOW CYTOMETRY ANALYSIS OF GLASS - REINFORCED HYDROXYAPATITE - INDUCED CHANGES IN CELL PROLIFERATION AND FUNCTION

I. Olsen[1], M. A. Lopez[2], J. D. Santos[2], F. J. Monteiro[2] and J. C. Knowles[3]

Departments of [1]Periodontology and [3]Biomaterials, Eastman Dental Institute, University of London, UK; [2]Department of Metallurgical Engineering and Institute of Biomedical Engineering, University of Porto, Portugal.

ABSTRACT

Glass-reinforced hydroxyapatite (GR-HA) composites have been developed in order to improve the mechanical properties of HA for use in orthopedic and dental surgery. However, the precise biological effects of these implant materials on host cells are not yet known. In this study we found, using flow cytometry (FCM), that GR-HA caused a decrease in the size of osteoblast-like MG63 cells and also resulted in a low level of inhibition of cell growth, possibly by delaying the progression of the cells from the G0/G1 into the S phase of the cell cycle.

FCM was also used to examine HA- and GR-HA- induced changes in osteocalcin (OC), a bone cell marker, fibronectin (FN), which imaintains the integrity and organisation of the extracellular matrix, and collagen type I (COL I), a major antigen of all connective tissues. Although the level of COL I was unaffected, the GR-HA was found to down-regulate both OC and FN. These findings indicate that the GR-HA used in this study has potentially deleterious effects on the proliferation and functional activity of bone-like cells. They also demonstrate that the FCM technique is a useful tool for evaluating subtle but possibly important biological responses to implant materials.

KEYWORDS
HA, bone cells, flow cytometry, cell cycle, extracellular matrix

INTRODUCTION
The precise biological responses to implant materials for orthopaedic and dental surgery are still not well characterised, thus raising the possibility of unexpected deleterious effects *in vivo*. In order to assess subtle but potentially important biological effects, we have used the technique of flow cytometry (FCM) to examine certain key aspects of the response of osteoblast-like MG63 cells to hydroxyapatite (HA) and a glass-reinforced hydroxyapatite composite material (GR-HA).

The FCM technique measures the light scattered by individual cells as they pass a laser beam, sensing devices detecting light scattered at small angles (forward scatter; FSC), which is considered proportional to cell size, while the orthogonal light scatter (side scatter; SSC) is proportional to the granularity of the cell. In addition, the application of fluorescent antibodies and cytoplasmic and nuclear dyes as 'tags' have enabled many cellular components to be accurately measured. Although used primarily for the analysis of lymphocyte sub-sets in immunologically-based diseases, we have adapted the FCM procedure[1-3] and in this study have used it to examine the effects of HA and GR-HA on the cell cycle and on the size, granularity and expression of specific connective tissue components by MG63 human osteosarcoma cells.

MATERIALS AND METHODS

Preparation of discs

HA was obtained from Plasma Biotal (Tideswell, England) and a composite made by mixing the HA with 2.5% (w/w) of a P_2O_5-based glass (50%mol P_2O_5, 16.5%mol CaO and 33.5%mol MgO), as previously described.[4] The powders were uniaxially pressed and 30 mm diameter discs were fired to 1300°C for 1 h, then mechanically polished using a 1 µm diamond aerosol spray. After ultrasonic de-greasing, the discs were sterilised at 180°C for 1 h.

Cell culture

MG63 cells were cultured at 37°C in a humidified atmosphere of 5% CO_2 in air, in 75 cm^2 flasks containing 10 ml of a complete medium consisting of α-MEM (Gibco; Paisley, Scotland), 10% foetal calf serum (FCS) (PAA Laboratories; Consett, England), 2 mM L-glutamine, 50 IU/ml penicillin and 50 µg/ml streptomycin. They were sub-cultured by incubating with 0.25% trypsin-1mM EDTA for 5 min at 37°C to detach the cells, and then re-seeded and grown in new culture flasks.

Aliquots of the cells were placed onto the 30 mm discs in 6-well Falcon culture plates (Becton Dickinson; Oxford, England) and allowed to attach for 2 h at 37°C, after which 2.5 ml of complete medium was added. In control cultures the cells were placed, at the same density, directly into the plastic culture dishes in 2.5 ml of medium.

Cell cycle analysis

The cells were plated at 5000 cells/cm^2 on the discs and on the plastic dishes, as described above. After 36 h of incubation the cells were detached by treatment with trypsin-EDTA, washed with phosphate-buffered saline (PBS) and suspended in 2 ml of 70% ethanol for 30 min, then centrifuged and resuspended in 400 µl of PBS. They were incubated with 100 µl of RNase A (1 mg/ml) (Sigma; Poole, England) and 100 µl of propidium iodide (PI) (400 µl/ml) (Sigma) at 37°C for 45 min to stain for DNA. The cells were gated to eliminate cell debris and cell aggregates and the content of DNA per cell was analysed by FCM as described below, in order to determine the distribution of cells in the 5 main phases of the cell cycle .

Immunofluorescent staining of antigens

The cells were plated at 10000/cm^2 on 30 mm discs and directly on plastic dishes and incubated for 6 days. They were detached using 20 mM EDTA. Trypsin was not used because its activity would be likely to remove some cell surface-associated antigens. The cells were centrifuged, resuspended and immediately fixed in 1% paraformaldehyde in PBS for 30 min. After washing by centrifugation, the cells were resuspended in a washing buffer of PBS containing 2% FCS and 0.1% saponin (Sigma) to permeabilize the fixed cells in order to facilitate the entry of the antibodies. Aliquots of 10^5 cells were used to measure the relative levels of osteocalcin (OC), fibronectin (FN) and collagen type I (COL I) by FCM, as follows.

The cells were incubated for 1 h at room temperature in the following primary antibodies: rabbit polyclonal antibody against human OC (Biogenesis; Poole, England), diluted 1:100; mouse monoclonal antibodies (mAbs) against human FN (Gibco) and COL I (Sigma), diluted 1:100 and 1:100 respectively. Normal pre-immune rabbit serum and mouse IgG$_1$ (Dako; High Wycombe,

England) were used as negative controls. Cells were then washed and fluorescein isothiocyanate (FITC)-conjugated swine anti-rabbit IgG (Dako) (diluted 1:20) and FITC-conjugated rabbit anti-mouse IgG (Dako) (diluted 1:50) were added for 30 min at room temperature. The cells were washed, resuspended in 400 µl of washing buffer and analysed as below.

FCM analysis

The forward and side scattering properties of laser light (FSC and SSC, respectively) and the fluorescence intensity of cells stained with PI (red fluorescence) and FITC (green fluorescence) were measured using a FACScan flow cytometer (Becton Dickinson). The excitation source was an argon-ion laser emitting a 488 nm beam at 15 mW. The FSC, SSC and PI values were measured on a linear scale of 1024 channels, while FITC-emission was detected on a four decade logarithmic scale. The signals arising from cell debris and cell aggregates were eliminated from the analysis of both DNA content and antigen expression , as noted above. In each of the experiments the negative control was cells treated with non-specific immunoglobulin instead of primary antibody; this value was subtracted from each of the test samples. Data were collected, stored and analysed with CellQuest Software (Becton Dickinson) and are presented as arbitrary units of FSC, SSC and fluorescence intensity. These values depend on the electronic input and detection settings of the FACScan, which were kept constant in the experiments described, and on the specific antibodies used.

Statistical analysis

The median values of triplicate FCM profiles were used to calculate the averages of the light scattering and fluorescence intensities ± standard deviation (SD). Analysis of the statistical significance of the results was carried out using the Mann-Whitney U-test ($p < 0.05$).

RESULTS AND DISCUSSION

Effects of HA and GR-HA on cell cycle progression

During the cell cycle the genetic material is replicated and divided equally among the two new, identical daughter cells. With mammalian cells, this process generally occupies approximately one day, and in an exponentially growing culture the cells are distributed in G0 and G1 (resting phases), S phase (DNA synthesis), G2 (post-DNA synthesis) and M (mitosis). The proportion of cells in each of these is assessed by their DNA content, which can be accurately measured by FCM of cells stained with PI. The results in Table 1 show the effects of culture on HA and GR-HA discs on the proportion of cells in each of the phases of the cell cycle, compared with control MG63 cells grown on plastic.

Table 1. Effects of HA and GR-HA on the progression of the MG63 cell cycle.
The results are shown as the % of cells in each phase compared with plastic-grown cells.

Phase of Cell Cycle	% of Control Cells	
	HA	GR-HA
G$_0$/G$_1$	92.0	138.0*
S	87.5	62.5*
G$_2$/M	122.0	104.5

* Denotes statistically significant differences from control cells (p<0.05).

While HA appeared to have no statistically significant influence on the distribution of MG63 cells among the phases of the cycle, cells grown on GR-HA significantly accumulated in G0/G1 and were concomitantly reduced in the S phase compared with control cultures. The proportion of G2/M cells was statistically unaffected in all cultures. These results thus suggest that culture of the cells in the presence of GR-HA may have inhibited cell cycle progression, possibly by delaying the entry of G0/G1 cells into the S phase.

Effects of HA and GR-HA on cell size and granularity

Microscopic examination indicated that most cells adhered to the discs after plating, and during subsequent incubation *in vitro*, little if any debris was observed in the culture dish, indicating that the HA and GR-HA were not cytotoxic. After removal of the cells from the discs and control plastic surfaces, FCM was used to assess whether growth on the discs altered the size and granularity of the cells compared with that on the plastic, as described in the Materials and Methods. Fig. 1 is the result of triplicate experiments, in each of which 10000 individual cells were examined, and shows that although both the average size and average granularity of the HA- and GR-HA- grown cells were somewhat reduced compared with the plastic-grown cells, there was no statistically significant difference between them (p>0.05).

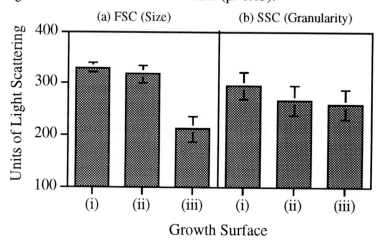

Fig. 1.   Effects of HA and GR-HA on the size and granularity of MG 63 cells.
MG63 cells were grown on (i) plastic dishes, (ii) HA discs and (iii) GR-HA discs. They were then analysed by FCM for (a) size (FSC) and (b) granularity (SSC), as described. The results are shown as the average (±SD) of 3 relicate experiments.

Expression of HA and GR-HA on OC, FN and COL I expression

The disc- and plastic- grown cells were immunostained for the expression of 3 major connective tissue antigens, OC, FN and COL I, and the relative levels of each measured by FCM as described in the Materials and Methods. Table 2 is the result of 3 separate experiments and shows that, while the average relative expression of OC, FN and COL I by cells grown on HA was very similar to that of the plastic-grown cells (approximately

90, 82 and 88%, respectively, of the control cells), OC and FN were expressed at significantly lower levels in the GR-HA-grown cells than in the control cells (68% and 69% of control cultures, respectively; $p<0.05$).

Table 2. Effects of HA and GR-HA on antigen expression by MG63 cells.
MG 63 cells were incubated for 5 days on HA and GR-HA discs and stained with antibodies against OC, FN and COL I. The cells were analysed by FCM and the average levels of fluorescence intensity ($\pm$SD) compared with control cells.

Culture conditions	Antigen Levels (% of Control Cells)		
	OC	FN	COL I
HA discs	90 $\pm$6.3	82 $\pm$9.3	88 $\pm$ 2.1
GR-HA discs	68* $\pm$6.1	69* $\pm$5.2	87 $\pm$10.7

* Denotes statistically significant difference from control, plastic-grown cells ($p<0.05$).

CONCLUSION

Despite our observation of apparently good attachment to the HA and GR-HA discs and very little if any debris in the culture dishes, our FCM experiments nevertheless demonstrated that GR-HA in particular may have a deleterious effect on the cell cycle of MG63 cells. This is consistent with our finding that the GR-HA cells are also of somewhat smaller size than plastic-grown cells. Moreover, as well as differences in cell cycle progression, OC and FN expression in the GR-HA cells was found to be only two-thirds of the levels of control cells. The results of these FCM experiments suggest that the GR-HA used in the present *in vitro* study may be significantly less than optimal for facilitating the cell proliferation and connective tissue production which are essential for effective tissue re-building processes *in vivo*,

REFERENCES

1. H. Sumner, D. Abraham, G. Bou-Gharios, C. Plater-Zyberk., and I. Olsen, "Simultaneous measurement of cell surface and intracellular antigens by multiple flow cytometry," *J. Immunol. Methods*, 136, 259-267 (1991).
2. J.R. Beauchamp, D.J. Abraham, G. Bou-Gharios, T.A. Partridge, and I. Olsen, "Expression and function of adhesion molecules during differentiation of human skeletal muscle in culture," *Am. J. Pathol.*, 140, 387-401 (1992).
3. G. Bou-Gharios, J. Osman, C. Black, and I. Olsen, "Excess matrix accumulation in Scleroderma is caused partly by differential regulation of stromelysin and TIMP-1 synthesis," *Clin. Chim. Acta*, 231, 69-78 (1994).
4. J.D. Santos, J.C. Knowles, R.L. Reis, F.J. Monteiro, and G.W.Hastings, "Microstructural characterisation of glass-reinforced hydroxyapatite composites," *Biomaterials*, 15, 5-10 (1994).

Bioceramics Volume 11, edited by R. Z. LeGeros and J.P. LeGeros
(Proceedings of the 11th International Symposium on Ceramics in Medicine)
New York, NY, USA, November 1998

EFFECTS OF BIOACTIVE GLASS ON MACROPHAGES ACTIVATION

M. Bosetti^, L.L. Hench*, J. Wilson*, M. Cannas^

^Department of Medical Sciences, Human Anatomy, University of Torino, Novara, Italy
*Imperial College of Science Technology and Medicine, Department of Materials, University of London

ABSTRACT

In this study we compares quantitatively the effect of 45S5 Bioglass® with commercial crystalline silicon dioxide (quartz) powders evaluating peripheral human blood macrophages activation by chemilluminescence assay. The two powders were studied alone or in a situation of chemical macrophage activation using Phorbol myristate acetate (PMA) as a direct stimulator of protein kinase C and N-formylmethionylleucylphenilalanine (fMLP) as receptor linked activator.

The two powders were not toxic for macrophages and Bioglass® evidenced a statistically significant increase in oxidative activity respect to non stimulated cells and SiO2; PMA and fMLP did not increase Bioglass® macrophages activation.

These results indicate that the well established early release of Na+ and Ca++ from Bioglass® may be driving the activation of macrophages in culture as the cells activation involves Na+ and Ca++ receptor sites. This effect could contribute to the rapid repair of soft and hard tissues (also for wound healing) and proliferation of bone in clinical use.

KEYWORDS: Bioglass®, macrophage activation, in-vitro biocompatibility

INTRODUCTION

It has been shown *in vivo* and *in vitro* that macrophages respond differently to bioactive and bioinert materials; it is known that cell-biomaterials contact evokes the release of chemotactic mediators and growth factors that may elicit and sustain inflammatory responses at the implant site[1-3]. Previous studies indicated that a wide variety of particles can prime macrophages to give a marked increase in their oxidative response [4].

This study compares quantitatively the effect of 45S5 Bioglass® particles with crystalline silica (quartz) with and without an intracellular macrophage activator (PMA) and an extracellular macrophage activator (fMLP). PMA enhances macrophage production of oxidative proteinases, such as H2O2 and free radicals of oxygen by passing through the cellular membrane, triggering the arachidonic acid cascade and activating production of the protein kinase C (PKC)[5]. PMA also enhances the ability of the macrophage to signal phagocytosis. fMLP, a chemotactic peptide, is a less potent extracellular activator of macrophages.

MATERIALS AND METHODS

Macrophages were obtained from peripheral human blood of healthy volunteers by centrifuging in Ficoll-Hipaque gradient (Histopaque 1077, Sigma, Milano, Italy) at 400 X g for 30 minutes followed by two washing at room temperature in Hanks' Balanced Salt Solution (HBSS, Sigma), cells were used for chemilluminescence assay or cultured in RPMI (Sigma) containing 10% heat-inactivated fetal calf serum, 2mM glutamine, penicillin (100 units/ml) and streptomycin (100 μg/ml). Cell viability and number were determined by Tripan Blue staining and counting in a hematocytometer.

Cell activation was determined by chemilluminescence assay (CL) using two hundred microliters of purified peripheral human blood monocytes/macrophages (5×10^6/ml) suspended in 3 ml of HBSS (37°C) in propylene vials (Packard Company, Milano). CL was monitored in a Beckman CPM-100 liquid scintillation counter normalized and programmed in the single photon counting mode with a five minute counting delay (dark adaption), one minute counts per well and ten counting cycles. Luminol (Sigma) was added to the cell suspensions to give a final concentration of 0.1 mM. Subsequently, CL was elicited by addition of 400 μg/ml of the powders to test: Bioglass® powder (710-90 μm in diameter) and Silicone dioxide powder (0.5-10 μm diameter, from Sigma), were tested to evaluate cell toxic effect and oxidative burst response.

PMA in a final concentration of 0.5 μg/ml and fMLP in a final concentration of 26.7 ng/ml were used respectively as direct stimulator of protein kinase C and receptor linked activator in presence and absence of the materials tested; cells with luminol were used as negative control. Results are the average of nine experiments and statistical evaluation was made using an independent sample t test; p value was obtained from the ANOVA table and the conventional 0.05 level was considered to reflect statistical significance.

RESULTS AND DISCUSSION

Cellular interactions which occur at the tissue implant interface represent an important determinant of biomedical materials biocompatibility[6]. Inflammatory cells are the predominant component of cell/polymer interactions, in particular macrophage activation induce the cells to further differentiate, phagocytose or secrete products to the surrounding environment[7]. This is an important macrophages property that influences their ability to recognize foreign surfaces.

Bioglass® and $SiO2$ powders were not toxic for peripheral human blood monocytes/macrophages during 48 h of incubation at 37°C *in vitro*; this data was determined looking cell at morphology using the inverted phase microscope. The viability of cells incubated with silicone dioxide and Bioglass particles was comparable to cells incubated without particles for the same period (results not shown).

Statistical analysis of the lumino-enhanced chemiluminescent assay results, to study the cascade of events leading to the production of tissue-damaging reactive oxygen intermediates, are rapresented in Table 1.

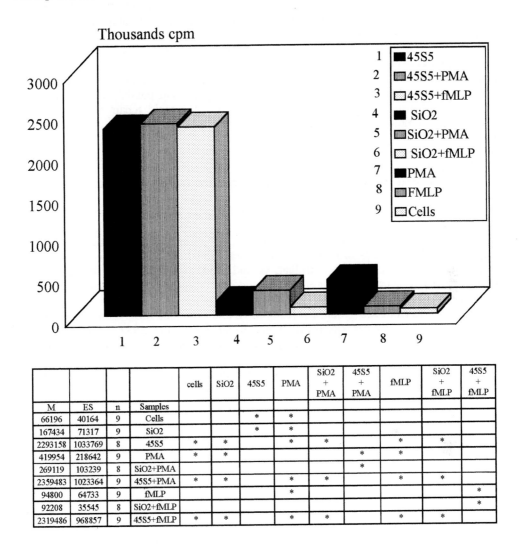

M	ES	n	Samples	cells	SiO2	45S5	PMA	SiO2 + PMA	45S5 + PMA	fMLP	SiO2 + fMLP	45S5 + fMLP
66196	40164	9	Cells			*	*					
167434	71317	9	SiO2			*	*					
2293158	1033769	8	45S5	*	*		*	*		*	*	
419954	218642	9	PMA	*	*				*	*		
269119	103239	8	SiO2+PMA						*			
2359483	1023364	9	45S5+PMA	*	*		*	*		*	*	
94800	64733	9	fMLP				*					*
92208	35545	8	SiO2+fMLP									*
2319486	968857	9	45S5+fMLP	*	*		*	*		*	*	

Table 1: Statistical analysis of macrophages activation by chemilluminescence assay.
M = mean; ES = standard error; * = p<0,05

Results showed that cells alone (#9) show very little oxidative activity. Addition of the intracellular activator, PMA, significantly increases oxidative activity (#7) whereas the extracellular activator, fMLP, has no significant effect (#8). Silicon dioxide (#4) does not alter the macrophage oxidative activation; SiO2+PMA (#5) is equivalent to the effects of PMA alone (#7); SiO2+fMLP (#6) is similar to fMLP alone (#8) and SiO2 alone (#4). However, addition of 45S5 Bioglass® to the macrophage cultures results in an enormous increase in oxidative activity of the cells, both with PMA (#2) and fMLP (#3) and even without the biological activators (#1).

These results indicate that the well established early release of Na+ and Ca++ from Bioglass ® may be driving the activation of macrophages in culture and possibly also in the early stages of wound healing. This effect could contribute to the rapid repair of soft and hard tissues and proliferation of bone in clinical use, which have already been observed for the material.

REFERENCES

1.   Bloom, B.R. and Bennet, B., Mechanism of a reaction in vitro associated with delayed-type hypersensitivity, *Science* 1966, **153**, 80-82

2.   David, J.R., Al-Askari, S., Lawrence, H.S. and Thomas, L., Delayed Hypersensitivity *in vitro, J.Immunol.* 1964, **93**, 264-282

3.   Nathan, C.F., Karnovsky, M.L. and David, J.R., Alterations of macrophage functions by mediators from lymphocytes, *J. Exp. Med.* 1971, **133**, 1356-1372

4.   Myrvik, Q.N., Gristina, A.G., Giridhar, G. and Hayakawa, H., Particle-induced in vivo priming of alveolar macrophages for enhanced oxidative responses: a novel system of cellular immune augmentation, *J. Leuk. Biol.* 1993, **54,** 439-443

5.   Kaplan S.S, Basford R.E., Mora E., Jeong M.H. and Simmons R.L., Biomaterial-induced alterations of neutrophil superoxide production, J. Biomed. Mat. Res. 1992, 26, 1039-1051

6.   Remes A., Williams D.F., Immune response in biocompatibility, *Biomaterials* 1991, **13,** 731-743

7.   Trevor Rae, The macrophage response to implant materials - with special reference to those used in orthopedics, *Critical Reviews in Biocompatibility* 1990, **2, 2,** 97-126

Bioceramics Volume 11, edited by R. Z. LeGeros and J.P. LeGeros
(Proceedings of the 11th International Symposium on Ceramics in Medicine)
New York, NY, USA, November 1998
© 1998 by World Scientific Publishing Co. Pte. Ltd.

BIORESORBABLE BONE SUBSTITUTE MATERIALS MADE OF SINTERED CARBONATE APATITES

Y.Doi[1], S.Saku[2], H.Iwanaga[3], T,Kajimoto[2], Y.Moriwaki[1], K.Yamamoto[2], T.Shibutani[3], Y. Iwayama[3], Y.Mizuta[4], and Y.Ikeda[4]

Departments of [1]Dental Materials & Technology, [2]General Dentistry & Operative Dentistry and [3]Periodontology, School of Dentistry, Asahi University, Gifu 501-02, Japan and [4]Japan Fine Ceramics Center, Nagoya 456, Japan

ABSTRACT

Sintered carbonate apatites have been evaluated in vitro and in vivo as bone substitutes. In an osteoclastic cell culture, the number of tartrate-resistant acid phosphatase (TRAP) positive cells on sintered disks with smooth surfaces was essentially the same as that on bone slices after two-day incubation, although it was greater by about 40% on disks with rough surfaces. With every disk examined, however, the osteoclasts were capable of resorbing sintered carbonate apatite. Micro-focus computed tomographs showed that in vivo very little bone formed in defects unfilled surgical untill at least 3 weeks after implantation but in defects filled with the sintered apatite bone formed by two weeks. Staining of sectioned specimens by TRAP showed that there were many TRAP-positive cells around the resorbing material. This finding was also confirmed by transmission electron micrographs, suggesting that the resorption of the sintered carbonate apatite particles is, in part, similar to osteoclastic bone resorption.

KEYWORDS: Sintered Carbonate Apatites, Osteoclasts, Bioresorbable, Bone Substitutes

Introduction

Calcium phosphate biomaterials are often used as bone substitutes. Two important features of bone substitutes are their biocompatibility and their ability to resorb at a rate similar to bone growth [1,2]. Factors governing bioresorption of calcium phosphates are not fully understood, but appear to be mainly regulated by solution- and cell-mediated degradation [2-4]. In the present study, apatite specimens containing about 12wt% carbonate were sintered at 750°C [5,6] and the usefulness of sintered specimens as bone substitutes [7] was evaluated in vitro and in vivo. Sintered carbonate apatite particles were implanted in skull defects of Wister rats, and the rats were sacrificed at 1-4 weeks after implantation for micro-focus X-ray computed tomography (MFX-CT), light microscopy and transmission electron microscopy. The MFX-CT used [8] has a spatial resolution of the order of 10μm, which is approximately 10-20 times finer than that of usual medical CT systems [9,10]. This level of resolution provides CT images comparable with images obtained by contact microradiography with sectioned specimens.

MATERIALS AND METHODS
Sintered specimens

Sintered hydroxyapatite (HAp) and carbonate apatite (CAp) specimens were produced by heating compacted samples in a manner described previously [5,6]. Approximately 1-mm-thick sections were cut from the sintered specimens with a diamond saw, some of whose surfaces were polished with 1μm diamond paste or with #1000 water-proof sand paper. The sections were subsequently cleaned ultrasonically and placed in 24-well plates for cell culture experiments. For animal experiment, non-compacted samples of carbonate apatite particles with sizes between 300 and 500μm were sintered under the same conditions as with the compacted samples of carbonate apatite.

Osteoclastic cell culture

Osteoclasts were obtained from the long bones of 1-day-old neonatal rabbits (Japan white) as described before [7,11]. Cell suspension (100μl) containing 50-100 multinucleated osteoclasts per 100μl was plated onto each sintered apatite section in the small wells of microculture plates. After incubation at 37°C in 5% CO_2 for 90 minutes, the non-attached cells were gently washed off and the substrates transferred into 35mm culture medium and then incubated at 37°C in 5% CO_2 for periods of up to 48 hours. Osteoclasts were identified by staining for tartrate-resistant acid phosphatase after cyanuric chloride pretreatment as described before[11] and the number of TRAP positive cells with diameter greater than 20μm were counted using a stereomicroscope (SZX12,Olympus).

Skull defects

Twelve Wistar rats weighing 300-350g were used. A 4 mm diameter defect was made through each parietal bone with a trephine [12]. Some defects were filled with about 5 mg of either coarse or fine particles (300-500μm; coarse particles and ≤200μm; fine particles) of sintered carbonate apatite and the rest were left empty. The animals were sacrificed at 1,2,3 and 4 weeks after implantation. The skullcaps were removed and fixed with 10% neutral formalin, decalcified with neutral ethylene diamine tetraacetic acid, embedded in paraffin and sectioned. Sections of 5-8μm thickness were stained with either hematoxylin and eosin (HE) or with TRAP for light microscopy. Some animals were perfused with a linger's solution, immediately followed by pefusion with 4% paraformaldehyde-1% glutaraldehyde in 0.1M sodium cacodylate buffer at pH 7.3,postfixed in a 2% osmium tetraoxide solution, and embedded in Epon 812 resin for transmission electron microscopy (TEM).

Micro-focus X-ray computed tomography (MFX-CT)

All the skull defects were scanned with a micro-focus X-ray computed tomograph (MFX-CT) [8] before sectioning for light and TEM microscopy. Five to six MFX-CT images were measured in planes parallel to each skull defect and each MFX-CT scan was taken with about a 20μm slice thickness. Images were reconstructed in matrices of 512X512 pixels and the two-dimensional resolution of the MFX-CT was less than 12μm at the magnification used.

RESULTS AND DISCUSSION
Osteoclastic cell culture

Figure 1 shows the number of TRAP-positive cells on sintered specimens. For comparison the number of TRAP-positive cells on sintered hydroxyapatite specimens was also included. The number of TRAP-positive cells was significantly higher (p<0.02) on the sintered specimens compared to bone slices, except the sintered carbonate apatite with smooth surface (CAp-S). The number of TRAP-positive cells on the latter specimen was essentially the same as that on bone slices.

SEM micrographs showed that many resorption pits or lacunae were evident on sintered carbonate apatite as well as bone after 2 day incubation, but no pits or

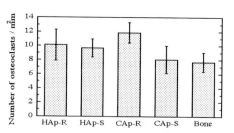

Figure.1 The number of TRAP-positibe cells on substrates of sintered hydroxyapatite with rough (HAp-R) and smooth surfaces (HAp-S), sintered carbonate apatite with rough (CAp-R) and smooth surfaces (CAp-S) and bone slices after 2-day incubation.

lacunae were observed on sintered hydroxyapatite substrates, irrespective of the difference in the roughness (HAp-S and HAp-R). Nevertheless the osteoclasts appeared to attach to the surface of the HAp substrate in essentially the same way as that seen for the bone and carbonate apatite.

Skull defects

Figure 2 shows roentgenographs of skull defects without particles (a), filled with fine (b) and coarse particles (c) at 4 weeks postoperationally. It is evident that the unfilled defect is somewhat more x-ray transparent, indicating that no significant bone formed spontaneously by 4 weeks after implantation. Figure 3 compares micro-focus X-ray computed tomographs (MFX-CT) of the three skull defects shown in Fig.2. For each specimen, two CT slices that correspond to the cen-

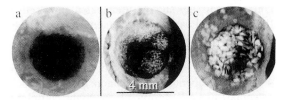

Figure 2. Roentgenographs of skull defects filled with no material (a), fine (b) and coarse particles (c) of sintered carbonate apatite at 4 weeks after implantation.

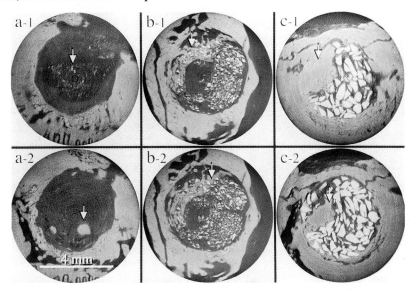

Figure 3. Representative mico-forcus x-ray computed tomographs of the three specimens shown in Fig.2.

Arrows indicate new bone formed in the defect at 4 weeks after implantation.

tral part of the defect, separated from each other by about 40µm are shown. In the defect with no implanted material (a-1 and a-2), only a small area has an X-ray translucency that favorably compares with that of the surrounding host bone. In the defects filled with particles, however, a much larger area is comparable in X-ray translucency to the host bone, indicating that bone formed to an appreciable extent in the presence of the sintered apatite particles. In the defect filled with finer particles (b-1 and b-2), many particles appear to be embedded in the newly formed bone. Irrespective of the difference in the particle size used, however, the defects were not completely filled with bone at 4 weeks postoperationally.

Figure 4 shows a toluidin blue-stained, non-decalcified specimen of a defect filled with the finer particles of sintered carbonate apatite at 4 weeks

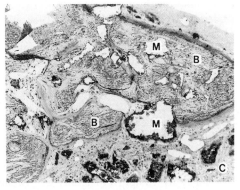

Figure 4. Bone formation in contact with the finer particles of sintered carbonate apatite. B:bone, M:materials and C:connective tissues.

postoperationally. In the area where particles were embedded in newly formed bone, no matrix material appears interposed between the particles and the bone. On the other hand, the coarser particles appeared not to have became embedded in new bone. Nevertheless, many particles were in direct contact with the bone. In areas where no bone formation occurred, particles were surrounded with connective tissues and multinucleated giant cells were observed around some particles and newly formed bone. Possible involvement of osteoclasts in resorption of the sintered material was confirmed with TRAP-stained, decalcified specimens, indicating that multinucleated giant cells identified with HE or TB-stained specimens were also TRAP-positive.

Figures 5 and 6 show some typical TEM micrographs of defects filled with the coarser particles at 4 weeks postoperationally, demonstrating osteoclast-like cells resorbing the particles (Fig.5) and osteoblast-like cells forming bone on the particles (Fig.6). Distribution of sintered particles beneath the osteoclast-like cells appeared to be somewhat sparse and some particles appeared to be phagocytosed in vesicles (Fig.5). In the area where bone formation was in progress, osteoid was found between the osteoblast and bone, which contained some osteocytes as shown in Fig.6. These findings suggest that sintered carbonate apatite would be useful as a bioresorbable bone substitute.

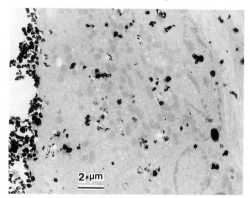

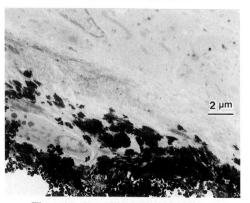

Figure 5. Osteoclast-like cell resorbing the material.

Figure 6. Osteoblast-like cell forming new bone on the material.

REFERENCES

1. De Groot K. Biomaterials 1986; **7**:137-143.
2. Jarcho M. Dent Clin North Am 1986; **30**:25-47.
3. Blair HC, Teitelbaum SL,Tan H-L, Koziol CM, Schlesinger PH. Am J Physiol (Cell Physiol)1991; **29**:c1315-c1324.
5. Doi Y, Koda T, Wakamatsu N, Goto T, Kamemizu H, Moriwaki Y, Adachi M, Suwa Y. J Dent Res 1993; **72**:1279-1284.
6. Doi Y, Koda T, Adachi M, Wakamatsu N, Goto T, Kamemizu H, Moriwaki Y,Suwa Y. J Biomed Mater Res 1995; **29**:1451-1457.
7. Doi Y, Shibutani T, Moriwaki Y, Kajimoto T, Iwayama Y. J Biomed Mater Res 1998; **39**:603-610.
8. Ikeda Y,Mizuta Y, Tobita H. Proceedings of the Eights Asia-Pacific Conference on Nondestructive Testing (8th APCNDT)1995:33-40.
9. Yancey RN,.Klima SJ. Ceram Eng Sci Roc 1991;**12**:2029-2041.
10. Kinney JH, Haupt DL, Nichols MC, Breunig TM, Marshall GW, Jr, Marshall SJ. Nucl Instr and Meth in Phys Res 1994; **A347**:480-486.
11. Shibutani T, Heershe NM. J Bone Miner Res 1993; **8**:331-336.
12. Dersot JM, Septier D, Llorens A, Saffar JL. Cell Mater 1993; **31**:395-405.

Bioceramics Volume 11, edited by R. Z. LeGeros and J.P. LeGeros
(Proceedings of the 11th International Symposium on Ceramics in Medicine)
New York, NY, USA, November 1998
© 1998 by World Scientific Publishing Co. Pte. Ltd.

55S BIOGLASS PROMOTED DIFFERENTIATION OF CULTURED RAT OSTEOBLASTS AND CREATED A TEMPLATE FOR BONE FORMATION

C. Loty[1], J.M. Sautier[1], S. Loty[1], E. Jallot[2], and N. Forest[1]

[1]Laboratoire de Biologie-Odontologie, Institut Biomédical des Cordeliers, Escalier E, 2è étage, 15-21, rue de l'Ecole de Médecine, 75270 Paris Cedex 06, France; [2]Laboratoire de Microscopie Electronique, INSERM U314, Université de Reims, France.

ABSTRACT

We investigated the behavior of fetal rat osteoblasts cultured on bioactive glass with 55wt% silica content (55S) and on bioinert glass (60S). Morphological observations revealed that cells attached and spread to all substrata and formed multi-layered nodular structures by day 10 of culture. Cytoenzymatic localization of alkaline phosphatase (AP) and immunolabeling with bone sialoprotein antibody revealed a specific staining for the bone nodules formed in the 55S cultures. Furthermore, biochemical determination of AP activity after 12 days in culture revealed a significantly higher content of the isoenzyme for the 55S cultures than for the controls. Ultrastructural observations of undecalcified sections revealed the presence of an electron-dense layer, composed of needle-shaped crystals at the periphery of the material, that seemed to act as a nucleating surface for biological crystals. This data indicate better osteoblast expression on 55S bioactive glass compared to non-bioactive glass and revealed that mineralization can be initiated *in vitro* with 55S bioactive glass serving as a template for bone formation and controlling nucleation of biological crystals.

KEYWORDS: Bioglasses, osteoblasts, differentiation, cell culture, interface.

INTRODUCTION

Bioactive materials, such as calcium phosphate ceramics, bioactive glasses and glass ceramics, have been shown to form a strong chemical bond with living tissue. This rate of bonding is dependent upon the bulk composition of the glass. 45S5 bioactive glass has been shown to be the optimal composition in terms of maximum bonding to bone and soft tissue[1]. As such, 45S5 has been studied extensively while less attention has been paid to melt derived glasses of varying silica contents. Although 55S glass have been shown to bond to bone but not to soft tissue[2], the biological mechanisms concerning the interfacial interactions between the glass and cells remains poorly understood. For this reason, this work was undertaken to examine the behavior of fetal rat osteoblasts cultured on 55S bioactive glass and the interfacial interactions between the material and bone cells. An *in vitro* system was used with osteoblasts derived from the fetal rat calvaria.[3] Morphological, immunocytochemical and biochemical parameters were used to investigate the osteoblast phenotype. The bone/bioactive glass interface was studied using TEM and EDX.

MATERIALS AND METHODS

US Biomaterials Corporation (Alachua, FL) prepared the 55S and 60S glass compositions as previously described[3]. Samples were supplied in the form of disks with a 1 cm diameter and 1 mm thickness. Osteoblasts were enzymatically isolated form calvaria of 21-day-old fetal rats using the protocol described by Nefussi et al.[4] The osteoblast phenotype was monitored by SEM, cytoenzymatic localization of AP and immunolabeling with bone sialoprotein antibody. The specific activity of AP was assayed in the cell layer by monitoring the release of p-nitrophosphenol from p-nitrophenolphosphate. After 15 days in culture, 55S disks were embedded in epon and cut into ultrathin sections (100 nm) for TEM and EDX analysis.

RESULTS AND DISCUSSION

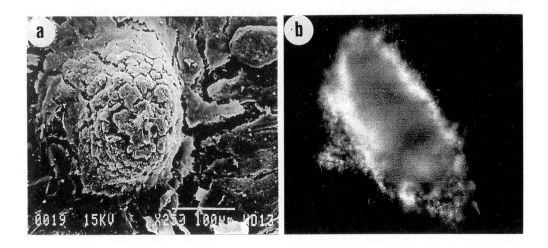

Figure 1. SEM observation of (a) a bone nodule formed on 55S bioactive glass on day 10 of culture and (b) immunolocalization of bone sialoprotein (x 200).

SEM observations revealed that cells attached and spread to all substrate and formed multi-layered nodular structures by day 10 of culture (Figure 1a). Immunolabeling with bone sialoprotein antibody revealed a specific staining for the bone nodules in 55S cultures (Figure 1b). Furthermore, cytoenzymatic localization of AP showed a significant increase in the isoenzyme after cells reached confluence and showed concentrations of AP on clustered round (Figure 2a). In addition, the AP activity measured by enzyme assay gradually increased after 3 days in culture. After 12 days, the AP activity measured in cultures exposed to 55S was twice that of cultures exposed to non-reactive glass (Figure 2b). Results indicate a positive effect of 55S bioactive glass on osteogenic differentiation.

Findings were very similar to that observed by Vrouwenvelder et al.[5-6] for 45S5 glass. They hypothesize that the reaction kinetics of the glass and the formation of the hydroxyl carbonate apaptite layer that occurred in the culture medium provided a favourable environment for osteoblast differentiation. The 55S glass appears to create a similarly favourable environment. Also interesting to note are the observations of Keeting et al.[7] which showed that soluble silica induced proliferation and differentiation of human osteoblast-like cells. The 55S has a greater silica content than 45S5 glass but is more durable and therefore does not release as much soluble silica into the surrounding environment. It appears form these results, however, that it releases enough to induce active proliferation and differentiation of the rat osteoblasts.

TEM observations of undecalcified sections revealed the presence of active osteoblasts and a dense collagenous matrix surrounding the bioactive glass particles (Figure 4). An electron-dense layer, composed of needle-shaped crystals, was observed at the periphery of the material. EDX analysis revealed that this zone contained Ca and P but no Si. In addition, it was observed that collagen fibrils coalesced with this layer, which seemed to act as a nucleating surface for biological crystals. Such observations suggested that at early stages of osteogenesis, calcified foci might serve to bridge the collagen fibrils and thereby create a continuous mineralized bone tissue and allow fusion with the surface layer of the glass. The bonding to bioactive glasses by interdigitation of collagen fibers with the material surface was first reported by Hench et al.[8] Lastly, in a previous study, we observed that the onset of bone formation occurred directly on the apatite surface of a glass ceramic [9].

In conclusion, there appears to be a better osteoblasts expression on 55S bioactive glass compared to 60S glass as demonstrated by enzyme cytochemical, immunocytochemical and biochemical parameters. Futhermore, mineralization can be initiated *in vitro* with 55S bioactive glass serving as a template for the organization of the matrix and for generating bone tissue.

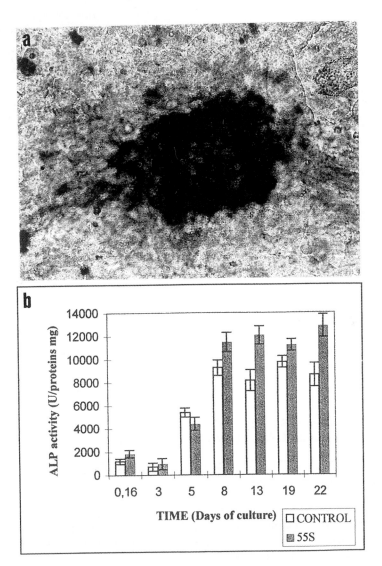

Figure 2. (a) Cytoenzymatic localization of alkaline phosphatase (x 200) (b) time course of alkaline phosphatase activity.

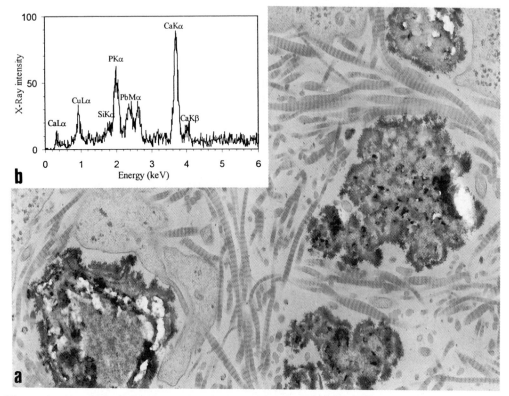

Figure 3. (a) TEM observation of the bone/bioactive glass interface. X 20.000. (b)   EDX, diffraction pattern of the periphery of 55S particle.

ACKNOWLEGDMENTS

This work was supported by US Biomaterials Corporation, Alachua, Florida.

REFERENCES

1. Hench LL. *J Am Ceram Soc* 1991; **74(7)**: 1487-1510.
2. Hench LL. In: Anderson OH, Ali-Urpo A, eds. *Bioceramics 7*. Buterworth-Heinemann Ltd, 1994: 3-14.
3. Greenspan DC, Zhong JP, LaTorre GP. In: Anderson OH, Ali-Urpo A, eds. *Bioceramics 7* Buterworth-Heinemann Ltd, 1994: 55-60.
4. Nefussi JR, Boy-Lefèvre ML, Boulekbache H, Forest N. *Differentiation* 1985; **29**: 160-168.
5. Vrouwenvelder WCA, Groot CG, de Groot K. *J Biomed Mater Res* 1993; **27**: 465-475.
6. Vrouwenvelder WCA, Groot CG, de Groot K. *Biomaterials* 1994; **15**: 97-106.
7. Keeting PE, Oursler MJ, Wiegand KE, Bonde SK, Spelsberg TC, Riggs BL. *J Bone and Mineral Res* 1992; **7(11)**: 1281-1289.
8. Hench LL, Paschall HA. *J Biomed Mater Res Symp* 1973; **4**: 25-42.
9. Sautier JM, Kokubo T, Ohtsuki T, Nefussi JR, Boulekbache H, Oboeuf M, Loty S, Loty C, Forest N. *Calcif Tissue Int* 1994; **55** : 458-466.

Bioceramics Volume 11, edited by R. Z. LeGeros and J.P. LeGeros
(Proceedings of the 11th International Symposium on Ceramics in Medicine)
New York, NY, USA, November 1998
© 1998 by World Scientific Publishing Co. Pte. Ltd.

IMMUNOSUPPRESSANT FK506 PROMOTES OSTEOBLASTIC DIFFERENTIATION OF MARROW STROMAL CELLS

H. Nakajima[1,2], T. Yoshikawa[1,2], H. Ohgushi[1], S. Tamai[1], Y. Dohi[3] and K. Ichijima[2]

Departments of Orthopaedic Surgery[1], Pathology[2] and Public health[3], Nara Medical University, Kashihara City, Nara 634-8521, JAPAN. Tel:+81-744-22-3051. Fax:+81-744-29-1460

ABSTRACT

Immunosuppressants are known to suppress immunologic rejections resulting in success of allogenic transplantation, however, the effect of immunosuppressants on bone metabolism has not well been characterized. In vitro cultured marrow stromal cells can differentiate into osteoblast when the culture medium contains dexamethasone (Dex). Here we report that FK506 (Fujisawa Pharmaceutical Co., Ltd., Osaka, Japan), a widely used immunosuppressant, enhanced the Dex induced in vitro osteogenic differentiation evidenced by high levels of alkaline phosphatase (ALP) activity, osteocalcin and calcium contents of the marrow culture. Based on our previous finding of in vivo bone forming capability of the in vitro cultured marrow cells in porous hydroxyapatite ceramics, present data suggest the usefulness of FK506 for marrow/ceramic composite transplantation in bone reconstruction surgery.

KEY WORDS: marrow stromal cell, FK506, dexamethasone, osteoblast, differentiation

INTRODUCTION

Immunosuppressants have been used for allogeneic cells and organ transplantation[1,2], and we reported that allogeneic marrow cells in porous ceramics can show osteogenic potency under the influence of the immunosuppressants[3,4]. The success of the allogeneic transplantation is due to the suppress of immunologic rejections by the immunosuppressants. It is also reported that immune system is an integral part of bone metabolism[5] and therefore, the immunosuppressants may have a critical role on osteogenesis. Although, only a few reported the effects of immunosuppressants on bone metabolism and suggested that adminstration of an immunosuppressant such as FK506 causes high-turnover osteopenia in vivo[6] and thus the immunosuppressants may cause the negative effects on osteogenesis. We focused on the effect of FK506 on osteoblast differentiation of marrow stromal cells which contains precursors of osteoblasts. Previously, Maniatopolous et al. demonstrated in vitro culture system that rat bone marrow stromal cells form calcified bone-like tissues in the presence of ß-glycerophosphate and dexamethasone[7]. In the present study, using this culture method, we analyzed the effect of an immunosuppressant on proliferation of the cultured bone marrow stromal cells and differentiation of the cells into osteoblasts. The analysis of markers of osteoblast phenotypes showed the positive effect of FK506 on osteoblastic differentiation of marrow cells.

MATERIALS AND METHODS
Preparation and Culture of Marrow Stromal Cells

Marrow cells were obtained from the femoral shafts of a seven-week-old male Fischer rats. The femora were taken and cut at both ends of epiphysis under aseptic conditions. The marrow plug was flushed out with the 10ml standard culture medium using a 10-ml syringe with a 21 gauge needle. The standard medium consisted of an Eagle minimal essential medium (MEM) containing 15% fetal bovine serum (ICN Biomedicals Japan Co. Ltd.) and antibiotics (100U/ml penicillin, 100μg/ml streptomycin and 0.25μg/ml amphotericine B, Sigma). The released cells were collected in a T-75 flask (COSTAR) containing 15ml of the culture medium. In primary culture, non-adherent cells were washed off leaving only the adherent cell (marrow stromal cell) layer. After 10 days in primary culture with the standard medium, confluent cells were harvested after treatment with 0.25% trypsin solution and seeded at 10^4 cell /cm^2 density on 35mm tissue culture plates. The subculture medium was supplemented with 10mM sodium-b-glycerophosphate, 82μg/ml vitamin C phosphate (L-ascorbic acid phosphate magnesium salt n-hydrate) and 10nM Dex.   To analyze the effect of immunosuppresants, FK506 (10ng/ml) was added into the Dex-containing medium.   For negative control, the culture was done in the abbsence of Dex and FK506.   FK506 was dissolved in ethanol and diluted with culture medium. Drugs were freshly prepared and the culture medium and supplementation were renewed 3 times a week.

Mesurement of ALP activities and DNA contents

Cells were grown in tissue culture plates for 6 and 12 days to quantitate DNA content and alkaline phosphatase (ALP) activity. Detail methods have already been reported[8]. The outline is as follows: The cultured cells in a well were immersed in 1 ml of 0.05M sodium phosphate buffer (pH7.4), 2mM EDTA and 2M NaCl, and scraped from the well.   The collected cells were homogenized, sonicated and centrifuged. After these treatment, the supernatant was assayed for both of DNA content and ALP activity. The DNA measurements were done in the presense of 0.5μg/ml Hoechst 33258 (Calbiochem-Novabiochem Corp. San Diego, CA). The fluorescence was measured at 356nm excitation and 492nm emission by spectrophotometer (Hitachi 650-10S). We used calf thymus DNA as standard. ALP activity was measured as previously reported[9]. Briefly, the supernatant was added into 1ml of 50mM p-nitrophenyl phosphate containig 1mM $MgCl_2$, and the mixture was incubated for 30mim at $37^{\circ}C$. Two ml of 0.2N NaOH was added to stop the enzymatic reaction, and the absorption at 410nm was measured with spectrophtometer. ALP activities were represented as μmol of p-nitrophenol released per well after 30 minutes incubation.

Calcium and Osteocalcin assay

The precipitates of the sonicated and centrifuged samples were used to quantitate mineralization in each well. They were demineralized with 1ml of 20% formic acid for 24 hrs and calcium concentraion of the aliquots were assayed by atomic absorption (Flame Spectrophotometer, Shimadzu, AA610S). Another aliquots were also assayed for osteocalcin which is most specific maker of bone tissue. The intact form of rat osteocalcin was measured with a sandwich enzyme immunoassay as described previously[10].

RESULTS

Immunosupressant FK506 treatment increased all the biochemical parameters in comparison to others. As shown in Fig. 1, alkaline phosphatase activity (ALP) of Dex treated culture increased as time passed, whereas negative control (without Dex and FK506) showed only basal levels of

ALP. The addition of FK506 to the Dex treated cells showed marked increase of ALP and DNA contents. Calcium and osteocalcin contents were detected on 12th day of subculture in Dex treatments but could not be detected in the negative control (Fig. 2). The calcium and osteoclacin contents of the cells supplemented with FK506 were about twice those of the Dex treated cells without FK506. These data indicate that FK506 promotes osteoblastid differentiation of marrow stromal cells.

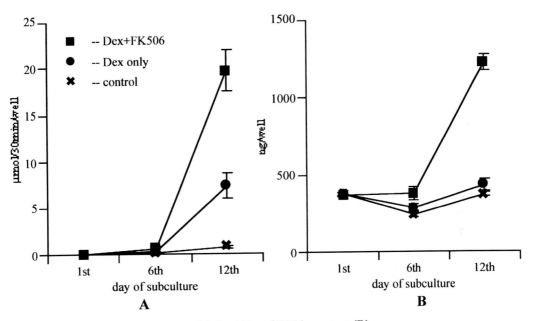

Figure 1. Time course of ALP acitivity (A) and DNA content (B)

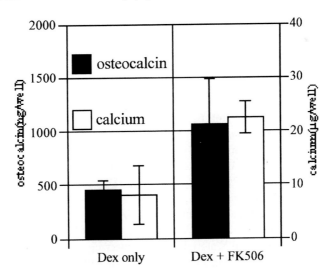

Figure 2. Osteocalcin and calcium content on 12th day of subculture

DISCUSSION

We have reported the appearance of osteogenic cells in porous ceramics by transplantation of marrow/ceramic composites at heterotopic (extraosseous) sites[9,11] and also reported that not only fresh marrow but also cultured human fibroblastic cells can show the osteogenic response resulting in bone formation at heterotopic sites[12]. Recently, we established the method to show marrow derived in vitro bone formation in porous ceramics using tissue culture technique in the presence of Dex[13]. Importatnly, the in vitro bone can show continuous active cellular function including osteoblastic activity after in vivo implantation of the ceramics[14]. Although, the quantity of thus formed in vitro bone is limited and therefore, if we can increase the in vitro osteoblastic activity in the tissue culture condition, the in vitro bone can show more osteogenic capacity in vivo.

Present data showed that immunosupressant of FK506 can enhance the Dex induced osteogenic differentiation of marrow cells. The enhancement was confirmed by the increase of ALP activity, calcium and osteocalcin contents. The ALP demonstrates the osteoblastic acvitity and the latter parameters of calcium and osteocalcin correlate with the amount of bone matrix. Therefore, supplementation of FK506 amplifies the in vitro bone formation together with increased cellular (osteoblast) activity. Based on the facts that in vitro bone can be formed in porous area of hydroxyaptite ceramics that can show continuous in vivo bone forming response, we can construct more potent osteogenic hydroxyapatite by the supplementation of FK506. These results suggest the clinical application of porous ceramics as the scaffold for the marrow cell culture together with the osteogenic supplementation of FK506.

ACKNOWLEDGEMENT

The authors wish to thank T. Ohta (Teijin Institute for Bio-Medical Research) for mesurement of intact osteocalcin.

REFERENCES

1. Fukunaga, T., Masumi, S., Yano, H., Ikebe, S. and Shimizu, K. *Acta Orthop Scand*, 1995, **66**, 557-560.
2. Yoshikawa, T., et al. In: *Bioceramics 9*, Pergamon, Oxford, 1996, 65-68.
3. Sempuku, T., Ohgushi, H., Okumura, M. and Tamai, S. In: *Bioceramics 8*, Pergamon, Oxford, 1995, 397-400.
4. Fealy, M.J., et al. *Ann. Surg.*, 1994, **219**, 88-93.
5. Horowitz, M.C. *Science*, 1993, **260**, 626-627.
6. Cvetkovic, M., et al. *Transplantation*, 1994, **57**, 1231-1237.
7. Maniatopolous, C., Sodek, J. and Melcher, A.H. *Cell Tissue Res.*, 1988, **254**, 317-330.
8. Ohgushi, H., et al. *J. Biomed. Mat. Res.*, 1996, **32**, 333-340.
9. Yoshikawa, T., et al. *Calcif. Tissue Int.*, 1992, **50**, 184-188.
10. Ohta, T., et al. *Calcif. Tissue Int.*, 1996, **59**, 283-290.
11. Ohgushi, H., Goldberg, V.M. and Caplan, A.I. *J. Orthop. Res.*, 1989, **7**, 568-578.
12. Ohgushi, H. and Okumura, M. *Acta Orthop. Scand.*, 1990, **61**, 431-434.
13. Yoshikwa, T. et al. Bio-Medical Materials and Engineering., 1997, 7, 49-58.
14. Yoshikawa T. et al. *J. Biomed. Mat. Res.*, 1996, **32**, 481-492,

Bioceramics Volume 11, edited by R. Z. LeGeros and J.P. LeGeros
(Proceedings of the 11th International Symposium on Ceramics in Medicine)
New York, NY, USA, November 1998
© 1998 by World Scientific Publishing Co. Pte. Ltd.

IN VITRO INTERACTIONS OF OSTEOCLAST-LIKE CELLS AND HYDROXYAPATITE CERAMICS

Y. Fujimori, H. Mishima*, K. Sugaya, T. Sakae*, R.Z. LeGeros**, Y. Kozawa* and H. Nagura

Department of Oral Surgery, Nihon University School of Dentistry at Matsudo
(2-870-1, Sakecho-Nishi, Matsudo, Chiba 271-8587, Japan)
*Department of Anatomy, Nihon University School of Dentistry at Matsudo
**Department of Dental Materials Science, New York University College of Dentistry

ABSTRACT

There is a lack of agreement on the resorption of HA ceramic *in vitro* and *in vivo*. The purpose of this study was to investigate the *in vitro* interactions between osteoclast-like cells and hydroxyapatite (HA) ceramics. Osteoclast-like cells from bone marrow and bones of one-day old rabbits and sections of HA ceramic were used in this study. The cells were seeded onto the HA sections in tissue culture dishes incubated at 37°C under 5% CO_2 for 72h. After this period, the HA sections were rinsed with 0.05 M sodium cacodylate buffer (pH 7.4) and fixed with 2.5% glutaraldehyde with the buffer at 4°C for 40 min. TRAPase activity was detected using the azo dye method. Specimens were prepared to scanning electron microscopy and energy dispersive spectroscopy analyses.

Numerous TRAPase-positive cells were observed on the HA sections. The osteoclast-like cells did not form any resorption lacunae on the HA sections but had many short cell projections on the cell surfaces and filopodiae around the cell bases.

The cells appeared to have caused the HA ceramic to partially disintegrate into smaller particles but active resorption was not observed.

Keywords: HA ceramic, osteoblast-like cells, resorption.

INTRODUCTION

Synthetic hydroxyapatite (HA) ceramics sintered at 1100-1200°C are used clinically as bonegraft materials and are found to be biocompatible and osteoconductive [1,2]. It has been speculated that HA ceramic is neither resorbed or affected by cells *in vivo* [3] and *in vitro* [4]. The aim of this study was to investigate the interaction between osteoclast-like cells and HA ceramics *in vitro*.

MATERIALS and METHODS

Materials. HA (Apaceram[R], PENTAX, Tokyo) in the form of porous block resembling the natural bond structure was used in this study. The block was sectioned and then polished with whetstones to a final thickness of 140-250 μm. The sections were washed and sterilized in an autoclave.

Cell isolation and culture. Osteoclast-like cells were obtained and cultured as described by Chambers and Magnus [5]. Femora, humeri and tibiae of one-day old rabbits (Japanese white, Saitama experimental animals) were dissected out, cut into small pieces including the bone marros, then placed in alpha-minimal essential medium (α-MEM, GIBCO, Grand Island, NY) containing 10% fetal calf serum (FCS, Flow Laboratories, McLean, VA), 100 μg/ml penicillin G (Sigma Chmical Co., St. Louis, MO), 100 μg/ml kanamycin, and 0.25 μg/ml amphotericin B (Flow Laboratories, McLean, VA) and supplemented with 5 μg/ml ascorbic acid (Wako, Osaka, Japan). The medium containing bone marrow cells and bone fragments was transfered to a screw-capped tube, spun at 1200 rpm for 10 min. The collected cells were added to fresh α-MEM and stirred, and this suspension of bone marrow cells flowating in the medium containing osteoclast-like cells, was used for the experiments. The cells were seeded onto the HA sections in tissue culture dishes (Nunc Inc., Naperville, IL) incubated at 37°C under 5% CO_2 for 72 hr.

Detection of tartrate-resistant acid phosphatase (TRAPase). After culture, the HA sections were rinsed with 0.05 M sodium cacodylate buffer (pH 7.4) and fixed with 2.5% glutaraldehyde with the buffer at 4°C for 40 min. TRAPase activity was detected using the azo dye method [6] and TRAP-ase positive cells were considered to be osteoclast-like cells. The axo dye solution comprised of napthol AS-MX (Sigma, St. Louis, MO) as the substrate, fast red Violet (Sigma) as the diasonium chloride and 10 mM sodium tartrate (Wako) [7,8]. The HA specimens were incubated in this solution at 37°C for 10 min.

Scanning electron microscopic (SEM) observations and analysis. Specimens were post-fixed with 2% osmium tetroxice in 0.05 M sodium cacodylate buffer (pH 7.4) for 2 hr at 4°C. Following acetone dehydration, they were critical-point dried with CO_2. Finally, the specimens were coated with gold-palladium (not carbon) and observed using SEM (S-2700, Hitachi/T-200, JEOL) at 15 kV. After the observation, the HA-like crystals in question on the osteoclast-like cells were analyzed using energy dispersive spectroscopy analysis (EDS: Kevex Delta Plus, Fisons Insturments Inc., San Carlos, CA) at 15 kV (W.D. 12 mm) by standardless calculations.

RESULTS and DISCUSSION

Apaceram[R] was examined by X-ray diffraction and EDS and was shown to be composed of highly crystalline hydroxyapatite (Fig. 1, Table 1)

Numerous TRAPase-positive cells were observed on the HA slices under bionocular microscope. TRAPase-positive cells identified as the osteoclast-like cells, were then observed under SEM. After 75 hr in the culture medium, the osteoclast-like cells were round in shape and about 40 μm in diameter. The osteoclast-like cells did not form any resorption lacunae on the HA sections but had many short cell projections on the cell surfaces and filopodiae around the cell bases. The projections and filopodiae attracted many small rounded polygonal shaped particles (Fig. 2).

EDS qualitative analysis of the particles on the osteoclast-like cells showed that the particles consisted mainly of Ca and P. SEM analysis showed that the particles containing mainly Ca and P were situated on the round surface of the osteoclast-like cells. It was evident that these particles on the cell surfaces were derived from the HA substrate. The cultured Osteoclast-like cells on HA did not form lacunae (resorption pits) such as those observed in dentin [9] or bone [10]. Instead,

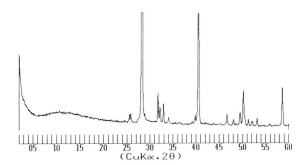

(CuKα.2θ)

Fig.1: X-ray diffraction shows that Apaceram®
consists of well crystalline hydroxyapatite.

Table 1   Composition of HA (Apaceram)

Element	Weight (%)	Atomic (%)
Ca	64.3	60.33
P	30.79	37.38
Sr	4.61	1.98
Cl	0.3	0.31
Total	100	100

Table 1: EDS shows that Apaceram® mainly
composes of Ca and P.

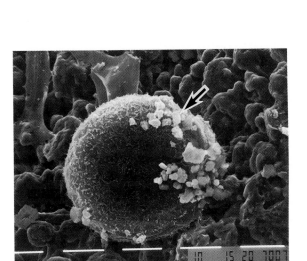

Fig. 2 : Osteoclast-like cell on HA cultured for
72 hr. The osteoclast-like cell formed no
resorption lacunae, and was picking up the
particles (arrow) of the HA substitute on the cell
surface. (bar : 10 µm)

the osteoclast-like cells appeared to have caused the HA ceramics to partially disintegrate to smaller particles. The fate of these particles were not clear in this study.

CONCLUSION

This study demonstrated that the osteoclast-like cells did not form resorption lacunae on the HA ceramic surface and did not actively resorb the HA ceramic. However, these cells appeared to cause partial disintegration of the HA particles. Studies on the nature of the reaction between tne HA particles and the osteoclast-like cells will be continued.

Acknowledgements

This work was supported by the Nihon University Research Grant no. C98-016 (T. Sakae) and the Nihon University School of Dentistry at Matsudo Research Grant (Suzuki Grant) no. 98-0002 (H. Mishima). The HA ceramic materials were generously provided by PENTAX (Asahi Kogaku).

REFERENCES
1. Tei N, Sato M, Sakata K, Yamaguchi F, Oikawa T, Izumi H. *Nihon Univ J Oral Sci* **19**: 35-41, 1993.
2. Doi Y, Moriwaki Y. *Dental J* **36**: 355-370, 1992.
3. Ogison M. *J Stomatol Soc Jpn* **50**: 1-22, 1983.
4. Takeuchi M. *J Jpn Prosthodont Soc* **36**: 1148-1161, 1992.
5. Chambers TJ, Magnus CJ. *J Pathol* **136**: 27-39, 1982.
6. Burstone MS. *J Histochem Cytochem* **6**: 322-339, 1958.
7. Minkin C. *Calcif Tissue Int* **38**: 268-274, 1982.
8. Domon T, Wakita M. *Am J Anat* **192** 35-44, 1991.
9. Boyde A, Ali HN, Jones SJ. *Brit Dent J* **156**: 216-220, 1984
10. Chambers TJ, Revell PJ, Fuller K, Athanasou NA. *J Cel Sci* **66**: 383-399, 1984.

V. TISSUE RESPONSE TO BIOCERAMICS

Bioceramics Volume 11, edited by R. Z. LeGeros and J.P. LeGeros
(Proceedings of the 11th International Symposium on Ceramics in Medicine)
New York, NY, USA, November 1998
© 1998 by World Scientific Publishing Co. Pte. Ltd.

CONDENSED CALCIUM PHOSPHATES FOR SOFT TISSUE AND BONE REPAIR / REGENERATION

M. J. Filiaggi[1], J. D. Wells[1], S. A. F. Peel[2], R. M. Pilliar[1], M. D. Grynpas[1,2], R. A. Kandel[2]

[1] Centre for Biomaterials, University of Toronto, 170 College St., Toronto, Ontario, Canada M5S 3E3; [2]Connective Tissue Research Group, Mt. Sinai Hospital, Suite 600, Toronto, Ontario, Canada M5G 1X5

ABSTRACT

Repair or regeneration of skeletal tissues, particularly bone and cartilage, remains an ongoing clinical challenge. This report describes the preliminary development and use of degradable condensed calcium phosphates (CCP) for augmenting repair and in some cases assisting in the regeneration of viable skeletal tissues. In this study, CCP glass was produced from calcined calcium phosphate monobasic monohydrate crystals $\{Ca(H_2PO_4)_2 \cdot H_2O\}$ by quenching from the melt phase. Subsequent gravity sintering of sized powders resulted in porous crystalline CCP of controlled pore size and density. CCP rods (6 mm in length x 4 mm in diameter) placed in the distal femur of New Zealand white rabbits for up to 1 year demonstrated the ability of this material to support bone ingrowth, with degradation rates of the scaffold inversely proportional to particle size used for implant fabrication. In parallel cell culture studies, porous CCP disks of similar morphology were found to support the attachment of bovine articular chondrocytes. Within two weeks the cells formed a continuous layer of cartilagenous tissue which was anchored to the CCP, suggesting the potential of this construct for joint repair.

KEYWORDS: calcium phosphate; biodegradation; tissue regeneration; bone; cartilage

INTRODUCTION

Replacing or repairing skeletal tissues after traumatic injury or disease continues to be an ongoing clinical challenge in the orthopædic and dental fields. In the case of substantial bone loss, current therapies that include the use of autograft or allograft bone have significant limitations and concerns with respect to availability, disease transmission and controlled degradation. Tissue engineering approaches aimed at repairing or regenerating lost or damaged articular cartilage also present a formidable task, particularly given that cartilage possesses a limited ability to repair. Strategies utilizing synthetic or biologically-based degradable "scaffolds", with or without additional cell therapy, to support tissue development and growth remain promising. To date, however, synthetic materials under investigation have been limited to certain degradable polymers or conventional calcium phosphates and glasses possessing inadequate mechanical properties and/or degradation characteristics. Studies[1-3] in our laboratory have indicated the potential of a condensed calcium phosphate (CCP) as a biodegradable scaffold capable of supporting and promoting the growth of viable skeletal tissues. Unique to this calcium phosphate is a Ca to P ratio of 0.5 $\{[Ca(PO_3)_2]_n\}$ resulting in a polymeric structure consisting of phosphate chains; *in vitro* evaluation suggests hydrolytic degradation of this material via chain scission.[3] In this study we describe the *in vivo* degradation characteristics of CCP in a rabbit bone defect model, as well as the use of porous CCP on which to culture chondrocytes *in vitro*.

MATERIALS AND METHODS

Fabrication and Characterization of Porous CCP Bodies

To obtain CCP glass powders, commercially available calcium phosphate monobasic monohydrate crystals, $Ca(H_2PO_4)_2 \cdot H_2O$, calcined at 500°C were melted at 1100°C in a platinum crucible, followed by quenching of the melt in deionized distilled water to produce a frit. This frit was subsequently ground and screened by conventional methods to produce CCP glass powders with the desired particle size distribution.

Porous CCP (pCCP) disks were prepared by gravity sintering the CCP powder in platinum tubes using vibration to achieve initial packing together with an appropriate sintering temperature for 2 hours under ambient conditions. Sintered rods nominally 4mm in diameter were sectioned using a diamond wafering blade to produce porous plugs or disks for the *in vivo* and cell culture studies.

X-ray diffraction (XRD) was used to confirm the structure of the glass powders and sintered rods, while neutron activation analysis (NAA) provided confirmation of the Ca to P ratio. Information on the morphology of the sintered disks was obtained via scanning electron microscopy (SEM), with image analysis (Quantimet 570, Leica) of serial sections allowing for density measurements.

In vivo Degradation Studies

pCCP plugs nominally 4 mm in diameter and 6 mm in length were implanted into 4mm x 6mm defect sites in the distal femur of New Zealand white rabbits (1 implant / rabbit). In the initial short-term study using a coarser particle size range (150-250 μm), 4 rabbits (n=4) were euthanized at 2 days (t=0), 2 weeks, 6 weeks and 12 weeks. In subsequent animal studies utilizing sintered rods derived from finer particulates (45-106 μm; 106-150 μm), the rabbits were euthanized at 6 weeks and 1 year, with 5 rabbits (n=5) per time period.

After sacrifice the rabbit femurs were dissected and x-rayed. Blocks containing the implants were fixed in formalin and dehydrated in ascending grades of alcohol and embedded undecalcified in Spurr resin. Sections (90 μm) were cut and stained with toluidine blue and H&E for histological examination, while additional sections were used for SEM backscattered image analysis. The resulting digital images of the cross-section of the implant in bone were analyzed morphometrically using the Quantimet 570 to determine the volume percent of CCP particles or bone within the porous implant.

Cell Culture Studies

Chondrocytes were isolated by sequential enzyme digestion from the deep zone of bovine articular cartilage and plated onto pCCP disks derived from powder having a 45-106 μm particle size distribution. The seeded disks were placed in Ham's F12 medium supplemented with 10% fetal bovine serum and maintained at 37°C in a humidified incubator (5%CO_2). The cultures were harvested at varying times up to 14 days. Cell attachment and proliferation were quantified by measuring DNA using Hoescht 33258 dye and fluorometry, while SEM was used to monitor the morphology of the attached cells. On day 14 the chondrocyte-CCP construct was harvested, fixed in formalin and imbedded in Spurr resin. Sections were cut and stained with toluidine blue, and the histological appearance of the construct was examined.

RESULTS

Porous CCP Properties

SEM examination of the as-sintered rods confirmed the presence of interconnected porosity, with a wide pore size distribution; extensive sinterneck formation throughout suggested good initial loadbearing capabilities. NAA confirmed a molar P/Ca = 2 for this CCP. Additionally, XRD indicated a highly crystalline structure for sintered disks derived from amorphous powder.

In vivo Degradation

No surgical complications or infections were noted throughout the course of the study and all rabbits resumed normal activity following surgery. Histological sections demonstrated bone ingrowth into the pores, the amount of which varied with the duration of the implant. Additionally, no adverse tissue reaction or fibrosis were seen in any of the histological sections examined at any time point. Table 1 summarizes the morphometric quantitation of bone ingrowth

Table 1. CCP Implant Degradation and Bone Ingrowth[*]

Implant Time	45-106 μm		106-150 μm		150-250 μm	
	%CCP	%Bone	%CCP	%Bone	%CCP	%Bone
0,2 days (t=0)	61.37±2.79	0	59.24±2.72	0	58.09±2.31	0
2 weeks	n/a	n/a	n/a	n/a	51.41±1.56	4.46±2.52
6 weeks	32.43±2.10	12.53±4.27	48.29±3.67	10.98±5.97	52.61±0.85	6.76±5.81
12 weeks	n/a	n/a	n/a	n/a	49.90±4.95	15.70±4.45
52 weeks	26.49±7.67	18.22±4.00	n/a	n/a	n/a	n/a

* Data indicate % of total implant volume based on serial cross-sections

and CCP of the thick sections for the time points available. Degradation rates of the scaffolds were found to be inversely related to the particle size used for implant fabrication, with the 45-106 μm rods demonstrating the most significant degradation at comparable time points.   Also noteworthy at 1 year was the volume occupied by bone in the implant region having reached a volume similar to that of trabecular bone at such site (~ 20%).

Cartilage / CCP Constructs

In cell culture, chondrocyte attachment was evident by 24 hours, with the cells retaining their round morphology. Cell number increased threefold by 2 weeks.   Histological examination showed that the cells had accumulated extracellular matrix, forming a continuous layer of cartilagenous tissue with a thickness of 400±10 μm on the pCCP surface.

DISCUSSION AND CONCLUSIONS

Porous condensed calcium phosphate ($[Ca(PO_3)_2]_n$) structures were found to support the ingrowth of new bone into a defect site in the rabbit femur.   Generally, *in* vivo degradation rates were dependent on the starting particle size, with higher rates observed for the finer particle size distribution. The corresponding increase in CCP surface area as well as the increase in the number of sinternecks, or bonding zones between particles, suggest the importance of sinterneck and surface regions in general on degradation rates.   Overall, implants derived from 45-106 μm particles proved most appropriate with respect to enhanced degradation and %bone fill. Longer term animal studies beyond 1 year would be required to determine if complete resorption will occur.

Cell culture studies also indicated that chondrocytes can attach to porous CCP, retain their phenotype, and form cartilagenous tissue within two weeks.   Future studies will investigate whether these CCP-cartilage constructs can be used in joint resurfacing applications where full-thickness defects are present.

ACKNOWLEDGEMENTS

This study was supported by the Natural Sciences and Engineering Research Council (NSERC) of Canada, and by Innova Technologies Corporation (Toronto, ON).

REFERENCES

1. Wells JD, Grynpas MD, Pilliar RM. *Trans 5th World Biomat Congress* 1996; 321.
2. Guo W, Kim S, Grynpas MD, Pilliar RM. *Trans 20th Meet Soc for Biomat* 1994; 286.
3. Wells JD. *The Processing and In Vitro Degradation Properties of Gravity Sintered Calcium Polyphosphate Powders.* M.A.Sc. Thesis, University of Toronto, Canada, 1997.

Bioceramics Volume 11, edited by R. Z. LeGeros and J.P. LeGeros
(Proceedings of the 11th International Symposium on Ceramics in Medicine)
New York, NY, USA, November 1998

BIOACTIVITY AND BIODEGRADABILITY:
MELT VS. SOL-GEL DERIVED BIOGLASS® *IN VITRO* AND *IN VIVO*

Greenspan DC[1], Zhong JP[1], and Wheeler DL[2]

1. USBiomaterials Corporation, One Progress Blvd. #23 Alachua, FL 32615, USA
2. University of Florida, Department of Orthopaedics, Gainesville, FL 32511, USA

ABSTRACT

The formation of HCA in melt-derived 45S5 Bioglass® and the release of soluble silica to surrounding tissue have been cited as key factors in its rapid bonding to bone and the stimulation of bone tissue growth. The newly developed sol-gel Bioglass® also acts like the melt-derived Bioglass® but with a different rate of silica release and HCA formation as reported previously. In this work, the bone formation and degradability of sol-gel derived 58S Bioglass®, and the melt-derived 45S5 Bioglass® have been evaluated *in vivo* using a transcortical rabbit model, and the *in vivo* data have been compared with *in vitro* bioactivity tests. The 58S glass showed a faster rate of silica degradation and HCA formation *in vitro* compared with 45S5 Bioglass®. Although a clear difference in bone formation can not be determined by histological micrographs, the *in vivo* data from the analysis of the implanted particles from 4 weeks to 12 weeks showed the faster silica degradation rate in 58S compared to 45S5. These data should help to understand the details of the correlation between the rate of soluble silica release, HCA formation and the stimulation of bone growth *in vivo*.

KEYWORDS: Bioglass®, Sol-gel, Degradability, Soluble silica, HCA.

INTRODUCTION

45S5 melt-derived Bioglass® has been used as a human implant material with clinical success for over 10 years[1]. Its biocompatability has been attributed to its rapid surface reactivity including the formation of a porous silica gel layer with high surface area, hydroxy-carbonate apatite (HCA) layer and release of soluble Si[2,3]. In an attempt to achieve higher reactivity, sol-gel bioactive glasses have been developed[4]. These gel glasses can be processed at lower temperatures than melt derived Bioglass®, and have the ability to control their pore structures which change the bioactivity and biodegradability. Previously, 45S5 dense Bioglass® has been compared with sol-gel porous Bioglass® *in vitro* [5], and the sol-gel Bioglass® showed a greater bioactivity and degradability than 45S5 Bioglass®. The sol-gel Bioglass® could function as a synthetic bone graft material which would completely resorb within a desired period of time and be replaced by natural tissue while maintaining its bioactive behavior, the ability to stimulate bone growth.

An *in vivo* test has been done using 58S and 45S5 Bioglass® to examine and compare their degradability *in vivo* and to verify the *in vitro* results of these two materials.

MATERIALS AND METHODS

45S5 melt derived Bioglass® with particle size range 710-90μm was used in this test. The 58S sol-gel derived glass was prepared by acid hydrolysis of tetraethoxysilane, $Si(OC_2H_5)$, with additions of triethylphosphate, $OP(OC_2H_5)_3$, and calcium nitrate as previously described[6]. The 58S was heat treated to 700°C in ambient air with a resulting average pore radius of 43Å and surface area 207m²/g. The material was then ground to the particle size range of 710-300μm.

Animal testing was conducted in rabbits which had bilateral surgical removal of a 6 mm cylindrical core of cancellous bone from the distal femoral metaphyses. Details of this model have been published elsewhere[7]. The defects were filled with 45S5, and 58S graft materials with unfilled defects as controls. The animals were sacrificed at 4, 8 or 12 weeks and the distal femurs were harvested and the condyles bisected and prepared to slides for SEM and histological examination. The SEM analyses were conducted on the 4 and 12 week implants using EDXA for the concentration of Si, Ca, P and Na of the particle cross section and to examine the resorption of the materials *in-vivo*.

RESULTS AND DISCUSSION

Fig. 1 shows typical histological micrographs of the 45S5 Bioglass and 58S sol-gel bioactive glass, 12 weeks post operatively. The stimulation of rapid bone growth is seen with both compositions, and significant resorption of the 58S particles can be seen, as indicated by the arrow, whereas there is less resorption of the 45S5 particles.

The EDXA analysis of the histologic samples at both 4 and 12 weeks is presented in Fig.2, along with EDXA of unimplanted controls (Fig.2a,b). It is very clear from the analysis of the 58S

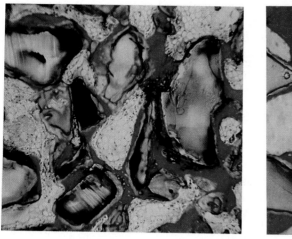
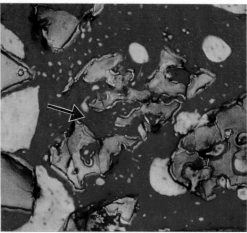

(a)   (b)

Fig. 1. Histological micrographs of 45S5 (a) and 58S (b) Bioglass® implanted in Rabbit
for 12 weeks (arrow indicates resorbing particles)

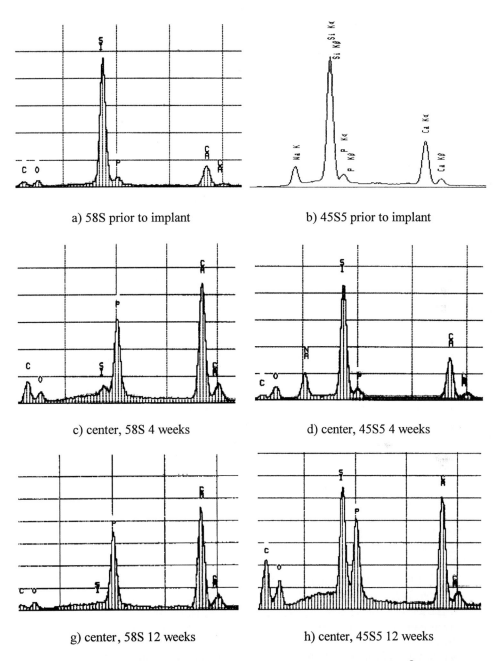

a) 58S prior to implant

b) 45S5 prior to implant

c) center, 58S 4 weeks

d) center, 45S5 4 weeks

g) center, 58S 12 weeks

h) center, 45S5 12 weeks

Fig. 2 EDXA of Si, Ca, P and Na on implanted 58S and 45S5 Bioglass® particles

sol-gel material that by 4 weeks *in-vivo,* significant silica has been leached from the particles, and that by 12 weeks, nearly all of the silica has been depleted, resulting in essentially a calcium phosphate residue. The 45S5 Bioglass® shows slight spectral changes at 4 weeks, and much more pronounced changes at 12 weeks, including the loss of sodium, and a much more significant calcium-phosphate layer.

Work previously reported on the *in-vitro* reactivity of sol-gel bioactive glass compared to 45S5 Bioglass® demonstrated that by seven days in a simulated body fluid (SBF), virtually all of the silica had been leached from the particles, resulting in a calcium phosphate construct[5]. This leachability was shown to be dependent on the rate of replenishment of the solution. The 45S5 composition showed that silica continued to leach from the glass surface up to 28 days, and that the total amount of silica released was less than that from the 58S composition. This study also demonstrated an HCA layer formation in only one hour on the 58S glass, compared to six hours for the 45S5 composition. A recent implantation study by Al Bazie, et al.[8], in a rabbit femoral model, showed more stimulation of bone formation by the 58S composition than for the 45S5 composition at 4 weeks.

The *in-vitro* studies on 58S and 45S5 Bioglass® reported previously[5,9] have shown that different classes of bioactive glasses are sensitive to the particular test conditions in which they are placed. One problem facing researchers has always been the lack of consistent correlation of the *in-vivo* results with *in-vitro* 'bioactivity' studies. The data presented here show that the rate of degradation of the 58S sol-gel glass *in-vitro* and the rate of HCA layer formation previously reported, correlates to the rate of bone formation and degradation of the particles *in-vivo*. The high rate of soluble silica released from the 58S sol-gel glass shown *in-vitro*, and *in-vivo* as seen in Fig. 2, seems to support the theory proposed by Hench that the soluble silica in bioactive glasses plays a vital role in the stimulation of rapid bone formation by both intra, and extra cellular processes[10].

CONCLUSIONS

The previous *in vitro* results demonstrated that sol-gel 58S formed an HCA layer and degraded soluble Si more rapidly than 45S5 Bioglass®. More biodegradability has been observed for the sol-gel 58S than 45S5 Bioglass® *in vivo*. Si was released from 58S completely before 12 weeks while a significant amount of Si was still detected on 45S5 implanted particles in 12 weeks which agrees with the previous *in vitro* results. The reported early bone formation and the greater biodegradability would certainly make sol-gel Bioglass® suitable for a bone graft material.

REFERENCE
1. Wilson, J., et al., "Bioglass® Middle Ear Devices - Ten Year Clinical Results," Bioceramics 8, Elsevier Science Ltd., 239-45, 1995
2. Hench, L.L, J. Am. Ceram. Soc., 74, 1487, 1991
3. Hench, L.L, Bioceramics 9, Elsevier Science Ltd., 3-6, 1996
4. Li, R., et al., J. Appl. Biomater., 1991, 2, 231-39
5. Greenspan, D.C. et al., Bioceramics 10, Elsevier Science Ltd., 391-94, 1997
6. Zhong, J.P., and Greenspan, D.C., Bioceramics 10, Elsevier Science Ltd., 265-68, 1997
7. Wheeler, D.L., et al., Bioceramics 10, Elsevier Science Ltd., 349-52, 1997
8. Al-Bazie, S., Chou, L. et al., J. Dent. Res. 77:839, 1664, 1997
9. Greenspan, D.C., et al., Transactions of 24th Annual Meeting, Soc. for Biomaterials, 437, 1998
10. Hench, L.L, Bioceramics 7, Butterworth-Heinemann, 3-8, 1994

Bioceramics Volume 11, edited by R. Z. LeGeros and J.P. LeGeros
(Proceedings of the 11th International Symposium on Ceramics in Medicine)
New York, NY, USA, November 1998
© 1998 by World Scientific Publishing Co. Pte. Ltd.

NEW PUTTY COMPOSITE MATERIALS FOR BONE DEFECTS IN DENTISTRY

A. .M. Gatti[1], L. L. Hench[2], E. Monari[1], J. Thompson[2], D. Tanza[1]

[1]Centro di Studio dei Biomateriali, Dip. Chirurgia, Univ. di Modena, Via del Pozzo 71, 41100, Modena, Italy; [2]Imperial College of Science, Techn. and Medicine, Dpt. of Materials, London, U.K.

ABSTRACT

Two types of composite materials for bone repair were produced at Imperial College of London, one of Bioglass® dextran resorbable matrix and the second of Bioglass® and a non resorbable polysulphone polymer matrix. Three samples of the first and a fourth sample of the second were sterilized and implanted in drilled holes in a sheep's mandible and also in tibial defects. After 3 months the materials with the surrounding tissues were explanted, fixed and radiographed in order to have the macroscopic relationship between the material and bone. Sections were prepared for scanning electron microscopic observations and X-ray microanalyses to detect any resorption of the materials and the interface developed with bone.

Results show good biocompatibility for all four materials. The polysulphone/glass showed a small surface degradation. The bioactive glass-dextran composite showed maximum resorption and at times it was difficult to recognize the site of implantation. The dextran-glass composite was very promising in mandibular bone augmentation or repair of bone defects. The polysulphone- bioactive glass composite may be more useful for long term implants.

KEYWORDS: Active glasses, bioactivity, dental materials.

INTRODUCTION

Bioglass® particulate has been used in numerous bony defect sites[1,2] and some soft tissue applications[3]. However, the hard tissue sites have been limited as Bioglass® alone in not sufficiently cohesive to augment convex or large concave bone defects. To improve the handling characteristics high molecular weight dextran has been added. This addition results in a more mouldable "putty" like material.

MATERIALS AND METHODS

The Bioglass® is one of the first active glasses used in Medicine and its bioactivity has been already well demonstrated[4,5].

The materials used for this research are composites employing Bioglass® and they are:
1. Sample A: 13.8 g of Bioglass® granules (710-90micron size), mixed with low molecular weight dextran and sterile water.
2. Sample C: 16.7 g of Bioglass® granules (710-90micron size), mixed with low molecular weight dextran and sterile water.
3. Sample D: 16.7 g of Bioglass® granules (710-90micron size), mixed with high molecular weight dextran and sterile water.
4. Sample E: 6mm diameter rods of polysulphone and Bioglass® granules.

These materials were sterilized separately by ethylene oxide. In the operating room the first 3 materials were prepared and implanted in 8 mm size holes surgically drilled with a microengine in mandibular bone and tibia of a sheep. After 90 days the sheep was sacrificed and the materials with the surrounding tissue were explanted, fixed in paraformaldheyde and radiographed. After drying in ascending concentration of alcoholic solutions, the samples were embedded in methylmetahcrylate and sectioned with a diamond saw (Accutom, Struers, Denmark). 200 micron thick sections were prepared for the histologic and scanning electron microscopic observations (SEM XL40 Philips, The Nederlands).

Microanalyses for detecting the inorganic elements present in the materials and their topographic distribution were carried out by means of an Energy Dispersive System (EDS by EDAX).

RESULTS

The results in mandibular bone were better than those in tibia, but in both sites the composite materials showed similar bioactivity. The samples A, C and D after implantation in the mandible filled the 8mm size defects completely after 3 months. Sometimes it was very difficult to find the sites of implantation, since the granules reabsorbed almost completely and the bony reconstruction of the hole was total. The unfilled control site was partially filled with new bone. Sometimes the site of implantation was recognized by the difference in electron density in back scattered mode between the new and the old bone. The old one is more calcified, so whiter, the new one, darker.

In Fig. 1a and b some granules of sample D are surrounded by new bone. Few granules are still present and it can be noted that their size is reduced by reabsorption; some of them have the core void. These fragments are chemically completely changed, now they are composed of a calcium and phosphorus only, as detected by EDS analyses.

Fig. 2a and b show the complete reconstruction of the hole and few granules of sample C still present outside. Now they are composed of calcium and phosphorus only. In Fig. 3a and b the granules of sample A are completely degraded and bone grew inside the granules (Fig. 3b). The same degradation occurred in samples A, C, D.

Only specimen E (polysulphone) remained unchanged (Fig. 4a, b). In this case there is some bone growth that surrounded the sample, but the glass granules are not degraded, since the polysulphone has a slower degradation, but overall it is not bioactive.

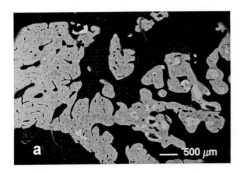
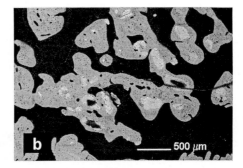

Fig 1a, b - Microphotographs, at different magnifications, of new mandibular bone with some granules of sample D. Note some void granules (b).

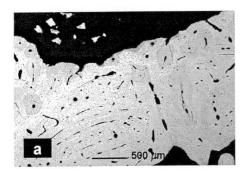
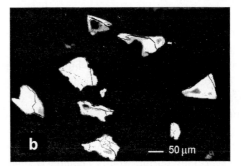

Fig. 2a, b - Microphotographs of new mandibular bone with granules of sample C.

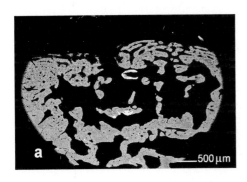
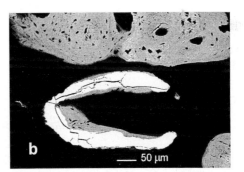

Fig. 3a, b - Microphotographs of new mandibular bone with sample A. Note the bone growth inside a granule (b).

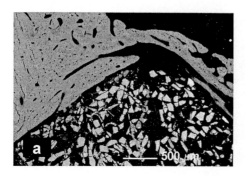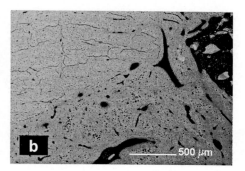

Fig. 4a, b - Microphotographs of sample E, at different magnifications, surrounded of new bone.

CONCLUSIONS

The composite material dextran/Bioglass® showed very interesting results <u>in vivo</u>, more than those obtained with the Bioglass® granules alone[4,5]. The first test showed that there is no difference in bioactivity between low or high molecular weight dextran. Perhaps a difference, if there is, can be noted at the first time of implantation, infact the degradation of the low molecular weight dextran is faster than that of high molecular one. Also the quantity of water added during the preparation does not influence the bioactivity, but only the viscosity of the material and the handability of the material by the surgeon.

The putty system is very effective, because the granules can be "glued" together and will not be displaced, especially during wound healing. Displacement is a problem for the surgeon, who sometimes covers the filled cavity with membranes. This system will probably be useful for bone augmentation in the maxilla, since the material maintains the shape given by the surgeon.

The composite with polysulphone may be more useful for solid implants designed to function long-term and it can be used in Dentistry and Orthopaedics.

AKNOWLEDGEMENTS

This work was supported by National Research Council (CNR) of Italy. The Authors are indebtful with Ms. S. Piaggi and R. Salvatori for their technical assistance.

REFERENCES

1. Hench LL. In: Mitchell J, ed. *Bone Grafts and Bone Substitutes*, W.B. Saunders Company, 1992: 263-275.
2. Wilson J, Lowry G and Courtney S. In: Sedel L, Rey C, eds. *Bioceramics Vol. 10*, New York: Elsvier Science Ltd, 1997: 65-68.
3. Wilson J, Clark AE, Walker RD & Ramer M. In: Bonfield W, Hastings GW & Tanner KE, eds. *Bioceramics Vol 4*. New York: Elsevier Science Ltd ,1991.
4. Gatti AM, Hench LL, Monari E, Gonella F, Caccavale F.In: Sedel L., Rey C, eds. *Bioceramics Vol.10*, New York: Elsevier Science Ltd., 1997: 287-290.
5. Gatti AM, Hench LL, Monari E, Chiarini L, Bulgarelli S, Tanza D. In: Wilson J, Hench LL, Greenspan D, eds. *Bioceramics Vol. 8*, New York: Elsevier Science Ltd, 1995: 41-46.

Bioceramics Volume 11, edited by R. Z. LeGeros and J.P. LeGeros
(Proceedings of the 11th International Symposium on Ceramics in Medicine)
New York, NY, USA, November 1998
© 1998 by World Scientific Publishing Co. Pte. Ltd.

DEGRADATION OF HYDROXYLAPATITE, FLUORAPATITE AND FLUORHYDROXYAPATITE - COATING OF DENTAL IMPLANTS IN DOGS

P. Frayssinet[□][○], L. Gineste*, M. Gineste*, A. Ellefterion**, A. Guilhem[□], N. Rouquet[□],

- * Parodontology Dpt, Dental School, Chemin des Maraïchers, 31400 Toulouse, France
- ** Mathematical Dpt, Université Paul Sabatier, 133 Rte de Narbonne, 31400 Toulouse, France
- [□] Bioland 132 Rte d'Espagne 31100 Toulouse, France
- [○] Laboratoire du Tissu Osseux et des Pathologies Ostéo-articulaires, Université Paul Sabatier, Toulouse, France

ABSTRACT:

We investigated the degradation rate of dental implants with 50 and 100 μm coatings of hydroxylapatite (HA), fluorapatite (FA) or fluorhydroxyapatite (FHA). The implants were inserted in dog jaws and retrieved for histological analysis after three, six and twelve months. They were embedded in PMMA, and sections were performed using a low speed diamond saw and were ground until a thickness of 30 μm. The thickness of the calcium phosphate coatings was evaluated using an image analysis device. A relative resorption index and its standard deviation were studied.

HA and FA coatings, even 100 μm thick, were almost totally degraded within the implantation period. In contrast, the FHA coatings did not show significant degradation during the same period. The standard deviation showed that the resorption process for FHAP with thicknesses of 50 or 100 μm was the same. Such a difference was not observed between 50 and 100 μm thick coatings of FA and HA.

In conclusion, the FHA coatings showed good integration in the bone tissue and lasted much longer than classic calcium phosphate coatings.

KEYWORDS: calcium phosphate coatings, fluorapatite, fluorhydroxyapatite, hydroxylapatite, degradation

INTRODUCTION:

Several reports have demonstrated that calcium phosphate coatings are degraded both by dissolution in extracellular fluids and by cell degradation within cell compartments of low pH. Degradation does not have any clinical consequences in hip arthroplasty. However, concerns have been raised as a result of emission of calcium debris during resorption as to the effect of coating disappearance on fixation of the material in bone. Fluorated apatites are known to be less soluble than HA (1, 2). Several authors have reported histological studies of fluorapatite (FA) coated implants inserted within long bones of goats (3). Bone apposition at the material surface was apparently identical to that at the surface of HA-coatings while resorption was lower.

This is why we carried out this study to test the stability in a biological environment of different calcium phosphate coatings - hydroxylapatite (HA) : $Ca_{10}(PO_4)_6(OH)_2$, fluorapatite (FA) : $Ca_{10}(PO_4)_6F_2$ and fluorhydroxyapatite (FHA) : $Ca_{10}(PO_4)_6(F, OH)_2$ - on dental implants which were not put in charge and implanted in dog jaw. The degradation of the coatings was evaluated and compared on histological sections.

MATERIALS AND METHODS:

Dental implants

The dental implants used in this study were manufactured with Ti-6AI-4V alloy and were of 3.5 mm diameter and 10 mm length. They were coated either by 50 μm or 100 μm thick coatings of HA, FA and FHA. The coating characteristics were given table 1, 2 and 3.

Table 1: coating characteristics determined by X-ray diffraction.

	Crystallinity	Amorphous	Ca/P	TCP	CaO
FA	87%	<5%	1.728	0%	0.5%
FHA	89%	<5%	1.672	1.4%	0.3%
HA	66%	<25%	1.762	3.1%	1.7%

Table 2: coating fluoride analysis:

	Fluoride concentration (mg) /100 mg of coating
FA	$4.03.\ 10^{-2}$
FHA	$1.45.10^{-2}$

Table 3: coating roughness

	Ra (μm)	Rt (μm)
FA	12.8	82
FHA	11.1	74
HA	12,2	55

Implantation protocol

This study was carried out on 6 male 18 month old Beagle dogs. The right half jaw received a 100 μm thick coated implant of each group. The left side was implanted with 50 μm thick coated material. Grit blasted titanium alloy implants were used as controls. 36 coated implants were made i.e. 6 implants per dog in 6 dogs.

The animals were sacrificed after an implantation period of : 3 months (D 90) for 2 dogs, 6 months (D 180) for 2 dogs and 1 year (D 360) for 2 dogs. Then undecalcified histological sections were performed.

Histomorphometry

The coating thickness measurements before and after implantation were obtained at X 200 magnification. The measures were taken 20μm apart from 2 sections of the same 5 mm long zone for each implant. All the implants were measured.

Statistical analysis

-An intra-group study was performed (Anova) in order to compare the mean coating thickness modifications at dates D_0, D_{90}, D_{180} and D_{360}.

- An inter-group study (anova) dealing with comparisons of intra-groups studies was carried out.
- The main variables measured in this study were:
   - - mean coating thickness and standard deviation ($\chi \pm \sigma$).
   - - relative resorption index of the mean coating thickness (R) defined at 2 different dates for each kind of material. For example R (D_0, D_{90}) gave the coating thickness variation from D_0 to D_{90} as follows : $R[D_0, D_{90}] = [\chi D_{90} - \chi D_0 / \chi D_0]$ %. This index indicated the evolution of the average thickness of coated implants.
   - - A variation index of the standard deviation (Δs) between dates D_0 and D_{90} was calculated as follows : $\Delta s[D_0, D_{90}] = [sD_{90} - sD_0 / sD_0]$ % This index indicated the evolution of surface roughness during this period : if Δs was almost equal to zero, this meant that the resorption could be characterized as homogenous. When Δs was positive, it indicated that $sD_{90} > sD_0$ and that roughness had increased during the measurement period. In this case, resorption occurred mostly in the hollow of the roughness. In contrast, when Δs was negative, indicating that $sD_0 < sD_{90}$, the roughness decreased due to resorption of the crest.
   - An « equal activity » zone has been defined at ±20% of the R and Δs value at D_0 due to the irregularity of the coating thickness. Within this zone, the variations were not considered as significant.

Results:

Intra-group study:

☞Fluorohydroxyapatite (FHA):

It was noted that FHA thickness varied from D_0 to D_{360} by less than 20%. This variation was not considered significant as it was within the range of coating roughness variation (fig. 1).

☞Fluoroapatite (FA):

R and Δs were over 20% at D_{360} and increased with time. The same evolution was found for Δs indicating a roughness increase at D_{360} for both coatings (Fig. 2).

☞Hydroxyapatite (HA).

R and Δs increased with time and were over 50% from D_{180} onwards (Fig. 3).

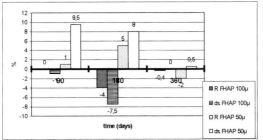 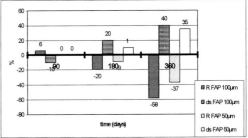

Fig 1 and 2: relative resorption index (R) and variation index of the standard deviation (ds) of FHA and FA coatings

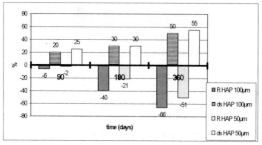

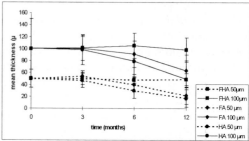

Fig. 3: relative resorption index (R) and variation index of the standard deviation (ds) of HA-coatings

Fig. 4: evolution of the coating mean thickness during the implantation time

Inter-group study:

As the FHA coatings did not show a significant thickness variation, the study was limited to a comparison of the results obtained with HA and FA.

☛The mean thickness variation between D_0 and D_{360} was (Fig. 4):

-significantly higher for 100 µm thick than 50µm thick coatings for both HA and FA.

-significantly faster for HA than FA.

☛Δs variation between D_0 and D_{360} was:

-identical for 50µm thick and 100µm coatings.

-significantly higher, for HA than for FA as early as D_{180}

Conclusions :

FHA- coatings are good candidates for low degradation rate coatings as they keep a non significantly decreased thickness throughout a one year implantation period. The reasons for higher durability of FHA coatings are multiple: high crystallinity of the continuous phase; low amount of CaF_2 contamination; higher stability of FHA in a biological environment. The better stability of fluorinated powder during the plasma-spraying can also be considered as a factor of longevity for these coatings. In so far as the adhesion of these coatings to metal was as least as good as that of HA-coatings they could be a part of the answer to the concerns raised by calcium phosphate degradation.

References:

1/ Montel G, *Ann Chim* 1969, **4**: 255-266.

2/ LeGeros, RZ. In: Brown PW, Constantz B, ed. *Hydroxyapatite and Related Materials*, Bocca Raton: CRC Press, 1994: 3-28.

3/ Dhert WJA, Klein CPAT, Wolke JGC, Van Der Velde EA, De Groot V, Rozing PM. *J Biomed Mater Res* 1991, **25**: 1183-1190

Bioceramics Volume 11, edited by R. Z. LeGeros and J.P. LeGeros
(Proceedings of the 11th International Symposium on Ceramics in Medicine)
New York, NY, USA, November 1998

α-BSM™: A RESORBABLE APATITIC CALCIUM PHOSPHATE BONE SUBSTITUTE

David Knaack[1], Maria Aiolova[1], Ali Tofighi[1], Anthony Catalano[1], Christian Rey[2], Berthold Nies[3], D. Duke Lee[1]

[1]ETEX Corporation, University Park at MIT, 350 Mass Avenue, Cambridge MA 02139, USA; [2]Institut National Polytechnique de Toulouse, France; [3]Merck Biomaterial Gmb.H., Darmstadt, Germany.

ABSTRACT

α-BSM™ is an endothermically setting apatitic calcium phosphate bone substitute material. Its injectability and ability to harden at body temperature in the presence of physiological saline, as well as other buffering agents, makes it an attractive clinical bone substitute and delivery vehicle for therapeutic agents. α-BSM™ remodeled into bone and promoted bone healing in two critical size defect animal models. In the rabbit radius model, α-BSM™ promoted defect healing by four weeks. Sheep tibial full segmental defects, repaired with internal fixation and α-BSM™, were restored to near normal torsional strength within 12 weeks. Biologically active agents (*e.g.*, enzymes, growth factors, antibiotics) have been shown to be compatible with the α-BSM™ setting reaction. RhBMP-2 with α-BSM™ was demonstrated to be effective in stimulating ectopic bone, *in vivo*.

KEYWORDS: Apatitic calcium phosphate, bone remodeling, bone substitute, critical size defect, therapeutic agent delivery vehicle

EXPERIMENTAL RESULTS AND PRECLINICAL STUDY OBSERVATIONS

α-BSM™ Properties and Applications

α-BSM™ is provided as a single powder that is hydrated with physiological saline to form a workable paste, which remains formable at room temperature for hours and is easily injectable through a 16-gauge needle. Upon implantation, α-BSM™ hardens at body temperature. Chemically, hardened α-BSM™ is virtually identical to the mineral component of normal bone (Figure 1).

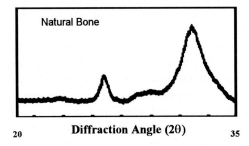
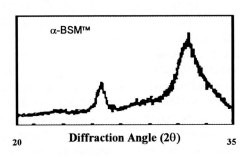

Figure 1. Comparison of X-Ray Diffraction Spectra: Natural Bone Mineral versus α-BSM™

Hardening characteristics of the α-BSM™ paste at different temperatures are shown in Figure 2. α-BSM™ can be formulated with compressive strengths ranging from less than 5 MPa to greater than 40 MPa, as shown in Figure 3. One such formulation exhibited a compressive strength of 12.36 ±0.41 MPa (n=30), and flexural 3-point bending strength of 5.58 ±0.48 MPa (n=25). The density was determined to be 2.59 g/cm^3 by mercury picnometry. The porosity was 60% with an average pore size of approximately 80Å via mercury porosimetry.

Hardened α-BSM™ displays limited solubility at 37°C, with an estimated solubility constant of 5.7 x 10^{-54} (±0.8 x 10^{-54}). Solubilities were confirmed by *in vitro* mass loss studies, at both neutral and acidic pH; after 30 days, approximately 90% of the α-BSM™ remained undissolved; and was recovered as a single solid mass.

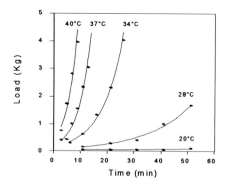

Figure 2. α-BSM™ paste hardening kinetics

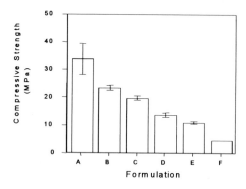

Figure 3. α-BSM™ compressive strengths

α-BSM™ is Remodeled into Bone

New bone formation and α-BSM™ resorption were studied in a canine femoral slot model. Autograft recipients were used as positive controls. Defect filling with woven bone occurred by the third week for both treatment groups. By 12 weeks, bone within the original defect region was largely lamellar and it was difficult to identify the defect site boundaries; the medullary canal apparently underwent remodeling with restoration of normal looking marrow tissue. Figure 4 compares α-BSM™ implanted femur cross sections at 3 and 12 weeks.

Microscopic examination of the femoral defects indicated that sites implanted with either autologous bone or α-BSM™ had similar histological appearances. α-BSM™-associated bone formation appeared to occur intramembranously in the absence of typical fracture-healing callus. Residual α-BSM™ could be reliably detected only in specimens from animals sacrificed at three and four weeks. Small amounts of residual α-BSM™ could also sometimes be detected in samples from later time points. In all samples, residual α-BSM™ frequently was found to contain islands of cells, both internal to the residual material and along its periphery. These cellular islands often appeared as classic cutting cones with an abundance of presumptive osteoclast, osteoblast and vascular elements. Residual α-BSM™ also was frequently observed to be penetrated with new bone and occasional Haversian systems. These observations, coupled with the relative insolubility of α-BSM™, suggest α-BSM™ is recognized and remodeled by normal cellular bone remodeling mechanisms.

Healing and resorptive processes were quantified by undecalcified, von Kossa stained section histomorphometric analysis. Figure 5 compares the time course resorption of α-BSM™ to the formation of new bone in animals receiving α-BSM™ or autologous implants. The initial time zero value for residual α-BSM™ was assumed to be 100% and was not measured.

This histomorphometric analysis confirms that the bone healing time course in the presence of autograft was similar to healing in the presence of α-BSM™, and indicates that autograft healing may occur slightly in advance of healing with α-BSM™. Further, this analysis also showed that at four weeks, 1.7% ±0.83% (n=8) of the implanted α-BSM™ was still present, while only 0.36% ±0.36% (n=4) remained at 26 weeks.

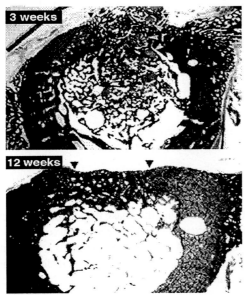

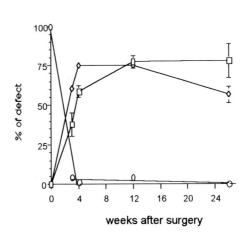

Figure 4. Defect healing and α-BSM™ remodeling in canine femur defect. (Undecalcified, von Kossa stained cross sections)

Figure 5. Femoral slot defect healing and α-BSM™ remodeling time course: α-BSM™ [□], autograft [◊], residual α-BSM™ [o]. (Error Bars represent the Standard Error of the Mean)

Critical Size Defects Studies

The performance of α-BSM™ in mediating bone healing in critical size defects (CSDs) has been studied in both small and large animal models. Because these models do not readily undergo spontaneous healing, they represent a stringent test to assess the bone promoting capability of a graft material.

The rabbit radius CSD has been used in a number of studies to investigate the osteopromotive effects of a variety of carrier systems, with and without rhBMP-2.[2,4,6] The defect is prepared surgically by complete removal of roughly a 2-cm length of the radius. Schmitt, *et. al.* (*in preparation*) have studied the osteopromotive effect of α-BSM™ in this model. Figure 6 compares the amount of new bone formed after four and eight weeks in CSDs treated with α-BSM™ to new bone formation using other implant materials.[6] These data show that α-BSM™ alone, without exogenous growth factor, has a similar osteopromotive capacity when compared to previously studied growth factor-carrier combinations.

Wippermann, *et. al.*[5] have obtained similar results with a large animal CSD model. In this study, a 3-cm defect was surgically prepared in sheep tibias. Figure 7 compares α-BSM™ torsional strength results to those of the autograft control. At 12 weeks, tibia treated with α-BSM™ had significantly greater restoration of torsional strength than autograft controls. While an average value of 60% of the contralateral strength was obtained, at least one animal treated with α-BSM™ had recovery of full torsional strength at 12 weeks; no animal receiving autograft recovered full torsional strength over the same time period.

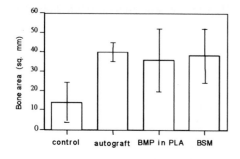

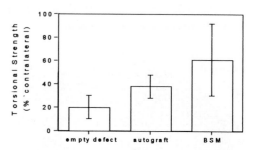

Figure 6. Rabbit radius CSD model: 8-week bone formation comparison [6]

Figure 7. Sheep tibia critical size defect model: torsional strength comparison

Delivery of Therapeutic Molecules

The α-BSM™ setting reaction has a number of favorable characteristics that make it an attractive vehicle for therapeutic agent delivery. Specifically, α-BSM™ setting occurs under relatively benign conditions at neutral pH and body temperature, and is compatible with a range of aqueous hydrating agents, including physiologically useful buffers and blood or serum. Recent investigations using antibiotics, rhBMP-2, and the enzyme alkaline phosphatase show that the α-BSM™ hardening process does not affect the biological activity of these therapeutic agents.

α-BSM™ has been prepared with up to 350 mg/mL of gentamicin in hydration media. Neither the hardening kinetics nor compressive strength was significantly affected by the addition of this amount of gentamicin. Greater than 85% of the gentamicin was released by free diffusion from hardened α-BSM™ within 24 hours.

We have confirmed the use of α-BSM™ as an effective protein delivery vehicle *in vivo* by determining the ability of rhBMP-2 loaded α-BSM™ to induce ectopic bone formation at a soft tissue site in the rat.[1] Hardened α-BSM™ disks were prepared containing either 0.02 mg/mL or 0.2 mg/mL rhBMP-2 and implanted into the rat dorsal subcutis. Results are given in Figure 8. Ectopic bone was found at the implant site at both 14 and 28 days for only the highest dose of BMP used. The amount of bone present at 28 days was approximately three-fold greater than that observed at 14 days.

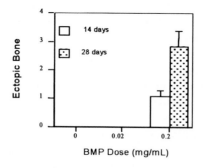

Figure 8. Ectopic bone formation using rhBMP-2 delivery with α-BSM™

Discussion

α-BSM™ paste hardens in less than 20 minutes at body temperature to form an apatitic calcium phosphate with a nano-crystalline structure. Following implantation into a bony site, α-BSM™ remodels to form new bone. The establishment of new bone is accompanied by disappearance of excess α-BSM™ from the defect region, as well as from the medullary canal. The remodeling of α-BSM™ to natural bone presumably promotes the restoration of normal biomechanical properties, appropriate to the implant site, and minimizes the risk of potential refracture around the regions of unresorbed material.

The endothermic nature of the α-BSM™ setting process allows extended ease of use and favorable injectability characteristics in surgical settings. The mild setting characteristics and controlled resorption rate of α-BSM™ is conducive to the excellent stability of therapeutic molecules incorporated into α-BSM™; the biological activity of enzymes and growth factors is retained over the course of the setting reaction.

The favorable physical, chemical, and biological characteristics of α-BSM™ are applicable to its use as both a bone substitute material and a delivery vehicle for therapeutic agents. Studies have shown bone healing within normal healing periods, with restoration of biomechanical properties. Further, studies with antibiotic and growth factors have demonstrated the potential effectiveness of α-BSM™ as a therapeutic delivery system.

ACKNOWLEDGEMENTS

We would like to thank our collaborators in parts of this work: Jeffery O. Hollinger, Oregon Health Sciences University and John Wozney, Genetics Institute. Special thanks are given to Anthony M. Majahad, ETEX Corporation, for his assistance in preparing this manuscript.

REFERENCES

1. ETEX Corporation and Genetics Institute, *unpublished results,*1998
2. Goad MEP, Aiolova M, Tofighi A, Jacobs M, Lee DD. *J Bone Joint Surg (Am)* 1997; **12-1**: s518
3. Knaack D. *NMHCC* 1997; (Boston, MA,)
4. Schmitt JM, Buck DC, Joh SP, Lynch SE, Hollinger JO. *J. Periodontol.* 1997; **68(11)**
5. Wippermann B. *Proceedings of the German Traumatology Union* 1997 (Berlin, Germany)
6. Zegzula HD, Buck DC, Brekke J, Wozney JM, Hollinger JO. *J Bone Joint Surg (Am)* 1997; **79A**: 1779-1780

Bioceramics Volume 11, edited by R. Z. LeGeros and J.P. LeGeros
(Proceedings of the 11th International Symposium on Ceramics in Medicine)
New York, NY, USA, November 1998
© 1998 by World Scientific Publishing Co. Pte. Ltd.

IN VIVO EVALUATION OF RESORPTION, BONE MATRIX OSTEOCLASTIC AND DEPOSITION AND ESTIMATION OF OSTEOBLASTIC ACTIVITY OF BIOCEMENT D IN A CANCELLOUS BONE DEFECT

R. Wenz[1], F. C. M. Driessens[1], M. G. Boltong[1], M. Dard[1], B. Nies[1]

' Merck Biomaterial GmbH 64271 Darmstadt, German, [2]Department of Dental
Material Science, University of Gent, Belgium

ABSTRACT

Biocement D, a newly developed calcium phosphate based cement was implanted in a rabbit defect model. Eight weeks after implantation histology revealed no signs of inflammation. The resorption of the cement through ostcoclasts and concomitant new bone formation through osteoblasts seems to mimic the natural remodeling of bone. Osteoclastic activity was determined by histochemical staining of the tartrate-resistant-acidic-phosphatase (TRAP), osteoblastic activity by alcaline-phosphatase (APh) staining and bone matrix formation by means of osteocalcin detection.

Keywords: Calcium phosphate cements, osteoclasts, ostcoblasts, osteocalcin, bone defect model.

INTRODUCTION

Calcium phosphate cements (CAPC) have attracted an increasing interest in traumatology, orthopedic and maxillo-facial surgery for the treatment of bone defects, Because of their inorganic nature they bear no risks of transmissible diseases like allograft bone and are in contrast to autologous bone of unlimited availability.

The investigated Biocement D powder reacts with aqueous liquids by forming a carbonated hydroxyapatite. Carbonated hydroxyapatite can subsequently be incorporated in newly formed bone 1. In vitro studies on osteoclast responses to a CaPC with a similar composition revealed osteoclastic resorption 6. The purpose of this study was to investigate the handling properties under the conditions of an operation theatre, the biological behavior and the nature and quantity of resorption in a cancellous bone defect without interfering periosteal activity.

MATERIALS AND METHODS

CAPC based on a α-tertiary calcium phosphate monetit and calcium carbonate was prepared as described by Driessens et al 3. After the wetting of 1-g cement powder with 0.35 ml of a 2.5 % Na2HPO4 solution in water in a mortar, a toothpaste consistency is filled into a syringe and applied into the defect.

Eight female mixed-bred one-year old rabbits were used for the implantation study. Anesthesia was obtained by intramuscular injection of a combination of ketamine and xylazine. After hair clipping and disinfection, an incision was made at the lateral aspect of the knee joint, the patella was mobilized to the medial side and 5.4 mm x 10mrn milling-cutter defects were created in both femura by a water cooled diamond bone cutting system (OBCS) to be sure not to create a heat necrosis. Biocement D was applied with a syringe into the defect. The cement was smoothened to obtain congruence on the joint with a resorbable suture material. Detection of tartrate-resistant-acidic phosphatase and alcaline-phosphatase were used as indications for the activity of osteoclasts and osteoblasts respectively. Osteocalcin deposition was detected immunohisto-chemically as described by Bareille et al 4.

RESULTS AND DISCUSSION

After wetting of the cement powder with a liquid to powder ratio of 0.35 ml/g and an accelerator concentration of 2.5% Na_2HPO_4 in water, a tooth-paste consistency of the mass was achieved which could easily be filled into a I ml syringe. In a working time of 4 minutes at 24'C room temperature the paste could easily be applied through a syringe. While hardening of the Biocement D in the defect site (38.7°C) occurred within 1 minute, the bleeding out of the defect site was stopped immediately. These results arc in accordance to the findings of Ginebra et al 6.

During the follow-up period of 8 weeks there were no clinical *signs of* inflammation, which was confirmed by a histological examination at the end of the investigation. After 8 weeks 8% - 10% of the implanted cement was resorbed by active osteoclasts, demonstrated through TPAP expression with concomitant bone matrix deposition demonstrated by immunohisto-chemical osteocalcin detection. In out model the resorption rate was rather slow in contrast to findings of Jansen et al 3 who found a higher resorption rate in a precursor cement formulation. This might be due to the different implantation sites. In our defect model, the patella-groove, no undifferentiated mesenchymal cells can be provided to the cement because of the lack of periosteum in this implantation site.

CONCLUSIONS

Biocement D has excellent working properties combined with a favorable setting behavior for the clinician. Its rapid setting in situ stops bleeding without disintegration of the cement. Resorption of Biocement D seems to mimic the natural remodeling process of bone by specific bone cells and concomitant disposition of newly formed bone. No macrophages or giant cells seem to be included in the resorption process. Resorbability and good working properties combined with a high mechanical strength make Biocement D to an ideal material for the use in traumatology and orthopedics

ACKNOWLEDGEMENTS

The authors grateful acknowledge Mrs. Bareille and Mr. Lafarge for preparation of the histological slides.

REFERENCES

1. LeGeros RZ, LeGeros JP. In: Schnettler Markgraf ed. *Knochenersatzmaterialen und Wachstumsfakroren, 1997:* 1 2-1 8.
2. de Bruijn JD, Borell YP, Planell JA, Driessens FCM. Fifth World Biomaterials Congress. Toronto 1996: 121.
3. Driessens FCM, Khairoun I, Bolfong MG, Planell JA. In: Sedel L, Rey C, ed. *Bioceramics 1997;* 10; 279-282.
4. Bareille R et al. 13th European Conference on Biomaterials 1997: 124.
5. Jansen JA et al. *J Mat SC.- Mat in Med* 1995, 6: 65 3 -65 7.
6. Ginbera MP et al. In: Andersson, Yli-Urpo. ed. *Bioceramics* 1994; 7: 273-278.

Bioceramics Volume 11, edited by R. Z. LeGeros and J.P. LeGeros
(Proceedings of the 11th International Symposium on Ceramics in Medicine)
New York, NY, USA, November 1998
© 1998 by World Scientific Publishing Co. Pte. Ltd.

IN VIVO REACTIONS OF β-TRICALCIUM PHOSPHATE AND HYDROXYAPATITE SINGLE CRYSTALS WITH BONE MARROW OF RATS I. REACTIONS OF HYDROXYAPATITE SINGLE CRYSTALS

Takayuki Kobayashi, Satoshi Nakamura, Masataka Ohgaki and Kimihiro Yamashita

Division of Inorganic Materials, Institute for Medical and Dental Engineering,
Tokyo Medical and Dental University, 2-3-10 Kanda-Surugadai, Chiyoda-ku, Tokyo 101-0062
Japan

ABSTRACT

Single crystals of hydroxyapatite (HAp) were implanted in femoral bones of rats.   *In vivo* reactions of the crystals with the bone marrow were estimated by histological and cytochemical techniques.   The crystals of HAp were synthesized by hydrothermal methods. The obtained crystals was hexagonal prismatic shape lengthened along *c*-axis and $0.1 \times 0.1 \times 5$ mm^3 in maximum.   The single crystals were inserted in the femoral medullary cavities of 6-week-old Wister rats using spinal needles from the drilled hole of 1.1 mm in diameter on the trochlea femoris.   A new bone formation around the HAp single crystals was observed at 5 days after the implantation by H-E stained sections.   The area of newly formed bone decreased with time in the range from 5 to 14 days.   Osteoblasts being positive for ALP existed around the crystals and newly formed bones at 5, 7 and 14 days after the implantation.   TRAP-positive multinucleate great cells assigned to osteoclast appeared at 7 and 14 days.   The reaction of HAp single crystals with bone marrow has no considerable difference from that of the sintered HAp ceramics.

KEYWORDS: Hydroxyapatite, single crystal, ALP, TRAP

INTRODUCTION

Ceramics of hydroxyapatite (HAp) and β-tricalcium phosphate have been applied in dental and orthopedic fields.   These applications of the polycrystal ceramics are based on a number of studies on tissue reaction by various methods.   On the contrary, it is difficult to find the articles concerning with the tissue reaction of HAp single crystals [1].   The comparative study on tissue reactions of   the HAp ceramics made of bladed particles dominated by c faces and acicular single crystals lengthened along c-axis as well as dominated by a faces is important for investigation of anisotropic tissue reactivity.

In the present study, Single crystals of HAp were implanted in femoral bones of rats.   *In vivo* reactions of the single crystals with bone marrow were estimated by conventional histological methods and phosphatase staining technique.

MATERIALS AND METHODS

Materials

Single crystals of HAp were synthesized by hydrothermal methods at 290°C under CO_2 atmosphere.   The obtained HAp crystals were colorless transparent and had hexagonal prismatic shape lengthened along c-axis and $0.1 \times 0.1 \times 5$ mm^3 in maximum.   The carbonate substitution (0.1% in CO_2 weight) for OH group was indicated by the IR spectra.

Experimental Procedures

Single crystals of HAp were implanted in the femoral medullary cavities of   6-week-old Wister rats.   The HAp single crystals washed by diluted water and ethanol were sterilized by heating at 180°C for 120 min.   After the rats were anaesthetized by intraperitoneal injection of   Nembutal (pentobarbital sodium solution),   trochlea femoris were exposed by lateral luxation.   A hole was obtained on the trochlea femoris with a drill of 1.1 mm in diameter.   The HAp crystals were inserted in the femoral medullary cavities using spinal needles under sterile conditions (Fig. 1). The crystals were placed away from the hole to prevent from reparative calcification effect around the hole.

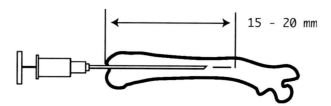

15 - 20 mm

Fig. 1   Implant method of HAp single crystals femoral cavities of rat using spinal needle.

The bones containing single crystals were extracted at 5, 7 and 14 days after the implantation with perfusing of 2 % paraformaldehyde fixing fluid (with $pH=7.4$ cacodylate buffer).   The extracted specimens, after being soaked in the fixing fluid, were examined by soft X-ray radiography to determine the position of slicing.   The specimens decalcified with 10% EDTA solution for 7 days.   Sections were cut using a tungsten carbide blade on a cryo-microtome at - 20°C. The sections were estimated by hematoxyin eosin (HE), alkaline phosphatase (ALP) and tartrate resistant acid phosphatase (TRAP) methods [2-4].

The H-E staining was performed according to Mayer's method.   The ALP staining was examined according to the azo dyes method of Burstone.   After   being soaked in magnesium chloride solution for the reactivation of enzymes, the sections were incubated for 10 min at 37°C in 0.2 M Tris-HCl buffer (*pH*=8.5) containing naphthol AS-MX phosphate (Sigma) as a substrate and Fast Red Violet LB salt (Sigma) as a stain for reaction product. The TRAP staining was performed according to the fast garnet GBC method. The sections were incubated for 10 min at 37°C in 0.1M sodium acetate buffer (*pH*=5.0) containing naphthol AS-MX phosphate (Sigma) and Fast Red Violet LB salt (Sigma) under prevention of light [5-7].

RESULTS AND DISCUSSION

A new bone formation around the HAp single crystals was observed at 5 days after the implantation by H-E stained sections (Fig. 2). The area of newly formed bone decreased with the passage of time in the range from 5 to 14 days. The appreciable disappearance of the bone at 7 days was attributed to the occurring of absorption.

Some parts of the cells around the HAp single crystals and newly formed bone exhibited positive for ALP at 5, 7 and 14 days (Fig. 3). The existence of ALP positive cells showed that osteoblastic cells generated new bones with being affected by the single crystals. No positive area for TRAP was detected in the sections of day-5 specimens as shown in Fig. 4. In the cases of 7 and 14 days, however, TRAP-positive multinucleate great cells were observed around newly formed bones. The positive cells were assumed to be assigned to osteoclast although it was undeniable that the cells were macrophage without NSE staining assay.

In the present study, no considerable difference was found concerning with reaction between the HAp single crystals and sintered ceramics in the femoral medullary cavities. No anisotropic tissue reaction reactivity was detected.

CONCLUSION

It was revealed by histological and cytochemical estimations that the reaction of HAp single crystals with bone marrow has no considerable difference from that of sintered HAp ceramics.

ACKNOWLEDGMENTS

The authors extends their thanks to Professor Hiroo Miyairi in Division of Applied Mechanics, Institute for Medical and Dental Engineering, Tokyo Medical and Dental University for technical supports and use of cryo-microtome. Parts of the present study were supported by Japanese Grant in Aid for Scientific Research (A) #10305047, The Sumitomo Foundation and Tokuyama Science Foundation.

REFERENCES

1. Aoki H, Akao M, Nakamura S, Ito A, Fujii O, Yoshizawa K. *Bioceramics* 1989; **2**: 19-24.
2. Burstone MS. *Enzyme Histochemistry*. New York : Academic Press, 1962: 88-113.
3. Minkin C. *Calcif. Tissue Int.* 1982; **34**: 285-290.
4. Robison R. *Biochem. J.* 1923; **17**: 286.
5. Fushimi M. *J. Japanese Society for Biomaterials* 1995; **13**: 224-235.
6. Hammarstom LE, Hanker J S, Toverud SU, *Clin. Orthop. Relat. Res.* 1971; **78**: 151-167.
7. Yoshiki S, Umeda T, Kurahashi Y. *Histochemie* 1972; **29**: 296-304.

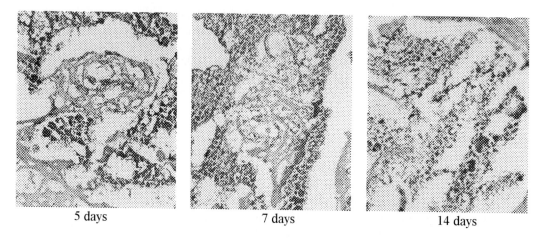

5 days   7 days   14 days

Fig. 2   Sections of bone marrow stained with H-E (×100).

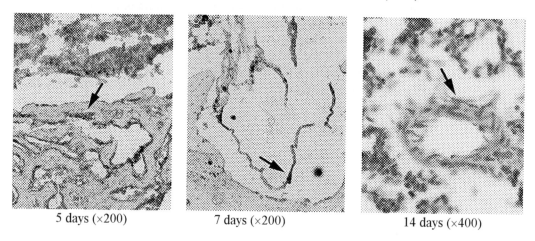

5 days (×200)   7 days (×200)   14 days (×400)

Fig. 3   Sections of bone marrow stained with ALP.   Arrows indicate ALP-positive cells.

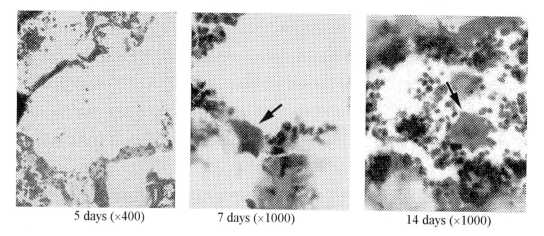

5 days (×400)   7 days (×1000)   14 days (×1000)

Fig. 4   Sections of bone marrow stained with TRAP. Arrows indicate TRAP-positive cells.

Bioceramics Volume 11, edited by R. Z. LeGeros and J.P. LeGeros
(Proceedings of the 11th International Symposium on Ceramics in Medicine)
New York, NY, USA, November 1998

BIOACTIVE COMPOSITE: COMPARISON OF CERAMIC FILLERS ON OSTEOCONDUCTIVITY AND BONE-BONDING STRENGTH

M. Kobayashi[1,2], T. Nakamura[2], Y. Okada[2], S. Shinzato[2], T. Kokubo[3], and T. Kikutani[4]

[1]Department of Orthopaedic Surgery, Otsu Red Cross Hospital, Nagara 1-1-35, Otsu 520-0046, Japan; [2]Department of Orthopaedic Surgery, Faculty of Medicine, Kyoto University; [3]Division of Material Chemistry, Faculty of Engineering, Kyoto University; [4]Nippon Electric Glass Co. Ltd.

ABSTRACT

A study was conducted to compare osteoconductivity and bone-bonding strength of composites (AWC, HAC, TCPC, ABC, ALC, and SGC) each consisting of either apatite and wollastonite-containing glass-ceramic (AW-GC), hydroxyapatite (HA), β-tricalcium phosphate (β-TCP), amorphous phase-containing alumina bead, α-alumina, or amorphous fused silica powder as a filler and bisphenol-*a*-glycidylmethacrylate(Bis-GMA)-based resin as a matrix. Filler was added to the composite in 70% w/w. Each composite polymerized *in situ* using radical polymerization, which had uncured surface layer. Affinity indices for AWC, HAC, TCPC, ABC, ALC, and SGC calculated from contact microradiogram specimens of rat tibiae 8 weeks post-implantation were $80.0 \pm 14.9, 57.1 \pm 15.3, 29.5 \pm 11.9, 81.0 \pm 10.4, 5.2 \pm 2.5$, and 8.4 ± 5.6 % (n=12), respectively. Prefabricated and abraded rectangular plates (10x15x2 mm) of each composite were implanted into the tibial metaphyses of rabbits at random and the failure loads were measured by a detaching test 10 weeks after implantation. The failure loads of AWC, HAC, TCPC, and SGC were $3.95 \pm 0.84, 2.04 \pm 0.44, 2.03 \pm 0.65$, and 0.00 ± 0.00 kgf, respectively (n=8). The failure loads of AWC were significantly higher than those of the rest. Results indicate that both AWC and ABC have higher osteoconductivity than HAC and TCPC, and that AWC has superior bone-bonding strength compared to the rest.

KEYWORDS; Composite, AW-GC, Alumina, Osteoconductivity, Bone-bonding strength

INTRODUCTION

We developed a bioactive bone cement consisting of apatite- and wollastonite-containing glass-ceramic (AW-GC) powder as an inorganic filler and bisphenol-*a*-glycidyl methacrylate (Bis-GMA)-based resin as an organic matrix using a system of radical polymerization for prosthesis fixation[1,3,5,10,11] This cement shows much higher mechanical strength than conventional polymethylemethacrylate bone cement and bonds to bone directly under both non-weight loading and weight loading conditions. Recently, we also developed a hybrid bioactive bone cement containing both AW-GC and fused silica glass powders, which showed improved mechanical and molding properties.[2] These desirable properties are attributable to the early formation of a dense and uniform apatite layer on the cement surface due to coordinated coupling of the highly bioactive glass or glass-ceramic powder and leaching of incompletely polymerized monomers from the cement surface.[4,6,8] In this study, six types of particulate filled composite (AWC, HAC, TCPC, ABC, ALC, and SGC) were made in order to compare osteoconductivity and bone-bonding strength of composites each consisting of either AW-GC, hydroxyapatite (HA), β-tricalcium phosphate (β-TCP), amorphous phase-containing alumina bead, α-alumina, or amorphous fused silica powder as a filler

MATERIALS AND METHODS

Preparation of bioactive composite

Powders 4 μ m in an average particle size of AW-GC powder with a nominal composition of MgO 4.6, CaO 44.7, SiO_2 34.0, P_2O_5 16.2, and CaF_2 0.5 by weight ratio which was synthesized by the method previously reported[7], those 4.3 μ m of pure crystaline HA powder sintered at 1200°C and those 3.7 μ m of β-TCP powder sintered at 1150°C, both of which were supplied by Mitsubishi Material Co. Ltd., were used. The α-alumina particles under 10 μ m in diameter were fused and quenched subsequently to produce alumina bead powder containing amorphous and δ-crystal phases of alumina in its main crystal structure. The average particle size was 3.0 μ m. Pure α-alumina powders were re-manifactured by fusing alimina bead. Spherical particles of amorphous silica glass powder (SG-P) were also prepared by the fusing method from highly purified quartz ($>$ 99.7% pure), which had average particle size of 3.0 μ m.

Each powder was silane-treated, and benzoyl peroxide at 0.4% per unit weight of the treated powder was added. Bis-GMA and triethyleneglycol dimethacrylate (TEGDMA) were mixed in equal weight. N,N-dimethyl-p-toluidine, at 1.0% per unit weight of the mixture of Bis-GMA and TEGDMA, was dissolved.[2-4,6] The weight ratio of the filler powder mixed into the composite was 70%. The composite was prepared by mixing the appropriate powder into the mixture of Bis-GMA and TEGDMA and stirring it for 1 minute. It was polymerized within 5-6 minutes. The six types of composite, containing either AW-GC, HA, β-TCP, alumina bead, α-alumina, or amorphous silica powder, were designated AWC, HAC, TCPC, ABC, ALC, or SGC, respectively.

The mechanical properties of each composite except for ALC, measured after soaking in simulated body fluid (SBF) at 37°C for 1 day, were shown in Table 1.

Table 1. Mechanical properties of five types of composite measured after soaking in SBF for 1 day

	Compressive Str.(MPas)	Bending Str.(MPa)	Tensile Str.(MPa)	Fracture Toughness(MPam$^{0.5}$)
AWC	194±6	124±7	47±4	1.52±0.10
HAC	158±9	72±11	23±4	1.16±0.07
TCPC	128±9	69±1	21±3	1.14±0.05
ABC	196±4	151±10	58±3	1.44±0.05
SGC	237±14	157±10	59±5	1.69±0.11

Str.=Strength

Examination of osteoconductivity and measurement of affinity index

Ten-week-old male Wistar rats were operated on under general anesthesia (Nembutal: 40 mg/kg body weight). Cortical bone defects measuring 2 X 5 mm were created on the medial aspect of the proximal metaphysis of both tibiae, and the bone marrow was curetted. The intramedullary canals from both bone defects in each individual animal were packed with the same kind of composite, and allowed to cure *in situ*. Three rats received each composite, being killed at 8 weeks after the operation.[1-4,6,10]

All tibial segments containing composite samples were excised and dehydrated in serial dilutions of ethanol, then embedded in polyester resin. Thin sections (500 μ m thick) were cut with a band saw   perpendicular to the axis of the tibia. Two sections from each tibia (i.e. 12 specimens in total for each composite) were ground to a thickness of 100 μ m using a diamond lap disk for contact microradiography. From these specimens, circumferential bone to the cement in the tibia without any intervening connective tissue were measured using an image analyser (integrated by Tectron, Kyoto, Japan). An affinity index for each composite was calculated by dividing this length by the total length of the cement surface in the tibia and multiplying this value by 100.[2-4,6,10]

Measurement of failure load

The bone-bonding ability of AWC, HAC, TCPC, and SGC was evaluated in rabbit tibiae. Rectangular plates (10 x 15 x 2 mm) of composites were abraded with #2000 alumina powder and sterilized in ethylene oxide gas. The average roughness for AWC, HAC, TCPC, and SGC was 0.26, 0.37, 0.39, and 0.31 μ m, respectively, and the maximum roughness for each plate was 2.50, 3.31, 3.55, and 3.08 μ m , respectively.[5,11]

The plates were implanted into the metaphyses of the bilateral tibiae of mature male Japanese white rabbits weighing between 3.0 and 3.5 kg. The rabbits were anesthetized by an intravenous injection of pentobarbital (50 mg/kg body weight) and local administration of 0.5% (w/v) lidocaine. Using sterile surgical techniques, a 3 cm incision was made on the antero-medial aspect of the proximal metaphysis of the tibia. Using a dental burr, a critical size hole was made from the medial cortex to the lateral cortex parallel to the longitudinal axis of the proximal metaphysis. Both tibiae were surgically treated, and one of four types of plates were implanted in each tibia at random in the frontal direction perforating the tibiae and protruding from both the medial and lateral cortex symmetrically to the longitudinal axis of the tibia.[5,11]

Sixteen rabbits were sacrificed with an overdose of pentobarbital at 10 weeks after implantation. A segment of the tibiae containing the implant was excised, the bone was dissected transversely 2 mm above and below each end of the implant by making parallel cuts with a disc cutter, and prepared for the detaching test by Nakamura's method [9]. During the detaching test, each segment was held by a hook connected to an Instron-type autograph (Model-1323, Aikoh Engineering, Nagoya, Japan). The bone segment with the implant was placed horizontally and pulled in opposite directions at a cross-head speed of 3.5 cm/min. The failure load, when an implant detached from the bone, or the bone or the implant itself broke, was measured.

RESULTS AND DISCUSSION

Evaluation of osteoconductivity

Values for affinity indices of each composite are shown in Table2. The values for both AWC and ABC are significantly higher than those for HAC, TCPC, ALC, and SGC (ANOVA p<0.05).

Table 2. Affinity indices (%) of six types of composite 8 weeks
after implantation in rat tibiae (n=12)

AWC	HAC	TCPC	ABC	ALC	SGC
80.0 ± 14.9	57.1 ± 15.3	29.5 ± 11.9	81.0 ± 10.4	5.2 ± 2.5	8.4 ± 5.6

Table 3. Detaching failure loads (kgf) of four types of composite
10 weeks after implantation in rabbit tibiae (n=8)

AWC	HAC	TCPC	SGC
3.95 ± 0.84	2.04 ± 0.44	2.03 ± 0.65	0.00 ± 0.00

Evaluation of bone-bonding ability
Bone-bonding strengths of AWC, HAC, TCPC, and SGC measured by detaching failure loads are shown in Table 3. The values for AWC are significantly higher than those of the rest (ANOVA $p<0.05$).

Results indicate that both AWC and ABC have higher osteoconductivity than HAC and TCPC, and that AWC has superior bone-bonding strength compared to HAC and TCPC. Kokubo et al. reported that AWC had formed apatite earlier than HAC or TCPC had *in vitro* study using SBF.[8] Another study demonstrated that ABC showed both mechanically strong and highly osteoconductive properties.[4] Both AWC and ABC show promise as a basis for developing a bioactive and mechanically strong composite.

REFERENCES

1. Kawanabe K, Tamura J, Yamamuro T, Nakamura T, Kokubo T, Yoshihara S. *J Appl Biomater* 1993; **4:** 135-141.
2. Kobayashi M, Nakamura T, Tamura J, Iida H, Fujita H, Kokubo T, Kikutani T. *J Biomed Mater Res* 1997; **37:** 68-80.
3. Kobayashi M, Nakamura T, Tamura J, Kokubo T, Kikutani T. *J Biomed Mater Res* 1997; **37:** 301-313.
4. Kobayashi M, Kikutani T, Kokubo T, Nakamura T. *J Biomed Mater Res* 1997; **37:** 554-565.
5. Kobayashi M, Nakamura T, Okada Y, Fukumoto A, Furukawa T, Kato H, Kokubo T, Kikutani T. *J Biomed Mater Res* in press.
6. Kobayashi M, Nakamura T, Kikutani T, Kawanabe K, Kokubo T. *J Biomed Mater Res (Appl Biomater)*, in press.
7. Kokubo T, Ito S, Shigematsu M, Sakka S, Yamamuro T. *J Mater Sci* 1985; **20:** 2001-2004.
8. Kokubo T, Morita Y, Miyaji F, Nakanishi K, Soga N, Nakamura T. In: J. Wilson, L. L. Hench, and D. Greenspan, eds. *Bioceramics 8*, New York: Elsevier Science, 1995: 213-217.
9. Nakamura T, Yamamuro T, Higashi S, Kokubo T, Ito S. J Biomed Mater Res 1985; **19:** 685-698.
10. Tamura J, Kawanabe K, Kobayashi M, Nakamura T, Kokubo T, Yoshihara S, Shibuya T. *J Biomed Mater Res* 1996; **30:** 85-94.
11. Tamura J, Kitsugi T, Iida H, Fujita H, Nakamura T, Kokubo T, Yoshihara S. *Clin Orthop* 1997; **343:** 183-191.

Bioceramics Volume 11, edited by R. Z. LeGeros and J.P. LeGeros
(Proceedings of the 11th International Symposium on Ceramics in Medicine)
New York, NY, USA, November 1998
© 1998 by World Scientific Publishing Co. Pte. Ltd.

IN VIVO HISTOLOGICAL EVALUATION OF HA/N-CARBOXYMETHYLCHITOSAN FILLERS

C. Mangano[1], A. Scarano[1], M. Piattelli[1], A. Piattelli[1], R. Martinetti[2]

[1]Dental School, University of Chieti, Via Dei Vestini, 11 66013 Chieti Scalo, Italy; [2]FIN-CERAMICA, Via Ravagnana, 186 48018 Faenza (RA), Italy

ABSTRACT

A problem concerning alveolar bone reconstruction is the time required to achieve a suitable quantity of newly-formed bone to allow a dental implant insertion with succesful long-term prognosis. To obtain such a reconstruction, dentists currently use today calcium phosphate based fillers.
Hydroxyapatite / N-Carboxymethyl chitosan (HA / N-CMC) fillers were prepared, studied, and proposed as a new biomaterial for medical use to solve the problems of bone healing for alveolar reconstruction.
The fillers, in the granulometric range of 600-900 μm, were made by granulation method (patent n. BO93A 000435) starting from hydroxyapatite powder and adding N-CMC.
The target of this study was to evaluate the physico-chemical behaviour of HA / N-CMC filler *in vivo*.
Chitosan is an important interface between bone and hydroxyapatite because it promotes an osteoconductive reaction during the filling of irregular bone defects.
Preliminary hystological results obtained from specimens retrieved after *in vivo* tests on rabbit tibiae showed that HA / N-CMC fillers have a good biocompatibility with bone and that there is a direct contact with newly formed bone.

KEYWORDS: filler, hydroxyapatite, chitosan

INTRODUCTION

Chitosan seems to increase the restorative processes of the tissues. Literature on *in vitro* studies with osteoblasts[1] reports that, when chitosan is present, the Gla-protein- a protein able to control the hydroxyapatite crystal deposition- is detected. Chitosan is an important interface between bone and hydroxyapatite because it promotes an osteoconductive reaction during the filling of irregular bone defects [2]. It stimulates bone tissue regeneration and helps the wound healing; in association with calcium phosphate compounds it can reduce the healing of bone defects. Chitosan allows strong Van der Waals bonds [3], with phosphate calcium salts.

The mixture between chitosan-hydroxyapatite, calcium oxide and zinc oxide produces the formation of a material that can assume different shapes as that of the spongy sheet used for the regeneration of the bone tissue. In N-CMC the repeating units are N-Acetylglucosamine and N-Carboxymethyl glucosamine and its polimer chain is linear.

The carbonate group of N-CMC may integrate itself in the hydroxyapatite structure lattice on the interface planes trying to produce the correspondent carbonate-apatite. In some way the Van der Waals bond increases constituting a kind of chelating for epithetical deposition of the N-CMC molecules.

N-CMC could so promote enlargement of specific crystallographic planes of HA. The promoted planes will be those on which PO_4^{3-} can be easily substituted by the carbonate groups of N-CMC. This is particularly true when the distance between a carbonate group and the other along the N-CMC molecula is equal to a lattice distance between a suitable PO_4^{3-} lattice site and another on the interfacial plane exhibited by HA.

The presence of glycine units on the biopolymer is a further reason of affinity to the human tissues which contain collagen mainly constituted by glycine

MATERIALS AND METHODS

The N-CMC used in this study is a glycosaminoglycan obtained from chitosan. It carries glycine units and its molecular weight is 700 K Dalton. Its nature and its general chemical behaviour are those of an amphoteric polysaccharide, where the cationic nature is prevailing. It combines in itself the main characteristics of chitosan and glycine. It can be fully mixed with water and water solutions; it is included in the field of biopolymers, which exhibit positive actions on the human body. It is an excellent film-forming agent. It has been already shown that it stimulates the healing processes of damaged tissues.

The HA granules, used to prepared the proposed fillers in association with N-CMC, have low density, were made by granulation method (patent n. BO93A 000435) [4] starting from hydroxyapatite powder.

A solution of N-CMC with 1.0 wt% concentration was prepared and by aerosol method, used to obtain a thin coating of about 1.0 μm on hydroxyapatite granules. The samples prepared were dried at 37° C for 6 hours and then sterilised by γ - ray irradiation at 25 kGγ. The N-CMC solution was characterised from the reological point of view using a Rotovisco RV20 (Haake device). The IR spectra in the solid state, were collected for N-CMC, HA and HA / N-CMC with a Bruker 113v FT IR spectrometer on KBr pellets as support in the spectral range 4000 – 400 cm^{-1}. SEM (Leica Cambridge mod. 360 Stereoscan, Englan) was used to study the microstructure and the morphology òf the starting materials and of the final sample.

Preliminary *in vivo* tests were performed on rabbit tibiae. The animals were anesthetized with intramuscular injections of fluanizone (0,7 mg/kg b.wt.) and diazepam (1.5 mg/kg b.wt.). Local anaesthesia was given using 1 mL of 2% lidocain/adrenalin solution. Surgery was performed under sterile conditions. Fourteen New Zealand rabbits has been used in this study.

In each rabbit's tibiae two 6 mm. holes were created; one was filled with Hydroxyapatite/ N-Carboxymethyl chitosan and the other one was use as control. Each tibia was exposed by a skin incision and a periosteal flap. Appropriate 5.5 mm. large burs were used for preparing bone defects of about 6 mm of diameter under generous irrigation with saline. The periosteum and fascia were sutured with a catgut suture; the skin was sutured with silk. Postoperatively the animals were administered intramuscular injections of penicillin (2.000.000 IE/5 mL;0,1 mL/kg b.wt.). No animal died in the postoperative period. The animals were killed with an overdose of intravenous pentobarbital with the following schedule: two after one week, two after two weeks and two after three weeks, two after four weeks, two after five weeks, two after six weeks and two after twelve weeks. The specimens and surrounding tissues were washed in saline solution and immediately fixed in 4% parapholmaldehyde and 0.1% glutaraldehyde in 0.15 M cacodylate buffer al 4 °C and pH 7.4, to be processed for histology. The specimens were processed to obtain thin ground sections according to the cutting-grinding system[10]. Briefly the specimens were dehydrated in an ascending series of alcohols and embedded in a glycolmethacrylate resin (Technovit 7200 VLC, Kulzer, Germany). After polymerization the specimens were sectioned with a diamond saw at a thickness of about 200 μ and ground down to about 30 μ.. About 3 sections were cut for each bone defect, in a way parallel to the major axis. After polishing, the slides were stained with basic fuchsin-methylene blue and with basic fuchsin- toluidine blue and were observed with a Leitz Laborlux microscope (Leitz, Wetzlar, Germany) in normal light.

RESULTS AND DISCUSSION

The pH of N-CMC solution was controlled during the coating process: it was 4.5; the viscosity was measured at D (1 / s) = 1000, the following data was determined: Eta = 27.6 (mPas).

The sample studied is identified by the infrared spectrum: a general overlap of N-CMC spectra and HA is deducible with intensification of the main bands, in particular in the range between 1700 and 1200 cm^{-1} it is not possible to determine if an interference exists between the materials. The microstructure of   starting materials, of the surface of N-CMC coating on HA granule and of the interface HA/N-CMC were examined [5], in particular the microstructure of HA granules shown a crystals size of 0.05 - 0.1 μm.

Bone defects filled with HA/N-CMC showed a faster healing process than the control defects. An higher osteoblastic activity was observed in test sites. In the test sites, in the first week it was possible to observe many activ osteoblast that were in the process of secreting osteoid matrix. This activily secreting osteoblast are present until the first week after this time there is a sharp decrease. The HA/N-CMC particles have a concentric shape and they seem to be completly surrounded by newly formed bone.

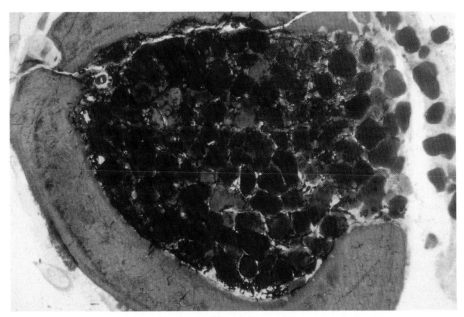

Figure 1.
Bone defect in rabbit tibiae: HA /N-CMC particles surrounded by small trabeculae of newly
formed bone after three weeks (13 x).

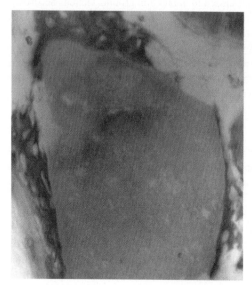

Figure 2. HA /N-CMC particles cemented by newly formed bone with large osteocytic lacunae after five weeks (100 x).

Figure 3. Resorption of HA /N-CMC particles and replacement of newly formed bone after twelve weeks (200 x).

In the control defects in the first three weeks have a poor quantity of new bone.

After the third week (figure 1) it is possible to observe new bone with presence of large osteocytic lacunae.

Preliminary histological results of specimens retrieved after *in vivo* tests on rabbit tibiae proved that HA / N-CMC fillers have good biocompatibility with bone and show a direct contact with newly formed bone (figure 2, 3). Further tests are in progress.

REFERENCES

1. F. Lo Bianco, C. Parodi, S. Spinato, L. Lo Bianco: *DENTAL CADMOS* , 1993, **10,** 40-46.
2. M. Mattioli, G. Biagini, R. Muzzarelli, C. Castaldini, M.G. Gandolfi, A. Krajewski, A. Ravaglioli, M. Fini, R. Giardino: J. of Bioactive and Compatible Polymers , 1995, **10,** 249-257.
3. M. Takechi, Y. Miyamoto, K. Ishikawa, M. Yuasa, M. Nagayama, M.Kon, K. Asaoka: J. of Material Science: Material in Medicine, 1996, **7,** 317-322.
4. A. Ravaglioli, A. Krajewski, A. Piattelli, C. Mangano, R. Martinetti: Tadashi Kokubo, Takashi Nakamura, Fumiaki Miyaji, Japan, *Bioceramics* Vol. **9,** 1996, 185-188.
5. R. Martinetti, L. Dolcini, A. Ravaglioli, A. Krajewski, C. Mangano, *Bioceramics* Vol. **10,** 1997, 503 - 506.

Bioceramics Volume 11, edited by R. Z. LeGeros and J.P. LeGeros
(Proceedings of the 11th International Symposium on Ceramics in Medicine)
New York, NY, USA, November 1998
© 1998 by World Scientific Publishing Co. Pte. Ltd.

BIOGLASS®-DEXTRAN COMPOSITE TESTED IN RABBIT FEMUR

I. Thompson[2], C. Chan[1], P. Robinson[1], P. Pevell[3], J. Wilson[3] and L. L. Hench[2]

[1]Department of Materials, Imperial College, London, UK; [2]Department of Oral & Maxillofacial Surgery, Guy's Hospital, London, UK; [3]Department of Histopathology, Royal Free Hospital, London, UK.

ABSTRACT

The ability of particulate 45S5 Bioglass® to provide bone augmentation has been previously described in femoral[1], spinal[2] and dental[3] applications. In certain circumstances, notably maxillofacial applications, a mouldable form of the material is advantageous so long as the bioactivity remains uncompromised. In this study such a material has been tested in the rabbit femoral condyle model. Bioglass particulate (90-710µm) was mixed with high-molecular weight dextran solution sufficient to give a composite which could be handled satisfactorily by surgeons. It was placed in 5mm defects in NZ white rabbit femurs and sites were evaluated at 2 days, 1,2,3,6 and 12 weeks, using special stains and bone labelling techniques. The study was designed to determine the effects of dextran, if any, on the Bioglass®, when used alone or when combined with autograft. There was no evidence of toxicity, the dextran was undetectable even at 2 days. All sites were filled by 3 weeks, the particulate was incorporated into new trabecular bone and was almost undetectable after 12 weeks. There was no difference in the rate of bone repair in any test site. Sites with autograft, particulate and a mixture of the two healed completely and were unaffected by the addition of dextran, which markedly improved handling properties, allowing a wider range of applications than the particulate alone.

KEYWORDS: Bioglass®, Dextran, Particulate

INTRODUCTION

Bone grafting procedures are required in the oral and maxillofacial region for a variety of reasons including bone loss due to trauma, congenital deficiency and other pathology, alveolar ridge augmentation and preparation for osseointegrated dental implants. The use of autologous bone remains the gold standard despite the drawbacks of donor site morbidity, unpredictable resorption of the graft and availability. Bioglass® has unique bioactivity which allows it to bond to both hard and soft tissues. Bioglass® particulate is not sufficiently cohesive to use in augmenting convex or large concave bony surfaces. The addition of high molecular weight dextran improves handling by producing a mouldable putty which can eventually be used for more complex defects.

OBJECTIVE

To evaluate the influence of dextran upon the bioactivity of Bioglass®.

MATERIALS AND METHODS

The technique described by Oonishi et. al.[4] was used in 51 male New Zealand white rabbits. Five materials were evaluated:

    (1)   Autologous bone
    (2)   Bioglass® particulate
    (3)   Bioglass® particulate mixed with dextran to a putty-like consistency
    (4)   Mixture of Bioglass® particulate and autologous bone
    (5)   Mixture of Bioglass® putty and autologous bone

The 45S5 Bioglass® particulate (90-710μm) was supplied by US Biomaterials Corp., individual packets were prepared and sterilised by steam autoclave. The high molecular weight dextran (Sigma) was packaged and sterilised using ethylene oxide. The Bioglass® putty was formed by mixing Bioglass® particulate with dextran and sterile de-ionised water at room temperature. Eight animals were killed after 2 days, 1, 2, 3, 6 and 12 weeks, of the 16 available site, at each time period, fifteen were filled with test materials, (n=3) and one site was unused. Three animals (six defects) were used as unfilled controls. Rabbits were housed individually and allowed dry pellet food and water *ad lib.*

Animals were anaesthetised and an approximate 15 mm incision was made over the distal femur and lateral aspect of the knee joint. The periosteum was incised and the epiphysis identified. A 5mm diameter defect was created using a trephine under continuous water irrigation to a depth of 7-8 mm. Cavities were filled according to the protocol. Cancellous bone obtained from the trephine provided autogenous bone. The wound was closed in layers after haemostasis. The animals were then given a single subcutaneous injection of long-acting amoxycillin (Duphamox) (1mg/ Kg) and a depot of a non-steroidal anti-inflammatory analgesic (Zenecarp) (2.5mg/ Kg) subcutaneously.

To determine the rate and pattern of new bone formation four different bone markers were injected subcutaneously. These were Tetracycline 25mg/Kg, Calcein Green 25mg/Kg, Alizarin complexone 25mg/Kg, Calcein Blue 25mg/Kg.

All animals were killed by intravenous injection of pentobarbitone (Lethobarb) and defects removed together with surrounding bone. Material was embedded in plastic, sawn sections cut and stained with Von Kossa, toluidine blue as required.

RESULTS

Autograft was already colonised by osteoblasts and osteoclasts by one week and became connected by osteoid bridges by two weeks, with some focal deposition of new bone. At and after three weeks, sections showed 100% trabecular bone, although sites could not be positively identified.

Bioglass® was seen as a mass of particulate immobilised in soft tissue extending from the periphery. Lacy calcification between particles and bone bridging were seen at one week and occasional particles were surrounded by bone. By two weeks, bone had grown between and around particles for up to 7 layers of particles from the periphery. By three weeks, bone extended throughout the defect and a trabecular structure, with particles enclosed within the trabeculae, had begun to appear (fig 1). At six and twelve weeks sites contained trabecular bone with a gradually reducing content of particles, which eventually survived only in the central areas (fig 2).

Bioglass® and autograft was seen as a mass of particulate mixed with relatively large fragments of bone. At the later time periods the autograft could not be distinguished. Bony bridges and lacy calcification were seen as early as one week and by two weeks they extended to a depth of 10 particle layers. At and after three weeks bone with a trabecular pattern filled the defects and enclosed particles were seen as in the Bioglass®-filled defects.

Bioglass® mixed with dextran produced a response essentially similar to that of Bioglass® alone. Bone bridges and lacy calcification were seen at one week and had reached 2-6 layers deep by two weeks. At three weeks and after, 100% trabecular bone with enclosed particles was seen, although in one three week sample there were a few centrally placed particles which were not surrounded (fig 3).

Bioglass®, autograft and dextran was surrounded by soft tissue at one week without bone bridges. By two weeks bridging extended up to 7 layers from the periphery and thereafter the defects were filled with trabecular bone with enclosed particulate, which decreased in amount until only a few, centrally placed, particles survived at twelve weeks.

Control (unfilled) sites were examined at the two, three and six week time periods (fig 4). Repair was undetectable up to three weeks and at six weeks only small foci of new bone were seen.

Bone labelling studies showed that maximum ingrowth of bone after one and two weeks (expressed as a mean percentage of the radius of the defect) when measured on the three week samples by ultraviolet microscopy, showed no difference between any of the five test groups.

Figure 1: Bioglass® section (3 weeks) showing bone bridging between glass particles

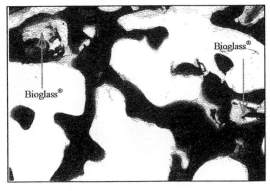

Figure 2: Bioglass® section (12 weeks) showing trabecular structure with two residual glass particles indicated

Figure 3 Bioglass®/Dextran section (3weeks) showing bone bridging between glass particles

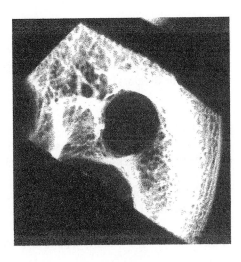

Figure 4: Radiograph of a 6 week control defect (no notable ingrowth)

DISCUSSION

The normal repair pattern is seen in autograft sites which were completely healed and remodelled by three weeks. Sites with Bioglass® filled with bone by three weeks and remodelled between three and six weeks to a trabecular structure, within which the particulate can be seen at first, but is gradually used up as the repair progresses from the periphery to the centre of the defect. The addition of autograft does not appear to alter the pattern or rate of repair (fig 5). The addition of dextran to Bioglass® or to the Bioglass®/autograft mixture does not alter the repair process. There is no evidence that dextran is deleterious, it produced no observable tissue reaction.

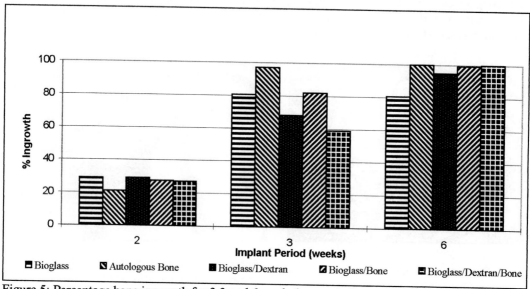

Figure 5: Percentage bone ingrowth for 2,3 and 6 week time periods, measured by UV bone labels

CONCLUSIONS

Sites filled with particulate Bioglass® healed almost as quickly as those filled with autograft. Addition of autograft to the Bioglass® did not appear to alter the tissue response. Addition of dextran to Bioglass® or Bioglass®/autograft mixtures did not affect the process of bone repair.

REFERENCES

1) Oonishi, H., Kushitani, S., Yasukawa, E., Iwaki, H,. Hench, L.L., Wilson, J., Tsuji,E., Sugihara,T., Clinical Orthopaedics and Related Research (1996), No334, p316-325.

2) Wilson, J., Lowery, G. and Courtney,S., Bioceramics Vol.10 (1997), Eds. Sedel,L. & Rey,C. Elsevier Science Ltd, p 65-68

3) Wilson, J. and Low, S., J. Applied Biomats. (1992), Vol. 3, p173-179

4) Oonishi et. al Bioceramics Vol. 4 (1991), Eds. Bonfield, Hastings & Tanner. Butterworth-Heinemann Ltd., England. p191-197

Bioceramics Volume 11, edited by R. Z. LeGeros and J.P. LeGeros
(Proceedings of the 11th International Symposium on Ceramics in Medicine)
New York, NY, USA, November 1998
© 1998 by World Scientific Publishing Co. Pte. Ltd.

REMOVAL PATHWAY OF SILICON RELEASED FROM BIOACTIVE GLASS GRANULES *IN VIVO*

W. Lai[1], P. Ducheyne[1,2], J. Garino[2]

Center for Bioactive Materials and Tissue Engineering, Department of Bioengineering[1], Department of Orthopaedic Surgery[2], University of Pennsylvania, Philadelphia, PA 19104

ABSTRACT

In this study we traced and quantified the silicon released from bioactive glass granules (BGG) in vivo (45S5, 300-355 μm). 1500 mg of BGG were implanted in the paraspinal muscle of 4 kg rabbits. Blood and urine samples were obtained weekly. After 6 weeks, the rabbits were euthanized and the following tissues and organs were harvested: local muscle, appendix, brain, heart, kidney, liver, lung, and thymus. Using flame atomic absorption spectrophotometry, the concentration of elemental silicon (Si) was measured in these fluid, tissues, and organs.

The concentrations of silicon measured in the urine were well below saturation and there was no significant increase in Si in the kidney or in the other organs. These data suggest that the elevated Si excretion rate was within the physiological range of the experimental animal. It can be concluded that the resorbed silica gel is harmlessly excreted in soluble form through the urine in the first few weeks of bioactive glass transformation and resorption.

KEYWORDS: bioactive glass, biocompatibility, degradation, dissolution, in vivo, silicon

INTRODUCTION

Bioactive glass granules (BGG) with a narrow size range (300-355 μm) fully react *in vivo* to form internal silica gel cores which are subsequently degraded, leaving external calcium phosphate shells. In the excavated particles, a unique process occurs in which osteoprogenitor cells undergo differentiation and start laying down new bone tissue.[10] Although the degraded material is no longer found at the local implant site, the path of removal of the resorption products has not yet been traced. To address this need, we have devised a rabbit study to quantify the resorption, transport, and excretion of the silica gel.

The study is designed to address the hypothesis that the glass is constantly reacting with its surroundings, and that the silica gel is removed by a combination of Si dissolution in the circulating interstitial fluid and active degradation by phagocytic action of macrophages contacting the silica matrix surface; the Si-containing product diffuses into the local tissue, then enters the bloodstream or lymph to be distributed to other parts of the body in soluble form; since there are no known physiological processes specific for the absorption and metabolism of soluble Si, the Si will finally be filtered out of the blood by the kidney; during this resorption, the Si concentration in the organs and body fluids remains within physiologically typical ranges.

MATERIALS AND METHODS

750 mg of 45S5 bioactive glass granules (300-355 μm; 45% SiO_2, 24.5% CaO, 24.5% Na_2O, 6% P_2O_5 by weight) were loaded into two intramuscular sites in the back of rabbits weighing 4 kg. A total of 1500 mg of BGG reflects a relevant dose of 30 cc used in a human clinical case, where BGG would be used as a bone graft substitute. The intramuscular implant site was chosen because the resorption rate of the Si would be enhanced in muscle tissue versus in a slower healing site such as a bone defect. There were a total of 9 rabbits in the study: 4 control rabbits, and 5 rabbits that were injected with the granules.

The surgical procedure was performed bilaterally, and by spreading fibers apart in the paraspinal muscle a defect was formed, approximately 0.5 x 0.5 inches and 0.75 inch deep. The sterile bioactive glass granules were received in specially designed syringes (Orthovita, Inc., Malvern, PA) and the granules were loaded dry, directly into the defect. The layers were then sutured closed with resorbable sutures. After surgery, the rabbit was immediately placed into a metabolic cage.

Blood samples were taken weekly, beginning one week after surgery from the middle ear artery. The blood was then stored in a refrigerator until chemical digestion. 24-hr urine samples were obtained weekly by using specially designed plastic metabolic cages, in which urine was filtered through two sieves, which separated feces and food matter. The volume of urine was measured and the urine was stored at room temperature in sealed, plastic vials.

After a period of 6 weeks the rabbits were euthanized and the following organs were removed for chemical analysis: appendix, brain, heart, kidney, liver, lung, and thymus. The bolus of implanted granules was located and a sample of muscle tissue was taken near the implant. The tissues were frozen in a deep freezer, -70°C, until digestion. The duration until sacrifice was determined by using previous histological data showing that the granules implanted in the mandible were excavated after one to two months.[10]

The tissue and blood samples were chemically digested in concentrated nitric acid using a microwave digester. The concentrations of elemental Si was determined by flame atomic absorption spectrophotometry (AAS, Perkin Elmer 5100, Norwalk, CT). One way ANOVA was performed to determine the statistical significance of the differences between the implanted and the control groups.

RESULTS

The urinary excretion rates of Si from control and implanted groups are shown in Figure 1: they were not significantly different until week 5 and 6 ($p < 0.05$). The concentrations of Si measured in the urine was 60±11 ppm, well below saturation (~180 ppm).[9]

The first initial drop of urinary Si of the implanted group was most likely due to the fact that all the experimental animals exhibited a decrease in urinary output during the first week. This temporary reduction can be attributed to the surgical trauma. In this study, no fluids were supplemented during or after surgery.

It appears that more Si was excreted in the implant group starting sometime between the second and third week, thus representing the removal of Si from the implanted BGG. The increase was about 3 mg/day (10 - 7 mg/day, from Figure 1). The increased rate remained constant and did not appear to increase or decrease. There was a total of 315 mg of Si implanted in the rabbit. (1500 mg of bioactive glass implanted; 45% of bioactive glass is silica; 46.7% of silica is Si.) At 3 mg/day, 13% of the Si was removed in the last two weeks.

Table 1 compares the Si concentrations of the harvested organs from both groups. The appendix was analyzed because it is a large lymphoid tissue found in the peritoneum. No significant accumulation of Si was found in any of the peripheral organs. Elevated Si was only found in the muscle tissue surrounding the implant. No significant differences in blood Si concentrations were found between implanted and control groups (data not shown).

Table 1. Concentrations of Si in organs harvested from control and implanted groups. * The only significant difference between groups was found in the muscle tissue close to the implant.

Tissue	Control ppm of Si	Implanted ppm of Si	P value
Appendix	11.2±0.99	10.3±0.70	0.506
Brain	2.80±0.12	2.71±0.10	0.581
Heart	2.88±0.10	2.94±0.09	0.672
Kidney	5.16±1.05	4.46±0.94	0.637
Liver	3.46±0.78	2.45±0.70	0.371
Lung	2.46±0.08	2.23±0.07	0.080
Muscle	7.0±5.8	29.1±5.2	0.024 *
Thymus	3.8±0.38	2.4±0.31	0.066

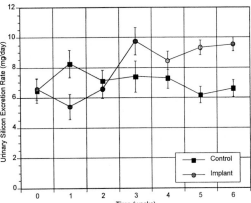

Figure 1. Urinary Si excretion rate for control and implant groups (n=4,5 respectively). There was a significant elevated excretion rate for the implant group for weeks 5 and 6 (p = 0.0076,0.025 respectively). Week 0 was sampled the day before surgery and Week 1 was sampled immediately after surgery.

DISCUSSION

Since measurable levels of Si were found in the urine, the Si-release product in the blood must be relatively small in order for it to pass through kidney filtration. In humans, the size of molecules passing through filtration is approximately 18 Å.[1] This increased urinary Si supports the hypothesis that the silica gel from the reacted BGG is dissolved into the blood stream and removed by the kidney.

In a previous study, the BGG were fully excavated between one and two months.[10] In our study, after 1 month, 13% of the Si was excreted. This reduced rate is ascribed to the geometry of the implantation. The large amount of granules was placed into the muscle as a small bolus, which could have limited the effective surface area of the dissolution process. The observed rate of Si excretion was also much slower than results from an *in vitro* dissolution study performed by Radin et al.[8] in which 45S5 BGG (300-355 μm) were immersed in fluid with plasma electrolytes and serum proteins. As expected in the *in vitro* case, the Si release was much faster. All of the Si release occurred in the first week.

Assuming that the concentration of local muscle was uniform and the Si diffused into a volume of 64 cm^3 (4x4x4) per implant, the percent of Si from the implant bound in the local muscle at the end of the study is 1%. This pool of Si is significantly less than the amount of Si found in the urine.

Si was not found to be increased in any of the major organs. These data further corroborate the findings of the histological analyses of the same organs of animals in other studies employing the bioactive glass granules of narrow size range. BGG (45S5, 300-355 μm) were implanted in 8 mm drilled defects in each ilia of the rabbit. After one month, the regional lymph nodes, kidney, liver and spleen were histologically normal.[6] BGG granules (45S5, 300-355 μm) were also implanted in the femoral metaphyses of beagles. After six months, no deviations from the normal histological appearance were observed in the kidney, liver and spleen.[5]

In the present rabbit model, it was found that the body excreted the excess Si. However, in trace amounts Si is naturally found in the body, and the possible role of Si with respect to bone development has been previously suggested. The potential for an effect on bone tissue was first described by Carlisle, who found Si to be uniquely localized in active growth areas in young bone of mice and rats.[2] In subsequent studies, it has been suggested that dietary Si is an essential trace element required for normal growth and development of bone tissue and connective tissue, since Si-deficiency caused abnormalities in these tissues.[3,11] Support for Si's metabolic role in bone tissue at the cellular level is provided by evidence of its presence in bone cells. The Si concentration was found to be especially high in the metabolically active state of the cell, the osteoblast, where Si was found to be localized in the mitochondria.[3,7]

These reports regarding Si as an essential element required for bone tissue formation and the fact that bone tissue forms in the excavated granules and not on their exterior raises the idea that the differentiation of the osteoprogenitor cells may be related to the exposure of the internal silica gel during the resoprtion process. Regardless, differentiation of osteoprogenitor cells caused by a synthetic graft material is a unique, beneficial biological phenomenon that is not affected by previous Si resoprtion and removal.

CONCLUSION

In a rabbit model with intramuscular implants of bioactive glass granules we observed that Si diffused into the local tissue around the implant, entered the bloodstream or lymph, and was excreted in the urine. The concentrations of Si found in the urine were well below saturation and no accumulation of Si was found in the major organs. These data suggest that the increased Si excretion rate was within the animal's physiological range. In the initial stages, the resorbed silica gel is harmlessly excreted in soluble form through the urine.

ACKNOWLEDGEMENTS

In part, Orthovita, Malvern, PA.

REFERENCES

1.   Berne RM, Levy MN, *Physiology*, 2nd ed. St. Louis: C.V. Mosby, 1988: 733-135.
2.   Carlisle EM. *Science* 1970; **167**:279-280.
3.   Carlisle EM. *Ciba Foundation Symposium* 1986; **121**:123-139.
4.   Carlisle EM. *Federation Proceedings* 1975; **34**:927.
5.   Flaitz CM, Cohen C, and Vresilovic E, *Int J Oral & Maxillofacial Imp*, in prep.
6.   Flaitz CM, Ducheyne P, Metsger DS, Rieger MR, *Int J Oral & Maxillofacial Imp*, in prep.
7.   Landis WJ, Lee DD, Brenna JT, Chandra S, Morrison GH. *Calcified Tiss Int* 1986; **38**:52-59.
8.   Radin S, Ducheyne P, Falaize S, Hammond A. *Bioceramics* 1997; **10**:45-48.
9.   Sauer F, Laughland DH, Davidson WM. *Canadian J Biochem Phys* 1959; **37**:183-191.
10. Schepers E, De Clercq M, Ducheyne P, Kempeneers R *J Oral Rehab* 1991; **18**, 439-452.
11. Schwarz K, Milne DB. *Nature* 1972; **239**:333-334.

Bioceramics Volume 11, edited by R. Z. LeGeros and J.P. LeGeros
(Proceedings of the 11th International Symposium on Ceramics in Medicine)
New York, NY, USA, November 1998
© 1998 by World Scientific Publishing Co. Pte. Ltd.

INFLAMMATORY POTENTIAL OF *IN VIVO* AGED BASIC CALCIUM PHOSPHATE (BCP) CRYSTALS

F. Prudhommeaux[1,2], C. Rey[3], A. Meunier[2], T. Bardin[1]

[1]Laboratoire de Physiopathologie Synoviale, ER 254 , 6 rue Guy Patin, 75475, Paris Cedex 10, France.
[2]present address: Orthopaedic Research Lab., UPRES-A CNRS 7052, 10 av de Verdun, 75010 Paris, France.
[3]Lab. Physico-Chimie des Solides, URA CNRS 445, Toulouse, France.

ABSTRACT:

The aim of this study was to compare the inflammatory potential of synthetic native versus *in vivo* aged BCP crystals. Three synthetic BCP crystals were tested: stoechiometric hydroxyapatite (HAY), Carbonated Apatite (CA) containing 3.2% of carbonate and Octacalcium phosphate (OCP). Crystal aging was achieved by introducing BCPs in a diffusion chamber (DC) then implanted intraperitoneally in a rat for a period of time ranging from 6h to 2 weeks. Aged and native BCPs were tested using the conventional air pouch model. Aging and air pouch testing were performed in the same animal. All 3 tested crystals underwent surface modifications as revealed by FTIR analysis, consisting of protein adsorption and carbonate enrichment, through material-dependent processes: HAY adsorbed significantly less proteins and demonstrated a low carbonate enrichment onto the surface through a maturation process. Native CA crystals, grew through secondary nucleation. In the mean time, CA adsorbed significantly less proteins than OCP (p<0.02). OCP experienced much more surface modifications. As revealed by TEM, new crystals made of carbonated apatite grew through heterogeneous nucleation, while proteins were extensively adsorbed. These different aging processes induced variable inflammatory properties: native CA induced acute inflammation which was inhibited after aging, while native and aged HAY were not phlogistic, and native and aged OCP were responsible for acute inflammatory responses. Competition between protein adsorption (acting as a passivation process) and new CA deposition (responsible for a continuous inflammatory activation) was responsible for the differences in biological responses. This study suggests that aging of BCPs should be taken into account when considering their long term in-vivo tolerance.

KEY WORDS: Inflammatory potential; In vivo Aging; Basic Calcium Phosphate crystals;

INTRODUCTION:

The need for bone substitutes is still of major concern. Among nowadays studied biomaterials, basic calcium phosphates constitute promising candidates, due to their similarities in composition to native hard tissues [1] and their ability to bond directly to bone [2]. In fact, according to their physico-chemical characteristics BCP ceramics can evoke after implantation normal bone healing and/or controlled bioresorption. This direct bonding ability is related to their bioactivity [3]. When BCP materials are exposed to biological fluids, they experience aging, complex physico-chemical reactions occur on their surface leading to the formation of a carbonate-rich apatitic layer on which bone may grow and thus facilitates implant osteointegration. However some questions still need to be answered : biocompatibility studies of BCPs in particulate form have given rise to contradictory results [4-6]. Further more, no data are available about their biocompatibility, once aging has occurred. The aim of this study was to quantify surface modifications induced by *in vivo* implantation and to compare the inflammatory potential of *in vivo* aged versus native crystals.

MATERIALS & METHODS

Three synthetic BCP crystals were tested: Stoechiometric hydroxyapatite synthesized according to the Young method (HAY); AB Carbonated Apatite (CA) containing 3.2% of carbonate; Octacalcium phosphate (OCP), obtained by direct precipitation.
Crystal aging was achieved by injecting 10 mg of BCP in a diffusion chamber [7] (DC) implanted intraperitoneally in a rat for a period of time ranging from 6 hours to 2 weeks. Surface modifications were sequentially studied by FTIR spectroscopy where quantitative comparisons before and after aging were obtained by evaluating the ratios of carbonate and organic matter (OM) contents over phosphate contents for each sample [8, 9].

One week-aged or native BCP crystals inflammatory potential was tested using the conventional air pouch model [10]. Aging and air pouch testing were performed in the same animal. Six animals per crystal type (aged and native) were tested. Two animals implanted with empty DCs were used as negative control. Statistical analysis was performed using Mann & Whitney tests.

RESULTS

The physico-chemical characteristics of the 3 tested crystal types are summarized in table 1. When exposed to body fluids through *in vivo* implantation, the 3 tested BCP crystals exhibited diverse time-dependent evolution pathways as revealed by FTIR spectroscopy (Figure 1). These aging processes consisted in two phenomenon: a surface protein adsorption (as revealed by amide bands) and a carbonate enrichment.

Table 1: Physico-chemical characteristics	HAY	CA	OCP
Specific surface area (m²/gm)	7	110	26
Ca/P ratio	1.67	1.34	1.33

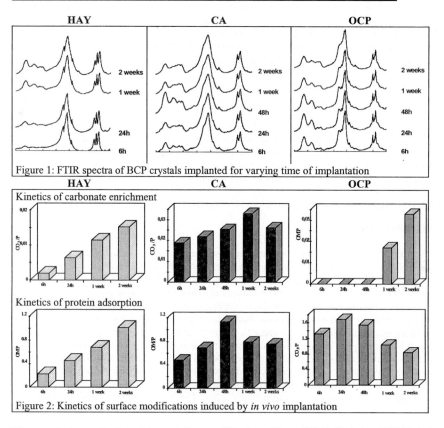

Figure 1: FTIR spectra of BCP crystals implanted for varying time of implantation

Figure 2: Kinetics of surface modifications induced by *in vivo* implantation

The quantitative evaluation of these surface modifications (Figure 2) revealed that OCP crystals adsorbed first a considerable amount of OM; after 24h, the amount decreased as OCP started to transform progressively into carbonate apatite. After 2 weeks the amount of OM was similar to that found on CA. Similar to biological apatites, CA crystals did not exhibit important modifications, but were associated at the earliest stage with OM which decreased after 48 hours. HAY crystals, often chosen as a reference for experimental studies, showed a very different reactivity. They adsorbed at first very low amount of OM, then the formation of carbonate apatite was observed and the amount of OM increased. The final major mineral surface appeared to be carbonated apatite in the 3 crystal types studied. Crystal TEM observation before and after 1 week of *in vivo* implantation revealed morphological as well as ultrastructural changes (Figure 3). For CA and HAY samples, individual crystals were no more distinguishable from amorphous like clumps. On the contrary, for aged OCP crystals, we were able to observe the native plate-like crystals among which small and tiny needle-shaped crystals had appeared. This new crystallographic phase was electron dense and appeared organized perpendicularly to native crystal faces.

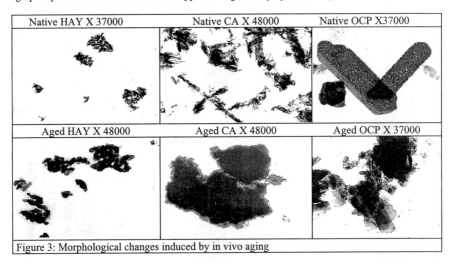

| Native HAY X 37000 | Native CA X 48000 | Native OCP X37000 |
| Aged HAY X 48000 | Aged CA X 48000 | Aged OCP X 37000 |

Figure 3: Morphological changes induced by in vivo aging

These different aging processes have modified the inflammatory properties of these BCPs (Figure 4). Their injection in the air pouch model induced variable volume of exsudates as well as cell densities. The volume of exsudates induced by aged CA and HAY remained low and were similar to those obtained with native crystals. On the contrary, aging OCP resulted in a significantly decreased volume of exsudate (p=0.02). Cellular densities significantly decreased with aged CA (p=0.03) and HAY (p=0.02), demonstrating a decrease in the inflammatory process. On contrary, this parameter remained identical between native or aged OCP and was larger than both aged CA and HAY (p<0.03).

DISCUSSION

Our results confirmed that when implanted in *in vivo* but acellular environment, tested BCPs underwent variable surface protein adsorption and carbonate enrichment according to crystal type and time allowed for aging. The formation of an intervening carbonated-apatitic layer on bioactive implants has already been reported both *in vivo* and *in vitro* [11-15]. However our results revealed that aging process may differ according to crystal type. Although the final crystal structure found on the surface of all aged BCPs was CA, the forming process was material dependent: it was either the result of secondary nucleation and/or maturation (CA and HAY) or heterogeneous nucleation and crystal growth of a 2nd phase (OCP). Since the inflammatory potential of particles is determined by their surface properties, the modifications induced by their *in vivo* implantation resulted in a change of their phlogogenic properties. Competition between protein adsorption (acting as a passivation process) and new CA deposition (responsible for a continuous inflammatory activation) was responsible for the various biological responses, observed in BCP-crystal-induced arthropathies: HAY was non inflammatory, CA induced acute reactions which spontaneously resumed, while OCP triggered acute inflammation which became chronic.

CONCLUSION

The biocompatibility study of a bioactive material performed with native crystals may not allow prediction of their long term biological response since their interactions with body fluids modify their inflammatory potential. As a consequence, aging should be considered as an intrinsic mechanism of long term tolerance.

1. Volume of exsudates

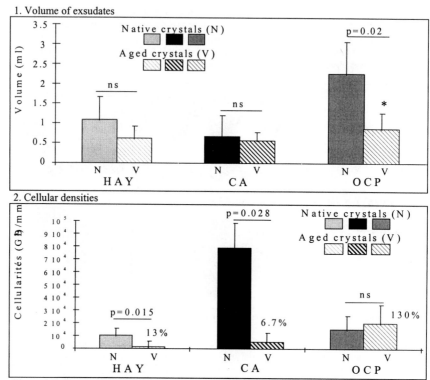

Figure 4: Inflammatory potential of *in vivo* aged versus native BCP crystals

REFERENCES:

1. Glimcher M, In: American Physiological Society, ed. *Handbook of physiology-Endocrinolgy VIII*, Washington 1976: 25-115.
2. Hench LL, Splinter RJ, Allen WC, Greenlee TK, *J Biomed Mat Res* 1971; **2**: 117-141.
3. Damien CJ, Ricci JL, Christel P, Alexander H, Patat JL, *Calcif Tissue Int* 1994; **55**: 151-8.
4. Nagase M, Baker DG, Schumacher HR, *J Rheumatol* 1988; **15**: 1334-1338.
5. Pizzoferrato A, Vespucci A, Ciapetti G, Stea S, Tarbusi C, *J Biomed Mater Res* 1987; **21**: 419-428.
6. Rae T, *Critical Reviews in Biocompatibility* 1986; **2**: 97-126.
7. Ashton B, Allen T, Howlett C, Eaglesom C, Hattori A, Owen M, *Clin Orthop Rel Res* 1980; **151**: 294-307.
8. Rey C, Shimizu M, Collins B, Glimcher MJ, *Calcif Tissue Int* 1990; **46**: 384-394.
9. Rey C, Renugopalakrishman V, Collins B, Glimcher MJ, *Calcif Tissue Int* 1991; **49**: 251-258.
10. Edwards J, Sedwick A, Willoughby D, *J Pathol* 1981; **134**: 147-156.
11. Amrah-Bouali S, Rey C, Lebugle A, Bernache D, *Biomaterials* 1994; **15**: 269-272.
12. Dalcusi G, LeGeros RZ, Heughebaert, Barbieux I, *Calcif Tisuue Int* 1990; **46**: 20-27.
13. Ducheyne P, Radin S, King L, *J Biomed Mater Res* 1993; **27**: 25-34.
14. Neo M, Nakamura T, Ohtsuki C, Kokubo T, Yamamuro T, *J Biomed Mat Res* 1993; **27**: 999-1006.
15. Royer P, Amrah-Bouali S, Freche M, Rey C, Rouquet N, Bonel G, *Bioceramic* 1992; **5**: 95-101.

ACKNOWLEDGMENTS:

This research has been supported in part by Roche France S.A. and CNRS.

Bioceramics Volume 11, edited by R. Z. LeGeros and J.P. LeGeros
(Proceedings of the 11th International Symposium on Ceramics in Medicine)
New York, NY, USA, November 1998
© 1998 by World Scientific Publishing Co. Pte. Ltd.

BONE-BONDING STRENGTH OF ALUMINA BEAD COMPOSITE

S. Shinzato[1], M. Kobayashi[1], H. Fujita[1], K. Choju[2], T. Kokubo[3] and T. Nakamura[1]

[1]Department of Orthopaedic Surgery, Faculty of Medicine, Kyoto University, 54 Kawahara-cho, Shogoin, Sakyo-ku, Kyoto 606-8507, Japan; [2]Nippon Electric Glass Co. Ltd., Otsu, Japan; [3]Division of Material Chemistry, Faculty of Engineering, Kyoto University, Kyoto, Japan.

ABSTRACT

We developed alumina bead composite (ABC), consisting of alumina bead powder (AL-P) and bisphenol-*a*-glycidyl metacrylate(Bis-GMA) based resin. AL-P was composed of amorphous and δ-crystal phases of alumina. Mechanical testing of ABC was strong enough for use under weight-bearing conditions. Another composite (αALC) filled with α-alumina powder was used as referential material. The composite-plate was made *in situ* by radical polymerization reactions in a rectangular mold (15X10X2 mm), which was soaked in saline. Solidified ABC had uncured surface layer on which saline contacted because of inhibition of polymerization by O_2 in saline and was soon implanted into the proximal metaphysis of tibiae of male Japanese white rabbits and the failure load was measured by detaching test 10 weeks after implantation. The failure load of ABC (1.91 ± 1.2 kgf, n=8) on its uncured surface was significantly ($p<0.001$) higher than those of α ALC (0.35 ± 0.33 kgf, n=8). Direct bone formation on the uncured surface of ABC and αALC was observed by CMR, Giemsa surface staining and SEM. Bone ingrowth into the composite was observed only on the uncured surface of ABC. ABC shows promise as a osteoconductive and mechanically strong biomaterial.

KEYWORDS: Alumina, Amorphous, Bis-GMA, Composite, Bone-bonding strength

INTRODUCTION

We developed new composite (ABC), consisting of alumina bead powder (AL-P) and bisphenol-*a*-glycidyl metacrylate (Bis-GMA) based resin and reported its excellent osteoconductivity in rat tibiae previously. [1,2] AL-P was manufactured by fusing crushed α-alumina powder and subsequently quenching it. Purpose of this study is to measure its bone-bonding strength by the detaching test and examine the bone-composite interface histologically.

MATERIALS AND METHODS

1) Preparation of the composite-plate

Bulk α-alumina (99.5% pure Al_2O_3) was put in an electrical melting furnace from calcined alumina powder (99% pure Al_2O_3), produced by Bayer's prosess. The bulk α-alumina was then pulverized and particles under 10 μm in diameter were collected. The collected powder was then fused and quenched subsequently to produce AL-P (99.7% pure Al_2O_3). According to powder X-ray diffraction, it was composed of amorphous and δ-crystal phases of alumina in its main crystal structure. Its average particle size was 3.5 μm and specific surface area was 0.7 m^2/g. AL-P was fused and quenched again in order to produce α-alumina powder as a referential material. Powder X-ray diffraction of the powder showed that it contained only α-crystal phase. Its average size was 3.4 μm and specific surface area was 1.1 m^2/g. Each powder was silane-treated with γ-methacryloxypropyltrimethoxy silane.

In order to make composite-plates of ABC, two types of paste (called B and T paste) were prepared. Monomers were prepared from mixing equal weights of Bis-GMA and triethyleneglycol dimethacrylate (TEGDMA). B paste contained AL-P, monomers, and benzoyl peroxide at 1.5% per unit weight of the monomers. T paste contained AL-P, monomers, and N,N-dimethyl-p-toluidine at 1.0% per unit weight of the monomers. The weight ratio of the filler powder mixed into the composite was 70%.

B and T paste were mixed and a composite-plate was made *in situ* by radical polymerization reactions in a rectangular mold (15X10X2 mm), which was soaked in saline at 37 ℃. Solidified ABC had **uncured** surface layer on which saline contacted, because of inhibition of polymerization by O_2 in saline. Solidified ABC had **cured** surface on which the bottom of the mold contacted. α ALC was also made by the same way as that of ABC. The ultimate bending strength, elastic modulus of bending (Young's modulus), compressive strength of ABC and α ALC were 151 ± 10 and 122 ± 8, 7.2 ± 0.2 and 8.8 ± 0.2, 196 ± 4 and 193 ± 17, measured after soaking in simulated body fluid (SBF) at 37℃ for one day. Average surface roughness of ABC and α ALC was 0.66 ± 0.03 μm and 1.28 ± 0.51 μm, respectively. There was no significant difference between those values. The thickness of the uncured surface layer of ABC and α ALC was less than 10 μm.

2) Animal Experiments

Mature male Japanese white rabbits weighting between 2.9 and 3.9 kg were reared and the experiments carried out at the Institute of Laboratory Animals, Faculty of Medicine, Kyoto University. The guidelines for animal experimentation of Kyoto University were carefully observed. Soon after the composite-plates were made, they were implanted into the proximal metaphysis of rabbit tibiae. The rabbits were anesthetized by an intravenous injection of Nembtal (50 mg/kg body weight) and local administration of 0.5% Lidocaine. Using sterile surgical techniques, a 3 cm incision was made on the anteromedial aspect of the proximal metaphysis of the tibia. a critical size hole was made from the medial cortex to the lateral cortex parallel to the longitudinal axis of the proximal metaphysis. Both tibiae were operated on and one of the plates was implanted in the direction that uncured surface layer faced anteriorly, perforating the tibiae and protruding from both the medial and lateral cortex symmetrically to the longitudinal axis of the proximal metaphysis (Fig. 1a). [3,4,5]

Each experimental group consisted of 6 animals (12 legs) which were sacrificed with an overdose of Nembtal at 10 weeks after surgery. A segment of the tibiae containing the implant was excised (Fig. 1b) and the detaching test by Nakamura's method was done for 4 animals (8 legs). Remained 2 animals (4 legs) in each group were prepared only for histological examination. During the detaching test, each segment was held by a hook connected to an Instron-type testing machine, an autograph (Model-1323, Aikoh Engineering, Nagoya, Japan). The bone segment with the plate was placed horizontally and pulled in the opposite direction at a cross head speed of 3.5 cm/min. [3,4,5] Firstly, the failure load when the bone detached from one side of the plate was measured (Fig. 1c). Secondly, the failure load at the other side of the plate was measured (Fig. 1d). Values are expressed as the mean ± standard deviation. Groups were compared using one-way analysis of variance (ANOVA). P values less than 0.05 were considered statistically significant.

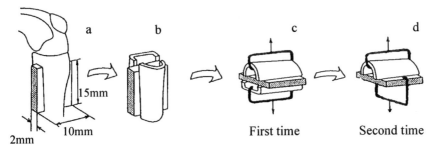

Figure 1. The preparation of rabbit tibia and the detaching test

3) Histological Examination

The specimens were fixed in 70% ethanol. The specimens were dehydrated in serial concentrations of ethanol and then embedded in polyester resin. Thin sections (300 μm thick) were cut perpendicular to the axis of the tibia with a band saw. The specimens were ground to a thickness of 120 μm using a diamond lap disk for evaluation by contact microradiography (CMR) and Giemsa surface staining. Additional sections (500 μm thick) were polished with diamond paper for analysis of the interface between the composite and the bone using a SEM connected to an EDX. X-ray intensities for calcium, phosphorus and alumina were analyzed across the composite-bone interface.

RESULTS

1) Evaluation of Bonding Ability and Failure Load

Of the tested samples, most of the plates were detached from the bone on the cured surface when they were connected to the hook. Therefore, the detaching failure load was recorded as 0 kgf. Macroscopically, every implant was detached at the bone-plate interface. The detaching failure loads of each plate and their statistical results are shown in Table 1. The detaching failure load of ABC was 1.91 ± 1.23 kgf (n=8) on its uncured surface, 0.24 ± 0.38 kgf (n=8) on its cured surface. The detaching failure load of αALC was 0.35 ± 0.33 kgf (n=8) on its uncured surface, 0.04 ± 0.09 kgf (n=8) on its cured surface. The failure loads of ABC on its uncured surface were significantly higher than those of αALC (p<0.001) and ABC on its cured surface (p<0.001).

Table 1. Failure Loads (kgf)

Composite	Uncured Surface	Cured Surface
ABC	1.91 ± 1.23	0.24 ± 0.38
αALC	0.35 ± 0.33	0.04 ± 0.09

Mean $\pm$ S.D.; n=8 ANOVA at 0.001 level of significance. Between ABC and αALC at uncured is significant. Between uncured and cured at ABC is significant.

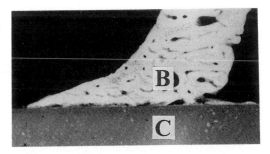

Figure 2. CMR of ABC B, Bone; C, composite
(Original magnification x40)

2) Histological Evaluation

Direct bone formation on the uncured surface of ABC (Fig. 2) and αALC without interposed soft tissue layer was observed by CMR, Giemsa surface staining, and newly formed bone connected to the uncured surface of ABC and α ALC was also observed. On the cured surface of ABC and α ALC, radiolucent zone or soft tissue layer was observed between bone and the cured surface. Examination by SEM showed that bone formed directly on the bone-composite interface of the uncured surface of both ABC (Fig.3) and α ALC (Fig.4). Moreover, bone ingrowth into the composite was observed only on the uncured surface of ABC (Fig. 3, between arrows).

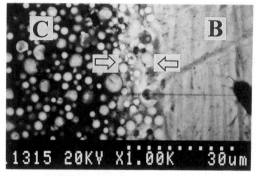

Figure 3. SEM of ABC C, composite; B, Bone

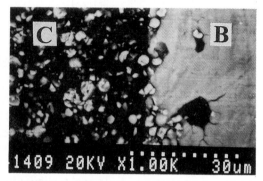

Figure 4. SEM of α ALC C, composite; B, Bone

DISCUSSION

The present study showed that both ABC and α ALC were in direct contact with bone on the uncured surface and that the bonding strength of ABC on the uncured surface was significantly higher than the rest. These result indicated that the uncured surface is needed for having the bone-bonding strength. When the composite is implanted in *vivo* and polymerized *in situ*, the uncured surface layer can form. Because O_2 in blood inhibits radical polymerization reactions. In the uncured surface layer, unpolymerized monomer were dissolved and AL-Ps were uncovered. The surface property of AL-P may have ability of cell adhesion or protein adsorption [1,2] so bone can grow into the gaps between AL-Ps. In fact, this bone ingrowth into the composite was observed only on the uncured surface of ABC. ABC shows promise as a basis for developing a highly osteoconductive and mechanically strong biomaterial. We're now planning to evaluate its mechanical and biological properties after long-term implantation *in vivo*.

REFERENCES

1. M. Kobayashi, T. Nakamura, T. Kikutani, Y. Okada, N. Ikeda, S. Shinzato, and T. Kokubo, "Mecanical and biological properties of alumina bead composite," *Bioceramics* **10**, Elsevier Science, 313-316 (1997).
2. M. Kobayashi, T. Kikutani, T. Kokubo, and T. Nakamura, "Direct bone formation on alumina bead composite," *J. Biomed. Mater. Res.*, **37**, 554-565 (1997)
3. T. Nakamura, T. Yamamuro, S. Higashi, T. Kokubo, and S. Ito, "A new glass-ceramic for bone replacement : Evaluation of its bonding ability to bone tissue," *J. Biomed. Mater. Res.*, **19**, 685-698 (1985).
4. T. Kitsugi, T. Yamamuro, T. Nakamura, S. Higashi, Y. Kakutani, K. Hyakuna, S. Ito, T. Kokubo, M. Takagi, and T. Shibuya, "Bone bonding behavior of three kinds of apatite containing glass ceramics," *J. Biomed. Mater. Res.*, **20**, 1295-1307 (1986).
5. J. Tamura, T. Kitsugi, H. Iida, H. Fujita, T. Nakamura, T. Kokubo, and S. Yoshihara, "Bone bonding ability of bioactive bone cements," *Clin. Opthop.*, **343**, 183-191 (1997).

Bioceramics Volume 11, edited by R. Z. LeGeros and J.P. LeGeros
(Proceedings of the 11th International Symposium on Ceramics in Medicine)
New York, NY, USA, November 1998
© 1998 by World Scientific Publishing Co. Pte. Ltd.

RESORPTION OF COLLAGEN-CARBONATE APATITE-COMPLEX IN SKULL DEFECTS

T,Kajimoto [1], T.Tanabe [1], K.Kondou [1],S.Saku [1], K.Yamamoto [1] and Y. Doi [2]

Departments of [1] General Dentistry & Operative Dentistry and [2] Dental Materials & Technology, School of Dentistry, Asahi University,Gifu 501-02,Japan

ABSTRACT

Collagen-carbonate apatite-complex has been prepared and its usefulness as bone substitute materials has been evaluated in skull defects. To prepare the complex, carbonate apatite particles were placed in a mold under finger pressure, and the block obtained was sintered at 750°C to make porous, sintered carbonate apatite. Porous carbonate apatite blocks were then placed in collagen gel under vacuum, washed with alkaline solutions and air-dried. After crosslinking in the presence of phosvitin and alkaline phosphatase, each block was immersed in calcium β-glycerophosphate solutions for 2 weeks to induce the formation of apatite on collagen fibrils on the pore. The collagen-carbonate apatite-complex thus obtained was implanted in skull bone defects of Wister-strain rats. Sixteen Wister rats were used and they were sacrificed at 2 and 4 weeks after implantation. At 2 weeks after implantation, collagen appeared to resorb almost completely, and new bone formed in contact with sintered carbonate apatite particles without any significant inflammatory cell involvement. At 4 weeks after implantation, carbonate apatite particles resorbed almost completely, and new bone continued to form on the periphery of the pore to an appreciable extent. The new bone contained osteocytes and was as mineralized and dense as the host bone.

KEYWORDS: Collagen, Carbonate Apatites, Collagen apatite complex, Bone substitutes

Introduction

Many kinds of bone substitutes are applied to periodontal defects and poor alveolar ridge [1]. Sintered hydroxyapatite is the most popular material in these bone substitutes. But sintered hydroxyapatite is rarely resorbed by osteoclasts. When sintered hydroxyapatite particles are implanted in periodontal defects, they flow out from recipient sites before their stabilization by connective tissue ingrowth and seem to be difficult to handle [2]. Important ability of bone substitutes is to fit to a form of a recipient site, stay at recipient sites for a certain period of time and resorb at a rate similar to bone growth [3]. Several methods have been proposed to eliminate this problem, including fixation with collagen [4]. In the present study, a collagen carbonate apatite-complex was prepared in calcium β-glycerophosphate solutions using reconstituted collagen gel, which was immersed in sintered, porous carbonate apatite blocks. The usefulness of collagen-carbonate apatite-complex as a bone substitute was evaluated in vivo. In skull defects of Wister rats, collagen-carbonate apatite-complex was implanted and the rats were sacrificed at 2 and 4 weeks after implantation for light microscopy .

MATERIALS AND METHODS

Preparation of carbonate apatite
Carbonate apatites were prepared in a way similar to that described previously [5], by mixing 8L of 2mol calcium nitrate solution and 2L of 1.2mol disodium hydrogen phosphate solution containing 6 mol disodium carbonate for 3 days at 100°C and pH 9.0±0.1. The pH was maintained constant by automatic addition of hydrochloric acid. Each precipitate was centrifuged, the supernatant decanted, and the centrifugate washed 10 times with de-ionized, double-distilled water and then freeze-dried. Carbonate apatite particles with sizes between 300 and 500 μm were placed in a mold under finger pressure and then were heated at 750°C for 2 hours to make sintered, porous carbonate apatite blocks.

Mixing carbonate apatite and collagen gel
Porous carbonate apatite blocks were placed in collagen gel and evacuated under vacuum to allow collagen gel to diffuse into inner macro pores of sintered carbonate apatite blocks (Fig. 1).

Crosslinking
Crosslinking procedures were essentially the same as those used previously [6]. Carbonate apatite-collagen mixture was incubated for 6 days at 37°C in 30 ml of 200mM tris solution containing alkaline phosphatase (0.13μg/ml.EC3.1.3.1;Sigma Chemical Co.), egg yolk phosvitin (0.13μg/ml;Sigma Chemical Co.), and a crosslinking reagent of dimethyl suberimidate hydrochloride (1mg/ml;Nakari Tesque,Inc.). The carbonate apatite-crosslinked collagen mixture was then washed several times with 200mM Tris solution to remove unreacted chemicals and by-products.

Collagen-carbonate-apatite complex
Freshly prepared, carbonate apatite-crosslinked collagen mixture was first incubated in 10ml of 200mM Tris solution containing alkaline phosphatase (0.13μg/ml) and egg yolk phosvitin (0.13μg/ml) for 3h at 37°C. After incubation, the supernatant was decanted and the carbonate apatite -crosslinked collagen was incubated for 20h in 40 ml of 6mM calcium β-glycerophosphate solution buffed at pH9.0 with 200mM tris at 37°C. The 3- and 20-h incubations were repeated 14 times, washed thoroughly each time, to induce and accumulate mineral deposits on the collagen fibers and carbonate apatite particles.
Skull defects

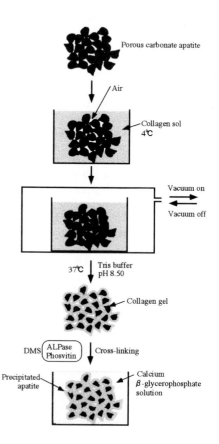

Figure 1. Flow chart for the preparation of collagen-carbonate apatite complex.

Sixteen Wister rats weighing 300-350g were used. A 4mm diameter defect was made through each parietal bone with a trephine. Defects of eight rats were filled with collagen-carbonate apatite-complex and eight defects were left empty. The animals were sacrificed at 2 and 4 weeks after implantation. The skullcaps were removed and fixed with 10% neutral formalin, decalcified with neutral ethylene diamine tetraacetic acid, embedded in paraffin and sectioned. Sections of 5-8 μm thickness were stained with hematoxylin and eosin (HE) for light microscopy.

RESULTS AND DISCUSSION

Figures 2 and 3 compare photomicrographs of defects filled with (Fig.2) and without (Fig.3) the collagen-carbonate apatite-complex at 2 weeks after implantation. Collagen, one of the constituents of the complex used, appeared to resorb almost completely within 2 weeks after implantation. No significant invasion of inflammatory cells and giant macrophages were evident. New bone formed to an appreciable extent from the edge of the defect and also in the central part of the defect as shown in Fig.1. Some particles of sintered carbonate apatite, the other constituent of the complex, appeared to be embedded in newly formed bone and no matrix material was evident between the particle and the newly formed bone. Most of the defect areas, however, were filled with connective tissues. On the other hand, in the defects left empty, no bone was evident, only connective tissues.

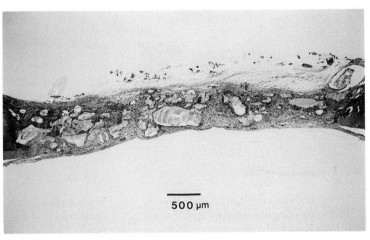

Fig.2 A photomicrograph of skull defects filled with collagen-carbonate apatite-complex at 2 weeks after implantation. Note that collagen, one of the constituents of the complex resorbed almost completely. New bone is evident on the edge of skull defect as well as in the central part of the defect.

Figures 4 and 5 compare photomicrographs of defects filled with (Fig.4) and without (Fig.5) the collagen-carbonate apatite-complex at 4 weeks after implantation. In the presence of the complex, most of the defect areas were filled with newly formed bone. Particles of sintered carbonate apatite

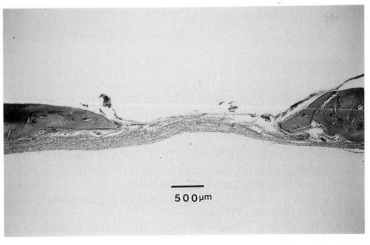

Fig.3 A photomicrograph of unfilled skull defects at 2 weeks after implantation. The defect is filled with connective tissues and no bone is evident.

are hardly identifiable, indicating that they resorbed almost completely within 4 weeks after implantation. In the defects left empty, no bone was evident, only connective tissues. These findings suggest that the collagen-carbonate apatite-complex resorbed almost completely, while forming new bone without any significant invasion of inflammatory cells and giant macrophages, indicating that the collagen-carbonate apatite complex examined in the present study would be quite useful as a bioresorbable bone substitute.

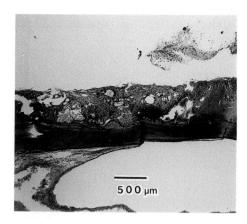

Fig.4 A photomicrograph of skull defects filled with collagen-carbonate apatite-complex at 4 weeks after implantation. Particles of sintered carbonate apatite, the other constituent of the complex, resorbed almost completely and was replaced with newly formed bone to an appreciable extent.

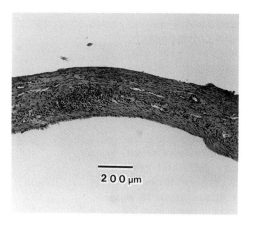

Fig.5 A photomicrograph of unfilled skull defects at 4 weeks after implantation. The defect is filled with connective tissues and still no bone is evident.

REFERENCES

1. Becker W, Lynch SE, Lekholm U, Becker BE, Caffese R, Donath K, Sanchez R. J Periodont 1992;**63**:929-940.
2. Kanazawa A, Kajimoto T, Doi Y, Moriwaki Y, Iwayama Y. J.Japan.Soc.Periodont.1995;**37**:483-493.
3. Metsger DS, Driskell JD, Paulstrud JR. J Am Dent Assoc 1982;**105**:1035-1038.
4. Mehlish DR, Taylor TD, Leibold DG, Hiatt R, Waite DE, Waite PD, Laskin DM, Smith ST, Koretz MM. J Oral Mxillofac Surg 1987;**45**:408-413
5. Doi Y, Koda T, Adachi M, Wakamatsu N,Goto T, Kamemizu H, Moriwaki Y, Suwa Y. J Biomed Master Res 1995;**29**:1451-1457.
6. Doi Y, Horiguchi T, Y Moriwaki, Kitago H,Kajimoto T, Iwayama Y. J Biomed Master Res 1996;**31**:43-49.

Bioceramics Volume 11, edited by R. Z. LeGeros and J.P. LeGeros
(Proceedings of the 11th International Symposium on Ceramics in Medicine)
New York, NY, USA, November 1998
© 1998 by World Scientific Publishing Co. Pte. Ltd.

PRELIMINARY *IN VIVO* EVALUATION OF SYNTHETIC CALCIUM PHOSPHATE MATERIALS

A. M. Gatti[1], R.Z. LeGeros[2], E. Monari[1], and D. Tanza[1]

[1]Centro di Studio dei Biomateriali, Dip.Chirurgia, Univ. di Modena, Via del Pozzo 71, 41100, Modena, Italy;
[2]College of Dentistry, New York University, 345 East 24th Street, New York, NY, USA

ABSTRACT

Hydroxyapatite (HA) and tricalcium posphate (ß-TCP) are two commercially available calcium phosphate materials presently used as bone grafts. The purpose of this preliminary study was to evaluate the biocompatibility and biodegradation of calcium phophate preparations differing in composition: calcium deficient apatite (dAP), ceramic hydroxyapatite (HA), carbonate hydroxyapatite (CHA), fluoride-substituted apatite (FA), and magnesium-substituted tricalciumphosphate (ß-TCMP). The materials were prepared and characterized using x-ray diffraction and infrared absorption spectroscopy and biologicaly through in-vivo implantation in muscles and femural diaphyses of 2 rabbits. After 30 and 60 days, the implants were retrieved, fixed in 4% formaldehyde and processed for the histological and electron microscopic evaluations. The sections were microradiographed and observed under optical and scanning electron microscope with an x-ray microprobe.
All the samples showed biocompatibility and a good interface with soft and hard tissues. The materials differed in the degree of biodegradation. Conclusion: Calcium phosphates (substitutted apatites and tricalciumphosphates) of varying degrees of biodegradation can be used as bone graft materials for different applications.

Keywords: Hydroxyapatite, tricalciumphosphate, bonegraft

INTRODUCTION

The use of natural and synthetic materials in medicine and dentistry in place of autogenous bone for bone repair, augmentation and substitution has become more popular during the last 30 years. Calcium phosphate materials which are commercially available as bone graft materials include hydroxyapatite, HA; tricalcium-phosphate (ß-TCP); biphasic calcium phosphates (BCP), a mixture of HA and ß-TCP; coral-derived HA and bovine-bone derived HA [1-5]. The purpose of the present study was to evaluate the biocompatibility and comparative biodegradation of 5 calcium phosphate materials differing in composition implanted in non-osseous ans osseous sites.

MATERIALS AND METHODS

The following calcium phosphate materials were prepared according to methods previously described [6,7]:
(A) calcium deficient apatite, CadAP; (B) carbonate hydroxyapatite, CHA; (C) Ceramic calciumhydroxyapatite, HA; (D) Fluoride-substituted apatite, FA; and (E) magnesium-substituted tricalcium phosphate, ß-TCMP.
The materials were characterized using x-ray diffraction and infrared absorption spectroscopy (FTIR):
The materials were pressed into 1mm thick disks using a hydraulic press. The discs were broken into two equal parts, sterilized with ethylene oxide and implanted in surgically created dorsal muscular pockets and surgically drilled 4mm holes in femural and tibial diaphyses in two rabbits. The implanted sites were treated with antibiotic spray. After 30 and 60 days the rabbits were sacrificed and the materials with the surrounding biologic tissues explanted and fixed in 4% paraformaldheyde. The dehydratation was carried out in ascending concentration alcohols and embedded in

in 4% paraformaldheyde. The dehydratation was carried out in ascending concentration alcohols and embedded in PMMA.

The explanted materials were analyzed with X-radiography (Castellini, 65KV, Italia) in order to localize the HA samples in bone and in soft tissues before cutting the slices with a diamond saw (Accutom, Struers, Denmark) sections were obtained for the bone implants and 200mm thick sections were obtained for the implants in bone, 50?m slices for the soft tissue implants. The sections were further reduced to 20 μm by lapping for histological staining (Toluidine-blue) and for the optical microscopy. Some of the sections were prepared for the Scanning Electron Microscopy (SEM, XL40 Philips, The Netherlands) with an X-ray microprobe (Energy Dispersive System by EDAX) for the elemental analyses as previously described [8].

RESULTS

Part of the disks fragmented into smaller pieces after insertion. These little fragments degraded more easily. Histological results indicate no inflammatory reaction around the specimens after both 30 or 60 days.
No significant biodegradation were observed for materials A, B and C. Samples E became finely fragmented and after 60 days, it was very difficult to recognize them.

Figs. 1, 2, and 3 show SEM microphotographs, in backscattered mode, of samples B, D and E after 30-day implantation in muscular tissue. The granules appear fragmented in very fine debris. The more interesting results were detected in the bone implantation in femoral and tibial diaphyses. All the materials demonstrated an osteoconductive capacity, also after 30 days. Fig. 4 shows fragments of the sample A, in the middle of the cavity, connected by new bone trabeculae. They surround very closely the surface of HA debris.
Samples D and E became fragmented during implantation and developed higer surface contact with cells and a higher quantity of bone. The degradation of the materials appeared to start after 60 days. Fig. 5 shows a debris of the sample (R) surrounded by new bone and the arrows indicate that the surface is not smooth, but rough and in some points which have been partially resorbed. Sample E underwent a high degree of resorption (Fig. 6). The sample fragments surrounded by new bone trabeculae earlier were still visible but the surface appeared rough. However, degradation of the fragments which remained in the collagenous matrix appeared to continue after 60 days, as shown in Fig. 6.

CONCLUSIONS

The calcium phosphate materials used in this preliminary study presented similar capacity to stimulate the bone growth, since all the samples develop a close contact with bone. Sample A, B, and C were observed to degrade slower than the samples D and E; which may B related to the fragmentation of sample D and E.
The chemical degradation, of course, depends on the amount of the surface exposed to the biological fluids, so if these samples are obtained as granules of small size, their bioactivity can increase. This solution can be suitable when these apatites are used to repair the bone defects. Instead if they are employed in a bone augmentation operation, the better thing is to use the sample C or A or B, since they are characterized by a slow rate of degradation and allow the bone to grow Further studies are planned to identify the factors determining biodegradation: composition vs. particle size.

Acknowledgements
This work was supported in part by the Ministry of University and Scientific Research and Technology, MURST, of Italy (Gatti) and research grant no. DE 12388 from the National Institute for Dental Research of the National Institutes of Health (LeGeros). The authors are grateful to Ms. S. Piaggi and R. Salvatori (Italy) and to Drs. S. Lin and M. Retino (New York) for their technical assistance.

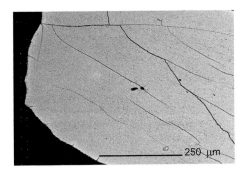

Fig. 1-BS microphotograph of granules of sample A in muscles after 30-day implantation.

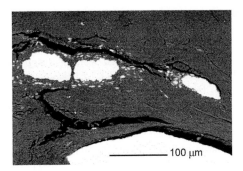

Fig. 2 -BS microphotograph of sample B in muscles after 30-day implantation.

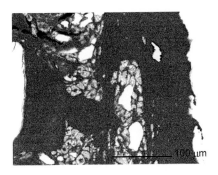

Fig. 3 - BS microphotograph of sample D in muscle after 30-day implantation.

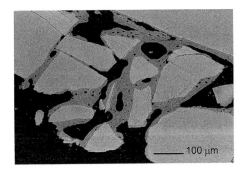

Fig. 4 - BS microphotograph of sample A after 60-day implantation in rabbit's femoral diaphysis.

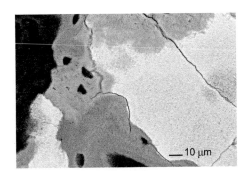

Fig. 5 - BS microphotograph of sample B after 60-day implantation in femoral diaphysis.

Fig. 6 - BS microphotograph of sample E after 60-day implantation in rabbit's bone.

REFERENCES

1. Jarcho M. *Clin Orthoped,* 1981, <u>157</u>: 259-269.
2. Wilson J. Merwin GE. *J Biomed Mater Res Appl Biomat,* 1988, <u>22:</u> 159-177.
3. Nery EB, LeGeros RZ, Lunch KL. *J Periodontol,* 1992; <u>63:</u> 729-735.
4. Piecuch JJ. *Dent Clin N Am,* 1992; 291-305.
5. Aoki H. *Science and Medical Application of Hydroxyapatite. 1991.* JAAS, Takayama Press, Tokyo.
6. LeGeros, RZ. *Calcium Phosphates in Oral Biology and Medicine.* Monographs in Oral Sciences, Vol 15, 1991, Karger, Basel.
7. Zapanta-LeGeros RZ. *Nature* <u>206:</u> 403-404.
8. Gatti AM, Zaffe D, Poli G. *Biomaterials,* 1990; 11: 513-517.

Bioceramics Volume 11, edited by R. Z. LeGeros and J.P. LeGeros
(Proceedings of the 11th International Symposium on Ceramics in Medicine)
New York, NY, USA, November 1998
© 1998 by World Scientific Publishing Co. Pte. Ltd.

BONE FORMATION WITH APATITE-COLLAGEN

I. Toda[1], N. Kitayama[2], H. Oonishi[3], M. Muraoka[2], F. Sugihara[4], Y. Gonda[2] and F. Suwa[1]

[1]Department of Anatomy and [2]First Department of Prosthodontics, Osaka Dental University, 8-1, Kuzuhahanazono-cho, Hirakata-shi, Osaka 573-1121, Japan; [3]Department of Orthopaedic Surgery, Artificial Joint Section and Biomaterial Research Laboratory, Osaka-Minami National Hospital, 677-6, Kido-cho, Kawachinagano-shi, Osaka 586-0001, Japan; [4]Research and Developmental Department, Nitta Gelatin Inc, 2-22, Futamata, Yao-shi, Osaka 581-0024, Japan.

ABSTRACT

This experimental study was performed to investigate vascularization and bone tissue reaction of apatite-collagen conjugated sponge implanted into jaw defects.

Octacalcium phosphate (OCP)-collagen conjugated sponge was employed as an experimental material, having hydration activity, together with type I collagen gel in a short time under physiological conditions.

Japanese monkeys were employed as experimental animals. Bilateral lower premolars and molars were extracted. After healing of the site, an artificial bone defect was made, and the material was inserted. These animals were sacrificed 2nd, 3rd and 8th week after operation. Acryl plastic was injected via the common carotid arteries utilizing the plastic injection method to prepare a microcast around the experimental region. The injected specimens were coated with gold in order to use scanning electron microscopy.

In first two weeks, this OCP-collagen sponge guided a dense capillary network and new bone formation was observed around apatitic OCP particles with osteoblasts in the experimental region. And it promoted osseous healing of the sight.

Application of this sponge in an alveolar bone defect promotes bone formation in preparation for prosthodontic treatment.

KEYWORDS: OCP, apatite-collagen sponge, bone formation, alveolar bone, microvasculature.

INTRODUCTION

We have investigated the bone tissue reaction of α-TCP conjugated collagen sponge applied to the tooth extracted socket [1].

Here, we inserted absorbable calcium phosphate conjugated collagen sponge to artificial bone defect, and then investigated the relationship between this material and osteogenesis, especially with the microvasculature changes, and qualitatively compared the bone tissue reaction of the sponge with that of α-TCP conjugated collagen sponge.

MATERIALS AND METHODS

Octacalcium phosphate (OCP)-collagen conjugated sponge (OCP-collagen sponge) (Fig. 1) was used as an experimental material. The procedure of preparing this material is modified of it α-tetracalcium phosphate conjugated collagen sponge (α-TCP-collagen sponge) in Bioceramics 9 [1].

Figure 1. OCP-collagen sponge material.

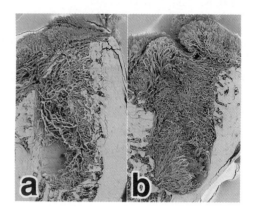

Figure 2. Two weeks after operation. x4.
a: Control site (SEM). b: Experimental site (SEM).

Six adult Japanese monkeys were employed in this study. The animals were anesthetized intraperitoneally with pentobarbital sodium. Bilateral lower premolars and molars were extracted. Over 10 weeks later, lingual and labial gingivoperiosteal flaps were risen on both sides of the experimental region. Artificial bone defects (4 mm in diameter and 8 mm in depth) were made on each side. On one side of the defects, OCP-collagen sponge was inserted immediately, but not on the other side of the defects for the control. After that gingivoperiosteal flap was carefully sutured. At 2nd, 3rd and 8th week after operation, the animals were euthanesized under the anesthesia. Blood vessels of the mandible were injected with methylmethacrylate plastics via common carotid arteries, according to the plastic injection method [2]. After the plastic had polymerized, experimental regions were cut out with a diamond belt-saw to produce a longitudinal section through the defect. The cut blocks were treated with 2% NaOCl for soft-tissue digestion, and sputter-coated with gold for a scanning electron microscopic examination (SEM).

Additionally the other cut blocks were fixed in a 10% formalin solution. These specimens were decalcified, embedded in paraffin and stained with hematoxylin-eosin for a light microscopic examination (LM).

RESULTS

Two weeks after operation

In the control site, newly formed capillaries which elongated from the defect wall filled the defect. But, new bone formation was not observed (Fig. 2a). In the experimental site, newly formed capillaries filled the defect similar to the control site. This newly formed capillary network was denser than the control (Fig. 2b). Using the decalcified sections of the experimental site, immature new bone formation was observed.

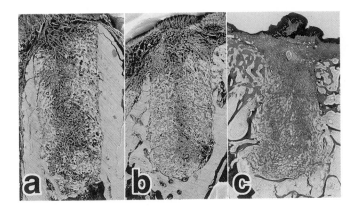

Figure 3. Three weeks after operation. x4.
a: Control site (SEM). b: Experimental site (SEM). c: Experimental site (LM).

Three weeks after operation

In the control site, new bone trabeculae filled the peripheral area of the defect. In the center of the defect, we observed a dense capillary network only (Fig. 3a). However, in the experimental site, the dense new bone trabeculae almost filled the defect (Fig. 3b, 3c). And new bone trabeculae formed around the apatitic OCP [3] particles with newly formed capillaries.

Eight weeks after operation

In the control site, the defect was filled with new bone trabeculae. These trabeculae were dense and alveolar bone-remodeling had not begun yet (Fig. 4a). In the experimental site, the bone defect was filled with newly-formed bone. And new bone trabeculae were similar to the preexisting bone with the bone-remodeling (Fig. 4b, 4c).

DISCUSSION

The guided tissue or bone regeneration (GTR, GBR) method was used for establish prosthodontic treatment to the jawbone. Authors have reported on the application of the GTR method to the tooth extracted socket [4]. In the GTR method, non-absorbable membrane is used and some materials are needed for keeping space under the membrane for the osteogenesis. However, it would be an absorbable material, it does not be needed a secondary operation to remove the membrane.

We investigated the bone tissue reaction of α-TCP-collagen sponge applied to the tooth extracted socket [1] and that of several kinds of calcium phosphate-collagen conjugated sponge to rabbit bone [5].

Now, we used OCP-collagen sponge in this study, in order to compare with α-TCP-collagen sponge especially in view of accelerating bone remodeling. The collagen sponge does not need anything to make space for osteogenesis. And after insertion, the sponge is stable. Furthermore, it is easy to operate and has a good hemostasis. On the experimental sight, osseous healing was much faster than on the control sight.

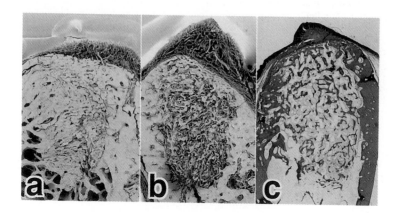

Figure 4. Eight weeks after operation. x4.
a: Control site (SEM). b: Experimental site (SEM), c: Experimental site (LM),

The inserted OCP-collagen sponge, which has a honeycomb structure, promotes the osteogenesis as the collagen fibers act as scaffolding (Fig. 2b). And apatitic OCP particles become the beginning points of calcifying, because the newly formed capillaries and bone marrow cells invaded into the sponge even if in the part far from preexisting bone at an early stage of the healing process (Fig. 3b). The sponge matrix is digested slowly with new bone formation. Accordingly, it promotes the osseous healing, prevents a down-growth of the epithelium and secures the space for the osteogenesis. Additionally, the bone remodeling begins at an early stage and the border is not clear between the newly formed and preexisting bone. Therefore, OCP-collagen sponge accelerates bone remodeling much than α-TCP-collagen sponge, and contributes to the osseous healing of the defect.

CONCLUSION

OCP-collagen sponge application to the bone defects accelerates bone healing and prevents the absorption of alveolar bone ridge. Additionally it helps hemostasis of the defects. Therefore, this material is useful for the vascularization and the bone healing of the jawbone defects. The OCP-collagen sponge has the ability of alveolar ridge augmentation and bone remodeling.

REFERENCES

1. Toda I, Kitayama N, Sugihara F, Minamigawa K, Suwa F, Oonishi H. *Bioceramics* 1996; **9**: 465-468.
2. Ohta Y, Okuda H, Suwa F, Okada S, Toda I. *Okajimas Folia Anat Jpn* 1990; **66**: 301-312.
3. Sugihara F, Oonishi H, Minamigawa K, Mandai Y, Tsuji E, Yoshikawa M, Toda T. *Bioceramics* 1996; **9**: 399-402.
4. Gonda Y, Kawamura K, Toda I, Kitayama N, Ohta Y. *Jpn J Oral Biol* 1994; **36**: 427-434.
5. Oonishi H, Sugihara F, Minamigawa K, Mandai Y, Nagatomi K, Kushitani S, Iwaki H, Kin N, Tsuji E. *Bioceramics* 1997; **10**: 403-406.

Bioceramics Volume 11, edited by R. Z. LeGeros and J.P. LeGeros
(Proceedings of the 11th International Symposium on Ceramics in Medicine)
New York, NY, USA, November 1998
© 1998 by World Scientific Publishing Co. Pte. Ltd.

HISTOLOGICAL STUDY OF CALCIUM PHOSPHATE CERAMICS IMPLANTED IN HUMAN LONG BONES

P. Frayssinet[1], C. Schwartz[2], B. Beya[3]

[1] Depuy-Bioland, 132 Rte d'Espagne 31100 Toulouse France, email: patrickf@worldnet.fr
[2] Hôpitaux civil de Colmar, Hôpital Pasteur, Colmar, France
[3] Centre Hospitalier de La Rochelle, Rue de Dr Schweitzer, 17019 La Rochelle, France

ABSTRACT:
Calcium phosphate ceramics implanted in bones are integrated following a sequence of biological events which has already been described. We had the opportunity to analyze histologically some HA-ceramic samples that had been implanted in humans for various periods of time.
Five biopsies were obtained from calcium phosphate ceramics implanted in different sites. All the samples were implanted for periods ranging from 4 to 9 months.
The samples were fixed in ethanol and embedded in hydroxyethylmetacrylate or polymethyl methacrylate. 5 μm thick sections were prepared and stained with Giemsa or by Von Kossa method. Alkaline phosphatase and tartrate resistant acid phosphatase (TRAP) were revealed by histochemical methods. Certain implants were integrated within mature bone. In other, hematoma remnants were still visible at any time after implantation. These implants were invaded by a loose connective tissue in which some cell condensations were apparent. They lead to the formation of bone trabeculae by direct ossification. Some osteoblasts differentiated at the ceramic surface and synthesized osteoid tissue at the material surface. The fibroblast-like cells of the loose connective tissue were TRAP+. Most of them had TRAP+ nucleus and contained cytoplasm vesicles. Multinucleate TRAP+ osteoclasts showing TRAP- negative nuclei were found in Howship's lacunae at the bone surface.

KEYWORDS: calcium phosphate, osteointegration, acid phosphatase

INTRODUCTION:

Calcium phosphate ceramics are integrated within bone following a well known sequence of events (1). After a physico-chemical modification of their surface in the early time of implantation, a loose connective tissue invades the implantation site and replaces the post-operative hematoma. Osteoblasts differentiate from the fibroblasts contained in this tissue and synthesize an ECM at the material surface which is the first stage of formation of immature bone. Then the remodeling of the immature bone concerns also the ceramic and leads to the replacement of the material by a layered bone.

This process has been described from experiments performed in bone of healthy animals. The integration process of this material in human long bones is not so well established although publications reported the osseointegration of calcium phosphate ceramics within human maxillo-facial bone (2).

We had the opportunity to study the histological integration of calcium phosphate ceramics implanted in human long bone.

MATERIALS AND METHODS:

Material to be implanted:

The ceramics were made of a mixture of HA (70%) and β-TCP (30%). Their porosity was 40% and the mean pore size was either 200 or 400 μm. The pores were not interconnected. The compression resistance was superior to 20 MPa. The grain size ranged between 3 and 8 μm.

Implantation procedure:

In each case, the implanted site was cleaned of any necrotic tissue. No bone marrow was associated to the ceramic. Small biopsies were performed during the retrieval of osteosynthesis material or for operations motivated by clinical failure with the patient consent.

The reasons for ceramic implantation were various:
- Case 1: patient 40 years old. Femur fracture around a hip prosthesis stem treated by osteosynthesis. Some ceramic blocks were inserted between the plate and the femur at the fracture site. Radiological and clinical results were good until another fracture occurred in a different site. Implantation time: 1 year.
- Case 2: patient 48 years old. Implantation of ceramic blocks in the necrotic zone of a femoral head. Good functional results. Implantation period nine months.
- Case 3: patient 66 years old. Side fracture of the distal radius treated by osteosynthesis and defect filling with ceramics granules. Implantation time: 1 year.
- Case 4: patient 50 years old. Necrosis of the femoral head. Implantation of the ceramic once the necrotic zone was removed. Then the head was replaced 9 months later by a hip prosthesis.
- Case 5: patient 33 years old. Pseudarthrosis of clavicle treated by implantation of ceramics granules and osteosynthesis. Good functional and radiological results. Biopsy at 4 months.

Histology procedure:

The biopsies were fixed in ethanol- acetone fixative (50/50 W/W). They were dehydrated in ethanol and embedded in hydroxy-ethyl methacrylate or polymethylmethacrylate without to be decalcified. 5 μm thick sections were then performed. The sections were stained with Giemsa. Alcaline and tartrate resistant acid phosphatase were evidenced using azo dyes reactives.

RESULTS:

All the implants showed different tissue structures at their contact. Several implants were integrated in layered bone. In these cases, there was an unusual amount of osteoid either at the surface of the surrounding bone or the ceramic itself (fig. 1). Fragments of ceramics were also found within bone tissue. Osteocytes could be evidenced at the fragment contact. Osteoblast layers were shown at the surface of the ceramic synthesizing an osteoid matrix.

In other sections, most of the surface was occupied by hematoma remnants. Bone fragments were also found (cases 1, 3, 5). A vasculo-connective tissue invaded the hematoma and bone trabeculae were formed within this tissue. Osteoid lined by alkaline phosphatase positive phosphatase cells was present at the trabeculae surface. Very few alkaline phosphatase positive cells were shown in the hematoma.

The fibroblast-like cells found in the connective tissue invading the implanted site were tartrate resistant acid-phosphatase positive (fig. 2). Their nucleus was in most of the case TRAP+. TRAP+ multinucleated cells were evidenced at the surface of the forming bone. Their cell nuclei were negative, the enzymes were found in cytoplasm vesicles.

DISCUSSION:

This study shows that integration of calcium phosphate ceramic in human bone could be different from that described in animal bone. The hematoma of the early stage stays in the implantation site for a longer time. The healing osteogenic tissue does not necessarily follow the ceramic surface. It seems that the osteogenic cells arrive in the site within the connective tissue invading the pore volume then fix at the implant surface. The majority of the fibroblast-like cells found in the healing site are TRAP+ cells. Two kinds of TRAP+ cells can be differentiated. The first type is constituted of cells located at the bone surface. They are multinucleated with TRAP-nuclei and have TRAP+ positive granules within the cytoplasm. These cells were identified as osteoclasts.

The fibroblast-like cells of the loose connective tissue invading the ceramic pores show TRAP+ nucleus with or without TRAP+ granules in their cytoplasm. These cells can also be located within a dense collagen matrix. The presence of these cells in the site precedes that of bone and of cells which show a membrane alkaline phosphatase activity. The quasi-totality of the cells found in the connective tissue which invades the hematoma are TRAP+, it suggests that the osteogenic stem cells are found in this cell group. TRAP activity has been first associated to the osteoclast. Then, it has been attributed to certain activated macrophages located in pseudosynovial membranes around aseptic loosened prostheses (3). None of the cells located within the collagen matrix have a macrophage morphology or phagocytosed calcium phosphate particles. They show a fibroblast-like morphology. The great number of TRAP+ cells contrasts with that of alkaline phosphatase stained cells which are maintained at the osteoid surface.

It must be noted that the amount of osteoid around the ceramic fragments seems to be higher than in the rest of bone tissue. Compared to the bone formation at the surface of ceramic implanted in healthy animal bone, the ossification process can be different. It is possible in certain cases to find osteoblasts differentiating at the material surface as it is visible in animals. It seems likely that in other cases the bone differentiates in the connective tissue invading the site then engulfs the material. Its is during this embodiment of the material by the healing bone that osteogenic cells appears at the material surface.

CONCLUSIONS:

It must be noted that at first TRAP+ positive mononucleated cells are found at the calcium phosphate fragment surface and in the ceramic pores. It indicates that these cells must be either removed from the material surface before osteogenic cells form osteoid at its surface or have a role in the ossification process taking place at the ceramic surface.

REFERENCES:

1. Frayssinet P, Trouillet JL, Rouquet N, Azimus E, Autefage A. *Biomaterials* 1993, **14**: 423-429.
2/ Marini E, Valdinucci F, Silvestrini G, Moretti S, Carlesimo M, Poggio C, Bonucci E. *Cells and Materials*, 1994, **4** : 231-246.
3/ Passuti N, Daculsi G, Rogez JM, Martin S, Bainvel JV. *Clin Orthop Rel Res* 1989, **248** : 169-176.
4/ Sabokbar A, Fujikawa Y, Neale S, Murray DW, Athanasou NA. *Ann Rheum Dis* 1997, **56**:414-420.

Fig. 1: Section of the case 2 biopsy. Osteoblasts (→) synthesize an osteoid matrix partially mineralized (MIN, mineralized; NM unmineralized) at the ceramic surface (HA). Von Kossa, bar 100 μm

Fig. 2: Connective tissue invading the pores of the ceramic (HA) implanted in case 3. This tissue contains numerous fibroblast-like cells with TRAP+ nucleus (dark spots). Bar 50 μm.

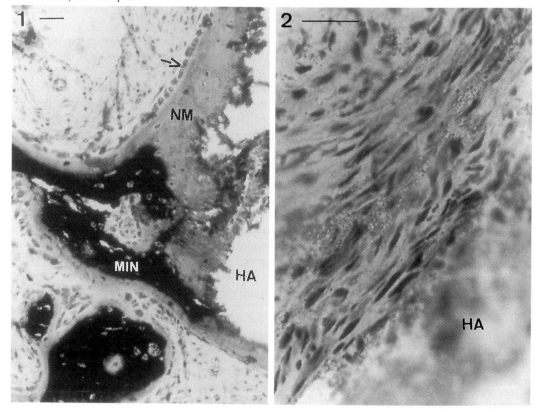

Bioceramics Volume 11, edited by R. Z. LeGeros and J.P. LeGeros
(Proceedings of the 11th International Symposium on Ceramics in Medicine)
New York, NY, USA, November 1998
© 1998 by World Scientific Publishing Co. Pte. Ltd.

COMPARISON OF BONE GROWTH BEHAVIOUR INTO SPACES OF HYDROXYAPATITE AND AW GLASS CERAMIC PARTICLES

H. Oonishi, N. Murata, M. Saito, S. Wakitani, K. Imoto, N. Kim, and M. Matsuura

Department of Orthopaedic Surgery, Artificial Joint Section and Biomaterial Research Laboratory, Osaka-Minami National Hospital, 2-1, Kidohigashi-Machi, Kawachinagano-Shi, Osaka, 586-0008, JAPAN   Tel : 0721-53-5761, Fax : 0721-53-8904

ABSTRACT

HA particles of 300 to 600 μ m sintered at 1,150℃ with porosity of 35 to 48% and pore size of 50 to 300 μ m and AW glass ceramic particles of 300 to 600 μ m with an average porosity of 25% and an average pore size of 1 to 100 μ m were implanted into drilled holes made in the femoral condyles of mature rabbits.   These animals were sacrificed 1, 3 and 6 weeks after implantation.   Non-decalcified specimens were observed by light microscopy and back-scattered electron microscopy. Bone ingrowth rates were measured by means of an image processor for analytical pathology.

At one week, bone growth began at the periphery of the holes filled with HA or AW particles. At three weeks, new bone reached to the center of the holes filled with HA or AW particles.

Bone growth rates into the spaces of HA and AW glass particles were 2 and 3% at one week, 12 and 22% at three weeks and 23 and 28% at six weeks, respectively.

KEY WORDS: Hydorxyapatite, A-W glass ceramics, Particle, bone growth

INTRODUCTION

Bioceramics can be divided in to three categories:
1) Bioinert ceramics, 2) Surface bioactive ceramics, and 3) Resolvable bioactive ceramics.

Bone growth behaviour and reactions to the bone of bioinert ceramics and resolvable bioactive ceramics had been discussed [1-3], and comparisons of bone ingrowth between HA and Bioglass, as a surface bioactive ceramics, had been reported [4,5].

In this study, bone reactions to fine granules of HA and AW-glass ceramics (AW-GC) are compared.

MATERIALS

HA particles of 300 to 600 μ m sintered at 1,150℃ with porosity of 35 to 48% and pore size of 50 to 300 μ m, and AW glass ceramic (AW-GC) particles of 300 to 600 μ m with an average porosity of 25% and an average pore size of 1 to 100 μ m were used.   Mature rabbits were used for this experiment.

METHODS

Drilled holes 6 mm in diameter were made bilaterally in the femoral condyles of mature rabbits, and sufficient hemostasis was achieved by filling and compressing the holes with gauze for five minutes. Immediately following, particles of HA and AW-GC were placed in sufficient amounts to fill the holes in the femoral condyles, one material on each side, providing each with its own control.   Three rabbits were used for each time period.

The animals were sacrificed at intervals, and non-decalcified specimens were observed by light microscopy and backscattered electron imaging.

Bone ingrowth rates were measured by means of an image processor for analytical pathology (Figure 1(a,b)).

COMPARISON OF BONE GROWTH BEHAVIOUR INTO SPACES OF HYDROXYAPATITE AND AW GLASS CERAMIC PARTICLES

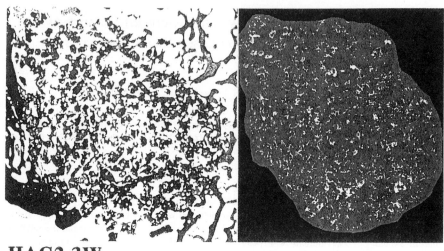

HAG2-3W.

(a) ; 3 weeks after implantation of HA particles of 300 to 600 μ m

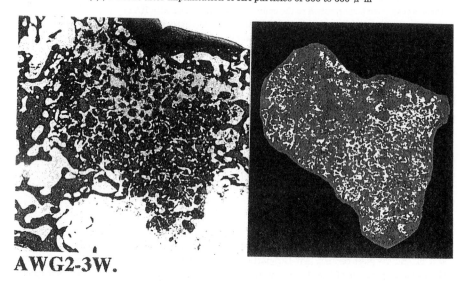

AWG2-3W.

(b) ; 3 weeks after implantation of A-W glass ceramic particles of 300 to 600 μ m

Figure 1(a), (b) ; Bone ingrowth rates were measured by means of an image processor for analytical pathology.

RESULTS AND DISCUSSION

Hydroxyapatite:

One week after implantation of the HA particles, new bone entered into the spaces of the first layer of the HA particles, and surrounded the periphery of the HA granules.

At three week, new bone growth reached the seventh and eighth outer layers of the HA particles. New bone surrounded large parts of the surface of HA particles of layers two and three (Figure 1(a)).

COMPARISON OF BONE GROWTH BEHAVIOUR INTO SPACES OF
HYDROXYAPATITE AND AW GLASS CERAMIC PARTICLES

At six weeks, new bone entered into the spaces of the ten outer layers ; that is to the center of the hole filled with HA particles.   New bone surrounded the surfaces of all particles of the outer three layers.

However, in the deeper layers, the new travecular bone only partially surrounded the HA particles.   In the deep layers, only a few of the spaces between the HA particles were filled with new bone.

AW-glass ceramics:

One week after implantation of AW-GC, bone growth behaviour was similar to that of HA.

At three weeks with AW-GC, new bone reached the spaces of the center of the hole and surrounded large part of the surfaces of the AW-GC particles in the center.

At six weeks, the new bone that filled the spaces between AW-GC particles was more extensive and denser than the bone around HA particles (Figure 1(b)).

Bone growth rate:

Bone growth rates into the spaces of HA and AW-GC particles were 2 and 3% at one week, 12 and 22% at three weeks and 23 and 27% at six weeks in average, respectively.

At one week, bone growth rate into the spaces filled with HA and AW-GC particles were almost the same, at three weeks, those with AW-GC particles were twice those with HA particles ; and at six weeks, those with AW-GC particles were 25% higher than those with HA (Figure 2).

Bone Ingrowth Rate into The Space of HA and
AW Granules (300 - 600 μm)

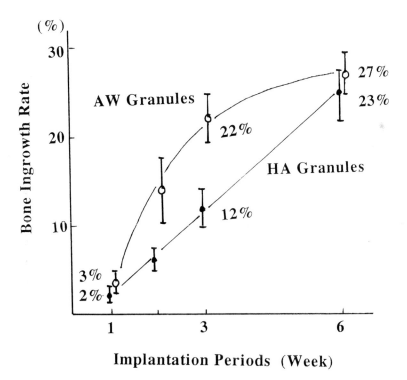

Figure 2 ; Comparative bone ingrowth rate into the space of HA and A-W glass ceramic particles of
300 to 600 μ m

COMPARISON OF BONE GROWTH BEHAVIOUR INTO SPACES OF HYDROXYAPATITE AND AW GLASS CERAMIC PARTICLES

CONCLUSION

The speed of bone growth around AW-GC particles was faster and the new bone was denser than bone associated with HA granules until six weeks.

REFERENCES

1) Oonishi, H., Tsuji, E., Mizukoshi, T. and Kushitani, S. in Bioceramics 4. W. Bonfield, G. W. Hastings and K. E. Tanar, eds., Butterworth-Heinemann Ltd., Guildford, England, 1991, 191-197.
2) Wilson, J. and Low, S. J. Appl. Biom. 1992, 3, 123-129.
3) Oonishi, H., Kushitani, S., Yasukawa, E., Kawakami, H., Hench, L. L., Wilson, J. and Tsuji, E. in Bioceramics-7, O. H. Anderson, R-p. Happonen, A. Yli. Eds., in Bioceramics-7 Butterworth Heinemann Ltd., finland, 1994, 139-144.
4) Oonishi, H., Kushitani, S., Iwaki, H., Sugihara, T., Hench, L. L., Tsuji, E. in Bioceramics-8, J. Wilson, L. L. Hench, D. Greenspan, eds. In Bioceramics-11,1995, 137-144.
5) Oonishi, H., Kushitani, S., Yasukawa, E., Hench, L. L., Wilson, J. Clinical Orthop ; 1997, 334, 316-325.

Bioceramics Volume 11, edited by R. Z. LeGeros and J.P. LeGeros
(Proceedings of the 11th International Symposium on Ceramics in Medicine)
New York, NY, USA, November 1998
© 1998 by World Scientific Publishing Co. Pte. Ltd.

BIOGLASS® SURFACE REACTIVITY: FROM *IN VITRO* TO *IN VIVO*

Zhong J.P. and Greenspan D.C.

USBiomaterials Corporation, One Progress Blvd. #23 Alachua, FL 32615, USA

ABSTRACT

Numerous studies have been conducted using various solutions to simulate the biological environment in an attempt to correlate the surface reaction on Bioglass® and its bioactivity *in vitro* with *in vivo* results. In this work, we compared the surface reactivity of Bioglass® in tris buffer, a simulated body fluid (SBF) and a cell culture medium (Dulbecco modified eagle medium, DMEM), respectively. The changes in surface reaction from tris, the simplest solution, to DMEM, a complex medium allows us to predict the *in vivo* behavior of Bioglass®. It has been found that in tris solution, Bioglass® showed faster surface reaction than in SBF and the DMEM. It is likely that the cell culture medium more accurately reflects the *in vivo* conditions. In DMEM, the modest pH change, the formed HCA crystals, similar in size to the mineral phase of bone and the gradual HCA growth which allows more cells and growth factors to adsorb or attach to the silica gel layer, provided more evidence for the excellent biocompatibility of Bioglass®.

KEYWORDS: Bioglass®, Reactivity, DMEM, *in vitro*, HCA

INTRODUCTION

It has been well established that the clinical success of Bioglass® as a bone graft material is attributed to its rapid bonding to living tissue arising from its high level of surface reactivity[1]. The sequence of the surface reactions when Bioglass® is exposed to physiological environment is the initial formation of a silica rich gel layer due to ion-exchange, dissolution and poly-condensation followed by the formation of HCA on the gel layer.

It has been proposed that during the formation of the HCA layer, biological species including cells and growth factors will adsorb and attach to the surface resulting in a composite matrix[2,3]. A strong bond is formed at the interface and the colonization of cells together with continuous surface reactions stimulate the surrounding tissue growth. Many research groups have used various biological solutions to simulate and simplify the *in vivo* environment in an attempt to find a correlation between the surface reaction on Bioglass® and its excellent biocompatibility and bioactivity.

In this work, we compared the surface reactivity on Bioglass® in tris buffer, a simulated body fluid (SBF)[4] and a cell culture medium(Dulbecco modified eagle medium, DMEM, Gibco,), respectively. The changes in surface reaction from tris, the simplest solution to DMEM, a complex medium allow us to predict the *in vivo* behavior of Bioglass®.

MATERIALS AND METHODS

1 cm discs of 45S5 Bioglass® were polished to 600 grit with SiC polishing papers and tested in tris(hydroxyaminomethane) buffer (pH, 7.25), SBF(pH, 7.25) and DMEM(pH, 7.30) at 37°C with the SA/V ratio of 0.1cm⁻¹. For testing in DMEM, an incubator supplied with 5% CO_2 was used to maintain the pH of the solution. After various reaction times, samples were removed and dried with acetone. The surfaces were characterized by FTIR and SEM to examine the formation of HCA and the crystal morphology. For surface area evaluation, Bioglass® particles were reacted dynamically using an orbital shaker rotating at 175 RPM at 37°C. After various reaction times, the reacted particles were separated by vacuum filtration through 8μm filter paper, dried with acetone and analyzed by BET(NOVA 2000, Quantachrome, FL) to evaluate the change of surface area. All of the reacted solutions were saved for pH measurement.

RESULTS AND DISCUSSION

Fig. 1 shows the pH change in the three solutions as a function of reaction time. The tris solution showed the largest pH change while SBF and DMEM showed minor change. Fig. 2 shows the FTIR spectra of the HCA formation on the reacted samples. HCA crystals occur on Bioglass® after 2 hours in tris, 6 hours in SBF and 7 days in DMEM. Additionally, the crystal size reached to 0.5 to 1 μm in tris and SBF and less than 0.1 μm in DMEM as shown in Fig. 3.

The surface area development of Bioglass® has been evaluated in tris and SBF, and a greater surface area has been seen in tris than in SBF as has been reported in previous work[5]. It should be noted that the evaluation of the surface area is not available so far in the DMEM under the CO_2 test condition.

Generally, tris is a simple organic buffer solution, SBF is tris buffer containing similar ion concentrations to human blood plasma. DMEM contains both the inorganic and biological organic components. The first reaction at the bioactive glass surface is ion-exchange, in which cations such as Na^+ from the glass exchange with H^+ from solutions, increasing the pH of the reaction solution. It has been reported that the early precipitation of Ca and P in SBF blocked the further ion exchange, dissolution and silica gel layer formation on Bioglass®, thus slowing the surface reaction stages, including the change of pH and surface area as well as HCA formation[5].

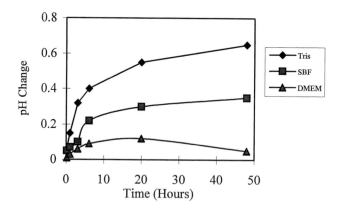

Fig. 1. Solution pH change as a function of reaction time

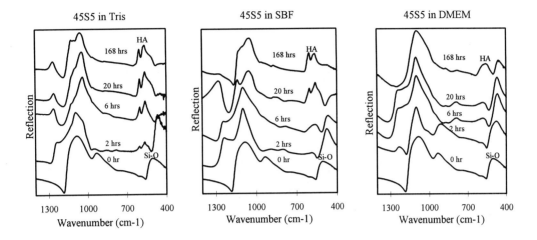

Fig. 2 FTIR spectra of Bioglass® reacted in tris, SBF and DMEM

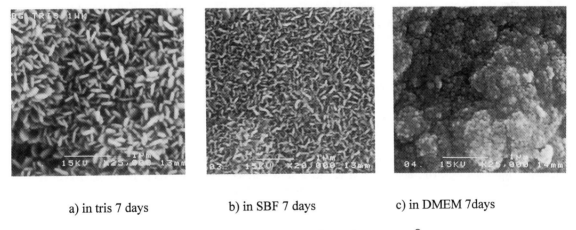

a) in tris 7 days   b) in SBF 7 days   c) in DMEM 7days

Fig. 3 SEM morphology of HCA formed on Bioglass®

In DMEM, both the early precipitation of inorganic ions and adsorption of organic species could explain the slow surface reaction. However, it has been found that the CO_3 groups from the carbonate buffer system of DMEM probably play a major role in the inhibition of HCA formation and crystal growth as shown in Figs. 2 and 3. Fig. 4 demonstrates the inhibition by CO_3 compared with tris and SBF. Usually, HCA is well developed on Bioglass® after 20 hours in tris or SBF. However, HCA crystallization might just be starting after 20 hours in the CO_3 group buffer solution. The mechanism for the inhibition of HA crystal growth by CO_3 groups has been studied early by LeGeros[6], who stated that CO_3 group substitution in type B carbonate apatites would decrease the a-axis, increase the c-axis and crystal stain, and thus, depress the crystal growth.

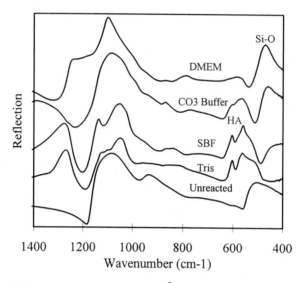

Fig. 4. FTIR Spectra of Bioglass® reacted 20 hours *in vitro*

Our results have shown that the pH change is modest in DMEM and the HCA crystal size is similar to that of the mineral phase of bone *in vivo*. In addition, the delay in HCA formation allows more biological species, including cells and growth factors, to adsorb or attach to the silica-gel layer on Bioglass® since the gel layer with a high concentration of silanol groups has been reported to be more able to adsorb and attach proteins than does the HCA layer[7]. As a result, the adsorbed and attached biological species will be stabilized by the late formed HCA, ultimately leading to a bonding and the stimulation of surrounding bone tissue growth.

CONCLUSIONS

Among the three *in vitro* solutions tested, tris buffer caused the fastest surface reaction on Bioglass®, followed by SBF, and DMEM led to a slow surface reaction. Since the DMEM cell culture medium reflects more accurately *in vivo* conditions, Bioglass® causes modest pH change, forms fine HCA crystals with size similar to the mineral phase of nature bone, and probably has more capability to adsorb and attach cells and growth factors which confirms the biocompatibility of Bioglass® *in vivo*. We believe that DMEM is the best choice of solution when testing new bioactive materials *in vitro*.

REFERENCE

1. Hench, L.L, J. Am. Ceram. Soc., 74, 1487, 1991
2. Hench, L.L, Bioceramics 9, Elsevier Science Ltd, 3-6, 1996
3. Zhong, J.P., LaTorre, G.P., and Hench, L.L., Bioceramics 7, Butterworth-Heinemann Ltd, 61-66, 1995
4. Kokubo, T. et al., J. Biomed. Mater. Res. 24, 721 1990
5. Greenspan DC et al, Transactions of 21st annual meeting of the Soc. For Biomaterials, , 41, 1995
6. LeGeros, R.Z., *Calcium Phosphates in Oral Biology and Medicine*, Karger, 1991
7. Lobel K.D., and Hench, L.L., J. Biomed. Mater. Res., 39, 575-79, 1998

Bioceramics Volume 11, edited by R. Z. LeGeros and J.P. LeGeros
(Proceedings of the 11th International Symposium on Ceramics in Medicine)
New York, NY, USA, November 1998
© 1998 by World Scientific Publishing Co. Pte. Ltd.

ULTRA-HIGH-STRENGTH HYDROXYAPATITE/POLY(L-LACTIDE) COMPOSITE RODS FOR INTERNAL FIXATION OF BONE FRACTURES : *IN VIVO* STUDY

T. Furukawa[1], Y. Matsusue[1], T. Yasunaga[1], M. Kobayashi[1], H. Fujita[1], Y. Shikinami[2]
M. Okuno[2], and T. Nakamura[1]

[1]Department of Orthopaedic Surgery, Faculty of Medicine, Kyoto University,
  Kawahara-cho 54, Shogoin, Sakyo-ku, Kyoto 606-8507, Japan,
[2]Takiron Co. Ltd., Nagano Yasutomi-cho 405, Shisou-gun, Hyogo 671-24, Japan.

ABSTRACT

Ultra-high-strength hydroxyapatite (HA)/poly (L-lactide) (PLLA) composites were produced by a new compression molding for biodegradable fracture fixation devices. The purpose of this study was to investigate *in vivo* biodegradation and bioactivity of the composites. The rods made of composites containing 40 wt % HA or unfilled PLLA were implanted in the medullary cavity of rabbit femora. Two, 4, 8 and 25 weeks after implantation the samples were examined histologically using Giemsa surface staining, and a scanning electron microscope (SEM). The histomorphometrical analysis of bone-implant interface was conducted using an image analyzer and the affinity index was calculated. The histological examinations showed the direct bone contact to the composites from early period. The affinity index of all composites were significantly higher than that of unfilled PLLA rod during the follow up period. No inflammatory cells like macrophage has been found by 25 weeks. The HA/PLLA composites used in this study was demonstrated to have good bioactivity, which indicate that this material may be useful for a bone fixation device.

KEYWORDS: Hydroxyapatite, poly(L-lactide), composite, internal fixation.

INTRODUCTION

Absorbable fixation devices made of synthetic polymer have become increasingly used in the fields of orthopaedic surgery. The major advantage of the use of absorbable implants is avoidance of removal procedure. Another advantage is to prevent stress shielding atrophy and weakening of the fixed bone usually caused by the rigid metallic fixation. However, several problems have been indicated, including mechanical weakness and lack of bone bonding ability. These disadvantages result in the mechanical failure of the implant or the aseptic loosening during the fracture healing period. Therefore, if the absorbable fixation device bonds directly to bone, the fracture fixation is expected to be more stable.

Recently, we have developed ultra-high strength hydroxyapatite (HA)/poly (L-lactide) (PLLA) composite rods for internal fixation of bone fractures, which have the highest mechanical strength of any reinforced bioactive ceramics fibers or particles/polymer.[1, 2, 5] The bending strength reached 280 MPa and was maintained over 200 MPa at 25 weeks in the *in vitro* test,[4] indicating that these composites possess sufficient mechanical strength for internal fixation device.

In the present study, the bioactivity and biodegradability of HA/PLLA composite rods were investigated in a rabbit model. Bone-implant interaction was examined histologically by light microscopy and scanning electron microscopy (SEM), and quantitative evaluation of osteoconductivity was performed by using image analyzer.

MATERIALS AND METHODS

Preparation of hydroxyapatite/poly-l-lactide composites

Two types of synthetic hydroxyapatite, sintered HA and unsintered HA, were used as a filler in this study. The particle size was limited within the rage of 0.3-20 μ m and about 3 μ m in the average.

Poly-l-lactide(PLLA) was polymerized in the similar way as described in the other literature.[3] The viscosity-average molecular weight of PLLA powder was 400 KDa before blending with HA particles. The PLLA powder were purified with few times of precipitating from polymer/dichloromethane solution by dropping ethanol. The small granules uniformly distributed u-HA or s-HA microparticles within a PLLA matrix were collected by precipitation polymer solution, which were extruded to make a thick billet. Thereafter, this billet was molded into a thin billet by a new process for compression molding at 103℃ and cut into a rod with a diameter of 3.2 mm and a length of 3 cm. The composites were filled with 40 weight fraction of u-HA or s-HA particles (s-HA40 and u-HA40 composite rods). Unfilled PLLA rods made by the same method were used as the control.

In vivo implantation

A total of 56 Japanese white rabbits weighing 2.8-3.4 kg were used for the intramedullary implantation of the rods. The rabbits were anesthetized by an intravenous injection of (50 mg/kg body weight) and local administration of 0.5% (w/v) lidocaine. The operations were performed with standard aseptic conditions. A medial parapatellar incision was made and the patella was laterally dislocated. Subsequently a longitudinal drill channel 3.2 mm in diameter was made through the intercondylar area of the femoral condyle with 3.2 mm dental bur (Morita, Kyoto, Japan). The cavity was washed thoroughly with a sterile physiological saline solution, and then rods were inserted with a press fit into the cavity. The capsule and incision were closed with 3-0 nylon sutures. The rabbits were sacrificed in groups of four or five at 2, 4, 8, and 25 weeks after implantation by overdose pentobarbital.

Histological evaluation

The samples for histological examination taken from rabbits were fixed in 10% phosphate-buffered formalin, dehydrated with a graded ethanol series(70,80,90,99 and 100%(v/v)), soaked serially with styrene(50, 70 and 100%(v/v)) and embedded in polyester resin.

Thin sections(500 μ m) were cut with a diamond band saw (BS-3000, EXACT cutting system, Norderstedt, Germany), perpendicular to the longitudinal axis of the bone .

Several 500-μ m sections taken from the composite and PLLA groups at every time interval studied were polished with diamond paper. These sections were used to study the bone-composite interface and the degradation of the rods, using a SEM (Hitachi S-2460N, Tokyo) connected to an energy-dispersive X-ray microanalyzer (Horiba EMAX-5770, Kyoto).

Table 1
Affinity Indices (%) of Composites and PLLA 2, 4, 8 and 25 Weeks
After Implantation in Rabbit Femur

Type	Weeks after implantation			
	2	4	8	25
u-HA40	25.9±5.6	30.6±4.2	27.8±3.4	22.0±4.0
s-HA40	29.3±3.7	41.0±3.8	34.9±2.5	28.4±5.7
PLLA	7.3±1.6	6.5±0.6	8.5±1.0	5.2±1.7

The values were analysed by ANOVA at a 0.05 level of significance between affinity index of two types of the composites and PLLA. At each experimental period, all the composites v.s. PLLA; significant. In s-HA40, 4weeks v.s. 2 and 25 weeks; significant. At 4 weeks, s-HA40 v.s. u-HA40; significant.

Histomorphometrical evaluation

Two sections from each rod were ground down to 60 μ m thickness with a speed lap(ML-511, Maruto, Tokyo, Japan) for Giemsa surface staining. From these specimens, the lengths of bone directly apposed to the composite without any intervening connective tissue were measured using an image analyzer (integrated by Tectron, Kyoto, Japan) . An affinity index for each specimen was calculated by dividing this length by the total length of the composite surface in the femur and multiplying the value by 100. An affinity index of each rod was calculated as the mean of the affinity index of the two specimens which were taken from the same rod.

RESULT

Histological results

The composite rods were in close contact with woven and old bone as early as 2 weeks after implantation (Fig. 1a). A trabecular structure of immature bone was seen in the gap between the composite rods and the surrounding cancellous bone. The new bone was noted growing along the composite rods with time and partially being contact with the surface of the composite rod without any intervening fibrous tissue (Fig. 1b). Also, SEM demonstrated that there was direct contact of bone with the surface of the composite rods.

At no time was there any sign of infiltration by inflammatory cells such as neutrophils and histiocytes in all composites and PLLA rods.

Histomorphometrical analysis

The affinity index of the composites and PLLA are shown in Table 1. During the follow-up period, there were significant differences between all types of composite rods and the PLLA rods, and the affinity index of the s-HA40 was relatively higher than that of the u-HA40, but only at 4 weeks they were significantly different .

DISCUSSION

Histological results indicated the increased bone contact for the composites compared to the PLLA, which demonstrated the fibrous encapsulation. Also, throughout the experimental period, there was a significant difference between the affinity index of the composites and of the PLLA. This fact

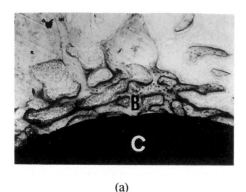 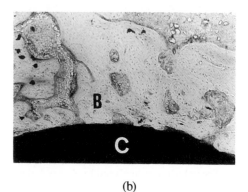

(a)   (b)

Figure 1. Giemsa surface staining of specimens from u-HA40 composites, showing the implant surface bonded directly with bone. (a) at 2 weeks ($\times$200), (b) at 25 weeks ($\times$200). C: composite, B: bone.

suggests that the osteoconductive property of HA should be well remained in the PLLA matrix, where the environment was different from HA alone. In addition, it should be noted that 40 weight percentage of HA correspond to 24 volume percentage, which values are relatively low, however, enough bone apposition was observed, in which the maximum value of the affinity index is 30-41%. In our composite, the mean HA particle size was relative small size (3 μ m), and the distribution of particles in the PLLA matrix was homogenous. These factors achieve large area of the particles on the surface of the composite and result in the ample bone apposition in spite of relative low weight fraction of HA.

There have been reports indicating that HA is both bioinert and subject to biodegradation. Many factors such as ratio of Ca/P, crystallinity or sintering temperature affect the degradation property of HA. In the current study, the affinity index revealed that s-HA40 composite has relatively greater osteoconductivity than u-HA40 throughout the experimental period. These findings suggest that the degradability of HA filler might affect the osteoconductivity of the composite.

Tissue reaction to the composites is the most important problem for the clinical application. Polymer debris seemed to be related with the tissue reaction. In this study, at no time was there any sign of infiltration by inflammatory cells such as neutrophils and histiocytes in all composites, suggesting that these composites have good biocompatibility until 25 weeks.

REFERENCES

1. Bonfield W, Grynpas MD, Tully AE, Bowman J, Abram J. *Biomaterials* 1981; **2**: 185-186.
2. Higashi S, Yamamuro T, Nakamura T, Ikada Y, Hyon SH, Jamshidi K. *Biomaterials* 1986; **7**: 183-187.
3. Hyon SH, Jamshidi K, Ikada Y. *Polymers as Biomaterials*, Plenum Press, New York, 1984, 51-65.
4. Shikinami Y, Hata K, Okuno M. In: *Bioceramics volume 9*, Elsevier Science 1996: 391-394.
5. Verheyen CC, de Wijn JR, van Blitterswijk CA, de Groot K. *J Biomed Mater Res* 1992; **2 6**: 1277-1296.

Bioceramics Volume 11, edited by R. Z. LeGeros and J.P. LeGeros
(Proceedings of the 11th International Symposium on Ceramics in Medicine)
New York, NY, USA, November 1998
© 1998 by World Scientific Publishing Co. Pte. Ltd.

BIOACTIVITY OF ORGANICALLY MODIFIED CERAMICS FILM COATED ON POLYMER SUBSTRATE

Kanji Tsuru, Satoshi Hayakawa, Chikara Ohtsuki and Akiyoshi Osaka

Biomaterials Lab., Faculty of Engineering, Okayama University,
Tsushima, Okayama-shi 700-8530, Japan

ABSTRACT

Polyamide and silicone substrates were coated with sols prepared from poly(dimethylsiloxane) (PDMS), tetraethoxysilane (TEOS) and calcium nitrate ($Ca(NO_3)_2 \cdot 4H_2O$). Adhesive strength between the coated layers and the substrates was not less than about 1.5MPa. Bioactivity was examined by using Kokubo solution. The films from the sol containing 1 molar DMF for 1 molar TEOS (film-DMF) deposited apatite within 7 days of soaking in the Kokubo solution while the films from the DMF-free sol could not deposit apatite within 14 days. ^{29}Si MAS NMR measurements suggested that the film-DMF contained less amount of hydrophobic PDMS chains than the DMF free films. We concluded that apatite-forming ability of the film-DMF has been derived by incorporation of DMF in the coating solution.

KEYWORDS: Bioactivity, organically modified ceramics, apatite, Kokubo solution, DCCA

INTRODUCTION

Artificial polymers such as silicone and polyamide (Nylon6®) with high flexibility are employed as implant materials in clinical use.[1] However, they do not directly bond to surrounding tissues because of formation of fibrous tissues on them when embedded in the body. As a result, they may cause pain, bleeding, inflammation or other inconvenience. Thus such implant materials are demanded that not only have bioactivity but are provided with better mechanical properties.

Biologically-active apatite formed on the bioactive ceramics in the body shows high biocompatibility with soft tissue.[2] Recently, we synthesized organically modified silicates starting from poly(dimethylsiloxane) (PDMS,-$(SiO(CH_3)_2)_n$-), tetraethoxysilane (TEOS, $Si(OC_2H_5)$) and calcium nitrate ($Ca(NO_3)_2 \cdot 4H_2O$) through sol-gel processing, and found that thus synthesized materials formed the apatite layer on their surface in Kokubo solution.[3] If the solutions acquired in the course of the gelling reaction are coated on various artificial polymers, one can expect to provide those polymers with bioactivity and to expand their commercial application as new bioactive implant materials. In this study, we synthesized such coating solutions starting from PDMS, TEOS and Ca(NO₃)₂·4H₂O through sol-gel processing and coated them on the polyamide (Nylon6®) substrates. Then we investigated apatite formation of the organic-inorganic films.

MATERIALS AND METHODS

A typical composition for the coating solutions was TEOS:PDMS:HCl:H_2O:Ca(NO₃)₂·4H₂O = 1 : 1.64 : 0.1 : 3 : 0.1. Detailed procedure of preparing the sols was given in the previous report.[3] A solution of PDMS, TEOS and solvents (2-propanol, tetrahydroflune (THF)) was added to an aqueous solution of calcium nitrate, distilled water, hydrochloric acid and a solvent (2-propanol) to be refluxed for 30 min at 80°C. To prevent quick evaporation of the solvents in the drying process, we also prepared some sols that contained N,N-dimethyformamide (DMF) known as a drying control chemical additive (DCCA).[4] After refluxing, the sols were dip-coated on Nylon6® (10x10x1 mm in size) where the pull-up speed was 1 mm/s. The coated substrates were kept at room temperature (25°C) for 10 min. After 5 iteration of the dip-coating they were placed in an oven for 2 days at 40°C and for 2 days at 60°C. The gel-film prepared by using DMF was denoted as "film-DMF", while the DMF free gel-film was denoted as "film". Sample aged for gelation without coating was denoted as "bulk sample".

The samples were soaked up to 14 days in Kokubo solution[5,6] : it has the inorganic ion composition similar to that of human blood plasma, and *in vitro* experiments can well reproduce the reactions that may take place the *in vivo*. It was kept at 36.5°C and buffered at 7.25 in pH with tris(hydroxymethylaminomethane). The samples treated with Kokubo solution were examined with thin-film X-ray diffraction (TF-XRD), Fourier transform infrared (FT-IR) reflection spectroscopy, and scanning electron microscopy (SEM).

Local structure around Si atoms in the samples was discussed by analyzing ^{29}Si magic angle spinning (MAS) NMR spectra for the pulverized samples. In the NMR measurement, the sample spinning speed was 4.5kHz at the magic angle (54.7°) to the external field. ^{29}Si NMR spectra of the samples were measured at 7.05T on a VARIAN^UNITY INOVA300 NMR spectrometer. The spectra were acquired at 59.59MHz with 7.0-μs pulses, 90.0s recycle delays, 10.0μs dead time. The signals for 960 pulses were accumulated. The chemical shift (δ in ppm) of ^{29}Si was determined using tetramethylsilane (TMS) (δ=0 ppm : where δ denoted the isotropic chemical shift) as an external reference substance. Poly dimethyl silane (δ=-34.0 ppm) was used as the secondary external reference.

RESULTS AND DISCUSSION

Figure 1 shows the FT-IR spectra of the bulk sample (a), film (b) and film-DMF (c) with the composition above before and after the soaking in the Kokubo solution up to 14 days. Assignments of the IR peaks shown in the figures follow the previous report.[3] One may find that the film did not deposit apatite within 14 days while the bulk sample deposited apatite within 1 day. The same was obtained by TF-XRD and SEM observation. Thus the degree of bioactivity was different between the bulk sample and the film. On the other hand, the film-DMF deposited apatite within 7 days of soaking in the Kokubo solution. This indicates that the surface for the film was favorably improved by addition of DMF. Furthermore, the coated layers were tightly bonded to the substrates. Adhesive strength between the coated films and substrates was not less than about 1.5 MPa.

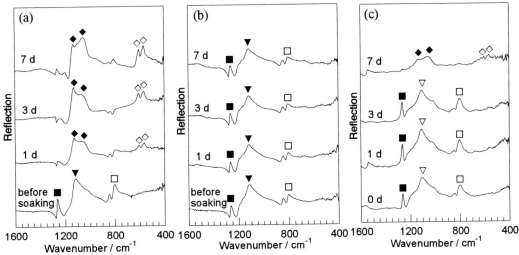

Figure 1. FT-IR spectra of bulk sample (a), film (b) and film-DMF (c) prepared with a typical composition before and after soaked in the Kokubo solution up to 14 days.
O:Apatite, $\triangledown$: ν(Si-O), $\square$: $\delta(CH_3)$ & ν(Si-C), $\blacksquare$: $\delta(CH_3)$, $\diamondsuit$: δ(P-O) ,$\blacklozenge$: ν(P-O)

Figure 2 shows the ^{29}Si MAS NMR spectra of the bulk sample (a), film (b) and film-DMF (c). The NMR spectra showed two groups of peaks on the basis of the chemical shift: the first peak (-10 to -25 ppm) was due to O_2SiMe_2 (Me=-CH_3) units (D groups) from PDMS while the other one (-100 to -110 ppm) was due to SiO_2 units (Q groups) originated from TEOS.[7] In the former peak, the sharpest peak is assigned to long PDMS chains (D).[7] Fig. 2 indicates that the film remained much more non-reactive PDMS in the structure than the bulk sample and the film-DMF. The NMR profile of the silica matrix (Q groups) does not show a significant difference between the film-DMF and DMF free one. Since the film was exposed to the air as soon as it was coated on the substrates, then, the film dried faster than the bulk sample. As a result, the film remained long chains of non-reactive PDMS on the surface since the polycondensation reaction could not proceed very much. On the other hand, addition of DMF kept the surface wet for the drying process. Thus, the film-DMF formed Si-OH groups on the surface by soaked in Kokubo solution since the polycondensation reaction proceeded successfully.

CONCLUSION

Organically modified silicate sols were prepared from the PDMS-TEOS-$Ca(NO_3)_2 \cdot 4H_2O$ solutions with / without DMF were doped. The sols were coated on Nylon6®. The coating film from the sols without DMF did not deposit apatite within 14 days while the bulk gel sample deposited apatite within 1 day of soaking in the Kokubo solution. The film-DMF from the sol with DMF deposited apatite within 7 days. Bioactivity of the gel-coated films was thus enhanced by incorporation of DMF into the coating sols. The difference in structure between film-DMF and DMF-free film affected bioactivity. Adhesive strength between the coated films and substrates was not less than about 1.5 MPa. We concluded that DMF was also a good drying control chemical additive for the present system and therefore apatite-forming ability of the film-DMF has been derived by incorporation of DMF in the coating solution.

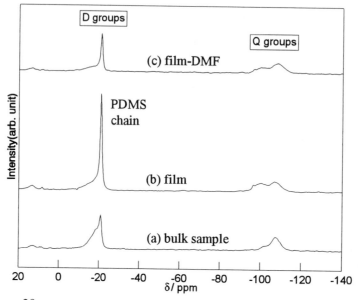

Figure 2. ^{29}Si MAS NMR spectra of bulk sample (a), film (b) and film-DMF (c)

ACKNOWLEDGEMENTS

This work was financially supported by the Grant-in-Aid for Scientific Research (B)(2)(09450246), the Ministry of Education, Science, Sports, and Culture, Japan. One of the authors (K. T.) gratefully acknowledges the Research Fellowship of the Japan Society for the Promotion of Science for Young Scientists. One of the authors (C. O.) gratefully acknowledges the Association for the Progress of New Chemistry.

REFERENCES

1. Ikada T. *Baiomateriaru (Biomaterial)*, 1st ed. Japan: Nikkan Industry Newspaper Company, 1988: 30-41.
2. Kageyama Y, Yokoyama Y, Suzuki K, Harada T, Kokubo T. In: Anderson ÖH, Yli-Urpo A, ed. *Bioceramics Volume 7*. Oxford: Butterworth-Heinemann Ltd, 1994: 165-170.
3. Tsuru K, Ohtsuki C, Osaka A. *J Mat Sci Mat Med* 1997; **8**: 157-161.
4. Wallace S, Hench LL. *Mat Res Soc Symp Proc* 1984; **32**: 47-52.
5. Cho SB, Nakanishi K, Kokubo T, Soga N, Ohtsuki C, Nakamura T, Kitsugi T, Yamamuro T. *J Am Ceram Soc* 1995; **78**: 1769-1774.
6. Kokubo T, Kushitani H, Sakka S, Kitsugi T, Yamamuro T. *J Biomed Mater Res* 1990; **24**: 721-734.
7. Florence B. *Mat Res Soc Symp Proc* 1994; **346**: 949-960.

Bioceramics Volume 11, edited by R. Z. LeGeros and J.P. LeGeros
(Proceedings of the 11th International Symposium on Ceramics in Medicine)
New York, NY, USA, November 1998
© 1998 by World Scientific Publishing Co. Pte. Ltd.

OSTEOCONDUCTIVE PROPERTIES OF BIOACTIVE GLASSES IN A BULK FORM AND AS A COATING ON ALUMINA

M. Hamadouche, R. S. Nizard, A. Meunier, C. Blanchat, P. Masquelier, L. Sedel
Laboratoire De Recherches Orthopediques,Upres A CNRS 7052
Universite Denis Diderot Paris VII, 10 Ave De Verdun, Paris. France

ABSTRACT

In a previous in-vivo study[2] evaluating the osteoconductive potential of bioactive glasses coated alumina, lack of mineralization was observed in the bone in direct contact with the materials. The present experiment was aimed to investigate the osteoconductive properties of the same glasses implanted in a bulk form in order to understand the underlying parameters involved in this mineralization inhibitory process. Three bioactive glasses were investigated : (i) a silica glass (SiG) similar in composition to Bioglass® 45S5, (ii) the original Bioglass® 45S5 and (iii) a silica free glass (PG). These materials were studied in a bulk form and compared to their coated-on-alumina counterparts. Plain alumina was used as a control. All materials were implanted in a rabbit lateral condyles defect model. Histomorphometry was performed to analyse the tissues found at the interface after 3, 12 and 24 weeks of implantation. Osteoid tissue was only present when using bulk silica free glass implants (PG) or all coated implants. On contrary, this type of tissue was always absent in cas of bulk silicate glasses (either SiG or Bioglass® 45S5 or plain alumina.
This lack of mineralization was probably related to an Al^{3+} release from the silica free glasses, or from the alumina substrates after the thermal treatment. The high temperature (1,300 to 1,500°C) could be responsible for an allotropic transformation of alumina from its α stable phase to a more soluble γ phase.

INTRODUCTION

In order to avoid polyethylene wear and its consequences, P. BOUTIN[1], in the early 70's, was the first surgeon to propose alumina on alumina bearing surfaces as an alternative to metal on plastic friction couple.. Until 1977, improvements in the manufacturing process have made alumina a reliable material. Between 1977 and 1982, in the Orthopaedic Surgery department of St Louis hospital in Paris, conventionnal cementing techniques were used to fix the acetabular component. Loosening of the acetabular cemented component was found to be the main reason for long term failure[6,4]. For this reason, a clinical trial using cementless fixation of the plain alumina socket was conducted. The bulk alumina socket was implanted with a press-fit technique (Cerapress). The results were satisfactory with a survivorship of 91.2 % at a 6 year follow-up. However the main cause of failure remained the anchorage of the alumina socket indicating that the bone/alumina interface was still the weakest point and required further improvements. Coating of alumina with bioactive glasses was one way of research. As an alumina coating, both silicate and silica free glasses failed to demonstrate any osteoconductive property but were rather « osteoid-conductive »: this tissue covered over 50% of the interface after 12 weeks and over 70% after 24 weeks of implantation[2]. Hypothesis advocated to explain this inhibitory phenomenon were: - (i) a flaw in the manufactoring process of the glasses, - (ii) a contamination of the glasses from the substrates during the coating procedure.
In order to explore these hypothesis, the same glasses as used previously were implanted as a bulk material. The results were compared to those obtained with the coated implants. Bulk 45S5 Bioglass® was used as a control.

MATERIALS AND METHODS

Three types of implants were surgically inserted (press-fit) in both lateral condyles of 45 New-Zeland adult male rabbits:
- bulk silicate glass (SiG)
- bulk phosphate glass (PG)
- and original Bioglass® 45S5 as controls.

The glasses composition is provided in table 1.

Table 1

Weight %	SiO$_2$	P$_2$O$_5$	CaO	Na$_2$O	ZrO$_2$	Fe$_2$O$_3$	Al$_2$O$_3$
Bioglass® 45S5	45	6	24,5	24,5	0	0	0
SiG	45	6	24,5	24,5	0	0	0
PG	0	45,5	14,8	13,2	12,6	2,6	11,3

Sacrifices were performed after 3, 12 and 24 weeks of implantation. Lower extremities of both femur were retrieved *en bloc* and embedded in PMMA. Cross sections perpendiculary to the implants long axis were obtained using a law speed diamond saw (Leitz 1600). Slices were ground down to 150-120 μm with the use of an Exakt machine. Histological sections were stained with Stevenel blue & Van Gieson, Von Kossa and Goldner trichrome.

Histological qualitative analysis included the identification of the tissues surrouding the implants with an optical microscope (X100). The biological tissues/material interface evaluation measured the percentage of contact area of these tissues using an image analyser.

RESULTS

Concerning both silicate glasses (SiG and Bioglass® controls), three tissues were present at the interface: bone, cartilage and zones of resorption corresponding to remodelling bone. In the other hand, phosphate glasses demonstrated, whatever the duration, a negligible percentage of bone in direct contact with the implants. However, as observed in the previous study (alumina coated with SiG and alumina coated with PG), osteoid tissue was present. Table 2 summarizes all quantitaive data measured in this study.

Table 2: tissues found in contact with the implant (% of total contact area)

Tissues / Implants	Bone	Resorption areas	Fibrous tissue	Osteoid	Cartilage
PG	1.07± 1.04	10.95±12.99	0	75.02±27.09	12.95±16.83
45S5	93.76± 4.96	4.52± 2.13	1.53± 4.34	0	0.19 ± 0.40
SiG	87.63± 5.90	12.37 ± 5.90	0	0	0
2 a: 3 weeks					
PG	6.12± 4.58	30.45± 9.92	0	61.64±10.15	1.79± 2.47
45S5	83.18±12.14	16.38±12.40	0	0	0.44± 0.99
SiG	90.53± 6.85	5.81± 5.73	0	0	3.67± 8.20
2 b: 12 weeks					
PG	4.12± 3.18	26.34± 6.66	0	69.35± 7.25	0.20± 0.44
45S5	94.04± 2.22	4.73± 2.51	0.82± 1.83	0	0.41± 0.92
SiG	96.36± 3.68	3.64± 3.68	0	0	0
2 c: 24 weeks					

3 weeks
Bone percentage was significantly higher for both silicate glasses when compared to phosphate glasses (p< 0.0001). There was no significant difference between the two types of silicate glasses (p= 0.1). The mean percentage of resorption zones was significantly higher for 45S5 in comparison to SiG (p< 0.05).

12 weeks
The main tissue at the interface was bone for both silicate glasses (SiG: 90.6% ans 45S5: 83.2%, NS). Osteoid tissue was present o,ly in contact with phosphate glasses (61.6%).

24 weeks

Over 93% of the interface was bone for both silicate glasses with no significant difference. The main tissue for phosphate glasses was osteoid (69.4%).

Time evolution of the tissues present at the interface are presented on figures 1-4.

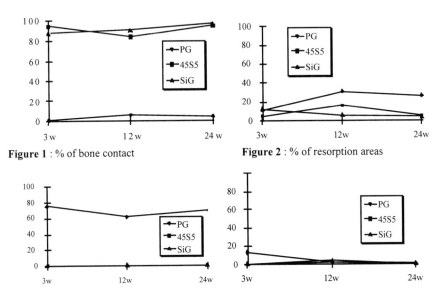

Figure 1 : % of bone contact

Figure 2 : % of resorption areas

Figure 3 : % of osteoid

Figure 4 : % of cartilage

DISCUSSION AND CONCLUSION

The results obtained with the original Bioglass® 45S5 were similar to those observed in the literature[3]: its osteoconductive properties were clearly observed. Resorption areas only indicated a remodelling activity and had no pejorative meaning.

Moerover, SiG glass demonstrated very similar behavior when compared to Bioglass® 45S5 in term of percentage of bony contact and osteoconductivity. However the significant difference found at 3 weeks in the number of resorption areas may be related to a slight difference in bioactivity. These results are not surprising as chemical composition of both glasses is identical. These data indicate that the initial composition of SiG glass used as a coating was not responsible for the absence of osteoconductivity found in the previous study.

On contrary, bone percentage in contact with PG implants was neglegible whatever the duration (< 5% after 24 weeks of implantation). Osteoid was the main tissue at the interface (70% after 24 weeks of implanation). In this respect, PG glass can not be considered as osteoconductive but « osteoid conductive » at least in the first 24 weeks of implantation. Similar lack of mineralization was also observed when used as a coating.

The whole results could be summarized as follow:

- Bioglass® 45S5: osteoconductive
- Glass SiG: osteoconductive
- Glass PG: osteoid conductive
- Alumina coated with SiG: osteoid conductive
- Alumina coated with PG: osteoid conductive.

Amongst the hypotheses that could explain this mineralization inhibitory process, the one involving Al3+ ions is the likeliest. PG glass composition was made of 10.8% Al2O3 and did not demonstrate almost no bony contact either in the bulk form or as a coating. On the other hand, alumina substrates seemed to inhibit bone formation of alumina coated implants even when coated with glasses that demonstrated osteocondictivity in a bulk form. Both observations lead to the concclusion that aluminum contamination was most probably responsible for the lack of local mineralization. However, this phenomenon was never observed in case of plain alumina implants. For this reason, one may suspect that a release of Al3+ ions from the substrate probably occured because of alumina transformation from the initial α stable phase to a γ soluble phase, in relation with the thermal treatment during coating procedure (1,300°C). Similar observations was made by Savarino et al.[5] when investigating retreived cobalt-chrome implants coated with plasma sprayed alumina. When considering PG glass, this transformation may have occured directly during the manufacturing process of the glass itself.

In conclusion, implantation of phosphate glasses in a cancellous bone environement leaded to pathological mineralization 6 months after implantation and initial stability of such implant is certainly a cause of major concern. Similar observations can be made on coated alumina implants, whatever glasses used as a coating. Use of bioactive glasses coated alumina should require extensive investigation of aluminum contamination of the surface during the material processing prior to any further developpement.

ACKNOWLEDGEMENTS

This study was supported in part by US Biomaterials (Alachua, Fl, USA), CERAVER-OSTEAL (Roissy, France) and CNRS.

REFERENCES

1. Boutin P, Blanquaert D. *Rev Chir Orthop* 1981;**67** (3):279-87.
2. Hamadouche M, Meunier A., Nizard R S et al, 42nd Annual Meeting ORS, Atlanta, 1996.
3. Hench LL, Wilson J. *Science* 1984;**226** (4675):630-6.
4. Nizard RS, Sedel L, Christel P, Meunier A, Soudry M, Witvoet J. *Clin Orthop* 1992;**282**:53-63.
5. Savarino L, Cenni E, Stea S, et al. *Biomaterials* 1993;**14** (12):900-905.
6. Sedel L, Kerboull L, Christel P, Meunier A, Witvoet J. *J Bone Joint Surg* [Br] 1990;**72** (4):658-63.

Bioceramics Volume 11, edited by R. Z. LeGeros and J.P. LeGeros
(Proceedings of the 11th International Symposium on Ceramics in Medicine)
New York, NY, USA, November 1998
© 1998 by World Scientific Publishing Co. Pte. Ltd.

BLAST COATING METHOD -TISSUE RESPONSE TO TITANIUM IMPLANT COATED WITH HYDROXYAPATITE AT ROOM TEMPERATURE-

Takamitsu Mano[1], Yoshiya Ueyama[1], Kunio Ishikawa[2], Takahiro Koyama[1], Tomohiro Matsumura[1], Kazuomi Suzuki[2]

[1]Department of Oral and Maxillofacial Surgery II, Okayama University Dental School, 2-5-1 Shikata-cho, Okayama 700-8525, Japan
[2]Department of Dental Materials, Okayama University Dental School, 2-5-1 Shikata-cho, Okayama 700-8525, Japan

ABSTRACT

We have previously reported blast coating method as a new coating method of titanium with hydroxyapatite (HAP) at room temperature. Blast coating method gives much stronger HAP coating on titanium surface when compared with those obtained by other coating method at room temperature. As an initial step to evaluate the usefulness of blast coating method, we evaluated tissue response and stability of HAP coated titanium implant made with blast coating method using experimental animals. The HAP coating stuck tightly on the titanium surface even after implant procedure. HAP coated titanium implant showed excellent tissue response and much better osteoconductivity when compared with pure titanium implant. Therefore we concluded, HAP coated titanium implant made with blast coating method has a potential value as osteoconductive implant materials.

KEYWORDS: blast coating, hydroxyapatite, titanium

INTRODUCTION

Although plasma spray method is widely accepted for the hydroxyapatite (HAP) coating because it gives tight adhesion between HAP and the titanium, extreme high temperature during the coating process produce serious problems such as an alteration of structure [1], formation of HAP with extremely high crystallinity [2]. To avoid shortcomings in the plasma spray method, many alternative coating method that do not require high temperature were studied extensively including ion beam sputtering, dipping, electrophoretic deposition, and electrochemical deposition [3- 6]. However, none of the above methods provide a tight bond between the HAP and titanium. Recently, we proposed blast coating method for the coating method of titanium surface with HAP [7]. Blast coating method gives relatively tight HAP coating. Theoretically HAP coated titanium implant made with blast coating method should show more excellent tissue response and better osteoconductivity when compared with pure titanium implant. However, no implantation study has been made so far and thus we have no histological results with respect to the HAP coated titanium implant made with blast coating. In addition we have no results with respect to the stability of HAP coating. Although blast coating method provide much stronger bonding between the HAP and titanium when compared with other coating method at room temperature, the absolute value is much weaker when compared with that of plasma spray. Therefore, the aims of this investigation was to evaluate the tissue response, osteoconductivity and the stability of HAP coated titanium made with blast coating method by implanting the HAP coated titanium in the bone of the experimental animals.

MATERIALS AND METHODS
Implant preparation
Pure titanium rods of grade 4 with a diameter of 2.0mm and a length of 5mm were blasted with HAP powder for 10s using an ordinary sandblaster (Hi-blaster SHB-20, Shofu, Kyoto, Japan). Commercially obtained HAP powder (Central Glass, Tokyo, Japan) was used in this experiment. After blast coating, titanium rods were cleaned ultrasonically to remove adsorbed HAP powder.

Surgical procedure
Seven-week-old male rats of the Wister strain, obtained commercially were used for the experiments. The rats were anesthetized by intraperitoneal injection of sodium pentobarbital (Nembutal®; Abbott Co., Chicago, IL). The legs were shaved and the medial end of tibia was exposed. A hole was made in the tibia using 2.0mm twist drill and the titanium implant was inserted in the hole. Titanium with no HAP coating was used as control.

SEM observation and hstological examination
The experimental rats were sacrificed at 3 and 6 weeks after surgery and perfused with a solution of 10% neutral buffered formalin. The tibias were taken with surrounding tissue. All specimens were dehydrated in a series of graded alcohol, and embedded in polyester resin. Each undecalcified block was cut into two sections on a slicer using a diamond blade. The cut surfaces were analyzed by SEM and EDXA. Sections were ground to a thickness of $50\,\mu$m and stained with toluidine blue.

RESULTS AND DISCUSSION
SEM observation revealed that the surface of titanium was coated with HAP homogeneously and completely even after implantation (Figure 1). Although the absolute bonding strength of HAP coating to titanium surface is unknown, it was enough at least to maintain bonding during the implantation procedure. Since HAP is known to show excellent tissue response and good osteoconductivity, it is expected that HAP coated titanium implant made with blast coating method shows excellent tissue response and good osteoconductivity. In fact we found

Figure 1. Scanning electron microscopic findings of the interface between HAP and titanium implant at 3 weeks after implantation.

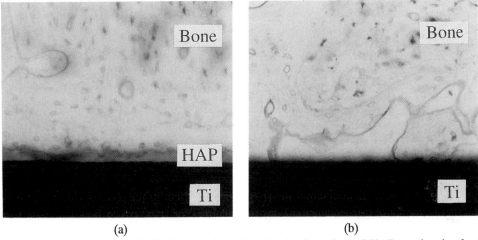

(a)   (b)

Figure 2. Light microscopic findings at 6 weeks after implantation of HAP coating implant (a) and non HAP coating implant (b). (toluidine blue stain, original magnification×200)

no inflammatory reaction and excellent tissue response during the whole experimental periods. 3 weeks after implantation, most of the HAP coated titanium implant was covered with new bone. The amount of new bone attached to the HAP coated titanium implant was larger than that attached to the titanium with no HAP coating. No connective tissue was observed between HAP coated titanium implant and new bone. At 6 weeks, new bone formation became more marked (Figure 2). Although, the length of implantation was only up to 6 weeks, better osteoconductivity observed in HAP coated implant demonstrated clearly that this material could be a good osteoconductive implant. One of the possible advantage of this blast coating method is the replacement of HAP coated layer with bone since HAP can be coated at low temperature, i.e., bone like apatite can be coated on the surface of titanium. We feel further implant study, i.e., longer observation should be done to understand the behaviour of this osteoconductive implant based on the encouraging results obtained in this study.

REFERENCES

1. Ducheyne P, Cuckler J, Radin S, Nazar E. CRC Handbook of Bioactive Ceramics, Boca Raton, FL: CRC Press, 1990; 123-131.
2. Cheang P, Khor KA. *Biomaterials*, 1996; **17**: 537-544.
3. Ong JL, Lucas LC, Lacefield WR, Rigney ED. *Biomaterials* 1992; **13**: 249-254.
4. Lee J, Aoki H. *Biomed Mater Eng* 1991; **5**: 49-58.
5. Ducheyne P, Radin S, Heughebaert M, Heughebaert JC. *Biomaterials* 1990; **11**: 244-254.
6. Butterworth-Heinemann Ltd.; Andersson OE, Yli-Urpoi A, Eds. Bioceramics 7, Turku, Finland, 1994, 261-266.
7. Ishikawa K, Miyamoto Y, Nagayama M, Asaoka K. *J Biomed Mater Res* 1997; **38**: 129-134.

Bioceramics Volume 11, edited by R. Z. LeGeros and J.P. LeGeros
(Proceedings of the 11th International Symposium on Ceramics in Medicine)
New York, NY, USA, November 1998
© 1998 by World Scientific Publishing Co. Pte. Ltd.

IN VIVO EVALUATION OF A NOVEL CALCIUM PHOSPHATE CEMENT FOR USE IN REPAIR AND RECONSTRUCTION OF BONE TISSUE

S.J. Gadaleta, R.S. Sapieszko, and E.M. Erbe
Orthovita Inc., 45 Great Valley Parkway, Malvern, Pennsylvania 19355

ABSTRACT

A novel, self-setting, injectable calcium phosphate cement is described. Low temperature, fine powder synthesis of the precursor materials generates a cement with properties well suited for repair and reconstruction of bone tissue. In this paper, we describe the histological and physico-chemical evaluation of the cement.

The cement was generated by reacting fine particle calcium and phosphate powders with a basic solution. The cement was injected into the medullary canal of the proximal metaphysis of both femora in six New Zealand White rabbits. Specimens were harvested at 4, and 8 weeks. Specimens were embedded in methyl methacrylate, sectioned on a Reichert-Jung microtome, and stained with Toluidine Blue and Goldner's Trichrome stains. The *in vivo* cement was analyzed by Fourier transform infrared microspectropscopy (FTIRM).

Analysis of the specimens revealed direct bone contact between the cement and host bone without fibrous/connective tissue at the cement-bone interface. Inflammation was not noted. Inspection of the 8-week specimens revealed further healing of the defect and bone growth in and around the cement. Resorption of the cement was observed, followed by osteoblasts secreting new osteoid. The material appeared to be intact and whole in all histology specimens. Furthermore, no changes in blood chemistry were noted. Both *in vitro* and *in vivo* FTIR analysis revealed the cement to be a poorly crystalline apatite similar to that of normal bone.

The current study describes a novel calcium phosphate cement generated by low-temperature, fine-particle synthesis. The powders used in the formulation result in a cement with a relatively uniform particle size. The cement sets at physiological pH without an exothermic reaction. Histological evaluation revealed normal bone growth and remodeling around the cement. Furthermore, remodeling of the cement was observed.

KEYWORDS: Calcium Phosphate Cement, Bone, Histology, Remodeling

INTRODUCTION

Bone grafting materials are used for a variety of indications including filling bony defects following tumor removal, reconstruction of failed joint arthroplasty, and spinal fusions, to name a few. Ideally, these materials should provide four basic elements for successful clinical outcomes:

- an osteoconductive matrix, a scaffold which supports bone in-growth[1]
- osteoinductive factors, chemical agents responsible for inducing various stages of bone regeneration and repair[1]
- osteogenic cells, capable of differentiating into the requisite cells for these processes[1]
- structural integrity[1]

The current gold standard for grafting procedures is the autograft. Autografts provide three of the four basic elements mentioned above; they provide an osteoconductive matrix, osteoinductive factors, and osteogenic cells. Although these procedures generally produce good clinical outcomes, harvesting the bone results in frequent donor site morbidity, increased surgical time, and pain. Allografts provide many of the attributes of autograft procedures, however, transmission of disease and immunogenic responses to the material are possible. The development of a biocompatible, synthetic, hardening bone graft substitute would eliminate the negative aspects of auto- and allograft, and provide a material with structural integrity.

Currently, there are a variety of products targeting the synthetic bone graft market. These include processed coral blocks, calcium sulfate pellets, demineralized bone matrix, and calcium phosphate bone cements. Coralline hydroxyapatite blocks offer macroporous structure, which afford bony and vascular in-growth and provide mechanical strength. However, this material remains at the site of implantation for a number of years and may be difficult to shape to fill the defect completely. Calcium sulfate pellets offer mechanical support to the defect site but are quickly resorbed/remodeled and are not capable of being shaped to fit the contour of the defect. Calcium phosphates cements offer an injectable, hardening material which resorb/remodel in an efficient length of time, provide mechanical support, and easily fit the shape of the defect. Incorporation of osteogenic factors and cells make this material an ideal substitute for bone autografts.

The following study was undertaken to examine the remodeling characteristics of a novel, self-setting, injectable calcium phosphate cement. In addition, the *in vitro* physico-chemical properties of the cement were also examined.

MATERIALS AND METHODS

Characterization of Precursor Powders. Physical and chemical properties of the powders were assessed by three methods: Fourier transform infrared spectroscopy (FTIR), x-ray powder diffraction (XRD), and scanning electron microscopy (SEM). FTIR spectra of the powders were acquired on a Nicolet Magna 560 spectrometer equipped with a wide-band MCT detector (Madison, WI). XRPD patterns were collected on a Rigaku Miniflex x-ray powder diffractometer using Cu-Kα radiation (Danvers, MA). Patterns were obtained between 15 - 50° (2θ). Electron micrographs were acquired using a JEOL 840A scanning electron microscope (Peabody, MA). Inductively coupled plasma spectroscopy (ICP) was used to assess the calcium and phosphate molar ratios of the monetite powder only (performed at CELS-Laboratory Services, Corning, NY).

Blood Chemistry Measurements. Blood levels of Ca, P, Na, K, Cl, and HCO^3 were assessed, both pre-operatively and 2 weeks post-operatively.

Formulation of Cements. Three unique formulations were generated for this study:

- 25:75 (weight %) Monetite:β-TCP/Hap
- 50:50 (weight %) Monetite:β-TCP/Hap
- 75:25 (weight %) Monetite:β-TCP/HAp.

The powders were hand-mixed with an alkaline solution and loaded into a 1cc syringe. Each formulation was injected into an aspirated and bloody site in the proximal metaphysis of the right and left femur. In addition, a pre-set slug of each formulation was inserted in the diaphysis of the left femur and a polyethylene cylinder, used as a control, was implanted into the distal metaphysis of both femora.

Preparation of Femoral Defects. A 3mm hole was drilled into the distal, diaphyseal, and proximal regions of the left and right femora of 6 New Zealand White rabbits. A single formulation of the experimental cement was injected into the distal defect of the right and left femora of each animal, a polypropylene rod was inserted into the proximal defect of the right and left femora of each animal, and a pre-set form of the cement was inserted into the diaphyseal defect of the left femur of each animal. The diaphyseal defect of the right femur was allowed to heal without introduction of any foreign material.

Preparation of Specimens for Histology. Femora were dissected from each animal and stored in 10% phosphate buffered formalin for 48 hours. Faxitrons of each specimen were obtained. The distal, diaphyseal, and proximal sections of bone were dehydrated, infiltrated with methyl methacrylate monomer, and polymerized into PMMA blocks. The blocks were subsequently sectioned to a thickness of ~80 μm and stained with Paragon and Goldner's trichrome stains.

Fourier Transform Infrared Microspectroscopy. Thin sections from each of the histology blocks were cut to a thickness of ~5 μm for analysis by Fourier transform infrared microspectroscopy (FTIRM). A 20 x 20 μm aperture was used to characterize the phase of the cement *in situ* at 4 and 8 weeks. FTIRM spectra were acquired on a BioRad FTS-40 infrared spectrometer coupled to a UMA 500 infrared microscope equipped with a narrow-band MCT detector. Spectra were obtained as described above.

RESULTS

Injectability, Set Behavior, and Blood Chemistry. Each of the three formulations was easily injected into the 3mm defect sites through a 1cc syringe. In addition, each formulation "set" in aspirated and bloody defect sites. "Set" behavior was judged by probing the exposed surface of the cement with a Gilmore needle. Moreover, histology sections revealed a solid, intact bolus of material at the site of implantation. Blood chemistry measurements revealed no significant increases in any of the tests.

In Vitro Analysis. Each of the formulations converted to hydroxyapatite as confirmed by x-ray powder diffraction and FTIR spectroscopy. Further analysis of the FTIR contour revealed this material to be a poorly crystalline hydroxyapatite with CO_3^{2-} and HPO_4^{2-} substitutions ((REFS)).

In Vivo Analysis. Analysis of the histology sections at the 4-week time point illustrated a solid intact bolus of material in direct contact with the surrounding cortical bone. Normal healing at the periosteum was noted. A tight seam between the cement and the cortical bone was also evident. Fibrous encapsulation of the material was not evident. Resorption of the cement was observed in the medullary canal. This resorption was followed by osteoblastic secretion of new osteoid. Analysis of the 8-week specimens revealed similar findings.

In Vivo FTIRM Analysis. The *in vivo* cement was characterized using infrared microspectroscopy. These spectra also reveal the material to be a poorly crystalline hydroxyapatite with CO_3^{2-} and HPO_4^{2-} substitutions in the lattice structure[2]. Moreover, the entire body of cement was characterized at discreet locations throughout the periphery and interior of the bolus. No variation was seen in the spectral properties of the material.

DISCUSSION

In recent years, much attention has been given to the development of calcium phosphate bone cements. This is attributable to the fact that these materials are biocompatible and may be used for a variety of clinical applications; they provide an osteoconductive scaffold for bone grafting

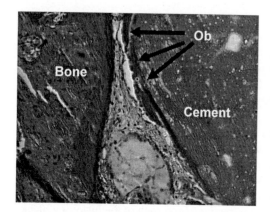 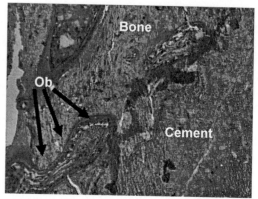

Figures A and B. Figure A (left) illustrates osteoblastic activity on the surface of the cement. Figure B illustrates resorption of the cement followed by osteoblastic secretion of osteoid. (Ob = osteoblast)

applications; they may be used to stabilize fractures; and they serve as carriers for proteins, cells, and pharmaceutical agents.

Brown and Chow pioneered the development of a calcium phosphate bone cement.[3] The chemistry consists of mixing tetracalcium phosphate and dicalcium phosphate dihydrate or dicalcium phosphate anhydrous with water or dilute phosphoric acid. The reactants dissolve and reprecipitate to form hydroxyapatite. The rate of hydroxyapatite formation may be increased or decreased by seeding the mixture with finely divided hydroxyapatite crystals or by using a liquid phase containing glycerin, respectively.

Constantz et al also developed a calcium phosphate bone cement.[4] The chemistry of this cement involves mixing monocalcium phosphate monohydrate, α-tricalcium phosphate, and calcium carbonate with a sodium phosphate solution. The product of this reaction is a poorly crystalline hydroxyapatite with a highly broadened x-ray diffraction pattern similar to that of natural bone.

The challenge of developing a calcium phosphate bone cement lies in balancing the resorption/remodeling characteristics with the mechanical properties of the cement. A material with high mechanical properties will probably have poor resorption/remodeling characteristics and vice-versa. This may be attributable to the fact that materials with superior mechanical properties typically have very high bond energies that may retard resorption/remodeling of the material.

The current study describes a novel calcium phosphate cement generated by low-temperature, fine-particle synthesis. The powders used in the formulation result in a cement with relatively uniform particle size and illustrate resorption/remodeling as early as 4 weeks. Future experiments include further characterization of resorption/remodeling characteristics and inclusion of the material in orthopedic applications.

REFERENCES

1. Gazdag AR, Lane JM, Glaser D, Forster RA. *J. Am Acad Orthop Surg* 1995; **3**: 1-8.
2. Gadaleta SJ, Paschalis EP, Betts F, Mendelsohn R, and Boskey AL. *Cal. Tissue Int.* 1996; **58**: 9-16.
3. Brown WE, Chow LC, US Patent 4,518,430, May 21, 1985.
4. Constantz BR, Ison IC, Fulmer MT, Poser RD, Smith ST, VanWagoner M, Ross J, Goldstein SA, Jupiter JB, and Rosenthal DI. *Science* 1995; **267**: 1796 - 1798.

Bioceramics Volume 11, edited by R. Z. LeGeros and J.P. LeGeros
(Proceedings of the 11th International Symposium on Ceramics in Medicine)
New York, NY, USA, November 1998
© 1998 by World Scientific Publishing Co. Pte. Ltd.

AUGMENTATION OF CANCELLOUS SCREW FIXATION
WITH A BIOACTIVE CEMENT (CAP) IN VIVO

Kazuyoshi Kawagoe[1], Takaaki Shibuya[2], Masanobu Saito[3], Toshihide Nakashima[4], Kenichi Hino[4] and Takahiro Ochi[5]

[1]Department of Orthopaedic Surgery, Nissei Hospital, 6-3-8, Itachibori, Nishi-Ku, Osaka 550-0012, Japan

  Tel : +81-6-543-3581   Fax : +81-6-532-6482

[2]Department of Orthopaedic Surgery, Saiseikai Izuo Hospital

  3-4-5, Kitamura, Taisho-Ku, Osaka 551, Japan

[3]Department of Orthopaedic Surgery, Osaka-Minami National Hospital

  2-1 Kidohigashi-machi, Kawachinagano 586-8521, Japan

[4]Kuraray Co., Ltd, 1621 Sakazu, Kurashiki 710, Japan

[5]Department of Orthopaedic Surgery, Osaka University Medical School, 2-2 Yamadaoka, Suita 565, Japan

ABSTRACT

We studied the effect of bioactive cement (CAP) and polymethylmethacrylate (PMMA) cement on augmentation of cancellous screw fixation in rabbit tibia. CAP is composed of 77% w/w hydroxyapatite granules and bisphenol-A glycidyl methacrylate-based resin. CAP has superior mechanical strength and osteoconductive property. A cancellous screw was placed in the proximal end of tibia to the point where threads engaged cancellous bone. One side was randomly selected to be augmented with PMMA or CAP. The contralateral side had a screw without cement (control). Thirty-six rabbits were operated on and sacrificed 1 and 3 months after surgery, and then the pull-out strength was determined for each screw. At 1 month mean values of pull-out strength of screws augmented with CAP and PMMA ($319 \pm 58N^*$ and $284 \pm 100N^{**}$, respectively) were higher than those for controls (control for CAP; $105 \pm 41N^*$ and control for PMMA; $132 \pm 71N^{**}$). Although all values of pull-out strength increased at 3 months, the CAP augmented screws maintained the greatest value (CAP vs control; $387 \pm 109N^{***}$ vs $196 \pm 107N^{***}$, PMMA vs control; $372 \pm 145N$ vs $242 \pm 100N$)

($*, **, ***$; $p < 0.05$). The effect of augmentation using CAP was equal with that for PMMA. In addition, CAP may promote and not impede fracture healing because of its osteoconductive property and low curing temperature. These results suggested that CAP had a good potential for clinical indication.

KEYWORDS: bone substitutes, bone cement, screw fixation, hydroxyapatite

PURPOSE

Stabilization of fractured bone with hardwares is very important for orthopaedic surgery. But because of poor quality of osteoporotic bone, ligid fixation can not be often acquired in elderly patient and occasionally result to failure. Although some researchers have tried to augment cancellous bone screws with polymethylmethacrylate (PMMA) cement,[1,3,6,8] several problems such as the impediment of fracture healing are still remaining.[2] We developed bioactive bone cement (CAP) that had superior mechancal strength to PMMA cement and osteoconductive property.[5] So, we expected that well stabilized fixation between bone and hardwares could be obtained with augmentation using CAP. In this study we assess the mechanical properties of cancellous bone screw fixation augmented with CAP in comparison with those augmented with PMMA.

MATERIALS AND METHODS

CAP is a composite resin, composed of HA granules (77% w/w) with a mean particle size of 2 μ m, as well as acrylic monomers. The acrylic monomers are bis-phenol-A glycidyl methacrylate (BIS-GMA), 2,2'-bis-(4-methacryloyloxyethoxyphenyl) propane (BIS-MEPP) and triethyleneglycol dimethacrylate (TEG-DMA) in a 30:20:50 w/w ratio. The average setting time of CAP is about 5 min and the peak curing temperature is about 46.0℃.

The mechanical effect of augmentation with cement was evaluated with screw pull-out testing constructs in rabbit tibia. Drilled and tapped hole with 2.0 mm in diameter was placed in proximal tibia of Japanese White Rabbit, followed by overdrilling of the outer cortex. After washing and drying of medullary space, cancellous bone screw 4 mm in diameter was inserted in the hole to the point where threads engaged cancellous bone. One side of each rabbit was randomly selected to be augmented with CAP or PMMA cement. After immediately each cement was injected into the hole, the cancellous screw was inserted. Same procedures were performed without cement on the other side of each rabbit. Thirty-six rabbits were operated on and nine rabbits of each group were sacrificed 1 and 3 months after surgery. Samples of proximal tibia were prepared for mechanical evaluation. Pull-out strength was measured for each sample with using an Instron universal material testing machine at a cross-head speed of 1 mm/min.

RESULTS

The mean pull-out strength of screws augmented with CAP and PMMA cement 1 month after surgery were $319 \pm 58N$ and $284 \pm 100N$, respectively, and those values were significantly greater than those for controls (control for CAP; $105 \pm 41N$ and control for PMMA; $132 \pm 71N$). Compared with the values of pull-out strength 1 month after surgery, all values of each group 3 months after surgery were increased. The mean pull-out strength of screws augmented with CAP ($387 \pm 109N$) and PMMA cement ($372 \pm 145N$) 3 months after surgery were also greater than those for controls (control for CAP; $196 \pm 107N$ and control for PMMA; $24 \pm 100N$).

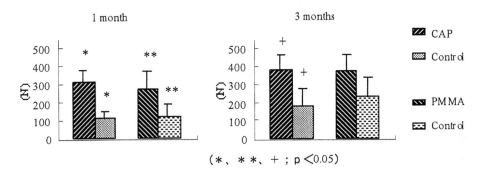

Figure 1. The mean pull-out strength of screws augmented with CAP and PMMA
1 and 3 months after surgery (n =9)

DISCUSSION

Occasionally, we experience the situation that it is hard to obtain the ligid stabilization between bone and hardwares in elderly patients with osteoporosis. PMMA cement was used for augmentation of screw in spite of its adverse effect to fracture healing.[2-3,6,8] In this study we tried to stabilize between the rabbit bone and the cancellous bone screw with CAP. Proximal end of rabbit tibia was sellected to use because this site was easy to treat and had a lot of cancellous bone with the moderate cavity. The mechanical properties of augmented screws with both CAP and PMMA cement were obviously superior to those of non-augmented screws at any time. Furthermore the mean pull-out strength of screws augmented with CAP were higher than those augmented with PMMA both 1 and 3 months after surgery, although there were no significant differences between them. CAP can not only bond to bone directly without intervening fibrous tissue, but also has superior mechancal properties to PMMA.[5] Therefore, the secure fixation of screws was thought to be obtained with using CAP. Recently, calciumphosphate cement (CPC) was used for augmentation of screw fixation. [4,7] CAP does not replaced by bone as is case with CPC, but its superior mechancal properties would stabilize the cancellous screws for long periods. These suggest that CAP has a good indication for clinical use, especially for augmentation of screw fixation in osteoporotic bone.

REFERENCES

1. Cameron HU, Jacob GS, Macnab I. J Bone Joint Surg 1975; **57**: 655-656.

2. Enis JE, McCollough NC, Cooper JS. Clin Orthop 1974; **105**: 283-294.

3. Keeman BC, Takeuchi T, Gerhart T. Clin Orthop 1986; **203**: 99-112.

4. Mermelestein LE, Chow LC Friedman C. J Orthop Trauma 1996; **10**: 15-20.

5. Saito M, Maruoka A, Mori T. Biomaterials 1994; **15**: 156-160.

6. Soshi S, Shiba R, Kondo H. Spine 1991; **16**: 1335-1341.

7. Stankewich CJ, Swiontkowski MF, Tencer AF. J Orthop Res 1996; **14**: 786-793.

8. Struhl S, Szporn MN, Cobelli NJ. J Orthop Trauma 1990; **4**: 151-157.

Bioceramics Volume 11, edited by R. Z. LeGeros and J.P. LeGeros
(Proceedings of the 11th International Symposium on Ceramics in Medicine)
New York, NY, USA, November 1998
© 1998 by World Scientific Publishing Co. Pte. Ltd.

HISTOLOGICAL STUDIES IN CLINICAL CASES ON INTERFACE BIOACTIVE BONE CEMENT INTERPOSING HA GRANULES BETWEEN BONE AND PMMA BONE CEMENT

H. Oonishi, N. Murata, M. Saito, S. Wakitani, K. Imoto, N. Kim, and M. Matsuura

Department of Orthopaedic Surgery, Artificial Joint Section and Biomaterial Research Laboratory, Osaka-Minami national Hospital, 2-1, Kidohigashi-Machi, Kawachinagano-Shi, Osaka, 586-0008, JAPAN   Tel : 0721-53-5761, Fax : 0721-53-8904

ABSTRACT

In order to improve the bone interface problems of PMMA bone cement in orthopaedic surgery we have used the interface bioactive bone cement technique (IBBC) by interposing 0 to 2 layers of HA granules of 100 to 300 μ m in diameter, between bone and PMMA bone cement. This is done by smearing HA granules on the bone surface at cementation in about two thousands cases since 1987. Very few radiolucent lines appeared at the interface between bone and PMMA bone cement on the radiograph even after ten years. Three ceses were retrieved due to late infections and loosening between the metal back of the socket and bone cement one to ten years after surgery.

Non-decalcified specimens were observed by light microscopy and back scattered electron microscopy. In OA case around cortical bone, new cortical bone was formed with the HA granule layer smeared on the cortical bone. Around cancellous bone, new cancellous bone was formed with the HA granule layer. On the whole layer, a functional gradient material layer was formed by bone, HA granules and PMMA bone cement. Therefore, the adequate fixation between bone and PMMA bone cement by interposing HA franules was acquired. In RA case a bone growth is not always expected.

KEY WORDS: Bone cement, Bioactive, Hydraxyapatite

INTRODUCTION

In order to solve the interface problems of traditional PMMA bone cement, we studied a method of making bioactive bone cement only at the interface by interposing 0 to 2 layers of porous fine HA particles of 100 to 300 μ m between bone and PMMA cement [1,2](Figure 1). In this technique PMMA cement boun to the HA mechanically and HA particles bound to the bone physicochemically after bone growth into the spaces of HA particles which was proved by animal experiments [3-5]. Total hip prostheses cemented by using this technique can be considered as a complete total contact cementless prosthesis with low density HA coating. This method was named "interface bioactive bone cement" technique (IBBC), and had been used since 1987 on over 2,000 cases.

MATERIALS AND METHODS

The specimens in which IBBC technique was performed in a patient were obtained from the acetabulum and the femur. They were retrieved due to the late infection at the femur four years after joint replacement to the osteoarthritis (OA) hip joint of 60 years old male patient, the movement between metal-backed socket and bone cement 10 years after replacement to the osteoarthritis (OA) hip of 65 years old male patient and the late infection at the acetabulum one year after replacement to the rheumatoid arthritis (RA) of mutilance type of 62 years old male patient. In mutilance type, severe osteoporotic, atrophic and fatty marrow changes and resorption of the bone and joint were observed.

Hard tissues were made from the specimens. Ground hard tissues were observed by back scattered electron image and hard tissue specimens stained by methylene blue or toluidin blue were observed by light microscopy. The interfaces between bone, HA and bone cement were observed.

HISTOLOGICAL STUDIES IN CLINICAL CASES ON INTERFACE BIOACTIVE BONE CEMENT INTERPOSING HA GRANULES BETWEEN BONE AND PMMA BONE CEMENT

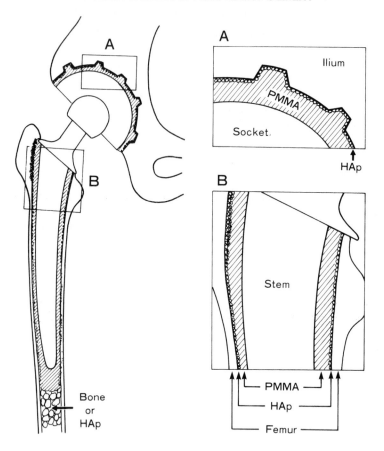

Figure 1: Scheme of interface bioactive bone cement (IBBC) technique

RESULTS

OA case:

On the dense bone, such as a cortical bone in the femur and a subchondral bone in the acetabulum, new dense bone grew into the spaces of HA particles smeared on the dense bone and new dense bone layers were formed by new bone and HA particles (Figure 2).

On the cancellous bone, new cancellous bone grew into spaces of HA particles with the same density of cancellous bone (Figure 3).

RA case:

As RA case is of the multilance type, the cortical bone of the femur changed to cancellous bone in a large part, and new bone grown into the spaces of HA particles was similar to cancellous bone. Consequently, a distribution of the new bone was not dense.

In some area, HA particles were found in only a bone cement, the spaces were found between the bone cement and the bone. In this case, it was supposed that IBBC was performed on the fatty bone marrow area, and there was no contact between bone and HA by interposing fatty tissues.

In the greater trochanter, as the cancellous bone changed to the fatty bone marrow bone ingrowth into the spaces of HA was very few.

HISTOLOGICAL STUDIES IN CLINICAL CASES ON INTERFACE BIOACTIVE BONE CEMENT INTERPOSING HA GRANULES BETWEEN BONE AND PMMA BONE CEMENT

Even on the coarse bone, new bone entered into the over ten layers of HA particles. However, the density of new bone growth was very low.

As the weight had been conducted on the bone plug by auto-bone graft, a lot of bone growth was found into the spaces of HA particles which were filled on the bone plug.

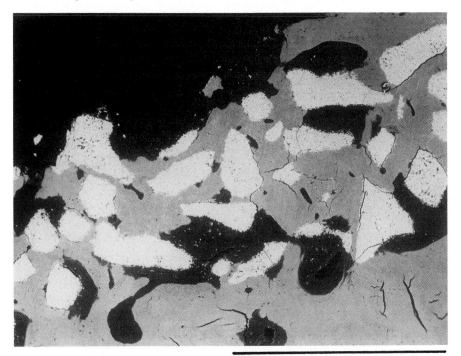

Figure 2: 10 Years after replacement to OA hip. New dense bone layers were formed by new bone and HA particles on the femoral cortical bone

1000 μm

DISCUSSION

It had been proved by our previous animal experiments that the dense bone entered into the spaces of particles on the bases of the dense bone and the cancellous bone entered into the spaces of particles on the bases of the cancellous bone.

At the interface of bone HA particles contact the bone in some areas and bone cement contacts the bone in other areas ; that is the bone does not bind to HA across the whole area.

In comparisons between IBBC and Non-IBBC cases using X-ray findings, the appearance rate of radiolucent lines in IBBC cases was much lower than Non-IBBC cases in both the acetabulum and the femur. Judging from experimental studies and histological studies retrieved from patients, HA particles interposed between bone and bone cement did not completely separate bone and bone cement, but in some parts HA contacted the bone directly and other parts bone cement contacted the bone directly. Therefore, bonding strength of the bone cement to the bone was not extremely high but moderate. In orther words, total hip prostheses cemented by using the IBBC technique can be considered as a complete total contact cementless prosthesis with low density HA coating. In consequent, there is no break in HA layer nor too strong fixability in comparison with prosthesis with HA coating on a smooth surface. By all accounts from clinical and experimental results, by using

HISTOLOGICAL STUDIES IN CLINICAL CASES ON INTERFACE BIOACTIVE BONE CEMENT INTERPOSING HA GRANULES BETWEEN BONE AND PMMA BONE CEMENT

IBBC technique correctly, the appearance of radiolucent lines will be prevented and an adequate fixability will be obtained.

In RA case, especially in mutilance type, as the bone changed to fatty bone marrow and lots of fatty and soft tissues entered into the spaces of HA particles, a new bone growth was very coarse.

From these results, it was supposed that the appearance rate of a radiolucent line is much higher than that of OA case and an adhesion strength, especially shear strength, at the interface of the bone is much lower than that of OA case.

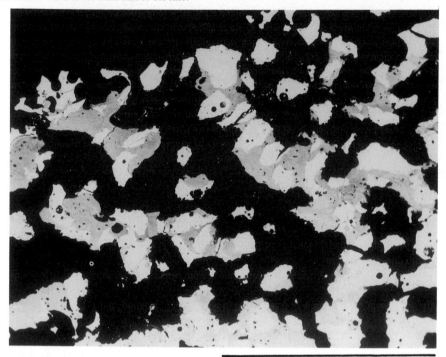

Figure 3: Four years after replacement to OA hip.
New cancellous bone grew into spaces
of HA particles with the same density of cancellous bone

1000 μm

CONCLUSION

By all accounts from clinical and experimental results, by using IBBC technique correctly, a strong fixability was not obtained but an adequate fixability was obtained at the interface between bone and bone cement by interposing HA particles. In the fatty bone marrow IBBC effect is not always expected.

REFERENCES

1) Charnley, J. J. Bone Joint Surg., 1960 ; 42-B, 28-30.
2) Hench, L. L. Splinter, R. J. J. Biomed. Mater. Res. ; 1971, Symposium, 2, 117-141.
3) Oonishi, H., Kushitani, S., Aono, M. Bioceramics-1, 1989,102-107.
4) Oonishi, H. The Bone Biomaterials Interface, University of Toronto Press, 1991 ; 321-333.
5) Oonishi, H., Kushitani, S., Yasukawa, E. Hip Surg., Materials and developments, Martin Duniz,1998 ; 67-74.

Bioceramics Volume 11, edited by R. Z. LeGeros and J.P. LeGeros
(Proceedings of the 11th International Symposium on Ceramics in Medicine)
New York, NY, USA, November 1998
© 1998 by World Scientific Publishing Co. Pte. Ltd.

COMPARISON OF THE TISSUE RESPONSE TO CALCIUM PHOSPHATE CEMENTS WITH VARIOUS SETTING ACCELERATOR

Kunio Ishikawa[1], Youji Miyamoto[2], and Kazuomi Suzuki[1]

[1]Department of Dental Materials, Okayama University Dental School, 2-5-1 Shikata, Okayama 700-8525 Japan, and [2]First Department and Oral and Maxillofacial Surgery, School of Dentistry, Tokushima University, 3-18-15 Kuramoto, Tokushima 770-8504 Japan

ABSTRACT

Conventional calcium phosphate cement (c-CPC) causes an inflammatory response when its paste, not the set mass, was implanted subcutaneously in a rat whereas fast-setting CPC (FSCPC) shows excellent tissue response. FSCPC accelerated setting reaction of CPC by accelerating apatite formation. As a result, FSCPC transforms to apatite faster than c-CPC in addition to higher mechanical strength from the initial stage. Therefore it is unclear which factor, composition or mechanical strength, plays more dominant role for the appearance of excellent tissue response. In this investigation therefore, faster setting was achieved by the method other than accelerating apatite formation and evaluated histologically. CPC(citric), CPC mixed with citric acid and set quickly by the chelate formation, and CPC(acrylic), CPC mixed with polyacrylic acid and set quickly by the acid base reaction, were implanted subcutaneously in rat. CPC(acrylic) caused inflammatory response whereas CPC(citric) caused no inflammatory response. Therefore, we concluded higher mechanical strength from the initial stage plays more dominant role than compositional change to apatitic mineral for the appearance of excellent tissue response at least in the initial implantation periods.

KEYWORDS: calcium phosphate cement, tissue response, fast-setting, mechanical strength

INTRODUCTION

We have previously reported that calcium phosphate cement consisting of an equimolar mixture of tetracalcium phosphate (TTCP: $Ca_4(PO_4)_2O$) and dicalcium phosphate anhydrous (DCPA: $CaHPO_4$) do not always show excellent tissue response [1-2]. When the paste of conventional CPC (c-CPC) was implanted subcutaneously in a rat immediately after mixing, it was found that c-CPC crumbled completely and caused a severe inflammatory reaction. In contrast fast-setting CPC (FSCPC) [3,4], and its anti-washout type (aw-FSCPC) [5,6] kept the same shape as at implantation and showed excellent tissue response. Also we found that all calcium

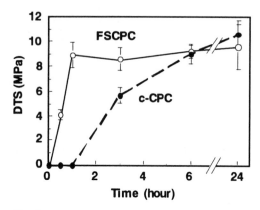

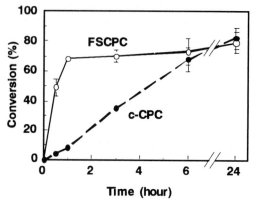

Fig. 1 Diametral tensile strength of CPCs when kept an incubator kept at 37 ℃ and 100% relative humidity.

Fig. 2 Time course of the conversion ratio to apatitic mineral when the CPC pastes were kept an incubator kept at 37 ℃ and 100% relative humidity.

phosphate powders including apatite powder caused inflammatory response when they were implanted subcutaneously in rat [7]. Therefore one of the causes of the inflammatory response to c-CPC maybe its crumbling property. c-CPC takes 30 - 60 min to set whereas FSCPCs set within approximately 5 min. As a result of fast setting, FSCPC shows higher mechanical strength from the initial stage (Fig. 1). In the case of FSCPC, fast setting is achieved by accelerating apatite formation with the addition of neutral sodium hydrogen phosphate. In the other words, FSCPC not only shows higher mechanical strength from the initial stage but also transforms to apatite faster than c-CPC (Fig. 2). Although both factors could contribute the excellent tissue response to FSCPC, it is not certain which factor plays more dominant role for the appearance of excellent tissue response.

In this investigation, therefore, faster setting was achieved by methods other than accelerating apatite formation and evaluated histologically.

MATERIALS AND METHODS
Cement powder and liquids
The powder phase of CPC was made by mixing an equimolar amount of TTCP and DCPA as reported previously [8,9]. Liquid phase of c-CPC, FSCPC, CPC(citric) and CPC(acrylic) were distilled water, 0.2 mol/L neutral hydrogen phosphate solution, 35 wt% citric acid solution, and 50% polyacrylic acid solution.

Animals and implantation procedure
Ten-week-old male rats of Wistar strain obtained commercially (Inoue, Kumamoto, Japan) and given standard pellets and water *ad libitum*, were used for the implantation study. The rats were anaesthetized by *i.p.* injection of sodium pentobarbital (Nembutal®, Abbott Co., Chicago, IL). For the implantation of cement paste, the abdomen of the rat was shaved, washed and disinfected with iodine. Three longitudinal incisions of about 1 cm were made through the full thickness of the skin. Subsequently, lateral incisions to the subcutaneous pockets were created by blunt dissection with scissors. Each experimental material was implanted using a cylindrical mold made by cutting the front portion of a 1 cm^3 plastic syringe (Terumo, Tokyo, Japan). Set CPC was also implanted subcutaneously in rat as control materials. Finally, the wounds were carefully closed.

Histological preparations

At the end of the implantation period the rats were killed with an excess dose of Nembutal®. After soft x-ray photographs were obtained to record the behaviour of calcium phosphate powers in each rat, the implant materials, including all surrounding tissues, were removed, fixed in 10% neutral buffered formalin and embedded in methylmethacrylate (HistoDur®, Leica Co., Nussloch, Germany). After polymerization, thin serial sections were cut using a rotary microtome. The sections were stained with hematoxylin-eosin and investigated by light microscopy.

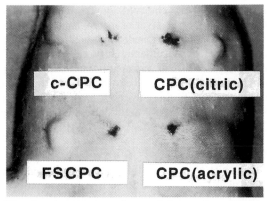

Fig. 3. Appearance of a rat abdomen 1 week after implantation.

RESULTS

Figure 3 shows the typical appearance, at 1 week after surgery, of the abdomen of a rat where c-CPC, FSCPC, CPC(citric) and CPC(acrylic) were implanted 1 min after mixing. Severe swelling with fluctuation by palpation is apparent around the c-CPC and CPC(acrylic). When the skin covering the c-CPC or CPC(acrylic) was cut with scissors, copious inflammatory effusion was observed. In contrast, no effusion was observed where the FSCPC and CPC(citric) had been implanted. Set mass was covered only by a thin fibrous capsule. Fig. 4 shows histological specimens of subcutaneous tissue surrounding implants of various CPCs at 1 week after implantation. c-CPC was surrounded by thick granulation tissue contains many macrophages and foreign body giant cells and moderate inflammatory cell infiltration, consisting of lymphocytes, plasma cells. Also, many of these cells were collected in some places around small particles of cement which had become scattered in the cutaneous tissue during the implantation procedure. In contrast, FSCPC and CPC(citric) were surrounded by thin fibrous tissue with a slight inflammatory response. Few macrophages and foreign body

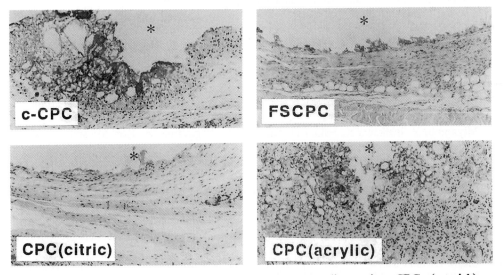

Fig. 4 Light micrographs of rat subcutaneous tissue surrounding various CPCc (asterisk).

giant cells were observed in the connective tissue adjacent to cement implants. In CPC(acrylic), some layer of macrophages and foam cells were present along the surface of the cement and were surrounded by the fibrous connective tissue and granulation tissue which contained moderate inflammatory cell infiltration, consisting of lymphocytes. XRD analysis revealed that FSCPC was apatitic mineral 1 week after implantation whereas the XRD patterns of CPC(acrylic) after 1 week were similar to CPC powder. Namely, no formation of HAP was confirmed in CPC(acrylic) even 1 week after implantation. In the case of CPC(citric), very small amount of HAP formation was observed even though most phase was still the mixture of TTCP and DCPA.

DISCUSSION

The results obtained in this study clearly demonstrated that higher mechanical strength plays more dominant role than faster transformation to apatitic mineral for the appearance of excellent tissue response to CPC. CPC(citric) that set quickly by chelate formation but does not transform to apatite, caused no inflammatory response. Therefore it can be concluded that fast setting plays more dominate role than quick transformation to apatitic mineral for the appearance of excellent tissue response to FSCPC. Of course this does not mean that compositional factor has no influence on tissue response. On the contrary, compositional factor does influence the tissue response. CPC(acrylic) caused inflammatory response even though it set quickly. Therefore, quick setting is not a sufficient condition but a necessity condition.

SUMMARY

We concluded fast-setting thus higher mechanical strength from the initial stage play one of the dominate roles for the appearance of excellent tissue response to FSCPC. CPC should have higher mechanical strength from the initial stage, one of the requirement for anti-crumbling property, using a method that does not induce inflammatory response for the appearance of excellent tissue response.

ACKNOWLEDGMENT

This investigation was supported in part by a Grant-in-Aid for Scientific Research from the Ministry of Education, Science, Sports and Culture, Japan.

REFERENCES

1. Miyamoto Y, Ishikawa K, Takechi M, Toh T, Yuasa T, Nagayama M, Asaoka K. *J Biomed Mater Res; Appl Biomater*, in press.
2. Miyamoto Y, Ishikawa K, Takechi M, Nagayama M, Asaoka K. *Bioceramics 9*, 1996; 263-266.
3. Ishikawa K, Takagi S, Chow L.C. and Ishikawa Y. *J Mater Sci: Mater Med* 1995, **6**, 528-533.
4. Miyamoto Y, Ishikawa K, Fukao H, Sawada M., Nagayama M, Kon M. and Asaoka K. *Biomaterials* 1995; **16**, 855-860.
5. Ishikawa K, Miyamoto Y, Kon M, Nagayama M and Asaoka K. *Biomaterials* 1995; **16**, 527-532.
6. Miyamoto Y, Ishikawa K, Takechi M, Yuasa M, Kon M, Nagayama M. and Asaoka K *Biomaterials* 1996; **17**, 1429-1435.
7. Ishikawa K, Miyamoto Y, Nagayama M, Suzuki K. *Bioceramics 10*, 1997; 301-304.
8. Brown WE and Chow LC In: *Cements Research Progress*, American Ceramic Society, Westerville 1986; 351-379.
9. Chow LC and Takagi S. In: *Specialty Cements with Advanced Properties*, Materials Research Society, Pittsburgh 1989; 3-24.

Bioceramics Volume 11, edited by R. Z. LeGeros and J.P. LeGeros
(Proceedings of the 11th International Symposium on Ceramics in Medicine)
New York, NY, USA, November 1998
© 1998 by World Scientific Publishing Co. Pte. Ltd.

A COMPARATIVE STUDY OF ULTRASTRUCTURES OF THE INTERFACES BETWEEN THREE KINDS OF BIOACTIVE BONE CEMENT AND BONE

Y. Okada[1], M. Kobayashi[1], H. Fujita[1], Y. Katsura[1], H. Takadama[2], T. Kokubo[2] and T. Nakamura[1]

[1]Department of Orthopaedic Surgery, Faculty of Medicine, Kyoto University, Kawahara-cho 54, Shogoin, Sakyo-ku, Kyoto 606-8397, Japan.
[2] Department of Material Chemistry, Faculty of Engineering, Kyoto University.

ABSTRACT

We have developed a bioactive bone cement which consists of apatite and wollastonite containing glass-ceramic (AW-GC) powder and bisphenol-α-glycidyl methacrylate (Bis-GMA)-based resin. In this study, we made three types of cement (designated AWC, HAC and TCPC) consisting of either AW-GC, hydroxyapatite (HA) or β-tricalcium phosphate (β-TCP) powder as the inorganic filler and Bis-GMA-based resin as the organic matrix. These cements were implanted into rat tibiae and cured *in situ*. Specimens were prepared 2, 4 and 8 weeks after the operation and observed using transmission electron microscopy.

Each of the bone cements was in direct contact with the bone. In AWC-implanted tibiae, the uncured surface layer of Bis-GMA-based resin was completely filled with newly formed bone-like tissue 2 weeks after implantation. The AW-GC particles were surrounded by bone and were in contact with bone through an apatite layer. No intervening soft tissue was seen. In HAC-implanted tibiae, it took 4 weeks for the uncured layer to completely fill with newly formed bone-like tissue. In TCPC-implanted tibiae, it took 8 weeks for the uncured layer to fill with newly formed bone-like tissue, and an intervening apatite layer was not evident. Results indicated that AWC had higher bioactivity than either HAC or TCPC.

KEYWORDS: Bioactive bone cement, AW glass-ceramic, Hydroxyapatite, β-TCP, Transmission electron microscopy.

INTRODUCTION

We have developed bioactive bone cements which combine $MgO-CaO-SiO_2-P_2O_5-CaF_2$ apatite and wollastonite containing glass-ceramic (AW-GC) powder with a bisphenol-α-glycidyl methacrylate (Bis-GMA)-based resin.[2,11,12] This cement shows direct contact with living bone through a so-called "Ca-P-rich layer". Kobayashi et al.[3] investigated the characteristics of three types of cement consisting of either AW-GC, hydroxyapatite (HA) or β-tricalcium phosphate (β-TCP) powder as the inorganic filler and Bis-GMA-based resin as the organic matrix (AWC, HAC and TCPC, respectively) both *in vitro* and *in vivo*. They concluded that AWC had stronger mechanical properties than HAC and TCPC, that AWC had higher bioactivity than HAC and TCPC in rat tibiae 2, 4 and 8 weeks after implantation, and that AWC had a more stable bone-cement interface than HAC and TCPC. They also demonstrated that AWC had higher bone-bonding strength than HAC and TCPC in rabbit tibiae evaluated by a detaching test.[4]

The aim of the present study is to compare the influence of AW-GC filler on the biological characteristics of the cement with those of the HA and β-TCP fillers, by transmission electron microscopy (TEM) .

MATERIALS AND METHODS

AW-GC powder was supplied by Nippon Electric Glass Co. Ltd. (Shiga, Japan). Glass-ceramic with a nominal composition of MgO 4.6, CaO 44.7, SiO_2 34.0, P_2O_5 16.2 and CaF_2 0.5 by weight, containing apatite and wollastonite crystal was synthesized as previously reported.[5] The average particle size was 4.0 μm. HA powder and β-TCP powder were supplied by Mitsubishi Material Co. Ltd. (Tokyo, Japan). HA powder was sintered at 1200℃. The average particle size of the HA powder was 4.3μm. β-TCP powder was sintered at 1150℃. The average particle size of the β-TCP powder was 3.7μm.[3] Each of the three powders was silane treated with γ-methacryloxypropyl-trimethoxysilane and benzoyl peroxide added at a rate of 1.0% per unit weight of the treated powder. Bis-GMA-resin was prepared from equal weights of Bis-GMA and triethyleneglycol dimethacrylate (TEGDMA). N,N-dimethyl-p-toluidine at 1.0% per unit weight of resin, was dissolved in the mixture of Bis-GMA and TEGDMA. The proportion by weight of the powder mixed into the cement was 70%.

Ten-week-old male Wistar rats weighing 250-300 g were operated on under general anesthesia (nembutal). Cortical bone defects measuring 2×5 mm were created on the medial aspect of the proximal metaphysis of both tibiae, and the bone marrow was curetted. Each of the cements was implanted and cured *in situ*. The rats were killed at 2, 4 and 8 weeks after the operation. Segments of the tibiae containing the cement samples were excised, fixed in 0.2 M cacodylate buffered 2.5% glutaraldehyde for 1 day, dehydrated in serial concentrations of ethanol, and embedded in polyester resin. Thin sections, about 500μm thick, were cut with a band saw (EXACT BS-3000, Norderstedt, Germany) perpendicular to the axis of the tibia. These sections were ground on a grinding machine with a diamond lap disc (Maruto Co. Ltd., Tokyo, Japan) to a thickness of about 40μm. These 40-μm-thick sections were embedded in epoxy resin. Then ultrathin sections, about 0.1μm thick, were cut with a diamond knife and stained with uranyl acetate. Non-decalcified sections were observed using a transmission electron microscope operating at a voltage of 75 kV (H7000, Hitachi, Japan) and were analyzed using an energy-dispersive X-ray microanalyzer (kevex7000, KEVEX, USA.).

RESULTS

In AWC-implanted tibiae, the uncured surface layer of Bis-GMA-based resin was completely filled with newly formed bone-like tissue 2 weeks after implantation (Fig. 1). The uncured layer was about 30μm thick. AW-GC particles in the uncured layer were surrounded by bone and were in contact with bone through an intervening fine crystal layer about 0.4μm thick (Fig. 2). Energy-dispersive X-ray microanalysis (EDX) showed that this fine crystal layer consisted of calcium, phosphorus and a little silicon. (This machine cannot detect elements from ^1H to ^{10}Ne.) Electron diffraction showed that the fine crystal layer consisted of apatite crystal. There was no intervening soft tissue. Such bone formation was seen more frequently in 4- and 8-week specimens.

In HAC-implanted tibiae, although fine crystals had formed on the surface of the HA particles in the uncured layer, new bone was rarely seen between the HA particles 2 weeks after implantation (Fig. 3). At the surface of the HAC, HA particles were in contact with bone through an intervening fine crystal layer. In 4-week specimens, the uncured layer was completely filled with newly formed bone-like tissue (Fig. 4). HA particles in the uncured layer were surrounded by bone and were in contact with bone through an intervening fine crystal layer about 0.3μm thick, and fragmentation of the HA particles was seen. (Fig. 5). EDX showed that this fine crystal layer consisted of calcium and phosphorus. Electron diffraction showed that the fine crystal layer also consisted of apatite crystal. There was no intervening soft tissue. In 8-week specimens, bone formation was seen more frequently.

In TCPC-implanted tibiae, neither newly formed bone-like tissue nor fine crystals were seen in the uncured layer 2 weeks after implantation. At the surface of the TCPC, β-TCP particles were in contact with bone directly. In 4-week specimens, bone ingrowth had not occurred in the uncured layer yet. In 8-week specimens, the uncured layer was filled with newly formed bone-like tissue, but the new bone on the TCPC was not as dense as that on the AWC or HAC and an intervening apatite layer was not evident (Fig. 6).

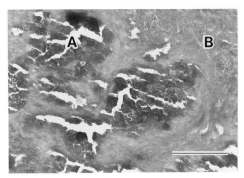

Figure 1.
 TEM of the AWC 2 weeks after implantation.
 (A=AW-GC particle, B=Bone, Bar=2.0 μm)

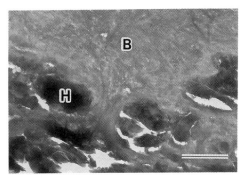

Figure 4.
 TEM of the HAC 4 weeks after implantation.
 (H=HA particle, B=Bone, Bar=1.0 μm)

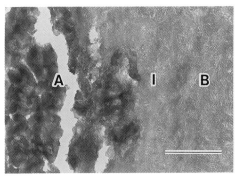

Figure 2.
 TEM of the AWC 2 weeks after implantation.
 (A=AW-GC particle, B=Bone, I=Intervening
 fine crystal layer, Bar=0.5 μm)

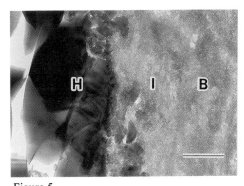

Figure 5.
 TEM of the HAC 4 weeks after implantation.
 (H=HA particle, B=Bone, I=Intervening fine
 crystal layer, Bar=0.3 μm)

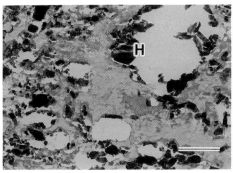

Figure 3.
 TEM of the HAC 2 weeks after implantation.
 (H=HA particle, Bar=2.0 μm)

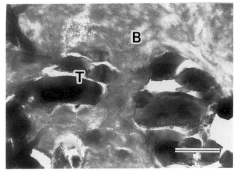

Figure 6.
 TEM of the TCPC 8 weeks after implantation.
 (T=β–TCP particle, B=Bone, Bar=1.0 μm)

DISCUSSION

In the present study, an apatite layer had formed on the surface of the AW-GC particles and the HA particles. Both types of particles were in contact with bone through an apatite layer. On the other hand, an apatite layer did not form on the surface of the β-TCP particles. By contrast, Daculsi et al. [1] demonstrated, using TEM, that new apatite crystal formed on the surface of β-TCP particles in their study. We sometimes observed a fine crystal layer between the bone and the β-TCP particles, but no pattern was observed by electron diffraction. Therefore, the fine crystal layer was probably amorphous calcium phosphate or degraded β-TCP.

The mechanism of apatite formation on each type of ceramic may not be the same. The calcium ions in the glassy phase and the wollastonite of AW-GC dissolve in body fluid[6] and increase the degree of supersaturation of the surrounding fluid with respect to apatite, so new apatite crystals precipitate on the surface of the ceramic particles. When this occurs, silanol groups (SiOH) may induce apatite nucleation.[7] In fact, the apatite layer we observed on the AW-GC included a little silicon. Once apatitic nuclei form, they can grow spontaneously by consuming the calcium and phosphate ions of the surrounding body fluid.[9] On the other hand, HA has no glassy phase, is much less soluble than AW-GC and does not contain silicate ions, so the mechanism of apatite formation on HA may differ from that of AW-GC. Daculsi et al.[1] suggested that the partial dissolution of HA and precipitation of new apatite crystals incorporating ions from the biological fluid occurs in the immediate microenvironment and that the HA crystals act as nucleators or seeds.

In the present study, bone-like tissue formed on AWC earlier than on HAC and TCPC. Sautier et al.[10] demonstrated, by TEM, the capacity of AW-GC to initiate biomineralization in osteoblast cultures. Ohgushi et al.[8] studied osteoblastic differentiation of marrow cells on the surface of AW-GC in vitro. They demonstrated that osteoblastic activity was enhanced by AW-GC, especially by AW-GC that had formed an apatite layer. AW-GC appears to be a favorable material for osteoconduction.

In conclusion, each of the bone cements tested showed osteoconductivity and AWC had higher bioactivity than HAC and TCPC in rat tibiae.

ACKNOWLEDGMENTS

We thank M.Fujioka for technical assistance and Nippon Electric Glass Co., Ltd. for supplying materials.

REFERENCES

1. Daculsi G, LeGeros RZ, Heughebaert M, Barbieux I. *Calcif. Tiss. Int.* 1990; **46**: 20-27.
2. Kawanabe K, Tamura J, Yamamuro T, Nakamura T, Kokubo T, Yoshihara S. *J. Appl. Biomater.* 1993; **4**: 135-141.
3. Kobayashi M, Nakamura T, Tamura J, Kokubo T, Kikutani T. *J. Biomed. Mater. Res.* 1997; **37**: 301-313.
4. Kobayashi M, Nakamura T, Okada Y, Fukumoto A, Furukawa T, Kato H, Kokubo T, Kikutani T. *J. Biomed. Mater. Res.* in press.
5. Kokubo T, Ito S, Shigematsu M, Sakka S, Yamamuro T. *J. Mater. Sci.* 1985; **20**: 2001-2004.
6. Kokubo T, Kushitani H, Ohtsuki C, Sakka S, Yamamuro T. *J. Mater. Sci. Mater. Med.* 1992; **3**: 79-83.
7. Li P, Ohtsuki C, Kokubo T, Nakanishi K, Soga N, Nakamura T, Yamamuro T. *J. Am. Ceram. Soc.* 1992; **75**: 2094-2097.
8. Ohgushi H, Dohi Y, Yoshikawa T, Tamai S, Tabata S, Okunaga K, Shibuya T. *J. Biomed. Mater. Res.* 1996; **32**: 341-348.
9. Ohtsuki C, Kokubo T, Yamamuro T. *J. Non-Cryst. Solids* 1992; **143**: 84-92.
10. Sautier JM, Kokubo T, Ohtsuki T, Nefussi JR, Boulekbache H, Oboeuf M, Loty S, Loty C, Forest N. *Calcif. Tiss. Int.* 1994; **55**: 458-466.
11. Tamura J, Kawanabe K, Yamamuro T, Nakamura T, Kokubo T, Yoshihara S, Shibuya T. *J. Biomed. Mater. Res.* 1995; **29**: 551-559.
12. Tamura J, Kawanabe K, Kobayashi M, Nakamura T, Kokubo T, Yoshihara S, Shibuya T. *J. Biomed. Mater. Res.* 1996; **30**: 85-94.

VI. BIOMIMETICS, TISSUE ENGINEERING, GROWTH FACTORS, DRUG DELIVERY

Bioceramics Volume 11, edited by R. Z. LeGeros and J.P. LeGeros
(Proceedings of the 11th International Symposium on Ceramics in Medicine)
New York, NY, USA, November 1998
© 1998 by World Scientific Publishing Co. Pte. Ltd.

PREFABRICATION OF BIOLOGICAL APATITE ON A BIOACTIVE GLASS CERAMIC PROMOTES *IN VITRO* OSTEOBLAST DIFFERENTIATION AND ALLOWS CONTACT OSTEOGENESIS

C. Loty[1], J. M. Sautier[1], S. Loty[1], T. Kokubo[2], N. Forest[1]

[1]Laboratoire de Biologie-Odontologie, Université Paris VII, Paris-France; [2]Kyoto University, Faculty of Engeneering, Japon.

ABSTRACT

We examined the behavior of fetal rat osteoblasts cultured on three different substrata : apatite-wollastonite-containing glass ceramic (AW), AW ceramic on which an apatite layer was formed by incubation in simulated body fluids (AWa) and control glass coverslips. The specific activity of alkaline phosphatase determined biochemically was about twice on AWa than of the control glasses and showed about a 30% increase compared to that of AW. SEM observations of the material surfaces after scraping of the cell layer showed that spongy mineralized nodules were in contact only with the ceramic but were twice on AWa. In addition, SEM analysis of the fractured surface revealed bone bonding with the surface apatite layer of the ceramic. These results demonstrated the positive effect of biological apatite formation on *in vitro* bone formation with contact osteogenesis on bioactive glass-ceramic but not on non-bioactive glass.

KEYWORDS: Osteoblasts, differentiation, *in vitro*, interface, bone bonding.

INTRODUCTION

An increasing array of synthetic materials is available for filling or reconstructing osseous defects. Among them, bioactive materials such as bioglasses or bioactive glass-ceramics bond to bone through an apatite layer formed on the material surface after implantation.[1,2] Glass-ceramic containing apatite and wollastonite crystals (AW) have been found to have high mechanical strength and display the ability to bond directly to living bone by forming an apatite layer on their surface in the body environment. Interestingly, the biological apatite layer can also be formed *in vitro* after immersion under simulated physiological conditions.[3] We have shown previously that prefabricated biological apatite layer on AW promoted differentiation of cultured chondrocytes.[4]

This work was therefore undertaken to study the possible stimulatory effect of the bioactive layer on osteoblastic differentiation and the bonding phenomena at the bone/apatite layer interface in an *in vitro* bone forming system.

MATERIALS AND METHODS

AW was synthesized by a method described[3] previously. Mirror-polished disks (diameter = 15 mm, thickness = 1 mm) were provided by Nippon Electric Glass Co Ltd (Japan) and some disks were incubated in simulated body fluids to generate a surface apatite layer. Osteoblasts were enzymatically isolated from 21-day-old rat fetus calvaria according to the method of Nefussi et al.[5] and plated at 4×10^4 cells/cm^2 onto AW, AWa disks and control glass coverslips. The specific activity of alkaline phosphatase (AP) was assayed in the cell layers by measuring the release of p-nitrophenol from p-nitrophenolphosphate and expressed as U/proteins mg. The extraction buffer (0.1 M sodium carbonate bicarbonate, MgCl^2 1 M, 0,2% Nodinet NP40) used for enzyme assays completely eliminated the organic matrix and the resulting disks were prepared for SEM examinations. A number of the disks were fractured to examine the bone/AWa interface using a scanning electron microscope connected to an energy dispersive X-ray micro-analyser (EDX II, Link Analytical, Oxford Instruments).

RESULTS AND DISCUSSION

Figure 1a showed the morphology of an osteoblast attached to the surface of AWa after 4 h of culture. The cell was anchored to the corroded apatite surface of the material by the means of numerous cytoplasmic extentions but they possessed a spherical morphology with a surface studied with numerous bleds. Previous studies showed that osteoblasts flattened closely onto positive ion exchange beads but adopted a "stand-off" morphology when cultured on negatively charged beads.[6] The bioactive layer of AWa containing highly charged phosphate groups certainly influenced the morphology of cultured osteoblasts. During the following days of culture, cells proliferated and synthesized large amounts of extracellular matrix. In addition, the specific activity of alkaline phosphatase determined biochemically gradually increased after 3 days of culture, but was about twice on AWa than of the control culture and showed about a 30% increase compared to that of AW on day 24 of culture (Figure 1b). The enhancement of osteoblastic activity on prefabricated biological apatite was also reported by Ohgushi et al.[7] with cultured marrow stroma stem cells. Furthermore, we previously demonstrated the promotion of the chondrocyte phenotype by the formation of a biological apatite layer on AW ceramic surface.[4]

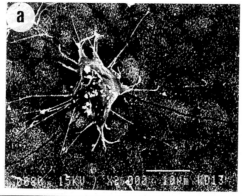

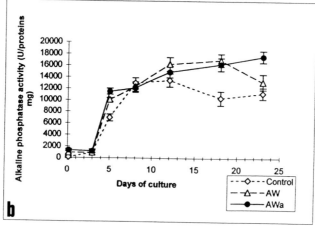

Figure 1. (a) SEM observation of cell morphology after 4 h of culture. (b) Time course of alkaline phosphatase activity (AW = apatite-wollastonite glass-ceramic. AWa = apatite-wollastonite glass-ceramic with prefabricated apatite layer. Control = glass coverslip.).

Interestingly, the extraction buffer used for enzyme assays completely eliminated the cells and the organic matrix from the surface of the disks. However, SEM observations of the resulting surface showed mineralized bone nodules attached to the surface of AW and AWa disks dut not to the control non-bioactive glass coverslips (Figure 2a,b). In addition, bone nodule number was about twice on AWa compared to AW (Data not shown). This finding, suggested that the biological carbonated apatite layer, very similar to natural bone mineral, not only promoted osteoblast differentiation but also allowed contact osteogenesis.

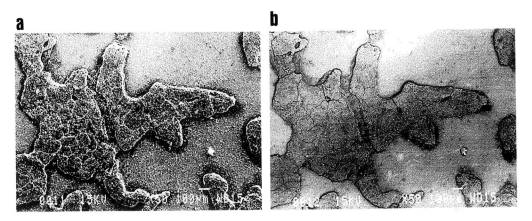

Figure 2. (a) SEM of a bone nodule on the surface of AWa after scrapping of the cell layer. (b) Same image using backscattered electron microscopy.

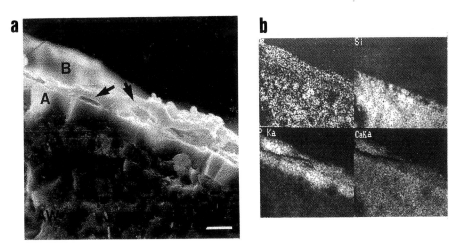

Figure 3. (a) SEM observation of the fractured surface showing the AWa/bone nodule interface (AW = ceramic bulk, A = bioactive apatite surface, B = Bone nodule, Bar = 10 μm). Note osteocyte lacunae (arrows). (b) X-ray microanalytical mappings of the AWa/bone nodule interface (Mg = magnesium, Si = silica, P = phosphorus, Ca = calcium).

The interface was examined by SEM and an energy dispersive X-ray microanalyser of fractured disks (Figure 3a,b). A Ca-P rich layer (about 10 μm) was observed at the surface of the ceramic and directly bond with the bone nodule that exhibited osteocyte lacunae. X-ray microanalytical mappings of the bone/AWa interface indicated that (1) magnesium (Mg) and calcium (Ca) were equally distributed, (2) that phosphorus (P) lesser extend in the ceramic bulk, and (3) that silicate ions (Si) were mainly located in the ceramic bulk. Our results are in accordance with previous TEM studies that demonstrated bone-bonding properties of AW *in vivo*[8] and *in vitro*.[9] Additionnally, detaching tests performed between implanted AW and bone have shown that failure did not occurred through the interface thus confirming the bone-bonding properties of this biomaterial.[10]

In conclusion, we have shown in this study that prefabrication of biological apatite on AW glass-ceramic promoted rat osteoblast differentiation. Futhermore, mineralization occurred directly onto the surface of the ceramic but in large amounts on AWa and observations of the interface revealed a direct bond of bone tissue with the biological surface.

ACKNOWLEDGMENTS.

This work was supported by a grant from CANAM - Assistance Publique - Hôpitaux de Paris.

REFERENCES

1. Hench LL. In: Davies JE, ed. *The Bone-Biomaterial Interfac*, University of Toronto Press, 1991; 33-48.
2. Kokubo T, Kushitani Y, Ebisawa T, Kitsudji S, Kotani S, Ohura K, Yamamuro T. In: Oonishi H, Aoki H, Sawai K, eds. *Bioceramics 1*. Ishiyaku EuroAmerica, Tokyo, 1989; 157-162.
3. Kokubo T, Kitsugi T, Yamamuro T. *J. Biomed Mater Res* 1990; **24**: 331-343.
4. Loty C, Loty S, Kokubo T, Forest N, Sautier JM. In: Sedel L, Rey C, eds. *Bioceramic 10*. Elsevier Science Ltd, 1997; 219-222.
5. Nefussi JR, Boy-Lefèvre ML, Boulekbache H, Forest N. *Differentiation*. 1985; **29**: 160-168.
6. Davies JE, Causton B, Bovel Y, Davy K, Sturt CS. *Biomaterials*., 1986; **7**: 231-234.
7. Ohgushi H, Dohi Y, Yoshilawa T, Tamai S, Tabata S, Okunaga K, Shibuya T. *J Biomed Mater Res* 1996; **32**: 341-348.
8. Neo M, Kotani S, Nakamura T, Yamamuro T, Ohtsuki C, Kokubo T, Bando Y. *J Biomed Mater Res* 1992; **26**: 1419-1432.
9. Sautier JM, Kokubo T, Ohtuki T, Nefussi JR, Boulekbache H, Oboeuf M, Loty S, Loty C, Forest N. *Calcif Tissue Int*. 1994; **55**: 458-466.
10. Yamamuro T. In : *Bone grafts, derivatives and substitutes*, Philadelphia : W.B. Saunders, 1992 : 245-259.

Bioceramics Volume 11, edited by R. Z. LeGeros and J.P. LeGeros
(Proceedings of the 11th International Symposium on Ceramics in Medicine)
New York, NY, USA, November 1998
© 1998 by World Scientific Publishing Co. Pte. Ltd.

ANALYSIS OF BIOGLASS® SURFACE LAYERS: COMPARING IN VITRO MODELS OF HCA FORMATION

T.A. Mahmood and J.E. Davies

Institute for Biomaterials and Biomedical Engineering, University of Toronto
170 College Street, Toronto ON, M5S 3E3, Canada.

ABSTRACT

In recent experiments we have revealed the incorporation of amino acids, DNA and RNA within Bioglass® surface reaction layers (SRLs) after exposure to minimal essential medium (α-MEM). The purpose of the experiment described herein was to compare the *in vitro* growth of the SRLs formed on 45S5 Bioglass® after immersion in either Simulated Body Fluid (SBF), or in SBF which contained serum proteins. Low resolution compositional XPS showed significant elemental concentrations of nitrogen present in the surface when incubated in the presence of proteins (>10%). Incubation in only SBF for identical (and longer) periods resulted in insignificant amounts of detectable nitrogen. Immersion in serum-containing SBF resulted in the creation of a calcium phosphate (CP) SRL as demonstrated by EDX, but negligible Ca and P signals were seen by XPS. These findings indicated that the newly forming CP-SRL was covered with a layer of adsorbed serum proteins. High resolution XPS confirmed that the deconvoluted N1s envelope corresponded to that of the peptide backbone characteristic of proteins. Deconvolution of the C1s envelope showed similar results. These results demonstrate that immersion in SBF is too simple a model of *in vivo* growth of Bioglass® SRLs. Since SRLs which form in the presence of proteins are compositionally different from those which form in SBF, tissue bonding hypotheses based on interfacial reactions with only CP-SRLs should be modified because adsorbed proteins covering the CP will be presented to the biological milieu.

KEYWORDS: bioactive glass, surface characterization, proteins, simulated body fluid

INTRODUCTION

Current *in vitro* techniques to grow calcium phosphate rich surface reaction layers (CP-SRLs) implicated in the tissue-bonding behaviour of bioactive glasses, such as Bioglass®, include immersion in simple inorganic ionic solutions such as Simulated Body Fluid (SBF).[1] The basis of this approach is the presence, in SBF, of ions in similar concentrations to those found in human blood plasma. After Bioglass® has been exposed to SBF, or other ionic solutions, a series of surface reactions occur, which have been described extensively by others, and result in the nucleation of calcium and phosphate ions at the surface.[2] The accumulation of these ions form an initially amorphous calcium phosphate layer, which after incorporation of carbonate ions results in a polycrystalline hydroxycarbonate apatite phase (HCA), which is considered (by FTIR and FT-Raman analyses) to be similar to bone mineral.[3]

The drawback of immersion in SBF is that reaction layer formation is solely a result of calcium and phosphate ion nucleation events on the material surface, to the exclusion of more complex species found *in vivo*. Indeed, Kokubo has shown that similar CP layers can be formed on various types of biomaterials exposed to SBF.[4] However, what has generally not been investigated is how the organic constituents of true body fluid (TBF), which may adsorb prior to, or concomitant with CP formation, will affect the resultant SRL. It was to address this question that we had earlier demonstrated the incorporation of amino acids, DNA and RNA within growing Bioglass® SRLs after immersion in minimal essential medium (α-MEM).[5]

In this experiment we compared the SRLs formed on 45S5 Bioglass® with, and without, the presence of fetal bovine serum proteins, by X-ray photoelectron spectroscopy (XPS). The presence of serum proteins represents a considerably more complex system than the simple amino acid dominated α–MEM, and is a step closer to *in vivo* reality. Not only does serum contain over 100 different proteins but the proteins themselves have complicated and variable conformations.

MATERIALS AND METHODS

45S5 type Bioglass® discs (kindly supplied by USBiomaterials Corporation, Gainesville FL) of 1cm diameter and 3 mm thickness were polished on one side with 600 grit paper. They were then immersed at 37°C for 72 hours in 25 ml (to ensure that the surface area:volume ratio was maintained at 0.1 cm^{-1}) of either SBF, or in SBF containing 15% Fetal Bovine Serum (FBS). An "as received" Bioglass® disc was also analyzed, and as a negative control, another was immersed in SBF for 4 weeks.

Chemical Analysis (XPS): This technique enabled the determination of elements present at the surface, their relative concentrations as well as detailed chemical information of the binding energies associated with the elemental surface constituents. The XPS was performed on a Leybold LH Max 200 using a MgKα x-ray source at 15kV and 20mA emission current. All Bioglass® samples underwent survey scans to detect elements at the surface and low resolution analysis to obtain relative percent compositions of elemental oxygen, nitrogen, calcium, carbon, phosphorous and silicon.

The C1s peaks of the SBF as well as the SBF + serum immersed samples were further analyzed by high resolution XPS modes, with spectrum calibration achieved by setting the C1s peak for adventitious carbon at 284.6 eV. The nitrogen (N1s) peak of the sample immersed in SBF + serum was also examined by high resolution XPS. In each case, the individual peaks were deconvoluted using a Gaussian-Lorenzen curve-fitting process.

RESULTS

Evidence of nitrogen was clear from the low-resolution XPS scans of samples exposed to proteins. Whereas insignificant nitrogen was detected at the Bioglass® surface after immersion in only SBF (even for the longer-term 4 week period), incubation in the serum containing SBF resulted in approximately 10% nitrogen (relative atomic %) at the surface (Figure 1). In addition, carbon concentration was 25% in the SBF immersed samples, and 66% in those immersed in SBF + serum. Calcium and phosphorus levels were found to be very low in the SBF + serum samples (≈ 0.2% each), which were barely distinguishable from background spectral noise. This was in contrast to the concentrations obtained in the SBF only samples ($\approx$ 11% each). Similarly, silicon concentration was only 0.38% when proteins were present, and 1% in their absence.

From the samples immersed in only SBF, high resolution denconvolution of the C1s envelope revealed 4 sub-peaks, at 284.6, 286.13, 287.63 and 289.03 eV (Figure 2). Negligible nitrogen signals precluded the analysis of N1s. On the contrary, high resolution analysis of Bioglass® immersed in SBF + serum showed that the nitrogen N1s envelope contained 2 sub-peaks, at 399.83 and 401.54 eV (Figure 3). Deconvolution of the broad carbon C1s envelope showed 4 sub-peaks, at 285, 286.45, 287.82 and 288.67 eV (Figure 4).

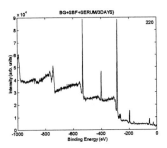

Figure 1. Survey spectrum (SBF only)

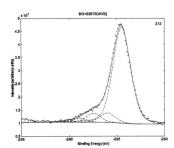

Figure 2. High-res. C1s (SBF only)

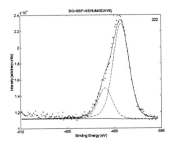

Figure 3. High-res. N1s (SBF + proteins)

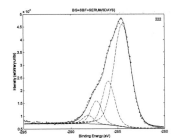

Figure 4. High-res. (SBF + proteins)

DISCUSSION

The data obtained from low-resolution XPS compositional analysis demonstrated that nitrogen containing entities were part of the Bioglass® SRL when proteins were present. This demonstrated that proteins had been incorporated within the forming surface reaction layer. Due to the lack of any significant calcium and phosphorous signal, the adsorbed protein coating must have been of sufficient thickness, probably greater than 100 Å which is the higher limit of XPS sampling penetration, to mask the underlying CP. This also suggested that proteins had not adsorbed in patches but rather that the CP-SRL was completely coated with proteins. This was not surprising, since many proteins are known to contain Ca^{+2} binding domains.[6] Energy dispersive x-ray analysis (not shown) demonstrated the presence of CP in these samples, beyond the sampling depth of XPS.

Low resolution compositional analysis also showed considerably greater carbon present in the reaction layer grown in the presence of proteins (66%), compared to growth in simple SBF (25%). The greater carbon found at the surface was likely due to the incorporation of proteins.

SBF: From high-resolution XPS analysis of SRLs grown in the absence of proteins, the C1s as well as N1s envelopes were deconvoluted to show the sub-peaks which constituted each envelope. Those comprising the C1s envelope of the samples immersed in only SBF were found to correspond to adventitious carbon, thereby requiring spectrum calibration at 284.6 eV. In addition, carbonate was very likely present, due to the appearance of a peak at 289.03 eV. Deconvolution of N1s was precluded due to the lack of sufficient nitrogen signal.

SBF + proteins: High-resolution deconvolution into 4 sub-peaks of the C1s envelope of Bioglass® exposed to proteins showed that the binding energies of 2 sub-peaks (285.68 eV , 286.9 eV) were within the range characteristic of carbon-nitrogen bonds (285.5 – 288.5eV).[7] These bonds are present in abundance in proteins, which were believed to have attached within the SRL.

It should be noted that the shape of the C1s envelope was very different from that obtained after immersion in simple SBF. After deconvolution, the spacing of the sub-peaks was seen to be very similar to those obtained from polymer samples, thus the spectrum was calibrated accordingly at 285 eV. This further strengthens the argument that the overall envelope, as well as the sub-peaks, were determined in a large part by the organic bonds present in proteins attached within the reaction layer. Similarly, high-resolution analysis of the N1s peak (SBF + proteins) revealed 2 sub-peaks, which at 399.83 eV and 401.54 eV were typical of nitrogen present in organic species, specifically peptide bonds.

These results demonstrate that immersion in SBF is too simple a model of *in vivo* growth of Bioglass® SRLs. Since SRLs which form in the presence of proteins are compositionally different from those which form in SBF, tissue bonding hypotheses based on interfacial reactions with only CP-SRLs[8] should be modified because adsorbed proteins covering the CP will be presented to the biological milieu.

CONCLUSIONS

Immersion in simple SBF is not an appropriate model of *in vivo* growth of calcium phosphate surface reaction layers on bioactive materials, since proteins alter the composition of the growing reaction layer.

ACKNOWLEDGEMENTS

TAM gratefully acknowledges the support of this project by USBiomaterials Corporation.

REFERENCES

1. Kokubo T, Kushitani H, Sakka S, Kitsugi T and Yamamuro T. *J. Biomed. Mater. Res.,* 1990: **24** 721-734
2. Hench LL and Andersson O. In: Hench LL and Wilson J, eds. *An Introduction to Bioceramics*, London: World Scientific, 1993: 41-62
3. Rehman IA, Hench LL, Bonfield W and Smith R. *Biomaterials*, 1994; **15**: 865-869
4. Kokubo T. In: Ducheyne P, Kokubo T and van Blitterswijk CA, eds. *Bone-bonding biomaterials*, Leiden: Reed Healthcare, 1993: 31-46
5. Mahmood TA and Davies JE, *J. Mater. Sci. Mater. in Medicine* 1998 (in press)
6. Mihalyi E. *Biochemistry*, 1988; **27**: 967-976
7. Moulder JF, Stickle WF, Sobol PE and Bomben KD. Handbook of X-ray Photoelectron Spectroscopy. Eden Prairie, MN: Perkin Elmer Corporation, 1992
8. Hench LL, Splinter RJ, Allen WC and Greenlee TK. *J. Biomed. Mater. Res. Symposium*, 1971: **2** 117-141

Bioceramics Volume 11, edited by R. Z. LeGeros and J.P. LeGeros
(Proceedings of the 11th International Symposium on Ceramics in Medicine)
New York, NY, USA, November 1998
© 1998 by World Scientific Publishing Co. Pte. Ltd.

BIOMIMETIC HYDROXYAPATITE COATING ON TI6AL4V INDUCED BY PRE-CALCIFICATION

Pierre Layrolle[1], Clemens A. van Blitterswijk[1,2] and Klaas de Groot[2]

[1]IsoTis BV; [2] Biomaterials Research Group, Leiden University, Professor Bronkhorstlaan 10, 3723 MB Bilthoven, The Netherlands. Email: pierre.layrolle@isotis.com

ABSTRACT

Hydroxyapatite (HA) coatings on titanium alloy (Ti6Al4V) were produced by a biomimetic method. After cleaning, Ti6Al4V plates were etched with an acid mixture to obtain microporous and rough surfaces. The samples were then treated with a saturated solution of $Ca(OH)_2$ at boiling temperature for 4 hours. This treatment induced the deposition of a calcium-rich layer over Ti6Al4V, due to the retrograde solubility of $Ca(OH)_2$ with increasing temperature. Following pre-calcification, Ti6Al4V samples were treated in the temperature range 50-600 °C and studied by scanning electron microscopy (SEM) together with energy dispersive analysis for X-ray (EDAX), Thermal analyses (TGA), X-ray photoelectron spectroscopy (XPS) and infrared spectroscopy (FT-IR). After heating at 400 °C, the calcium-rich layer became dense and well adhered to the Ti6Al4V substrates. The untreated and pre-calcified samples were soaked for 2 days at 37 °C in a calcium phosphate super-saturated (CPS) solution buffered at pH 7.4. SEM/EDX, FT-IR spectroscopy and thin-film X-ray diffraction (TF-XRD) showed uniform and well-adhered HA layer of about 20 μm in thickness on pre-calcified Ti6Al4V samples. These results show the potential of this biomimetic method for coating medical implants with an osteo-conductive HA layer.

KEYWORDS: Biomimetic, hydroxyapatite, coating, titanium alloy

INTRODUCTION

It has been demonstrated that hydroxyapatite (HA) coatings on metal prostheses enhance bone growth because of their osteoconductive property. Several techniques, such as plasma-spraying, have been developed for coating HA on metals. However, HA plasma-spray coatings are limited by specific drawbacks such as high temperatures, delamination and particle release. Recently, there is an increasing interest to develop a biomimetic strategy for the preparation of hydroxyapatite coatings on metal implants. This method, that resembles the biomimeralization process of bones and teeth, involves the nucleation and growth of bone-like apatite crystals on metal surface from calcium phosphate super-saturated (CPS) solutions at ambient temperature. Several authors have described a way to induce the bioactivity of titanium by means of a chemical treatment with alkaline solutions. This induced bioactivity was indicated by the potential of the chemically treated metal to form a surface carbonate-apatite layer from CPS solutions.[1-4] In the present study, a pre-calcification treatment of Ti6Al4V and its ability to induce the deposition of HA from CPS solution are studied.

MATERIALS AND METHODS

Pieces of titanium alloy of 10 x 10 x 1 mm^3 were cut from a sheet of commercially available Ti6Al4V (Smitford Staal BV, The Netherlands). The plates were ultrasonically cleaned for 15 min in acetone, then ethanol (70 %) and finally demineralised water. The Ti6Al4V samples were etched for 30 min under ultrasounds with a concentrated acid mixture containing demineralised water and an equivalent volume of hydrochloric acid (18 wt%) and sulfuric acid (48 wt%) to obtain specific surface roughness. The etched Ti6Al4V plates were thoroughly washed with demineralized water. A saturated calcium hydroxide solution was prepared at room temperature by adding ~3 g of Ca(OH)$_2$ reagent (Merck, Germany) in 1000 ml of demineralised water with stirring for 10 min and then filtration through filter paper (Whatman). The saturated Ca(OH)$_2$ solution has a calcium concentration and a pH of ~0.02 mol/l and 12.5, respectively. The Ti6Al4V samples were treated with the saturated Ca(OH)$_2$ solution at 60 or 100°C for 30 min, then thoroughly rinsed in demineralised water for 10 min and finally, dried at 50 °C or heated to 200, 400 and 600 °C in air. CPS solution was prepared by dissolving reagent grade NaCl, CaCl$_2$.2H$_2$O and Na$_2$HPO$_4$.2H$_2$O in demineralised water with the following ion concentrations: [Na$^+$]=140.4, [Ca^{2+}]=3.10, [HPO$_4^{2-}$]=1.86 and [Cl$^-$]=144.5 mM. The CPS solution was buffered at pH 7.4 with 50 mM of tris-hydroxymethylaminoethane and hydrochloric acid 1 M at room temperature. Each Ti6Al4V sample was immersed into 50 ml of CPS in a sealed polystyrene vial. The vials were placed in a shaking water-bath at 37 °C for 2 days. Finally, the samples were rinsed with demineralised water for 10 min and dried in air at room temperature. The surfaces of the samples were observed by SEM (Philips SEM 525) together with EDAX (Noran Instruments, Voyager). The pre-calcified and heat-treated plates were also characterized by XPS (Escalab, Mk 5). The biomimetic coatings were analyzed by FT-IR spectroscopy (Perkin-Elmer, spectrum 1000).

RESULTS AND DISCUSSION

Pre-calcification of titanium

During pre-calcification, the saturated Ca(OH)$_2$ solution turned opaque due to its retrograde solubility with increasing temperature.[5] After the treatments, all the samples were randomly covered by precipitates (figure 1). Numerous particles were several microns in size, but fine precipitates were also detected on the whole titanium alloy surface. EDAX analysis indicated that these particles, as well as free-precipitation areas, were composed of calcium and oxygen. The quantity of precipitates was maximum on the samples treated at 60°C. In average, the particle sizes were also higher for a treatment temperature of 60°C as compared to 100°C. At boiling temperature, too large particles might form that easily detach from the plates. On all treated plates, calcium, oxygen and carbon were found while titanium alloy peaks were not detected by XPS (figure 2). This indicates that the calcium hydroxide layer was very thick and uniformly deposited on the surface. In order to increase the adhesive properties of this calcium layer, the samples were heated at different temperatures. After firing at 400 or 600 °C, additional titanium peaks were observed by XPS (figure 2). The titanium, calcium and oxygen peak positions were in good accordance with those of calcium titanate ($CaTiO_3$). This compound resulted from a chemical reaction between the calcium layer and the titanium substrate. After firing at 400 °C, the surface layer appeared dense and uniform under SEM. Although the mechanical properties were not measured, the resulting $CaTiO_3$ layer was well adhered to the substrate.

Figure 1. SEM picture of the Ti6Al4V surface after pre-calcification at 60 °C (bar= 100 μm)

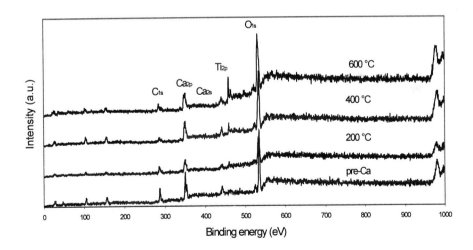

Figure 2. XPS spectra of pre-calcified Ti6Al4V before and after heating at 200, 400 and 600°C

Biomimetic hydroxyapatite coating

After pre-calcification and immersion in CPS solution, a calcium phosphate layer was uniformly deposited on the Ti6Al4V surface (Figure 3). The calcium phosphate coatings were approximately

20 μm in thickness and were composed of thin crystal plates of 10 x 0.2 μm. FT-IR spectroscopy showed the typical bands of apatite. The deposition of such layer was only induced by the pre-calcification treatment. The calcium and hydroxyl released from the pre-calcified layer might result from an increase of sursaturation at the vicinity of the plate and therefore precipitating apatite on the titanium alloy surface.

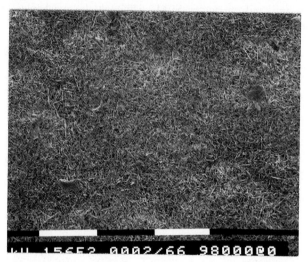

Figure 3. SEM picture of the biomimetic HA coating on Ti6Al4V (bar= 100 μm)

CONCLUSIONS

The pre-calcification treatment formed a calcium-rich layer on the titanium alloy surface. After heating, a calcium titanate layer appeared to be dense, uniform and well-adhered to the substrate. By immersion in CPS solution, it induced the deposition of bioactive HA coating.

REFERENCES

1. Kokubo T. In: Ducheyne, et al. eds. *Bone-Bonding Biomaterials*, Leiderdorp, The Netherlands: Reed Healthcare Communications 1992; 31-46.
2. Miyaji F, Zhang X, Yao T, Kokubo T, Ohtsuki C, Kitsugi T, Yamamuro T, Nakamura T. In: Andersson OH, Yli-Urpo A, eds. *Bioceramics 7*, London: Butterworth-Heineman Ltd., 1994: 119-24.
3. Mucalo MR, Yokogawa Y, Toriyama M, Suzuki T, Kawamoto Y., Nagata F, Nishizawa K, *J Mater Sci Mater Med* 1995; **6**: 597-605.
4. Hanawa T, Kon M, Ukai H, Murakami K, Miyamoto Y, Asaoka K. *J Biomed Mater Res* 1997; **34**: 273-8.
5. In: Hodgman CD ed. *Handbook of Chemistry and Physics, 44th Edition*, Cleveland, Ohio: The Chemical Rubber Publishing Co. 1963; 1696.

Bioceramics Volume 11, edited by R. Z. LeGeros and J.P. LeGeros
(Proceedings of the 11th International Symposium on Ceramics in Medicine)
New York, NY, USA, November 1998
© 1998 by World Scientific Publishing Co. Pte. Ltd.

FACTORS CONTROLLING CRYSTALLIZATION OF CALCIUM PHOSPHATES ON SOLID SURFACES

Wenju Wu and George H. Nancollas

Department of Chemistry, State University of New York at Buffalo, Buffalo, New York 14260

ABSTRACT

The heterogeneous nucleation of the calcium phosphates, octacalcium phosphate (OCP), hydroxyapatite (HAP) and fluorapatite (FAP), has been studied on polymer surfaces, poly(methyl methacrylate (PMMA) and poly(tetrafluoroethylene-*co*-hexafluoropropylene) (FEP), silicone rubber, titanium oxides. The influence of radiofreqency glow discharge treatment (RFGD) has also been investigated. Surface properties were characterized by contact angle measurements. Although the Lifshitz-van der Waals surface tension components (γ^{LW}) are approximately the same for all these material, the Lewis acid-base surface tension components (γ^{AB}) vary greatly. In supersaturated solutions, effective nucleation of calcium phosphates was observed only on those surfaces with relatively high values of Lewis acid-base surface tension component ($\gamma^{AB} > 5.0 \times 10^{-3}$ J/m^2) or, more specifically, Lewis base parameters ($\gamma^- > 20 \times 10^{-3}$ J/m^2). At the same relative supersaturation (σ), the induction period (τ) for calcium phosphate nucleation on hydrophilic surfaces is less than that on more hydrophobic surfaces. Thus, at $\sigma_{OCP} = 1.67$, the experimental values of τ were 63 and 85 minutes on anatase ($\gamma^- = 48 \times 10^{-3}$ J/m^2) and rutile surfaces ($\gamma^- = 16 \times 10^{-3}$ J/m^2), respectively.

KEYWORDS: crystallization, interfacial tension, contact angle, glow discharge, titania, implants.

INTRODUCTION

The effective use of implant materials in biological system is probably related either to the ease with which their surfaces will nucleate calcium phosphates or to the prevention/minimization of heterogeneous nucleation.[1,2] For example, rapid nucleation of calcium phosphates may be desired in many load-bearing dental and orthopedic implants to achieve fast bony adaptation, absence of fibrous tissue seams, reduced healing time, and increased tolerance of surgical inaccuracies.[3,4] In other situations, where calcification would destroy the utility of the implants,[5-7] nucleation must be controlled. Therefore, one key to the success of biomaterials is an understanding of the factors that control crystal nucleation and growth in aqueous solutions.

At constant temperature and pressure, the crystallization process is commonly described by two major elements; solution composition and interfacial free energy. Although the former has been extensively studied [8,9] the latter has received little attention. The objective of this work is to elucidate the role of surface (or interfacial) properties of the substrate and the growing crystal phases in the crystallization kinetics, by using both contact angle and crystallization kinetics measurements.

METHODOLOGY

Kinetics of crystallization

The constant composition (CC) method[10] was used to investigate the crystallization kinetics. In a typical calcium phosphate crystal growth experiment, a metastable supersaturated solution was prepared in stirred, double-walled Pyrex glass vessels maintained at 37.0±0.05°C, in an atmosphere of nitrogen gas, presaturated with water vapor, in order to exclude carbon dioxide. Sodium chloride or potassium nitrate solution was used to adjust the ionic strength. The solution pH was brought to the desired value by the careful slow addition of dilute base (potassium hydroxide). A pH electrode coupled with a single junction reference electrode along with an Orion pH meter was used to monitor changes in hydrogen ion activities. Once equilibrium was attained, as indicated by a steady electrode emf reading, the solid phase seeding surfaces were introduced to initiate the crystallization. Any changes in the hydrogen ion activities sensed by electrodes triggered the addition of titrants from stepper motor-driven burettes. The volume of titrant, V, added as a function of time was recorded. The induction time, τ_{in}, taken as the time needed to reach steady-state nucleation and growth at the solid surfaces, was measured as the time from seeding surfaces addition to the intersection of a tangent (dV/dt) with the time axis.

<u>Characterization of solid surfaces</u>

Contact angle measurements were made using a Gaertner (Chicago, IL) telemicroscope with an eyepiece goniometer and Teflon/glass syringes equipped with stainless-steel Luer-tipped hypodermic needles (Gilmont Instruments, Chicago, IL). The advancing contact angles (θ) were directly measured with a drop of the liquids [11, 12], placed on smooth flat surfaces.

For the determination of the contact angle formed between a liquid (and air, or vapor) and finely divided powder particles, for which direct contact angle measurements cannot be performed, a thin layer wicking capillary rise procedure was used[11,12]. In this method, the measured rate of capillary rise (i.e. the capillary rise h, in a time t) of a liquid L, through a packed column of powder supported on a glass microscope slide, was substituted into the Washburn Eq. (1)[13]:

$$h^2 = \frac{tR_{eff}\gamma_L \cos\theta}{2\eta} \tag{1}$$

In Eq. (1), R_{eff} is the effective interstitial pore radius, η the viscosity of the liquid, θ the contact angle between the solid (S) and the liquid (L), and γ_L the liquid surface tension against its vapor. The detailed procedure can be found in previous publications [12,15].

The surface tension component and parameters of the solid particles were calculated by means of Young's equation (2)[11]:

$$(1+\cos\theta)\gamma_L = 2(\sqrt{\gamma_S^{LW}\gamma_L^{LW}} + \sqrt{\gamma_S^{+}\gamma_L^{-}} + \sqrt{\gamma_S^{-}\gamma_L^{+}}) \tag{2}$$

where γ^{LW} is the Lifshitz-van der Waals (LW) surface tension component (apolar), γ^{+} the electron-acceptor (Lewis acid) parameter, and γ^{-} the electron donor (Lewis base) parameter. The interfacial tensions between solid surfaces and aqueous solutions were calculated from Eq. (3)[11]:

$$\gamma_{SL} = (\sqrt{\gamma_S^{LW}} - \sqrt{\gamma_L^{LW}})^2 + 2(\sqrt{\gamma_S^{+}\gamma_S^{-}} + \sqrt{\gamma_L^{+}\gamma_L^{-}} - \sqrt{\gamma_S^{+}\gamma_L^{-}} - \sqrt{\gamma_S^{-}\gamma_L^{+}}) \tag{3}$$

MATERIALS

Solid substrate surfaces for calcium phosphates crystallization included silicone rubber, poly(methyl methacrylate (PMMA) and poly(tetrafluoroethylene-*co*-hexafluoropropylene) (FEP), anatase and rutile. PMMA thin film was made by casting 2% (w/v) PMMA particles (Lot No. 2L-33-10; Polysciences, Warrington, PA) on micro glass slide. Anatase (99.9+%) was obtained from Aldrich Chemical Company (Cat. No. 23,203-3), and rutile (99.9+%) from Johnson Matthey (Lot K20F38, Ward, MA).

RESULTS AND DISCUSSION

The surface tension components and parameters on the natural and RFGD-treated polymer surfaces are shown in Table 1. It can be seen that RFGD treatment resulted in a marked decrease in water contact angle,[14] an increase in the values of the Lewis base parameter (γ^{-}), and very little change in γ^{LW}.

In agreement with the observed absence of titrant demand in the CC experiments, scanning electron microscopic examination of untreated surfaces of silicone, FEP, PMMA and even RFGD-treated silicone rubber whose surfaces had values of γ^{LW} ranging from 12 - 41 x10^{-3} J/m^2, and relatively small values of Lewis base, $\gamma^- < 10 \times 10^{-3}$ J/m^2, revealed no mineral phase crystallization. However, SEM and EDS examinations showed that calcium phosphates were nucleated on RFGD-treated PMMA, and FEP, which were characterized by relatively high values of Lewis base, γ^-, ranging from 24-40 x10^{-3} J/m^2.

Table 1 Surface Tension Components and Parameters of PMMA, RFGD-treated PMMA, FEP, RFGD-treated FEP, Silicone, and RFGD treated silicone at 20°C.

Substrate	$\gamma^{LW}/10^{-3}$ J/m^2	$\gamma^+/10^{-3}$ J/m^2	$\gamma^-/10^{-3}$ J/m^2	$\gamma_{SL}/10^{-3}$ J/m^2
PMMA	41.1	0	12.0	19.0
RFGD-PMMA	40.7	0	24.7	3.7
FEP	14.2	0	1.2	40.7
RFGD-FEP	24.2	1.7	38.4	-8.5
Silicone	11.9	0	1.8	38.9
RFGD-Silicone	19.0	0	8.8	21.1

The heterogeneous nucleation of calcium phosphates including OCP, HAP and FAP on anatase and rutile surfaces are shown in Table 2. Induction periods preceding the initial crystal growth of the calcium phosphate phases varied markedly with relative supersaturation. At the same relative supersaturation, the induction time for calcium phosphate nucleation on anatase surfaces was much shorter than that on rutile surfaces.

Table 2 Nucleation and Crystal Growth of OCP, HAP and FAP on Anatase and Rutile Surfaces.

Growth Phase	pH	Ionic Strength	σ	τ_{in} /min on anatase	τ_{in} /min on rutile
OCP	6.8	0.05	1.87	60	83
HAP	7.4	0.15	13.4	685	910
FAP	6.5	0.15	13.5	500	600

The thin layer wicking observations showed that the contact angle of water on a rutile surface is much larger than that on anatase; however, other liquids show little difference.[15] The calculated surface tension components and parameters for anatase (Table 3) show very high Lewis base values as compared with rutile surfaces.

Table 3 Surface Tension Components , in 10^{-3} J/m^2, of Anatase and Rutile at 20°C.

Solid	γ^{LW}	γ^+	γ^-	γ_{SL}
Anatase	42.1	0.8	47.7	-12.1
Rutile	40.6	1.7	15.6	11.1

In the classical nucleation model, the tendency for a crystal to grow at foreign surfaces depends upon two factors. The first is the driving force for crystallization expressed either as the relative supersatuation or as the Gibbs free energy of transfer from a supersaturated to an assumed saturated solution at the interface. This factor has been extensively studied and is readily controlled, notably by using the constant composition technique.[8,9] The second is the "image" contact angle (θ) formed between the embryo and the solid substratum, which is related to the overall free energies for the heterogeneous (ΔG^{het}) and homogenous (ΔG^{hom}) formation of the critical nucleus.[16] At the limit, $\theta = 180°$, there is a complete mismatch between the crystalline lattices of the substrate and that of the overgrowth, while $\theta = 0°$, implies a perfect match. However, these two limiting conclusions do not explain the heterogeneous nucleation processes and, in particular, the role of substrate.

Since in present work the metastable solutions were held at constant supersaturation with respect to each phase, it is suggested that the interfacial thermodynamics between the condensed phases plays a significant role in facilitating calcium phosphate nucleation on the solid surfaces. OCP, HAP and FAP have interfacial tensions with water of 4.3, 10, and 18.5 x10^{-3} J/m^2, respectively.[17] With respect to the tendency for crystallization, a much smaller interfacial tension value between the aqueous solution and the crystal phase indicates that the phase would have a greater tendency to be nucleated either on itself or on foreign surfaces. Thus, OCP crystals nucleate readily on titanium oxide surfaces while HAP and FAP crystals require much longer induction periods prior to crystallization on titania particles.[12, 15, 17, 18] For different substrata, the occurrence of crystallization depends not only upon the interfacial free energies of the growing phases but also upon the surface properties of the foreign phases. It can be seen from Tables 1-3 that surfaces with high Lewis base parameter (γ) and low interfacial tension with water (γ_{SL}) will readily facilitate the nucleation of calcium phosphates. In addition to the free energy for the formation of a critical nucleus in aqueous solution, the actual physicochemical meaning of crystal nucleation at solid surface can be regarded as follows: each unit of area covered involves the energy (γ_{SL}) required to displace unit area of solid-liquid interface (SL), the energy (γ_{LE}) to remove unit area of liquid-crystal embryo interface (LE), and the energy (γ_{SE}) required to form unit area of solid-crystal embryo interface (SE). Therefore, the ability of calcium phosphates to nucleate on foreign surface may be also described by a parameter, π, (Table 4) using Eq. (6)

$$\pi = \gamma_{SL} + \gamma_{LE} - \gamma_{SE} \qquad (6)$$

Lower π values suggest that a crystal phase in the system would readily nucleate on a substrate while higher values of π indicates that a phase may require a significant induction time preceding nucleation and growth on a foreign surface. OCP crystals are readily nucleated, especially on anatase surfaces.

Table 4 π values for calcium phosphates nucleation on anatase and rutile surfaces

	on anatase	on rutile
OCP	-8.3	12.3
HAP	-1.9	21.2
FAP	5.0	28.2

ACKNOWLEDGMENT

We thank the National Institute of Health (Grant DE 03223) for support of this work.

REFERENCES

1.   Hench LL. *Sciences* 1980; **208**: 826-831.
2.   Bunker BC, Rieke PC, et al., *Sciences* 1994; **264**: 48-55.
3.   Lemons LE. *Clinical Orthop. Rel. Res.* 1988; **235**: 220-228.
4.   Kay JF. *J. Biomed. Matr. Res.* 1988; 22: 1127-1135.
5.   Johnston TP, Schoen FJ, Levy RJ. *J. Pharm. Sci.* 1988; 77: 740-744.
6.   Chanda J. *Artif. Organs.* 1994; **18**: 752-757.
7.   Peters W, Smith D. *Ann. Plast. Surg.*, 1995; **34**: 8-11.
8.   Mullin JW. *Crystallization*, Oxford: Butterworth-Heinemann, 1993.
9.   Zhang JW. Nancollas GH. *Reviews Mineralogy*, 1990; **23**: 365-396.
10. Tomson MB, Nancollas GH. *Science*, 1978; **200**: 1059-1060.
11. Van Oss, C. J. *Interfacial Forces in Aqueous Media* New York: Marcel Dekker, 1994.
12. Wu W, Nancollas GH. *Langmuir*, 1997; **13**: 861-865.
13. Washburn EW. *Phys. Rev.* 1921; **12**: 273-283.
14. Wu W, Nancollas GH. *J. Biomed. Matr. Res.* 1997; **35**: 93-99.
15. Wu W, Nancollas GH. *J. Colloid Interface Sci.* 1998; **199**, 206-211.
16. Volmer, M. "Kinetik der Phasenbildung" Steinkopff, Dresden/Leipzig, 1939.
17. Nancollas GH, Wu W. *J. Dispersion Sci. Tech.* 1998; **19** (in press).
18. Wu W, Nancollas GH. *Colloids and Surfaces B:*, 1997; **10**: 87-94.

Bioceramics Volume 11, edited by R. Z. LeGeros and J.P. LeGeros
(Proceedings of the 11th International Symposium on Ceramics in Medicine)
New York, NY, USA, November 1998

FORMATION OF CALCIUM PHOSPHATE OVER PHOSPHORYLATED CHITOSAN FILM

H.K.Varma,[1,2] Y.Yokogawa[1], Y.Kawamoto[1], K.Nishizawa[1], F.Nagata[1] and T.Kameyama[1]

[1]Bioceramic Laboratory, National Industrial Research Institute of Nagoya, 1-1 Hirate-cho, Kita-ku, Nagoya 462, Japan; [2]Biomedical Technology Wing, Sree Chitra Tirunal Institute for Medical Science and Technology, Trivandrum 695012, India

ABSTRACT

A coating of porous calcium phosphate compound was produced over phsophorylated chitosan films by a $Ca(OH)_2$ soaking and SBF(simulated body fluid solution) immersion method. Chitosan films having 0.1 to 0.2 mm thickness were prepared from chitosan powder and phosphorylated using H_3PO_4 and urea . The P content of the film was ~0.2 wt%. These films were then soaked in saturated lime solution for 8 days before immersing in 1.5 x SBF solution for several days so that a calcium phosphate phase started depositing all over the film surface. Initially a mono layer of 200 nm size particles were deposited within 3-6 days and over that layer secondary nucleation had occurred leading to the formation of a continuous thick and porous coating as immersion time increases. The $Ca(OH)_2$ treatment facilitates the formation of a calcium phosphate precursor over the phosphorylated film, which in turn encourages the growth of a calcium deficient apatite coating over the surface upon immersion in SBF solution.

KEYWORDS: Calcium phosphate, coating, chitosan, biomimetic

INTRODUCTION

The search for new and better materials for various biomedical application has been the subject of intensive research as the number of tissue replacement applications increase. Biomimetic research has resulted in calcium phosphate coated polymeric and/or metallic materials that can be produced at biological conditions unlike other material processing techniques(1,2). Recent studies in the above area have shown the practicability of different surface functionalization techniques for creating favorable local conditions that can lead to the nucleation and growth of calcium phosphate phase over different substrate surfaces in simulated body fluid solutions(3,4,5). Phosphate group as the fuctionalisation radical was found to be very effective for the deposition of HAP over cotton, chitin etc(6,7). Prior to immersion in SBF, the phosphorylated substrate is subjected to soaking in saturated $Ca(OH)_2$ solution. This treatment creates a number of calcium phosphate precursor sites over the surface which will eventually create favorable condition for the nucleation and growth of HAP growth.

In this work, a calcium phosphate coating was produced over chitosan films by a process based on phosphorylation, $Ca(OH)_2$ treatment and SBF immersion steps.

EXPERIMENTAL

All chemicals were supplied by Wako Pure Chemicals Co. and were used without further purification. The growth medium (1.5x SBF) was prepared by procedures reported elsewhere(6).

The chitosan film was prepared by dissolving approximately 2 grams of chitosan powder in 100 ml of 2% acetic acid solution and the syrupy solution was allowed to dry in a petri-dish at 35°C in vaccum. Saturated sodium hydroxide solution was then introduced into the petri dish and the chitosan film could easily peal off. The film was then washed thoroughly with distilled water and phosphorylated by a procedure reported earlier (8). Approximately 1 gm of chitosan film was taken in a round bottomed flask fitted with a condenser, thermometer and nitrogen gas inlet tube. About 3 gm of 98% H_3PO_4 , 15 gm of urea and 30 ml of dimethyl formamide were added to it. The flask was then heated to $120\,^{\circ}C$ with the reactants refluxed for one hour under gentle stirring using a magnetic stirrer. After cooling the contents, the film was removed and thoroughly rinsed with distilled water.

The phosphorylated films were suspended in freshly prepared saturated $Ca(OH)_2$ solution for a period of 8 days. The solution was replaced with fresh $Ca(OH)_2$ after 3 days. After treatment, the films were thoroughly washed with distilled water. The above films were then vertically suspended in plastic jars with cotton threads and 50 ml of 1.5 x SBF solution was added. The jars were then covered with an air-tight cap and put into an air oven kept at $36.5\,^{\circ}C$.

The SBF solution was replaced each day. Samples were retrieved after 3, 7, 21 and 30 days of soaking. The retrieved samples were thoroughly rinsed with distilled water and dried at 65 ° C before performing various characterization studies such as Micro-Fourier Transform Infrared Spectroscopy (Micro-FTIR), Scanning Electron Microscopy(SEM), Energy Dispersive X ray Analysis(EDAX), Thin Film X Ray Diffractometry (XRD)etc.

RESULTS AND DISCUSSION

The original chitosan films as well as the phosphorylated varieties were transparent. The surfaces of both samples were appeared as smooth by SEM and the EDAX spectrum of phosphorylated sample showed strong P signals. As per the ICP analysis, P content in the film is ~ 0.2 wt %. This value is smaller than the obtained for chitosan powder samples subjected to similar phosphorylation reaction (8). This could be due to the smaller surface area of the film compared to the powder samples. The Micro FTIR spectrum of the Chitosan and Phosphorylated chitosan samples were taken. Apart from the characteristic chitosan peaks, phosphorylated sample showed additional peaks at 1150 and 620 cm^{-1} corresponding to the P-O stretch and bend respectively.

The phosphorylated films were then immersed in saturated $Ca(OH)_2$ solution for 8 days. SEM and EDAX results showed that after $Ca(OH)_2$ treatment, the entire surface was covered with a coating of fine particles identified as calcium phosphate particles. The EDAX showed that the Ca/P ratio was 1.34. The micro-FTIR spectrum showed the peaks corresponding to that of an amorphous calcium phosphate phase.

The $Ca(OH)_2$ treated phosphorylated chitosan films were immersed in 1.5 x SBF solution for different periods and Fig 1 a,b and c show the SEM pictures of the surface coating produced after 3, 7 and 21 days respectively. After 3 days of immersion, a single layer of calcium phosphate was found to deposit over the surface. After 7 days, the surface was almost covered by sinble layer of calcium phosphate particles accompanied by secondary nucleation of particle aggregates over the initial layer, as seen in the Fig 1b. Within 21 days the entire surface was covered with a coating of porous calcium phosphate aggregate(Fig.1c).

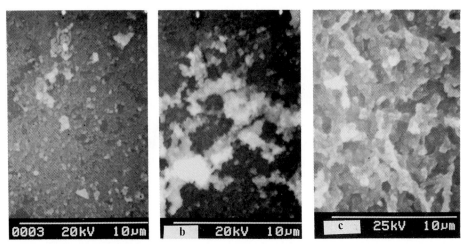

Figure 1   Scanning electron micrographs of phosphorylated and Ca(OH)$_2$ treated chitosan films after immersion in 1.5 x SBF solution at 36.5 °C for (**a**) 3 days (**b**) 7 days and (**c**) 21 days

Fig 2 is the micro FTIR spectrum of the calcium phosphate coating produced on sample immersed in SBF for 21 days. The major peaks around 1100 and 600 cm^{-1} are corresponding to the PO$_4$ of a poorly crystalline hydroxy apatite. It is also clear that the apatite is carbonate substituted from the appearance of peak at 1400 cm^{-1}. This is usually expected because the SBF is rich in carbonate ions. The Ca/P ratio of the coating was found to 1.6 , which indicates that the coating is basically a calcium deficient apatite.Fig 3 shows the thin film XRD pattern of the coating produced over the film after immersion   for 21 days. The broad peak of 2θ around 32-34° is ascribed to the diffraction of 211, 300 and 202 planes of HAP crystals. The other broad peak around 20° is due to the chitosan film.

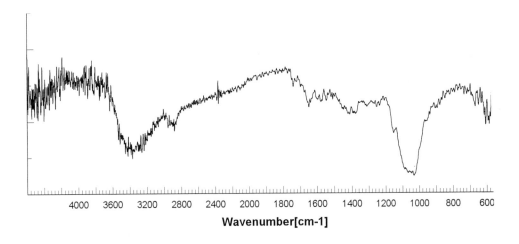

Figure 2. Micro-FTIR pattern of the of the calcium phosphate rich area of the fuctionalized chitosan film immersed in SBF solution for 21 days

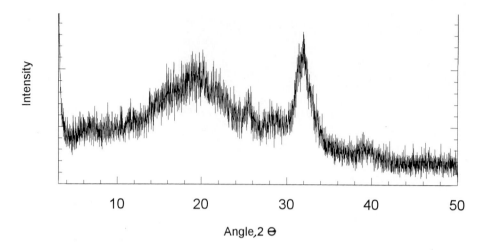

Figure 3. Thin film XRD pattern of surface functionalized chitosan film after immersing in SBF solution for 21 days

The possible mechanism for the above observations is that $Ca(OH)_2$ treatment produces a calcium phosphate precursor phase over the phosphorylated substrate which will later hydrolyse and facilitate the deposition of calcium deficient apatite upon immersion in the SBF solution. The phosporylated samples not subjected to the $Ca(OH)_2$ treatment did not show any the calcium phosphate growth over their surfaces upon immersion in SBF.

CONCLUSIONS

A biomimetic process is described for the deposition of calcium deficient carbonate apatite phase over functionalized chitosan film surface. Phosphorylated chitosan films were first soaked in saturated lime solution and then immersed in SBF solution for several days to facilitate the deposition of a porous calcium phosphate layer over the film surface.

ACKNOWLEDGEMENT

H.K.V.is grateful to Science and Technology Agency of Japan for awarding a post doctoral fellowship to carry out the work in Japan.

REFERENCES

1.   Mann S, *Biomimetic Materials, Chemistry*. New York:VCH, 1996
2.   Abe Y, Kokubo T, Yamamura T. *J.Mater.Sci.Mater.M*ed 1990;**1**:233-238.
3.   Dalas E, Kallitis JK,Koutsoukos PG, *Langmuir* 1991;7:1822-1826.
4   Tretinnikov ON, Kato K, Ikada Y, *J.Biomed.Mater.Res* 1994; **28**:1365-1373.
5.   Hato K, Kokubo T, Nakamura T,Yamamura T, *J. Am.Ceram.Soc* 1995; **78**:1049-1053.
6.   Mucalo MR, Yokogawa Y,Toriyama M, Suzuki T, Kawamoto Y, Nagata F, Nishizawa K, *J.Mater.Sci.Mater.Med* 1995; **6**:597-605.
7.   Yokogawa Y, PazReyes J, MucaloMR, Toriyama T, Kawamoto Y, Suzuki T, Nishizawa K, Nagata F, Kameyama T, *J.Mater.Sci.Mater.Med* 1997;**8**:407-412.
8.   Sakaguchi T, Hirokoshi T, Nakajima A, *Agric.Biol.Chem* 1981;**45**:2191-2195.

Bioceramics Volume 11, edited by R. Z. LeGeros and J.P. LeGeros
(Proceedings of the 11th International Symposium on Ceramics in Medicine)
New York, NY, USA, November 1998
© 1998 by World Scientific Publishing Co. Pte. Ltd.

APATITE PRECIPITATION AFTER INCUBATION OF BIPHASIC CALCIUM-PHOSPHATE CERAMIC IN VARIOUS SOLUTIONS: INFLUENCE OF IONS AND PROTEINS

R.Rohanizadeh, M. Padrines, J.M. Bouler, D. Couchourel, Y. Fortun and G. Daculsi

Centre de recherche sur les matériaux d'intérêt biologique - UPRES 2159, 1 Place A. Ricordeau, 44042 Nantes cedex 01, France.

ABSTRACT

The dissolution/precipitation process for calcium-phosphate ceramics in contact with biological fluid was studied by incubating biphasic calcium phosphate composed of hydroxyapatite and β-tricalcium phosphate in different solutions: distilled water, ionic simulated body fluid (SBF) without protein, and SBF containing various proteins and macromolecules separately [fibronectin, vitronectin, albumin and poly-L-glutamic acid (Poly-Glu)]. Transmission electron microscopy studies revealed that (i) apatite-precipitated microcrystals appeared around ceramic crystals in all solutions as a result of secondary nucleation; (ii) precipitates were poorly crystallized in water, and their form and size were not homogeneous compared to those precipitated in SBF; (iii) precipitates were smaller when fibronectin, vitronectin and Poly-Glu were present in SBF as compared to SBF without protein; and (iv) fibronectin and vitronectin initiated crystal nucleation in void spaces between ceramic crystals.

KEYWORDS: Ultrastructure, Calcium-phosphate ceramic, Precipitation, Simulated body fluid, Proteins.

INTRODUCTION

Biphasic calcium-phosphate ceramics composed of hydroxyapatite (HA) and β-tricalcium phosphate (β-TCP) have been extensively explored as bone graft materials[2]. After implantation *in vivo* or incubation in various solutions *in vitro*, the dissolution of the ceramic causes a supersaturation of Ca^{+2} and $PO4^{-3}$ ions in microenvironments, resulting in precipitation of carbonated apatitic microcrystals in the microporosity of the ceramic surface[6]. *In vivo*, biological factors such as proteins, enzymes and cells are important in establishing the density, size, shape and spatial distribution of precipitated microcrystals. Proteins play a dual role in the mineralization process, either promoting crystal nucleation by serving as nucleating agents or inhibiting crystal growth by binding to certain crystal planes. The present study was carried out in two phases: First, blocks of BCP were incubated in an ionic simulated body fluid (SBF) and distilled water in order to investigate the morphology and structure of precipitates and the influence of biological ions present in SBF on the precipitation process. Secondly, the influence of various proteins on the size and spatial distribution of precipitates was studied by incubating the BCP blocks in SBF in the presence or absence of proteins and macromolecules.

MATERIALS AND METHODS

Three blocks of macroporous BCP (5 x 5 x 5 mm, Triosite[TM], Zimmer, France) composed of 60% HA and 40% β-TCP were incubated under sterilized conditions in 2 ml of distilled water, or SBF without proteins, or SBF to which 5 μg/ml of different proteins were added separately: fibronectin (FN), vitronectin (VN), albumin and poly-L-glutamic acid (Poly-Glu). Recent investigations have shown that FN and VN have high affinities for calcium ions and HA crystals[1]. Poly-Glu is an acidic amino-acid sequence of proteins which acts as an inhibitor in solution[5] and as a promotor of apatite microcrystal growth in a gel system[4]. Albumin has inhibitory effects on apatite crystal growth[3]. SBF was prepared according to a previously described method[9]. The blocks of macroporous BCP were stored in an oven at 37°. After 2 weeks, fragments of the block surface were embedded in LR White and cut into ultrathin sections (90 nm) for transmission electron microscopy analysis at 200 kV (TEM-Jeol-200 CX). The structures of ceramic and precipitated microcrystals were determined by electron diffraction.

Dark field images were used to measure apatitic precipitated microcrystals. In this mode, crystals that strongly scatter an electron beam appear bright against a dark background (Fig. 1), allowing the selection of those which can be cut similarly. However, a hexagonal diffraction pattern corresponding to the [001] zone axis of apatite must be obtained first in order to measure thickness and width. The electron beam is then tilted to position the (010) spot at the central point of the diffraction pattern. Thus, all crystals cut parallel to the a-axis became bright in the dark field image (Fig. 1). Because of the flattened hexagonal morphology of precipitated apatite crystals, those cut parallel to the a-axis can be considered as being cut perpendicularly to the c-axis.

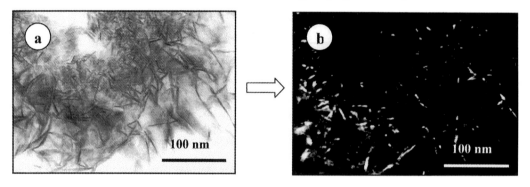

Fig. 1: (a) TEM image of apatitic precipitated microcrystals; b) dark field image of the same crystals as in (a). Crystals cut parallel to the a-axis of apatite structure became bright against a black background.

RESULTS AND DISCUSSION

TEM observations and electron diffraction showed that apatitic microcrystals precipitated around ceramic crystals in all solutions. The precipitates in SBF were needle-shaped, very well crystallized, and more or less homogeneous in shape and size (Fig. 2), whereas those in distilled water were poorly crystallized and inconsistent in shape and size (varying from small round to flattened microcrystals) (Fig. 3).

Apatite microcrystals could be precipitated in water only by dissolution of the ceramic crystal (especially β-TCP) and saturation of the microenvironment of Ca^{+2} and PO_4^{-3} ions. However, the presence of Ca^{+2} and PO_4^{-3} in SBF could have increased the crystallinity. Other biological ions present in SBF, such as Mg^{+2}, Na^{+1} and CO_3^{-2}, could have easily been substituted in the apatite structure and modified crystal growth and therefore crystal size and morphology.

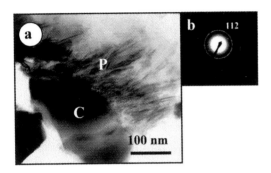

Fig. 2: (a) Precipitation (P) around the ceramic crystals (c) in BCP incubated in SBF; (b) electron diffraction pattern revealing the apatitic structure of precipitates.

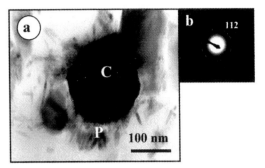

Fig. 3: (a) Precipitation (P) around the ceramic crystals (c) in BCP incubated in distilled water; (b) electron diffraction pattern revealing the apatitic structure of precipitates.

Our previous studies[7, 8] showed that more precipitates localized around HA ceramic crystals in implanted or incubated BCP in SBF than in β-TCP. These studies also revealed that precipitates were in continuity with the lattice planes of HA and oriented in a direction different from that of β-TCP lattice planes. The presence of proteins in SBF did not alter the shape and crystal structure of precipitates but modified their size and spatial distribution. In the presence of FN, VN and Poly-Glu, precipitates were significantly smaller than in SBF without protein, indicating that these macromolecules could bind to the surface of precipitates and inhibit their growth. Albumin had no influence on the size of precipitates. The average width of precipitates in distilled water was lower than in SBF.

Table 1: Size of precipitated microcrystals in the different solutions.

	Width	Thickness
SBF	39.7 ± 9.2	6.4 ± 1.4
SBF + FN	$32.6 \pm 10.2^*$	$4.6 \pm 0.6^*$
SBF + Albumin	43.1 ± 10.6	6.8 ± 2.0
SBF + VN	$29.9 \pm 11.5^*$	$3.1 \pm 0.9^*$
SBF + Poly-Glu	$29.0 \pm 5.6^*$	$3.9 \pm 1.1^*$
Distilled water	$27.0 \pm 11.6^*$	6.7 ± 3.9

* $P < 0.05$, i.e. a significant difference compared to SBF values.

In the presence of FN and VN, precipitation also occurred in void spaces between ceramic crystals (intercrystalline spaces) (Fig. 5a-b). In the presence of albumin and Poly-Glu, the distribution of precipitates (Fig. 5c-d) was similar to that in SBF without protein. This study did not allow quantification of the extent of precipitation, although the formation of precipitates in intercrystalline voids in the presence of FN and VN suggests that these proteins promote the nucleation of apatitic microcrystals.

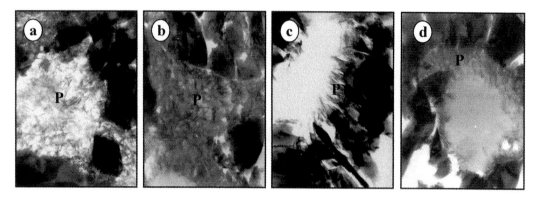

Fig. 5: Spatial distribution of precipitated microcrystals (P) in BCP incubated in SBF in the presence of (a) fibronectin, (b) vitronectin, (c) albumin or (d) Poly-Glu.

REFERENCES

1. Baccarani Contri B, Boraldi F, Taparelli F, De Paepe A, Pasquali Ronchetti I. *Am J Patho* 1996; **148:** 569-677.

2. Daculsi G, Passuti N, Martin S, Deudon C, LeGeros RZ, Raher S. *J Biomed Mater Res* 1990; **24:** 379-396.

3. Gilman H, Hukins DWL. *J Inorg Biochem* 1994; **55:** 31-39.

4. Hunter GK, Goldberg HA. *Biochem J* 1994; **302:** 175-179.

5. Hunter GK, Kyle CL, Goldberg HA. *Biochem.J* 1994; **300:** 723-728.

6. LeGeros RZ. In: Myers HM, ed. *Monographs in oral science*, Karger, San Fransisco, 1991.

7. Rohanizadeh R, Padrines M, Bouler JM, Couchourel D, Fortun Y, Daculsi G. *J Biomed Mater Res* 1998; (in press).

8. Rohanizadeh R, Trécant-Viana M, Daculsi G. *Calcif Tissue Int* 1998; (in press).

9. Yamada S, Nakamura T, Kokubo T, Oka M, Yamamuro T. *J Biomed Mater Res* 1994; **28:** 1357-1363.

Bioceramics Volume 11, edited by R. Z. LeGeros and J.P. LeGeros
(Proceedings of the 11th International Symposium on Ceramics in Medicine)
New York, NY, USA, November 1998

APATITE-FORMING ABILITY OF SODIUM TANTALATE GELS

T. Miyazaki,[1] H.-M. Kim,[1] F. Miyaji,[1] T. Kokubo[1] and T. Nakamura[2]

[1]Department of Material Chemistry, Faculty of Engineering, Kyoto University, Kyoto 606-8501, Japan; [2]Department of Orthopaedic Surgery, Faculty of Medicine, Kyoto University, Kyoto 606-8507, Japan

ABSTRACT

The present authors recently showed that a NaOH- and heat-treated tantalum (Ta) metal forms a bonelike apatite layer on its surface in a simulated body fluid (SBF) within 1 week in contrast with 4 weeks for the untreated Ta. The reason for this was assumed that Ta-OH groups formed on the surface of the NaOH- and heat-treated Ta by the exchange of Na^+ ion in its surface amorphous sodium tantalate layer with H_3O^+ ion in SBF induce the apatite nucleation, and the released Na^+ ion accelerates the apatite nucleation by increasing OH^- concentration of SBF. In order to confirm this assumption, sodium tantalate gels with various Na/Ta ratios were prepared via hydrolysis of sodium tantalum double alkoxide and coated on a SiO_2 glass plates. Apatite formation on these gels was examined in SBF. Although even Na-free tantalate gel formed the apatite, the induction period for the apatite formation decreased with increasing Na/Ta ratio of the gels. These results prove that the apatite-forming mechanism assumed above for the NaOH- and heat-treated Ta is correct.

KEYWORDS: Sodium tantalate gel, tantalum metal, bioactivity, apatite

INTRODUCTION

It is believed that the essential requirement for an artificial material to bond to living bone is formation of a bonelike apatite layer on its surface in body environment and that this bonelike apatite layer can be reproduced on its surface in a simulated body fluid (SBF) with ion concentrations nearly equal to those of human blood plasma[1]. The present authors previously showed that even a pure tantalum metal forms the bonelike apatite on its surface in SBF but it takes a time as long as 4 weeks. The same metal forms it within 7 days, however, when it was previously subjected to NaOH- and heat-treatments.[2, 3] Thus prepared bioactive tantalum metal is expected to be useful as bone-repairing material even under load-bearing conditions, since it shows high fracture toughness, high ductility and high malleability[4] as well as bone-bonding ability.

The subject of this paper is the mechanism of apatite formation on the surface of the tantalum metal. It was assumed that for the untreated tantalum metal Ta-OH groups formed by hydration of Ta_2O_5 layer on the surface of the metal in SBF induced the apatite nucleation, and that for the NaOH- and heat-treated tantalum metal the apatite nucleation induced by the Ta-OH groups was accelerated by the released Na^+ ion due to increase in the ionic activity product of the apatite in SBF. In the present study, in order to prove these assumptions, sodium tantalate gels with various Na/Ta ratios were prepared by a sol-gel method, and their structures and apatite-forming abilities were investigated in SBF.

MATERIALS AND METHODS

Tantalum ethoxide ($Ta(OC_2H_5)_5$) and sodium ethoxide ($NaOC_2H_5$) at various Na/Ta ratios were dissolved into ethanol and mixed, maintaining the tantalum ethoxide concentration at 0.1M. The mixed-ethoxide solution was refluxed in dry N_2 atmosphere at 78.5°C for 12 h to form the double alkoxide solution. Then the 0.1M H_2O ethanol solution in 4 ml was added to the double alkoxide solution in 4 ml for hydrolysis. The mixture was spin-coated on a rectangular specimen $10 \times 10 \times 1$ mm^3 in size of a high purity silica glass rotated at 410 rpm and repeated 15 times. Thus coated sodium tantalate gels were soaked in 30 ml of SBF at 36.5°C for various periods. The surface structures of the gels were characterized by laser Raman spectroscopy (Model T64000, ISA Jobin Yvon Co., France), thin-film X-ray diffraction (Thin-film attachment CN2651A1, Rigaku, Co., Tokyo, Japan), and scanning electron microscopy (SEM; S-2500CX, Hitachi Co., Tokyo, Japan). Variations in element concentrations of SBF with soaking of the gels were analyzed by inductively coupled plasma atomic emission spectroscopy (SPS-1500VR, Seiko Instruments Inc., Tokyo, Japan).

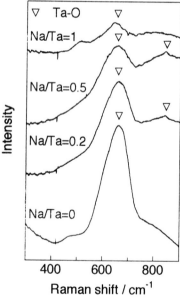

Figure 1. Raman spectra of the surfaces of sodium tantalate gels with various Na/Ta ratios.

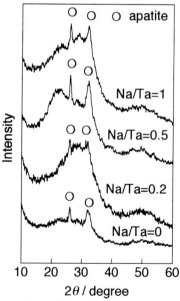

Figure 2. Thin-film X-ray diffraction patterns of the surfaces of sodium tantalate gels with various Na/Ta ratios soaked in SBF for 1 w.

RESULTS AND DISCUSSION

Figure 1 shows Raman spectra of the surfaces of sodium tantalate gels with various Na/Ta ratios. The peaks were observed around 600 and 800cm^{-1}. These peaks are ascribed to Ta-O bond in TaO_6 octahedra.[5] The peaks of the sodium tantalate gels coincided with those observed for the sodium tantalate layer formed on the surface of the NaOH- and heat-treated Ta metal. Figure 2 shows thin-film X-ray diffraction patterns of the surfaces of sodium tantalate gels with various Na/Ta ratios soaked in SBF for 1 w. The peaks ascribed to the apatite were observed for all the specimens, including the Na-free gel. The intensities of the apatite peaks were, however, larger for Na-containing gels than for Na-free gel. Figure 3 shows SEM photographs of the surfaces of the sodium tantalate gels with various Na/Ta ratios soaked in SBF for 4 days. The apatite was formed within 4, 4 and 2 days for the gels with Na/Ta ratio of 0, 0.5, and 1 respectively.

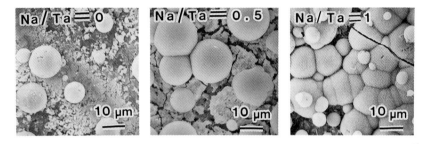

Figure 3. SEM photographs of the surfaces of the sodium tantalate gels with various Na/Ta ratios soaked in SBF for 4 days.

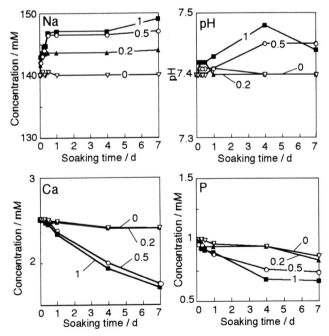

Figure 4. The variations in pH and element concentrations of SBF with soaking of sodium tantalate gels with various Na/Ta ratios.

Figure 4 shows the variation in pH value and element concentrations of SBF with soaking of sodium tantalate gels with various Na/Ta ratios. It can be seen from Fig. 4 that the Na concentration and pH value increased with increasing soaking time for the sodium-containing gels, and the Ca and P concentrations decreased with increasing soaking time for all the gels. The magnitude of the increases in the Na concentration and pH values and of the decreases in Ca and P concentrations increased with increasing Na/Ta ratio of the gels. These results indicate that the Ta-OH group itself can induce the apatite formation in SBF, and its apatite-forming ability is enhanced by the Na^+ ion released into the surrounding fluid.

On the basis of these results, the reason why even the untreated tantalum metal formed the apatite on its surface in SBF but it took a long induction period is interpreted as follows. The Ta_2O_5 passive layer on the surface of the tantalum metal was partially hydrated in SBF and the Ta-OH groups formed on the surface induced the apatite nucleation, but it took a long time for the hydration. The reason why the NaOH- and heat-treated tantalum metal formed the apatite on its surface in SBF within a short period is interpreted as follows. An amorphous sodium tantalate layer was formed on the surface of the tantalum metal by the NaOH- and heat-treatments. This sodium tantalate layer released rapidly the Na^+ ion into SBF to exchange the H_3O^+ ion in SBF. As a result, a large number of Ta-OH groups were rapidly formed on the surface of the tantalum metal. This Ta-OH group induced the apatite nucleation and the released Na^+ ion accelerated the apatite nucleation by increasing ionic activity product of the apatite in SBF due to increase in OH- ion concentration. Once the apatite nuclei are formed, they grew spontaneously by consuming the calcium and phosphate ions from SBF, since SBF is already supersaturated with respect to the apatite even under the normal condition. This means that the previous assumptions for the apatite formation on the tantalum metal were proved by the present model experiments using sodium tantalate gels.

CONCLUSIONS

The Ta-OH group itself can induce apatite nucleation in SBF, and its nucleation can be accelerated by the Na^+ ion released into the surrounding fluid. The apatite forming ability of the NaOH- and heat-treated tantalum metal as well as of the untreated tantalum metal in SBF can be well interpreted in terms of the Ta-OH groups and the Na^+ ion.

ACKNOWLEDGMENT

This study was supported by Grant-in-Aid for Scientific Research, the Ministry of Education, Science, Sports, and Culture, Japan.

REFERENCES

1. Kokubo T. *J Ceram Soc Japan* 1991;99: 965-973.
2. Miyazaki T, Kim H M, Miyaji F, Kokubo T and Nakamura T. In: *Bioceramics* Vol. 9, ed. by Kokubo T, Nakamura T and Miyaji F. Oxford: Elsevier, 1996: 317-320.
3. Miyazaki T, Kim H M, Miyaji F, Kokubo T and Nakamura T. In: *Bioceramics* Vol. 10, ed. by Sedel L and Rey C. Oxford: Elsevier, 1997: 11-14.
4. Black *J. Clin Mater* 1994; 16: 167-173.
5. Imoto F, Nakatani T, Shiozaki K, Iwamoto H and Yamamoto T. *Yogyo-Kyokai-Shi* 1987; 95: 520-525.

Bioceramics Volume 11, edited by R. Z. LeGeros and J.P. LeGeros
(Proceedings of the 11th International Symposium on Ceramics in Medicine)
New York, NY, USA, November 1998
© 1998 by World Scientific Publishing Co. Pte. Ltd.

ELECTROSTATIC AND STRUCTURAL ANALYSES OF PHOSPHATE/ORGANIC MATERIALS INTERFACES

K. Sato, Y. Suetsugu, M. Kikuchi, Y. Kumagai and J. Tanaka

National Institute for Research in Inorganic Materials, Namiki 1-1, Tsukuba, Ibaraki 305-0044, Japan.

ABSTRACT

Langmuir-Blodgett (LB) monolayers with carboxyl groups and amino groups were prepared using arachidic acid and stearyl amine to investigate an interfacial interaction between organic-inorganic materials. The surface of the arachidic acid monolayers was negatively charged and that of the stearyl amine monolayers was positively charged, corresponding to the electric charge of the respective functional group. The LB monolayers were soaked in simulated body fluid. Calcium phosphate precipitates formed on the arachidic acid monolayer, whereas no precipitate formed on the stearyl amine monolayer. It was indicated that the carboxyl groups could be nucleation sites for calcium phosphate but the amino groups could not be.

KEYWORDS: Langmuir-Blodgett monolayer, functional group, calcium phosphate, nucleation.

INTRODUCTION

Bone is a nanocomposite material in which as assembly of small apatite particles is effectively reinforced by collagen fibers. This fact suggests that bioactive artificial bones like bone-repairing materials can be obtained through organic-inorganic nanocomposite materials. In order to develop new kinds of bioactive composite material, it is important to understand an organic-inorganic interfacial interaction in simulated body environment. The previous study[1] indicated that oriented apatite crystals could be induced on carboxyl groups in organic materials. In the present paper, an interfacial interaction between functional groups and inorganic materials under the simulated body environment. Electrostatic and structural analyses of the interfaces were made for Langmuir-Blodgett monolayers.

EXPERIMENTAL TECHNIQUES

Preparation of Langmuir-Blodgett monolayer

Slide glasses and calcium fluoride crystals of 13 x 38 x 1 mm^3 in size were used as substrate. The slide glass substrates were hydrophobized with 1, 1, 1, 3, 3, 3 - hexamethyldisilazane and then dried at 95℃ for 1 hour. Ion-exchanged distilled pure water was used as aqueous subphase. Arachidic acid ($C_{19}H_{39}COOH$) and stearyl amine ($C_{18}H_{37}NH_2$) were dissolved in chloroform to obtain spreading solutions of concentration 1 mM. The chloroform solutions of 300 μl were spread onto the aqueous subphase. The resultant films were allowed to equilibrate with subphase for about 5 minutes prior to compression. Subsequently, the films were slowly compressed up to the surface pressure needed for film transfer, i.e. 25 mN·m^{-1} and kept at the constant pressure for 5 minutes in order to facilitate structural rearrangement. The monolayers of arachidic acid and stearyl amine were transferred onto the substrates at a dipping speed of 4 mm·min^{-1}. After dipping, the substrates were dropped into the subphase. The LB monolayers formed on the slide glass and the calcium fluoride were supplied for in vitro evaluation and infrared transmission measurement.

Infrared spectra and zeta-potential measurements

Infrared transmission spectra were measured with a Fourier transform infrared spectrometer (Spectrum 2000, Perkin Elmer, U.S.A.), whose sample chamber was purged with nitrogen gas to minimize the amounts of water vapor and carbon dioxide. The resolution of spectrum was 4 cm^{-1} and iteration was performed for 256 times in 3000-1200 cm^{-1}.

The zeta potential of the LB monolayers accumulated on the slide glass were measured by an electrophoretic light scattering method (LEZA-600, Otsuka Electronics Co., Ltd., Japan). The solution employed in the zeta potential measurement was buffered at pH 7.4 at 36.5 ℃ with 10 mM of tris (hydroxymethyl) aminomethane ($(CH_2OH)_3CNH_2$) and 10 mM hydrochloric acid (HCl).

In vitro evaluation

A simulated body fluid was prepared by dissolving reagents NaCl, NaHCO$_3$, KCl, K$_2$HPO$_4$·3H$_2$O, MgCl$_2$, CaCl$_2$ and Na$_2$SO$_4$ in distilled water after Kokubo *et al.*[2] In order to enhance the rate of nucleation of crystals on the LB monolayers, we prepared simulated body fluid with calcium ion concentration 1.25 times the value of the human blood plasma. The fluid was buffered at pH 7.4 (at 36.5 ℃) with 50 mM of tris (-hydroxymethyl) - aminomethane ($(CH_2OH)_3CNH_2$) and 45 mM hydrochloric acid. Slide glasses with LB monolayer were withdrawn from subphase and soaked in 30 ml of simulated body fluid for various periods.

After the substrates were soaked in the simulated body fluid for various periods, they were taken out of the fluid and gently washed with ion-exchanged distilled water. The substrates were dried at room temperature. Their surfaces were analyzed by thin-film X-ray diffraction (RINT 2000, Rigaku Co., Japan) and infrared specular reflectance measurement. IR spectra were taken with the Fourier transform infrared spectrometer.

RESULTS AND DISCUSSIONS

Fig. 1 shows the infrared transmission spectra of the LB monolayers of arachidic acid and stearyl amine. The peaks at 2919 and 2850 cm^{-1} are assigned to CH$_2$ antisymmetric and symmetric stretching vibration, respectively. The peaks at 1470 cm^{-1} are due to CH$_2$ scissoring vibration. Absorption features caused by alkyl chain evidence the presence of the LB monolayer accumulated on the substrates. The band observed at 1702 cm^{-1} only in the spectrum of arachidic acid is assigned to the C=O stretching vibration.[3] Absence of striking absorption feature except for the peaks corresponding to alkyl chain in the stearyl amine spectrum is caused by surface selection rule of infrared absorption.

The zeta potentials were -61 and 41 mV for the arachidic acid monolayer and the stearyl amine monolayer, respectively. The fact that the former is negatively charged and the latter is positively charged is attributed to the existence of the functional groups which are oriented toward the outside of the monolayers. The electrostatic properties of the LB monolayer surfaces are under the domination of the functional groups.

Figs. 2 and 3 show thin-film X-ray diffraction patterns and infrared reflection spectra of the LB monolayer surfaces before and after soaking in the simulated body fluid. The main peaks in Figs. 2 and 3 were assigned based on the data previously published.[4-6] In Fig. 2, it could be seen that new diffraction peaks due to apatite appeared on arachidic acid monolayer soaked in simulated body fluid. In the reflection spectra of arachidic acid monolayer after soaked, the peaks at 550 to 600 cm^{-1} increased

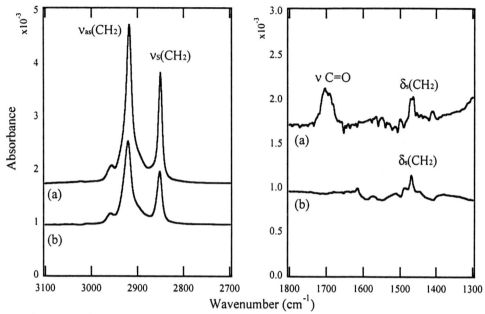

Figure 1. Infrared transmission spectra of the LB monolayers of (a) arachidic acid and (b) stearyl amine.

and those at about 1000 to 1200 cm^{-1} changed to two distinct peaks as shown in Fig. 3 and the peaks are attributed to apatite crystals. From the results of the XRD patterns and infrared spectroscopy, it is clear that apatite crystals were formed on arachidic acid monolayer but not formed on stearyl amine monolayer.

CONCLUSION

In order to elucidate the interaction between organic-inorganic phases in natural bone, the LB monolayers with functional groups the same as those on collagen fibers were prepared and soaked in simulated body fluid. The electrostatic properties of the LB monolayers were dominated by the functional groups. Apatite precipitates formed on the surfaces of arachidic acid monolayer which possess carboxyl groups, whereas the stearyl amine monolayer with amino groups did not form apatite at all. From these results, it was indicated that carboxyl groups play a more important role in the interaction of the organic-inorganic interface than amino groups.

REFERENCES

1. Cho SB, Kikuchi M, Tanaka J, Azumi R, Matsumoto M. *Bioceramics Vol 9*: 403-406.
2. Kokubo T, Ito S, Huang Z T, Hayashi T, Sakka S, Kitsugi T, Yamamuro T. *J Biomed Mater Res* 1990; **24**: 331-343.
3. Kimura F, Umemura J, Takenaka T. *Langmuir* 1986, **2**: 96-101.
4. Elliott JC. *Structure and chemistry of the apatite and other calcium orthophosphates*. Amsterdam: Elsevier, 1994.
5. Hench LL. *J Am Ceram Soc* 1991; **74**: 1487-1510.
6. Otsuki C, Kokubo T, Yamamuro T. *J Non-Cryst Solids* 1992; **143**: 84-92.

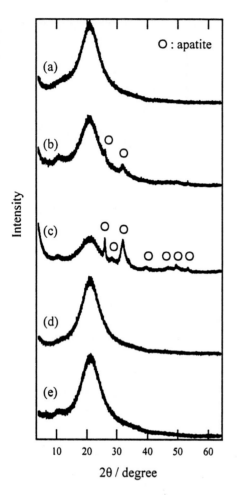

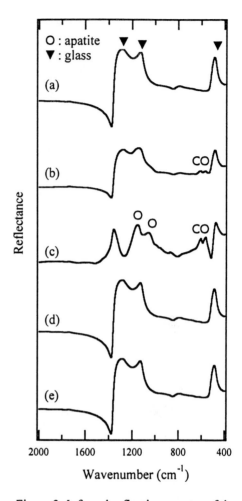

Figure 2. Thin-film X-ray diffraction patterns of the LB monolayers soaked in simulated body fluid for various periods. (a) Before soaking; (b) Arachidic acid soaked for 3 days; (c) Arachidic acid soaked for 7 days; (d) Stearyl amine soaked for 3 days; (e) Stearyl amine soaked for 7 days.

Figure 3. Infrared reflection spectra of the LB monolayer surfaces soaked in simulated body fluid for various periods. (a) Before soaking; (b) Arachidic acid soaked for 3 days; (c) Arachidic acid soaked for 7 days; (d) Stearyl amine soaked for 3 days; (e) Stearyl amine soaked for 7 days.

Bioceramics Volume 11, edited by R. Z. LeGeros and J.P. LeGeros
(Proceedings of the 11th International Symposium on Ceramics in Medicine)
New York, NY, USA, November 1998
© 1998 by World Scientific Publishing Co. Pte. Ltd.

EFFECTS OF CATIONS ON SURFACE REACTIONS AND APATITE NUCLEATION ON SILICATE GLASSES IN A BODY ENVIRONMENT

Akiyoshi Osaka, Satoshi Hayakawa and Chikara Ohtsuki

Biomaterials Lab., Faculty of Engineering, Okayama University,
Tsushima, Okayama, 700-8530, Japan

ABSTRACT

Apatite deposition was examined on a series of pseudo binary silicate glasses of composition $xM_mO_n \cdot (50-x/2)(CaO \cdot SiO_2)$ (x<10 mol %; M= Co, Zn, Mn, Cr, W, V,Ta) with thin-film X-ray diffraction, infrared spectroscopy and scanning electron micrograph after they were soaked in a simulated body fluid (Kokubo solution, SBF). The Zn glass was little corrosive. Zn ions remained in the resulted silica gel layer preventing apatite deposition. The Mn and Co ions were released into the SBF as well as stayed in the gel layer where adsorbed calcium phosphates remained amorphous. The Cr-containing glass was similar to the Zn glass regarding bioactivity. Addition of WO_3 shortened the induction time τ of apatite formation. The V glass had a longer τ than the mother glass but causes no effect on the growth of the apatite nuclei.

KEYWORDS: Bioactivity, apatite deposition, effects of cations, corrosive reactions, deactivation of body fluid

INTRODUCTION

A few groups of ceramic materials can deposit apatite when they are soaked in a body fluid, including a calcium silicate glass of wallastonite composition $CaO \cdot SiO_2$. However, addition of only 1 mol % of Al_2O_3 or TiO_2 to the glass fully suppressed the apatite deposition after Ohtsuki *et al.*,[1] while Osaka *et al.*[2] reported that addition of B_2O_3 in several mol % stimulated the deposition. Those third metal oxides modify water reactivity of the mother glass so that they either depress or enhance the formation of a silica gel layer which is considered to

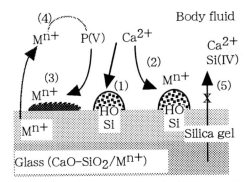

Fig. 1. Possible effects of the third metal ions M^{n+} on apatite deposition on a mother glass. Nuclei (1) are activated/activated by adsorption of M^{n+} (2). Calcium phosphates adsorbed is kept from crystallization (3). P(V) in the body fluid is deactivated by M^{n+} - P(V) interaction (4). The glass becomes even corrosion-resistant due to M incorporation to suppress the dissolution of Ca^{2+} ions and formation of a nucleation-inducing silica gel layer (5). Apatite formation scheme after Li *et al.*[3]

induce nucleation of apatite.[3] However, the mechanism proposed for apatite deposition[3] includes release of Ca^{2+} ions from the glass surface and adsorption of the Ca^{2+} ions together with phosphate anions on to the nucleation sites to form embryos and to grow the nuclei. Fig. 1 illustrates not only the scheme[3] leading to apatite deposition but the steps working favorably/unfavorably for it due to the third metal cations. Here, some cations added to the mother glass may be released into the contacting body fluid to increase the degree of supersaturation of apatite to destabilize the fluid, or be adsorbed on the nucleating sites of apatite as the calcium ions to favor / retard the apatite crystallization, while some cations released may be interacted with the phosphate ions to deactivate them or may occupy the nucleating sites to keep the calcium ions from adsorption, and behave unfavorably for bioactivity. Most of the implant materials clinically used now cannot deposit such apatite under the body environment. Providing them with bioactivity surely widens their applications. It is thus important to distinguish which ones are favorable by examining their effects on the apatite deposition, because such analysis serves to design bioactive implant materials.

In the present study, we examined the apatite deposition of a series of calcium silicate glasses, and discussed the effects of the cations added to the mother glass in terms of the corrosion of the glasses, release of the cations into the body fluid, adsorption on to the gel layer of the glass surface, and deactivation of the ions relevant to apatite deposition.

EXPERIMENTAL

Ternary silicate glasses of composition $xMmOn \cdot (50-x)CaO \cdot 50SiO_2$ ($x<10$ mol %; M= Co, Zn, Mn, Cr, W, V, Ta) were prepared by a conventional melt-quenching method using relevant reagent grade oxides and carbonates. Kokubo solution (SBF) was prepared as described by Cho et al.[4] The SBF had a composition (in mM: 142.0 Na^+, 5.0 K^+, 2.5 Ca^{2+}, 1.5 Mg^{2+}, 147.8 Cl^-, 4.2 HCO_3^-, 1.0 HPO_4^-, 0.5 SO_4^{2-}) and was adjusted 7.25 in pH. Polished glass specimens 10x10x1 mm in size were soaked in the SBF at 36.5°C up to 7 days. Their surface structure was analyzed before and after the soaking with a thin film X-ray diffractometer, reflection infrared (IR) spectrophotometer, and a scanning electron micrograph equipped with an energy dispersion X-ray detector. The ion composition of the SBF was monitored by inductively coupled plasma emission spectroscopy (ICP). We here took no notice on equilibrium accomplished in the glass melts between the valence states of manganese, chromium, vanadium, and tungsten ions for discussing the effects of each metal oxide on the bioactivity.

RESULTS AND DISCUSSION

Figure 2 illustrates thin film X-ray diffraction patterns for the glass specimens as well as their compositions after soaked in the SBF for 7 days where the diffractions assigned to apatite was indicated ○ after JCPDS-ICDD card.[5] The glasses with 0.5 mol% CoO and MnO_2 deposited apatite within a week while the addition of only 0.5 mol% ZnO kept from the deposition. All the glasses containing 5 mol% metal oxides could not deposit apatite. We confirmed from IR reflection spectra of the mother glass that an silica gel layer was yielded on the glass surface and deposition of certain amorphous calcium phosphates before apatite was crystallized on the surface. With increase in the amount of CoO and MnO_2 the formation of the calcium phosphates was delayed hence the crystallization of apatite until apatite could not be detected on the glasses with 1 mol% MnO_2 or 2 mol% CoO within 7 days of soaking. We could observe, however, the silica gel layer for the glasses containing MnO_2 or CoO up to 5 mol%. Observed was a similar but significant effect of ZnO to depress series of reactions leading to apatite deposition, i.e., the glass with 0.5 mol% ZnO yielded the silica gel layer but no apatite within 7 days in the SBF.

Release of cations accompanying the surface corrosion was monitored with ICP analysis of the SBF composition. Increase in Si indicates degradation of the surface layer while decrease in Ca and P indicates deposition of the phosphates and crystal growth of apatite. The greatest release of Si was observed for the Co glass among those containing 5 mol% metal oxide, and the least but a finite amount of Si was released from the Zn glass. Fig. 3 shows that Co and Mn ions were dissolved from the glasses containing 5 mol% metal oxide into the SBF but Zn ions remained in the glass or surface layer. SEM-EDX analysis of the glasses with 5 mol % MnO_2, CoO, and ZnO after soaked for 7 days showed deposition of P-containing particles on the glass surface. Thus the Zn glass released the silicate anions associated with Ca ions in the bulk glass while the anions associated with Zn ions remained in the surface layer and prevented the adsorbed calcium phosphates from crystallization. Mn and Co ions were both present in the SBF and were adsorbed on the surface gel layer, and they obstacled not

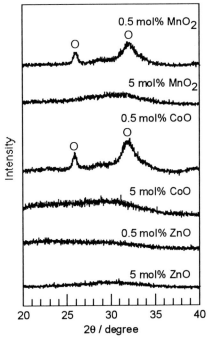

Figure 2 TF-XRD patterns for some of CaO-SiO$_2$ glasses soaked in the SBF for 7 days. O : Apatite

only the adsorption of the phosphate and calcium ions but their transformation into apatite. Chromium glass behaved as the Zn one, while no surface corrosion was observed for the glass containing 1 mol% Ta$_2$O$_5$ as in the alumina and titania glasses.[1]

The glasses with 5 mol% WO$_3$ and V$_2$O$_5$ were very corrosive in the SBF compared to the Zn or Co counterparts. ICP analysis indicated that the Ca concentration of the SBF continued increasing at soaking the V glass in the SBF whereas it saturated at a certain level for the W glass. Moreover, the V glass released twice as much Si as the W glass. Therefore the network of the mother glass turned corrosive due to the presence of V ions while the presence of W caused a limited effect. X-ray diffraction detected apatite on the V glass in 4 days of soaking in the SBF, while within 1 day for the W glass. The X-ray intensity for the (002) plane (~26° in 2θ (CuKα)) of apatite grew with the soaking time. One may assume that the first derivative of the X-ray intensity versus period curves represents the rate of apatite growth. The rate was then plotted in Fig. 4 as a function of the soaking period for the W and V glasses together with that for the mother glass. It decreased significantly at the first stage of rapid crystal growth, then it gradually approached the horizontal line because the phosphate ions in the SBF were consumed out. One can linearly extrapolate the curve at the first stage to the horizontal axis; the soaking period for the zero growth rate from extrapolation is the induction period τ of apatite crystallization. The W glass had a very high rate of growth and the shortest τ among the three glasses. The V glass was similar in curve profile to the mother glass while τ was about one day longer. Thus the V ions retarded the nucleation but did not affect the growth process in the later state. Since both W and

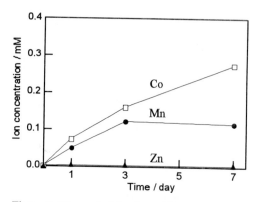

Figure 3 Change in Mn, Co and Zn concentration of the SBF due to soaking of the glasses with 5 mol% CoO, MnO$_2$ and ZnO.

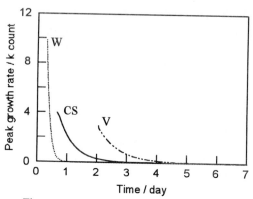

Figure 4 Apatite growth rate for the glasses with 5 mol% WO$_3$ and V$_2$O$_5$.
CS : CaO•SiO$_2$ glass.

V glasses were rigorously dissolved in the SBF, the difference in τ or degree of bioactivity was attributed to either the structure of the gel and glass network or the metal ion - phosphate anion interaction in the SBF as Blumenthal and Posner suggested that V^{5+} ions may form complexes with the phosphate anions in solution but not affect the adsorption of the anions.[6]

SUMMARY

The effects of a few third component oxides were examined on the bioactivity of the mother glass of a composition 50CaO•50SiO$_2$ by using the SBF. Addition of Ta$_2$O$_5$ kept the glass from corrosion as that of Al$_2$O$_3$ and TiO$_2$.[1] The Zn glass was reacted little with the SBF and Zn ions remained in the resulted silica gel layer that could not deposit apatite. The Mn and Co ions were released into the SBF as well as stayed in the gel layer that deposit amorphous calcium phosphate not transformable to apatite. The Cr-containing glass was similar to the Zn glass regarding bioactivity. Addition of WO$_3$ shortened the induction time τ of apatite formation. The V glass had a longer τ than the mother glass but caused no effect on the growth of the apatite nuclei.

REFERENCES

1. Ohtsuki C, Osaka A, Kokubo T. In: Anderson ÖH, Yli-Urpo A, ed. *Bioceramics Volume 7.* Oxford: Butterworth-Heinemann Ltd, 1994: 73-78.
2. Osaka A, Hayakawa S, Tsuru K, Ohtsuki C. In: *Proc II Internatl Conf Borate glasses crystals & melts.* Sheffield: The Society of Glass Technology, 1997: 490-497.
3. Li P, Ohtsuki C, Kokubo T, Nakanishi K, Soga N, Nakamura T, Yamamuro T. *J Am Ceram Soc* 1992; **75**: 2094-2097.
4. Cho S B, Nakanishi K, Kokubo T, Soga N, Ohtsuki C, Nakamura T, Kitsugi T, Yamamuro T. *J Am Ceram Soc* 1995; **78**: 1769-1774.
5. Powder diffraction file, sets 9-10, International Centre for Diffraction Data, Newton Square, Pa, 19073, USA, 1970, Card 9-432.
6. Blumenthal N C, Posner A S. *Appl Biomat* 1989; **23**: 13-22.

Bioceramics Volume 11, edited by R. Z. LeGeros and J.P. LeGeros
(Proceedings of the 11th International Symposium on Ceramics in Medicine)
New York, NY, USA, November 1998
© 1998 by World Scientific Publishing Co. Pte. Ltd.

BIOCOMPATIBILITY AND CRYSTAL GROWTH OF POLED HYDROXYAPATITE CERAMICS AND COATINGS

M. Ohgaki[1], T. Komiya[2], J. Hamagami[2], K. Yamashita[1]

[1]Institute for Medical and Dental Engin., Tokyo Medical and Dental Univ., Chiyodaku, Tokyo, Japan.; [2]Dept.of Applied Chemistry, Tokyo Metropolitan Univ., Hachioji, Tokyo, Japan.

ABSTRACT

Bone-like crystal growth and biological behavior on the electrically poled hydroxyapatite and it's coating films were investigated. Sintered hydroxyapatite and plasma sprayed hydroxyapatite coatings on titanium plate were used as specimens. These specimens were electrically poled in a dc field of 1 to 1000V/cm for 1h at 300°C. Crystal chemistry of the poled specimens were investigated by X-ray diffraction and thermal analysis. Bone-like crystal growths were studied in a simulated body fluid (SBF) with pH=7.25 at 36.5°C, and in Eagle's minimum essential medium with osteoblastic cells. Grown crystal layers were observed by scanning electron microscopy, and were analyzed by X-ray diffraction and Infrared spectroscopy. As a result, the bone-like hydroxyapatite crystals grew rapidly on the negatively poled surface, while the growth was restricted on the positively poled surface in SBF. Hydroxyapatite films prepared by different methods had the same effects of poling. It was considered that the aligned dipoles of substrate accelerated the crystal growth on the negative-pole surface, and decelerated on the positive-pole surface.

KEYWORDS: hydroxyapatite, poling, crystal growth, biocompatibility.

Introduction

The osteogenesis is exited by mechanical stress of bone, that based on the piezoelectric effect of bone. It was reported that dry bone is piezoelectric in the classic sense of mechanical stress polarization and application of electric field produces strain[1]. Hydroxyapatite (HAp, $Ca_{10}(PO_4)_6(OH)_2$) have good biocompatibility. To obtain a bioactive biomaterial with excellent mechanical properties for load bearing, bioactive HAp have been applied on to titanium implant by plasma-spraying technique[2]. Titanium coated with HAp and α-TCP ($Ca_3(PO_4)_2$) layers were prepared by plasma spraying by authors[3].   Recently, the accelerations and decelerations of bone-like crystal growth were discovered on the surfaces of polarized HAp ceramic in simulated body fluid[4-9].

The authors described the characterization and cell reaction of α-TCP and HAp coatings on titanium plate in detail[9-10]. The authors also studied electrically poled HAp coatings prepared by various methods, and described the bone-like crystal growths on the coatings and it's biocompativility[11-12]. In this study, we investigated that the effects on crystal growths and biological behaviors of electrically polarized HAp ceramics and coatings.

MATERIALS AND METHODS

Materials

Ceramics of HAp were obtained by sintering of HAp powders at 1200 $^{\circ}$C,   which were synthesized by a wet-chemically method.

Films of HAp were prepared on substrates of titanium plate. In this study, four types of coating methods were adopted to make HAp films: sputtering, biomimetic coating, plasma spraying, and metal chelate dissociation   method.   Sputtered HAp films were deposited in Air on titanium metal by r.f.magnetron sputtering method using $CaHPO_4$ powder as the target.   The films were annealed under saturated water vapor pressure at 200 $^{\circ}$C for 24 hours in an autoclave. To make biomimetic coatings, the   titanium substrate was placed on granular   particles of CaO, SiO_2-based glasss soaked in a simulated body fluid (SBF)[8]. After several days, the substrate was removed from SBF.   For plasma spraying, β-TCP powders were used as spraying materials. The coatings were applied by an atmospheric plasma spray technique. The plasma flame was composed of   plasmatized Ar-H_2 gas using an arc method. The β-TCP powders changed into α-TCP coating layers by plasma spraying. Then HAp coatings obtained by hydrothermal reaction of α-TCP coating layer in an autoclave.   The HAp films from metal chelate dissociation   method were prepared using the thermal dissociation of calcium-EDTA chelate complex in phosphate($Ca(edta)^{2-}$-$NH_4H_2PO_4$)   solution under hydrothermal condition of 175 $^{\circ}$C for 24 hours.

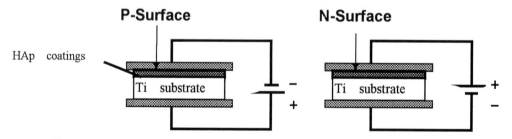

Figure 1. Schematic representation of electrode configurations to N- and P- surfaces for poling.

Experimental Procedures

The specimens were sandwitched between electrode plates, heated to 300°C in air, and treated electrically poling in a dc field of 1000V/cm for 2 hours, then cooled to room temperature under polarization.   For the poled HAp films, negative-poled surface and positive-poled surface were denoted   as N-surface and P-surface, respectively(Fig.1). The surfaces of specimens without poling were signified 0-surface. The electrically poled specimens were immersed in a 1.5SBF, having the 1.5 times concentration of inorganic ions in the human body, with pH 7.25, at 36.5°C (Fig.2). The poled specimens were also immersed in a MEM (Eagle's minimu essential medium) with osteoblastic cells at 37°C. After several days immersion, grown crystal layers were observed by scanning electron microscopy (SEM), and analyzed by X-ray diffraction (XRD) and Infrared spectroscopy (IR).

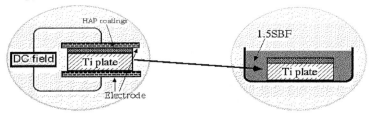

Figure 2. Schematic illustration of samples arrangement for poling and immersion in SBF.

RESULTS AND DISCUSSION

The coating films, obtained by sputtering, biomimetic coating, plasma spraying, and metal chelate dissociation method, had respective HAp phase under X-ray diffraction. SEM photographs of the surface of electrically poled HAp ceramics were shown in Fig.3. Bone-like crystal growth was accelerated on the N surface, whereas crystal growth was less observed on the P surface.

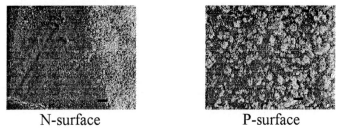

Figure 3. SEM photographs of the surfaces of electrically poled HAp ceramics after 12 hours immersion in 1.5SBF.

Fig.4(a-c) shows SEM photographs of the N-, 0-, P-surfaces of plasma splayed HAp coatings after 1 days immersion in 1.5SBF. On the N-surface(Fig.4(a)), remarkable growth of bone-like crystals were observed, while no crystals were grown on the P-surface. Further, the crystal growth on the positive side (P surface) was less than that on the 0-surface, thus, the growth was rstricted on the P-surface. These results agree with the result of HAp ceramics above mentioned.   It was also revealed that HAp films, prepared by sputtering and   biomimetic coating   method, had the same poling effects on crystal growth.   We considered that the N surface attracts cations, calcium ions in this case, and increase the rate of local HAp nucliations. It was considered   that   the aligned dipoles of substrate accelerated the crystal growth on the N surface, and decelerated on the P surface, caused from reorientation of the dipole moments in the HAp structure.

SEM photographs of the surfaces of   plasma splayed HAp coatings after 42 hours incubation with osteoblastic cells(MC3T3-E1) were shown in Fig.4, (d): cells on N-surface, (e):cells on P-surface. The cells proliferated well on both the N   and P surface of substrata. The cells were observed on the new grown layer of bone-like crystals for the N surface, whereas the cells directly on plasma coating layer for P surface.

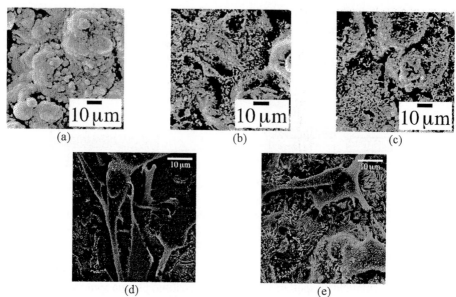

Fig.4   SEM photographs of the surfaces of   plasma splayed HAp coatings after1 days immersion in
1.5SBF; (a):N-surface, (b):0-surface, (c):P-surface, and SEM photographs of those after 42
hours incubation with osteoblastic cells; (d): N-surface, (e):P-surface.

ACKNOWLEDGMENTS

This work was partly supported by Grant-in-Aid for Scientific Research (A) #10305047,
The Sumitomo Foundation, and Tokuyama Science Foundation, to which the author's thank are
due. The authors are grateful to Mr. Y.Umezu of Advance Co. Ltd. for his kind help in the
preparing of samples with plasma sprayings.

REFERENCES

1. Fukada E, Yasuda I. *J Phys Soc Japan* 1957; **12**: 1158–1162.
2. de Groot K, Geesink R, Klein CPAT, Serekain PJ. *Biomed   Mater Res* 1987; **21**: 1375-1381.
3. Kuroyama Y, Aoki H, *et al*. *J Japanese Soc Dent Mater Dev* 1993; **12**: 528-534.
4. Yamashita K, Oikawa N, Umegaki T. *Chem Mater* 1996; **8**: 2697-2700.
5. Yamashita K, Yagi T, Umegaki T. *Phos Res Bull* 1996; **6**: 123-126.
6. Yonehara E, Yamashita K, Umegaki T. *Phos Res Bull* 1996; **6**: 301-304.
7. Yamashita K, Oikawa N, Umegaki T. *Proc. 2nd Pac Rim Cont. Ceramicsr* 1996.
8. Hata K, Kokubo T, Nakamura T, Yamamoto T. *J Am Ceram Soc* 1995; **78**: 1049-1053.
9. Ohgaki M, Nakamura S, Akao M. *Bioceramics* 1997; **10**: 50–53.
10. Ohgaki M, Yamashita K. *Phos Res Bull* 1998; **8**: (in press).
11. Ohgaki M, Yamashita K, Nakamura S, *et al*.   *Am Ceram Soc 100th Annual   Meeting* 1998.
12. Ohgaki M, Hamagami J, Umegaki T, Yamashita K.   *To be   published* 1998.
13. Yamashita K, Kitagaki K, Umegaki T. *J Am Ceram Soc* 1995; **78**: 1191-1195

Bioceramics Volume 11, edited by R. Z. LeGeros and J.P. LeGeros
(Proceedings of the 11th International Symposium on Ceramics in Medicine)
New York, NY, USA, November 1998
© 1998 by World Scientific Publishing Co. Pte. Ltd.

TISSUE ENGINEERING OF GOAT BONE: OSTEOGENIC POTENTIAL OF GOAT BONE MARROW CELLS

Joost D. de Bruijn[1,2], Ineke van den Brink[1], Yvonne P. Bovell[2] and Clemens A. van Blitterswijk[1,2]

[1]Biomaterials Research Group, Leiden University; [2]IsoTis BV, Professor Bronkhorstlaan 10, 3723 MB Bilthoven, The Netherlands. *E-mail: joost.de.bruijn@isotis.com*

ABSTRACT

Goat bone marrow cells were isolated from the iliac crest of adult Dutch milk goats and grown under culture conditions facilitating osteogenic differentiation. The culture medium comprised of α-MEM supplemented with 15% foetal bovine serum and with or without dexamethasone, L-ascorbic acid-2-phosphate and β-glycerophosphate. The in vitro osteogenic potential of the cells was examined by the production of a bone-like mineralised extracellular matrix. After seeding and culturing the cells for 1 week in porous calcium phosphate particles followed by subcutaneous implantation in nude mice for 4 weeks, the in vivo osteogenicity of these hybrid samples was examined by determining *de novo* bone formation.

Primary or subcultured cells grown in the presence of dexamethasone gave rise to the formation of bone-like nodules that subsequently became mineralised. In contrast, irrespective of the culture medium used, *de novo* bone formation in the porous calcium phosphates was observed with all culture conditions. These results indicate the potential of this hybrid, tissue engineering technology for bone reconstruction and provides a good base to initiate functionality studies on bone tissue engineering in large animal models.

KEYWORDS: Hybrid Technology, Tissue Engineering, Culture, Bone Marrow Cells, Goat

INTRODUCTION

Bone tissue engineering is a rapidly expanding field with numerous potential applications in dentistry and orthopaedics. The culture of autologous osteogenic cells and their bone-like extracellular matrix on scaffold implant materials is expected to improve the healing of large bone defects. Several investigators have shown the osteoinductive capacity of cultured bone marrow cells from a variety of species after seeding the cells in porous scaffolds and implanting the hybrid structures subcutaneously in syngeneic animals or nude mice[1-5]. We have recently shown that cultured rat bone marrow cells and their extracellular matrix do not only possess osteoinductive properties when grown in porous implants[2,5], but also when grown on flat metallic surfaces that had been coated with a biomimetic calcium phosphate coating[6].

In order to evaluate various bone graft materials in large animals, we recently developed a critical size defect model in goat iliac bone[7] that is also suitable to evaluate the potential of our hybrid, bone tissue engineering technology. For this purpose, we examined herein the osteogenic potential of cultured goat bone marrow cells when grown in porous calcium phosphate scaffolds. The bone marrow cells were obtained from an iliac crest punction and grown in α-MEM supplemented with 15% FBS and either or not in the presence of dexamethasone, ascorbic acid-2-phosphate and β-glycerophosphate. Second or third passage cells were seeded in various concentrations into porous calcium phosphate implants and after one week of culture, facilitating the formation of an in vitro formed bone-like extracellular matrix, the samples were subcutaneously implanted in nude mice for 4 weeks. After explantation, *de novo* bone formation was examined in undecalcified histological sections by light microscopy.

MATERIALS AND METHODS

After anaesthesia, the pelvic area of a goat was shaved, disinfected and a skin incision was made over the long axis of the iliac crest. The iliac was freed from overlying muscles and fat tissue by sharp and blunt dissection and the Os Ilium was exposed. After rinsing a syringe and attached biopsy needle with 5,000 I.E./ml heparin, a bone marrow biopsy of approximately 10 ml was taken from the Cresta Iliaca. The marrow was collected in 30 ml culture medium to which 5,000 I.E./ml heparin was added and transported to the laboratory on ice.

Clumps of cells were gently broken up by resuspending the bone marrow in a syringe with a 20G needle attached. The number of mononuclear cells were counted in a small sample of the bone marrow suspension to which a red blood cell lysing buffer had been added, and after centrifugation and resuspension, the bone marrow population was plated at a density of 2.8×10^4 mononuclear cells/cm^2 in 80 cm2 culture flasks. Culture medium comprised of α-MEM supplemented with 15% FBS and either or not 10 nM dexamethasone (Dex), 0.1 mM L-ascorbic acid-2-phosphate (AsAP) and 10mM β-glycerophosphate (BGP) added.

Second or third passage cells were seeded in porous calcium phosphate particles (approximately 2x2x3 mm, mean pore size of 435 μm; Pro-Osteon 500) in concentrations of 100,000 cells per particle (second passage cells) or 500,000, 1 million or 3 million cells per particle (third passage cells). Eight particles per condition were evaluated. After one week of culture in the two types of culture media (with or without the supplements AsAP, Dex and BGP), the bone tissue/material hybrids were washed with PBS and subcutaneously implanted in nude mice. Control samples incubated in culture medium, without cultured cells, were also implanted. Control cultures on pronectin-coated tissue culture plastic were used to monitor the in vitro osteogenicity (mineralised extracellular matrix production) of the primary, second and third passage subcultured cells by light and scanning electron microscopy.

RESULTS AND DISCUSSION

The cultured goat bone marrow cells showed a typical spindle-shaped osteoblastic morphology irrespective of the culture medium used (figure 1a). As previous studies had revealed that the cells easily rolled up at near confluence, we used pronectin-coated culture dishes that could prevent this. From 1-2 weeks onward, cells grown in culture medium to which Dex, AsAP and

BGP had been added, started to form bone-like nodules that became mineralised between 2 and 4 weeks of culture (figure 1b, c). Scanning electron microscopy revealed the presence of a cell multi-layer with abundant collagen and, after removal of this cell layer with compressed air, a cement line like layer was visible on the tissue culture polystyrene (figure 2a, b). This layer was comprised of mineralised globular deposits, as indicated by scanning electron microscopy and x-ray microanalysis, and was similar in morphology to cement lines that have previously been shown to form in osteogenic bone marrow cell cultures of rat[8] and human[9].

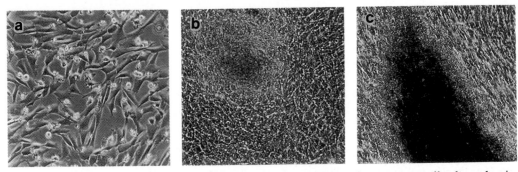

Figure 1a-c. Phase-contrast light micrographs of (a) 8 day primary goat bone marrow cell culture showing spindle-shaped osteoblast-like cells, and (b, c) 16 day second passage goat bone marrow cells grown in the presence of Dex, forming mineralised bone-like nodules. Field width: 500 μm

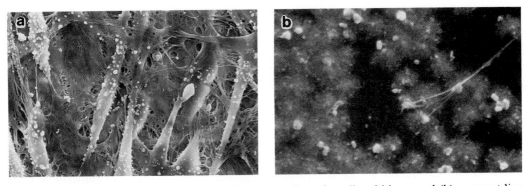

Figure 2a, b. Scanning electron micrographs of (a) the surface of a cell multi-layer, and (b) a cement-line like substance of mineralised globules produced by cultured goat bone marrow cells on the tissue culture polystyrene substrate. Field width: 113 μm (a) and 15 μm (b)

After subcutaneous implantation, irrespective of the culture medium used (with or without the osteogenic differentiation supplements Dex, AsAP and BGP), abundant *de novo* bone formation could be observed in all samples in which cells had been cultured (figure 3a, b). In contrast, none of the control samples, devoid of cultured cells showed bone formation (not shown). There was no difference between the amount of *de novo* bone formation between second or third subcultured cells. Similarly, no difference could be observed in the amount of *de novo* bone formation between the different concentrations third subcultured cells (500,000, 1 million or 3 million cells per Pro-Osteon particle). Blood vessels were often associated with and in close proximity to newly formed bone. In many samples, areas with complete bone marrow formation could be identified that were always associated with, and surrounded by *de novo* formed bone.

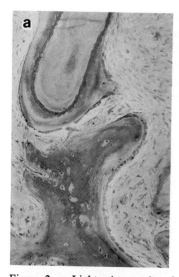 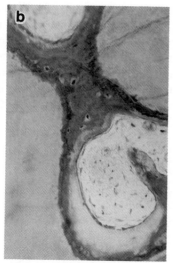 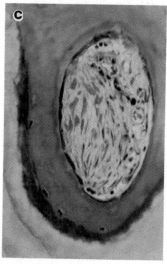

Figure 3a-c. Light micrographs of second subculture goat bone marrow cells grown for 7 days in porous calcium phosphate particles (100,000 cells per particle) and subcutaneously implanted for 4 weeks in nude mice. Note the abundant *de novo* bone formation. Field width: 900 μm (a, b); 560 μm (c)

CONCLUSIONS

These results show that goat bone marrow cells have a potential to generate bone formation in vitro and in vivo and maintain their in vivo osteogenic potential until at least the third passage, irrespective of the culture medium used. We are currently preparing functionality studies in which this hybrid, bone tissue engineering approach will be examined in a critical size defect in goat iliae.

REFERENCES

1. Yoshikawa T, Ohgushi H, Tamai S. *J. Biomed. Mater. Res.* 1996; **32**: 1-12.
2. De Bruijn JD, Dekker R, van den Brink I, Leenders H, Bovell YP, van Blitterswijk CA. *Trans. 23rd Ann. Mtg. Soc. Biomat.*, New Orleans, USA, 1997; 51.
3. Kadiyala S, Jaiswal N, Bruder SP. *Tissue Engineering* 1997; **3**: 173-185.
4. Krebsbach P, Kuznetsov S, Satomura K, Emmons R, Rowe D, Robey P. *Transplantation* 1997; **63**: 1059.
5. De Bruijn JD, van Blitterswijk CA. In: Walenkamp G, ed. *Biomaterials in Surgery*, Amsterdam: Georg Thieme Verlag, 1998: 77-87.
6. Dekker RJ, de Bruijn JD, van den Brink I, Bovell YP, Layrolle P, van Blitterswijk CA. *J. Mater. Sci., Mater. in Med.*, Special Issue, December 1998 (in press).
7. Anderson MLC, van Blitterswijk CA, Taylor M, Tanner KE, Verbout AJ, de Bruijn JD, Dhert WJA. *Trans. 24th Ann. Mtg. Soc. Biomat.*, San Diego, USA, 1998; 459.
8. Davies JE, Chernecky R, Lowenberg B, Shiga A. *Cells Mater.* 1991 **1**: 3-15.
9. De Bruijn JD, van den Brink I, Bovell YP. In: Kokubo T, Nakamura T, Miyaji F, eds. *Bioceramics 9*, Kyoto: Elsevier Science Ltd., 1996: 45-48.

Bioceramics Volume 11, edited by R. Z. LeGeros and J.P. LeGeros
(Proceedings of the 11th International Symposium on Ceramics in Medicine)
New York, NY, USA, November 1998
© 1998 by World Scientific Publishing Co. Pte. Ltd.

EFFECT OF BIOGLASS ® AND LOADING ENVIRONMENT ON WHOLE BONE ORGANS CULTURED "*IN-VITRO*"

Jason Maroothynaden [1] -, Xaio Zang[2]; L. L. Hench'; P.A. Revell[2].
'Department of Materials, Imperial College of Science, Technology and Medicine, Prince Consort Rd, London SW7 2BP. [2]Department of Histopathology ., Royal Free Medical School, UK.

ABSTRACT

16-day-old gestation fetal mouse long bones were cultured "in-vitro" in one of 5 culture environments for 4 days. After culture, the fetal mouse long bones were fixed and mounted histologically. Image analysis was used to quantify the mineralization of the fetal mouse long bones. The fetal mouse long bones successfully mineralized after 4 days of culture where increasing concentration of Na-β-glycerophosphate decreased the long bones' rate of mineralization. The long bones cultured on 45S5 substrata showed a greatly enhanced the rate of mineralization. Mineralization of the long bones grown in 45S5 extracts was also enhanced but the rate of mineralization was not as large as with the substrates.

KEYWORDS : 45S5 Bioactive glass, supplemented a.-MEM, substrata, in-vitro, fetal mice long bones, extracts, mineralization.

INTRODUCTION

The chemical effects responsible for enhanced osteoblast differentiation and proliferation observed *in vitro and in vivo* at 1 -gravity with bioactive glasses, may be sufficient to prevent the genetic 'turn-off of bone cells that is occurring in microgravity or other reduced loading environments. This hypothesis implies that biochemical effects ma3T, at least in part. be used to circumvent biochemical effects in bone metabolism. A fetal mouse long bone model' makes it possible to examine the coupling of biochemistry and biomechanics inherent to the functioning of Wolffs' Law thereby enhancing understanding of the mechanisms involved in stress shielding of bone by orthopedic prostheses, osteoporosis and osteopenia associated with aging as well as microgravity-induced demineralization.

MATERLA,LS AND METHODS

Using standard dissecting instruments, the long bones from 16-day gestation fetuses of Balb-C mice were dissected and cleared from adhering tissues without disturbing the perichodrium. The long bones were then rinsed in Puck's buffer G (Gibco, Paisley, Scotland). After rinsing, the long bones were place in five culture environments. Standard 24-well tissue culture plates were used, placed in a standard air/5% CO_2 incubator set to 37°C and 100% humidity for four days. After culture. the long bones were fixed in 10mls-gluteraldehyde solution.

In the first environment each long bone was cultured in 400 µl of control culture medium'. In the second environment each long bone was cultured in 400 µl of supplemented αMEM solution with exactly the same composition as the control culture medium with a higher Na-β-glycerophosphate composition of l.0mMol'. The third culture environment consisted of 10mm diameter 45S5 melt derived glass substrates each immersed in 400 µl of control culture medium.

The fourth culture environment consisted of each long bone being cultured in 400 µl of 15g/l concentration 45S5 glass extract while the fifth culture environment consisted of each long bone being cultured in 400 µl of 30g/l concentration 45S5 glass extract.

The control culture medium consisted of αMEM medium without nucleosides (Gibco) supplemented with 10% heat-inactivated normal rat serum (Harlan, Oxen) plus 100 units/ml 0.2 mMol penicillin / streptomycin (Difco). An organic phosphate source of 0.1 mMol Na-β-glycerophosphate (Sigma) was then added to sustain good mineralisation of the foetal mouse long bones[1].

Before immersion in the supplemented αMEM solution and exposure to the foetal mouse long bones, the 10mm diameter 45S5 glass substrates (U.S. Biomaterials, Florida) were polished on one side to 3µm using a non-aqueous lubricating medium and then sterilised, on both sides, via exposure to a fully isolated and contained ultra-violet radiation source for 24 hours. After sterilisation, the substrates were then "pre-reacted" by immersion in the supplemented αMEM solution for 30 minutes. After this, the glass substrates were used for tissue culture.

The 15g/l and 30g/l concentration 45S5 glass extracts were prepared by placing 15g and 30g of 20µm 45S5 glass powder (U.S. Biomaterials, Florida) in 1 litre of control culture medium respectively. The powder was held in suspension for 24 hours, under clean conditions, and then filtered. Hydrochloric acid was then added to the solution to bring down the pH to 7.4. After autoclave sterilisation, the solution was ready for tissue culture use.

After fixation, the long bones were sectioned and mounted. They were stained with toludine blue and all sections analysed using the image analysis program Scion Image version.

RESULTS

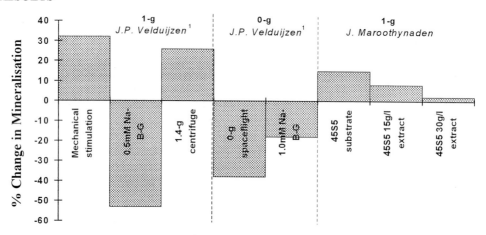

Culture Environment

Figure 1. Showing loading and chemical effects on the rates of mineralisation for foetal mice long-bones cultured for 4 days. The 4 day culture in control culture medium has been used as the base-line.

Referring to Figure 1, Mechanical stimulation = bones cultured under a continuous pressure of 113 ± 0.5 KPa ; 0.5 mM Na-B-G = bones cultured in supplemented αMEM solution containing 0.5 mM Na-β-glycerophosphate; 1.4-g centrifuge = bones cultured in Veldhuijzen and Van Loon hardware onboard centrifuge during space-flight[1] ; 0-g space flight = same conditions as 1.4-g centrifuge but container placed in an onboard incubator ; 1.0 mM N-B-G = bones cultured in supplemented αMEM solution containing 1.0 mM Na-β-Glycerophosphate; 45S5 substrate = bone cultured on 45S5 substrate disk and totally immersed in control supplemented αMEM solution; 45S5 15g/l = bone cultured in supplemented αMEM extract solution of glass composition of 15 grams glass per litre; 45S5 30g/l = bone cultured in control supplemented αMEM solution extract of glass composition of 30 grams glass per litre.

DISSCUSSION

Figure 1 shows the effect of culture environment on rates of mineralisation as compared to a base-line of mouse long-bones cultured for 4 days in a supplemented αMEM solution under static 24 well tissue culture plate conditions as described by Veldhuijzen and Van Loon[1]. The 10-fold increase in Na-β-Glycerophosphate concentration from the standard control culture medium of 0.1mMol to 1.0mMol resulted in a decreased rate of mineralisation. This trend confirmed the dose dependency of this foetal mouse long bone model to Na-β-Glycerophosphate as previously described by Veldhuijzen and Van Loon[1].

Figure 1 shows that when 45S5 glass is introduced *in-vitro* it has a positive influence on the rate of mineralisation. However Figure 1 also shows that the rate of mineralisation is influenced by the form of the 45S5 glass. Where the long bones were grown on the substrate disks they showed greatly enhanced rates of mineralisation compared to the femurs grown in the 45S5 extracts. The enhanced *in-vitro* effects of substrates over extracts is probably due to the physical presence of the substrate. During "pre-conditioning" preparation of the 45S5 substrates, large amounts of proteins and other growth factors, from the control culture medium, may be absorbed into the dynamically evolving silica-gel layer formed on the surface of the 45S5 disk during immersion[2]. Hence during culture on substrata, the bones are exposed to an environment with high protein and growth factor concentrations that were higher than the control culture environment while the opposite is the case for the extract environment. The data also show that the 45S5 enhances the rate of mineralisation as compared with the control culture environment. This suggests that the presence of various proteins and growth factors is not as important as the concentration of chemical constituents that have been leached into the supplemented α-MEM solution during extract preparation. The altered solution chemistry may exert a response at the genetic level[3] where the presence of divalent cations, in the extract medium, may enhance matrix organisation and molecular interactions similar to the extracellular matrix molecule/cell interactions found in the foetal mouse long bone[3,4]. The altered solution chemistry provides an alkaline environment for bone growth which is favoured by osteoblasts[5]. This is shown by the decrease in the rate of mineralisation with an increase in 45S5 concentration extract. This indicates that the rate of mineralisation is dose dependant on certain chemical constituents of the extract environment which include soluble silicon[4].

The enhanced rate of mineralisation when the 45S5 glass present as substrata may be due to:

- the extracellular matrix in/on substrata exerts a response at the genetic level[4,6].
- the degradation of the glass substrata provides cations into the local culture environment that enhances matrix mineralisation and molecular interactions similar to extracellular matrix / cell interactions[3].
- the substrata network dissolution provides an alkaline environment that is preferred by osteoblasts[5].
- the protein, growth factor-enriched silica gel layer is formed on substrata during early glass preparation and during immersion for 4 days, is transformed and enhanced by precipitation of hydroxy-carbonate apatite on substrata.

Finally, Veldhuijzen and Van Loon have shown that the local loading environment greatly affects the rate of mineralisation[1]. A hyper-gravity environment enhances the rate of mineralisation and the opposite occurs for culture under hypo-gravity conditions. It has been shown that if 45S5 glass is introduced chemically into the bones local environment, faster rates of mineralisation occur (fig.1). Hence it follows that the chemical effects responsible for enhanced osteoblast differentiation and proliferation observed *in vitro* and *in vivo* at 1-gravity with bioactive glasses may be sufficient to prevent the genetic 'turn-off' of bone cells that occurs in micro-gravity or other reduced loading environments, implying that biochemical effects may be used to circumvent biochemical effects in bone metabolism.

CONCLUSION

The foetal mouse long bone model is sensitive to both its local biochemical and biomechanical environment, with 45S5 bioactive glass enhancing the rate of mineralisation. The local biochemical environment seems to have a more dramatic effect on the rate of mineralisation compared with effects of local loading environment.

ACKNOWLEGEMENT

This project was funded by the Engineering and Physical Research Council, United Kingdom. The authors thank Dr. D. Greenspan (U.S. Biomaterials) for the supply of 45S5 bioactive glass substrates.

REFERENCES

1. Veldhuijzen JP, Van Loon JJWA. *Development of Tissue Techniques and Hardware to Study Mineralisation Under Microgravity Conditions.* Adv. Space Res. 1994; **14 (8)**, 289-298.
2. Lobel KD, Henche LL. *In-Vitro adsorption and activity of enzymes on reaction layers of bioactive glass substrates.* J Biomed Mater Res. 1996; **39**.
3. Lanza RP, Langer R, Chick WL. *Principles of Tissue Engineering.* Texas: R.G. Landes Company, 1997: 95.
4. Keeting et al. *Zeolite-A increases proliferation, differentiation, and transforming growth-factor-Beta production in normal adult human osteoblast-like cells-invitro.* J Bone and Mineral Res. 1992; **7 (11)**: 1281-1289.
5. Yamamuro T, Hench LL, Wilson J. *Handbook of Bioactive Ceramics. Volume 1: Bioactive Glasses and Glass-Ceramics.* Boca Raton, Florida: CRC Press, 1990; 241.
6. Hench LL. *Bioactive Ceramics : Theory and Clinical Applications. Volume 7: Proceedings of the 7th International Symposium on Ceramics in Medicine.* Oxford: Butterworth-Heinemann, 1990; 241.

Bioceramics Volume 11, edited by R. Z. LeGeros and J.P. LeGeros
(Proceedings of the 11th International Symposium on Ceramics in Medicine)
New York, NY, USA, November 1998
© 1998 by World Scientific Publishing Co. Pte. Ltd.

IN VIVO OSTEOGENIC POTENT OF CULTURED BONE/HYDROXYAPATITE CONSTRUCT: A COMPARISON WITH THAT OF MARROW CELL/HYDROXYAPATITE COMPOSITE

Toshimasa Uemura[1], Takafumi Yoshikawa[2], Hajime Ohgushi[2], Susumu Tamai[2], Tetsuya Tateishi[1]

[1]National Institute for Advanced Interdisciplinary Research (NAIR), Tsukuba Research Center, Tsukuba, Ibaraki, 305-8562, Japan; [2]Nara Medical University

ABSTRACT

The ideal bone graft is autogenous bone graft. However, it is not available in quantities needed for bone reconstruction and involves invasion of healthy tissue. To overcome this problem, we employed dexamethasone-treated marrow cell culture technology developed by Maniatopoulos et al., which produces bone tissue *in vitro*. We previously reported that the osteogenic construct, which combines bone formed *in vitro* and porous hydroxyapatite (HA), has high osteogenic potential when grafted *in vivo*. In the present study, we compared the *in vivo* osteogenic capacity of bone/HA construct with marrow cell/HA composite. Results obtained suggest that the cultured bone /HA graft construct procedure is an excellent method for obtaining more bones in a shorter time compared with the cell/HA composite.

Keywords: coralline hydroxyapatite, bone marrow, bone implantation, ALP activity

INTRODUCTION

The most ideal material in bone grafting is an autogenic bone graft. However, there are drawbacks: there is a limit to its quantity and normal tissues have to be invaded. It would be ideal if we can employ *in vitro* cell culture techniques to generate bone tissue to be used as bone graft. However, active bone tissues seldom occur even if bone cells from bone are isolated and cultured in a regular medium. Maniatopoulos et al[1] succeeded in confirming differentiation of marrow cells into osteoblasts and osteocytes together with active formation of extracellular matrix, by adding dexamethasone (Dex) into the medium of rat marrow cell culture. The osteogenesis seen with this culture is morphologically and biochemically similar to the primary stage of *in vivo* osteogenesis[5]. Therefore, the research group at Nara Medical University speculated that this cultured bone could be clinically applied to bone reconstructive surgery. In this point of view, they established the cultured bone/HA graft composite model. Briefly, the marrow cells from Fischer rat were cultured for 10 days. Then the cells were released from the culture dish and coincubated with the porous hydroxyapatite blocks in the medium including Dex. for 2 weeks. After that, the composites were implanted into rats. In this study, we compared *in vivo* osteogenic capacity of the bone/HA construct with marrow cell/HA composite to confirm the efficacy of this model.

MATERIALS & METHODS

Materials

Coralline hydroxyapatite ceramic (Interpore 500, manufactured by Interpore International, Irvine, CA, USA) was used in this experiment. A hydrothermal chemical exchange with phosphate converts the original calcium carbonate exoskeleton of coral into a completely inorganic replica of HA. The solid and porous components of the microstnicture are completely interconnected. The average pore diameter is 600 μm and their average interconnections is 260 μm in diameter. The coralline HA is a cancellous biomatrix which is normally placed in a cancellous bone environent. Cubic HA blocks (5x5x5mm) were used in this study.

Marrow cell preparation and culture

Marrow cells were obtained from the bone shaft of femora of 7-week old Fischer 344 mate rats. Both ends of the femora were cut away from the epiphysis, and the marrow was flushed out, according to the method developed by Maniatopoulos et al.[1]. The released cells were collected in two T-75 flasks containing 15 ml ofthe standard medium described below. The medium was changed after the first 24 hours to remove non-adherent cells. The medium was renewed three times a week. Cultures were maintained in a humidified atmosphere of 95% air with 5% CO_2 at 37°C.

Standard medium consisted of Eagles Minimal Essential Medium (MEM) containing 15% fetal bovine serum (JRH Biosciences, Lenexa, KS. Lot. No. 564010) and antibiotics (100 units/ml Penicillin, 100 mg/ml Streptomycin, and 0.25 mg/ml amphotericine B, Sigma Chemical Co., St. Louis, MO, USA).

After 10 days in primary culture, marrow stromal cells were released from the culture substratum using 0.1% trypsin. The trypsinized cells were prepared for subculture in porous hydroxyapatite and for implantation with porous hydroxyapatite.

Preparation for cultured bone/HA construct

The 24 HA blocks were soaked in 4 ml of trypsinized cell suspension (10^6 cells/ml) for 2 hours in a CO_2 incubator, as we previously reported[7]. After 2 hours of incubation, each block was transferred into a 24-well plate (Falcon, Franklin Lakes, NJ, USA) for subcultures. One HA block was subcultured in one well with I ml of the standard medium supplemented with 10 mM Na ß-glycerophosphate (Merck Japan Co., Tokyo, Japan), 82 mg/ml vitamin C phosphate (L-Ascorbic Acid Phosphate Magnesium Salt n-Hydrate, $C_6H_6O_9PMg_2.nH20$, Wako Pure Chemical Industrials, Osaka Japan) and 10^{-8} dexamethasone (Dex, Sigma). The medium was renewed three times a week and the subcultures were maintained for 2 weeks. These subcultured marrow/HA constructs were washed twice with Eagles MEM and prepared for subcutaneous implantation into syngeneic rats.

Implantation

Syngeneic 7-week-old male Fischer rats were anesthetized by intramuscular injection of pentobarbital (Nembutal 3.5 mg/lOOg B.W.), allowing light ether inhalation. Three cultured bone/HA constructs after 2 weeks, were separately implanted in the right side of the back of each syngeneic rat, and three HA blocks mixed with trypsinized cells were separately implanted in the left side (4 rats).

Histological analysis

These implants were harvested 2 weeks postimplantation and prepared for decalcified sections. The specimens were fixed in 10% buffered formalin, decalcified (K-CX solution, Falma Co., Tokyo, Japan) and stained with hematoxylin and eosin. These specimens were examined with light microscopy,

Biochemical analysis

These implants were harvested at 2 weeks (2 rats) after implantation, for biochemical analysis. The alkaline phosphatase activity was determined according to the method reported previously[8]. Briefly, each marrow/HA composite was immediately crushed, homogenized in 0.5 ml of 0.2% Nonidet P40 containing 1 mM $MgCl_2$, and centrifuged at 13,000 rpm for 10 minutes at 4°C. The supernatant was assayed for alkaline phosphatase activity using p-nitrophenylphosphate as a substrate. An aliquot (5 ml) of supernatant was added to 1 ml of 50 mM p-nitrophenylphosphate containing 1 mM $MgCl_2$ and the mixture was incubated for 3O minutes at 37°C. Then, 2ml of O.2 N NaOH was added to stop the reaction and the absorption at 410 mn was measured with a spectrophotometer. Alkaline phosphatase activity was represented by mmol of p-nitrophenol released per composite after 3O minutes of incubation at 37°C[9].

RESULTS and DISCUSSION
The alkaline phosphatase (ALP) activities in cell/HA graft and cultured bone/HA graft harvested 2 weeks post implantation are shown in Fig. 1. Results obtained demonstrated that the ALP activity of cultured bone /HA graft is about 4 times higher than that of cell/HA graft.

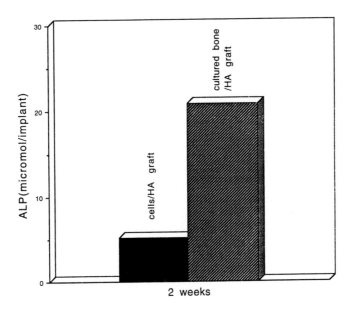

Fig. 1: Alkaline phosphatase (ALP) activity in cell/HA graft and cultured bone/HA graft harvested two weeks post implantation. The activity is shown in micromol/each implanted HA block.

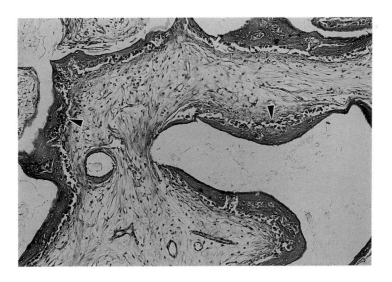

Fig 2: Cultured bone HA graft harvested two week post implantation. Arrows indicate active osteoblasts (hematoxylin stain x 100)

Fig. 2 shows the light microscopic image of the cultured bone/HA graft harvested 2 weeks postimplantation. In the pores of the HA block, bone tissue, together with active osteoblasts (indicated by arrows), was observed on the surface of the pores, where the white area shows the ghost of HA ceramics produced by decalcification procedure. Black area indicates the new bone which formed in the porous area. On the contrary, the cell/HA graft showed no significant bone formation at two weeks (not shown).

CONCLUSION

Both biochemical and morphological study suggested that the cultured bone/HA graft procedure is a much more efficient method for obtaining more bones in two weeks, compared with the marrow cell/HA graft. Results of this study indicate that in our implantation procedure, the *in vitro* culture of bone marrow cells treated with Dex is essential and indispensable for getting immediate *in vivo* bone formation after implantation.

Detailed experiments, such as time course and osteocalcin (BGP) expression, are now in progress and are expected to provide confirmatory results which will be published elsewhere.

REFERENCES

1.   Maniatopoulos C, Sodek J, Melcher AH. *Cell Tissue Res.* 1988; **254**:317-330.
2.   Davies JE, Chernecky R, Lowenberg B, Shiga A. *Cells Mater.* 1991; **1**:3-15.
3.   Davies JE, Ottenmeyer P, Shen Y, Hashimoto M, Peel SAF. In Davies JE ed. *The Bone Biomaterial Interface,* University of Toronto Press; 1991: 214-228.
4.   Lowenberg B, Chernecky R, Shiga A, Davies JE. *Cells Mater.* 1991; **1**:177-187.
S.   Yao K-L, Todescan R, Sodek J.J. Bone and Mineral Res. 1994; **9**:231-240.
6.   Holmes RE, Bucholz RW, Mooney V. *J Bone and Joint Surg.* 1986; **68A**:904-91 1.
7.   Yoshikawa T, Ohgushi H, Tamai S. *J Biomed. Mat. Res. 1* 996; 32:481-492.
8.   Yoshikawa T, Ohgushi H, Okumura M, Tamai S, Dohi Y, Moriyama T. *Calcif. Tissue Int.* 1992;50:184-188.
9.   Reddi AH, Sullivan NS. Endocrinology 1980; **107**:1291-1299.

Bioceramics Volume 11, edited by R. Z. LeGeros a: '
(Proceedings of the 11th International Symposium ,
New York, NY, USA, November 1998
© 1998 by World Scientific Publishing Co. Pte. Ltd.

PREPARATION OF A NOVEL CALCIUM PHOSPHATE-COATED SCAFFOLD FOR BONE TISSUE ENGINEERING

C.E. Holy[1], M.S. Shoichet[1], A.A. Campbell[2], L. Song[2] and J.E. Davies[1]

[1]Centre for Biomaterials, University of Toronto, 170 College Street, Toronto, Ontario, Canada M5S 3E3.
[2]Battelle, Pacific Northwest National Laboratories, 902 Battelle Blvd, PO Box 999, Richland WA USA 99352.

ABSTRACT

Calcium phosphates (CaP) have been recognized for decades as bone-bonding biomaterials and have therefore been used either as block implants or coatings. Biodegradable polymers, shaped in 3D foams have generated considerable interest as potential scaffolds for bone tissue engineering. We have recently developed a new method to produce three-dimensional poly (lactide-co-glycolide) 75:25 foams specifically designed for bone tissue engineering and demonstrated cell invasion and tissue formation within the scaffold *in vitro*. In this study, we have grown CaP crystals by the Surface Induced Mineralization (SIM) technique, on our novel biodegradable foams and implanted these foams, as well as control foams with no coating, in adult Wistar rat femoral defects. The coated and non-coated foams remained in the animals for 6 days. The animals were then sacrificed, the implants removed and observed by SEM. Histological sections were also prepared from the implants and stained with Haematoxylin and Eosin. CaP coated and non-coated samples were both filled with tissue throughout their structures, confirming the usefulness of these foams for tissue engineering applications. Interdigitation of bone matrix with the CaP coating indicated that the modified scaffold surface was bone-bonding.

KEYWORDS: bone, biodegradable scaffold, poly (lactide-co-glycolide), calcium phosphate

INTRODUCTION

Calcium phosphates (CaP) have created considerable interest as potential hard biomaterials because they bond directly to bone, forming a uniquely strong bone-implant interface.[1] CaP have been employed as block implants, but are less than ideal due to: 1) their inherent brittleness and 2) their unpredictable rate and degree of resorption.[2] CaP have therefore been utilized as coatings to promote bone-bonding to other synthetic materials.[3] These coating procedures have been shown to successfully accelerate bone formation along implant surfaces.[4]

CaP have also been used as tissue engineering scaffolds.[5] The concept of bone tissue engineering is to harvest osteogenic cells, seed them on a 3-D biodegradable foam and allow them to create a new tissue after which the scaffold eventually degrades. The degradation rate of the scaffold should therefore be equal to, or slower than, the rate of tissue formation. The unpredictability of CaP resorption limits their use for tissue engineering applications.

Biodegradable polymers like poly (lactide-co-glycolide) 75/25, have been used as scaffolds for bone tissue engineering. They can be molded in 3-D foams similar to trabecular bone, and their degradation profile can be controlled.[6] However, PLGA 75/25 implants do not allow bone-bonding interactions *in vivo,* but tend to be encapsulated.[7]

This study provides preliminary results from the use of a CaP-coated 3-D PLGA 75/25 foam used *in vivo* in a femoral defect. Bone ingrowth in CaP-coated and non-coated foams were compared.

MATERIALS AND METHODS

PLGA 75/25 foams were prepared as described previously.[8] Briefly, PLGA 75/25 solutions in dimethylsulfoxide (DMSO)(BDH, Toronto, ON) were mixed with glucose crystals. The crystals were allowed to leach out in ddH$_2$O and the obtained foams were dried under vacuum for 72 h. Half of the foams were kept as control, whereas a CaP coating was grown on the other foams, by surface induced mineralization, as described elsewhere.[9]

Coated and non-coated foams were implanted in femoral defects of adult Wistar rats. Both coated and non-coated foams remained in the rats for 6 days, after which the animals were sacrificed and the implants removed and processed for SEM and LM studies.

RESULTS AND DISCUSSION

Structure of the foams

The foam porosity observed under the light microscope showed a uniform distribution of macropores (~1 mm) throughout the polymer matrices. The large pores that were observed throughout the matrix were interconnected with substantial fissured porous walls ~300 μm thick. Foams were successfully coated with CaP, as shown in Figure 1b. CaP crystals of leaflet morphology covered the entire surface of the polymer foam.

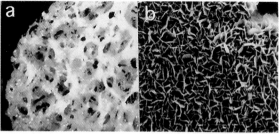

Figure 1: Light micrographs of a non-coated (a) foam at low magnification. (Field width = 1.8 cm). The pore wall of a CaP coated foam is shown (b) at high magnification (Field width = 32 μm).

No damage to the polymer surface was seen after treatment, indicating that the method did not degrade the polymer. (The weight average molecular weight of the polymer did not change during the CaP coating procedure, as estimated by GPC before and after the treatment.)

In vivo analysis:

SEM observations

Foams were maintained *in vivo* in the femora of Wistar rats for 6 days, after which they were freeze-fractured. One half was kept for SEM observation whereas the other half was processed for histological studies.

When observed by SEM, both the coated and non-coated samples showed a complex morphology indicating that, in both cases, new tissue invaded the foams. Microporosity within the bulk of the polymer was visible in both cases. Larger micropores were observed on the non-coated samples than on the coated samples, which may suggest that the degradation of the coated polymer *in vivo* was retarded when compared to that of the non-coated samples.

The CaP layer on the coated foams was still clearly observable after 6 days *in vivo*. The thickness of this layer was estimated, from the SEM micrographs, to 3-4 μm. Newly formed bone tissue was juxtaposed to the CaP coating.

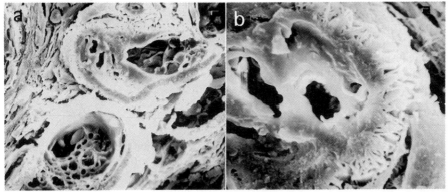

Figure 2: SEM micrographs of CaP coated foams, maintained *in vivo* for 6 days. At low magnification (a) the close apposition of the newly formed tissue to the polymer implant is seen (field width = 45 μm). At higher magnification (b) the CaP layer of the coated foam is clearly seen (field width = 16 μm).

Histological observations

During the processing of the bone samples, most of the polymer degraded. Thus, histological sections show only the newly formed tissue surrounding spaces previously occupied by the polymer.

In both coated and non-coated samples the entire foams were filled with new tissue. Many multinucleated giant cells were visible facing the hollow space previously occupied by the polymer.

Previous *in vivo* studies have reported large numbers of giant cells at sites occupied by polyester implants and these cells may play an important role in polymer degradation. However, no direct correlation between giant cell activation and polymer by-products was established.[10]

While bone growth was seen throughout both non-coated and coated polymer foams, it was only in the CaP coated samples that newly formed bone tissue was found juxtaposed to the implant pore walls.

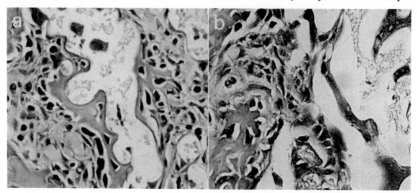

Figure 3: Histological sections of CaP coated and non-coated foams; a) Bone tissue was found juxtaposed to the hollow space previously occupied by the polymer whereas b) ingrown bone was not juxtaposed to the non-coated polymer. (Field width = 0.62 mm)

CONCLUSION

In conclusion, the results demonstrated that coating PLGA 75/25 3-D scaffolds with CaP was feasible, that the apatite layer was stable *in vivo* for up to 6 days and that bone-bonding could be observed between the scaffold and the newly-formed tissue.

ACKNOWLEDGMENT

The authors would like to thank A. Shiga and R. Chernecky for technical assistance. This work was supported by a Medical Research Council, grant # 11439 to JED, and an MRC graduate student scholarship to CEH.

REFERENCE

[1] Hench LL, Splinter RJ, Allen WC, Greenlee TK. *J Biomed Mater Res* 1971; **2**: 117-141.
[2] Jarcho M. *Clin Orthop and Rel Res* 1981; 157:259-278.
[3] Geesink RGT, de Groot K, Kleins CPAT. *Clin Orthop* 1987; **225**: 147-170.
[4] Tisel CL, Golberg VM, Parr JA, Bensusan JS, Stikoff LS, Stevenson S. *J Bone Joint Surg* 1994; **76A**: 159-171
[5] Eckert KL, Roesler U, Mathey M, Mayer J, Wintermantel E, Hofman J. In: Ducheyne P, Christiansen D, eds. *Bioceramics (Vol 6)*. Oxford: Butterworth-Heinemann, 1993:251-255.
[6] Von Recum HA, Cleek RL, Eskin SG, Mikos AG. *Biomaterials* 1995; 16:441-447.
[7] Bergsma JE, Rozema FR, Bos RRM, DeBruijn WC, Boering G. *Cells Mater* 1994; 4(1): 31-36.
[8] Holy CE, Davies JE, Shoichet MS. *Proc Am Inst For Chem Eng* 1997; 272-275.
[9] Campbell AA, Fryxell GE, Linehan JC, Graff GL. *J Biomed Mater Res* 1996; 32: 111-118.
[10] Visscher GE, Robinson RL, Maulding HV, Fong JW, Pearson JE and Argentieri J. *J Biomed Mater Res* 1985; **19**:349.

Bioceramics Volume 11, edited by R. Z. LeGeros and J.P. LeGeros
(Proceedings of the 11th International Symposium on Ceramics in Medicine)
New York, NY, USA, November 1998
© 1998 by World Scientific Publishing Co. Pte. Ltd.

BIOCERAMIC HOLLOW MICROSPHERES FOR 3-D BONE TISSUE FORMATION IN ROTATING BIOREACTORS

Q. Qiu[1], P. Ducheyne[1, 2] and P. S. Ayyaswamy[3]

Center for Biomaterials and Tissue Engineering, [1]Department of Bioengineering; [2]Department of Orthopeadic Surgery Research; [3]Department of Mechanical Engineering and Applied Mechanics, University of Pennsylvania, Philadelphia, PA 19104, USA

ABSTRACT

Novel bioceramic hollow microspheres with apparent density in the range 0.8-1.0g/cm^3 have been developed as microcarriers for 3-D bone tissue formation in rotating-wall bioreactors (RWV). The hollow ceramic microspheres have an inner shell with composition of 58-72% SiO_2, 28-42% Al_2O_3 (in % by weight) and a porous calcium phosphate (CaP) surface. This CaP surface was deposited using a fine particle sedimentation method. Subsequently, the hollow microspheres were sintered for 1 hour at 600, 800 and 1000^{0}C. A comparative analysis using FTIR indicated that crystalline calcium hydroxyapatite (HA) was present in the porous surface sintered at 600 and 800^{0}C. The trajectory analysis in both an inertial frame and a rotating frame demonstrated that these microspheres remained suspended in a RWV during the entire cell culture period and experienced a low shear stress (~0.6 dyn/cm^2). Cell culture studies in a RWV showed that osteoblastic cells (ROS 17/2.8) formed 3-D aggregates with hollow microcarriers in a RWV. Extracellular matrix and mineralization were observed in the aggregates. These data suggest that the bioceramic hollow microspheres can be used as microcarriers for 3-D bone tissue formation and for the study of the effects of microgravity on bone cell function in a rotating-wall bioreactor.

KEYWORDS: calcium phosphate; coating; microgravity; bone cell; shear stress

INTRODUCTION

Collagen-coated polymer beads, e.g. Cytodex-3, and polymer scaffolds have been used for 3-D cultures of various anchorage-dependent cell types in NASA rotating-wall vessels (RWVs).[1,2] Despite the fact that bioactive glass and calcium phosphate-based ceramics have been extensively used for bone implants, they have not been used as microcarriers for 3-D bone tissue formation in a rotating-wall vessel until recently. In a recent study from our laboratory, bioactive glass particles treated to have a calcium phosphate (CaP) surface were used as microcarriers for 3-D bone cell cultures in RWVs.[3] Three-dimensional aggregates of bone cells and calcium phosphate surface layers were observed. However, the growth and coverage of cells on the glass microcarriers were limited. The analysis on dynamics of a particle in a RWV revealed that when the density of a microcarrier is greater than that of the culture medium, the microcarrier migrates toward and eventually hits the outer wall of the vessel.[4] With increasing density difference between a microcarrier and the culture medium, the shear stress imparted to the surface of the microcarrier will also increase.[3,4] These experimental and numerical analyses indicated that the collisions with the wall and the high shear stress may have contributed to poor cell attachment. In order to reduce the shear stress and avoid the collisions, microcarriers with an apparent density less than and close to that of the culture medium are desired.

In this study, fabrication, characterization and evaluation of hollow bioceramic microspheres with an apparent density 0.8-1.0 g/cm³ are described. The motion trajectories of a hollow microsphere and osteoblastic cell culture on hollow microcarriers in a high aspect rotating-wall vessel (HARV) are also included to validate the concept of their use in microgravity conditions.

MATERIALS AND METHODS

Fabrication and characterization of hollow bioceramic microspheres

Hollow microspheres with a size range 100-200µm, a composition of 58-72% SiO_2, 28-42% Al_2O_3 (in % by weight) and an apparent density 0.8-1.0 g/cm³ were used (The PQ Corp., Philadelphia, PA). Calcium hydroxyapatite particulate sol was synthesized according to procedures described previously.[5] The hollow microspheres pretreated in 1.0N NaOH for 2 hours were mixed with the synthesized CaP sol on a shaker at 37°C for 2 hours, and subsequently washed, filtered and dried at 100°C. The coated microspheres were sintered for 1 hour at 600, 800 and 1000°C. The morphology of the surface of the microcarriers was analyzed using scanning electron microscopy (SEM, JOEL6300). The phases present in the CaP-coated microspheres sintered at different temperatures were determined using Fourier transform infrared analysis (FTIR: 5DXC, Nicolet, Madison, WI).

Microcarrier validation experiments

Trajectory recording. The trajectories of a hollow bioceramic microsphere (~150 µm in diameter) in a HARV at a rotational speed of 18 rpm were recorded in both inertial and rotating frames.

Cell culture. Rat osteosarcoma cells (ROS 17/2.8) and the CaP-coated hollow microspheres sintered at 800°C were used in RWV experiment. The mixtures of cells and hollow microspheres suspended in DMEM supplemented with 10% fetal bovine serum, penicillin G (100 units/ml), streptomycin (10 µg/ml), and 3 mM β-glycerophosphate were inoculated into a 50 ml HARV at a density of 10^5 cells/ml and cell/bead ratio of 10:1. The cultures were maintained in a humidified atmosphere of 95% air with 5% CO_2 at 37°C for 10 days at a rotating speed of 18 rpm. Cell cultures destined for morphological analysis were prepared according to the procedures described previously,[4] and were examined in a scanning electron microscope (JOEL 6300).

RESULTS AND DISCUSSION

In this study, hollow bioceramic microspheres with an apparent density of 0.8-1.0g/cm³ were developed (Fig.1A). During the investigation of CaP deposition conditions, we attempted to coat untreated microspheres with the particulate sol using the identical procedures for the treated microspheres. We found out that the CaP coverage on the untreated microspheres was poor and no

P-O bands appeared in their FTIR spectra. After being treated with NaOH and then immersed in CaP particulate sol, a layer of CaP was deposited on the microsphere (Fig.1B). The thickness of the coating varied from 0.5 to 4 μm. The particle size in the surface layer increased with the sintering temperature. The FTIR spectra of the CaP-coated microspheres sintered at different temperatures are shown in Figure 2. The spectrum of the uncoated microspheres was subtracted from these spectra. The apatitic OH^- bands (•) at 3572 and 632 cm^{-1} are present in the spectra of the microspheres sintered at 600 and 800°C. The $(PO_4)^{3-}$ bands (o) at 1090, 1045, 962, 603 and 566 cm^{-1} are also present. These OH^- apatitic bands and $(PO_4)^{3-}$ bands can be assigned to crystalline calcium hydroxyapatite. When the sintering temperature was increased to 1000°C, the intensity of the OH^- apatitic bands and P-O bands decreased. In addition, a new OH^- band (arrow) at 3544cm^{-1} and new P-O bands (♦) at 1135, 1103, 1086-992, 959, 591 and 573cm^{-1} appeared. These new P-O bands can be assigned to α-tricalcium phosphate (α-TCP).

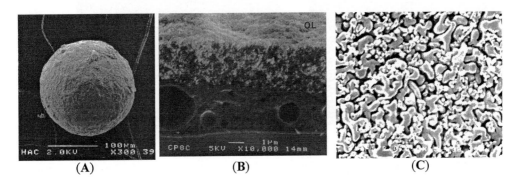

Figure 1 SEM micrographs of CaP-coated hollow microspheres. (**A**) A CaP-coated hollow microsphere. (**B**) Cross-section of a microsphere sintered at 800°C for 1h. Higher magnification. (**C**) Surface of a microsphere sintered at 1000°C for 1h.

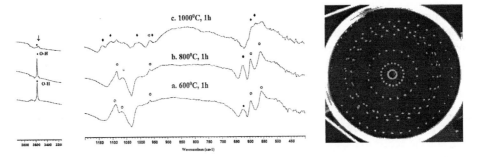

Figure 2 FTIR spectra of HA-coated microspheres sintered at 600, 800 and 1000°C for 1h, respectively.

Figure 3 Trajectory of a hollow Microsphere in an initial frame.

A hollow microcarrier of size 150 μm in dia. sintered at 800°C was placed in a HARV and its trajectories in both an inertial frame and a rotating frame were recorded. Particle locations were displayed at every 1/6 of a second along the loops that the particle traversed. Since the loops tended to overlap each other, a time lapse of 10min was chosen between each loop displayed beyond the first few loops. In an inertial frame, the hollow microsphere moved in a spiral fashion towards the center of the HARV (Fig.3). In a rotating frame, the microsphere moved in a small circle while moving towards the center of the vessel. In about 1 hour, the particle reached the central region of the vessel. These observations are consistent with the theoretical calculations reported previously.[4] Based on the data obtained from the trajectory recorded in a rotating frame, the maximum shear stress was calculated to be 0.6 dyn/cm^2 using the equation reported previously.[3]

In a 10-day co-culture of ROS 17/2.8 cells and hollow microspheres in a HARV, aggregates of ROS cells and hollow microcarriers were observed (Fig.4A). In the region between microcarriers, extensive extracellular matrix was observed in the aggregates (Fig.4B). Nodules associated with the extracellular matrix indicated early stage of mineralization.

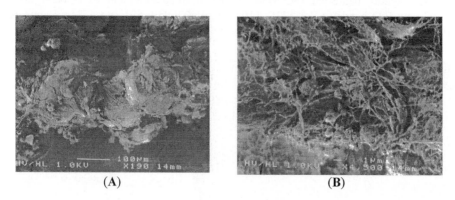

(A)   (B)

Figure 4 SEM micrographs showing co-culture of ROS 17/2.8 cells and hollow microcarriers in 10 day cell culture in a HARV. (**A**) A portion of an aggregate formed by cells and microcarriers. (**B**). Higher magnification, nodules associated with the extracellular matrix indicating early stage of mineralization.

With a biocompatible surface and an overall density less than and close to that of the culture medium, the hollow bioceramic microspheres can support 3-D cell cultures in a rotating-wall vessel. Shear stresses at their surfaces are low. These bioceramic microspheres allow the study of the effect of microgravity on the function of anchorage-dependent cells without complications from collisions with the outer wall of a rotating-wall vessel.

ACKNOWLEDGEMENTS

The authors gratefully acknowledge the technical assistance of Mr. Eric Johnston for the trajectory recording, and the access to the trajectory recording facility provided by Dr. Elliot Levine. This work was supported by NASA-NRA Grant NAG 9-817.

REFERENCES

1.   Becker JL, Prewett TL, Spaulding GF, Goodwin TJ. J Cellular Biochem 1993; **51**: 283-289.
2.   Freed LE, Vunjak-Novakovic G. Biotechnology and Bioengineering 1995; **46**: 306-313.
3.   Qiu Q, Ducheyne P, Gao H, Ayyaswamy P. Tissue Engineering 1998; **4(1)**: 19-34.
4.   Gao H, Ayyaswamy PS, Ducheyne P. Microgravity Science and Technology. 1998. In press.
5   Qiu Q, Vincent P, Lowenberg B, Sayer M, Davies JE. Cells and Materials 1993; **3(4)**:351-360.

Bioceramics Volume 11, edited by R. Z. LeGeros and J.P. LeGeros
(Proceedings of the 11th International Symposium on Ceramics in Medicine)
New York, NY, USA, November 1998
© 1998 by World Scientific Publishing Co. Pte. Ltd.

ENHANCEMENT OF *IN VIVO* OSTEOGENIC POTENTIAL OF MARROW/HYDROXYAPATITE COMPOSITES BY BIOLOGICAL FACTORS

T. Noshi[1], T. Yoshikawa[2], Y. Dohi[3], H. Ohgushi[2], M. Ikeuchi[1], K. Horiuchi[1] and M. Sugimura[1]

Departments of oral and maxillofacial surgery[1], orthopedic surgery[2] and public health[3], Nara Medical University, Kashihara City, Nara 634-8522, Japan.

ABSTRACT

The composite of cultured marrow cells and porous hydroxyapatite (HA) has *in vivo* osteogenic potential. To investigate factors which enhance the osteogenic potential of the HA/marrow composites, we prepared the protein fraction obtained by Heparin-Sepharose affinity chromatography after guanidine/HCl extraction of the bovine bone. The HA/marrow composites and the composites of HA, the protein fraction and marrow cells (HA/protein/marrow composites) were implanted at the subcutaneous sites of 7-week-old male Fischer rats. The HA/protein composites and HA alone were also implanted. The implants were harvested at 2 and 4 weeks postimplantation. Histologically, obvious *de novo* bone formation together with active osteoblasts began to appear at 2 weeks and more extensive bone formation occured at 4 weeks in many pore regions of the HA/protein/marrow composites. The HA/marrow composites did not show bone formation at 2 weeks but showed moderate amount of bone formation at 4 weeks. In contrast, the HA/protein composites and HA alone did not show obvious bone formation at any time. These results indicate that the bone derived protein fraction synergistically enhanced the osteogenic potential of marrow cells in porous HA and therefore, this graft method can be utilized in bone reconstruction surgery.

KEYWORDS: Hydroxyapatite, Marrow cells, Bone morphogenetic factors, Osteogenesis.

INTRODUCTION

We have reported that the composite of marrow cells and porous hydroxyapatite (HA) has *in vivo* osteogenic potential[1-6]. Not only fresh marrow[1-3] but cultured cells[4-6] can show the osteogenic potential in porous area of HA. The extensive osteogenic potential begins to occur at 3 to 4 weeks postimplantation. If the potential is accelerated by the addition of biological factors, its clinical application can be expanded. It is repored that the protein fraction of bone matrix extract separated by Heparin-Sepharose affinity chromatography contains various bone morphogenetic factors[7]. Therefor, we investigated the stimulative effect of the protein fraction on marrow cells-induced bone formation in porous HA.

MATERIALS AND METHODS

Preparation of protein fraction; Freshly obtained bovine metatarsal bones were crashed. The bone particles were washed with 10mM NaN_3 and defatted with Chloroform/methanol (1:1). The processed bone particles then were demineralized in 0.6N HCl. The bone matrix protein was extracted from the demineralized bone particles with 4M guanidine/HCl containing protease inhibitors (10mM N-ethylmaleimide)[8]. The extracts were dialyzed (SPECTRA/POR 1 MW cutoff 6,000-8,000, SPECTORUM MEDICAL) against 7 volumes of water and were centrifuged (25,000 rpm, 30 min, 4°C). The precipitates were lyophilized, dissolved in 0.15M NaCl, 50 mM Tris-HCl, and 6M Urea, pH 7.4, and applied on a Heparin-Sepharose CL-6B column (Pharmacia LKB: 2.6 x10 cm). The applied sample was eluted with 0.7M NaCl, 50 mM Tris-HCl, and 6M Urea, pH 7.4. The Heparin-Sepharose column eluted fraction was extensively dialyzed against water and lyophilized. The eluted protein fraction contains bone morphogenetic proteins (BMPs) and can induce differentiation of mesenchymal cells into bone.

Preparation of Marrow cells and Culture; Marrow cells were obtained from the bone shaft of femora of Fischer 344, male, 7-week-old rats. Both ends of the femora were cut away from the epiphysis, and the marrow was flushed out by using 10 ml of culture medium expelled from a syringe through a 20 gauge needle. The released cells were collected in two T-75 flasks (COSTAR) containing 15 ml of the below-mentioned standard medium. Subsequently, the medium was renewed three times a week. Cultures were maintained in humidified atmosphere of 95% air with 5% CO_2 at 37°C. A standard medium consisted of an Eagle-Minimal Essential Medium (MEM) containing 15% fetal bovine serum (ICN BIOMEDICALS JAPAN Co. Ltd.) and antibiotics (100 units/ml Penicillin, 100μg/ml Streptomycin, and 0.25μg/ml amphotericine B, Sigma). After 7 days in primary culture, marrow stromal cells were released from their culture substratum using 0.1% trypsin. The cells were concentrated by centrifuge at 900 rpm for 5 minutes at room temperature, resulting in 10^7 cells/ml.

Ceramics; Coralline hydroxyapatite ceramics (HA, Interpore International Co, Irvine, CA) were used in this experiment. It is made by conversion of the calcium carbonate skeletal structure of reef-building sea corals into pure hydroxyapatite by means of a hydrothermal chemical exchange reaction[9]. The solid and porous components of the microstructure are completely interconnectrd. The average pore size of this implant is 230μm in diameter and average void volume is 50-60%. In this study we used disk-shaped coralline hydroxyapatite 5 mm in diameter and 2 mm in thickness.

Combination of Ceramics and protein fraction; The 200μg (lyophilized weight) Heparin-Sepharose column eluted protein fraction was dissolved in 20μl of 0.1% Trifluoroacetic acid (TFA), applied on each HA disks and dried under decompression for 3 days.

Implantation of Ceramics; The porous HA disks containing the protein fraction were soaked in cultured rat marrow cell suspension (HA/protein/marrow composites) and were implanted at the subcutaneous sites of syngenetic Fischer rats. The porous HA alone, HA/protein composites (without marrow), and HA/marrow composites (without protein) were also implanted at the subcutaneous sites. These implants were harvested at 2 and 4 weeks postimplantation, and prepared for histological examination.

Histological analysis; For decalcified histological sections, the harvested implants were fixed in 10% buffered formaline, decalcified with K-CX solution (Falma Co., Tokyo) and stained with hematoxylin and eosin. These specimens were examined under light microscopy.

RESULTS

Histologically, obvious *de novo* bone formation together with active osteoblasts began to appear

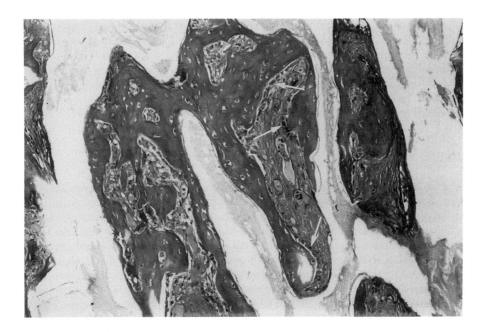

Figure 1. The HA/protein/marrow composites 2 weeks after implantation. White area shows the ghost of hydroxyapatite ceramic produced by decalcification procedures and black area shows the bone formed in the ceramic pore regions. Arrows indicate active osteoblasts forming bone (hematoxyline and eosin stain, x100).

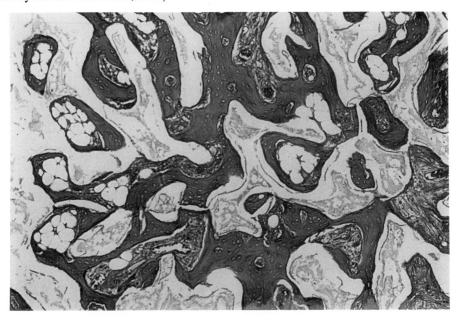

Figure 2. The HA/protein/marrow composites 4 weeks after implantation. White area shows the ghost of hydroxyapatite ceramic produced by decalcification procedures and black area shows the bone formed in the ceramic pore regions (hematoxyline and eosin stain, x40).

in many pore regions of the HA/protein/marrow composites at 2 weeks (Fig.1). At 4 weeks, total number of the osteoblasts and area of the bone increased (Fig.2). The HA/marrow composites did not show bone formation at 2 weeks but showed *de novo* bone together with active osteoblasts and osteoblastic cells in pore areas at 4 weeks. In contrast, the HA/protein composites did not show obvious bone formation at any time and showed fibrous tissue with foreign body giant cells in the pores regions. The HA alone showed minimum foreign body giant cells and good vasculature invasion but did not show bone formation.

DISCUSSION

Compared with the HA/marrow composites, the HA/marrow/protein composites showed earlier and more extensive bone formation. This is well characterized by the histology of the HA/marrow/protein composites at 2 weeks postimplantation (Fig. 1). The histology demonstrated many active osteoblasts, whish fabricated *de novo* bone. At the time of 2 weeks, the HA/marrow composites showed fibro-vascular invasion into the pore areas, but did not show any evidence of the appearance of active osteoblasts. At 4 weeks postimplantation, the HA/marrow/protein composites showed the bone formation in almost all pore areas (Fig. 2). These results suggests that the Heparin-Sepharose column eluted protein fraction enhanced the osteogenic activity of marrow stromal stem cells in porous HA. The nature of the protein factor to enhance the activity is not clear, one possibility is existence of the bone morphogenetic proteins (BMPs) reside in the protein fraction. In this regard, we already reported the BMP activity in the protein fraction[7]. Although, we could not demonstrate the bone forming capability of HA/protein composites, probably due to the small amount of the protein fraction loaded on HA ceramics.

All of these results indicate that the combination of cultured marrow cells, HA and the Heparin-Sepharose column eluted protein fraction synergistically enhance the the osteogenic potential. Based on our previous report[4] of the bone forming capability of cultured human marrow cells, this graft method can be utilized in bone reconstruction surgery.

ACKNOWLEDGEMENTS

We thank Dr. Edwin C. Shors (Interpore International, CA) for supplying the ceramics.

REFERENCES

1. Ohgushi H, Goldberg VM, Caplan AI. *J Orthop Res* 1989; **7**: 568-578.
2. Yoshikawa T, Ohgushi H, Okumura M, et al. *Calcif Tissue Int* 1992; **50**: 184-188.
3. Ohgushi H, Dohi Y, Tamai S, et al. *J Biomed Mater Res* 1993; **27**: 1401-1407.
4. Ohgushi H, Okumura M. *Acta Orthop Scand* 1990; **61**: 431-434.
5. Goshima J, Goldberg VM, Caplan AI. *Biomaterials* 1991; **12**: 253-258.
6. Yoshikawa T, Ohgushi H, Tamai S. *J Biomed Mater Res* 1996; **32**: 481-492.
7. Horiuchi K. *J Nara Med Ass* 1991; **42**: 335-352.
8. Mizutani H, Urist MR. *Clin Orthop* 1982; **171**: 213-223.
9. White E, Shors EC. *Dent Clin North Am* 1986; **30**: 49-67.

Bioceramics Volume 11, edited by R. Z. LeGeros and J.P. LeGeros
(Proceedings of the 11th International Symposium on Ceramics in Medicine)
New York, NY, USA, November 1998
© 1998 by World Scientific Publishing Co. Pte. Ltd.

ALLOGENEIC TRANSPLANTATION OF CULTURED BONE/POROUS HYDROXYAPATITE CONSTRUCT

T. Yoshikawa[1,2], H. Nakajima[1,2], H. Ohgushi[1], M. Akahane[1], S. Tamai[1], E. Yamada[2], K. Ichijima[2] and T. Uemura[3]

Departments of Orthopaedic Surgery[1] and Pathology[2], Nara Medical University, Kashihara City, Nara 634-8522, JAPAN.
National Institute for Advanced Interdisciplinary Research (NAIR)[3], Tsukuba Research Center, Ibaraki 305 8562, JAPAN

ABSTRACT

In vitro bone tissue in porous areas of hydroxyapatite (HA) can be constructed by marrow cell culture treated with dexamethasone (Dex). To investigate *in vivo* osteogenic potential of the cultured bone derived from allogeneic marrow cells, the HA blocks mixed with ACI rat marrow cells were cultured in a Eagle Minimum Essential Medium containing 15%fetal bovine serum and Dex for 2 weeks. The constructs of cultured bone and HA were subcutaneously implanted into 7-week-old male Fischer rats. An immunosuppressant, FK-506 or saline was intramuscularly given to the recipients every day for two weeks postimplantation and an additional injection was given every two days for two more weeks. The implants were harvested 8 weeks postimplantation and prepared for undecalcified section and alkaline phosphatase activity assay. When FK-506 was injected until 4 weeks, uptake of calcein given at 6 weeks after implantation was evident and significantly increased alkaline phosphatase activity was detected at the time of harvesting. These results indicate that the present graft method shows the possibility of allogeneic cultured bone transplantation having osteogenic property in HA, and may have a clinical relevance because normal tissue of a patient has not to undergo invasion.

KEYWORDS: Hydroxyapatite, Allogeneic graft, Osteogenesis, Alkaline phosphatase, FK506.

INTRODUCTION

According to Maniatopoulos et al., it is possible to obtain bone tissue by culturing bone marrow cells from rats[1]. The bone formation process seen *in vitro* is reported to morphologically resemble the early bone formation process that occurs *in vivo*. Bone protein and gene expression have been analyzed in detail during this culture process and have been proven to be the same as observed during bone formation *in vivo*[2-6]. We previously reported a high bone-forming capacity of cultured bone tissue obtained by this method after subcutaneous implantation using porous hydroxyapatite (HA) as the scaffolding for tissue culture. The construct with cultured bone tissue shown had a higher bone-forming capacity than the composite graft of fresh bone marrow cells and HA that was studied previously [7,8], and is expected to be clinically applicable for bone reconstruction [9,10]. In the present study, we biochemically and bone-dynamically investigated the possibility of allogeneic implantation of cultured bone constructs under immunosuppressant therapy.

MATERIALS AND METHODS

Marrow cell preparation and Culture: Marrow cells were obtained from the bone shaft of femora of 7-week-old, Fischer 344, male rats. ACI and Fischer strain rats were selected since they are known as strong immunologic mismatches. Both ends of the femora of a rat were cut away from the epiphysis, and the marrow was flushed out using 10 ml of culture medium expelled from a syringe through a 20 gauge needle, according to the method developed by Maniatopoulos et al.[1]. The released cells were collected in two T-75 flasks (Costar, Cambridge MA, USA) containing 15 ml of the standard medium described below. The medium was changed after the first 24 hours to remove non-adherent cells. Subsequently, the medium was renewed three times a week. Cultures were maintained in a humidified atmosphere of 95% air with 5 % CO_2 at 37°C. Standard medium consisted of Eagle Minimal Essential Medium (MEM) containing 15% fetal bovine serum (JRH Biosciences, Lenexa, KS. Lot.No. 564010) and antibiotics (100units/ml Penicillin, 100µg/ml Streptomycin, and 0.25µg/ml amphotericin B, Sigma Chemical Co., St. Louis, MO, USA). After 10 days in primary culture, marrow stromal cells were released from the culture substratum using 0.1% trypsin. The cells were concentrated by centrifugation at 900 rpm for 5 minutes at room temperature, and resuspended at 10^6 cells/ml. The HA blocks (Interpore 500, 5x5x5mm, cube, Interpore International Co., Irvine, CA, USA)[11] were soaked in 4 ml of cell suspension (10^6cells/ml) for 2 hours in a CO_2 incubator. After 2 hours of incubation, each block mixed with marrow cells was transferred into a 24-wellplate (Falcon, Franklin Lakes, NJ, USA) for subcultures. One HA block was subcultured in one well with 1 ml of the standard medium supplemented with 10mM Na β-glycerophosphate (Merck Japan Co., Tokyo, Japan), 82 µg/ml vitamin C phosphate (L-Ascorbic Acid Phosphate Magnesium Salt n-Hydrate, $C_6H_6O_9PMg_{2/3}.nH_2O$, Wako Pure Chemical Industrials, Osaka Japan) and 10^{-8}M dexamethasone (Dex, Sigma). The medium was renewed three times a week and the subcultures were maintained for 2 weeks. These subcultured marrow/HA constructs were washed twice with Eagle MEM and prepared for subcutaneous implantation into Fischer rats.

Implantation and administration of an immunosuppressant: Six subcultured marrow/HA constructs after 2 weeks of subculture were implanted subcutaneously at 6 sites of the back of each Fischer 7-week-old male rat: three subcultured constructs of Fischer marrow cells and HA were separately implanted in the right side, and the other three subcultured composites of ACI rat marrow cells and HA were separately implanted in the left side. An immunosuppressant, FK-506 (1 mg/ kg B.Wt) or saline was intramuscularly given to the recipients every day for two weeks postimplantation and an additional injection was given every two days for two more weeks. The medication was discontinued 4 weeks postimplantation and the implants were harvested 8 weeks postimplantation.

Biochemical analysis: Subcultured marrow/HA constructs 8 weeks after implantation were harvested and used for biochemical analysis. Alkaline phosphatase activity in the harvested HA blocks were determined as we previously reported [8,10]. Briefly, each construct was immediately crushed, homogenized within 0.5 ml of 0.2%Nonidet P40 containing 1mM $MgCl_2$ and centrifuged at 13,000 rpm for 10 minutes at 4 °C. The supernatant was assayed for alkaline phosphatase activity using p-nitrophenylphosphate as a substrate. An aliquot (5ml) of the supernatant was added into 1 ml of 50 mM p-nitrophenylphosphate containing 1 mM $MgCl_2$ and the mixture was incubated for 30 minutes at 37°C. 2ml of 0.2N NaOH was added to stop the enzymatic reaction and the absorption at 410 nm was measured with spectrophotometry. Alkaline phosphatase activity represented mmol of p-nitrophenol releases per one composites after 30 minutes of incubation at 37°C [12].

Histological analysis: To determine bone dynamics in the allogeneic ACI construct after discontinuance of an immunosuppressant at 4 weeks, some rats were given one dose of calcein (15mg/kg, intravenously) 6 week after implantation. The ACI constructs were harvested 8 weeks postimplantation and prepared for undecalcified histology. For the undecalcified histological processing, harvested implants were fixed in 70% ethanol. These were then dehydrated in an alcohol series, defatted, embedded in methyl methacrylate, and cut using a microtome. These specimens were examined under light microscopy and fluoromicroscopy.

Table 1. Alkaline Phosphatase Activity
8 weeks postimplantation

Fischer (isograft)	ACI (allograft) FK-treated	ACI (allograft) FK-untreated	
12.5±0.2	3.7±0.2	1.1±0.1	(μmol/implant)

mean±SE (n=12)

RESULTS AND DISCUSSION

At 8 weeks after implantation, ALP activity in the FK-treated ACI group was lower than in the FK-treated Fischer group, but was significantly higher than in the FK-untreated ACI group ($p<0.01$) [Table 1]. Calcein was administered at 6 weeks and calcein uptake was recognized on the surfaces of the bone in many pores areas in the undecalcified sections of FK-treated ACI construct grafts, indicating new bone formation by osteoblasts [Fig.1]. Significant osteoblast activity was still evident at 8 weeks after implantation, despite the discontinuation of FK506 administration at 4 weeks. These results indicate that the cultured-bone/HA constructs maintained allogeneic osteoblastic function even after discontinuance of an immunosuppressant.

Sempuku et al. previously reported good new bone formation in grafts composed of HA discs soaked in fresh bone marrow cells during FK506 administration [13]. However, the nuewly formed bone in most HA became necrotic after the FK506 was discontinued. In the present study, apparent osteoblastic activity was maintained even after discontinuation of FK506 by using a grafting method that expanded the bone-forming capacity of bone marrow cells through the application of culture techniques.

Furthermore, the cultured bone/HA construct that we developed has the same bone-forming capacity as cancellous bone [14]. Therefore, bone marrow cells from young donors with a high allogeneic bone-forming capacity could be used to treat bone disease in patients whose bone marrow cells have a reduced bone-forming capacity (e.g., the elderly) [15].

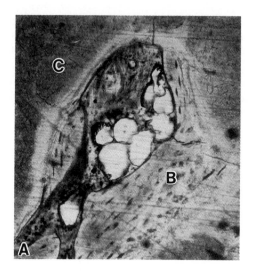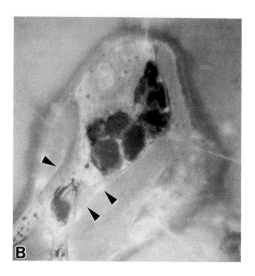

Figure 1. FK-treated ACI construct at 8 weeks after implantation. (A) Undecalcified section under light microscopy. B indicates bone and C indicates hydroxyapatite ceramic. (x100) (B) The same section under fluoroscopy. Arrowheads indicate the calcein labeling, administered 6 week after implantation. (Villanauva bone stain, x100)

ACKNOWLEDGMENTS

We thank Dr. Edwin C. Shors (Interpore International Co., CA) for supplying the ceramics.

REFERENCES

1. Maniatopoulos C, Sodek J, Melcher AH. *Cell Tissue Res* 1988; **254**: 317-330.
2. Davies JE, Lowenberg B, Shiga A. *J Biomed Mat Res* 1990; **24**:1289-1306.
3. Davies JE, Chernecky R, Lowenberg B, et al. *Cells Mater* 1991; **1**: 3-15.
4. de Bruijn JD, Klein CP, de Groot K, et al. *J Biomed Mater Res* 1992; **26**:1365-1382
5. Ohgushi H, Dohi Y, Katsuda T, et al. *J Biomed Mat Res* 1996; **32**: 333-340.
6. Yao K-L, Todescan RJ Sodek J. *J Bone Miner Res* 1994; **9**:231-240.
7. Ohgushi H, Goldberg VM, Caplan AI. *J Orthop Res* 1989; **7**: 568-578.
8. Yoshikawa T, Ohgushi H, Okumura M, et al. *Calcif Tissue Int* 1992; **50**: 184-188.
9. Yoshikawa T, Ohgushi H, Dohi Y, et al. *Biomed Mater Eng* 1997; **7**: 49-58
10. Yoshikawa T, Ohgushi H, Tamai S. *J Biomed Mater Res* 1996; **32**: 481-492.
11. Holmes RE, Bucholz RW, Mooney V. *J Bone Joint Surg* 1986; **68-A**: 904-911.
12. Reddi AH, Sullivan NS. *Endocrinology* 1980; **107**: 1291-1299.
13. Sempuku T, Ohgushi H, Okumura M, et al., *J Orthop Res* 1996; **14**:, 907-913.
14. Yoshikawa T, Ohgushi H, Akahane M, et al., *J Biomed Mater Res* in press.
15. Inoue K, Ohgushi H, Yoshikawa T, et al., *J Bone Miner Res* 1997; **12**: 989-994.

Bioceramics Volume 11, edited by R. Z. LeGeros and J.P. LeGeros
(Proceedings of the 11th International Symposium on Ceramics in Medicine)
New York, NY, USA, November 1998
© 1998 by World Scientific Publishing Co. Pte. Ltd.

MACROPOROUS BIPHASIC CALCIUM PHOSPHATE CERAMIC, A CARRIER FOR HUMAN GROWTH HORMONE

[1] Daculsi G. [1,2] Gauthier O., [1] Guicheux J., [1] Bouler J.M., [1,2] Aguado E.,
[1] UPRES EA2159 Faculté de Chirurgie Dentaire de Nantes, France
[2] Laboratoire de chirurgie, Ecole Nationale Vétérinaire de Nantes

ABSTRACT

Calcium phosphate ceramics have been recently used for administering therapeutic agents in bone. The present work investigated the efficacy of MBCP (Biomatlante France) implants as a matrix for local delivery of human growth hormone (hGH, Lilly France). MBCP loaded release hGH essentially during the 48 first hours and sustained for 11 days. The MBCP cylinders were loaded with 1, 10, 100 µg of hGH and implanted into the femurs of 8 rabbits. Bone ingrowth and MBCP resorption were determined using undecalcified sections in light microscopy and SEM. Quantitative data were obtained by image analysis. Results are expressed as the mean ± SD of at least 3 experiments.. Results indicated that hGH increased bone ingrowth and ceramic resorption significant versus control unloaded MBCP. Biochemical parameters monitored in rabbit plasma showed that hGH did not produce detectable systemic effects. Thus the use of MBCP appears to be effective for local delivery of hGH, and increase the bone ingrowth at the expense of the materials implants.

KEYWORDS: Growth hormone, drug release, calcium phosphate ceramic, MBCP

INTRODUCTION

Calcium phosphate (CaP) ceramics, such as Macroporous Biphasic Calcium Phosphate MBCP mixture of hydroxyapatite HA and B-tricalcium phosphate b-TCP, have been used successfully in bone surgery since they display controlled bioactivity (3,14,16). These materials have been extensively studied, and their biological and physicochemical properties have recently been considered suitable for bone drug delivery systems (1,2,4,15,18-20), which should facilitate bone substitution through incorporation of osteogenic factors for local delivery at the bone/implant interface

Growth hormone, because of its effect on longitudinal bone growth, has been selected as an osteogenic factor (11-13,17). Recombinant Human Growth Hormone (hGH) is one of the major factors affecting bone metabolism through stimulation of the osteoblastic synthesis of extracellular matrix and regulation of osteoclastic resorption. These features and its availability as a result of recombinant technology make hGH a good candidate for local administration via a bone bioactive drug delivery system. Previous studies have demonstrated that recombinant human GH (hGH) can be adsorbed and released by CaP powder, ensuring satisfactory kinetics for the conservation of its biological activity (8-9). The present study investigated the loading and release properties of MBCP *in to* improve bone ingrowth and ceramic resorption in a rabbit bone defect model.

MATERIALS AND METHODS

Recombinant hGH (Umatrope Lilly Co.France) concentrations were determined by radioimmunoassay (RIA) using hGH IRMA.

Macroporous biphasic calcium phosphate (MBCP) (Triosite, Zimmer™ Co., France) consisting of a ceramic with a 60/40 hydroxyapatite/B-tricalcium phosphate weight ratio was used. Macroporosity was about 50%, and mean macropore diameters 565 ± 33 µm. Cylindrical implants, 6mm long and 6 mm in diameter, were prepared. The cylinders (n=6) were loaded with 1, 10 and 100 PG of hGH, or vehicles (n=10), as described above. Eight mature female New Zealand white rabbits were randomly divided into four groups. A cylindrical defect was created with a 6 mm drill at the distal end of rabbit femurs at the epiphyso-metaphyseal junction and MBCP cylindrical implants positioned to fill the defects. Each rabbit received an hGH-loaded MBCP implant in the right femur and an equivalent~sized implant containing only a commercial additive of hGH in the left (contralateral) femur. Control rabbits received only implants without hGH in both femurs.

Histological analysis: After the animals were sacrificed at three weeks, the distal femoral extremities were excised and fixed in 1 % glutaraldehyde and 4% formaldehyde in cacodylate buffer (pH 7.4). Specimens were embedded in glycolmethacrylate. For each sample, two serial sections (100 µm thick) separated by at least 200 pm were cut perpendicular to the long axis of the implant. Sections were prepared for scanning electron microscopy (SEM) observation using backscattered electrons at 15kV. Quantitative determination of newly-formed bone and resorbed ceramic was performed with a semi-automatic image analyzer (LEICA Quantimeter 500, Japan).

RESULTS

Measurement of newly-formed bone in MBCP with or without hGH after three weeks of implantation are reported on table 1. hGH stimulated bone ingrowth significantly as compared to contralateral or control implants. hGH 100, 10 and 1 µg stimulated bone ingrowth respectively by about 45, 76 and 53% as compared to the control (p respectively 0.015, 0.0018 and 0.00205). No statistically significant differences were observed between contralateral and control implants in all tested conditions.

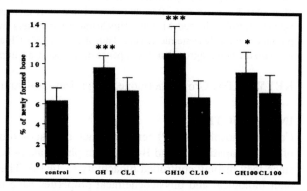

Table 1: Newly formed bone stimulated by hGH compared to control

The effects of locally administered hGH on MBCP ceramic resorption are reported in table 2. Significant differences were observed with hGH 10 and 1 µg, showing, an increase of about 87 and 134% respectively compared to the control, while hGH 100µg failed to produce a significant difference compared to the control. As reported for bone ingrowth, no significant differences were observed between contralateral and control implants in all tested conditions, indicating the absence of hGH systemic effects on bone ingrowth and ceramic resorption.

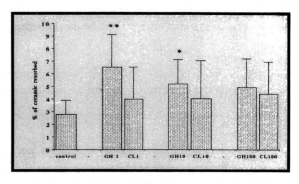

Table 2: Stimulatory effect on ceramic resorption

DISCUSSION

Several studies have focused on the use of CaP as a matrix for bone delivery of a therapeutic agent, and most have demonstrated local release of antibiotics during the critical postoperative period of bone surgery. Growth factors such as transforming growth factor, platelet-derived growth factor or bone morphogenic protein are now being investigated as means of improving, the therapeutic application of CaP. Numerous works have studied the CaP bioactive drug delivery system, but few have investigated the association between CaP ceramic and hGH.

The present study demonstrates that hGH loaded onto MBCP implants can be released with satisfactory kinetics to conserve the biological activity of the drug. Previous studies (5,6) reported the use of HA and B-TCP as drug carriers for growth hormone but did not determine whether the biological activity of the therapeutic agent was conserved during, the loading and release steps

As described extensively in the literature, GH exerts a stimulatory effect on bone ingrowth. Recent studies have also reported a possible implication of GH in the control of osteoclastic bone resorption. As a GH receptor has not been described on osteoclasts, it was hypothesized that GH acts on osteoclastic bone resorption through an unknown soluble local factor synthesized by bone stromal cells. GH is reported to be a macrophage-activating factor able to prime monocytes/macrophages, and recent investigations in our laboratory have demonstrated that hGH stimulates the degradation of CaP ceramic by activated human monocytes (10). This evidence of GH stimulatory effects on cell lines implicated in the ceramic resorption/degradation process led us to study whether locally administered hGH could stimulate not only bone ingrowth but also the ceramic resorption/degradation process. The bone ingrowth study showed statistically that hGH has a stimulatory effect on newly formed bone inside the ceramic, whereas the ceramic resorption study indicated that hGH also exerts significant stimulatory effects on ceramic resorption. In the bone ingrowth and ceramic resorption study, contralateral implants never showed a statistically significant difference with controls.

This pilot study demonstrated that macroporous calcium phosphate implants allow effective loading and release of hGH, providing satisfactory kinetics and conservation of biological activity. It is also shown that hGH has a potential therapeutic role as an osteogenic agent administered locally via calcium phosphate biomaterial. Further studies using injectable bone substitute (7) for release therapeutic agents in situ using "a minima" surgery will be developed.

Acknowledgments

The authors wish to thank Lilly France for providing hGH, The Nantes veterinary school surgery department, and particular the technical assistance of Paul Pillet, Severine Couillaud and Mireille Cottrel.

REFERENCES
1. Arm DM., Tencer AF, Brain SD, Celino D. *Biomaterials* 1996 ; *1* 7 : 703-709
2. Bajpal PK, Benohtizzi HA, *J Biomed Mater Res* 1988 ; 2 2, 1245-1266
3. Daculsi D, Passuti N, Martin S, Deudon C, Legeros RZ, Raher S. *J Biomed. Mater Res* 1990 ; **24** : 379-396
4. Denissen D, Van Beck E, Lowick C, Papapoulos S, Van den Hoof A. *Bone Miner 1993 ;* **25**, 123-134
5. Downes S, Di Silvio L, Archer RS, Kayser MV. In *Bone bonding,* Van Blitterswijk C.A. (ed.), 1992 ; 101-109, published by Reed Healthcare Communications, Leiden, The Netherlands.
6. Downes S, Di Silvio L, Klein CPAT, Kavser MK, *J Mat Sci Mat in Med* 1991 ; **2** :176-180
7. Grimandi G, Weiss P, Millot F, Daculsi G. *J Biomed Mater Res* 1998 ; **39** : 660-666
8. Guicheux J, Grimandi G, Trecant M, Faivre A, Takahashi S, Daculsi G. *J Biomed Mater Res 1997 ;* **34** : 165-170
9. Guicheux J, Heymann D, Trecant M, Gautier H, Faivre A, Daculsi G. *J Biomed Mater Res* 1997; **36**:258-264.
10. Guicheux J, Kimakhe S, Heymann D, Pillet P, Daculsi G. *J Biomed Mater Res* 1998 *;* **40** : *79-85*
11. Hedner E, Linde A, Niisson A. *J Bone Mine Res* 1996 *;* *1* 1 : 1952-1960
12. Isaksson, J0. Jansson, I. Gatise AM. *Science 1982 ;* 2 16 :1237-1239
13. Iscaard J, Niisson A, Lindabl A, Jansson JO, Isaksson OGP. *Am J Phvsiol* 1986 ; **250** : 367-372
14. Legeros RZ, *Clin Mater* 1983 ; *1* 4 : 65-88
15. Nguyen TH, Cromwell M, Wonc R, Beck LS, Plouhar P, Onpipattatanskul B. *Proceed Intern Svmp Control Rel Bioact Mater* 1994 ; 2 1 : 122-124
16. Passuti N, Daculsi G, Rogez JM, Martin S, Bainvel JV. *Clin Orthop Relat Res* 1989 ; **248** :12-19
17. Russel SM, Spencer EM, *Endocrinology, 1* 1985 ; **16** : 2563-2567
18. Shinto Y, Uchida A, Korkusuk F, Araki N, Ono K. *J Bone Joint Surg* 1992 ; 7 4 : 600-604
19. Uchida A, Shinto Y, Araki N, Ono K. *J Orthop Res* 1992 ; *1* 0 : 440-445
20. Wei G, Kotoura Y, Oka M, Yamaniuro T, Wada R, Hyon SH, Ikad Y. *J Bone Joint Surg* 1991 ; **73** : 246-253

Bioceramics Volume 11, edited by R. Z. LeGeros and J.P. LeGeros
(Proceedings of the 11th International Symposium on Ceramics in Medicine)
New York, NY, USA, November 1998
© 1998 by World Scientific Publishing Co. Pte. Ltd.

TISSUE REACTIONS TO CONTROLLED RELEASE SILICA XEROGEL CARRIERS

S. Radin[1], G. El-Bassyouni[1], E.J. Vresilovic[2], E. Schepers[3], P. Ducheyne[1,2]

Center for Biomaterials and Tissue Engineering, [1]Department of Bioengineering, [2]Department of Orthopaedic Surgery, University of Pennsylvania, Philadelphia, PA 19104
[3]Department of Dentistry, Catholic University of Leuven, Belgium

ABSTRACT

Silica xerogels of various compositions, either Ca-P free or Ca-P containing, with or without a hydroxyapatite (HA) surface film, were impanted as discs subcutaneously in the back or as granules in the iliac crest of New Zealand White rabbits. The animals were sacrificied at 2 or 4 weeks. Histological analysis indicated a tissue response which varied with xerogel composition, processing and surface conditions. Xerogels with optimal compositions and synthesis parameters showed a favorable tissue response in both implantation sites. Xerogel discs did not exibit a significant resorption after 4 weeks of implantation. Ingrowth of new bone tissue into the sites with granules coated with HA surface film was observed. Moreover, bone bonding, osteoconduction and formation of trabeculae between the particles in the center of the defect was observed for some compositions. The presence of HA surface film slowed down the granule resorption, and elicited a beneficial tissue response.

KEYWORDS: silica xerogel, in vivo, tissue response, biocompatibility, controlled release

INTRODUCTION.

Room temperature processed silica sol gels, termed xerogels, are novel materials intended for use as controlled release vehicles of molecules with biological functionality.[2,3] In vitro analysis of these materials showed that they were microporous and degradable.[1] Furthermore, they released biomolecules in a controlled, time dependent manner.[2,3] It was also shown that a hydroxyapatite (HA) surface film could be formed in simulated physiological solutions, with Ca-P containing xerogels forming the HA surface film considerably faster than Ca-P free xerogels.[1] In vitro experiments also demonstrated that the xerogel dissolution was significantly reduced by the presence of the HA surface.

In this paper, we describe the tissue response to these xerogels, either with or without a HA surface film. Various compositions of xerogels were implanted either as discs subcutaneously in the back or as granules in the iliac crest of New Zealand White rabbits. The animals were sacrificed at 2 or 4 weeks. The tissue response to the implanted materials was analyzed on thin stained sections using light microscopy techniques. A total of 16 bone and 32 subcutaneous sites were used in the analysis.

MATERIALS AND METHODS

<u>Synthesis</u>. Xerogels of various compositions, either Ca-P free or Ca-P containing, were synthesized at room temperature according to protocols developed in our laboratory. Variations in the compositions and processing also included incorporation of an antibiotic (Vancomycin) in one of the Ca-P containing compositions, and addition of polyethylene glycol (PEG, common drying control additive) to one of the xerogels (Table 1). Xerogel compositions, processing mode, shape and intended implantation site are indicated in Table 1.

Table 1. Composition and processing of xerogels used for implantation

Denomination	Composition W, %	Sol-gel process	Shape	HA film	Implantation site
S 100	100 SiO_2	AC	Discs	No	Subcutaneous
S 100 PEG	100 SiO_2	AC	Discs	No	Subcutaneous
S 70A-HA	70 SiO_2-25 CaO-5 P_2O_5	AM	Granules	Yes	Bone
S 85-HA	85 SiO_2-10 CaO-5 P_2O_5	AC	Granules	Yes	Bone
S 90	90 SiO_2-5 CaO-5 P_2O_5	AC	Discs	No	Subcutaneous
S 90-HA	90 SiO_2-5 CaO-5 P_2O_5	AC	Discs	Yes	Subcutaneous
			Granules	Yes	Bone
S 90V-HA	90 SiO_2-5 CaO-5 P_2O_5+Vanco	AC	Granules	Yes	Bone

AC=Acid catalyzed
AM=Alkoxide mixture

Tetramethylorthosilicate (TMOS), calcium methoxyethoxide (CME) or $CaCl_2$, and triethyl phosphate, were used as silica, calcium and phosphorus oxide precursors. All xerogels, except S70A, were processed by a one-step acid-catalyzed hydrolysis. Briefly, Ca-P free silica xerogel S100 was processed by mixing TMOS and deionized (DI) water at 1:10 molar ratio. PEG (MW 3350, J.T. Baker), dissolved in DI, was added to the sol at a TMOS:DI:PEG ratio of 1:10:0.0015 to form S100 PEG. Corresponding amounts of TEP and $CaCl_2$ were added to the sol to form S90 and S85. Vancomycin solution was added to the sol prior to the addition of TEP and $CaCl_2$ (20 mg Vanco per ml of sol) to form S90V. S70A was processed by mixing TMOS, TEP and CME alkoxides (no DI). The sols were cast in polystyrene vials. Discs, 8 mm diameter and 2 mm thick, resulting from gelling, aging and drying, were crack-free. Some of the discs were crushed and sieved to produce granules in a 710-1000 μm size range.

All granules of the various Ca-P containing xerogels (Table 1) and some of the S90 discs were subjected to an immersion treatment to form a surface HA-layer. Tris buffered (pH 7.4 at 37^0C) solution complemented with ions in a concentration reflecting that of plasma electrolytes plus, in addition, 2.5 mM Si (TE-Si) was used for the immersion treatment. For the treatment of Vancomycin-containing S90V, 2mg of Vancomycin per ml of TE-Si solution was added. Granules and discs were immersed for 24 hours at a weight-to-solution volume ratio of 2 and 3 mg/ml respectively. Formation of a surface HA-layer was confirmed by Fourier Transform Infrared (FTIR) analysis. The granules were packed into small-bore syringes (4mm diameter). Both granules and discs were sterilized by γ-radiation.

Xerogel discs with a diameter of 8 mm were implanted subcutaneously in the back of New Zeland White rabbits. Granules with a 710-1000 μm range were implanted in defects (5 mm diameter and 2 mm deep), created in the left and right sites of the iliac crest. The granules were applied directly from the syringes. Two granule samples and 4 disc samples were used per implantation duration, 2 or 4 weeks respectively. The subcutaneous implants retrieved with surrounding tissues and bony blocks, containing implanted granules, were immediately fixed in a solution of one part formaldehyde neutralized with 50 g $CaCO_3$/L and two parts of 80% ethanol. These segments were dehydrated in a series of graded alcohol. After embedding in methylmethacrylate, thin serial sections were cut, ground and polished to a thickness of 20-40 µm. The polished sections were stained with Stevenel's blue or a combination of this stain with Von Gieson picro-fuchsin.

RESULTS

FTIR analysis of as-synthesized xerogels showed that both Ca-P free and Ca-P containing xerogels were well-polymerized and completely hydrolyzed. The analysis confirmed that the granules of the various Ca-P containing xerogels and S90 discs, which were treated in TE-Si for 24 hours, formed a surface layer of carbonated hydroxyapatite (c-HA).

Histological analysis of subcutaneous implants indicated that all discs were encapsulated by a pseudo-synovial membrane of densely packed collagen fibres. After 2 weeks of implantation, the capsules surrounding discs without the surface HA film contained few inflammatory cells. Discs S90 with the surface film also showed very few cells in the capsule initially. In areas with progressive degradation of the surface film integrity, more phagocytosing cells could be observed. Histological observations of discs at 4 weeks were similar to those at 2 weeks with the following points of note. The already slight inflammatory response was further reduced around S100 discs: very few cells were observed. Even around cracks, the reaction was limited and the cracks were invaded by fibrous tissue. The number of cells, especially phagocytes, in the capsules around S90 discs without surface film, was greater than that after 2 weeks. Similar behavior at 2 and 4 weeks included an increased inflammatory response in areas of progressive surface film degradation and absence of evidence of disc resorption, except in areas of cracking.

Turning to the granules implanted in bone tissue, all granules that were produced using an acid-catalyzed hydrolysis (S85-HA, S90-HA and S90V-HA), showed a minimal inflammatory response. After 2 weeks of implantation the granules were surrounded by soft tissue and the fibrous tissue between the granules contained normal marrow components and few inflammatory cells. Where the surface film was detached, resorption had increased and an increased inflammatory cell population was present. Where the surface film was still adherent, dense collagen fibres covered the particles. At the borders of the defect where the periosteum was previously detached, and at the walls of the defects, there was extensive trabecular bone growth. These trabeculae were covered with a layer of osteoid tissue and a row of active osteoblasts. Direct bone contact with the S85-HA and S90-HA granules was only observed in few areas. However, bone bonding and osteoconduction along S90V-HA granules, were more extensive, and bone trabeculae grew between the particles towards the center of the defect. The results after 4 weeks of implantation were similar to those at 2 weeks: some granules resorbed while others did not visibly. On the latter, the HA-surface film was still adherent. Bone ingrowth was similar to that observed after two weeks, however less active.

The granules derived from the alkoxide mixture (S70A-HA) showed a considerable resorption and a strong inflammatory response after 2 and 4 weeks of implantation. The soft tissue around the granules were strewn with phagocytosing cells.

DISCUSSION AND CONCLUSIONS

These in vivo data reveal the effect of xerogel composition, and processing and surface conditions on the bone and subcutaneous tissue response. In addition, the data suggest that one can formulate xerogels that produce favorable tissue responses. Among subcutaneously implanted discs, S100 showed an excellent response; that is, after 4 weeks of implantation the discs were surrounded by densely packed collagen fibres containing only few inflammatory cells. In the bony defects, S90V-HA granules processed by acid-catalyzed hydrolysis showed evidence of bone bonding and osteoconduction. The HA-surface film helped to decrease granule resorption. The beneficial effect of Vancomycin suggests that the Vancomycin release at implantation site reduced the inflammatory response, thereby, enhancing biocompatibility and bioactive behavior.

This in vivo study is ongoing and will yield data on a larger sample population and, as such, statistically significant outcomes. Currently, all in vitro and in vivo data taken together suggest that silica xerogels are promising carrier materials for the controlled release of molecules with biological functionality.

ACKNOWLEDGMENTS

Egyptian Embassy fellowship CD 1386 (GEB).

REFERENCES

1. Falaize S, Radin S, Ducheyne P. *J Am Cer Soc*, in press
2. Nicoll SB, Radin S, Santos EM, Tuan RS, Ducheyne P. *Biomaterials* 1997, **18**: 853-859
3. Santos EM, Ducheyne P, Radin S, Shenker BJ, Shapiro IM. *J Biomed Mat Res*, in press.

Bioceramics Volume 11, edited by R. Z. LeGeros and J.P. LeGeros
(Proceedings of the 11th International Symposium on Ceramics in Medicine)
New York, NY, USA, November 1998
© 1998 by World Scientific Publishing Co. Pte. Ltd.

A PRELIMINARY STUDY ON THE USE OF POROUS CERAMIC BODIES FOR THE RELEASE OF PHARMACOLOGICAL SUBSTANCES

A. Krajewski[*], A. Ravaglioli[*], E. Roncari[*], P. Pinasco[▾], L. Montanari[♦], I. Pantieri[♦].

[*] Institute for Technological Research on Ceramics of C.N.R., Faenza, Italy; [▾] *"Polo Ceramico"* Agency Srl., Faenza, Italy; [♦] Interdisciplinary Clinical and Pharmacological Group, Faenza, Italy.

ABSTRACT

An approach to the production of ceramic drug delivery devices is proposed here. This presentation deals with two examples of possible ceramics: one is hydroxyapatite weakly modifiable by living tissue, the other is the bioinert alumina. Both examples take into consideration the possibility of controlling the formed porosity. The ratio among the acquired porosity and the quantity and quality of the agents inducing porosity is described and discussed. On the obtained porous ceramic bodies, a test on the role of porosity was performed with a study on the release of a substance with pharmacological activity from porous ceramic bodies of which they were previously impregnated. This paper represents the preliminary steps of further research into the preparation of ceramic drug delivery systems.

INTRODUCTION

The development of delivery systems is a method to ensure that pharmacological substances are brought only where they are needed, supplying them by a slow local continuous controlled flux (days, months or years). In several applications, it appears to be very advantageous to have a slow and/or localised delivery of drugs. It is expected that such a method will solve many of problems arising from the traditional ways by injection or via oral assumption. To solve these problems, it is necessary to understand the mechanism of drug movement through the formed architecture of the ceramics. Besides biocompatibility, ceramic's microstructure (porosity distribution) must provide controlled delivery to its target.

PREPARATION OF THE POROUS CERAMIC BODIES

Commercial powders of alumina (Al_2O_3) (Alcoa A/16-SG) and hydroxyapatite (HA) (Riedel de Haën), having an average diameter of the particles of 0.35 μm, were used as starting materials.

Table 1 -Formulations of alumina and HA mixtures with organic additives.

Sample	Composition of alumina mixtures (wt%)						
	A1	AB1	AB2	AC1	AC2	ABC1	ABC2
Alumina	77.54	73.64	65.88	79.18	76.80	72.57	65.06
Binder	0.37	0.37	0.33	0.40	0.38	1.45	1.30
Plasticizer	0.37	0.22	0.20	0.16	0.15	0.15	0.13
Water	21.71	18.41	20.42	14.40	18.82	20.32	23.10
Carbon fibres	-----	-----	-----	0.87	3.84	2.03	3.90
PVB	-----	7.36	13.18	-----	-----	3.48	6.51
Sample	Composition of HA mixtures (wt%)						
	H1	HB1	HB2	HC1	HC2	HBC1	HBC2
Hydroxyapatite	63.42	55.80	56.28	58.41	55.49	57.40	54.29
Binder	1.08	1.12	0.24	1.17	1.11	1.04	1.09
Plasticizer	0.11	0.11	0.15	0.12	0.11	0.10	0.11
Water	35.39	37.39	33.77	39.14	40.51	36.50	35.29
Carbon fibres	-----	-----	-----	1.17	2.77	1.83	3.26
PVB	-----	5.58	9.57	-----	-----	3.13	5.97

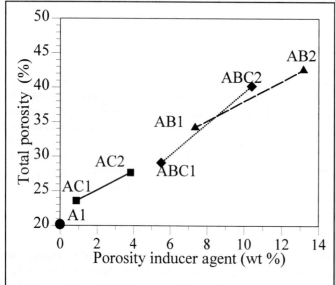

Figure 1 – Total porosity as a function of porosity inducing agents added in sintered extruded alumina.

HA powders were previously calcined at 900°C for 1 hour, so decreasing the specific surface from 61 to 5 m^2g^{-1}. Polyvinylbutirrale (PVB) (B-76 Monsanto Co.) and carbon fibres (diameter 7 μm, length < 3 mm; CFT3 - DuPont De Nemours Co.), coded B and C respectively, were utilised as porosity inducing agents (PIAs). Selected PIAs were utilised either alone or together in suitable mixture ratios. Different ratios of PIAs and ceramic powder were tested to produce ceramic bodies at different porosity. Cylindrical shaped bodies of the powders with PIAs were extruded using carbossimethylcellulose (CMC; Tylose) and a polysaccharide (Zusoplast PS-1) as binder and plastifier respectively. After a slow drying the extruded samples were sintered at 1300°C and at 1170°C, with a permanence for 1 hour, for Al_2O_3 and HA respectively. Porosity of the sintered samples was measured through a mercury intrusion analyser (Carlo Erba SpA 2000) and also examined by a scanning electron microscope (SEM) (Cambridge Stereoscan 360). The thermal cycle to submit the different cylindrical extruded green samples to firing was defined on the basis of thermogravimetric investigations. Table 1 reports composition of different Al_2O_3 and HA formulations (samples A1 for Al_2O_3 and H1 for HA were without PIAs). The trend of the total

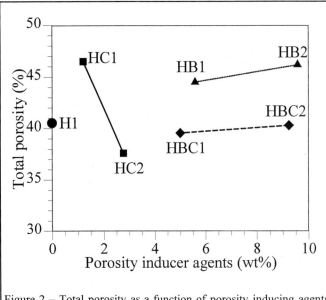

Figure 2 – Total porosity as a function of porosity inducing agents added in sintered extruded HA.

porosity of the samples as a function of the weight percentage of the utilised PIAs is reported in Figure 1 and Figure 2 for Al_2O_3 and HA ceramics respectively.

The porosity of sample A1 is essentially formed of pores of small size (average diameter 0.07 μm). in a very close range (0.01÷0.10 μm). Such a microporosity may be considered as "*structural*" and therefore present in all Al_2O_3 samples.

On the contrary of what ascertained for alumina, the total porosity in HA samples does not show a linear increase with the increase of the quantity of added PIAs as it results from Figure 2.

Using carbonium fibres (HC samples) the total porosity decreases increasing of concentration of PIAs. This apparently anomalous behaviour may be due to a different arrangement of the fibres at the interior of the body, difficult to be controlled.

IMPREGNATION WITH A DRUG AND RELEASE TEST

The cylindrical Al_2O_3 or HA ceramic samples, with diameter 9.5 (±0.3) mm and height 14.3 (±0.49) mm (volume 1020±100 mm^3), were impregnated with a methanol solution of hydrocortisone acetate (HCA, lot n. 950004) (Polichimica snc, Bologna) at a concentration of 3.5 mg ml^{-1}. Each cylinder was imbibed with 0.6 ml of such solution for a total amount of 2.1 mg of HCA. The adopted pharmacological substance, commonly used as antiphlogistic steroid, is insoluble in water (0.01 mg ml^{-1}) but highly soluble in methanol (3.9 mg ml^{-1}). The samples were left 24 hours in sterilised air (37°C) to allow the evaporation of the methanol. Every sample was then put into 100 ml of a physiological solution (NaCl

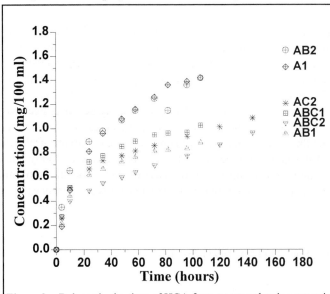

Figure 3 – Release in the time of HCA from porous alumina ceramic samples.

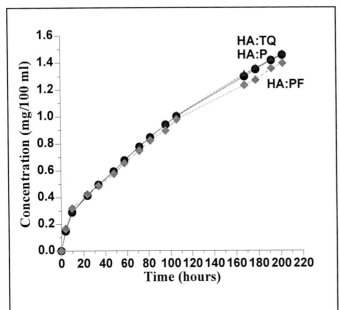

Figure 4 – Release in the time of HCA from porous HA ceramic samples (TQ = without porosity inducing agents; P with only binder PVB; PF = with both PVB and carbonium fibres).

0.9% in bi-distilled water) (Eurospital SpA, Trieste) to follow the release in the time. Absorbance measurements were performed at prefixed times for each solution through a spectrophotometer (Perkin-Elmer mod. 55B) at the wavelength of 242 nm on which the phenanthrene group of HCA molecule is activated. The test was carried out making reference to a curve drawn by measuring the intensity of absorbance of homologue standard solutions containing known concentrations of HCA. In all cases the measurements were placed in the linearity range of the calibration curve. The concentration of the released HCA in the time coming from the different samples is reported in Figure 3 for alumina samples whereas in Figure 4 that for HA samples. It should be noted that the rate of release (based on Fick's laws) can depend on the relative rates of dissolution of the pharmacological substance, on the bulk density of the ceramic, on its surface/volume ratio[1].

DISCUSSION AND CONCLUSIONS

Addition of PIAs has no significant effects on the properties of the HA ceramic. Having essentially the same porosity, the rate of release HA samples is consequently practically the same. On the contrary, changes were observed in the quantity and dimension of pores is connected to the addition of PIAs to the Al_2O_3 ceramic which has so proved to be a very interesting material for of drug delivery. Thus , to an extended duration of release, a recourse to porous capsules (porous shell including a wide cavity, as a reservoir, to be filled with the substance) becomes necessary. However, addition of PIAs causes a decrease in the number of smallest pores and formation of pores of wider dimensions. The flow through the porous wall is related to the amount of pharmacological substance, the viscosity of the liquid, the number of open pores inside the body and at the surface, their diameter, shape, length and tortuosity. In the case of this work, the imbibition involved the filling of the smallest pores (as expected by Kelvin's theory for wet substances).

REFERENCES

[1] W.J. Buykx; J. Australian Ceram. Soc. 29 (1/2) (1993) 23-31.

Bioceramics Volume 11, edited by R. Z. LeGeros and J.P. LeGeros
(Proceedings of the 11th International Symposium on Ceramics in Medicine)
New York, NY, USA, November 1998
© 1998 by World Scientific Publishing Co. Pte. Ltd.

OSTEOGENESIS WITH CORAL IS INCREASED BY BMP AND BMC IN A RAT CRANIOPLASTY

H. Petite, E. Arnaud*, C. De Pollak, A. Meunier, L. Sedel, C. Damien**

Laboratoire de Recherches Orthopédiques, Université D. Diderot, Paris VII,
URA CNRS 1432, 10 ave. de Verdun 75010 Paris, FRANCE
*Unité de chirurgie craniofaciale, Département de neurochirurgie, Hôpital Necker, 75743 Paris cedex 15, FRANCE
**Sulzer Orthopaedics, 4056 Youngfield Street, Wheat Ridge, Colorado 80033, USA

ABSTRACT

Autologous bone marrow cells (BMC), bone morphogenetic proteins (BMP) and natural coral exoskeleton (CC) were used to enhance the repair of large skull bone defects in a craniotomy model. Nine millimeter calvarial defects were performed on adult rats and were either left empty (control cavities) or implanted with CC alone, CC-BMC, CC-BMP, or CC-BMC-BMP. After 2 months, osteogenesis was insufficient to allow union when defects were left empty or filled with CC. Addition of BMC alone to CC had no positive influence on osteogenesis at any time and increased CC resorption at 2 months. In contrast addition of BMP or BMP/BMC to CC led to a significant increase in osteogenesis and allowed bone union after 1 month. At 2 months, the combination of CC-BMP-BMC was the most potent activator of osteogenesis. CC resorption was significantly decreased in the presence of BMP with or without BMC at both times. These data are in accordance with the presence of progenitor cells in bone marrow that are inducible by BMPs to the osteogenic pathway in cranial site. The increase in material resorption in cavities filled with CC-BMC could suggest that cells from the granulocyte-macrophage lineage survived the grafting procedure and are still active after 2 months.

KEYWORDS: ceramics; bone morphogenic protein; bone marrow cells; coral; calcium phosphate.

INTRODUCTION

The preferred treatment of large skull defects is the autologous bone graft due to its osteoconductivity, osteoinductivity and osteogenicity. It is, however, of limited supply and its harvest implies additional morbidity (infection, pain, hemorrhage, cosmetic disability, nerve damage and loss of function). The difficulty of fabricating a functional shape from the graft may result in less than optimal filling of the defect. To overcome these problems, bone allografts and bone substitutes have been developed but they have their own limitations [1]. Recent advances in the field of tissue engineering have allowed us to consider new substitutes combining biomaterial properties and biological activity originating from tissue-inducing substances such as BMPs or cells chiefly bone marrow cells [2]. The current investigation was designed to determine whether a calcium-carbonate-based biomaterial, coral, alone or supplemented with whole bone marrow, BMPs or both could regenerate a large bone skull defect that would otherwise not repair. We chose coral as a scaffold due to its interconnected porous architecture, high compressive breaking stress, good biocompatibility and resorbability. The intent is to determine the respective participation of the CC, BMC and BMP on osteogenesis. The clinical rationale for such a study is the search for a bone substitute that would have sufficient bone repair ability to avoid the use of autograft or allografts and to obviate their drawbacks.

MATERIALS AND METHODS

CC exoskeleton from *Porites sp.* was utilized in the form of granules (630-1000 μm) (Volume porosity 49±2% and mean pore diameter 250 μm). CC granules were sterilised by autoclaving. Bone protein extracts (Sulzer Orthopedics Biologics Inc. (Denver, Colorado). was prepared as previously described [3]. Freeze-dried extracts were reconstituted by addition 0.15 ml of 10 mM HCl per 1 mg of BP and kept until use at 4°C. Suspensions of bone marrow cells were prepared as previously described from 6 weeks-old syngenic Lewis rats[4] and diluted with α-MEM to an average of 1.5×10^7 nucleated cells/ 30μl. Preparation of the implants is summarized in table I.

Surgical procedure

A 9 mm craniotomy was performed in 11-12 weeks-old male Lewis rats (Charles River, Saint-Aubin les Elbeuf, France)) as previously described [5]. Defects were either left empty (control defects) or filled with CC granules, CC-BMC, CC-BMP and CC-BMC-BMP. After 1 or 2 months, the calvaria were harvested and soft tissue removed. Specimens were embedded in methyl methacrylate [6]. Histomorphometry was carried out using a microscope linked via a video-camera to an image processing system (CUE-2, OLYMPUS OIA01501 Version 2.2) on sections ground to a thickness of 100-120 μm and stained with stevenel blue and picrofuschine. The bone surface area, CC surface area and mean defect thickness were measured. Statistical significance was determined by one-way analysis of variance (ANOVA) and unpaired t-tests (p<0.05).

Experimental groups

Table I				
Preparation of composites and experimental groups				
group	**IMPLANT PREPARATION**		**months**	
	Coral	BMP	BMC	1	2
Control	no	no	no	6	6
CC		yes	yes	6	6
CC-BMC	yes	no	yes	6	6
CC-BMP	yes	yes	no	6	6
CC-BMC-BMP	yes	yes	yes	6	6

40 μl of BMCs suspension was seeded on top of CC granules one hour prior to surgery.
15 μl of BP (100μg) was added.

RESULTS

At 1 and 2 months, unfilled defects showed mainly fibrous tissue with a minimal amount of new trabecular bone formation originating from the defect margins. At 1 month, defects filled with CC or CC-BMC were invaded by a cellular loose connective tissue in which CC granules were embedded. In this tissue, most of the CC granules showed a resorption pattern characterized by needle-like crystals and adhesion of multinucleated cells. Occasionally, CC granules were surrounded by woven bone. At 2 months, three distinct patterns could be recognized: (1) fibrous tissue similar to the control defect with no residual CC granules, (2) mixture of fibrous tissue and CC granules surrounded by multinucleated cells, (3) area of resting bone surrounding CC granules. At 1 month, defects filled CC-BMP or CC-BMP-BMC were invaded with woven bone with active osteoblasts along all bone surfaces. CC granules were almost always embedded in bone and showed no characteristic pattern of resorption. At 2 months, active bone remodelling with osteoclast-like cells was observed with numerous Howship's lacunae of large size. On the external side of the defect, bone remodelling led to a lamellar bone with an organization similar to the adjacent calvaria. Hematopoietic zones and adipocytes were also observed.

Histomorphometry

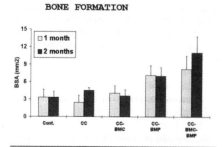

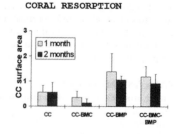

In defects left empty, no increase in bone formation was observed between one month (BS=3.3±1.3mm^2) and two months (BS=3.3±1.0mm^2). Addition of BMC alone to CC had no positive influence on osteogenesis at any time and increased CC resorption significantly at 2 months. No difference in bone area between defects filled with CC and BMP (7.17±1.65 mm^2) and defects filled with CC, BMP and BMC (8.23±2.2mm^2) were observed at 1 month. However, at 2 months, a statistical increase in bone formation was observed when defects were filled with CC, BMP and BMC (11.06 ± 2.76 mm^2) in comparison to cavities filled with CC and BMP (7.03 ± 1.45 mm^2). Bone formation was always superior in these implants in comparison to defects left empty or filled with CC or CC and BMC at both time. Similarly, calvaria thickness was greater in defects filled with CC-BMP-BMC in comparison to defects filled with any other materials at 2 months.

CALVARIA THICKNESS

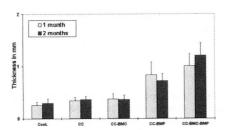

DISCUSSION

Limited success in regenerating large skull bone defects has been achieved by bridging them with osteoconductive materials. These substitutes lack osteogenic and osteoinductive properties of bone autograft. A direct approach that could quickly enter clinical reality would be to stimulate osteogenesis in these biomaterials by the addition of fresh bone marrow cells and or osteoinductive substances. In this study, we evaluate coral as a delivery vehicle for BMC and BMPs in 9 mm full-thickness cranial defects. In this model, the osteoconductivity of coral was insufficient to allow a bony union.

Supplementation of coral with BMC did not lead to an increase in osteogenesis contrasting with a number of studies demonstrating a positive influence of bone marrow in ectopic [7, 8] or orthotopic location [9-13]. Further investigations are necessary to establish the respective influence of the cell number as well as the age of the animal and the anatomical location in order to explain these discrepancies.

In contrast, supplementation of coral with BMP increased drastically bone formation and bone union was achieved at 1 month. This suggests that coral could be an interesting candidate as a carrier for BMP as observed with others ceramics (hydroxyapatite [14, 15], β-tricalcium phosphate [16]. The next step for these materials is to compare them in clinically relevant models. Despite their lack of influence on osteogenesis when used alone with coral, BMC significantly increased osteogenesis after 2 months when used in combination with BMP. These results were statistically significant in comparison to any other groups at 2 months. A possible explanation for these constrasting data is that bone marrow functions as a source of inducible osteoprogenitor cells (IOPC) rather than a source of determined osteoprogenitors(DOPC)[17]. In other words, the « skull environment » failed to provid the necessary clues for determination of IOPC.

A drawback of an osteoinductive agent could be its ability to induce bone in unsuitable site. In this study, bone formation was spatially limited to the defect as far as one can judge by gross macroscopic examination and histological study of the calvarium area. Bone surface did not increase between 1 and 2 months in defects filled with coral-BMP. This suggests a spatial and temporal regulation of the osteogenic process. Receptors with high affinity to BMP have been recently discovered in numerous cell types [18]. Additional studies to determine the influence of BMP on osteogenesis in surrounding tissues may be needed to check for their specific activity.

Choosing a biomaterial that is resorbable and that can be replaced by bone is a very attractive alternative. However, the balance between osteogenesis and biomaterial resorption is crucial to obtain a good clinical result. It is noteworthy that BMC alone increased biomaterial resorption at 2 months. This stressed the fact that among BMC are found not only osteoprogenitors but also cells from the granulocyte-macrophage lineage including osteoclast precursors. Careful study in appropriate model should be done to check for the optimal rate of biomaterial resorption.

Coral is rich in carbonate and poor in phosphate. Based on these data, it has been hypothesized that this could influence the exact composition of the newly formed bone. To answer this question, the mineral composition of the newly formed bone should be determined [19].

In conclusion , these results suggest that progenitor cells are present in bone marrow and are inducible to the osteogenic pathway by BMPs but not by the microenvironment of the cranial site itself. They also suggest that cells from the granulocyte-macrophage lineage survive the grafting procedure and are active after 2 months in the cranial site.

ACKNOWLEDGEMENTS

Inoteb (France) and Intermedics Orthopedics (USA) laboratories are thanked for their donations in pharmaceutical products. This study has been supported by a grant (AP-HP/CANAM-96) from Assistance Publique des Hôpitaux de Paris (Délégation à la recherche clinique) in combination with la Caisse Nationale d'Assurance Maladie des Professions Indépendantes. We thank Karim Oudina for its excelent technical assistance and Pepita Masquelet for her excellent animal care.

REFERENCES

1. **Damien C Parsons R,** *J of Applied Biomaterials* 1991; 2: 187-208.
2. **Langer R Vacanti JP,** *Science* 1993; 260: 920-6.
3. **Boden SD, J.H. SHutton WC,** *J Bone and Joint Surgery* 1995; 77-A: 1404-1417.
4. **Mardon HJ, Bee J, von der Mark KOwen ME,** *Cell Tissue Res* 1987; 250: 157-65.
5. **Marden LJ, Hollinger JO, Chaudhari A, Turek T, Schaub RGRon E,** *J Biomed Mater Res* 1994; 28: 1127-1138.
6. **Guillemin G, Meunier A, Dallant P, Christel P, Pouliquen JCSedel L,** *J Biomed Mater Res* 1989; 23: 765-779.
7. **Ohgushi H, Goldberg VMCaplan AI,** *J Orthop Res* 1989; 7: 568-78.
8. **Ohgushi H, Okumura M, Tamai S, Shors ECCaplan AI,** *J Biomed Mater Res* 1990; 24: 1563-70.
9. **Grundel RE, Chapman MW, Yee TMoore DC,** *Clin Orthop* 1991; : 244-58.
10. **Ohgushi H, Goldberg VMCaplan AI,** *Acta Orthop Scand* 1989; 60: 334-9.
11. **Louisia S, Petite H, Meunier A, Stromboni MSedel L.** *Repair of large bone defects with a hybrid material (coral seeded with bone marrow cells).* in *21st Annual Meeting of the Society For Biomaterials March 18-22.* 1995. San Francisco, California, USA.
12. **Johnson KD, Frierson KE, Keller TS, Cook C, Scheinberg R, Zerwekh J, Meyers LSciadini MF,** *J Orthop Res* 1996; 14: 351-69.
13. **Wolff D, Goldberg VMStevenson S,** *J Orthop Res* 1994; 12: 439-46.
14. **Horisaka Y, Okamoto Y, Matsumoto N, Yoshimura Y, Kawada J, Yamashita KTakagi T,** *Clin Orthop* 1991; 268: 303-312.
15. **Sato T, Kawamura M, Sato K, Iwata HMiura T,** *Clin Orthop* 1991; 263: 254-262.
16. **Urist MR, Nilsson O, Rasmussen J, Hirota W, Lovell T, Schmalzreid TFinerman GA,** *Clin Orthop* 1987; 214: 295-304.
17. **Takagi K Urist MR,** *Clin Orthop* 1982; 171: 224-231.
18. **Iwasaki S, Tsuruoka N, Hattori A, Sato M, Tsujimoto MKohno M,** *J Biol Chem* 1995; 270: 5476-5482.
19. **Daculsi G, Bouler JMLeGeros RZ,** *Int Rev Cytol* 1997; 172: 129-91.

Bioceramics Volume 11, edited by R. Z. LeGeros and J.P. LeGeros
(Proceedings of the 11th International Symposium on Ceramics in Medicine)
New York, NY, USA, November 1998
© 1998 by World Scientific Publishing Co. Pte. Ltd.

ANTITUMOR EFFECT BY SUSTAINED RELEASE OF TUMOR NECROSIS FACTOR USING POROUS CERAMIC DELIVERY SYSTEM

Yasuo Yamashita, Yasunari Hioki, Toru Yamakawa, Kou Kato, Atsumasa Uchida

Department of Orthopaedic Surgery, Mie University Faculty of Medicine, Edobasi 2-174,
Tsu-shi, Mie-ken 514-8507, Japan

ABSTRACT

We have developed a new delivery system of a tumor necrosis factor α (TNF-α) by enclosure into a block of porous calcium hydroxyapatite (CHA) ceramic together with atelocollagen (TNF-CHA). The slow release of TNF-α from this system was confirmed in *in vitro* experiments. The release of TNF-α from this system peaked on day 3, slowly decreased thereafter, but still detectable on day 21, resulting in excellent sustained release. This system was directly implanted into experimental osteosarcoma tumors in rats, and the inhibitory effects on tumor growth and survival of rats were evaluated. Inhibition of tumor growth was more marked after local implantation of this system than by non-treatment or CHA with only atelocollagen implantation. Moreover, an increased survival rate of rats bearing osteosarcoma was noted in the TNF-α treatment group. The present results suggest TNF-CHA local administration is effective as a slow-release drug delivery system for inhibiting tumor growth. This system is attractive as the mechanical strength of TNF-CHA permits simultaneous partial surgical excision and replacement of the bone defect.

KEYWORDS:

Tumor necrosis factor (TNF), hydoroxyapatite, drug delivery system, osteosarcoma

INTRODUCTION

In orthopedic oncology, the ideal setting for such regional delivery may be a delivery system for the sustained release of an anticancer drug by enclosure into materials having a high affinity for bone and bone marrow. We have previously reported that calcium hydroxyapatite ceramics (CHA), which have excellent biocompatibility with bony tissue[1,2], could be used as a sustainer of anticancer drugs because of its interlinked pore structure[3]. In bone tumors, it is attractive as the mechanical strength of CHA permits the simultaneous partial surgical excision and replacement of bone defect. We have developed a new delivery system for sustained release of TNF-α by enclosure into blocks of CHA. This system consists of CHA and atelocollagen derived from natural bovine skin together with TNF-α. In the present study, we demonstrated the slow release of TNF-α from TNF-CHA in *in vitro* experiments, and an anticancer effect on tumor growth and the survival rate of rats bearing osteosarcoma *in vivo*.

MATERIALS AND METHODS

TNF-α Release *In Vitro* : Porous CHA blocks 18×15×12 mm (Sumitomo Osaka Cement Co., Ltd., Japan) were sintered at 1150 °C for two hours to a porosity of 42% and a micropore diameter between 50 and 300 micrometers. An interconnecting pore structure was open to the surface of the blocks. A central cylindrical cavity 11 mm in diameter and 10 mm in depth was made for containing the drug. TNF-α (60 μg) was placed into a central cylindrical cavity in the CHA block together with 25 mg of atelocollagen derived from natural bovine skin. CHA blocks impregnated with TNF-α alone were prepared (TNF-CHA without collagen) for investigating the influence of atelocollagen. The cavity was sealed with a CHA plug 11 mm in diameter and 3 mm in height (Fig. 1).

Each was placed in a Falcon tube containing 10 ml of phosphate-buffered saline (PBS) and incubated at 37 °C. The PBS was replaced at 24- hour intervals for 30 days, and eluted fluids removed were preserved at -20 °C for later determination of TNF-α concentration measured by ELISA assay.

Therapy Experiments : S-SLM osteosarcoma, which was derived by subcutaneous injection, is syngeneic to Fischer 344 rats. This tumor was provided by the Department of

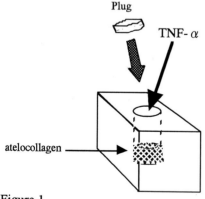

Figure 1.
Illustration of TNF-CHA.

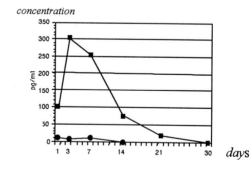

Figure 2.
Release profiles of TNF-α from CHA.
(■) TNF-CHA with collagen.
(●) TNF-CHA without collagen.

Oncological Pathology, Nara Medical University Japan[4], weighing 250-300 g, were used, and the transplantation was performed as follows. Tumor tissues were minced in physiological saline solution, and fragments (2×2 mm) were transplanted into the subcutaneous tissue of the back region of the rats. Three weeks after implantation, the solid tumor had developed to 2-3 cm³ in size. CHA ceramic for therapy experiments (cylindrical blocks, diameter 10 mm×height 10 mm) had a central cylindrical cavity 5 mm in diameter and 7 mm in depth. TNF-α (40 μg)was placed into a central cylindrical cavity in the CHA block together with 20 mg of atelocollagen. The cavity was sealed with a CHA plug 4 mm in diameter with a height of 3 mm. Three weeks after transplantation, rats were divided into three groups and 5 rats each group were treated as follows : no treatment (NT group), CHA containing 20 mg of atelocollagen without TNF was directly implanted into the tumor (CHA group), TNF-CHA composite containing 20 mg of atelocollagen was directly implanted into the tumor (TNF-CHA group). For assessment of antitumor effects of this delivery system, subcutaneous tumor volumes and body weight were measured every week, and estimates of tumor volume (V mm³) were calculated from the formula: V=(long diameter)×(short diameter)² / 2. During survival experiments, the rats were followed until their death.

RESULTS

TNF-α Release *In Vitro* : Figure 2 illustrates release patterns of TNF-α for materials. The release of TNF-α from TNF-CHA with atelocolagen increased rapidly during the first 1-3 days, decreased slowly thereafter, but was still and detectable on day 21. No increase release of TNF-α from TNF-CHA without collagen was found TNF-α was undetectable up to 14 days.

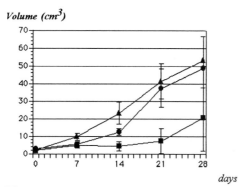

Figure 3.
Tumor growth curves for each group. Values are mean ± SD for five animals. (■) TNF-CHA group, (●) CHA group, (▲) NT group.

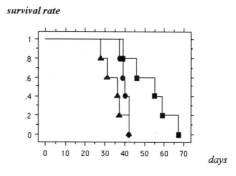

Figure 4.
Effects of administration of TNF- CHA on the survival. (■) TNF-CHA group, (●) CHA group, (▲) NT group.

Therapy Experiments : TNF-CHA with collagen composite was used for therapy experiments. In rats receiving the composite, the tumor growth curve remained flat up to 14 days after administration, and then rose slightly until day 21 at which time TNF-α was released from the composite *in vitro*. Therefore, the rate of tumor growth increased. Inhibition of tumor growth was more marked after local implantation of TNF-CHA than in either the NT or CHA group on day 28 ($p<0.05$). The tumor volumes in the CHA group, were slightly lower than those in the NT group, but no statistically significant difference was found (Fig. 3). Nor was any statistically significant difference in the body weight of three groups found. Implantation of TNF-CHA composite significantly prolonged the survival rate of rats, compared to both the NT group and the CHA group (Fig. 4) ($p<0.05$). The present results suggest local administration of TNF-CHA is effective as a slow-release drug delivery system for inhibiting tumor growth and lengthening the duration of survival.

DISCUSSION

The availability of TNF-α produced through recombinant DNA technology enabled the exploration of the therapeutic potential of TNF-α as an anticancer agent in human clinical trials. However, attempts to implement clinically this property have failed. Only anecdotal partial responses have been described in several hundred cancer patients treated with TNF-α systemically[5,6]. Immediately upon its systemic administration, TNF-α causes marked hypotension and systemic inflammatory response syndrome, with eventual multiorgan involvement. The novel idea of using TNF-α in regional therapy without exposing its lethal side effects seemed to be logical. Biomechanical properties of CHA are similar to those of bone, and atelocollagen is both a biocompatible and biodegradable material[7]. Therefore, a drug delivery system with CHA and atelocollagen may be effective for the application of TNF-α for bone tumors. Although the detailed release mechanism remains unclear, we believe that this TNF-α slow delivery system will prove to be an extremely effective means for local administration of TNF-α.

REFERENCES

1. Uchida A, Nade S, McCartney E, Ching W. *J Orthop Res* 1985; **3**: 65-77.
2. Uchida A, Nade S, McCartney E, Ching W. *J Bone Joint Surg* 1984; **66-B**: 269-275.
3. Uchida A, Shinto Y. *J Orthop Res* 1992; **10**, in press.
4. Mii Y, Tsutumi M, Shirakawa K, Miura S, Hohonoki K, Maruyama H, Ohgushi H, Masuhara K, Konishi Y. *Jpn J Cancer Res* 1988; **79**: 589-592.
5. Spriggs DR, Sherman KL, Michie H. *J Natl Cancer Inst* 1988; **80**: 1039-1044.
6. Feinberg B, Kurzrock R, Talpaz M. *J Clin Oncol* 1988; **6**: 1328-1334.
7. Rubin AL, Stenzel KH, Miyata T, White MJ. *J Clin Pharmacol* 1973; **13**: 309-314.

Bioceramics Volume 11, edited by R. Z. LeGeros and J.P. LeGeros
(Proceedings of the 11th International Symposium on Ceramics in Medicine)
New York, NY, USA, November 1998
© 1998 by World Scientific Publishing Co. Pte. Ltd.

DYNAMIC COMPACTION OF CALCIUM PHOSPHATE POWDER: A NEW PROCESS FOR DRUG DELIVERY SYSTEM

Daculsi G.[1], Trecant M.[1], Guicheux J.[1], Grimandi G.[1], Leroy M.[2],

[1] Centre de recherche sur les matériaux d'intérêt biologique UPRES EA2159 Faculté de Chirurgie Dentaire de Nantes, France
[2] Laboratoire FORSEM IUT de Nantes.

Abstract

Dynamic compaction requires no external heating for elaboration of CaP ceramics. A projectile with a velocity of 50 m/s was used, resulting in compacts having a compaction degree of 65 % and a tensile strength of 12.4 Mpa. The strength was very close to that obtained with sintered compact and indicate formation of grain boundaries. The process allows the integration of therapeutic agent into the ceramic and not only adsorbed at the surface. This reports presents the results of an in vitro study of therapeutic agent (Human Growth Hormone) associated with calcium phosphate powder. We have demonstrated the structural integrity of the two therapeutic agents after consolidation. 30 % only of the total hGH drug loaded was released during the 18 days study. This new compaction process should be useful in developing ceramics that contains a therapeutic agent.

Key words: growth hormone; drug delivery system; dynamic compaction; biphasic calcium phosphate

INTRODUCTION

Numerous biomaterials have been developed as alternatives to autogenous and allogenous bone grafts. Among these synthetic bone substitutes, calcium phosphate ceramics have been used successfully in orthopedics, dentistry and facial surgery [4,5,6,23]. Yet the incorporation of a therapeutic agent (antibiotic, growth factor, etc.) would appear to be of interest, allowing sustained release of the drug in adjacent bone. The conventional ceramic manufacturing process involves sintering. Heating is necessary to strengthen the material but prevents mixing of the therapeutic agent with CaP powder before compaction. Furthermore crystallinity and morphological features of the powder change with high temperatures [1,2,3,12,15] and unstable materials alter when heated [3].

Dynamic compaction is a technique used to produce bulk material from metallic powders at room temperature [7-9,14,16-20)) and appeared to have a great interest for the elaboration of new bioceramics particularly composites associating CaP and therapeutic agents. Consolidation is achieved by a shock wave produced by a piston impact or explosives placed around the powder. This wave deforms powder particles so quickly that interparticle melting and welding occur without external heating. A previous study demonstrated that human growth hormone (hGH) could be adsorbed on CaP powder and released with satisfactory kinetics. This *in vitro* study was based on the adsorption of hGH on the surface of sintered apatite beads, which then must be consolidated for clinical applications. However, the presence of a therapeutic agent prevents the use of classical calcium phosphate consolidation involving a sintering step. This new technique was developed to consolidate CaP powder without the use of external heating (Nantes University, Patent 92-12837).

MATERIALS AND METHODS

The apparatus was a pilot realized specifically for the elaboration of medical implant (Fig.1).
The shock compaction system was positioned horizontally so that static precompaction of the powder had

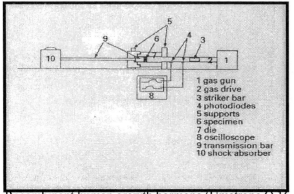

1 gas gun
2 gas drive
3 striker bar
4 photodiodes
5 supports
6 specimen
7 die
8 oscilloscope
9 transmission bar
10 shock absorber

to be performed before firing. The powder was compacted uniaxially in a 20 mm diameter cylindrical die10 mm/min. The Hopkinson bar apparatus fired a 20 mm diameter and 86 mm length projectile into the same lubricated die used for static compaction.

The biphasic calcium phosphate (BCP) powder used in this study consisted of a 40/60 weight mixture of beta-tricalcium phosphate (P-TCP) and hydroxyapatite (HA). BCP particles 40 to 80 microns in size were selected for dynamic compaction.

Recombinant human growth hormone (Umatrope O 16 1.U.) was associated with BCP powder by physical adsorption, as previously described (10,11) with a weight ratio of 1 mg hGH for 3 g BCP, and dynamic compaction was performed using a projectile with a velocity of 50 m/s.

Biological tests: The mouse L929 fibroblastic cell line was cultured in MEM supplemented with 10% fetal calf serum, 2 mM glutamine, and a mixture of antibiotics. Rat N-b2 lymphoma cells were routinely grown in a suspension culture. After a 24-h preincubation of compacted pellets in 6 well plates, cell numbers were after trypan-blue staining. The same experiments were conducted on glass coverslips. After 2 h, compacted pellets (with or without hGH) were deposited in each well and incubated for 96 h. The pellets then were removed, and the cells were gently rinsed with warm PBS and fixed with 4% formaldehyde in cacodylate buffer for 20 min at room temperature

The biological activity of hGH was assayed using an MTT-eluted stain bioassay (ESTA), as previously described (11). The compacted pellets were mechanically granulated in sterile conditions and hGH was extracted in PBS.

RESULTS

Degree of compaction and SEM observations of compacts elaborated using various static precompactions and stricter velocities ranging from 0 to 50 m/s [191 showed that similar final compaction degrees were achieved regardless of the static precompaction used before firing]. With the present compaction system, the highest densities obtained were about 70% (static precompaction of 310 MPa and projectile velocity of 50 m/s). From the point of view of the powder-compaction industry, the remaining micropores might appear as a drawback. However, microporosity is necessary in biomaterials since it allows internal biological fluids circulation, thus promoting bioactivity, while retaining sufficient mechanical properties.

Tensile strength depended on the compaction degree of the compacts (Figure 3). Mechanical strength improvement with sintering time (groups B to E) appears to be linked to the formation of bridges between particles.   Indeed samples from group B had low compaction degree (53%) indicating that no consolidation had occurred but only particle reorganization. On the other hand sintering at 1,050°C during 60 minutes (group D) permitted the formation of interparticle boundaries in the compacts and the beginning of densification (compaction degree of 59%) which resulted in higher tensile strength (10.9 ± 0.8 MPa). Since compacts obtained by dynamic compaction with a projectile velocity of 150 m/s (group G) possessed similar tensile strength (12.4 ± 2.7 MPa) as sintered compacts from group D, it is suggested that dynamic compaction had created interparticle boundaries.

Two different methods were used to assess the activity of hGH: immunological activity was analyzed by IRMA, and biological activity was assayed by an MTT eluted stain bioassay (ESTA) using a CH-sensitive Nb2 cell line. The quantities of hGH detected by both methods indicated that only about 65% of hGH loaded on the powder was recovered after 5 days of elution. The biological activity of eluted hGH was totally preserved, as shown by comparison of hGH integrity using both detection methods.

DISCUSSION

Association of drugs with biomaterials can be achieved by different techniques. One approach consists in coating the ceramic block surface with the drug (24), however, the low specific surface of the block prevents high amounts of drug from being loaded. Another approach consists in depositing the therapeutic agent in a cavity within the ceramic (11) thus the amount of drug loaded can be controlled, but the release is highly dependent on the porosity of the material. Moreover, in the event that the material is disrupted, all the drug loaded is instantly released. To overcome these limitations we have developed a new process known as dynamic compaction.This technique involves drug adsorption on the calcium phosphate powder surface followed by powder consolidation without external heating. This process provides regular distribution of the drug inside the pellets so that drug release is mainly dependent on the degradation rate of the ceramic, which can be controlled by both the chemical composition of the material and the compaction degree of the pellets. The present work demonstrates the *in vitro* biocompatibility of dynamically compacted CaP and the biological integrity of the loaded drug (human growth hormone).

The biocompatibility assay was based on a proliferation assay of mouse L929 fibroblastic cells and their fibronectin production in the presence of the material. The results indicate that the cellular behaviour of L929 cells was not altered by the calcium phosphate-compacted pellets and suggest that dynamic compaction can be used to produce biocompatible CaP.

The second result of biological evaluation was to determine the influence of dynamic compaction on the activity of the loaded therapeutic agent. The study demonstrated the biochemical of hGH released by pellets prepared by dynamic compaction. The comparison of hGH activity (immunological and biological activity) detected by radioimmunoassay and MTT-eluted stain bioassay showed that the biological activity of hGH is completely preserved after dynamic compaction. Despite the total biological integrity of hGH released from compacted pellets, only 65% of loaded hGH was recovered after release. The 35% of unrecovered hGH could be poorly accessible to the medium and be released only after a delay and under the influence of calcium phosphate dissolution *in vitro* or cellular degradation *in vivo*.

CONCLUSION

These data demonstrate for the first time that dynamic compaction process can be used as a new method to produce CaP drug delivery systems. Moreover, the preservation of the activity of the therapeutic agent indicates that this process can be used to release therapeutic agents *in situ*. Dynamic compaction of CaP powder produced compacts with a 65% compaction degree and a tensile strength of about 12.4 MPa. This tensile strength was close to that of sintered compacts which indicated that interparticle boundaries had been created during dynamic compaction. As this process does not require any external, dynamic compaction was used to produce drug-loaded CaP ceramics. Indeed it has been shown in a previous study that hGH and Vancomycin were not denatured during shock compaction (10,11,22). *In vitro* study also demonstrated that the biological activity of hGH was totally preserved. Therefore this compaction process appears useful to produce biomaterials incorporating a therapeutic agent. The kinetics of release of the therapeutic agent could be modified by changing, either the material solubility, or the compact porosity.

References

1. Best S., Bonfield W. et Doyle C., Proceedings of the 1st International Bioceramic Symposium (Dorishi H., Aoki H., Sawai K., Ishiyako America Inc., 1989) p. 68.
2. Bigi A., Incerti A., Roveri N. *et al., Bioniaterial* 1 (1980) 140-144.
3. Bohne W., Poutzat J.A., Peru L. et Daculsi G., *Cells and Materials* 3 (1993)) 419-424.
4. Daculsi G., LeGeros R.Z., Nery E. *et al., J Biomed Mater Res,* 23 (1989) 883-894.
5. Daculsi G., Passuti N., Martin S. *et al., J Biomed Mater Res,* 24 (1990) 379-396.
6. De Groot K., *Biomaterials,* 1(1980) 47-50.
7. Es-Saheb M.H., *J. Mat. Sci.* 27 (1992) 4151-4159.
8. Ferreira A., Meyers M.A. et Thadhani N.N., *Metall. Trans. A* 23A (1992) 3251-3261.
9. Ferreira A., Meyers M.A., Thadhani N.N. *et al., Metall. Trans. A* 22A (1991) 685-695.
10. Guicheux J., Heymann D., Trécant M., Gautier O., Faivre A., Daculsi G.., *J.Biomed. Mater. Res.* 36 1997) 258-264
11. J. Guicheux, G. Grimandi, M. Trécant, A. Faivre, S. Takahashi, and G. Daculsi, "Apatite as carrier for growth hormone:*In vitro* characterization of loading and release," *1. Biomed. Mater. Res.,* 34,165-170 (1997).
12. Krajewski A et Ravaglioli A.1, *Biomaterials* 2 (1981) 105-111.
13. M. Trécant, G. Daculsi, and M. Leroy *J. Mater. Sci. Mater. Med.,* 6, 545-551 (1995).
14. Meyers M.A., Wang S.L., *Acta Metall.* 36 (1988) 925-936.
15. Mordfin L., Kerper M.J., Mechanical and thermal properties of ceramics, Symposium on the mechanics and thermal properties of ceramic proceedings (1968) pp 243-262,
16. Morimoto Y., Hayashi T. et Nakanishi A., Inst. Phys. Conf Ser, No 70, paper presented at 3rd Conf Mech. Prop. High Rates of Strain, Oxford (1984) 427-434.
17. Morris D.G., *Metal Sci. 15* (1981) 116-124.
18. Page N.W et. Raybould D., *Mat. Sci. Eng.* A118 (1989) 179-195.
19. Raybould D., *J Mat. Sci.* 19 (1984) 3498-3514.
20. Raybould D., *J Mat. Sci.* 16 (1981) 5 89-598.
21. Trécant M., Daculsi G. et Leroy M., *J Mater. Sci. : Mater. in Med.* 6 (1995) 545-55 1.
22. Trécant M., Guicheux J., Grimandi G. *et al., Biomaterials 18* (1997) 141-145.
23. Van Blitterswijk C.A., Grote J.J., Kuijpers W. *et al., Biomaterials,* 7 (1986) 137-143.
24. Y. Shinto, A. Uchida, F. Korkusuz, N. Araki, and K. Ono, "Calcium hydroxyapatite ceramic used as a delivery system for antibiotics," *1. Bone Joint. Surg. Am.,* 74-B, 600-604 (1992).

Bioceramics Volume 11, edited by R. Z. LeGeros and J.P. LeGeros
(Proceedings of the 11th International Symposium on Ceramics in Medicine)
New York, NY, USA, November 1998
© 1998 by World Scientific Publishing Co. Pte. Ltd.

BONE AUGMENTATION BY BMP-COLLAGEN I AND BMP-POROUS BLOCK HYDROXYAPATITE COMPOSITE IN RAT CALVARIAL SUBPERIOSTEUM

H. Nagatsuka[1], M. Inoue[1], Y. Ishiwari[1], H. Tsujigiwa[1], B. Huang[1], N. Nagai[1], R. Z. LeGeros[2]

[1]Department of Oral Pathology, Okayama University Dental School, 2-5-1 Shikata, Okayama, JAPAN; [2] New York University, College of Dentistry, New York, NY, USA.

ABSTRACT

Bone morphogenetic proteins (BMP) are a group of cytokines that are characterized by their abilities to stimulate osteoblast differentiation and bone formation. In this study, we investigated the efficacy of type I attellocollagen (Col I) and porous hydroxyapatite ceramic block (PBHAP) as a carrier of BMP, and BMP-Col I and BMP-PBHAP composite as an onlay bone graft substitute in a calvarial model. BMP was mixed with type I attellocollagen and porous block hydroxyapatite . The BMP-Col I and BMP-PBHAP blocks were inserted beneath the cranial periosteum of 4 weeks old Wistar rats. Each composite were removed at 1, 2, 3, and 6 weeks after insertion and prepared for histological observations. Extensive bone formation occurred around the BMP- Col I and BMP-PBHAP blocks 2 weeks after implantation. At 6 weeks after implantation, the pores of BMP-PBHAP were filled with newly generated bone. The results demonstrated that the composite of BMP was osteoconductive and an effective material as an onlay bone graft substitute in rats.

KEYWORDS: BMP, Type I collagen, Hydroxyapatite, Bone augmentation

INTRODUCTION

Bone morphogenetic protein (BMP) was first described by Urist in 1965[1] and has been investigated for its bone inducing properties. Successful repair of craniomaxillofacial and other osseous defects has been accomplished using autogenous bone grafts. Now recombinant human BMP-1 through BMP-15 have been identified by genetic engineering techniques[2] and the time will come when BMP can be synthesized in large quantities and used in clinical practice

It is well known that a proper carrier is necessary in the BMP delivery system. Materials such as insoluble collagenous bone matrix, collagen and ceramics have been investigated as carriers for BMP [3,4]. Insoluble bone matrix (IBM), the guanidine-insoluble collagenous residue of the decalcified cortical bone matrix, has been a conventional organic carrier for natural or recombinant BMP for ectopic bone and cartilage formation in animal experiments [5]. IBM is solid particle with narrow space previously occupied by osteocytes and vessels. The disadvantages of IBM are its immunogenicity in host tissue and difficulty of sterilization. Unlike IBM, however, type I collagen and HAP has the properties of being biologically inert and has shown a good biocompatibility.

The purpose of this study, was to investigate the efficacy of type I attellocollagen (Col I) and porous hydroxyapatite ceramic block (PBHAP) as a carrier of BMP for bone repair in a calvarial model.

MATERIALS AND METHODS

Recombinant human morphogenetic protein-2 (rhBMP-2) and carrier
The rhBMP-2 used in this study was produced by means of genetic bioengineering techniques supplied by Yamanouchi Pharmaceutical Co., Ltd., Japan. The rhBMP-2 was prepared in 0.025mg/ml solution with phosphate buffered saline. Carriers of rhBMP-2 were the type I atelocollagen derived from bovine skin (Collagen PC-I, Koken, Japan) and porous block hydroxyapatite (5x5x3 mm, sintered at 1200   , 70% porosity, Mitsubishi Material). The rhBMP-2 (10fÊg) was mixed with 10mg of type I attellocollagen in the sterilized tube and lyophilized. The BMP/collagen I composites were compacted and shaped in a tube by a sterilized stainless steel stick. The rhBMP-2 (10mg) was mixed with the PBHAP and lyophilized.

Tissue preparation
All the animals were Wisteria strain rats (4 weeks, male, about 100g). BMP-Col I and BMP-PBHAP composites inserted beneath the cranial periosteum of Wistar rats under intraperitoneal anesthesia with pentobarbital sodium. The type I attellocollagen and porous block hydroxyapatite alone were inserted in the same manner as controls. At 1, 2, 3 and 6 weeks after insertion, the rats were sacrificed with overdose of diethylether anesthesia. The specimens were immersed in 4% paraformaldehyde solution in 0.1M phosphate buffer (pH7.4). A samples were dehydrated in ethanol series and decalcified with 15% EDTA (pH 7.4). Decalcified tissues were dehydrated and embedded in paraffin. Sections of 4 mm thickness were cut and mounted on 3-(triethoxylosilyl) -propylamin (Merck, Schuchardt, Munchen Germany) coated slides and stained with hematoxylin and eosin.

RESULTS

BMP-Col I composites
In the control group, at one and two week after insertion slight reactive osteogenesis was seen close to Col I in contact to with the cranial bone, by six weeks active bone formation was not seen.
In the BMP-Col I group, at one week after insertion a large number of proliferating mesenchymal cells were seen close to BMP-Col I composite.
On the side of composite, newly formed bones lined with a large number of osteoblasts and hypertrophic chondrocyte-like cells were seen (Fig 1). At two weeks after insertion, induced bones were observed in many regions of the composites, and trabecular bones lined with plump shaped osteoblasts. On the skull side, newly formed bones were seen. Carrier collagen remained in the central area of the composites. At three weeks after insertion, many trabecular bones were observed mainly in the extensive area with a large number of osteoblasts lining the trabecular bones. A few numbers of multinuclear giant cells were present beside the bone (Fig. 2). The carrier collagen still remained, but some of mesenchymal cells infiltrated in the carrier collagen. At six weeks after insertion, many trabecular bones with hematopoietic bone marrow were observed (Fig. 3). There were still flat shaped osteoblasts lining the trabecular bones, and bone marrow contained small round basophilic cells, as well as megakaryocytes. Carrier collagen was absent and replaced by trabecular bone and bone marrow.
BMP-PBHAP *composites*
In the control group, at one and two week after insertion, slight reactive osteogenesis was seen close to PBHAP in contact to with the cranial bone. By six weeks, active bone formation was not observed.
In the BMP-PBHAP group, at one week after insertion a large number of proliferating mesenchymal cells were seen close to BMP-PBHAP composite. On the skin side of composite, newly formed bones lined with a large number of osteoblasts were seen (Fig 4). Hypertrophic chondrocytes were absent and bone formation was predominantly intramembranous ossification. At two weeks after insertion, induced bones were observed on the side of the

composites, and trabecular bones lined with plump shaped osteoblasts. At three weeks after insertion, many trabecular bones were observed mainly in the extensive area with a large number of osteoblasts lining the trabecular bones. A few intramembranous bones were observed in the pore of the BMP-PBHAP composites (Fig. 5). At six weeks after insertion, many trabecular bones were observed. The pores of the BMP-PBHAP composites were filled with newly formed bones (Fig. 6). There were still flat or round shaped osteoblasts lining the trabecular bones, and bone marrow contained small round basophilic cells. Resorption of carrier PBHAP was not seen by six weeks after insertion.

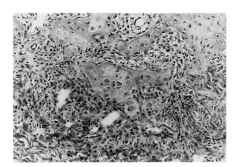

Figure 1. BMP-Col I, 1 week after insertion. A large number of proliferating mesenchymal cells ,newly formed bones and hypertrophic chondrocytes were observed. x100

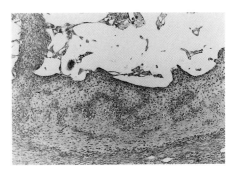

Figure 4. BMP-PBHAP, 1 week after insertion. Many proliferating mesenchymal cells and immature bones were seen close to BMP-PBHAP composite. x50

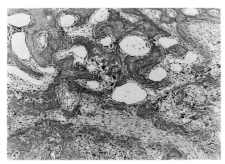

Figure 2. BMP-Col I, 3 week after insersion. Trabecular bone lining with a large number of osteoblasts were present. x50

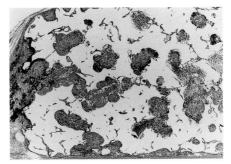

Figure 5. BMP-PBHAP, 3 week after insertion. A few intramembranous ossification were observed in the pore of the BMP-PBHAP composites. x50

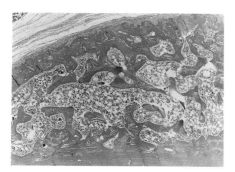

Figure 3. BMP-Col I, 6 week after insersion. Many trabecular bone with hematopoietic bone marrows were observed. x20

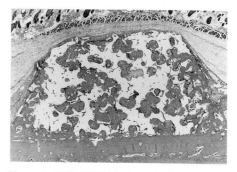

Figure 6. BMP-PBHAP, 6 week after insertion. The pores of the BMP-PBHAP composites were filled with newly formed bones. x10

DISCUSSION

Although rhBMP is now available for clinical use, the protein is not widely used because of the lack of suitable carrier for BMP. In recent years, attention has been directed to type I attellocollagen and hydroxyapatite as onlay bone graft materials in the field of plastic surgery, orthopedics, and dentistry [6,7,8]. The type I attellocollagen is biocompatible and resorbable. Hydroxyapatite is minimally resorbable, biocompatible, and osteoconductive. In this study, we compared bone formation of BMP-Col I with BMP-PBHAP as an onlay bone graft substitute in a rat calvarial model. Six weeks after insertion, complete resorption of carrier collagen and a change of shape and volume of BMP-Col I composites were observed. In contrast, the carrier PBHAP of BMP-PBHAP group remained six weeks after insertion, and maintained its shape and volume. These results suggest that both Col I and PBHAP are effective carrier materials of BMP as onlay bone graft, and PBHAP has the advantage of maintaining its shape and materials. The advantage of a resorbable onlay bone graft material combined with BMP is the potential for total replacement by bone tissues.

REFERENCES

1. Urist MR. Science 1965; 150: 893-899
2. Wozny JM, Rosen V, Celeste AJ, Mitsock LM, Witters MJ, Kriz RW, Hewick RM, Wang EA. Science 1988; 242: 1528-1534
3. Nagai N, Nagatsuka H, Murata M, Inoue M, Akagi T, Qin CL, Nakano K, Ishiwari Y, Konouchi H, Tsujigiwa H, Chigono Y, Takagi T. J Hard Tissue Biol 1995; 4: 25-23
4. Qin CL, Murata M, Nagatsuka H, Inoue M, Nagai N. Jpn J Oral Biol 1997; 39: 572-582
5. Nagatsuka H, Inoue M, Akagi T, Ishiwari Y, Liu G R, Huang B Z, Takagi T, Attia-Zouair M G, Nagai N. J Hard Tissue Biol 1997; 6: 10-15
6. Breitbart A S, Staffenberg D A, Thorne C H M, Glat P M, Cunningham N S, Reddi A H, Ricci J, Steiner G. Plast Reconstr Surg 1995; 96: 699-708
7. Miki T, Imai Y. Int J Oral Maxillofac Surg 1996; 25: 402-406
8. Ono I, Ohura T, Murata M, Yamaguchi H, Ohnuma Y, Kuboki Y. Plast Reconstr Surg 1992; 90: 870-879

Bioceramics Volume 11, edited by R. Z. LeGeros and J.P. LeGeros
(Proceedings of the 11th International Symposium on Ceramics in Medicine)
New York, NY, USA, November 1998
© 1998 by World Scientific Publishing Co. Pte. Ltd.

MULTIPLE INITIAL CALCIFICATION IN ECTOPIC BONE FORMATION INDUCED BY A BMP-COLLAGEN COMPOSITE

N. Nagai[1], M. Inoue[1], H. Nagatsuka[1], Y. Ishiwari[1], Y. Kinuta[1], K. Nakano[1], N. Nagaoka[1], R. Tamamura[1], and R. Z. LeGeros[2]

[1]Department of Oral Pathology, Okayama University Dental School, 2-5-1 Shikata, Okayama Japan; [2]New York University, College of Dentistry, 345 E. 24th Street, New York, NY, USA.

ABSTRACT

Subcutaneous implantation of a bone morphogenetic protein (BMP) - collagen type I composites induced direct bone formation. We then conducted an ultrastructural analysis of this bone formation.
The composite induced the bone without cartilage formation within 14 days after implantation. An initial calcification was observed not only on matrix vesicles within osteoid the tissue, but also on BMP- containing proteins and carrier collagen fibrils.
These results demonstrate that the initial calcification of direct bone formation induced by BMP appears at multiple-nucleation sites, and carriers not only stabilizes BMP, but also play a role as the site of the bone in nucleation and calcification.

KEYWORDS: Bone Morpogenetic Protein (BMP), ultrastructure, multiple initial calcification

INTRODUCTION

Bone morphogenetic protein (BMP) was first described by Urist in 1965.[1] It is well known that BMP induces chondro-osteogenic formation through connective cell differentiation, and that this chondro-osteogenic formation is similar to enchondral ossification of normal calcification.[2] However, recent studies have reported that BMP induced bone formation directly without cartilage, and that the cell differentiation pattern induced by BMP was highly dependent upon the nature of the cell environment that the carrier provided.[3,4,5]
In this study, we conducted an ultrastructual analysis of this direct bone formation to examine cell differentiation and initial calcification.

MATERIALS AND METHODS

Preparation of BMP
Fresh bovine metatarsal bone powder was cleaned of periosteum and marrow, pulverized, demineralized in HCl, and extracted with 4M guanidine HCl /0.05M Tris-HCl (pH7.4) containing protease inhibitors . The extract was filtrated and concentrated to limit the proteins within the molecular weight range between 10 KDa and 100 KDa. This molecular weight extract was dialyzed against cold distilled water, and the water-insoluble precipitation was collected by centrifugation. This fraction was designated as G-Ext BMP. The crude BMP was sequentially purified by heparin-Sepharose affinity chromatography (Pharmacia, 2.6 x 40 cm). In this study we termed this fractions as Heparin (Hep)-BMP. The BMP activity at each step of purification was determined by ectopic bone formation. Protein concentration was measured by the Bradford method.

Combination of BMP and Collagen
Hep-BMP (2.0mg) in 1.0 ml of 0.1% trifluoroacetic acid solution was mixed with 10mg of collagen (collagen type I, KOKEN) in a sterilized tube and lyophilized. The BMP-collagen composite was compacted and shaped in the tube by a sterilized stainless steel stick.

Collagen type I only was compacted as the control.

Tissue Preparation

Wistar strain rats (4 weeks, male, about 100g) were used. The BMP-collagen composite was implanted in the dorsal subcutaneous tissue of the rats. At 3, 5, 7, 10, 14, and 21 days after implantation, the rats were sacrificed under diethylether anesthesia. The specimens were immersed in 2% paraformaldehyde - 2% glutaraldehyde solution in 0.1M phosphate buffer (pH7.4).

The specimens were postfixed in 1% OsO4 solution. Then as prescribed in routine procedure, the material was dehydrated in ethanol and embedded in Epon 812. Ultrathin sections were double-stained with 2% uranyle acetate and lead citrate, and observed under a Hitachi H800 electron microscopy.

RESULTS

Bone formation without cartilage was observed by light microscopy at 7-14 days after composite implantation.
Three patterns of initial calcification were observed by electron microscopy, at the osteoid formation periods.
1) Initial calcification on matrix vesicles of the new osteoid

Osteoblast-like cells induced new osteoids close to the fine fibrils of the carrier (Fig.1). There were a number of mineralizing foci on the osteoids and carriers (Fig.2). Several membranous and granular structure acceptable as matrix vesicles were present between the collagen fibers in the new osteoid (Fig.3), and needle-shaped crystals deposits in the matrix vesicles.
2) Initial calcification on BMP-containing granular material of the carrier

This pattern was present at the border between the new osteoids and carriers. Collagen fibers in irregular sizes and low density areas of collagen fibers were observed in narrow osteoids between osteoblasts and the carrier. In these areas, osteoblasts with irregular shapes had some intracytoplasmic organelles. The granular materials on the borders between the osteoid and carrier showed mineral depositions (Fig.4). These calcification foci had a tendency for fusion, and calcification bundle on the carrier were observed.
3) Initial calcification of fine fibrillar materials of the carrier

Spike shaped mineral depositions were observed on the inner fiber side of the carrier collagen (Fig.5). Osteoids or osteoblasts were not seen around the carrier collagen. A similar pattern was observed with carrier pellets without BMP on 14 days to 21 days after implantation (Fig.6). In this case, osteoids or osteoblasts were not observed.

DISCUSSION

In normal bone formation, initial calcification occurs in or around matrix vesicles.[6] However, initial calcification in ectopic bone formation induced by our BMP-collagen composite occurred at three different areas.

Initial calcification on matrix vesicles was found mainly in ectopic bone formation. This pattern of calcification was similar to normal calcification. Our study showed that the carrier was important to direct bone formation, because most osteoids were observed close to the carrier fibers.

The subsequent pattern of calcification occurred on granular materials of the BMP-collagen composite. The calcification occurred on the border between osteoids and carriers, and spread to individual collagen fibers and carriers. In this pattern of calcification, osteoblasts had poor intracellular organelles. The density and shape of the osteoids were irregular, and not found in the matrix vesicles. The core of the calcification was on the granular materials of carrier and seemed to be partially purified BMP. This granular matrix had high affinity to calcium because of the presence of many proteins as histones in the partially purified BMP.[5] In this pattern, partially purified BMP was at the core of calcification.

The last pattern of initial calcification occurred on the fine fibrillar materials of the carrier collagen. Osteoblasts and osteoids were not observed, and a similar pattern of calcification was observed in carrier pellets without BMP as controls, so we suggest that this pattern is similar to that of nucleation sites of dystrophic calcification.[7]

These results demonstrate that the initial calcification of direct bone formation induced by BMP appears at multiple-nucleation sites, and the carrier not only stabalize BMP, but also plays a role as the site of the bone in nucleation and calcification.

REFERENCES

1. Urist MR. *Science* 1965; 150: 893-899
2. Reddi AH. *Cell Res* 1981; 1: 209-226
3. Missana L, Nagai N, Kuboki Y, *J Oral Biol* 1994; 36: 9-19
4. Nagai N, Nagatsuka H, Nakano K,, *J Hard Tissue Biol* 1995; 4: 15-23
5. Murata M, Tsujigiwa H, Kinuta Y, *J Hard Tissue Biol* 1997; 6: 95-104
6. Ham AW, Cormack DH. *Histology* Philadelphia and Toronto: Lippincott, 1969
7. Ferzo N. Ghadially, *Ultrastructural Pathology of the Cell and Matrix*, 3rd ed. London: Butterworths 1988: 1278-1289

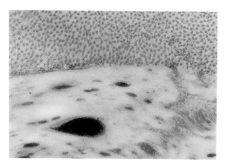

Figure 1. The border between the osteoid and carrier at 7-10 days after implantation. New collagen fibers are observed close to the fine fibrils of carrier. High density granular materials are present in the carrier.

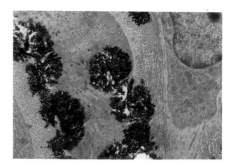

Figure 2. The border between the osteoid and carrier at 14-21 days after implantation. Some mineralized foci are observed on the fine fibrillar materials of the carrier.

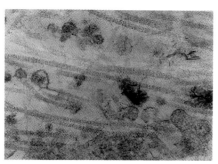

Figure 3. Osteoid. Needle-shaped crystals deposits in the matrix vesicles.

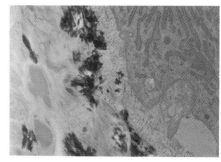

Figure 4. The border between the osteoid and carrier. Needle-shaped crystals deposits are seen on granular materials of the carrier.

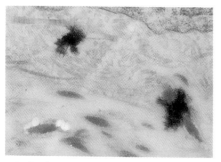

Figure 5. Carrier. Needle-shaped crystals deposits are present on fine fibrillar materials of the carrier.

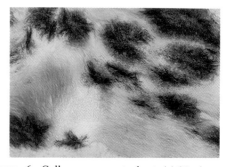

Figure 6. Collagen as control at 14-21 days after implantation. Mineralizing foci are observed on fine fibrils of the carrier. Osteoids or osteoblasts were not observed.

VII. CLINICAL APPLICATIONS

Bioceramics Volume 11, edited by R. Z. LeGeros and J.P. LeGeros
(Proceedings of the 11th International Symposium on Ceramics in Medicine)
New York, NY, USA, November 1998
© 1998 by World Scientific Publishing Co. Pte. Ltd.

MICROCHEMICAL ANALYSIS OF BIOACTIVE GLASS PARTICLES OF NARROW SIZE RANGE

E. Schepers, A. Huygh, L. Barbier, P. Ducheyne[⊕]

Department of Prosthetic Dentistry, Catholic University of Leuven, Kapucijnencoer 7, 3000 Leuven, Belgium
[⊕]Department of Bioengineering, University of Pennsylvania, Philadelphia, USA

ABSTRACT

Previous studies demonstrated the capacity of bioactive glass particles (BG) of narrow size range (300-355 μm, Biogran®) to stimulate the formation of new bone tissue by the formation of protective pouches. In these pouches, formation of new bone is detected without this bone being connected to the bone tissue outside the particles. These islands of newly formed bone tissue act as nuclei for enhanced bone repair. This osteostimulatory effect is a consequence of the chemical interactions between the bioactive glass and the surrounding tissue fluids. This study evaluates the chemical transformation of these bioactive glass particles. The particles are implanted in the jaws of beagle dogs and resected after 1, 2, 3, 6, 12 months. Microchemical analysis is performed using a scanning electron microscope equipped with an Energy Dispersive X-ray analysis system. The results show that after 1 month Na-ions are completely leached out and that the particle is transformed into a dual reaction layer; the centre is turned over into a Si-rich gel, while the outer surface consists out of a CaP-rich shell. After 2 months the concentration levels of the CaP-rich shell remain, while in the centre the Si-concentration decreases and the Ca- and P-concentrations increase. Histologically, phagocytosis of the Si-gel, resulting in excavated particles, is observed. These tendencies continue after 3 months and after 6 months Si has disappeared completely, while the Ca- and P-concentrations in the centre and in the outer shell are similar. At this time, bone formation in the excavated area is noticed. After 1 year the Ca- and P-concentrations in the transformed particles equal those of the bone tissue, further confirming the biological equivalence of the CaP-shell and bone tissue.

KEYWORDS: Bioactive glass, particulate, microchemical analysis

INTRODUCTION

Previous studies demonstrated that bioactive glass particles of narrow size range (300-355 μm) have besides their osteoconductive properties also osteostimulatory capacities [1,2]. It was shown that most of these particles eroded internally via small cracks. In these protective pouches new bone formation was observed which is not in connection with the external bone tissue. These islands of newly formed bone tissue act as nuclei for enhanced bone repair

This phenomenon of osteostimulation can be described as follows [3]. The interfacial ion exchange between the glass particles and the surrounding tissue fluids results in the formation of a Si-rich gel which extends throughout the centre of the particles. At the same time, a CaP-rich layer is formed at the outer surface. This complete transformation of the particles is possible due to the dimensions of the particles (300-355 μm) and the high fluid turnover in the surrounding tissues. This chemical transformation elicits also a physical change of the particle with crack formation in the outer CaP-rich layer as a consequence. Phagocytosing cells can penetrate the silica rich gel via these cracks and start the resorption of the gel. Subsequent to the resorption, mesenchymal cells penetrate the excavated centre via the small cracks. In this protected area centre with minimal fluid flow the osteoprogenitor cells can adhere to the inner side of the CaP-rich layer. When these primitive cells are immobilised on a bone-like substrate, differentiation into osteoblasts occurs and bone formation starts. In this way, bone tissue is formed without the need of osteoblast proliferation from the pre-existing bone.

In this study the chemical transformation of implanted bioactive glass particles is analysed using a scanning electron microscope equipped with an Energy Dispersive X-ray analysis system.

MATERIALS AND METHODS

Bioactive glass particles of narrow size range (300-355 µm) were supplied by FBFC International (Dessel, Belgium) and were prepared as follows. The glass components 45% SiO_2, 24.5% Na_2O, 24.5% CaO and 6% P_2O_5 by weight percentages, were premixed, melted in a platinum crucible at 1350 °C and poured into graphite moulds. These glass discs were cracked into pieces and reduced to small particles using a pestle and mortar. The particle size range from 300 µm to 355 µm was retained by sifting. These particles were cleaned ultrasonically and sterilised in ethylene oxide.

The premolars and first molar in the lower jaws of five beagle dogs were extracted at least three months prior to the implantation of the bioactive glass particles. In each of these partial edentulous lower jaws bone defects were surgically created using slowly rotating inner-cooled instruments. These defects were filled with bioactive glass particles and primary closure was obtained by non-resorbable sutures. The animals were sacrificed after 1, 2, 3, 6 and 12 months of implantation.

The resected specimens were embedded in methylmethacrylate and thin serial sections were made on a sawing microtome (Leitz, Wetzlar, Germany). Some of these sections were covered with a thin carbon layer for use in back-scattered or secondary electron scanning microscopy and energy dispersive X-ray analysis for Si, Na, Ca and P. These measurements were done on a cross-section with a mean value of 346 µm throughout the particle. Three histological sections of each time period were chosen at random and three particles in each section were analysed. The nine measurements of each time period were averaged and than plotted.

RESULTS AND DISCUSSION

Significant changes in the chemical composition of the particles are observed; some ions decrease in concentration or even disappear while others increase [4, 5].

The components of the glass are evenly distributed throughout the entire particle when the unreacted material is analysed. There are everywhere high amounts of Si and Na and lower amounts of ca and P.

After 1 month of implantation, an ion exchange between the particles and the tissue fluids have taken place. The chemical composition of the particles has completely changed; Na has leached out, the centre of the particle is Si enriched, while the outer surface became enriched in Ca and P. Morphologically, cracks can be observed in the outer CaP-rich layer as a physical consequence of the chemical transformation (*figure 1*).

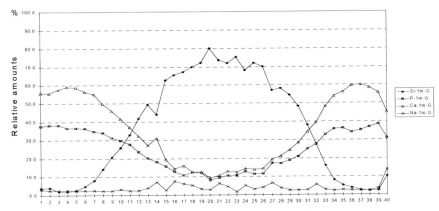

Figure 1: EDAX-profiles after 1 month of implantation

After 2 months of implantation, the Si-rich concentration in the centre of the particle is decreasing. Histologically, this corresponds with the resorption of the Si-gel by phagocytosing cells which entered the centre via cracks in the outer CaP-rich layer. The presence of these cells and also tissue fluids cause an increase of the Na-concentration in the centre of the particles. The concentrations of Ca and P in the outer CaP-rich layer remain stable.

The same evolution can be observed after 3 months, but now the concentrations of Ca and P start to increase in the centre of the particle. This coincides with beginning bone formation in the excavated centres of the particles, which is histologically confirmed (*figure 2*).

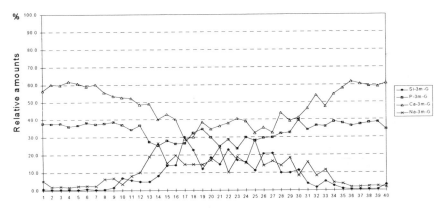

Figure 2: EDAX-profiles after 3 months of implantation

At 6 months, the differences between the centre and the outer part of the particle disappear. The concentrations of Ca and P in the outer shell remain stable, but their concentrations in the centre of the particles increase to a comparable level. The concentrations of Si and Na decrease. These observations correspond with further bone growth and complete fill with bone tissue of these excavated centres.

After 12 months of implantation, there are no differences anymore in the ion concentrations between the outer CaP-rich outer part of the particles and the centre of the particles. The excavated particles are completely filled with bone tissue. The concentrations of Ca and P are very high and equal to these of the internally formed bone, while the concentrations of Si and Na became very low (*figure 3*).

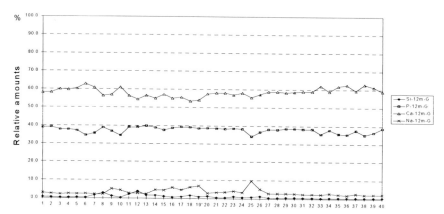

Figure 3: EDAX-profiles after 12 months of implantation

CONCLUSION

The chemical composition of the bioactive glass particles changes completely upon implantation. The outer surfaces enrich in Ca and P while the centre is turned over in a Si-rich gel. This gel will be resorbed and replaced by bone tissue. After 1 year of implantation the Ca and P- concentrations in the transformed glass particles equal those of bone tissue, further confirming the biological equivalence of the CaP-shell and bone tissue.

REFERENCES

1. Schepers EJG, De Clercq M, Ducheyne P, Kempeneers R. *J Oral Rehab* 1991; **18**: 439-452.
2. Schepers EJG, Ducheyne P. In: Ducheyne P, Christiansen D, ed. Bioceramics 6, Buttersworth-Heineman, 1993, 401-404.
3. Schepers EJG, Ducheyne P. *J Oral Rehab* 1997, **24**: 171-181.
4. Müller-Mai C, Turowsky G, Giersig M, Voigt C, Gross UM. In: Kokubo T, Nakamura T, Miyaji F. ed. Bioceramics 9, Pargamon, 1996, 37-40.
5. Hench LL, Pashall HA. J Biomed Mater Res 1973; 7: 25-42.

Bioceramics Volume 11, edited by R. Z. LeGeros and J.P. LeGeros
(Proceedings of the 11th International Symposium on Ceramics in Medicine)
New York, NY, USA, November 1998
© 1998 by World Scientific Publishing Co. Pte. Ltd.

BONE-GRAFTING OF CANINE EXTRACTION SOCKETS WITH AN INJECTABLE CALCIUM PHOSPHATE BIOMATERIAL

[1,2] O. Gauthier, [2] D. Boix, [2] G. Grimandi, [1,2] E. Aguado, [2] J. M. Bouler, [2] P. Weiss and [2] G. Daculsi

[1] Laboratoire de Chirurgie, Ecole Nationale Vétérinaire de Nantes, Route de Gachet, BP 40706, 44307 Nantes cedex 03, France, [2] Laboratoire de Recherche sur les matériaux d'intérêt biologique, Faculté de Chirurgie Dentaire, 1 place Alexis Ricordeau, 44042 Nantes Cedex 01, France

ABSTRACT

This experimental study evaluated the osteoconduction properties of an injectable bone substitute (IBS) composed of a polymeric carrier and a calcium phosphate mineral phase, which was used to fill mandibular and maxillary canine extraction sockets. The polymer was a cellulosic derivative (methyl-hydroxy-propyl-cellulose, MHPC), and the mineral phase consisted of granules of biphasic calcium phosphate (BCP) ceramics 200 to 500 μm in diameter. Mandibular and maxillary premolars were extracted from 3 dogs and 60 extraction sites were immediately treated with the IBS or left unfilled as control sites. Three months after implantation, histological studies showed that the IBS was able to support the extensive apposition of well-mineralized newly-formed lamellar bone over the entire socket surface and appeared to prevent alveolar ridge bone loss in treated extraction sites.

KEYWORDS : ceramics, calcium phosphate, injectable bone substitute, bone-grafting, tooth.

INTRODUCTION

Bone availability is an essential factor for efficient placement of implants in extraction sites[16]. Bone grafts and biomaterials, as demineralized freeze-dried bone allograft, autogenous cancellous bone and hydroxyapatite, are usually proposed to restore alveolar bone damage prior to implant placement[1,4-6,11]. More recently the development of biphasic calcium phosphate (BCP) ceramics has provided materials whose bioactivity is controlled by an association of HA and β-TCP in adequate ratios[7,14]. Most observations of bone ingrowth have concerned macroporous ceramics but calcium phosphate particles have proved more efficient than massive blocks for alveolar bone-filling, although they are difficult to handle[2,3]. It seemed of interest to develop a injectable calcium phosphate bone substitute (IBS) with conserved physicochemical and biological properties. The purpose of this study was to investigate the ability of this IBS to support new bone formation in fresh extraction sites and to compare its behavior in mandibular and maxillary animal sockets.

MATERIALS AND METHODS

1. Injectable bone substitute

The biomaterial used was obtained by combining a polymer and a calcium phosphate mineral phase. The ceramic, composed of 200 to 500 μm diameter BCP granules with a 60/40 HA/β-TCP weight ratio, was obtained by hydrolysis of commercial dicalcium phosphate dihydrate.

The associated polymer was a cellulose derivative (methyl-hydroxy-propyl-cellulose = MHPC) recently proposed as an efficient vehicle for the mineral phase[9]. The composite biomaterial was obtained by mixing a 2% MHPC solution with the 200-500 μm BCP granules in a 50/50 weight ratio and sterilized by steam at 121°C for 20 min.

2. Animal experiments

The extractions were performed on right and left second, third and fourth mandibular premolars and on right and left second and third maxillary premolars from three dogs. Thus, 10 teeth were extracted per animal so 20 alveolar extraction sites were available per animal for bone-filling, for a total of 60 extraction sites. After extraction, the depth of each socket was measured with a graduated probe. Extraction sites were grafted with the injectable biomaterial or left unfilled, i.e. the mesial socket of a tooth was left unfilled and the distal one filled with the composite biomaterial. The connective tissue surfaces of the buccal and lingual flap margins were carefully joined together with non-resorbable sutures.

Animals were sacrificed three months after implantation. Mandibular and maxillary osseous segments were immediately dissected from the animals and fixed in paraformaldehyde solution. The sockets were separated by cutting into the intra- and interdental septa with a diamond saw. Each socket was dehydrated in graded ethanol and embedded in a glycolmethylmethacrylate resin.

3. Histological evaluation

Both treated and control mandibular and maxillary sites were histologically evaluated with light microscopy. For each socket, 7-μm-thick sections were cut with a hard tissue microtome along the long axis of the root implantation site and then stained with solochrome-cyanine and Movat's pentochrome.

4. Bone ingrowth measurements

The resin block obtained from the central area of each socket was sputtered for scanning electron microscopy (SEM). Bone ingrowth was compared in filled and control mandibular and maxillary sites and quantitatively evaluated using a semi-automatic image analyzer from SEM observations of socket surfaces obtained with backscattered electrons. Their respective surfaces were calculated automatically and expressed as a percentage of the whole surface of the socket. Differences in bone ingrowth between mandibular and maxillary extraction sites were studied for statistical purposes with a Mann-Whitney U test. P values <0.05 were considered statistically significant.

RESULTS

1. Clinical results

Perfect mucoperiosteal and gingival healing was achieved 10 days after implantation in all animals.

53 extraction sites were available for further histological evaluation. After tooth extraction, the measured probing depth was significantly greater ($p<0.0001$) in mandibular (8.67 mm $\pm$ 1.02, n=32) than maxillary sockets (6.64 mm $\pm$ 0.57, n=21).

2. Histological results

Three months after implantation, extensive bone ingrowth was found in both filled and control mandibular and maxillary sites. In filled extraction sites, stainings showed the presence of highly mineralized newly-formed lamellar bone all around the BCP granules. New bone was observed throughout the extraction site, from the bottom of the socket to the top of the alveolar crest.

SEM observations confirmed the presence of newly-formed bone in both filled and control mandibular and maxillary sites, as well as close contact between newly-formed bone and ceramic particles. No BCP granules were found in control sites, indicating the absence of migration of material from the initial injection site. SEM also provided socket surface images, allowing evaluation of alveolar ridge height. Slight alveolar ridge bone loss was observed in almost every unfilled socket (-0.11mm ± 0.17, n=16). In filled ones, the IBS seemed to prevent a height decrease in the alveolar crest (alveolar ridge augmentation = + 0.41mm ± 0.66, n=16). Filled extraction sockets showed a wider and rounder contour, newly-formed bone was observed over the original crest and some osseous bridges between the two margins of the alveolar ridge.

3. Bone ingrowth results

Thirty-six sockets (18 mandibular and 18 maxillary sites) provided quantitative measurements of newly-formed bone. For both filled and control extraction sites, the rate of newly-formed bone was significantly higher ($p = 0.02$) in mandibular than maxillary sites. The mean rate of newly-formed bone was quite high in control sites. However, for the mineralized phase, the total hard tissue surface fraction was higher in treated sites than in control ones. 59% ± 8.6 of the treated sites surface (n=18) was filled with BCP ceramic and newly-formed bone. In control sites, 56% ± 12.1 of the sockets surface (n=18) was filled with bone. This difference in total hard tissue surface between treated and control sites was not significantly different.

DISCUSSION

Many experiments have been conducted in canine models to study the bone-filling of periodontal defects or extraction sites. We used both maxillary and mandibular sites to provide separate analysis of mandibular and maxillary sites. In spite of the gel consistency of the IBS, BCP granules remained in the filled mandibular and maxillary alveolar sites, and no BCP particles were found in the originally unfilled sites. Both mandibular and maxillary extraction sites showed notable newly-formed bone. Probing depth and bone ingrowth were greater in mandibular than maxillary extraction sockets. Finally, the differences between mandibular and maxillary sites were similar in control and treated sockets, indicating that the IBS did not disturb natural alveolar bone-healing conditions.

Different kinds of carriers have been proposed to improve the handling of calcium phosphate particles for periodontal applications[6,10]. Our results indicate that MHPC, which expressed good cytocompatibility properties[9], is an efficient in vivo vehicle for BCP ceramic particles.

Successful alveolar ridge augmentation, maxillary sinus grafting, or the grafting of defects near endosseous implants have been described with β–TCP, HA alone or HA mixed with autogenic or allogenic bone grafts[1,4,5,11,12]. BCP ceramics have also been used to treat periodontal osseous defects, promote bone ingrowth and new attachments on root sufaces and maintain alveolar ridges, providing a sufficient quantity of bone for the placement of endosseous implants[13,15]. In this study, newly-formed bone three months after implantation was well-mineralized lamellar bone.

The IBS expressed osteoconduction properties. Newly-formed bone was in close contact with BCP granules without any fibrous interface, as usually described with these calcium phosphate ceramics[7,8].

The association of SEM and image analysis proved to be an efficient method of obtaining reproducible quantitative data for newly-formed bone[8]. Quantitative evaluation showed that the amount of newly-formed bone was significantly higher in mandibular than maxillary extraction sockets for both treated and control sites. Our method indicated that the IBS used was efficient since the hard tissue fraction was not significantly different when all treated sites were compared with all control sites. Even though alveolar ridge augmentation was not our main goal, extraction site bone grafting with this IBS seemed to prevent bone loss of the alveolar ridges. Observations from SEM images indicated that alveolar ridge height remained nearly unchanged in control sites but was increased in treated extraction sites.

CONCLUSION

This experiment demonstrated the in vivo biocompatibility and osteoconduction properties of a composite cellulosic-calcium phosphate biomaterial. This injectable bone substitute promoted new bone formation in treated extraction sockets similar to that observed in controls, preserved alveolar bone volume and seemed to prevent alveolar ridge bone loss. This experimental work showed that a composite calcium phosphate biomaterial with injectability properties and conserved biactivity can promote bone ingrowth in alveolar extraction sites and seems promising for further periodontal applications

REFERENCES

1. Becker W, Becker BE, Caffesse RG. *J Periodontol* 1994; **65**: 1128-1133.
2. Bell DJ. *J Prosthet Dent* 1986; **56**: 322-326.
3. Block MS, Kent JN. *J Oral Maxillofac Surg* 1986; **44**: 89-93.
4. Bowen JA, Mellonig JT, Gray JL, Towle HT. *J Periodontol* 1989; **60**: 647-654.
5. Brugnami F, Then PR, Moroi H, Leone CW. *J Periodontol* 1996; **67**: 821-825.
6. Cook SD. *J Oral Implantol* 1994; **20**: 292-298.
7. Daculsi G, LeGeros RZ, Nery E, Lynch K, Kerebel B. *J Biomed Mater Res* 1989; **23**: 883-894.
8. Gauthier O, Bouler J-M, Aguado E , Pilet P, Daculsi G. *Biomaterials* 1998; **19**:133-139.
9. Grimandi G, Weiss P, Millot F, Daculsi G. *J Biomed Mater Res* 1998, in press.
10. Mehlisch DR, Taylor TD, Leibold DG. *J Oral Maxillofac Surg* 1987; **45**: 408-413.
11. Mentag PJ, Kosinski T. *J Oral Implantol* 1989; **15**: 114-123.
12. Moy PK, Lundgren S, Holmes RE. *J Oral Maxillofac Surg* 1993; **51**: 857-862.
13. Nery EB, Eslami A, Van SR. *J Periodontol* 1990; **61**: 166-172.
14. Nery EB, LeGeros RZ, Lynch KL, Lee K. *J Periodontol* 1992; **63**: 729-735.
15. Piatelli A, Scarano A, Mangano C. *Biomaterials* 1996; **17**: 1767-1770.
16. Schwartz-Arad D, Chaushu G. *J Periodontol* 1997; **68**: 915-923.

Bioceramics Volume 11, edited by R. Z. LeGeros and J.P. LeGeros
(Proceedings of the 11th International Symposium on Ceramics in Medicine)
New York, NY, USA, November 1998
© 1998 by World Scientific Publishing Co. Pte. Ltd.

TISSUE RESPONSE TO ANTI-WASHOUT APATITE CEMENT IN THE PREMAXILLA OF A RAT

Yoshiya Ueyama[1], Kunio Ishikawa[2], Takamitu Mano[1], Takahiro Koyama[1], Hitoshi Nagatsuka[3], Tomohiro Matsumura[1] and Kazuomi Suzuki[3]

[1]Department of Oral and Maxillofacial Surgery, [2]Department of Dental Materials and [3]Department of Oral Pathology, Okayama University Dental School, 2-5-1 Shikata, Okayama 700-8525 Japan

ABSTRACT

The anti-washout apatite cement (aw-AC) sets within approximately 5-6 min to form hydroxyapatite without crumbling, even when the cement paste is immersed in fluid immediately after mixing. Although aw-AC has good potential value to be a good candidate as biomaterials aimed at the reconstruction of bone defects, only a limited study has been done so far, and no study has been done with respect to the tissue response to aw-AC in the palatal region. Therefore, the aim of this study was to evaluate the tissue response to aw-AC when used for filling in bone defects in the palatal region and the course of healing of bone defects, compared with the conventional apatite cement (c-AC). Bone defect was made in the premaxiila of a rat with a round bar, filled with AC, and evaluated histologically. We found no inflammatory reactions in the surrounding areas of bone in the case of aw-AC and the bone defect was covered with new bone. In contrast, c-AC eaused inflammatory reactions in the area surrounding the cement filling and the degree of bone regeneration was poor. We conclude that aw-AC is superior to c-AC in biocompatibility, and, therefore, is a useful material for filling in bone defects.

KEYWORDS: anti-washout apatite cement, reconstruction of premaxilla in a rat, tissue response

INTRODUCTION

Recently, apatite cement (AC) has attracted a lot of attention since it forms hydroxyapatite after setting and shows excellent tissue response. The conventional apatite cement (c-AC), that powder phase consist of an equiamolar mixture of tetracalcium phosphate (TTCP) and dicalcium phosphate anhydrous (DCPA), and employed distilled water as liguid phase, has already been applied clinically.   The setting time of c-AC, however, is relatively long (30-60 min), and it washes out when it comes into contact with fluids before its setting reaction[1-3]. To improve shortcoming of the c-AC, we have proposed the anti-washout apatite cement (aw-AC).   It sets within approximately 5-6 min without washing out, even when the cement paste is immersed in fluid immediately after mixing[1-3].   Therefore aw-AC may be a good candidate for the biomaterials aimed at the reconstruction of bone defects since it can be also used where the complete hemostasis is difficult.   Although tissue response to aw-AC is the key factor for the feasibility of aw-AC, limited studies has been done so far, and none has been done which analyze the tissue response to aw-AC in the palatal region.   The aim of this study, therefore, is to evaluate the tissue response to aw-AC when used for filling in bone defects in the palatal region as well as the subsequent course of healing of these bone defects.

MATERIALS AND METHODS
Preparation of anti-washout apatite cement
An equimolar mixture of TTCP and DCPA was used as the power phase of c-AC and aw-AC. The liquid phase of aw-AC was 0.2ml/l Na1.8H1.2PO4 including 0.5% sodium alginate, whereas distilled water was used as the liquid phase of c-AC.   Each cement was designed to be mixed with the powder and the liquid (P/L=3.5).
Animals and implantation procedure
Seven-week-old male Wistar rats weighting about 200g, fed commercial rat food and water ad libitum, were used for the experiment.   The rats were anesthetized with intraperioneally injection sodium pentobarbital (0.08ml/Kg).   A straight incision was made in the midline mucosa of the premaxillary bone under sterile conditions.   The palatal mucosa flap, consisting of mucosa and periosteum, was then raised and the premaxillary bone was exposed.   A approximately 2-mm diameter bone defect was prepared in the midline of the premaxilla with a round bar.   The wound was flushed with isotonic saline to reduce heat generation.   Both types of cement were designed to be mixed with the powder and the liquid (P/L=3.5) on a glass using a spatula for 20 seconds. After that, the prepared bone defect was reconstructed with each cement. The mucosa flap was then closed and sutured.
Histological preparations
Each rat was anesthetized with sodium pentobarbital to the level at which respiration was markedly suppressed, and was perfused from the ascending aorta with phosphate-buffered saline (PBS) followed by 500ml of 4% formaldehyde in 0.1 mol/L phosphate buffer (pH 7.4).   After removing the premaxillary regions, specimens were further prepared with the same fixative for 24 hours.   They were then decalcified with 10% formic acid for 10 days.   After dehydration in an ascending   graded series of ethanol, the specimens were embedded in paraffin and sectioned 3mm thick.   The sections were stained with hematoxylin-eosin for light microscopy.

Result
2-Week Specimens
aw-AC: Surrounding the aw-AC area, there was almost no inflammatory reaction.   The filled aw-AC was enclosed with a fibrous connective tissue.   The osteocytes were partially recognized at the rims of the bilateral defects, but the greater part of the defects were still filled with aw-AC (Figure 1).

c-AC: Severe inflammatory reactions occurred around the c-AC. Moreover, c-AC flowed out and many gigantic cells of a foreign type appeared around it (Figure 2).

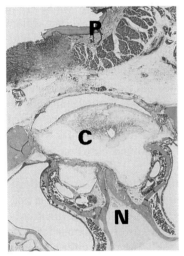

Figure 1. 2 weeks after filling with aw-AC
(H-E stain, x 40)

Figure 2. 2 weeks after filling with c-AC
(H-E stain, x 40)

C: apatite cement, P: palatal side, N: nasal side

8-Week Specimens

aw-AC: The surrounding area of the bone defect was repaired with new bone, and the fibrous connective tissue did not stand between the aw-AC and the bone. The appearance of phagocytosed cement was recognized in the new bone.

c-AC: The foreign body reaction remained in the area surrounding the cement, and the foreign granular tissue was also recognized.

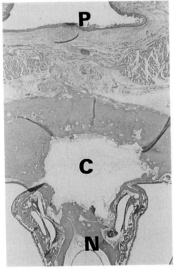
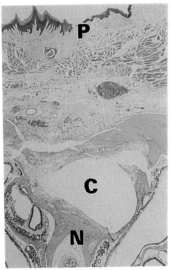

Figure 1. 8 weeks after filling with aw-AC
(H-E stain, x 40)

Figure 2. 8 weeks after filling with c-AC
(H-E stain, x 40)

C: apatite cement, P: palatal side, N: nasal side

Discussion

c-AC has been already applied clinically in Europe and North America, Costantino and Friedman[4,5] reported that c-AC converted substantially to hydroxyapatite within 4 to 6 hours, showed excellent tissue response, and was finally reabsorbed and replaced by natural bone within eighteen months. Their results, however, seemed to be valid only when c-AC set without crumbling. For example, bone defects of the palatal regions in rats in this study had a tendency to bleed, and the cement contacted with blood in the restoration even if the initial hemostasis was sufficient. As a result, c-AC failed to set and washed out when it contacted with blood. Consequently, the inflammatory reaction was arisen in the area surrounding the cement filling. Although the remarkable inflammatory reaction decreased with time, foreign body reactions even after 8 weeks were still recognized. Moreover, in c-AC, the closure of the wound based on bone was not complete even after eight weeks.

On the other hand, in aw-AC, no inflammatory reaction was recognized after two weeks. After four weeks the cement was covered with fibrous connective tissue and giant cells appeared next to the cement. After eight weeks, however, very few giant cells were recognized. The histological findings showed that the aw-AC was surrounded with new bone, and giant cells appeared next to the cemented area. The plain difference between c-AC and aw-AC may be due to the wash out property of the c-AC. We have previously reported that c-AC crumbled and caused inflammatory response when the paste was implanted subcutaneously in rat, whereas aw-AC caused no inflammatory response[6]. When the cement paste was implanted subcutaneously in rat, it is free from fluid exposure but suffer some pressure. c-AC takes longer time to set and shows lower mechanical strength in the initial stage. Thus it crumbled and caused inflammatory response. In the experimental condition used in this study, c-AC is free from pressure but faced with body fluid. As a result, it crumbled and caused inflammatory response. In both conditions, aw-AC set keeping the shape at implantation, thus caused no inflammatory reaction in the area surrounding the aw-AC filling. we have to pay attention for use of c-AC.

In conclusion, we understand that aw-AC is superior to c-AC in biocompatibility, and is a useful material for filling in bone defects. We have to pay attention and select clinical cases for use of c-AC so that its shortcoming , long setting time and washout property, would not appear a problem for the setting reaction of c-AC.

Reference

1. Ishikawa K, Miyamoto Y, Kon M, Nagayama M, Asaoka K. Biomaterials 1995; **16**: 527-532.
2. Miyamoto Y, Ishikawa K, Takechi M, Yuasa M, Kon M, Nagayama M, Asaoka K Biomaterials 1996; **17**: 1429-1435.
3. Takechi M, Miyamoto Y, Ishikawa K, Yuasa M, Nagayama M, Kon M, Asaoka K. J Mater Sci; Mater Med 1996; **7**: 317-322.
4. Costantino PD, Friedman CD, Jones K. Arch Otolaryngol Head Neck Surg 1991; **117**: 379-384.
5. Friedman CD, Costantino PD, Jones K. Arch Otolarygol Head Neck Surg 1991; **117**: 385-389.
6. Ishikawa K, Miyamoto Y, Nagayama M, Suzuku K. Bioceramics 1997; **11**: 301-304.

Bioceramics Volume 11, edited by R. Z. LeGeros and J.P. LeGeros
(Proceedings of the 11th International Symposium on Ceramics in Medicine)
New York, NY, USA, November 1998
© 1998 by World Scientific Publishing Co. Pte. Ltd.

BONDING OF BIOACTIVE GLASSES TO HUMAN DENTIN

S.E. Efflandt[1], P. Magne[2], W.H. Douglas[2], L.F. Francis[1]

[1]Department of Chemical Engineering and Material Science, University of Minnesota
151 Amundson Hall, 421 Washington Ave. SE, Minneapolis, MN 55455
[2]Minnesota Dental Research Center for Biomaterials and Biomechanics, University of Minnesota
16-212 Moos Tower, 515 Delaware St. SE, Minneapolis, MN 55455

ABSTRACT

The purpose of this study was to assess the potential of bioactive glasses to bond to human dentin. Bioactive glass beads in the $CaO-MgO-P_2O_5-SiO_2$ and $Na_2O-CaO-P_2O_5-SiO_2$ systems were prepared and polished to provide a flat surface for bonding. Human teeth were cut to expose dentin, kept hydrated and treated with a mild phosphoric acid. Each tooth was then placed against a sample of bioactive glass (or non-bioactive glass control) with a thin layer of whole saliva in the interface. The pairs were secured with an elastic band, immersed in whole saliva and placed in an incubator at body temperature for 3 or 6 weeks. Observations showed that the bioactive glasses adhered to dentin, but the non-bioactive glass did not. Bioactive glass/dentin pairs were prepared for analysis across the interface. SEM results showed the presence of a new material in the interface. Microdiffractometry on the glass side of debonded pairs showed crystalline peaks corresponding to those of apatite-like materials. From these results we conclude that a new material is formed at the interface between bioactive glasses and dentin, leading to bonding and promise for the development of new dental materials.

KEYWORDS: bioactive glasses, bonding, dental materials, SEM, microdiffractometry

INTRODUCTION

Bioactive glasses and glass-ceramics in bulk shapes as well as coatings and granules have been used or proposed for a variety of hard tissue replacement and repair applications.[1] Bioactive glasses and glass-ceramics form a layer of apatite on their surfaces *in vivo* and create a contiguous bond to bone.[2,3] In addition, these materials interact favorably with bone-producing cells and soft tissues, making them ideal for hard tissue regeneration applications such as bone grafts.[4] The *in vivo* bonding to bone correlates with the formation of apatite *in vitro* when materials are soaked in aqueous solutions with ionic composition and pH similar to plasma. Saliva has a very similar ionic composition as plasma, although it has a slightly lower pH and contains different organic species.[5] Recently, we have shown that bioactive glasses in the $CaO-MgO-P_2O_5-SiO_2$ system form an apatite-layer when soaked in human whole saliva[6], indicating the potential for bonding to dental hard tissues such as dentin.

Dentin is an intricate connective tissue with an average composition of ~ 50 vol % (70 wt%) inorganic crystals, 23 vol % (18 wt%) organic material, and 27 vol % (12 wt%) water.[7] In the natural formation process, dentinogenesis, an organic collegenous matrix is constructed by secretions from odontoblast cells and is mineralized with $Ca_{10}(PO_4)_6(OH)_2$ (hydroxyapatite, HA) crystallites. This process is quite similar to the formation process for bone.[7,8] Dentin and bone are close in structure; however, dentin is not vascularized. In fully formed dentin, dentinal tubules pass through the entire dentin structure; these tubules house the odontoblast process, act as biological mass transport canals and provide a means for dentin repair.[9] The similarity between dentin and bone as well as the observation of apatite formation on a bioactive glass in saliva provided the motivation for this study of the bonding of bioactive glass to dentin.

Usually, porcelain is bonded to dental tissue using composite resin combined etching procedures.[10-12] This makes the clinical bonding procedure a very complicated and time-consuming process. Moreover, the composite material does not represent an ideal luting agent because of its curing contraction and its thermal expansion mismatch with regard to dental hard tissues.[13,14] In this context, an innovative approach would consist of obtaining a direct bonding between the ceramic and the dentin, trying to simulate the dentioenamel junction.

MATERIALS AND METHODS

Two types of glass powder were used to determine their potential bonding to human dentin: (1) $44.9CaO-4.6MgO-16.3P_2O_5-34.2SiO_2$[15] and (2) $24.5Na_2O-24.5CaO-6P_2O_5.45SiO_2$[2]. Both glass powders are made by Specialty Glass Inc. in Oldsmar, Florida and were used as-received. Other materials used in this study were standard microscope slides as a control, human dentin, whole human saliva and phosphoric acid.

Glass beads were prepared by melting the powders separately in a platinum crucible for 1 hour at 1500°C, quenching the molten glass onto an aluminum block, and annealing the beads at 650°C for 4 hours to relieve internal stresses. The beads were then polished using several grits of silicon carbide paper to ensure a smooth surface. Human teeth were cut to expose a maximum dentin surface and then etched with 37% phosphoric acid. The dentin was also kept hydrated at all times. A layer of fresh saliva was placed on the dentin surface and the bioactive glass was placed against it. The two parts were then secured together with an elastic band and completely immersed in whole saliva in a glass bottle with an airtight seal. Additionally, a standard microscope slide was used as a control. These bottles were then placed in an incubator at body temperature (37°C) for 3 or 6 weeks. The 3-week samples included 1 $Na_2O-CaO-P_2O_5.SiO_2$ glass/dentin pair, 1 $CaO-MgO-P_2O_5-SiO_2$ glass/dentin pair and 1 microscope slide/dentin pair. Following the encouraging qualitative results of the 3-week samples, a 6 week immersion was performed using 2 pairs each of the two glasses.

The bonding at the interface between the glass and dentin was investigated by several methods. First, each pair was probed qualitatively to assess the degree of adherence. All pairs with a bioactive glass were adhered well enough for further interfacial studies, indicating that bacterial growth did not overwhelm the growing interfacial material creating the bond. Some pairs were mounted in resin and sliced perpendicular to the interface using a slow speed diamond saw. After drying, the cross-sections were mounted on a stub, coated with a thin metal layer and then examined by SEM. Other pairs were separated (by drying, see below), exposing dentin and glass surfaces. The glass surfaces had visible patches of interfacial material which were examined using microdiffractometry.

RESULTS AND DISCUSSION

After the allotted time, the glass/dentin pairs were removed from the incubator and bond strength assessed qualitatively. Adherence of the dentin to the bioactive glass was noted for all 6 pairs investigated in this study. By contrast, the microscope slide glass/dentin pair immediately fell apart when its elastic band was removed. This qualitative assessment of bonding strength did not allow any conclusions to be drawn about the relative effectiveness of the different bioactive glass compositions or the effect of incubation time on the bonding.

The bioactive glass/dentin pairs were then examined (after drying) with SEM to obtain visual evidence of an interfacial material. As dentin dries, the collagen collapses which leads to shrinkage and fracture at the interface. Despite this destruction, SEM examinations still revealed an interfacial material. An example is shown in Figure 1. The interfacial material has a different microstructure than the glass and the dentin. Interestingly, the shrinkage-induced fracture did not follow a straight path, but rather gave a jagged path which may indicate some microstructural mechanisms of crack deflection. The interfaces of other bioactive glass/dentin pairs had similar features, but comparisons between pairs could not be made due to the irregular nature of the fractures. We have also examined a bioactive glass/dentin interface before dehydration using a polymeric replica technique; these results showed that the interfacial material continuously spanned the glass and dentin.[16]

Microdiffractometry, which determines crystallinity of a small area (approximately 1 mm^2), was performed on the glass side of a dried sample. Since SEM indicated that the interfacial material would most likely be on both the glass and dentin sides after cleavage, the glass side was investigated so that any crystallinity could be ascribed to the interfacial material. The data shown in Figure 2 confirms the presence of a crystalline interfacial material. Peaks matching apatite-like phases (PDF#09-0432) were identified; additionally, several unidentified peaks appeared in the data. Further characterization is required for their identification. The apatite in the adhered interfacial material could have formed by growth in the interface during the immersion of the pair in saliva. Alternatively, the apatite may originate from dentin that was separated with the interfacial material and left on the glass surface. Both sources of apatite indicate a bond forming at the interface as a result of interaction between dentin, bioactive glass and saliva.

These results indicate the possibility of forming a mineralized bond to dentin perhaps similar to bonds which has been successfully used for bonding to bone. More research is needed to conclusively identify the interfacial material and to understand how the bond forms with time. Efforts are underway to prepare bioactive glass/dentin pairs without shrinkage-induced fracture for better analysis of the interface via techniques such as electron microprobe analysis.

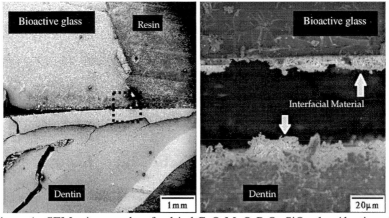

Figure 1. SEM micrographs of a dried $CaO-MgO-P_2O_5-SiO_2$ glass/dentin pair
after 3 weeks in saliva. Overall set-up is shown in (a) with outlined box of interface.
Higher magnification of interface from box is shown in (b)

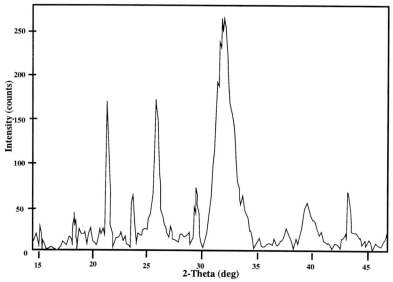

Figure 2. Microdiffraction data from adhered interfacial material on the $CaO-MgO-P_2O_5-SiO_2$ glass separated from dentin after 6 week incubation in saliva

ACKNOWLEDGEMENTS

We thank the NSF (DMR-9357502); the Minnesota Dental Research Center for Biomaterials and Biomechanics and the Dept. of Oral Science at the University of Minnesota; the Dept. of Prosthodontics and Dept. of Prevention and Therapeutics at the University of Geneva; and the Swiss Science Foundation (81GE-50071). We also thank H.Y. Huang for helpful discussions.

REFERENCES

1. Hench LL. *J Am Ceram Soc* 1991; **74**: 1487-1510.
2. Hench LL, Paschall H. *J Biomed Mater Res Symposium* 1973; **4**: 25-42.
3. Kokubo T, Ito S, Huang ZT, Hayashi T, Sakka S, Kitsugi T, Yamamuro T. *J Biomed Mater Res* 1990; **24**: 331-343.
4. Oonishi H, Kushitani S, Yasukawa E, Iwaki H, Hench LL, Wilson J, Tsuji E, Sugihara T. *Clinical Orthopaedics and Related Research* 1997; **334**: 316-325.
5. Ten Cate AR. *Oral Histology: Development Structure and Function.* St. Louis, MO: The C.V. Mosby Co., 1980: 312-340.
6. Huang HY, Francis LF. To be submitted.
7. Mjor IA. In: A. Linde, ed. Dentin and Dentinogenesis, Vol. I. Boca Raton, FL: CRC Press, Inc., 1984: 1-18.
8. Ten Cate AR. *Oral Histology: Development Structure and Function.* St. Louis, MO: The C.V. Mosby Co., 1980: 106-114.
9. Ten Cate AR. *Oral Histology: Development Structure and Function.* St. Louis, MO: The C.V. Mosby Co., 1980: 395-408.
10. Buonocore MG. *J Dent Res* 1955; **34**: 849-853.
11. Nakabayashi N, Kojima A, Masuhara E. *J Biomed Mat Res* 1982; **16**: 265-273.
12. Roulet JF, Soderholm KJ, Longmate J. *J Dent Res* 1995; **74**: 381-387
13. Magne P, Versluis A, Douglas WH. In press.
14. Versluis A, Douglas WH, Sakagushi RL. *Dent Mater* 1996; **12**: 290-294. .
15. Kitsugi T, Yamamuro T, Nakamura T, Kokubo T. *J of Biomed Res* 1989; **23**: 631-648.
16. Efflandt SE, Magne P, Douglas WH, Francis LF. In preparation.

Bioceramics Volume 11, edited by R. Z. LeGeros and J.P. LeGeros
(Proceedings of the 11th International Symposium on Ceramics in Medicine)
New York, NY, USA, November 1998
© 1998 by World Scientific Publishing Co. Pte. Ltd.

CLINICAL STUDY OF TEETH WHITENING PROPERTIES OF TOOTHPASTES CONTAINING HYDROXYAPATITE

H. Aoki, K. Matsuda*, H. Aoki*, T. Daisaku**, T. Sato***, and M. Niwa***

International Apatite Institute, 2-1 Surugadai Kanda Chiyoda-ku Tokyo, 101 -0062, Japan.
*Tokyo Bioceramics Institute Co. Ltd., 2-7-1 Honcho Nihonbashi Chuo-ku Tokyo,
**Kokonoe Orthodontic Clinic, 5-12-15 Honcho Koganei City Tokyo,
***Nippon Dental University, 1-9-20 Hujimicho Chiyoda-ku Tokyo.

ABSTRACT

Toothpastes containing hydroxyapatite (HA-toothpaste) were developed in 1978. Since then, clinical test had been performed in Japanese Dental Universities over ten years. In 1990, it was demonstrated that the toothpastes are dramatically effective in preventing caries. However, the effect on whitening teeth has not been investigated. In this study, the effect of the toothpastes on whitening teeth was examined clinically using two kinds of colorimeters with two specially made fiberscopes.

Keywords: hydroxyapatite, toothpastes, colorimeter, and whitening.

INTRODUCTION

Toothpastes are composed of flavoring, foaming, sweetening, viscous, and brightening agents, and have to be nontoxic and nonabrasive. The toothpastes available in Japan have been used as a tasty cleanser rather than a preventive against caries. In 1978, a toothpaste containing hydroxyapatite (HAp-toothpastes) was developed by Aoki (Japan Patents No. 1,553,260 and 1,557,631, 1990; and U.S. Patent No.4,327,079, 1982). The HAp toothpastes have three main clinical advantages: efficacy in preventing caries or treatment of periodontal disease; removal of mouth odor; and teeth whitening. The effect of preventing caries was demonstrated by the 10 years clinical studies at three universities in Japan. According to the results, it was concluded that the HAp-toothpastes are dramatically effective in preventing caries. The hydroxyapatite content of the toothpaste was reported to promote remineralization on tooth surfaces and arrest the progress of incipient caries. The effect of removal of mouth odor was clarified by the properties of absorption of hydroxyapatite with protein, lipids, polysaccharide, etc. However, the effect on teeth whitening has not been investigated.

In this study, changes in the brightness and whiteness of teeth were investigated clinically at Nihon Dental University using HAp- and non-HAp toothpastes.

MATERIALS and METHODS

<u>Materials</u>: Toothpastes containing hydroxyapatite: 0%, 3%, 15% by weight, were prepared.
<u>Apparatus</u>: Changes in the brightness and whiteness of the upper central incisor teeth were measured by two

colorimeters (SZ- Y -90 and SE-2000) with two specially made fiberscopes (inner diameter of 3.5 and 2.5mm).

Clinical tests: Subjects, 20 to 50 years old who have not used HA-toothpastes were selected for the study.
At the beginning of the study, brightness and whiteness of the teeth of the subjects were measured using colorimeters with fiberscopes. Then, toothpastes containing 15% HA, 3% hydroxyapatite and common toothbrushes were delivered to two groups of subjects. The subjects were instructed to use each toothpastes two times a day. After two, four weeks, and six months, the brightness, whiteness and color of the teeth were measured using the specially designed colorimeters. From the changes in brightness, whiteness, and color of the teeth, the effect of the HAp-toothpastes on teeth whitening teeth was determined.

RESULTS

Relationships of brightness, whiteness, and color.
Statistical testing of the values determined for each tooth revealed significant differences in L^*(brightness), a^*(red), and Y^* (yellow). L^* and whiteness increase with brightness increasing. When L^* is zero, it is black, while L^* is 100, it is physically perfect white. L^* decreases with a^* and Y^* increasing (Fig. 1).

Figure 1. L^*, a^*, Y^* streogram
for representation of color.

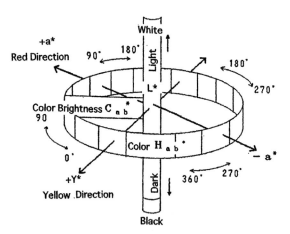

Brightness and whiteness values ranged from 30 to 60, and most values were approximately 50 units. Differences between left and right upper front teeth were less than 20%. Yellow color values of the teeth ranged from -10 to 40 units.

After 2 weeks: Measurements were carried out five times about one tooth. When the teeth were measured, saliva on the teeth was wiped off to obtain stable data. The brightness and whiteness of the teeth increased by 67%. In the case of toothpastes containing 15% HA, the increase was 71 %, compared to 60% with 3% HAp-toothpastes. The rate of increase was 19% with 15% HAp-toothpastes and 12.5% with 3% HAp-toothpastes. After a short time of 2 weeks, 15% HAp-toothpastes made teeth white and bright in 71% of the subjects and the average rate of increase in the brightness and whiteness of teeth was 19% (Fig. 2).

After 4 weeks: When teeth were brushed using 15% HAp-toothpastes, increase in values of brightness and whiteness were 64% higher than values after 2 weeks. On the other hand, in the case of 3% HAp-toothpastes the increase in values were 40% higher than those after 2 weeks. However, in the case of 3% HAp-toothpastes, a decrease of 60% in brightness and whiteness were observed (Fig. 2).

After 6 months: At six months the brightness and whiteness were stable and a slight decreas was observed. The brightness and whiteness of the teeth of a few subjects who stopped using the Hap toothpastes drastically decreased.

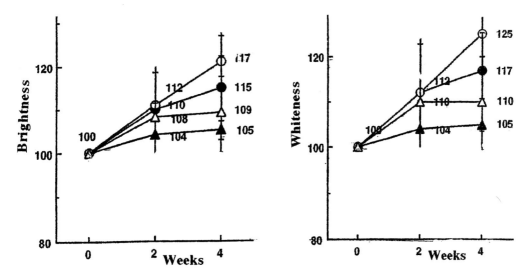

<u>Figure 2</u>. Changes in brightness and xN7hiteness after 2 and 4 weeks.

DISCUSSION

The brightness and whiteness of upper front teeth drastically increased for the short time by using toothpastes containing HA compared to toothpastes without HA. The degree and rate of brightness and whiteness increased with the amounts of hydroxyapatite present in the toothpastes.

The increase in brightness and whiteness of teeth may be explained by the removal of plaque, smoother surfaces, etc. In the Aoki's patents of 1978, the reasons were described as follows: polishing properties of HAp-toothpastes are lower than those of toothpastes without HA and remineralization causes the tooth surfaces to become smooth. *In vitro* and *in vivo* testing showed that HA promote remineralization of tooth surfaces causing them to be smooth. This phenomenon was demonstrated by SEM and optical microscope obervations. The flat surface increases the brightness and whiteness of teeth, Because the brightness and whiteness depend on the reflection rate of light

CONCLUSIONS

1. The toothpastes containing hydroxyapatite increased teeth brightness and whiteness.
2. The degree and rate of increase in brightness and whiteness increased with the amount of hydroxyapatite in the toothpaste.

REFERENCES

1. H. Aoki, U.S. Patent No.4,327,079(1982). Japan Patents, 1,553,260(1990), 1,557,631(1990).
2. N. Furuya, A. Shinya, and S. Yokozuka; Basic Studies on Conditions of Color Measurements, J. Shigaku (Odontology), Vol.80, No.5 (1993) pp. 1 125-1139.
3. K. Kobayashi, A. Shinya, and S. Yokozuka; Basic Studies on Color Stability of Teeth Using Photoelectric Colorimeter, J. Shigaku (Odontology) Vol. 82 No. 5(1995) pp. 1033 -1055.
4. H. Aoki, H. Aoki, K. Matsuda, Y. Kawai, T. Kutuno, T. Daisaku, M. Niwa and T. Sato-, Change in Color of Enamel, Trans. 13th Symp. Apatite Japan. (1997) pp.5.

Bioceramics Volume 11, edited by R. Z. LeGeros and J.P. LeGeros
(Proceedings of the 11th International Symposium on Ceramics in Medicine)
New York, NY, USA, November 1998
© 1998 by World Scientific Publishing Co. Pte. Ltd.

INTERPENETRATING-PHASE COMPOSITE DENTAL RESTORATIVE MATERIALS

J. J. Harris, H. Hornberger and P. M. Marquis

The University of Birmingham, Biomaterials Unit, School of Dentistry, St Chad's Queensway, Birmingham, B4 6NN, United Kingdom.

ABSTRACT

Interpenetrating-phase composites (IPCs) are systems where each phase is continuous and interconnected in three dimensions. These structures can possess unique and novel properties. In this paper we report a method for the fabrication of a metal/glass IPC and compare it with In-Ceram, an alumina/glass IPC currently in use in clinical dentistry. The average biaxial flexure strength of In-Ceram has been shown to be in excess of 600 MPa. Although weaker, with a biaxial flexure strength of approximately 200 MPa, the novel metal/glass IPC has been shown to demonstrate non-brittle composite failure behaviour indicating its potential suitability for use in dental crowns and bridgework.

INTRODUCTION

An interpenetrating-phase composite (IPC) may be defined as a multiphase material in which each of the component phases are continuous and interconnected throughout the microstructure[4]. Examples of such materials include spinodally decomposed silicate glasses[1], PZT/polymer piezoelectric transducers[15] and glass ceramic composites such as In-Ceram (Vita, Germany)[2,8,12,13].

Traditional composite materials are normally manufactured through the incorporation of isolated high strength, high modulus, reinforcing components into a softer homogenous matrix. Such materials, particularly with fibrous reinforcement, commonly display mechanical property anisotropy. IPCs, by contrast, display no such anisotropy due to their three-dimensional interconnected reinforcement providing isotropic resistance to crack growth[4].

Manufacturing techniques for IPCs are varied, depending on the constituent materials, and can include infiltration of preformed porous substructures with a secondary phase. In-Ceram manufacture involves capillary infiltration of low viscosity glass into a slip cast and sintered porous alumina core. Ceramic preforms can also be made by sintering a pre-ceramic polymer infused powder compact[9].

High gold dental copings are also produced by capillary infiltration of pure gold into a gold/platinum/palladium substructure made using an alloy particle/organic binder mixture; the CAPTEK process[14]. Upon heat-treatment the binder material volatilises and the alloy particles fuse together creating an interconnected network. Subsequent infiltration of pure gold gives rise to a composite coping comprising two distinct interpenetrating metal phases.

The principal advantage of IPCs lies in the potential to combine materials to tailor final component properties. Flexible composite piezoelectric materials have been produced through IPC technology by combining a highly piezoelectric, brittle ceramic with a non piezoelectric elastomer[10]. The CAPTEK process utilises IPC technology to eliminate the casting shrinkage inherent to dental coping production[11], improving marginal accuracy[3] and resulting in the production of high gold (88% 22 carat) copings with superior aesthetics to the finished crown.

IPCs therefore represent a major advance in materials processing as they provide a means to the fabrication of components in which the desirable features of each constituent material are exploited to produce a multifunctional, optimised composite.

Crowns and Bridges

Dental porcelain glasses have been used in the manufacture of dental crowns for many years due to their aesthetic qualities but are restricted in application due to their brittle nature and limited flexural strength (45-90MPa). Jacket crowns can be made using all ceramic approaches, utilising aluminous core porcelain, or by employing porcelains fused to metal. The excellent aesthetics associated with these all-ceramic systems are offset by deficiencies in mechanical properties, whilst the latter are optimised in the metal ceramic system at the expense of aesthetics. An IPC system offers the potential to combine the key features of both of these systems.

MATERIALS AND METHODS

In-Ceram Disc Manufacture

In-Ceram alumina (Al_2O_3) slip was prepared according to the manufacturers instructions and disc-shaped test-pieces produced using the methods described by Hornberger[6].

Metal-Glass IPC Disc Manufacture

A mould was constructed from a standard investment material according to the manufacturers instructions. Discs of 13 mm diameter were cut from a strip of Au/Pt/Pd particles dispersed in a polymeric binder) and placed onto the refractory block. The discs were then air fired at 1075°C for 4 minutes to burn out the polymer and point sinter the alloy particles. A thin slurry of In-Ceram glass was applied to the upper surface of the porous metal discs which were placed, uncoated side up, onto a sheet of platinum foil and fired at 1,100°C for 2 ½ hours.

Mechanical Testing

Biaxial flexure strength was calculated from load-at-failure data obtained using ball-on-ring apparatus in an Instron 5544 universal testing rig (Instron Ltd, England). Specimens were positioned on a circular knife-edge support, 10 mm diameter, and loaded in compression using a steel ball-bearing. Interposition of a thin sheet of rubber between sample and knife-edge minimised any stress concentrating effects produced by surface peculiarities of either component. The IPC specimen was tested using a crosshead speed of 0.001 mm/min to observe any slow crack growth effects. In-Ceram discs were tested at 1 mm/min.

RESULTS

The mean biaxial flexure strength of the 67 In-Ceram specimens was 605 ± 108 MPa (Weibull Moduli of 6.44)[7]. The single IPC disc tested to date possessed a strength of 204 MPa assuming a Poisson's ratio of 0.25 The In-Ceram discs demonstrated typically brittle behaviour whilst in contrast the metal glass IPC showed evidence of non-brittle composite behaviour, failing in a more graceful manner than In-Ceram, as shown in figure 1. The three peaks in fig. 1a, indicated by arrows ①, ② and ③, correspond to applied loads of 13.57, 12.9 and 12.39 N respectively.

Young's Modulus

The Young's modulus measured using ultrasonic methods for In-Ceram was 255±55 GPa. The relative Young's modulus of the IPC, determined through gradient measurements of the stress strain curves, was 71.68 GPa.

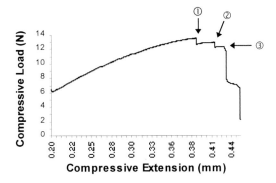

Figure 1a. Load Extension data as recorded during mechanical testing of IPC disc.

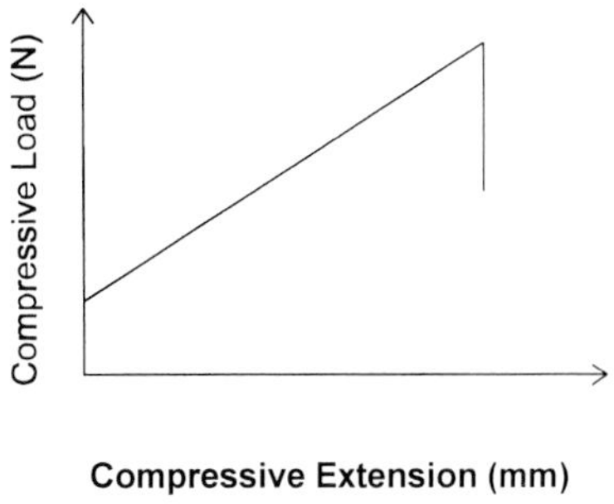

Figure 1b. Typical appearance of data produced by brittle materials such as In-Ceram.

Examination of the fracture surface produced as a result of failure of the IPC (see fig 2) reveals a highly convoluted morphology, consistent with composite failure.

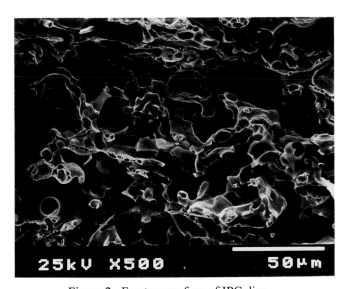

Figure 2. Fracture surface of IPC disc.

DISCUSSION

Load-extension curves plotted from data obtained from the testing of In-Ceram highlight the typical limitations of brittle materials; minimal deformation prior to sudden and catastrophic failure of the specimen. By comparison the curve obtained from the metal-glass IPC shows several novel features. Initiation of failure is associated with peaks ①,② and ③ (fig. 1a) which are indicative of failure mechanisms associated with crack formation and arrest. The SEM micrograph of the IPC fracture surface (fig. 2) reinforces the suggestion of brittle fracture but also presents evidence of failure of a ductile nature. The lack of linearity in the initial part of the curve implies that some plastic deformation has taken place whilst the absence of any evidence of discrete load reduction events in this region suggests that cracks in the glass phase are arrested by the metal phase.

The influence of the metal on the mechanical properties of the IPC are also reflected in the reduced Young's modulus. Although the strength of the IPC is significantly lower than that of In-Ceram it compares favourably with some clinically successful systems such as Empress (134-180MPa) and Dicor (152 MPa). The strength of the IPC disc was also calculated using an arbitrary Poisson's Ratio value of 0.25. Most engineering materials exhibit values of approximately 0.3 with metals falling in the range 0.25-0.5 [5]. The lower bounds value of 0.25 is characteristic of a ceramic, however the IPC may posses a higher value of Poisson's ratio which will affect the calculated biaxial flexure strength. Assuming the Poisson's ratio for the IPC is 0.5, the corresponding biaxial flexure strength is 238 MPa.

The behaviour patterns of the IPC demonstrate a series of characteristics which highlight the potential of such a composite system to be employed in bridgework where fatigue is recognised problem. IPCs may also be used for single crowns where they should offer a resistance to slow crack growth degradation in oral fluids combined with a potential for extremely good aesthetics.

REFERENCES

1. Cahn JW, Charles RJ. *Phys Chem Glasses* 1965; **6**, 4: 181-191.
2. Campbell D, Pelletier LB, Pober RL, Giordano RA. *J Prosthet Dent* 1995; **74**: 332-340.
3. Choi C, Sorensen JA. *J Dent Res* 1994; **73**: 191; Abstract No 715.
4. Clarke DR. *J Am Ceram Soc* 1992; **75**, 4: 739-759.
5. Flinn RA, Trojan PK. *Engineering Materials and their Applications*, 4th ed. Houghton Mifflin Co., 1990: 104.
6. Hornberger H. *J Mater Res* 1996; **11**: 1934-1942.
7. Hornberger H.. *Strength Microstructure Relationships in a Dental Alumina Glass Composite* 1995: PhD Thesis, The University of Birmingham.
8. Kelly JR, Nishimura I, Campbell SD. *J Prosthet Dent* 1996; **75**: 18-32.
9. Kelly JR, Smith SM, Antonucci JM. *J Dent Res* 1995; **74**: 166; Abstract No 1237.
10. Newnham RE, Skinner DP, Cross LE. *Mat Res Bull* 1978; **13**: 525-536.
11. Phillips RW. *Skinners Science of Dental Materials*, 9th ed. W.B. Saunders Co, 1991: 371-372, 379-380.
12. Pober R, Giordano R, Campbell S, Pelletier L. *J Dent Res* 1992; **71**: 253; Abstract No 1179.
13. Rosenblum MA, Schulman A. *JADA* 1997; **128**: 297-307.
14. Shoher I, Whiteman A. *European Patent Spec* 1987; Publication No. 0 270 084 B1.
15. Skinner DP, Newnham RE, Cross LE. *Mat Res Bull* 1978; **13**: 599-607.

Bioceramics Volume 11, edited by R. Z. LeGeros and J.P. LeGeros
(Proceedings of the 11th International Symposium on Ceramics in Medicine)
New York, NY, USA, November 1998
© 1998 by World Scientific Publishing Co. Pte. Ltd.

IMPLANTATION OF CUBAN GRANULATED HYDROXYAPATITE "APAFILL-G™" IN PERIAPICAL BONE DEFECTS

M.C.P. Alvarez[1], R.G. Corrodeguas[2], J.A.D. Garcia-Menocal[2], I.F. Diaz[2], D.M. Arguelles[2], J R. Hernandez[1], E.A. Hernandez[1], S.A. Guttierrez[1]

[1]Clinica Estomatologica Docente de bauta Ave. 251 No. 13201, Bauta, Prov Habanna Cuba; [2]Centro de Biomateriales de la Universidad de la Habanna Ave. Unversidad s/n Cuidad Habanna 10400, Cuba

ABSTRACT

The authors present their clinical experience implanting the Cuban granulated hydroxyapatite APAFILL-G™. Between 1990 and 1997, 708 patients, having periapical bone defects of diverse origin were treated. The follow up of cases consisted in initial and post-operatory periodical clinical and radiographic examinations over a period of one year.
The APAFILL-G™ implantation procedures were performed surgically or endodontically, depending on the nature and or characteristics of the bone defect. The results showed a treatment efficacy of 97.0%. No adverse reactions caused by the implanted material were observed during the follow-up period.
The clinical and radiographic examination showed complete bone repair after 6 months for surgically implanted cases, and 9 months for those implanted endodontically.

KEYWORDS: Hydroxyapatite, periapical bone defects, bone repair, endodontics, and periapical surgery

INTRODUCTION

Hydroxyapatite ceramics are similar to bone mineral in chemical composition and crystalline structure. It has been accepted that this similarity is responsible for the biocompatibility, bioactivity, and osteoconductivity exhibited by hydroxyapatite ceramics when implanted in bone tissue. Many scientific papers concerning hydroxyapatite implantation in bone defects in animal and human subjects have been published since 1970's. The results generally point out the efficacy of hydroxyapatite as a filling material able to bond and integrate to bone tissue [1,2,3].
Odontology was the first field of application of hydroxyapatite ceramics and at present, continues to be the main consumer of hydroxyapatite products[4]. They have been successfully employed in the treatment of periodontal and periapical bone defects, and pre-prosthetic remodeling of alveolar ridge[5].
Periapical osteolytic bone lesions are quite frequent cause of attendance to Cuban dentistry services. Its origin is generally related to pulp infection processes or traumas affecting the teeth 6.
APAFILL-G™ is a trademark of synthetic hydroxyapatite ceramic granules fabricated by the Centro

de Biomateriales de la Universidad de la Habana. "In vitro" tests have shown that no cytotoxic haemolytic or genotoxic activity is related to the material. Experimental implantation in dogs confirmed its biocompatibility, bioactivity and osteoconductivity.

This study presents the efficacy of APAFILL-G for treating periapical bone defects in several dental clinics in Cuba.

METHOD AND MATERIALS

The hydroxyapatite used in this study was APAFILL-G™ (BIOMAT), a dense synthetic hydroxyapatite in the form of granules of irregular shape which fulfills the requirements of International Standardization Organization 8.

The population (who volunteered for this study) included 708 patients having periapical bone defects. They attended several public dental services in the Cuban provinces of Habana, Pinar Del Rio, Matanzas, Santi Spiritu, and Sanriago de Cuba, between 1990 and 1997. All defects were classified in the categories 0, and 1, according to the World Health Organization. Subjects were between 8 and 70 years old, without background of neither neoplasm nor uncontrolled diabetes.

The bone defects were classified into circumscribed and diffuse, according to their radiographic appearance. In circumscribed bone defects, conventional apical surgery and curettage were used. Apicoectomy debridement and sealing of the canal of the affected teeth was made when needed. APAFILL-G™ particles with a grain size between 0.1mm and 0.4mm were mixed with distilled sterile water, blood or saline, then condensed in the defect site by gentle pressure and covered with a fibrin mesh to prevent particle migration. After restoring the mucoperiosteum and the flap, the surgical incision was sutured with 3.0 silk suture or with tissue adhesive Tisuacryl® (Biomat).

Diffuse bone defects were treated by techniques of periapical reparation techniques implanting hydroxyapatite via the root canal. After a pulpectomy and careful irrigation of the root canal with calcium hydroxide solution; a paste made of calcium hydroxide solution and APAFILL-G™ (particle size lower than 0.1mm) was implanted in root canal. The root canal was temporarily scaled with Cimpat (Septodont). Irrigation, implantation and temporary sealing were repeated monthly 2 more times. Between the sixth and ninth months, the canal was permanently sealed.

The follow-up consisted of monthly clinical and radiographic exams for one year after the implantation. Three assessment categories were established by comparison to the initial clinical and radiographic exams. (1) Satisfactory: complete disappearance of radiographic and clinical initial symptom. (2) Improvement: partial disappearance of radiographic and clinical initial symptoms, or partial disappearance of radiographic, and complete disappearance of clinical ones, or vice versa. (3) Failure: clinical and radiographic symptoms similar to those initially observed. x^2 and t-Tests were employed to compare the frequency distribution of the three assessment categories and the efficacy, among the two treatments, surgical and endodontical.

RESULTS

The following table summarizes the results in the study. An efficacy of 97.3% and 96.7% was found for surgical and endodontical implantation procedures, respectively considered as the obtained rate of satisfactory. Both values had no statistical difference ($\alpha = 0.05$), and the global efficacy was 97.0%.

The x^2-Test showed that the frequency of the three categories, S, D, and I was the same p=0.05) for both procedures, surgical and endodontical.

Table Frequency distribution (absolute) of the assessment categories.

Treatment	S	I	F	Total
Surgical	366	7	3	376
Endodontical	321	6	5	332
Total	687	13	8	708

S: Satisfactory, I: Improvement, F: Failure

Typical circumscribed defect, surgically treated

Male 30 years old carrying a typical circumscribed periapical bone defect related to a cyst that affected the central and lateral upper right incisors without clinical symptoms.

A well-delimited radiolucent area that corresponded to the bone defect occupied by cystic soft tissue was observed in the initial radiograph. The radiolucent area showed radiopacity similar to normal adjacent bone but implanted granules could be stilled distinguished. The picture was similar one month after surgery, but a radiolucent well-defined border between implanted material and adjacent bone appeared. After 6-months, the radiolucent border disappeared and no difference in optical density between the implanted site and surrounding normal bone could be detected in the radiograph picture after 1-year was the same, without any sign of regression.

Typical diffuse defect, endodontically treated

Female, 27 years old carry a typical periapical bone defect affecting central and lateral right lower incisors. Antecedent of trauma involving the affected teeth and clinical symptoms of pain, mobility-3, and active fistula were detected.

Pain and fistula completely disappeared two months after the endodontical implantation. Physiological mobility was achieved after 6 months.

Fetidness in the conduit was completely removed in the third month. Definitive scaling was carried out 6 months after implantation. No regression of clinical symptoms was detected at 1-year clinical exam.

Radiographically, a wide radiolucent area with diffuse limits was observed, indicating destruction of periapical alveolar trabeculae. Two months after implantation, radiolucency started to gradually disappear. The initial radiolucent area became indistinguishable 6 months after implantation. Radiological examinations after 1-year showed that the initial radiolucent area exhibited normal radiopacity and no evidences of regression were observed.

DISCUSSION

The main cause of failure in circumscribed periapical bone defects was the regression of radiolucency due the presence of false conduits originated in a previous root canal treatment, that were not detected during the surgical procedure (2 cases). Other cause of failure (1 case) was a post-operatory trauma, which caused root fracture of the affected tooth. In satisfactory, cases the initial clinical symptoms normally disappeared 1- month after the implantation. Radiographically, a demarcation line between hydroxyapatite granules and bone appeared in the 1-month radiograph and disappeared between the third and sixth month. Bleeding from the bone walls after the implantation may cause this phenomenon[9]. The initially distinguishable granules were apparently integrated by bone, which grew from the wall of the defect after the sixth month.

The causes of failure in the endodontial treatment of diffuse bone defects could not be identified. However, the authors presume that success it is related to the absence of soft tissue in the defect. The clinical symptoms in satisfactory cases disappeared 1 month after the implantation. The radiographic aspect of the defect gradually becomes similar to the adjacent wealth bone and indistinguishable between the third and sixth month.

No signs of rejection of the implanted material were observed neither in surgical nor endodontical treatments. The high rate of success obtained in this study suggested that surgical and endodontical implantation of granule hydroxyapatite APAFILL-G™ is an effective techniques for the repair of periapical bone defects. The success of the procedures strongly depends on the proper selection and evaluation of the patient and a previous preparation technique.

ACKNOWLEDGEMENTS

Authors acknowledge the financial support of the Cuban Ministries of Health, and Science, Technology and Environment. The work is part of the activities of the Joint Project CYTED VIII.6.

REFERENCES

1. LeGeros RZ, LeGeros JP, In Hench LL, Wilson J, Eds. *An Introduction to Bioceramics*, Singapore: World Scientific, 1993: 139-180.
2. Shors FC Holes RE. In Hench LL, Wilson J Eds. *An Introduction to Bioceramics*, Singapore; World Scientific: 1993: 181-198.
3. LeGeros RZ *Calcium Phosphates in Oral Biology and Medicine*. Monographs in Oral Science, Vol. 15 Eds. Myers HM, ed., Basel; Karger, 1991: 154-171.
4. Jarcho M. Dent Clin North AM 1992: 36: 19-26.
5. LeGeros RZ. Adv. Dent Res. 1988; 2; 164-180.
6. Alvarez L Endodoncia. La Habana : Ed Revolucionaria, 1977: 421-455.
7. APAFILL-G Technical information, La Habana, Centro des Biomateriales, 1997
8. ISO/DIS 13779-96 Implants for Surgery. Ceramic materials based on Hydroxyapatite. International Organization for Standardization 1996.
9. Hara Y. in Gold St. Midda M, Mutlu S, Eds. Recent Advances in Periodontology, Vol. II, Excerpta Medicia; Amsterdam, 1991: 69-76.

Bioceramics Volume 11, edited by R. Z. LeGeros and J.P. LeGeros
(Proceedings of the 11th International Symposium on Ceramics in Medicine)
New York, NY, USA, November 1998

ENZYME CYTOCHEMISTRY OF HYDROXYAPATITE-SOL APPLICATION TO RATS' MOLAR PULP

Tuantuan Li and Hideki Aoki

International Apatite Institute (IAI), 2-1 Surugadai Kanda Chiyoda-ku Tokyo, 101 -0062
Japan.

ABSTRACT

Tissue reaction in rat molar after direct pulp capping with hydroxyapatite-sol (HAp-sol) or suspension of hydroxyapatite heated at 800'C (HAp-800) was studied by enzyme cytochemistry using electron microscopy. HAp-sol was prepared by dispersing unheated hydroxyapatite microcrystals into distilled water. HAp-800 was used as a comparative material. 0.001ml of each sample was injected into the pulp of the upper first molar of Wistar male rats using a microliter syringe. At 7 days postoperatively in the group of hydroxyapatite-sol, ACPase activity was detected along all biosynthesizing pathways in odontoblast-like cells. In the group of HAp-800°C after 7 days postoperatively, ACPase activity was detected only along the membranes bounding cytoplasmatic vacuoles. LDH activity had shown phagocytosis of hydroxyapatite microcrystals by odontoblasts. However, in the group of HAp-800°C after 7 days postoperatively, phagocytosis of hydroxyapatite microcrystals by odontoblasts was not observed.
These findings suggest that HAL-sol material may be a source of Ca and inorganic phosphate through hydrolysis by alkaline phosphatase (ALP), and induces the early formation of tubular dentine. Hap sol is a safe biomaterial for dental pulp capping and induces early formation of dentine-bridge more so than HAp-800°C.

Keywords: Hydroxyapatite-sol, Enzyme cytochemistry, Molar Pulp.

INTRODUCTION

Hydroxyapatite-sol composed of hydroxyapatite microcrystals without heating was developed as a new biomaterial for use as a drug carrier, an absorbent of virus and an accelerator of bone formation (Aoki et al, 1992). Since then, many researchers have presented that hydroxyapatite-sol can be used as effective drug carriers (Aoki et al, 1994), and it has an excellent biocompatibility with macrophage cells (Fukuchi et al 1995, 1996), and absorbs HIV (Kobayashi et al. 1995). Recently serological and hematologists' studies of HAp-sol were presented. The HAp-sol can be used as a hydroxyapatite-coating agent on titanium for dental implants (Li et al, 1995). The author et a] reported that bone formation in femur marrow and dentine bridge in rat's molar pulp is more accelerated by injection of the HAp-sol than by HAp-800°C (Li et al, 1996). The tissue reaction of the HAp-sol to rats' molar pulp was examined histologically in order to investigate whether HAp-sol can be used as a successful direct pulp capping material.

MATERIALS AND METHODS

Calcium carbonate was calcined at 1050°C for 3 hours. The product was hydrated to $Ca(OH)_2$ by adding distilled water were vigorously stirred and a solution of H_3PO_4 (0.6 mol) in 750 ml distilled water was added drop-wise (100ml/15min) using an ultrasonic homogenizer to produce hydroxyapatite microcrystals at room temperature. The reaction mixture was aged for three days at room temperature. A little HAp-sol was filtered and dried at 60°C for 24 hours. The powder was heated at 800'C for 2 hours in air (HAp-800°C). The resulting HAp-800°C powder was suspended into distilled water. The concentration of HAp-sol and HAp-800°C was 14.8mg/ml. HAp-sol and HAp800'C suspensions were identified by X-ray diffractometry with a horizontal goniometer (RINT-Ultima, RIGAKU Co).

In vivo study

Wistar male rats of 6-week-old with average weight of 150 g were used, 0.001ml of each sample was injected into the pulp of the upper first molar which was exposed by a #1/2 round bur at low speed through the mesial surface of teeth using a microliter syringe. After injection, the pulp was covered by a temporary sealing material.

Enzyme Cytochemistry

After tissue dissection, the fresh teeth with pulp were immersed further at 4°C in the same fixative for 1-2 h. After immersion for 1-2 h in 20% dimethyl sulfoxide solution of pH 7.5, the samples were cut with a Vibratome (Oxford, UK) or freezing microtome at thickness 20-60 mm. Acid phosphates (ACPase) and Localized Dehydrogenate (LDH) activities were determined cytochemically. After incubation for enzymatic activity, the sections were postfixed, and embedded as mentioned above. Ultrathin sections were either left unstained or doubly stained with both uranyl acetate and lead citrate and examined under a Hitachi H-600 electron microscope at 75 kV.

RESULTS

Characterization of Materials

X-ray powder diffraction (XRD) patterns of the HAp-sol showed broad diffraction peaks while the HAp-800°C showed sharp peaks of hydroxyapatite. The broad peaks reflect the small hydroxyapatite crystals less than 0.1 mm, in HAp-sol

Enzyme Cytochemistry: ACPase Activity

After 7 days postoperatively, in the group A (HAp-sol), ACPase activity was detected along all the biosynthesizing pathways, including the perinuclear space, Golgi complex, vesicles and vacuoles of odontoblast-like cells attached to the HAp particles. The reaction product was seen on the eroded pulp surface and within the porous HA p structure.

LDH activity was localized along the inner membranes of the crest of the mitochondria as small dots on the plasma membrane and in some cases along the inner lamellae of Golgi apparatus. In the region of the Golgi apparatus, a relatively great number of LDH-positive small vesicles were seen.

In group B (HAp-800°C), LDH activity was not observed.

DISCUSSION

The size and crystallinity of apatite in HAp-sol was approximately 0.1 μm, almost the same as those of biological apatites in the bones and dentine of animals and human beings. Initial solubility in distilled water of the HAp-sol was two times higher than that of HAp-800°C. The solubility and the rate of dissolution depend on differences in crystal size or crystallinity of HAp. After the dissolution, the pH of the HAp-sol was almost neutral. Therefore, the HAp-sol will be quickly phagocytosized by cells and dissolved *in vivo*.

The study suggests that the HAp-sol could be a calcium and phosphate ion source, which could cause dentine bridge formation. Hukuchi et al revealed that macrophage cells are activated by phagocytosizing the HAp-sol, using a cell culture technique. The cell activation may depend on the crystal sizes of hydroxyapatite microcrystals in the HAp-sol.

In conclusion, ACPase and LDH activities in pulp after injection of HAp-sol were noted higher than after injection of HAp-800°C.

REFERENCES

1. Aoki H., Akao M., Kano S, Matusmoto K., Ogawa Y., and Sakatsume M: Effects of hydroxyapatite-sol on cell growth. *Report of Institute for Medical and Dental Engineering.* 26:15-21 (1992).
2. Aoki H., Kano S., Yoshizawa K., Kobayashi T., Ohgaki M., Akao M., and Nakamura S: *In vitro* interaction of carcinostatic substances desorbed on hydroxyapatite microcrystals with cells derived from cancers, 15:3-9. *Mat. Res. Soc. Jpn. (1994).*
3. Fukuchi N., Akao M. and Sato A: Effect of hydroxyapatite microcrystals on hydroxyapatite microcrystals on macrophage activity. *Bio-Medical Materials and Engineering.* 5: 219(1995).
4. Li T., Takikawa K., Yoshizawa K., Sakatsume M., and Aoki H: Reaction of hydroxyapatite-sol in bone marrow. *Bio-Medical Materials and Engineering,* 5:83 –92 (1995).
5. Li T., Lee J., Kobayashi T., Aoki H: Hydroxyapatite coating by dipping method, and bone bonding strength *Journal of Materials Science: Materials in Medicine.* 7: 355 (1996).
6. H. Aoki, Medical Applications of Hydroxyapatite, *Ishiyaku EuroAmerica, Inc.* Tokyo, St. Louis (1994).

Bioceramics Volume 11, edited by R. Z. LeGeros and J.P. LeGeros
(Proceedings of the 11th International Symposium on Ceramics in Medicine)
New York, NY, USA, November 1998
© 1998 by World Scientific Publishing Co. Pte. Ltd.

COLORED ZIRCONIA CERAMICS FOR DENTAL APPLICATIONS

Bernard CALES

Norton Desmarquest Fine Ceramics, Z.I. n°1, 27025 Evreux Cedex, France.

ABSTRACT

The objective of this study was to develop colored zirconia ceramics for restorative dentistry as an alternative to porcelains or glass-ceramics. The three iron oxide Fe_2O_3, cerium oxide CeO_2 and bismuth oxide Bi_2O_3 were selected as coloring additives and a large palette of tooth colors was produced. The physico-chemical properties of colored zirconias appear similar to that of the original zirconia ceramic. The coating of a zirconia core by veneers was also examined. No marked reaction at the zirconia core-veneer interface was detected and the fracture strength of the coated zirconia core remained unchanged.

KEYWORDS: Zirconia, colored ceramics, dental, restorations

INTRODUCTION

Ceramic materials have been successfully used for dental restorations for very long time. The two main functions of restorative ceramics are aesthetics and mechanical strength. However, most dental ceramics do not fulfill both requirements. For aesthetics applications, various porcelains and glass ceramics are used[1]. They exhibit tooth colors and translucency, but exhibit low or moderate fracture strengths (50-150 MPa), close or lower than dentin or tooth enamel[1,2]. For core manufacturing, higher strength ceramics were developed. These materials exhibit fracture strength in the range 150-500 MPa, significantly higher than natural dental materials, but are generally too opaque and need to be combined with veneers[1,2]. In addition the fracture toughness remains low when compared to metallic materials[2], making such ceramics sensitive to manufacturing flaws and /or stress concentrations, such as those used by non-optimized fitting between tooth and restorative ceramic.

Thus, there was a need for more fracture resistant dental ceramics, combining both aesthetics and high fracture strength. Surgical grade yttria-stabilized tetragonal zirconia (Y-TZP), is characterized by a high fractures strength, higher than 1500 MPa, with a high fracture toughness and an outstanding slow crack growth behavior[3]. Zirconia ceramic has thus far been successfully used in orthopeady for 12 years, as hip joint heads, to improve fracture resistance and wear behavior with more than 250 000 zirconia hip joint heads implanted in USA and Europe. Surgical grade Y-TZP zirconia has also been introduced for several years in dentistry for various applications, like abutments[4], post (Zircopost®, OHC France) and implants and it has been proved to lead to the lowest plaque accumulation, compared to other metallic and ceramic dental materials[5]. However, current surgical grade Y-TZP zirconia has a light ivory color which is not appropriate for dental restoration and specific colored zirconia grades have to be developed with color close to that of teeth. This was the objective of the present study.

MATERIALS AND METHODS

Colored zirconia ceramics were obtained by mixing 3 mol% Y2O3-doped zirconia powder with coloring additives, such as oxides or nitrates, selected from the literature review. The mixture was optimized by ball milling in alcohol, then dried with the help of a rotovapor. The mixture was pressed into pellets and sintered in air at about 1500°C for 3 hours.

The color of sintered colored zirconia samples was checked on polished surfaces and compared to dental color shades. For this study the Vita (Vita, Bad Säckingen, Germany) color shade sample was used as a reference. The stability of colored zirconia ceramics was controlled by X-rays diffraction before and after autoclave at 134°C-2 bars - 5 hours. The microstructure was controlled and the mean grain size measured on polished and thermally etched surfaces by SEM, with an accuracy of ± 0.05 μm.

RESULTS AND CONCLUSION

Most of the known coloring additives have been used for alumino-silicate compositions of veneers, porcelains and glass-ceramics. Thus, the reported colors are not representative of the color that may be obtained in sintered zirconia, because the coloring ions will be in completely different crystallographic network. Prior research efforts were used to select possible coloring additives. For instance, D.G. Grossman[6] indicated that a yellow colored glass-ceramic could be obtained using vanadium oxide, cerium oxide and terbium oxide in various amounts between 0.05 and 1wt.%. J.A. Klepacki[7] reported that iron, titanium, vanadium, zinc and bismuth oxides can be mixed to induce colors close to natural tooth. Finally Yoshida et al.[8] indicated a method to manufacture orthodontic zirconia parts by adding a mixture of erbium, praseodymium, iron and zinc oxides.

A selection of different coloring additives has been made based on literature data and the results are summarized in Table 1. Silver and manganese lead to inappropriate gray or black colors. Some additives, like zinc, vanadium or terbium, lead to severe ceramic degradation. Based on this first screening, three main coloring additives were selected because they give brown to yellow colors, their toxicity is expected to be very low or negligible and the amount of coloring additive is very small. They are: iron oxide Fe_2O_3, cerium oxide CeO_2 and bismuth oxide Bi_2O_3.

Table 1. Effect of various coloring additives in sintered Y-TZP zirconia

Coloring Additive	Form	Effective color	Comments
Silver	$AgNO_3$	gray	inappropriate color
Iron	Fe_2O_3	brownish	content must be < 1 wt%
Zinc	ZnO	uncolored	zirconia phase transformation
Erbium	Er_2O_3	light violet	solid solution with zirconia solid
Neodymium	Nd_2O_3	light pink	solution with zirconia
Cerium	CeO_2	cream	solid solution with zirconia
Bismuth	Bi_2O_3	deep cream	content must < 0.2 wt%
Vanadium	V_2O_5	orange	microcracking
Terbium	Tb_2O_3	light orange	rapid grain growth
Manganese	Mn_2O_3	black	inappropriate color
Praseodymium	Pr_2O_3	deep yellow	solid solution with zirconia

These three coloring oxides were thus mixed with zirconia to prepare a complete set of dental color shades. The selected compositions are indicated in Table 2, which also gives the correspondence with the Vita color reference. The combination of iron oxide Fe_2O_3, cerium oxide CeO_2 and bismuth oxide Bi_2O_3 in different ratios allows to reproduction of most of the colors of the Vita palette.

All the compositions indicated in Table 2 were characterized by SEM to measure the mean grain size and by X-rays diffraction on as-polished surface and after autoclaving at 134°C-2 bars for 5 hours. Such a treatment has been shown to be representative of an aging of 20 years in human fluid at 37°C9. All the selected compositions are characterized by a mean grain size identical to that of the uncolored Y-TZP zirconia surgical grade ceramic. In addition, the monoclinic content on the as-polished surface is close to 0 vol %, as for the uncolored zirconia and the monoclinic content after aging is lower than 5 vol % in all cases. It can thus be concluded that the addition of coloring additives, based on a mixture of iron oxide Fe_2O_3, cerium oxide CeO_2 and bismuth oxide Bi_2O_3 in the ratios indicated in Table 2, does not significantly change the physico-chemical properties of the Y-TZP ceramics.

Table 2. Compositions of colored zirconia ceramics

Zirconia grade	Coloring additives (%)			Color	VITA Ref.	Mean grain	Monoclinic content (%) As polished	After Autoclave
	Fe_2O_3	CeO_2	Bi_2O_3					
P00	-	-	-	white	-	0.50	0.0	2.5
P10	0.1	-	-	brownish	A4	0.48	0.0	2.4
P11	-	-	0.1	cream	A2	0.50	0.0	3.1
P14	-	1	-	light cream	B1	0.47	0.0	1.8
P16	-	1	0.1	cream	A2	0.48	0.0	3.0
P17	0.1	-	0.1	deep cream	A3,5	0.48	0.0	2.6
P18	0.1	1	-	deep cream	B3	0.49	0.0	2.2
P19	0.05	-	0.1	light brown	C2	0.49	0.7	3.7
P20	0.05	1	-	deep cream	B3	0.48	0.3	3.5
P21	0.05	1	0.1	light brown	C3	0.52	0.0	1.9
P31	0.03	0.5	0.1	cream	B2	0.48	0.0	2.3
P32	0.03	0.5	-	cream	B2	0.41	0.1	2.1
P33	0.03	0.5	0.05	cream	B2	0.47	0.1	2.4
P34	0.03	0.5	0.2	cream	B1	0.44	0.1	2.4

Despite their aesthetic function, the colored zirconias do not exhibit a marked translucency, as required for some tooth restorations. Therefore, the use of veneers on colored zirconia cores has also been studied. The surface of 4-point flexural test bars were ground by the techncian just before veneer coating using a dental driller. The tested veneer, Vitadur, was fired at 970°C and, in order to evaluate possible degradation of the core zirconia ceramics by phase transformation or thermal fatigue, the coated bars were cycled 10 times at the Vitadur temperature of 970°C. The results are summarized in Table 3.

Table 3. Flexural strength (MPa) of zirconia core with Vitadur coating

	As ground	with Vitadur coating 1st Series	(10 times) 2nd series
Mean value	1032	853	833
Standard déviation	85	89	90

Due to the observed standard deviation, it can be concluded that the coating with Vitadur veneer and the 10 thermal cycles does not significantly change the flexural strength of the zirconia ceramic. It should be noted that the mean flexural strength is quite low when compared to standard Y-TZP HIPed zirconia ceramic. The difference is due to the grinding of the surface of the bars before veneer coating and also because the bars were machined in non-HIPed zirconia ceramic. SEM examination of the fractured bars

(Fig. 1) also reveals the absence of any reaction between the veneer and the zirconia core and the strong adherence of the veneer on the zirconia ceramic surface, without any chipping close to the fracture.

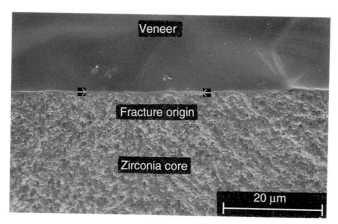

Figure 1. Microstructure of zirconia core-veneer interface

CONCLUSION

A set of colored 3 mol% Y-TZP zirconia ceramics has been developed for dental restorative applications, as an alternative to currently used porcelains and glass-ceramics. Iron oxide Fe_2O_3, cerium oxide CeO_2 and bismuth oxide Bi_2O_3 have been selected as coloring additives for Y-TZP zirconia ceramics. All the current dental color shades may be reproduced with appropriate ratios of these three oxides. The colored zirconia ceramics exhibit physico-chemical properties similar to that of the undoped "white" Y-TZP zirconia. For more aesthetic purposes, the colored zirconia grades could be coated with dental veneers, without degradation of their mechanical properties. Good veneer-zirconia interfaces were observed, without marked reaction between veneer and core and an apparent good adherence.

These colored Y-TZP zirconia ceramics are now commercially available and are developed for CAD/CAM machining of inlays, onlays and crowns.

REFERENCES

1. Kelly JR. Annu Rev Mater Sci: 1997; 27: 443-468.
2. Kappert HF. Transactions Academy of Dental Materials 1996; 9: 180-198.
3. Drouin JM, Calès B, Chevalier J, Fantozzi G. J Biomed Mat Res 1997; 34: 149-155.
4. Marzouk J. Quintessence International 1996; 27: 533-547.
5. Krämer A, Weber H, Geis-Gerstorfer J. Z Zahnärztl Implantol 1989; V: 283-286.
6. Grossman DG. US patent 5,387,558 1995.
7. Klepacki JA. US patent 5,125,970 1992.
8. Yoshida et al. German patent DE 42 07 179 A1 1992.
9. Chevalier J, Calès B. In: Sedel L, Rey C, ed.Bioceramics, Vol 10, Cambridge: Pergamon, 1997: 135-138.

Bioceramics Volume 11, edited by R. Z. LeGeros and J.P. LeGeros
(Proceedings of the 11th International Symposium on Ceramics in Medicine)
New York, NY, USA, November 1998
© 1998 by World Scientific Publishing Co. Pte. Ltd.

THE EFFECT OF HOT ISOSTATIC PRESSING AND SURFACE FINISH ON THE FLEXURAL STRENGTH OF ZIRCONIA DENTAL IMPLANTS

K. Srisukho[1], W. R. Lacefield[2]

[1]Department of Prosthodontics, Faculty of Dentistry, Mahidol University, Phaya Thai, Bangkok 10400, Thailand.
[2]Department of Dental Biomaterials, School of Dentistry, University of Alabama at Birmingham, Birmingham, AL 35294, USA.

ABSTRACT

Partially stabilized zirconia ceramics are an interesting group of materials for dental and orthopedic implant applications. One of their advantages over alumina ceramics is their higher fracture toughness. The strength and in general mechanical properties of ceramics depends to a large extent on the number and size of pores and flaws that arise during processing. Pressure-assisted sintering technique like hot isostatic pressing (HIP) is commonly thought to enhance the densification of the ceramics, resulting in improved strength. The purpose of this study was to determine the effect of the processing methods and surface finish on the flexural strength of yttria stabilized zirconia (3 mol% Y-TZP). Four different levels of surface finish of Y-TZP were investigated under two different production conditions (HIP'ed and unHIP'ed). The results showed that hot isostatic pressing significantly increased flexural strength, whereas surface finish had no significant effect at the $p \leq 0.05$ level. A trend of surface finish affecting the strength, however, was observed within the hot isostatically pressed sample in comparison to cold isostatically pressed and sintered group, indicating that the effect of surface finish on strength becomes more important when the internal pores and flaws have been eliminated by hot isostatic pressing.

KEYWORDS: Partially stabilized zirconia, surface roughness, hot isostatic pressing, mechanical properties.

INTRODUCTION

There are two basic types of zirconia suggested for surgical implants: tetragonal zirconia stabilized with yttria (Y-TZP) and magnesium oxide partially stabilized zirconia (Mg-PSZ). Compared to PSZ materials, the fine grained TZP ceramics show better material properties leading to higher safety when used as an implant material.

Most of the major qualifications of an implant material are derived from its mechanical properties. The strength of the ceramic depends to the large extent on the number and size of pores as well as flaws that arise during processing. Attention has been paid to the preparation and compaction of the ceramic powders in an effort to reduce the critical flaw size in the densified form[1], to give material with the optimum mechanical properties. The effective method of reducing the flaw size is by reducing the grain size of the powder, and by improving homogeneity of the microstructure[2]. The flaws (both surface and volume) do not disappear easily during pressureless sintering. Some pressure assisted sintering techniques, like hot isostatic pressing (HIP), hot pressing and sinter forging provide the opportunity to prevent the formation of, or to eliminate such flaws, therefore improving the mechanical properties and the reliability of the final material[3].

Studies on a number of metallic and ceramic systems have shown that HIP at pressure of the order of 100 MPa leads to higher rates of densification than those found in pressureless sintering experiments[1]. Recent data differ as to the efficiency of hot isostatic pressing in improving the mechanical properties of ceramic microstructure. Some evidence clearly supports improved properties, but more commonly the results are mixed when compared to alternate processing techniques. Occasionally, detrimental influences on material properties have been reported[4].

This study was aimed to investigate the effect of hot isostatic pressing and surface finish on the flexural strength of yttria stabilized zirconia (3 mol % Y-TZP).

MATERIALS AND METHODS

The material investigated was commercially available tetragonal zirconia polycrystal stabilized with 3 mol% yttria (Y-TZP). Specimens obtained from the manufacturer were rectangular rods (3 x 4 x 45 mm.) of four different surface roughness values (Ra, roughness average). The as-received specimens were subjected to two kinds of processing treatment:

1. Twenty-five samples of cold isostatically pressed then sintered at 1,500°C Y-TZP with no additional heat treatment, which will be refered to untreated samples.
2. Twenty-five samples of Y-TZP hot isostatically pressed in a molybdenum furnace at 1,500°C and 103 MPa (15,000 psi) in argon pressure for a 2 hour hold after being processed under the identical condition as in the first group. This group is referred to as treated samples.

For statistical purpose, both treated and untreated rods were equally divided according to the surface finish. The number of specimen of surface finish of 12 microinch were double of the other surface finishes, thus yielding a total of 5 groups of samples being tested.

Profilometery was performed in the analysis of surface roughness of the samples. For the investigation of mechanical property, a flexural strength test was carried out at the ambient temperature utilizing a four-point bending apparatus connected to the Instron loading machine (Instron Corp, Canton, MA) of a constant crosshead speed of 0.5 mm/min.

The fracture surfaces were then examined by scanning electron microscopy (SEM). Pore and flaw size was directly measured using SEM micrographs. The average amount of pores and flaws were determined by randomly placing a window area of 4 cm^2 over 10 different areas in each micrograph. Grain size was determined through representative microstructure from fractured specimen in all the three major planes (x, y, z) of the rectangular rod, to confirm the uniformity of the microstructure.

RESULTS

Average grain size in treated and untreated groups were 0.48 and 0.51 μm respectively. The SEM analyses of grain size from all the three major planes (x, y, z) of the rectangular rod specimens exhibited neither preferred plane or orientation, in both treated and untreated samples, nor significant difference of the grain structure.

Treated specimens revealed approximately 18% less pores and flaws than untreated specimens. The average pore size of the specimens was approximately 0.5-1 μm. while that of the treated specimens was about 0.2-0.5 μm., which was about 50-60% different.

Table 1 summarizes the flexural strength values of treated and untreated specimens in the order of surface roughness value. The effect of surface finish on flexural strength (MOR) was plotted in Figures 1 and 2 for untreated and treated samples respectively.

Table 1. Average flexural strength (MPa) and standard deviations of treated and untreated samples.

Surface finish (microinch)	No. of samples	Treated (MPa)	Untreated (MPa)
>24	5	835 ± 44	612 ± 101
24	5	880 ± 83	639 ± 33
12	5	928 ± 29	604 ± 26
12	5	886 ± 32	591 ± 40
2	5	968 ± 78	611 ± 51

The Ra values revealed no significant differences among the sample groups, though the SEM micrographs show the difference among surface finish groups.

Two-way analysis of variance (ANOVA) shows that the treatment had significant influence on the flexural strength. A linear trend related to surface roughness as a function of flexural strength is observed in the treated group. Surface roughness was not influential for untreated samples.

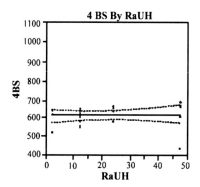

Figure 1. The effect of surface finish on flexural strength in untreated samples.

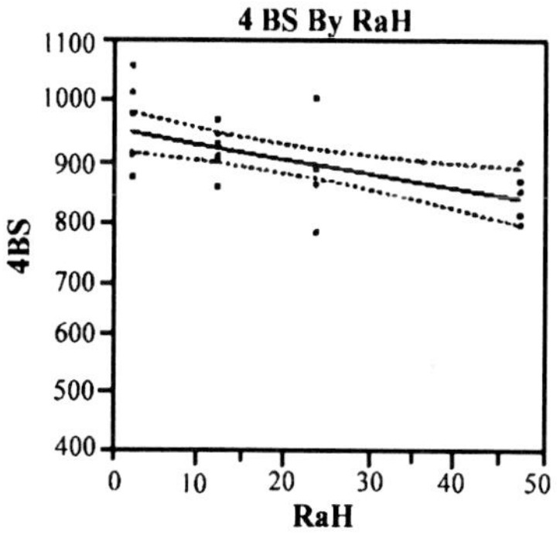

Figure 2. The effect of surface finish on flexural strength in treated samples.

DISCUSSION

The strength test data showed the treated specimens possessed significantly greater flexural strength as compared to the untreated specimens (Table 1) which suggests an improvement in the microstructure of the material after hot isostatic pressing. Typical micrographs and the statistical data illustrate a decrease in size and number of pores and flaws in the treated as compared to the untreated groups. This implied that the complementary HIP process does improve the microstructure, and therefore, the strength by reducing the pore and flaw size and their number.

The experimental steps included the measurement of the grain size to see if treating has any influence on the consolidation of grains. A quantitative method was applied in calculating the average grain size. It is not uncommon that there was no statistically significant difference in the size of the grains between the treated and untreated samples, since ceramic particles are crystalline and cannot be easily broken merely by processing pressure, otherwise the material would not be qualified as a load bearing material. The results showing grain sizes of both groups being nearly equivalent further indicated that the starting powder used in fabricating the specimens in both techniques was the same, which helped eliminate a nonvariable factor. Hence, it could be concluded that the difference in bending strength between treated and untreated zirconia was a result of the methods of production.

It has been shown that application of pressure at or above the sintering temperature accelerates the kinetics of densification by increasing the contact stress between particles and by rearranging particle positions to improve packing. A decrease in the size and number of pores in the treated samples indicated that hot isostatic pressing affected particle rearrangement by internal pores being eliminated and pinned down. Therefore, the critical factor in strength degradation is the porosity.

The relevance of surface roughness and flexural strength was determined. Figures 1 and 2 summarize the relationship between the surface roughness and flexural strength. The statistical analysis suggested that hot isostatic pressing had a significant influence on the flexural strength. At p value of 0.01, it is possible to observe a linear trend relating surface roughness and flexural strength in the treated group. In the untreated group, the results was unpredictable whether surface roughness could have affected the strength. Being isostatically pressed, the size of internal pores became so small that it is plausible for the surface flaws to be the strength-limiting factor. On the other hand, without treatment, the size of the internal pore seemed to be the strength determining factor. Therefore, no linear trend relating surface roughness and flexural strength were observed among the untreated samples.

CONCLUSION

Hot isostatic pressing is an effective method in improving densification of ceramic powder since it reduced the internal pores and flaws and their size to the degree that the surface roughness became of greater impact on the bend strength than the internal porosity of the hot isostatically pressed zirconia.

REFERENCES

1. Shin DW, Orr KK, Schubert H. *J Am Ceram Soc* 1990, **73**: 1181-1188.
2. He YJ, Winnubst AJA, Verweij H, Burggraaf AJ. *J Mater Sci*, 1994, **29**: 5868-5874.
3. He YJ, Winnubst AJA, Verweij H, Burggraaf AJ. *J Mater Sci*, 1994, **29**: 6505-6512.
4. Druschitz AP, Schroth JG. *J Am Ceram Soc*, 1989, **72**: 1591-1597.

Bioceramics Volume 11, edited by R. Z. LeGeros and J.P. LeGeros
(Proceedings of the 11th International Symposium on Ceramics in Medicine)
New York, NY, USA, November 1998
© 1998 by World Scientific Publishing Co. Pte. Ltd.

CORAL BIOIMPLANTS IN ORTHOPEDIC

F.Blardoni[1], H.Maestre[1], R.González[2].

[1]"Fructuoso Rodríguez" Orthopedic Hospital. Ave. G y 29 (s/n), Vedado 10400, Ciudad Habana, Cuba.
[2] Science Research National Center (CNIC), Ave. 25 y 158 (s/n), AP 6880, Ciudad Habana, Cuba.

Abstract

A report on the application of porous hydroxyapatite of coral origin in bone graft requirements is presented. Implants were practiced on 52 patients with diverse pathologies: tibial fracture, hip and cubit non-union, parostal osseous fibroma, bone cysts, Valgo's deformity of ankle and acetabular reconstruction.

Several advantages were observed over other materials. Not less than a 20% reduction of surgical time, less loss of blood and a 100% biocompatibility. The research proves the factibility of widespread use of the biomaterial and the availability and easy of processing of the same. In some cases, the evolution was followed for more than three years.

Keywords: Porous hydroxyapatite, orthopedic coral application, bone graft materials, implants, calcium phosphates materials.

INTRODUCTION

The need to replace, restore and/or regenerate bone tissue either damaged or lost in different sites of the human body has been a challenge faces with greater on lesser success throughout centuries, or perhaps millennia. The materials used for the above purpose make up a long list containing various types of metals, polymers, ceramics and glass and also various types of bone graft.[1,2]. It can be said that up the present time, no biomaterial has been found yet suitable to meet all the requirements of bone reconstructive surgery in different medical specialties. However, there is a fairly widespread consensus among specialists to the fact that, from the viewpoint of biocompatibility, tolerance, by the human organism and healing effectiveness, calcium phosphate and particularly hydroxyapatites are regarded to be the most promising biomaterials in this field [2,4,8,9]. This is because the chemical and structural identity of these substances greatly matches the mineral support of the bone, known as biological apatite. Hence, the successful results achieved with the clinical use of these compounds, notably in the last 20 years, which provide a safe choice as substitutes for bone graft in reconstructive surgery.

This paper presents a summary on major results achieved with the clinical use of Coral Porous Hydroxyapatite (HAP-200)[3] as a bone implant material in the treatment of various types of bone lesions in 52 patients treated in our Orthopedic and Traumatology Care Center.

MATERIALS AND METHOD

The trial covered 52 patients (18 to 65 years old age group), with different lesions in long bones and limbs, seen at "Fructuoso Rodríguez" Orthopedic Hospital. Criteria on deontology, inclusion and exclusion and termination of trial, were all taken into account. Classification of the host was made and the likely development of adverse reactions was anticipated.

All patients were made comprehensive clinical, x-ray and histological examinations as appropriate, enabling an histological accurate diagnosis and indication on the required treatment.

The biomaterial used in this trial was porous hydroxyapatite of coral origin (HAP-200) in the form of granulates of 2 – 2.5 mm particle size, or preformed blocks according to the lesion to be treated. The implant was done after proper dressing and careful washing of the recipient bone site, enabling the biomaterial to make direct contact with the healthy and well vascularized bone, ensuring extreme aseptic handling [1,6,7].

Post-surgical follow-up extended to 3 years, in line with a Protocol providing for the direct clinical evaluation of the patient, monitoring of vital signs and local examination of surgical site following an scale classification (from 0 to III) to evaluate edema, pain, swelling and sepsis. Mobility and stability of the affected zone was also studied. Longitudinal x-ray Studies, TAC and bone gammagraphy made it possible to observe the osteo-integration. The follow-up also included hematological test with complete hemograms, eritrosedimentation; determination of calcium, phosphorous and alkaline phosphatase. According to the clinical symptoms based on the major answers to the various parameters of evaluation and the functional restoration of the lesion, a four category scale to assess the final result was established: outstanding, good, moderate, negative.

RESULTS AND DISCUSSION

Table 1 shows the diagnosis, number of patients under treatments and final results. It shows the range of lesions and the high percentage of satisfactory results standing at 86% (both outstanding and good), with 13.5 % of non-satisfactory results with three septic complications and two fragmented implants with loss of stability.

The indications were: Interposition, filling and apposition graft. General contraindications were sepsis and necroses of implant recipient zone and intra-articular implantations. The required precautions at the time of laying the implant are: contact with vascularized recipient zone, stable and compressed implants and stable fixation.

Table 1. Diagnosis and the number of patients under treatments.

PATHOLOGIES	CASES	RESULTS			
		E	G	M	P
TRAUMATIC					
Tibial plate fracture	9	3	5	1	
Hip's non-union	5	2	2		1
Ulnar non-union	1		1		
TUMORS					
Enchondroma	1	1			
Fibroblastoma	3	1	2		
Parosteal bone fibroma	1		1		
PSEUDOTUMORS					
Bone cysts	5		5		
OTHERS					
Scoliosis	3		3		
Total Hip replacement	6		6		
Acetabular reconstruction	1			1	
Cervical disk herniation	5		5		
Lumbar disk herniation	2		2		
Extra-articular arthrodesis	2		2		
Bone sepsis (Implant + antibiotic)	8		4	2	2
TOTAL:	52	7	38	4	3

The material used for model bone implants in animals during pre-clinical tests, has proved to be highly biocompatible, non resorbable and osteoconductor. The fibroconnective tissue begins to penetrate through the pores to ultimately spread over the entire implant, thus starting the cellular differentiation process until generation of the new bone is observed after 21 days in both the entire volume and the bone –biomaterial contact surface. An approximate sequence of the actual occurrence can be described as follows: It has been generally observed that a slight inflammation phase develops during the early hours following the implantation. . During this time, various cells including macrophages invade the surgical site; the inactive cellular residues begin to phagocyte and attack against the HA surface starts. At the same time, preosteoblasts are set to become osteoblasts and migrate towards the edges of the bone defective site and also, towards the biomaterial surface, while revascularization occurs through the pores of the biomaterial, at the expense of both phosphate and calcium in the implant site. The HA and the osteoid formation act as epitaxial nucleation sites for the formation of biological apatite. Formation of the bone continues until the defect is corrected and successively remodeled and the area of osteoids between the newly generated bone and the biomaterial, diminishes.

Picture 1, 2 and 3 shows a patient with Hip non-union and disjoined of metallic implant, the reduction and was rechange with Bioimplant interposition graft Coralina HAP-200, notice the final result with stability, integration and biomaterial reabsorption at 3.5 years (classified as excellent result).

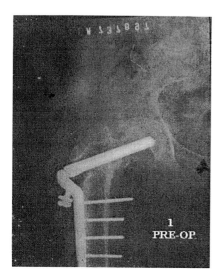
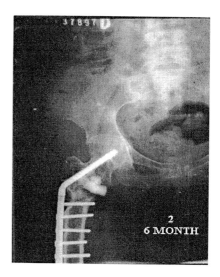
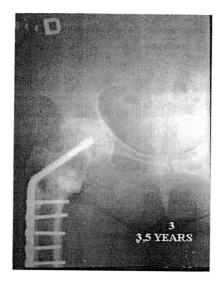

CONCLUSIONS

In over own experience, the immediate and long-term results achieved with this biomaterial for surgical implantation is similar to the one achieved with bone graft, with the following advantages: surgical time is cut in a 20% or more; less loss of blood and non-use of bone zone as donation. We conclude, therefore, that given its availability coupled with the beneficial and favorable results brought to the patients, this bone substitution biomaterial is of importance to our specialty.

ACKNOWLEDGMENTS

Our appreciation should go to the Cuban National Center of Scientific Research (CNIC) and to "Fructuoso Rodríguez" Orthopedic Training Hospital, co-sponsors of this work.

REFERENCES

1. Blardoni F, González R. Ortopedia '94. 1994:
2. González R, Guerra-López J. Materiales Bioactivos para Implantes Oseos. La Habana: CNIC. 1993.
3. González R et. Al. Quim. Nova. 1993;16: 509-512.
4. Holmes RE, Bucholz RW, Mooney V, J. Bone Surg. 1986; 68 A: 906-911.
5. Martínez Ruiz F. Biomecánica de la Columna Vertebral y sus Implantes. Madrid: Nueva Imprenta S.A. 1992: 261.
6. Pereda O, González R. Biomédica. 1994; 14: 22-29.
7. Pereda O, González R. Rev. Cub. Ortop. Traumatol. 1995; 9: 75-83.
8. Pouliquen JC, Noat M. Rev. Chir. Orthop. 1989; 75: 360-369.
9. Shimazaki K. J. Orthop. Res. 1985; 3: 301-310.

Bioceramics Volume 11, edited by R. Z. LeGeros and J.P. LeGeros
(Proceedings of the 11th International Symposium on Ceramics in Medicine)
New York, NY, USA, November 1998
© 1998 by World Scientific Publishing Co. Pte. Ltd.

MECHANICAL AND HISTOLOGICAL EVALUATION OF A NOVEL BIOACTIVE ORTHOPAEDIC COMPOSITE

Erik M. Erbe, Anthony M. Wilkes, and Sergio J. Gadaleta

Orthovita, Inc., 45 Great Valley Parkway, Malvern, PA, 19355

ABSTRACT

In this paper we discuss the evaluation of a novel, self-setting bioactive composite cement with properties significantly exceeding those of PMMA. This new cement, a hybrid of bioactive graft materials and polymer composites, was evaluated physically, mechanically, and histologically relative to PMMA. Safety and biocompatability of the cement were also established. Superior mechanical properties and generation of bone on the surface of the composite creates a tough, stable, chemically bonded bone-composite interface. Rabbit histology reveals bone-cement bonding and interdigitation. This initial evaluation leads to the justification for the use of this composite in orthopaedics.

KEYWORDS: Composite, cement, bioactive, PMMA, and histo-mechanical evaluation.

INTRODUCTION

A hybrid of bioactive graft materials and composite cements, a novel orthopaedic-composite (Orthocomp[TM], Orthovita, Inc., Malvern PA) has been developed. A bioactive, self-setting, bone bonding composite that offers ease of use in delivery and immediate function to load bearing bone reinforcing, implant stabilizing, and bone grafting applications. The composite nature allows for intimate conformation to the site of injection and polymerization leads to immediate load bearing strength. The composite is strengthened by the integration of the surface grafting and chemical bonding to bone and tissue surfaces. This interaction leads to improved fracture toughness of the entire implant system. The specially formulated thermoset resin matrix exhibits a low exotherm on polymerization and strong 3-dimensional bonding that prohibits residual monomer leaching. Orthocomp is easily visualized under radiographic or fluoroscopic imaging thus facilitating use as an orthopaedic cements.

Preliminary feasibility of delivery and injectability, as well as safety and efficacy was determined. Animal implantation of *in situ* polymerized cement was necessary to demonstrate the formation of bone at the composite interface. Safety and biocompatibility was established following a series of tests outlined by the FDA, ISO 10993 guidance documentation.

BIOACTIVITY MECHANISM

The key to Orthocomp's bioactivity is the nature of the interface that is formed between the surface of the composite and the surface within the body (e.g. bone tissue). The surface bioactivity depends on the chemical reaction of the bioactive glass-ceramic filler, which interacts with body fluids and cells to release ions that change the local environment on the surface of the entire composite. The result is a biologically active $CaO\text{-}P_2O_5$ surface gel that actually interdigitates between the composite and the bone tissue and ultimately converts to Hydroxylapatite (HAp) which chemically bonds to the bone. Similar reactions have previously been reported[1-3] for biologically active glasses (e.g. Biogran[TM]) and ceramics.

MATERIALS & FORMULATIONS

Superior mechanical properties are a result of the difunctional, 3-dimensional structure of the thermoset polymer system, whereas PMMA is a monofunctional, 2-dimensional thermoplastic polymer[4]. The following syringeable viscosity ($\sim$ 73 weight % filler) formulation was used for mechanical and implantation assessment. The two pastes were blended on delivery through a static mix tip.

- A -Paste = Resin [80% Bis-GMA {2,2 -bis -4(2-hydroxy-3 methacryloxy propoxy) phenyl propane} / 20% TEGDMA {Triethylene Glycol Dimethacrylate} + DHEPT {N,N,-Dihydroxy-p-toluidine}] + Combeite glass-ceramic filler {$Na_2O\text{-}CaO\text{-}P_2O_5\text{-}SiO_2$}.
- B-Paste = Resin [80% BisGMA/20% TEGDMA + BPO {benzoyl peroxide}+ BHT {2,6-Di-Tert-Butyl-4-Methylphenol}] + Combeite glass-ceramic filler.

PHYSICAL & MECHANICAL PROPERTIES

All of the specimen dimensions and protocols for mechanical testing (Table I) follow ASTM F-451 (exotherm, compressive strength), D-3967 (diametral tensile strength), D-4065 (fatigue) and D-790 (flexural strength), where applicable[5].

Table I. Physical and Mechanical Properties.

Property	Orthocomp[TM]	PMMA (Simplex P)*
Polymerization Exotherm (^{O}C)	60	88
Monomer leaching ($37^{O}C$ in saline)	12 ppm (0.001%)	119 ppm (0.012%)
Ultimate Compressive Strength (MPa)	222	82
Diametral Tensile Strength (MPa)	37	27
3-Point Flexural Strength (MPa)	105	60
Elastic Modulus (GPa)	4.6	2.5
Dynamic Creep (% deformation) @ 24 hr	<1%	25%
Fatigue (1.0E7 cycles): Compressive \ Tensile Strength (MPa)	100 \ 20	[<20] \ [<10]
Set time (min) at $37^{O}C$	4.5	8.5

* Howmedica, *Simplex P*, Lot PL12263/0001 hand mixed w/o vacuum.
 [specimens did NOT survive 1.0E6 cycles]

HISTOLOGICAL EVALUATION OF IMPLANTED CEMENTS

An *in situ* polymerization study (4, 8, 12, and 24 weeks implanted) was conducted in mature New Zealand White rabbits (n=6 per time period) using *in situ* polymerized Orthocomp™ cement with PMMA (Simplex P)* as a control. There were (n=3) implant sites per rabbit femora (n=6 /rabbit). Implants sites were prepared by drilling 5mm defects transcortically on the lateral side of the upper and lower metaphysis and diaphysis.

Figure 1 (A) and (B) depict an undecalcified (H&E stained) section through 8 week implanted (rabbit femora) Orthocomp at 25X and 100X magnification, respectively. The apparent mineralization front on the surface of the Orthocomp, suggest an ideal bioactive bond to bone. No fibrous encapsulation or interfacial gaps are present. Adjacent host bone appears healthy and normal.

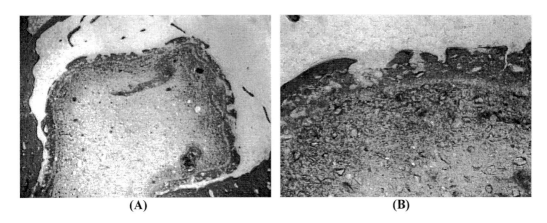

(A) (B)

Figure 1. Orthocomp™ after 8 weeks of implantation (A) 25X and (B) 100X magnification. All histology sections stained with H&E.

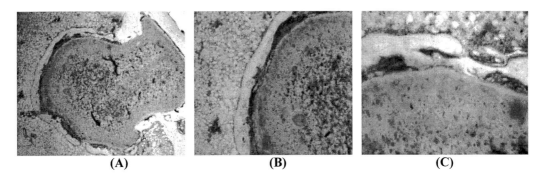

(A) (B) (C)

Figure 2. Orthocomp™ after 24 weeks of implantation (A) 25X (B) 100X and (c) 200X magnification. All histology sections stained with Paragon.

A reaction zone within the composite can also be noted by the color change around the periphery of the implant. The 4 week histology specimens show slightly less bone formation. The 12 and 24 week histology specimens reveal increased interdigitation and bone formation around the entire composite surface.

TOXICOLOGY & SAFETY

Following the safety protocol outlined by the ISO 10993 and FDA documents, the Orthocomp™ composite is deemed safe and non-toxic. The following tests were conducted and passed according to the guidelines of each test:

- Irritation Test using intracutaneous injection;
- Skin Sensitization Test (Kligman, Adjuvant and Patch Test);
- Cytotoxicity Tests (L929 MEM Elution and V79 Clonal Assay);
- Systemic Injection Test;
- Pyrogen Test;
- Mutagenicity Test (Ames, Chromosomal Aberration, CHO/HGPRT Forward Mutation);
- Long Term Bone Implant Test.

DISCUSSION

Preliminary safety and efficacy has been established with the new Orthocomp composite cement. The mechanical properties are significantly greater than PMMA, especially in fatigue. The existence of a bioactive surface leading to a chemical bond with surrounding bone tissue will lead to stronger and more stable implant constructs. The lower creep, bone-bonding surface, and a lower exotherm all suggest that this new cement will adhere more tenaciously to its mated implant and bone interface. The stability of the implant system will increase as the bone-composite interface strengthens its chemical bond over time.

CONCLUSIONS

PMMA has been the cement of choice in the orthopaedic community for nearly 30 years despite being plagued with a malady of insufficient mechanical properties and questionable matrix chemistries. Fixation properties due to micromechanical interdigitation of the cement - bone tissue interface are apparent. Improved setting strength and long term apatitic bonding leads to improved system outcomes over time. Aseptic loosening caused by high exotherms, monomer leaching, high creep, and a non-chemically-bonded interface is not the issue that it can be with PMMA. All of the attributes of Orthocomp™ will offer alternatives, replacements, as well as new surgical techniques given a new level of materials performance.

REFERENCES

1. K.H. Karlsson, *The Bioactivity of Glasses*, Ch.8, High-Performance Glasses (1993).
2. E. Schepers, et al, *Bioactive Glass Particulate As A Filler For Bone Lesions*, J. Oral Rehab., 1991.
3. E.Schepers, et al, US Patent # 5,204,106 (1993).
4. D.H. Kohn and Paul Ducheyne, *Materials for Bone and Joint Replacement*, Ch. 2, Materials Science and Technology; A Comprehensive Treatment, Vol 14, 1992.
5. ASTM F-451, "Standard Specification for Acrylic Bone Cement."

Bioceramics Volume 11, edited by R. Z. LeGeros and J.P. LeGeros
(Proceedings of the 11th International Symposium on Ceramics in Medicine)
New York, NY, USA, November 1998
© 1998 by World Scientific Publishing Co. Pte. Ltd.

WEAR CHARACTERISTICS OF EXPLANTED ALUMINA-ALUMINA HIP PROSTHESES

J.E. Nevelos[1], J. Fisher[1], E.Ingham[2], C. Doyle[3], A.B. Nevelos[4].

[1]Dept of Mech. Eng., University of Leeds, U.K. [2]Dept of Microbiology, University of Leeds.
[3]Howmedica International, UK. [4]Bradford Royal Infirmary, U.K.

ABSTRACT

The wear of ultra high molecular weight polyethylene (UHMWPE) and the resulting wear debris induced osteolysis is still one of the major problems facing modern total hip arthroplasty. As a result there has been renewed interest in alternate bearing materials for hip prostheses.

Wear surfaces and linear wear penetrations of eleven retrieved Mittelmeier Autophor ceramic hip components (average implantation time 8.6 years, range 1-13 years) were analysed and the different types of wear identified. All components were measured using a Kemco 3D co-ordinate measurement machine. Surface analysis was then performed using Talysurf contacting profilometry and scanning electron microscopy. Three types of wear were identified: low wear (1 case), stripe wear (6 cases) and severe wear (4 cases). Stripe wear was characterised as a stripe of worn area on the head 10-150µm deep whilst the rest of the head showed very low wear. The cups in the stripe wear cases were worn over about 40-50% of the surface. Severe wear cases had very large areas of heavy wear and visible volume loss. The four cases of severe wear were associated with abnormal clinical histories.

Keywords: Hip Arthroplasty, Retrieved Implants, Wear, Analysis

INTRODUCTION

The role of UHMWPE wear debris in osteolysis and component loosening in prosthetic hip replacement has been well documented[1, 2]. As a result, there is renewed interest in alternate bearing materials for hip arthroplasty. The alumina on alumina combination was first implanted by Boutin in 1970[3] with Mittelmeier following with the Autophor design in 1972. This bearing combination has been used in only limited numbers over the past twenty years. The clinical performance of these prostheses has been reported to vary between excellent[4] to very poor[5]. The poor performance of this prosthesis in trials in the USA resulted in the FDA restricting its use. This is in sharp contrast to its success with the under 55 age group in Europe[4]. The major problems with this prosthesis have been associated with fixation. The most common reason for revision being aseptic loosening of one or both components[3-6]. The acetabular cups have been reported to migrate over time with asymptomatic migrations of over 1mm reported by Mittelmeier[4]. This lack of primary stability has been criticised recently and has been suggested to be due to the lack of osseointegration into the component. However, in contrast to prostheses with polyethylene acetabular cups, few cases of osteolysis have been reported around ceramic on ceramic hips. The aim of this study was to evaluate the tribological performance of eleven explanted Mittelmeier ceramic on ceramic hips joints which had failed due to aseptic loosening after 1-13 years implantation time, with particular reference to the clinical histories of the patients.

MATERIALS

The Autophor design consists of a monolithic ceramic, threaded truncated cone socket which is screwed into an under-reamed acetabulum with a 32 or 38mm spherical head mounted on a cementless cobalt chrome alloy stem. The ceramic components were made of 'BIOLOX' alumina ceramic with a density of 3.94-3.96 Mg/m^3 and a mean grain size of about 3μm (range 1-5μm).

This study analysed retrieved components from a sixteen year series of Mittelmeier implants performed by one of the authors, Mr. A.B. Nevelos, at the Bradford Royal Infirmary, UK between 1980-1996. In all 307 Mittelmeier total hip arthroplasties were performed during this period of which 42 were bilateral. The age range of these patients was males: 17-58 (mean 39.4 years), females: 15-60 (mean 40.6 years). Twenty four hips were revised in total, the average time for revision was 7.4 years.

Eleven cases were selected for analysis. These cases were representative of the explant group and included all of the severe wear cases. All were revised for aseptic loosening of acetabulum (2 cases), loosening of femoral stem (4 cases) or loosening of both components (4 cases). The remaining case was thought to be loose, but on inspection was found to be stable. The femoral head was swapped but the rest of the components were left in place (the revised component forms low wear case 1). Table 1 shows patient details including the implantation angle of the cup which is believed to be a factor in implant life[4, 6].

All components were inspected macroscopically by eye before being measured. The components were categorised into three wear categories: Severe wear, Stripe wear and Low wear.

i.   'Severe wear' - Both the head and the cup showed large areas of wear and loss of sphericity.
ii.   'Stripe wear' – An elliptical wear stripe was visible on head, with roughening of part of the cup surface sometimes visible.
iii.   'Low Wear' - Little visible wear and the surfaces remained polished.

Table 1. Patient Details

Patient	Age (at implantation)	Sex	Cup Pen. / mm	Head Pen. / mm	Implant. Time/yrs	Acetabular Cup Angle.	Components Loose.
Severe 1	18	F	0.578	0.375	1	55^0	Acetabular
Severe 2	41	F	0.376	0.191	8	75^0	Both
Severe 3	46	F	2.946	1.967	13	40^0	Both
Severe 4	37	M	1.344	0.946	9	70^0	Both
Stripe 1	31	F	0.008	0.054	10.5	55^0	Femoral
Stripe 2	45	F	0.100	0.090	10	45^0	Both
Stripe 3	31	F	0.130	0.068	1	70^0	Acetabular
Stripe 4	24	M	0.007	0.047	13	45^0	Femoral
Stripe 5	51	M	0.101	0.128	12	60^0	Femoral
Stripe 6	45	M	0.004	0.027	10	45^0	Femoral
Low 1	45	M	No Data	0	3.25	45^0	N/A

METHODS

Volumetric measurements of the cups and heads were carried out using a Kemco 3D co-ordinate measuring machine. The measurements were taken as 2D profiles of the surface in the plane of greatest penetration. Co-ordinates of points were measured every 6^0 of curvature.

Surface roughness measurements were also taken of both worn and unworn areas using a Rank Taylor Hobson Talysurf 6 contacting profilometer.

RESULTS

Macroscopic examination showed one low wear, six stripe wear and four severe wear cases in this series. The unworn and polished areas had a roughness of 0.005μm Ra. Any areas rougher than this were assumed to have been worn. Severely worn areas were usually in the range 0.2-0.4μm Ra. Wear stripes had a typical roughness of 0.1-0.2μm Ra.

The maximum penetrations of the heads and cups are also shown in Table 1. The penetrations were calculated by comparing the radius of a measured point with the unworn radius, which was estimated using the manufacturers specifications. Due to manufacturers tolerances the accuracy of these penetration measurements was +/- 10μm.

The penetration values varied widely and did not appear to depend on the implantation time. This implied that wear was not proportional to time of implantation. In the four severe wear cases the penetration of the cups was at least 40% greater than the penetration of the heads. The stripe worn components did not show any relationship between head and cup wear.

DISCUSSION

For a normally positioned prosthesis with no other complications the linear penetration wear was less than 0.15mm. The wear was characterised by a stripe 10-150μm deep on the heads. This stripe wear may have been due to surface contact when fluid film lubrication had broken down leading to roughening of the surfaces. This roughening could then have accelerated the wear, as the lubrication moved more towards the mixed regime. This could, in turn, have led to an 'avalanche' type effect already mentioned in the literature[6]. Mittelmeier reported technical failures associated with too steep an acetabular implantation angle[4]. Refior et al also reported a major increase in wear for harsh repositioning in hip simulator tests, and minor increases in wear for an acetabular repositioning from 45^0 to 55^0[7]. From the data reported here the following observations can be made:

1. Of the stripe wear group, case 3 had the steepest acetabulum. The wear was a little higher than the average for the group but given that the implantation time was very short (1 year) the wear rate was considered very high. It is conceivable that if this particular prosthesis had not loosened so early, the high wear rate would have continued and led to severe wear.

2. Stripe wear cases 1 and 5 also had steep acetabular implantation angles (55^0 and 60^0 respectively) but with longer implantation times (10.5 and 12 years respectively). Stripe wear case 5 had slightly higher wear than the stripe wear cases with 45^0 acetabular angles but stripe wear case 1 did not.

In this series there was no evidence of osteolysis in any case. However severe wear and large amounts of wear debris of any material must be considered undesirable. The condition of the patients bone and activity levels were clearly additional important factors contributing to loosening.

CONCLUSIONS

1. Three categories of wear have been identified.
2. Severe wear was associated with an abnormal clinical history. Factors such as misalignment and dislocation appear to have influenced the wear rate.
3. The wear mechanism appeared to be polishing and subsequent grain pull-out with plastic deformation of the grains in severe wear areas.
4. Stripe wear was found in the majority of patients with linear penetrations less than 150μm.
5. Steep acetabular implantation angles ($>>55^0$) appeared to give rise to higher wear rates.
6. There did not appear to be a clear relationship between loosening and wear. Apart from the severe wear cases this series of explants may well be representative of the wear patterns in successful implants.

ACKNOWLEDGEMENTS

This work was funded by Howmedica International, U.K.

REFERENCES
1. Amstutz H., Campbell P., Kossovsky N., Clarke I. Mechanism and clinical significance of wear debris-induced osteolysis. *Clinical Orthopaedics and Related Research.* **276**: 7-18, 1992.
2. Mohanty M. Cellular basis for failure of joint prostheses. *Bio-Medical Materials and Engineering* **6**:165-172, 1996.
3. Boutin P. T.H.R. using alumina-alumina sliding and a metallic stem: - 1330 cases and an 11 years follow-up. *Orthopaedic Ceramic Implants. Vol. 1. Proc Japanese Society of Orthopaedic Ceramic Implants.* 1981.
4. Mittelmeier H. and Heisel J. Sixteen years' experience with ceramic hip prostheses. *Clinical Orthopaedics,* **282**: 64-72, 1992.
5. Mahoney O. and Dimon J. Unsatisfactory results with a ceramic total hip prosthesis. *Journal of Bone and joint Surgery* **72-A (5)**, 1990.
6. Nevelos A., Evans P., Harrison P., Rainforth M. Examination of alumina ceramic components from total hiparthroplasties. *Proc Instn Mech. Engrs.* **207**, **part H**.

Bioceramics Volume 11, edited by R. Z. LeGeros and J.P. LeGeros
(Proceedings of the 11th International Symposium on Ceramics in Medicine)
New York, NY, USA, November 1998
© 1998 by World Scientific Publishing Co. Pte. Ltd.

THE EFFECT OF HIP PROSTHESES COATING ON THE POSTOPERATIVE BIOMECHANICAL STATE OF THE FEMUR.

G. Baroud[1], G. Willmann[2], R. Kreissig[3]

[1]Human Performance Laboratory, The University of Calgary, Calgary, Alberta, CANADA T2N 1N4; [2]CeramTec AG, Medical Product Division, Fabrikstrasse 23-29, 73207 Plochingen, Germany; [3]Institute of Mechanics, University of Chemnitz, 09107 Chemnitz, Germany.

ABSTRACT

Femoral stems and acetabular cups used for total hip replacements (THR) are usually coated with hydroxyapatite (HA). Animal and clinical test results proved that HA-coating enhances the osseointegration of the implant. The purpose of the present study was to investigate the basic influence of coating on the biomechanical situation, in particular, the mechanical stresses within the femur and at the femur-implant interface.

Using the finite element method (FEM), three types of stems for the THR were investigated: non-coated, completely HA-coated, and proximally HA-coated. All three stems were otherwise identical. The results of this study 3D FE study show that, in terms of the nature of the coating, the HA-coated stem is biomechanically superior to the non-coated stem, and that the proximally coated stem is superior to the completely coated stem.

KEYWORDS: hydroxyapatite, hip prosthesis, bone remodeling

INTRODUCTION

Prosthesis surgery related to the skeleton, i.e. in the Total Hip Arthoplasty (THA), leads to a change of the natural load transfer mechanism within the bone[1,4]. It is well known that the changes in the physiological mechanical state result in growth reactions in the femur[4,2]. Several years later, bone resorption may occur which leads to the loosening of prosthesis.

Hyroxyapatite is one of the various calcium phosphates known. HA is bioactive and is available as granule or bulk material for the bone grafting and as coating on several kinds of implants[9]. For approximately 10 years, the influence of the HA-coating on the fixation of the implants, and consequently, the effect of the stem coating on the quality of the prostheses has been studied. There is a lot of basic research related to animal studies, and clinical reports[3,7,9]. Today, the bioactive HA coating is successfully used for component in the total hip replacement.

The purpose of this numerical study is to investigate:
1.   The influence of HA stem coating upon the mechanical situation within the proximal femur
2.   The influence of HA stem coating upon the contact stress at the interface between femur and implants.

The finite element methods allows for the evaluation of the mechanical state depending on variable boundary condition effectively. Based on the FEM, three types of stems for the Total Hip replacement (THR) were investigated: non-coated, completely HA-coated, and proximally coated. In order to compare the results, all three stems were the same design, and had identical material properties. In addition, all other boundary conditions were identical.

Material properties
The material behavior of the femur is very heterogeneous. The femur mesh is dived into seven isotropic, linear elastic and homogeneous areas with different elastic Modulus due to the work of Rohlmann[6]. Conventional prostheses systems are made from Titanium or Cobalt alloy. The Zweymueller prosthesis used in this study was modeled to be linear elastic.

EVALUATION THESIS
To evaluate the changing mechanical situation caused by insert the prosthesis, the following postulation was formulated based on the Wolff's law[10].
1.   The preoperative stresses state is regarded as optimal.
2.   Harmful reduction in bone mass can be avoided, when the deviation between the pre- and postoperative mechanical state is minimized.
3.   Quality of the prosthesis is given through the comparison between the pre- and postoperative mechanical state within the femur.
4.   The less the deviation, the higher is the compatibly of the prosthesis.

RESULTS AND DISCUSSION
According to Pauwels loading model, the femur is bent. The maximum stresses occur medially and laterally on the surface of the femur. Pressure stress occurred medially, while tensile stress laterally. The ventral and dorsal stresses maintain small values. For this reason, the change of stress distribution is represented by the evaluation of the results the frontal femur plane (fig. 2).
The insert of the hip endoprosthesis lead to a significant change in the mechanical situation of the bone, which may be classified as follows:
1.   change in the load transfer
2.   change in the mechanical stiffness of the entire structure.

Thus, a change in the postoperative stress situation in the bone occurs, which may be classified as follows:
1.   stress reduction within the proximal femur.
2.   high contact stresses in bone-prosthesis contact interface.

In figure 2, the stress situation caused by using the completely HA-coated stem, and the proximal coated stem is compared. The physiological stress (preoperative stresses) are presented in figure 2 as reference.

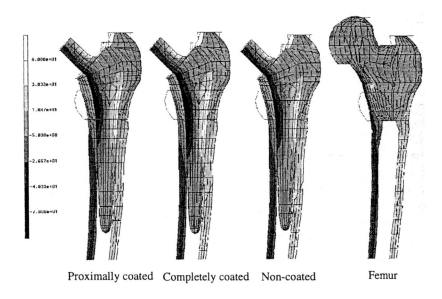

Proximally coated   Completely coated   Non-coated   Femur

Figure 2: Comparison the bending stress in the frontal femur plan

Figure 2 shows that, the proximal coated stem produces a postoperative stress state which is closer to the preoperative stress that postoperative stress state caused by the complete coated stem. Therefore, the proximal coated stem may creator less harmful bone reduction that the completely coated stem. therefor, the proximal coated stem may be considered as more compatible than the completely coated prosthesis.

The normal contact stresses that occurred at the proximal coated stem are compared with the proper stress that occurred in the non-coated stem (figure 3).

METHODS

Finite Element Analysis

The application of the FEM within the field of the biomechanics has been established[2,4]. The quality of the results depends on the quality of the FE-meshes. The FE-meshes introduced in this work were created manually, and they consisted of brick elements with 8 nodes. The data for the femur geometry are founded on CT-scans of right femur (length:1 70 cm, mass of body: 70kg and mass one leg: 10,5kg).

The mesh for the femur is defined on orthogonal coordinates with x-axis laterally, y-axis ventrally and z-axis proximally pointed.

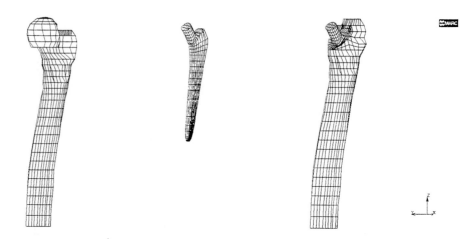

Figure 1: Used FE meshes consisting of brick elements

Table 1: FE meshes

FE Model	Nr. of Elements	Nr. of Node	Degree of Freedom
Femur	2974	3744	11232
Prosthesis	868	1247	3741
Femur/ Prosthesis	28565	3856	11568

Boundary condition

The load within the femur depends on the physiological and individual characteristics. In case of consideration of a characteristically movement condition such as walking, the load on the femur is mainly caused in the frontal plane by a body weight force and balancing muscle forces within the hip[5]. The whole load is reduced to a hip joint force and a muscle force, which substitute the muscle forces at the Trochanter major. In this study, the hip force was 2060N at a hip joint angle of 16°, while the muscle force was accepted by 1609 N at an angle of 21°. Both forces were divided over several FE-nodes.

All of the FE models were investigated, under the assumption that only the contact condition at the interface femur-implant was manipulated. The coated stem represent the ingrown state between femur and stem, therefore the transfer of compression and tension stresses is allowed. In comparison to the coated stem, the non-coated stem is modeled to transfer only compression tension. Moreover, micromovement between the non-coated stem and femur is not prohibited. The completely coated stem uses the entire contact area with femur for the load transfer.

In comparison to the completely coated prosthesis, the proximally coated prosthesis uses the proximal contact area for load transfer. In the distal part of the proximally coated stem, a non-coated contact condition between implant and femur is assumed.

Material properties

The material behavior of the femur is very heterogeneous. The femur mesh is dived into seven isotropic, linear elastic and homogeneous areas with different elastic Modulus due to the work of Rohlmann[6]. Conventional prostheses systems are made from Titanium or Cobalt alloy. The Zweymueller prosthesis used in this study was modeled to be linear elastic.

If the non-coated stem is used, considerable micromotion between stem and femur may occur. Such micromotion may damage the bone structure around stem. Thus, the attachment between stem and femur can not be guaranteed. consequently, the micromotion of the prosthesis into the femur causes higher contact stresses compared with the coated stem. A high stress in the interface may cause bone resorption[8], therefore the non-coated stem is mechanically considered to be less compatible in comparison with the coated stem.

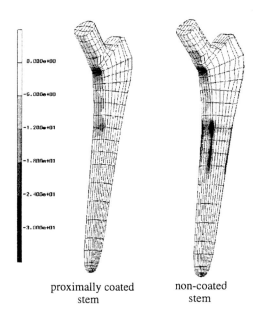

proximally coated
stem

non-coated
stem

Figure 3: Comparison of the contact normal stresses at the femur implant interface

CONCLUSION

Conventional stem hip prostheses lead to a change in the physiological force transmission. Such a change induces harmful bone remodeling and consequently loosening of the attachment between prosthesis and femur.

The HA-coating is considered to improve the biomechanical compatibility of the prosthesis. The results of this study show, that the HA-coated stem is biomechanically superior to the non-coated stem, and the proximally coated stem is superior to the completely coated stem.

ACKNOWLEDGEMENT

This study has been performed during my work at the University of Technology of Chemnitz, Saxony, Germany. The author has been supported by Prof. Dr.Ing. Reiner Kreissig (Institute of Mechanics) and the company CeramTec in Plochingen, Germany.

REFERENCES

1. Baroud G. On the THR. Institute of Mechanics: Univ. of Chemnitz, 1997.
2. Fyhrie DP, Carter DR. J of Biomechanics 1990; 23(2):1-10.
3. Gesink RGT, Clinical Orthopedics and related Research 1990; 261:39-44.
4. Huiskes R. Chir Organi 1992; Mov 77, 2:129-133.
5. Pauwels F. Gesamte Abhandlung der funktionellen Anatomie des Bewegungsapparat. Heidelberg: Springer-Verlag, 1965.
6. Rohlmann A, Bergmann G, and Koebel R. Z Orthop 1980; 118:122-131.
7. Soballe K. Acta Orthop. Scand. Suppl. 1993; No. 225.
8. Walker PS, Shneeweis D, Murphy S, Nelson P. J of Biomechanics 1987; 20(7):693-702.
9. Willmann G. Bioceramics 1997; 10:353-356.
10. Wolff J. The low of bone remodeling. Heidelberg: Springer-Verlag, 1986

Bioceramics Volume 11, edited by R. Z. LeGeros and J.P. LeGeros
(Proceedings of the 11th International Symposium on Ceramics in Medicine)
New York, NY, USA, November 1998
© 1998 by World Scientific Publishing Co. Pte. Ltd.

A CLINICAL STUDY ON HYDROXYAPATITE COATED EXTERNAL FIXATION PINS

Antonio Moroni, MD[1]; Cesare Faldini, MD; Jouni Heikkila, MD[2]; Soren-Toksvig Larsen, MD[3], Goran Magyar, MD[3]; Susanna Stea, Bsc[4]; Jie Zhou, MD[1]; and Sandro Giannini[1], MD

[1]Department of Orthopaedic Surgery, Bologna University, Rizzoli Orthopaedic Institute, Via G.C. Pupilli 1, Bologna, 40136, Italy

[2]Department of Orthopaedic Surgery, Turku University, Turku, Finland

[3]Department of Orthopaedics, University Hospital, 221 85, Lund, Sweden
[4]Laboratory for Biocompatibility Research on Implant Materials, Rizzoli Orthopaedic Institute, Via G.C. Pupilli 1, Bologna, 40136, Italy

ABSTRACT

The purpose of this study was to compare the biomechanical and clinical results of two groups of patients who underwent external fixation with tapered uncoated or tapered hydroxyapatite coated pins. Twenty-four patients from were randomized to receive uncoated (standard), tapered 5/6-millimeter pins (Group A) or hydroxyapatite coated, tapered 5/6-millimeter pins (Group B). Group A had 12 patients; 2 patients had external fixation in the femur and 10 in the tibia. Group B had 12 patients; 2 patients had external fixation in the femur and 10 in the tibia. Mean final insertion torque was 408 ± 251 Ncm in Group A and 301 ± 177 Ncm in Group B, (p=0.032). Mean extraction torque was 132 ± 177 Ncm in Group A and 579 ± 260 Ncm in Group B, (p<0.001). In Group A, the extraction torque was significantly lower compared to the corresponding insertion torque (p<0.001). In Group B, the extraction torque was significantly higher compared to the corresponding insertion torque (p<0.001). Group A had 20 pin track infections while Group B had 13 pin track infections (p<0.05). This study demonstrated that coating pins with hydroxyapatite was clinically effective in improving the bone pin interface strength of tapered pins. These results are due to the superior HA coating osteoconductivity and optimal surface roughness which improves initial mechanical stability.

KEYWORDS: hydroxyapatite, interface, pin, external fixation

INTRODUCTION

Pin loosening and infection at the bone to pin interface site is a major complication of external fixation.[1,2,4,6,7,9,10,14,15]. Pin loosening and infection can occur even with proper pin insertion[14]. Many authors have demonstrated that hydroxyapatite adheres to the bone[5,8,11] and consequently, hydroxyapatite has been proposed as a suitable coating material for external fixation pins[3,12,13]. The purpose of this study was to compare the biomechanical and clinical results of two groups of patients who underwent external fixation with tapered uncoated pins or tapered pins coated with hydroxyapatite in a randomized, multicenter clinical study.

MATERIALS AND METHODS

A total of 24 patients from three orthopedic centers who had external fixation of the femur or the tibia were included in this study. Patients were randomized to receive uncoated (standard), tapered 5/6-millimeter pins (Group A) or hydroxyapatite coated, tapered 5/6-millimeter pins (Group B). Group A consisted of 12 patients who received 45 pins; 2 patients had external fixation in the femur and 10 in the tibia. The average age of Group A was 46 ± 11 years. External fixation was used in 3 fracture fixations, in 8 knee osteotomies and in 1 bone-transport. A unilateral fixator was mounted in 11 patients and a circular fixator in 3 patients. Group B consisted of 12 patients who received 47 pins; 2 patients had external fixation in the femur and 10 in the tibia. The average age of Group B was 47 ± 12 years. External fixation was used in 2 fracture fixations, in 8 knee osteotomies, and in 2 bone-transport. A unilateral fixator was mounted in 10 patients and a circular fixator in 2 patients. No significant differences in patient sex, age, external fixation treatment type, external fixation frame and length of treatment were observed between the two groups.

RESULTS

Mean final pin insertion torque was 408 ± 251 Ncm in the uncoated pins (Group A) and 301 ± 177 Ncm in the hydroxyapatite coated pins (Group B), (p=0.032). Mean pin extraction torque was 132 ± 177 Ncm in Group A and 579 ± 260 Ncm in Group B, (p<0.001). In Group A, the pin extraction torque was significantly lower compared to the corresponding insertion torque (p<0.001). In Group B, the pin extraction torque was significantly higher compared to the corresponding insertion torque (p<0.001). In Group A there were 20 pin track infections and in Group B, 13 pin track infections. The pin track infection rate was lower in Group B compared to Group A (p<0.05). After pin removal, the hydroxyapatite coating looked intact without any exposure of the metallic substrate. In Group A, small bone fragments were observed in direct contact with the hydroxyapatite coating. In . In Figure 1 there is a BEI-SEM picture showing an unimplanted HA coated pin. In Figure 2 there is a BEI-SEM picture showing an HA pin after removal. There are no detachments of the bioceramic coating from the metallic core. Some bone trabeculae attached to the threads can be observed.

DISCUSSION

This study demonstrates that coating pins with hydroxyapatite was clinically effective in improving the bone pin interface strength of tapered pins. These positive results are due to the superior HA coating osteoconductivity and optimal surface roughness which improves initial mechanical stability. Consequently, the higher stability led to a decrease in pin loosening and infection rate. Deterioration of the bone pin interface strength can be avoided and external fixation complications minimized by using these pins.

FIGURE LEGEND

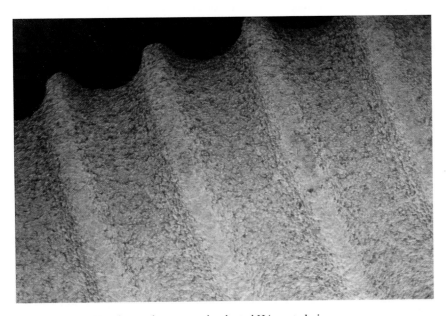

Figure 1. BEI-SEM picture shows an unimplanted HA coated pin.

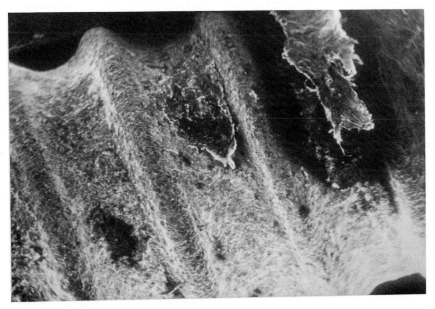

Figure 2. BEI-SEM picture shows an HA pin after removal. There are no detachments of the bioceramic coating from the metallic core. Some bone trabaculae attached to the threads can be observed.

REFERENCES

1. Aro HT, Markel DM, Chao EYS. Cortical bone reactions at the interface of external fixation half-pins under different loading conditions. *J Trauma* 1993; **35**: 776-785.

2. Briggs BT, Chao EYS. The mechanical performance of the standard Hoffmann-Vidal external fixation apparatus. *J Bone Joint Surg* 1982; **64A**: 567-573.

3. Caja VL, Moroni A. Hydroxyapatite coated external fixation pins. *Clin Orthop* 1996; **325**:269-275.

4. Chao EYS, Aro H. In: Mow VC, Hayes WC, eds. *Basic Orthopaedic Biomechanics*. New York: Raven Press, 1991: 293-336.

5. Cook SD, Thomas KA, Kay JF. Experimental coating defects in hydroxyapatite-coated implants. *Clin Orthop* 1991; **265**: 280-290.

6. DeBastiani G, Aldegheri R, Renzi-Brivio L. The treatment of fractures with a dynamic axial fixator. *J Bone Joint Surg* 1984; **66B**: 538-545.

7. Edwards CC. In: Epps CH (ed). *Complications in Orthopaedic Surgery*. Ed 2. Philadelphia: JB Lippincott Company, 1986:103-125.

8. Geesink RGT. Hydroxyapatite-coated total hip prostheses. Two-year clinical and roentgenographic results of 100 cases. *Clin Orthop* 1990; **261**: 39-58.

9. Green SA, Ripley MS. Chronic osteomyelitis in pin tracts. *J Bone Joint Surg* 1984; **66A**: 1092-1098.

10. Lewallen DG, Chao EYS, Kasman RA, Kelly PJ. Comparison of the effects of compression plates and external fixators on early bone healing. *J Bone Joint Surg* 1984; **66A**: 1984-1091.

11. Moroni A, Caja VL, Egger EL, Trinchese L, Chao EYS. Histomorphometry of hydroxyapatite coated and uncoated porous titanium bone implants. *Biomaterials* 1994; **15**: 926-930.

12. Moroni A, Caja VL, Maltarello MC, Savarino L, Marinelli F, Stea S, Visentin M, Giannini S. Biomechanical, scanning electron microscopy, and microhardness analyses of the bone-pin interface in hydroxyapatite coated versus uncoated pins. *JOT* 1997; **11**: 154-161.

13. Moroni A, Aspenberg P, Toksvig-Larsen S, Falzarano G, Giannini S. Enhanced fixation with hydroxyapatite coated pins. *Clin Orthop* 1998; **346**:171-177.

14. Pettine KA, Chao EYS, Kelly PJ. Analysis of the external fixator pin-bone interface. *Clin Orthop* 1993; **293**: 18-27.

15. Schatzker J, Horne JG, Sumner-Smith G. The effect of movement on the holding power of screws in bone. *Clin Orthop* 1975; **111**: 257-262.

Bioceramics Volume 11, edited by R. Z. LeGeros and J.P. LeGeros
(Proceedings of the 11th International Symposium on Ceramics in Medicine)
New York, NY, USA, November 1998
© 1998 by World Scientific Publishing Co. Pte. Ltd.

ANALYSIS OF WEAR BEHAVIOR OF ALUMINA-ALUMINA HIP PROSTHESES AFTER 10 YEARS OF IMPLANTATION

F. Prudhommeaux[1], J. Nevelos[2], C. Doyle[3], A. Meunier[1], L. Sedel[1]

[1]Orthopaedic Research Lab. UPRES-A CNRS 7052, 10 av de Verdun, 75010 Paris, FRANCE.
[2] Department of Mechanical Engineering, University of Leeds, UK.
[3] HOWMEDICA, Research & Development, Staines, UK.

ABSTRACT

The aim of this study was to investigate the surface topography of 8 Al_2O_3-Al_2O_3 hip prostheses retrieved for aseptic loosening, after a mean implantation time of 10 years. Massive wear was assessed by measuring dimensions' changes, using a coordinate measuring machine (CMM) and low wear features were evaluated by Talysurf analysis. Scanning electron microscopy (SEM) was used to look at wear mechanisms. Components were classified into 3 groups: G1 (n=2) with a visible loss of material on both components; G2 (n=4) with a visible oblong worn area on heads; G3 (n=2) with no sign of wear. For G1, wear was localized all around heads and cups, with a maximum of 2.70 and 1.02 mm respectively on head and cup. For G2 & G3, cups and heads showed penetration values below 50 µm. Talysurf data indicated that for G3, surfaces of both components were still very smooth, with Ra <0.035 µm, whereas for G1 & G2, components showed worn and unworn regions where Ra values differed by a factor of 10, while Rt remained below the size of one grain. The main difference between G1 & G2 was not the magnitude of roughness but the extent of the worn region over the unworn. SEM analysis confirmed that Al_2O_3 wear was the result of grain excavation, the worn and unworn regions differing in the number of removed grains. Dramatic wear seems to be the result of an implantation date prior to 1979 and/or the occurrence of unfavorable situations such as socket tilting. Otherwise, the wear of Al_2O_3-Al_2O_3 components remains of very low magnitude.

KEY WORDS: Total Joint Arthroplasty; Alumina; Retrieved implants; Wear;

INTRODUCTION

In the past 30 years arthroplasty of the hip joint has made progress and has taken new directions. One of these concerned the search for highly wear-resistant materials which would perform their function for decades despite the extremely severe conditions encountered in artificial joint.

Alumina (Al_2O_3) ceramic has been used as bearing components for THR since 1970 in France by Boutin[1]. The use of Al_2O_3-Al_2O_3 components has been advocated for its excellent biocompatibility[2] and for its tribological properties (wear and friction)[3]. Simulator tests have proved low friction, as in Charnley's material combination, but with much less wear (only about one twentieth of metal-polyethylene combination). However there has been many concerns about the in vivo wear behavior of Al_2O_3[4], and mechanisms leading to aseptic loosening have still not yet been satisfactory explained. As a consequence, examination of retrieved specimens are helpful to understand the failure mechanisms and subsequently improve material performances and surgical techniques. For this purpose, the aim of this study was to investigate the surface topography on a series of explanted Al_2O_3 components.

MATERIALS & METHODS

Eight matched pairs of Al_2O_3 heads and cups manufactured between 1977 and 1988 by Ceraver-Osteal® were retrieved at the time of revision for aseptic loosening of the socket. Prior to examination, components were cleaned in 10% formol baths for 48h.

A visual evaluation was performed in order to classify explants according to wear features. Two methods of wear quantification were used: 1) massive wear was assessed by measuring the change in dimensions of both components, using a coordinate measuring machine (CMM) [5]; 2) low wear features were evaluated by Talysurf analysis to assess surface roughness values (R_a and R_t) on worn and unworn regions. In addition, regions of interest were observed with a scanning electron microscope (SEM) to look at wear mechanisms.

Among patients, 4 were women and 4 men. The mean age at the time of operation was 58 years (range 33 to 74). Patients weights ranged from 55 to 86 Kg, with a median of 72.5 Kg. The mean implantation time was 10.6 years ranging from 1.8 to 17.4 years. A summary of clinical details is given in Table 1. In addition to clinical follow-up, radiological evaluation was completed by an independent observer. Stem and socket positions were sequentially recorded to detect any sign of loosening, migration, and/or tilting.

Table 1: Clinical data

Case	Gender	Age	Weight (Kg)	Height (cm)	Etiology	Date of implantation	Follow (yr.)	Group	Angle (°)	Tilt
1	Male	45.6	64	180	AVN	19/05/87	1.8	G2	40	no
2	Female	68.5	80	151	COX	12/09/80	14.8	G2	52	yes
3	Female	66.9	76	170	COX	18/01/83	12.3	G2	40	no
4	Female	74.7	55	153	COX	02/12/85	6.1	G2	52	no
5	Female	64.1	55	160	PTN	15/10/85	10.3	G3	42	no
6	Male	48.6	75	181	PTN	04/10/77	17.4	G1	50	yes
7	Male	64.5	70	167	PTC	22/11/88	6.7	G3	41	yes
8	Male	32.7	86	184	PTC	09/03/79	15.7	G1	53	yes

RESULTS

Gross examination allowed us to classify these components into 3 groups: G1 (n=2) with a visible loss of material on both components; G2 (n=4) with a visible oblong worn area on heads; G3 (n=2) with no sign of wear.

Quantification of dimensional changes revealed information for components belonging to G1 where obvious differences appeared between measured and theoretical data (Figure 1). For G1, wear was localized all around heads and cups, with a maximum near the apex of 2.47 and 1.02 mm respectively on head and cup. For G2 & G3, cups as well as heads, showed maximum penetration values below 50 µm.

Figure 1: Quantification of wear according to macroscopic wear features

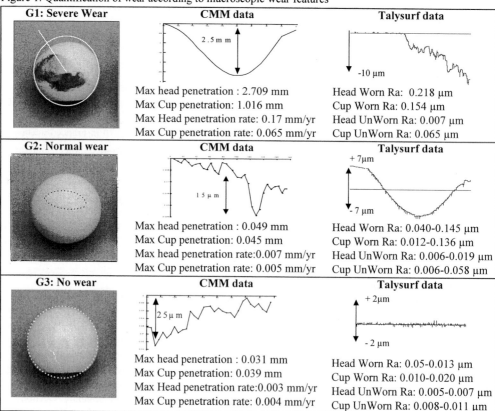

G1: Severe Wear	**CMM data**	**Talysurf data**
	2.5 mm	-10 µm
	Max head penetration : 2.709 mm Max Cup penetration: 1.016 mm Max Head penetration rate: 0.17 mm/yr Max Cup penetration rate: 0.065 mm/yr	Head Worn Ra: 0.218 µm Cup Worn Ra: 0.154 µm Head UnWorn Ra: 0.007 µm Cup UnWorn Ra: 0.065 µm
G2: Normal wear	**CMM data**	**Talysurf data**
	15 µm	+7µm -7 µm
	Max head penetration : 0.049 mm Max Cup penetration: 0.045 mm Max head penetration rate:0.007 mm/yr Max Cup penetration rate: 0.005 mm/yr	Head Worn Ra: 0.040-0.145 µm Cup Worn Ra: 0.012-0.136 µm Head UnWorn Ra: 0.006-0.019 µm Cup UnWorn Ra: 0.006-0.058 µm
G3: No wear	**CMM data**	**Talysurf data**
	25 µm	+2µm -2µm
	Max head penetration : 0.031 mm Max Cup penetration: 0.039 mm Max Head penetration rate:0.003 mm/yr Max Cup penetration rate: 0.004 mm/yr	Head Worn Ra: 0.05-0.013 µm Cup Worn Ra: 0.010-0.020 µm Head UnWorn Ra: 0.005-0.007 µm Cup UnWorn Ra: 0.008-0.011 µm

The computation of wear rates as a function of maximum penetration value per year of use revealed 2 different sets of data. For G1, it was of 0.04 and 0.17 mm per year respectively for cups and heads, while for G2 & G3, it was only between 0.002 to 0.007 mm per year for both components.

Talysurf data indicated that for G3, surfaces of both components were still very smooth, with Ra <0.035 μm and Rt <0.35 μm, whereas for G1 and G2, components showed a worn and an unworn regions with Rt below the size of one grain. The main difference between the surfaces of G1&G2 components was not the magnitude of roughness but the extent of the worn region over the unworn.

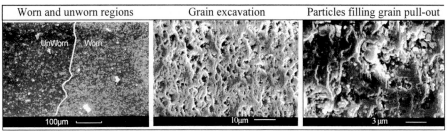

Figure 3: SEM observation of regions of interest

SEM analysis revealed, as shown on Figure 3, a clear boarder between the worn and unworn areas. The difference between these two areas appeared to be only the number of excavated grains. The loss of shiny appearance of the worn area might be the result of surface scattering. Both areas showed evidence of polishing. What we called « unworn area » should rather be called « less worn area », since grains pull out was also visible. In addition, we observed that many particles did actually fill intergranular pull out sites. Finally, this observation revealed that worn areas were the result of multiple grain pull-out but only one at a time explaining why roughness parameters remained small.

Our attempt to find correlations between wear features and clinical data revealed first that patients belonged to 2 different groups: one made of young, heavy and tall males and a second of older, lighter and smaller women. Even if observed wear features belonging to G1 differed drastically from the ones computed for G2 & G3, leading to a badly dispersed set of data, we were able to notice some relation between quantitative wear measurements performed on retrieved components and clinical data.

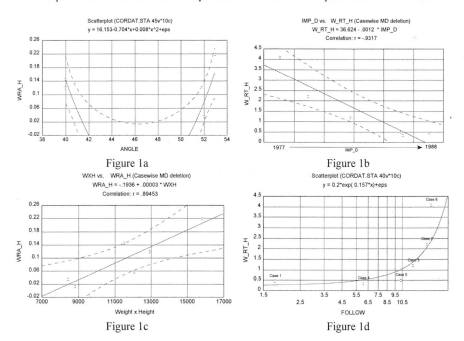

No simple relation could be observed between macroscopic wear features (CMM data) and any clinical data. However, on a microscopic scale (Talysurf data), we noticed that roughness increased when the initial socket angle moved away from a 46° value (Figure 1a). As implantation date went towards 1988, alumina quality improved leading to a decrease in roughness parameters measured on retrieved components (Figure 1b). In addition, we observed a linear correlation between differences of Ra and Rt values measured respectively on worn and unworn areas and a parameter computed by multiplying the weight by the height of patients (Figure 1c). Furthermore, as implantation time went, these Ra and Rt differences increased on both components in an exponential manner. Finally we noticed that all components belonging to G1 had tilted while those from G2 & G3 were equally distributed between tilted and untilted prostheses.

DISCUSSION

The classification we established macroscopically was confirmed by quantitative wear analysis. Two different wear behaviors appeared: under normal condition (no tilting), a localized area is submitted to high stress, leading to stripe formation; if tilting occurs, wear becomes dramatic, leading to massive loss of material all around components through the so called "avalanche effect". In fact, we did not observe components showing intermediate states of wear pattern (weak loss on extensive region).

The worn surface topography and more especially the observation of wear debris filling pull-out sites illustrates the important role that debris may play in the alumina wear process. Exaggerated wear appears to be initiated, as previously documented, by transgranular and subsequent intergranular pull out, leading to third body abrasive wear damage. As noticed by Nevelös et al[6], the role played by plastically deformed debris, which agglomerate and infill these pull-out sites, would however, appear to be important in the enhancement of the so called "avalanche effect". Due to its smeared and adherent nature, they would be likely to promote delamination of attached, virgin, subsurface grains over a relatively large region, via an environmental corrosion fatigue mechanism.

Our results show that some microscopic parameters increase with the activities and morphologies of patients as well as alumina quality the prostheses are made of. However the lack of relation between macroscopic and microscopic wear features on one hand and macroscopic wear features and clinical data on another hand suggests that no one mechanism is dominant in causing loosening. In addition the observation of explants with no sign of wear even on Talysurf analysis, indicates that numerous mechanisms are contributing in varying degrees to failure in a single prosthesis, and that aseptic loosening may not be due to Al_2O_3 wear as a sole factor.

CONCLUSION

Dramatic wear seems to be the result of the combination of two unfavorable factors: an implantation date prior to 1979, when Al_2O_3 quality was still questionable and the occurrence of socket tilting. Otherwise, the wear of Al_2O_3-Al_2O_3 components, even after 15 years, remains of low magnitude when compared to metal/PE bearings.

REFERENCES

1. Boutin P, *Rev Chir Orthop* 1972; **58**: 229-234.
2. Leray J, Christel P, In: GD Winter, DF Gibbons, H Plenk ed. *Biomaterials 1980*, New York: John.Wiley Ltd, 1982: 197-206.
3. McKellop H, Clarke I, Markolf K, Amstuz H, *J Biomed Mater Res* 1981; **15**: 619-653.
4. Griss P, Heimke G, *Arch Orthop Traumat Surg* 1981; **98**: 157-164.
5. Derbyshire B, Hardaker CS, Fisher J, Brummitt K, *Proc Instn Mech Engrs* 1994; **208**: 151-158.
6. Nevelös AB, Evans PA, Harrison P, Rainforth M, *Proc Instn mech Engrs* 1993; **207**: 155-162.

Bioceramics Volume 11, edited by R. Z. LeGeros and J.P. LeGeros
(Proceedings of the 11th International Symposium on Ceramics in Medicine)
New York, NY, USA, November 1998
© 1998 by World Scientific Publishing Co. Pte. Ltd.

INVESTIGATION OF 87 RETRIEVED CERAMIC FEMORAL HEADS

G. Willmann, A. Brodbeck

CeramTec, Medical Product Division, Plochingen, Germany

ABSTRACT

87 retrieved ceramic femoral heads have been investigated. All heads had articulated against PE cups. Examination of the heads did not show any change in diameter, sphericity, and surface roughness. Neither wear, nor fretting corrosion was detected in the conical bore of the heads. It was determined that the strength of the heads was still in compliance with FDA's minimum regulations. All 87 investigated retrieved Biolox heads are still according to specifications and standards valid at the time of manufacturing. The excellent condition of these retrieved heads after clinical use confirms one of the greatest benefits derived from the use of ceramic heads when compared to the substantial damage found in metal heads.

KEYWORDS: Total hip replacement, alumina ceramics, femoral heads, retrievals, reliability

WEAR IN TOTAL HIP REPLACEMENT

Aseptic loosening is the limiting factors for long-term application of implants for total hip replacement (THR). Nowadays mechanical failures of implants are quite seldom. The revision rate due to aseptic loosening is in the order of 10% after 10 years. This problem will stay to be a major one in THR when using metal heads articulating against polyethylene (PE). Aseptic loosening is caused by the PE wear particles. The wear rate of the couple metal/PE is 0.2 mm per year, sometimes up to 0.5 mm per year [1,6,7,10,11,16]. There are clinical reports that the wear rate, osteolysis, and revision rates [11,15] may be reduced when using ceramics, e g. heads articulating against PE or ceramic-on-ceramic [7]. The mostly used ceramic material is Biolox. Biolox is the trade name for alumina manufactured by Feldmühle, now CeramTec. It is an alumina according to ISO 6474, ASTM F 603, and FDA regulations. The in vivo wear rates per year are <0.1 mm for Biolox/PE [1,6,10,11,15,16] and 0.005 mm for Biolox/Biolox[1,7]. The results of in vitro tests are 0.001 mm/1million cycles for Biolox forte/Biolox forte. Biolox is sintered in air, Biolox forte has improved properties due to hiping.

More important are the revision rates. When using metal heads articulating against PE cups the revison rates due to aseptic loosening are 5-10%, when using Biolox heads the rates are reduced[1,15]. The goal was and still is to improve the performance and longevity of the total joint replacement. Ceramic femoral heads were introduced in Germany in 1974. So far more than 2 million ceramic heads have successfully been used. Today medical-grade alumina ceramics are standardized[5,3].

RETRIEVED CERAMIC FEMORAL HEADS

As far as we know there exists only one publication about an investigation of retrieved Biolox heads that articulated against a PE cup for a long time[12]. 87 retrieved Biolox heads became available. The hospitals RKU (Ulm, Germany) and LKH (Salzburg, Austria) and Lima, Lto. in Italy had collected retrieved Biolox heads. 26 heads had been in vivo up to 5 years, 33 between 6 and 10 years, and 29 for more than 10 years.The diameter of the retrieved heads was 32 mm with the 14/16 taper (angle 5°42,5'). All heads had been manufactured by CeramTec.

Biolox heads have an identification number. The reports about quality control of these heads are still available. So it is possible to check if properties may have changed in vivo. The objective of this investigation was to answer the folowing questions: Does the ceramic head show any wear after long-term application ? Does fretting or fretting corrosion occur when using ceramic heads ? Is there any strength degradation of the ceramic heads ?

RESULTS

The sphericity of the ceramic heads had been determined when manufacturing them. Using the same test methods when re-measuring the heads no change of their diameters was detected. The surface finish may be characterized by measuring its roughness and inspecting with a microscope. For 100 % quality control ceramic heads are still inspected using a microscope because this is easy to perform and cost effective. This inspection includes criterias like porosity, scratches, coloured regions etc.

Inspecting the retrieved heads it was found that they are still according to specification valid at the time of manufacturing. The surface finish of the retrieved heads did not change. Scratches on the articulating surfaces were not detected. This may be explained by to the extreme hardness of ceramic which can only be scratched by diamond.

On some of the retrieved heads metal traces on their polished surface were detected. These marks on these heads are due to contact with surgical instruments when explanting them or due to contact with the metal-back of a socket due to impingment or luxation or even due to total penetration of the head in the PE cup. Some people believe that these marks are scratches.

Metal heads are easily scratched when handled. A scratch on metal consists of a depression and an elevation. For metal heads wear, scratches, and changes of their surface can be observed[2]. The surface of a metal head may easily be scratched by a surgical instrument or by particles like hard tissue or bone cement particles. The depression of the scratch will not cause a problem, it is the elevation that will scratch the polyethene[2].

The hypothesis is that alumina ceramics are scratch resistant. When using a ceramic head the wear situation is much better. This hypothesis is based on the alumina's extreme hardness.

To prove this hypothesis the marks which were detected on some of the retrieved heads had to be investigated with SEM to find out if these are scratches or just metal prints on the ceramic heads. The profile of the mark was determined, too. The graphs shows an elavation, no scratches. After cleaning this head with acids the marks were gone and the surface was still polished. There were no signs of wear whatsoever.

The summary of this part of the investigation is: The retrieved heads were compared to the specification valid at the time of manufacturing. Diameter, sphericity, and surface roughness of the retrieved heads did not change. All the parameters of the heads were still according to the specifications at the time of their manufacturing.

For safe fixation of the head the roughness, the straigthness, and the taper angle of the bore and the metal taper are most important parameters. These specifications for the tapers are based on test results optimizing the compression strength of the ceramic heads, i. e. minimizing the risk of fracture[1,12,13]. For the specifications of the tapers see [8,12,13].

The parameters of the bore were re-measured. Comparing the results to the data in CeramTec's files no changes could be detected. Inspecting the conical bore of the retrieved heads there is no indication of any wear, corrosion, or fretting corrosion.

If the taper of a stem and the bore of a Biolox head have been manufactured according to specifications micromovement is impossible. High-purity alumina like Biolox is an electrical insulator with a specific resistance of 10^{15} Ωcm. Due to this extremly high electrical resistance galvanic effects are impossible. Therefore fretting corrosion is impossible if the tapers used and the bore of the ceramic heads have been manufactured according to specification.

There is proof that Biolox heads have an extremely low risk of fracture. The revision rate due to fractured ceramic heads is in the order of 0.02 %. This excellent result is based on large numbers of alumina ceramic heads, e. g. 0.01% based on 200,000 heads[8], 0.015% based on 511,000 heads[9], and less than 0.02% based on more than 1.5 million heads[1,14]. The revision rates for THR due to aseptic loosening are in the order of 10% after 10 years and about 1% for septic loosening. When comparing this to the fracture rate of modern ceramic heads fracture is not a primary problem.

A hip prosthesis is designed to withstand loads for 10 to 20 million cycles in vivo. The maximum loads for cyclic loading vary between 3 times body weight for walking and up to 6 times body weight for jumping. Regulations for safety of ceramic heads were edited by FDA[3], e. g. the average value for the static loading of a ceramic head must be above 46kN. No value shall be below 20kN. Materials strength degrades due to fatigue. Therefore it is very interesting to check if the strength of the retrieved heads is still according FDA's regulations and if there is strength degradation that may cause a higher risk of failure with incresing time in vivo. The force to fracture the retrieved heads was determined using the procudure recommended by the FDA[3] and ISO 7206-5. The results are: The avarage value is above 46kN. The lowest value was 42kN, the highest between 91kN and 99kN. All values were above 20kN as recommended by FDA. There is no evidence for a strength degradation (fatigue).

CONCLUSIONS

Examination of 87 Biolox retrieved heads did not show any change in diameter, sphericity, and surface roughness. Neither wear, nor fretting, nor fretting corrosion was detected. No scratches were detected. The strength of the retrieved heads was above 46kN. There is no proof for strength degradation of the ceramic heads (fatigue).

All 87 investigated retrieved Biolox heads are still according to specifications and standards valid at the time of manufacturing. The excellent condition of these retrieved heads after clinical use confirms one of the greatest benefits derived from the use of ceramics when compared to the substantial damage found in metal heads. No other analysis of a large number of retrieved ceramic heads has been found in the literature. Ceramics are very reliable for THR.

REFERENCES

1. Clarke IC, Willmann, G. in: Cameron, HU ed. *Bone Implant Interface.* St. Louis, 1994: 203 - 252

2. Fisher, J, Firkens P, Hailey J H , Isaac G H; Proc Inst Mech Engrs 1995; **209**: 263 - 264.

3. Food and Drug Administration 1995; Guidance Document for the Preparation of Premarket Notification for Ceramic Ball Hip Systems. FDA, Washington D C, USA.

4. Heimke G. Adv. Mater 1994; **6**: 165 - 170.

5. ISO 6474 2nd ed. 1994

6. Kusaba, A, Kuroki Y. Bone Joint Surgery 1997; **9B**: 331 - 336

7. Puhl, W. Performance of the Wear Couple Biolox forte in Hip Arthroplasty. Enke, Stuttgart 1997

8. Semlitsch, M, Dawihl W. in: Buchhorn, G H , Willert HG ed. *Technical Priniples, Design and Safety of Joint Implants.* Seattle, Hogrefe & Huber Publ 1994: 99 - 101.

9. Semlitsch, M, Weber H, Steger R. Biomed Technik 1995; **40**: 347 - 355.

10. Semlitsch M, Willert HG. J Eng in Medicine 1997; **211**: 73 - 88.

11. Weber, B G, Fiechter Th. Orthopädie 1989; **18**: 370 - 376.

12. Willmann, G, Kemmer U, Zweymüller K. Bioceramics 1994; 7: 377 - 384 .

13. Willmann, G. Mat wiss Werkstofftechnik 1993; **24**: 315 - 319.

14. Willmann, G. Mat wiss Werkstofftechnik 1996; **27**: 280 - 286.

15. Zichner, L P, Willert, HG. Clin Orthop Rel Res 1992; **282**: 80 - 94

16. Zichner L, Lindenfeld Th. Orthopäde 1997; **26**: 129 - 13

Bioceramics Volume 11, edited by R. Z. LeGeros and J.P. LeGeros
(Proceedings of the 11th International Symposium on Ceramics in Medicine)
New York, NY, USA, November 1998
© 1998 by World Scientific Publishing Co. Pte. Ltd.

HYDROXYAPATITE-TRICALCIUM PHOSPHATE AS A FILLER FOR ENCHONDROMA OF THE METACARPALS AND PHALANGES OF THE HAND

Katsuji Suzuki, Mitsuko Yamada, Kohsuke Yamamoto, and Tohru Tanaka

Department of Orthopaedic Surgery, Fujita Health University School of Medicine.
1-98, Dengakugakubo, Kutsukake, Toyoake, Aichi, 470-1192, JAPAN.

ABSTRACT

The efficacy of a hydroxyapatite-tricalcium phosphate (HAP-TCP) filler for metacarpal and phalangeal bone defects was studied by comparing 17 patients treated with HAP-TCP and 16 who received iliac autografts. There were no significant differences in age or the rate of pathologic fracture between the HAP-TCP and iliac autograft groups. There were also no significant differences in the total active motion (TAM) recovery time, grip power recovery time, autograft union time, HAP-TCP bonding time, and fracture union time.

KEYWORDS: Hydroxyapatite-tricalcium phosphate, enchondroma, iliac autograft, metacalpal, phalanx.

INTRODUCTION

Filling of bone defects is necessary after removal of enchondromas from the metacarpals or phalanges of the hand. Iliac autografts are often used, but problems can arise at the donor site. We compared the efficiency of filling curretted metacarpal and phalangeal bone defects with hydroxyapatite-tricalcium phosphate (HAP-TCP) granules or autogenous iliac bone chips.

SUBJECTS

Thirty-three patients with metacarpal and phalangeal enchondromas of the hand were operated on at our department between January 1987 and December 1996. All of them had solitary lesions.

Iliac autograft group

Iliac autografts were used in 16 patients from January 1987 to February 1992 (6 males and 10 females; mean age: 27.8 years; range: 6-65 years). There were 8 of the proximal phalanges, 6 of the middle phalanges, 1 of the distal phalanx, and 1 of the metacarpal. Eight of the patients had pathological fractures.

HAP-TCP group

HAP-TCP was used in 17 patients from March 1992 to December 1996 (7 males and 10 females; mean age: 27.1 years; range: 8-63 years). There were 7 lesions of the proximal phalanges, 6 of the middle phalanges, 2 of the distal phalanges, and 2 of the metacarpals. Nine of the patients had pathological fractures.

METHODS

Operative method

We made a rectangular window in the dorsal cortex of the metacarpal or phalanx, and resected and curetted the tumor. Then we filled the bone defect with autogenous iliac bone chips or HAP-TCP granules and fibrin paste, and closed the window with the original bone cortex (Figure 1).

Aftercare

The patients without pathological fracture used an aluminium splint for 2 weeks and then started active and assisted exercises after buddy taping to the adjacent finger. The patients with pathological fracture used an aluminium splint for 3 weeks and then started active and assisted exercises.

Evaluation

The time until total active motion recovered to above 90% of that on the healthy side (TAM recovery time), and the time until grip power recovered to above 90% of that on the healthy side (grip power recovery time) were compared between the two groups. The time required for autograft

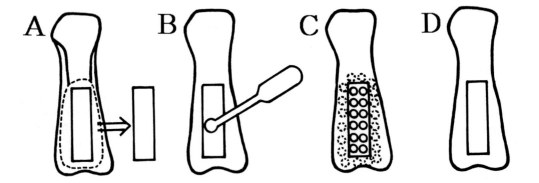

Figure 1. Operative methods. 1-A: A rectangular window is made in the dorsal cortex of the metacarpal or phalanx. 1-B: The tumor is resected and curetted. 1-C: The bone defect is filled with autogenous iliac bone chips or HAP-TCP granules using fibrin paste. 1-D: The window is closed with the original bone cortex.

union (autograft union time), the time until HAP-TCP bonded with the surrounding bone (HAP-TCP bonding time), the time until pathologic fractures were united (fracture union time), and the complications were also studied.

RESULTS

The TAM recovery time was 5.6±1.5 weeks (M.±S.D.) in the iliac autograft group and 5.3±1.2 weeks in the HAP-TCP group (P=N.S.; Wilcoxon test). The grip power recovery time was 10.8±1.4 weeks in the iliac autograft group and 10.9±1.1 weeks in the HAP-TCP group (P=N.S.). The autograft union time was 15.2±2.3 weeks and the HAP-TCP bonding time was 17.5±3.5 weeks (P=N.S.). The fracture union time was 4.2±1.2 weeks in the iliac autograft group and 4.0±0.9 weeks in the HAP-TCP group (P=N.S.). Postoperative infection did not occur in either group. Pain at the donor site occurred in 6 patients from the iliac autograft group, but no symptoms were noted in the HAP-TCP group.

CASE REPORTS

Cases 1 and 2 both had enchondroma with pathologic fracture of a proximal phalanx. Case 1 was a 41-year-old man (iliac autograft group) with enchondroma of the left 5th proximal phalanx. He suffered a pathologic fracture without trauma and then noticed the tumor. Autogenous iliac bone chips were used to fill the curretted bone defect. The TAM recovery time was 8 weeks, the grip power recovery time was 12 weeks, the autograft union time was 14 weeks, and the fracture union time was 4 weeks.

Case 2 was a 62-year-old man (HAP-TCP group) with enchondroma of the left 5th proximal phalanx. He suffered a pathologic fracture after strongly grasping an object. HAP-TCP granules were used to fill the curretted bone defect. The TAM recovery time was 6 weeks, the grip power recovery time was 12 weeks, the HAP-TCP bonding time was 18 weeks, and the fracture union time was 4 weeks.

DISCUSSION

HAP-TCP filler is a composite of hydroxyapatite (HAP) and tricalcium phosphate (TCP) which shows excellent biocompatibility and bone conductivity. TCP also fuses strongly with the surrounding bone because it acts as a bone substitute.

Nakamura [2] inserted fresh autogenous bone grafts into rats and found that the compressive strength was reduced by 25 % at 8 weeks after grafting. When autogenous bone was used as the filler, the graft was gradually substituted by new bone and its mechanical strength decreased during this process.

In experiments using rabbits, Hori et al. [1] found that the compressive strength of HAP was only 11 % of that of cancellous bone. However, the compressive strength of HAP increased to 71 % of that of cancellous bone when it was packed into a bone defect and then removed after 4 weeks. Therefore, HAP-TCP has greater compressive strength than autogenous bone grafts during 4 to 8 weeks after filling, the period when pathologic fractures unite and finger movement exercises are performed, which is clinically a very important time [3-5].

In the present study, there were no significant differences in age or the pathologic fracture rate between the HAP-TCP and iliac autograft groups, and there were also no significant differences in the TAM recovery time, grip power recovery time, autograft union time, HAP-TCP bonding time, and fracture union time.

CONCLUSION

There were no significant differences in TAM recovery time, grip power recovery time, autograft union time, HAP-TCP bonding time, and fracture union time between the HAP-TCP and iliac autograft groups. It was concluded that HAP-TCP was effective for filling bone defects after curettage of enchondromas of the metacarpals and phalanges of the hand.

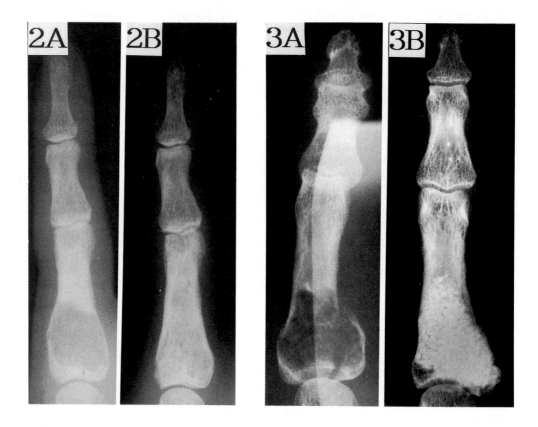

Figure 2. Case 1. A 41-year-old man from the iliac autograft group. 2-A: Enchondroma of the left 5th proximal phalanx with a pathologic fracture. 2-B: Twenty-four weeks after surgery, the iliac autograft is well united and the bone is homegenous.

Figure 3. Case 2. A 62-year-old man from the HAP-TCP group. 3-A: Enchondroma of the left 5th proximal phalanx with a pathologic fracture. 3-B: Twenty-four weeks after surgery, the bonding of HAP-TCP is good and the granules are homegenous with the bone.

REFERENCES

1. Hori M, Munemiya M, Takahashi S, Sawai K, Niwa S, Tagai H, Kobayashi M, Ono M, Takeuchi K. *Cent Jpn J Orthop Traumat* 1984; **27**: 2133-2135.
2. Nakamura S. *Kitazato Igaku* 1998; **18**: 406-419.
3. Suzuki K, Kurabayashi H. *Bioceramics* 1994; **7**: 435-440.
4. Suzuki K, Yamada M, Yamamoto K, Muramatsu K. *Bioceramics* 1995; **8**: 225-229.
5. Suzuki K, Yamada M. *Bioceramics* 1997; **10**: 341-344.

Bioceramics Volume 11, edited by R. Z. LeGeros and J.P. LeGeros
(Proceedings of the 11th International Symposium on Ceramics in Medicine)
New York, NY, USA, November 1998
© 1998 by World Scientific Publishing Co. Pte. Ltd.

CLINICAL EVALUATION OF A NEW BIOCERAMIC OPHTHALMIC IMPLANT

EJC Soares[1], VP Franca[1], L Wykrota[2], S Stumpf[1]
[1]Oculoplastic Service, Eye Clinic, Felicio Rocho Hospital Brazil
[1]Oculoplastic Service, Department of Ophthalmology, Federal University, Brazil
[2]Brazilian Institute of Biomaterials, Belo Horizonte, Minas Gerais, Brazil

ABSTRACT

The authors report on a new orbital implant for anophthalmic cavities, consisting of a bioceramic sphere (synthetic hydroxyapatite) with a titanium coupling system for connection of the implant to the cosmetic prosthesis. The clinical results of 92 patient implant surgery in a 5 year period are discussed, as well as the advantages of using Synthetic Bioceramics as compared to other materials including coralline hydroxyapatite.

KEY WORDS
Anophthalmic Cavity Reconstruction, Orbital Implants, Bioceramic, Hydroxyapatite.

INTRODUCTION
The use of an orbital implant for anophthalmic cavity reconstruction dates back to 1885, when Mules first placed a glass sphere within an eviscerated socket. Since, then, many types of implants have been devised and used, always aiming at improving prosthesis motility and providing the patient with the best cosmetic appearance.

A great advance has been achieved with the utilization of bioceramic material, mainly because it becomes integrated with the host orbital tissues, thus practically eliminating the risks of infection and implant extrusion. A considerable increase in the amount of movement of the prosthesis has been observed when the orbital implant is coupled to the prosthesis by means of a peg.

The article reports on the results obtained with the use of a buried, integrated implant made of synthetic hydroxyapatite (Bioceramic). Based on the successful utilization of this material in orthopedic surgery for bone reconstruction and odontological implantations[3,4], we have decided to study its clinical performance as an orbital implant in anophthalmic patients.

MATERIALS AND METHODS
A retrospective study was made of 92 patients who underwent enucleation, evisceration or secondary anophthalmic reconstruction with bioceramic implants at the Oculoplastic Services of the Eye Clinics of Felicio Rocho Hospital and Sao Geraldo Hospital (Federal University of Minas Gerais) in the period between January, 1992 and October, 1997.

In addition in data relating to the patients, the following variables were included in the protocol: surgical techniques, characteristics of the implants, postoperative problems, attachment of the coupling system, prosthesis fitting, degree of motility of the implants and prosthesis, results, and complications.

Of the 92 patients evaluated, 49 were female and 43 male. The right eye was the more frequently affects (60%). The patients' ages varied from 10 to 70 years.

Fifteen primary procedures (37 enucleation and 33 eviscerations) and 22 secondary reconstruction ere performed. Except for a few technical modifications described to allow the implantation of HA spheres[2,13], our surgical techniques did not differ from standard procedures used in enucleation, eviscerations and secondary reconstructions[5,6]

IMPLANT

The implant, a model designed in 1992 by Soares, Franca and Wykrota, is manufactured with technology by EINCO LTDA (Belo Horizonte). It consists of a sphere made of hydroxyapatite (75%) and calcium phosphate (25%) with a coupling system for attachment of the implant to the cosmetic prosthesis.

In the cases of enucleation and secondary implants, greater motility of the implant is obtained by attaching the sphere to the extraocular muscles [6]. For this reason, particularly in these procedures, the implant should be wrapped in some materials, to allow reinsertion of the four recti muscles. In wrapping integrated implants, two details are of particular importance: a) protecting the anterior third of the implant, so that the overlying tenon's capsule and conjunctiva closure will not be eroded from contact with the rough surfaces of the sphere and b) cutting adequately sized windows in the four quadrants of the implant, to permit fibrovascular ingrowth. The bioceramic sphere used in the enucleation and secondary implants were wrapped n Dacron[7] in some cases. Other covering materials used were sclera and dura mater. In two cases of secondary implantation, the spheres were placed directly into the orbit, unwrapped and without muscle attachment.

In the nine eviscerated patients, the spheres were inserted after openings had been cut in the four quadrants of the scleral shell. The 18 mm sphere was the most frequently used.

All patients were fitted with a temporary prosthesis 3 to 4 weeks after surgery. This initial prosthesis was temporary in that it was planned to be replaced with a permanent prosthesis after approximately 180 days, such being the period usually required for integration of the implanted material with the host tissue through fibrovascular invasion[8].

COUPLING SYSTEM

The coupling system consists of two parts, which are both made of commercially pure titanium.

One is an 8mm long cylindrical sheath measuring 3mm in diameter and containing a blind hole 2 mm in diameter and 7mm in depth. The sheath has a polished, concave neck on its external end, to facilitate the formation of an epithelial sealing zone. On its remaining portion, the surface of the sheath is treated with abrasive jet, to provide increased mechanical adherence to the cement upon attachment of the sheath into the ceramic sphere.

RESULTS

In the 92 cases studied, the early postoperative course showed no significant differences as compared to that of patients undergoing similar surgical procedures with other types of implants, The manifestations observed, whether objective (edema, inflammatory reaction, etc.) or subjective (sensation of compression, pain caused by movement, etc), were equally related to the nature of the surgery performed, the technical difficulties involved, and the operative manipulations, as well as to the patient's individual reaction to the surgical trauma.

All patients were fitted with a temporary prosthesis 3 to 4 weeks after surgery. The cosmetic and functional result was considered good and comparable to that obtained with completely buried, unpegged implants. In all cases, a light, thin shell prosthesis was sufficient to correct the orbital volume deficit, restore the patient's natural appearance, and provide a satisfactory prosthesis motility. Six patients were so satisfied with the result that they chose not to undergo peg placement.

In all of these patients, a marked improvement in the motility of the prosthesis was noted, as compared to that obtained with the temporary, unpegged prosthesis. It was also observed that with very thin prostheses such as those used in patients receiving larger-sized spheres, it become more difficult for the oculist to drill the posterior surface of the prosthesis to create a deep-enough hole to firmly accommodate the peg head. Large-degree movement can thus be affected since the shallower the hole, the more easily the peg head will be dislodged, with the articulation being broken.

The patients were followed up for a period that varied from 1 to 65 months.

The final result was judged good in 90 cases, corresponding to 98% of the total. The criteria for evaluation the result included recovery of the normal aspect of the orbito-palpebral region, good motility of the prosthesis, absence of residual deformities, and the patients' satisfaction with their final appearance. The presence of secretion was not considered as an impediment to a good result.

Of the 92 cases analyzed, there were no complications in 24 cases, corresponding to 74% of our series. In two patients the surgical removal of the implant was necessary. The occurrences of this complication were attributed to the patients' bad hygiene.

DISCUSSION

The loss of an eyeball is the cause of important orbito-palpebral alterations which, if not adequately corrected, can lead to physical deformities and psychological problems to the patient. To prevent or treat such deformities, an orbital ball is implanted, together with a cosmetic prosthesis, for restoring the orbital volume. Functional recover, which translates into good motility of the prosthesis, is absolutely necessary for the patients complete rehabilitation [6].

Among the various implant materials currently being used, coralline hydroxyapatite stands out especially because of its ability to become totally integrated with the host orbital tissues, thereby reducing to practically zero the risk of extrusion [13,14]. Fibrovascular invasion of the porous sphere progresses centripetally, and vascularization of the superficial portion of the implant can usually be observed within 4 weeks. Complete vascularization to its center is achieved approximately 6 months after implantation [9,10], at which time the peg can be inserted, to transmit to the prosthesis the full mobility of the implant.

The clinical performance of the bioceramic sphere proved to be comparable to that of natural hydroxyapatite, with total acceptance by the orbital tissues and absence of clinical reactions of intolerance rejection, even in those cases in which there was exposure of the implant.

As with the natural hydroxyapatite implant, the bioceramic implant allows a peg to be attached for coupling to the prosthesis, to improve motility of the prostheses. During the follow-up period, the sheath-peg coupling system was found to be efficient and safe. An important advantage offered by this system is that it does not allow conjunctival epithelium to grow into the implant, as no space is left between the peg and the sheath or between the sheath and the ceramic material. Another advantage is that it prevents the peg from causing erosion of the implant, a problem that can be seen in long term cases, when the peg is attached directly into the porous hydroxyapatite. In order to resist the impacts from transmission of the movements of the implants to the prosthesis, the coupling peg must be firmly supported along its entire shaft, particularly on the end located within the sphere. Otherwise, it can become loose and be easily dislodged, thus loosing its function. Finally, this system eliminates the problems related to skewed drilling or drilling of a peg hole larger in diameter than the peg shaft, which require complicated procedures to be adequately corrected [13].

Exposure of the hydroxyapatite sphere, caused by mechanical friction between the conjunctival covering and the rough surface of the implant, was the most frequent complication, occurring to 16 cases (18%). This compatible with the result reported by other investigators [11,12]. Also, it was observed that in the first cases, the exposure of the implant was coincident with the use of larger spheres encased in Dacron wrapping with a central orifice on the anterior face of the sphere.

The avoid tissue breakdown, we now use a continuous wrapping, with no apical opening of the anterior segment of the implant, which protects the overlying Tenon's fascia and conjunctiva against direct contact with the rough surface of the hydroxyapatite. In eviscerations, a similar protection is provided by preserving the cornea or using the sclera as a wrapping material. Another important preventive measure is to use smaller spheres. In addition to being less likely to cause exposure, a smaller orbital implant allows a shell-type prosthesis, a little thicker than a lens (2.5-3mm central thickness), to be fitted, thus permitting a deeper hole to be drilled for the peg head. In the more recent cases in which these cares were taken, exposure of the implant was no longer observed.

The most serious complication occurred in our second patient, a man from a lower social condition, with very bad hygiene. He developed chronic infection of the cavity, with several acute episodes affecting the orbit and inducing to removal of the implant. A similar case was described by Goldberg [12] with coralline hydroxyapatite implant.

CONCLUSION

Analysis of the results obtained during two-year follow up of the cases in our series have demonstrated that, in terms of the surgical technique, tolerance of the material by the orbital tissues, and improved motility of the prosthesis through a coupling system, primary or secondary implantations with the bioceramic implant (synthetic hydroxyapatite) do not differ, from a practical point of view, from those performed with (natural) coralline hydroxyapatite spheres.

The idea of coupling the orbital implant to the prosthesis by means of a peg that fits into a sheath previously cemented into the implant is a new concept that offers numerous advantages, the most important being the improvement of mechanical resistance, efficiency, safeness and absence of late complications.

Further investigations are needed to determine the material's capacity for fibrovascular tissue growth into its pores.

This implant does not require costly manufacturing processes. The improvements now available to treat the anophthalmic cavities with the integrated orbital implants can also be obtained using the bioceramic material.

REFERENCES

1. Perry AC. *Clin North Amer* 1991;4:173-182
2. Perry AC. *Adv Ophthal Plast Reconst. Surg* 1988;8:75-81
3. Croci AT, Camargo OP, Campos R, Oliveira R. *Rev Bras Ortop* 1992;27:849-852
4. Stahl SS. Froum SJ. *J. Periodontl* 1987;58:(10):589-695
5. Soares, EJC. *Anais do 2o Congresso Luso-Hispano-Brasilerio de Oftalmologia* 1972;II:155-168
6. Soares EJC. *Orbit* 1991;10:77-88
7. Franca VP, Soares EJC, Trigueiro SMB. *Rev Bras Oftalm* 1990;49:11-16
8. Shields CL, Shields JA, Eagle RC. *Amer J. Ophthalm* 1991;111:363-366
9. Ferrone PJ, Dutton J. *Ophthalmology* 1992;99:376-379
10. Grengo TE, Zins JE, Bauer TW. *Plast Reconstr Surg* 1989;245-249
11. Buettner H, Bartley G. *Amer J. Ophthal* 1992;113:669-673
12. Goldberg RA, Holds JB, Ebrahimpour J. *Ophthalmology* 1992;99:831-836
13. Dutton J. *Ophthalmology* 1991;93:370-377
14. Shields CL, Shields JA, Potter P. *Arch Ophthalm* 1992;110:333-338

Bioceramics Volume 11, edited by R. Z. LeGeros and J.P. LeGeros
(Proceedings of the 11th International Symposium on Ceramics in Medicine)
New York, NY, USA, November 1998
© 1998 by World Scientific Publishing Co. Pte. Ltd.

ALUMINA / BIOACTIVE COATING INTERVERTEBRAL SPACER FOR THE CERVICAL REGION

N. Francaviglia[1], R. Spaziante[1], Angelo Nataloni[2], Roberta Martinetti[2], Antonio Ravaglioli[3]

[1]Neurosurgery, University in Genoa, Genova, Italy; [2] Fin-Ceramica Faenza s.r.l., Via Ravegnana 186, 48018 Faenza (RA), Italy; [3] IRTEC-CNR Via Granarolo, 64 48018 Faenza (RA), Italy

ABSTRACT

The intervertebral spacers proposed for cervical fusions consist of alumina with bioactive coating and, compared to those currently in use, they represent a development both in terms of design and materials. The special "design" of these new products was conceived in parallel with finite element analysis[1] which took into consideration the loads to which they will be subjected together with the compressive and flexural strength stresses.
This study evaluated the preliminary results obtained with a follow-up of 2 years in terms of applicability, biocompatibility, side effects and complications.

KEY WORDS: cervical spine - anterior spinal fusion - bioceramic microporous alumina

INTRODUCTION

For the treatment of degenerative and traumatic pathologies, anterior cervical decompression requires anterior spinal fusion [2-3-4]. Therefore numerous natural materials (e.g. autologous or heterologous bone) or synthetic materials (e.g. Titanium, BOP, PMMA, hydroxyapatite) which are tolerated by the human body and promote osteoblastic activities, are subjects of great interest. Their advantages, however, do not always overcome the inconveniences to which the patient will be subjected.
During the last 3 years, FIN-CERAMICA Faenza in co-operation with the 2nd chair of Neurosurgery of the University in Genoa and IRTEC CNR in Faenza, designed, characterised and clinically tested a range of intervertebral spacers for cervical fusion. These spacers made of alumina with bioactive coating, are definitely more advantageous both for the surgical resolution of the pathology and for the patient.
The cuneiform shape characterised by rises and holes allows an immediate mechanical stability and promotes osseous regrowth both on the prosthesis surface and inside of it.
The insertion of the spacer occurs in the front section, with the possibility of a segmentary vertebral stabilisation (up to 2 intervertebral spaces) depending on the type of pathology.
The characteristics of this new prosthesis are represented by complete biocompatibility, anatomic design and bioactivity, which is fundamental for biological coupling.

MATERIALS

At the onset of the experiment, we took into consideration the surgical technique and the intervertebral faces. Then, after an accurate evaluation of the statics, dynamics and dimensions of the cervical rachis, together with the finite element analysis of the same region (C1-C7) (Figure 1), a series of Alumina/bioactive coating intervertebral spacers was created (Figure 2).

With reference to the specific application, we set up a bioinert ceramic material based on Alumina with a microporous structure and a bioactive coating at micrometric level.

The microporose alumina exhibits mechanical properties with security factors 10 times higher than those of the bone.

Figure 1. Finite element analysis of the cervical region

Figure 2. Alumina/bioactive coating intervertebral spacers for the cervical region

In terms of the chemistry of this material is concerned, the Alumina (made up of crystals of α-Al_2O_3 with a polycrystalline structure) meets the reference standard ISO 6474.

The product is characterised by a material with a microporous structure: this microporosity is obtained thanks to a particular production process and is characterised by pores contained in the range of 0.05 – 0.06 micron (of radius) and by an average grain dimension contained between 2 and 5 micron.

The microporosity and the surface-wrinkledness prove to be indispensable characteristics to foster the bioactive coating [5] (Figure 3).

The bioactive coating (Figure 4) is principally made up of silica and sodium and calcium phosphates besides minor constituents that give the characteristics required for the applications. The coating is a glass ceramic with microcrystalline phases opportunely studied to check bioreactivity, is able to activate and quicken the clasping to the osseous tissue.

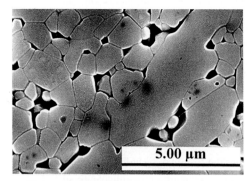

5.00 µm

Figure 3.   Section of an Alumina sample. Microporosity of the material

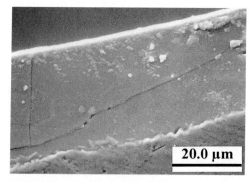

20.0 µm

Figure 4 .   Section of an Alumina sample. The bioactive coating

METHODS

Among the different techniques used for the pathologies of the cervical region, the most valid is, in our opinion, the one that provides for a surgical aggression per conventional anterior via. The target is to eliminate the causes of compression through the exeresis of the osteophytosis and the "uncosectomia", followed by a fusion with intervertebral graft of Alumina spacers with bioactive coating. After cutaneous incision, a first surgical step is necessary to remove the osteophytic alterations. Then the real somatotonia is made with a full thickness drilling of the cervical region corresponding to the intervertebral disks interested.

When the vertebral plane is reached, we proceed with the preparation of the prosthesis "housing". After pulling apart the upper and lower vertebral bodies, the graft is implanted under compression for the release of the bodies previously pulled apart. It is always advisable to evaluate with the amplifier the depth reached by the Spacers, which has to remain deeply a little bit distant from the "durale" surface and, on the surface the spacers do not have to fully reach the anterior plane of the vertebral bodies. In this way the possible mobilisation of the spacers themselves is avoided.

Also in the case of more or less complex fractures-luxations, the same technique can cause a regression of the deficiency syndromes. The joint arthrodesis with Alumina Cervical Spacers coated with bioactive glass gives a valid consolidation.

RESULTS AND DISCUSSION

In the year 1996/97 at the 2nd chair of Neurosurgery of the University in Genoa 20 patients were treated with a total of 29 FIN-CERAMICA Alumina/bioactive coating intervertebral implants (7 patients treated at one level, 11 patients at two levels). The patients were operated for degenerative or traumatic cervical pathologies (Table 1).

Table 1. Characteristics of the sample studied

Pathology	Patients treated
Herniated disk	10
Cervical spondyloarthrosis	5
Posttraumatic lysis	5

The follow-up of the patients operated, carried out with a direct Radiography, TC and RMN (Figures 5, 6), confirms the satisfying clinical results. No cases of collapse of the material or of the intervertebral restrictions and no displacement have been observed. In all the cases a rearrangement in the points of vertebral contact of the implant and a rehabilitation of the holes from the biological material took place. Thus, both stabilisation and the ossification process of the graft were efficacious.

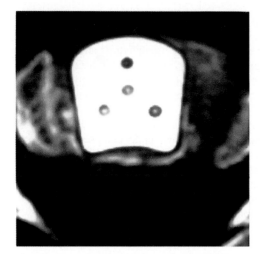 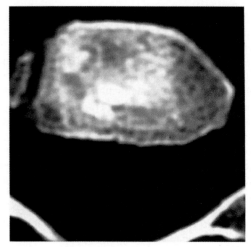

Figure 5.   Post-operating check CAT: Figure 6. Check CAT after 4 months: holes
empty holes   filled with osseous tissue

CONCLUSIONS

In the light of these results, the microprobes alumina with bioactive glass coating seems the most
suitable material for this type of graft. The high compression strength and the inertness are
indispensable and fundamental characteristics to enable the intervertebral spacers to support,
(without fracturing or changing) the thousands of "cycles" of asymmetrical compression caused
by the movements of the cervical rachis. Moreover, the coating speeds up the process of
osteoimpaction, which definitely improves immediate stability.
The material and the technique eliminate the necessity of taking from iliac crest and cause a real
fusion of the adjacent bodies, preserving the normal alignment of the vertebral bodies.

REFERENCES

1.   C. Farina; L. Dolcini; A.Nataloni; M. Fabbri N. Zaghini. Ceramica Acta n. 5/97 (1997)
2.   E.S. Stauffer; J.L. Neil. Clin Orthop 112:159-164 - (1975)
3.   T.Shima; M.D. J.T. Keller; M.M. Alvira; F.H. Mayfield; S.B. Dunsker. J. Neurosurg 51:533-518 (1979).
4.   S.D. Cook; M.C. Reynolds; T.S. Whitecloud; A.S. Routman; A.F. Harding; J.F. Kay; M. Jarcho. Spine - Vol. 11 n° 4 - (1986)
5.   A. Ravaglioli; A. Krajewski, A. Piancastelli; G. Berger; K. Adam; R. Gildenhaar. Interceram vol. 41 - n° 2 (1992).

Bioceramics Volume 11, edited by R. Z. LeGeros and J.P. LeGeros
(Proceedings of the 11th International Symposium on Ceramics in Medicine)
New York, NY, USA, November 1998
© 1998 by World Scientific Publishing Co. Pte. Ltd.

CLINICAL EVALUATION OF BIPHASIC CALCIUM PHOSPHATE CERAMIC USE IN ORTHOPAEDIC LESIONS

L. L. Wykrota**, C. A. Garrido*, F. H. L. Wykrota**, V. C. F. Cury**, and J. A. Filho*

*   Orthopaedic Surgery - São Bento Hospital, Belo Horizonte, M.G. Brazil.
** Instituto Brasileiro de Biomateriais - Belo Horizonte , M.G. Brazil

ABSTRACT

Direct osteomyelitis in traumatic large bone defects extrusive osteolysis in revision of total hip replacement prosthesis involving massive bone defects and bone tumoral lesions were grafted with a micromacroporous biphasic calcium phosphate (HA/ß-TCP) bioceramic granules to fill lost bone. Besides serving as a filler, this material was also used as a drug carrier in order to prevent infections during large invasive surgery procedures. The material has interconnective porous structure and good compression strength resistance and demonstrated a strong union with the surrounding bone, a high rate of bone ingrowth and no decrease in graft volume.

Keywords: Orthopaedic lesions, biphasic calcium phosphate, hydroxyapatite, ß-TCP.

INTRODUCTION

Several kinds of biomaterials, especially calcium phosphate bioceramics, have been used to rebuild and reconstruct hard tissues because of their biocompatibility and chemical and physical resemblance to bone mineral (1-4). These materials produce no immunological or toxic reaction and risk of other pathology transmission is avoided by stringent production control.

The micro- and macro- porous calcium phosphate ceramic with stable (HA) and more soluble (ß-TCP) phases presents interesting features as a filling material (5-7). Macroporosity, ranging from 50 to 350mm produce a more effective organic response and allow easy tissue ingrowth (8). Microporosity, ranging from 1 to 10 mm increase the ionic concentration in the area because of their great solubility in a larger surface area in contact area with physiological fluid. This macromicroporous architecture makes the ceramic adequate as drug carrier because it allows great absorptions, high rate of dissolution and high concentration in the implant site for a long period (9).

MATERIAL AND METHODS

The biphasic calcium phosphate ceramics were used in treating 12 patients (ages between 8 to 78 years old) who required different procedures, including: 3 cases of tumor, 6 cases of pseudoarthrosis, 3 cases of extrusive osteolysis, 2 cases of direct osteomyelits in pseudoarthrosis in traumatic large bone defects whose prognosis was amputation. The postoperative assessment period varied from 6 to 18 months. In cases of infection, antibiotic was used with the bioceramic.

The graft material used was a micromacroporous biphasic calcium phosphate (75% HA/25% ß-TCP) with microporosity of 1-10mm and macroporosity of 50-350mm (OSTEOSYNT[R]).

The bioceramic granules were prepared with marrow bone or blood of the patient when ever possible. To improve the manipulation, antibiotic was added, when especially indicated or for local protection. After the material was packed in the place of lost bone, a good compaction and procedures to contain the material were done. This was necessary to provide good immobilization in the beginning of the regeneration process.

Case evaluation was done by clinical and radiographic examinations.

RESULTS

Successful repair with the material was observed between 6 and 17 months even though the materials were used in different sites and in critical situations, including under great mechanical stress. No adverse reactions were evident from radiological and clinical analyses. Satisfactory clinical effects were obtained and minor recuperation time were required. No important complications were observed.

Case evaluations are summarized in Table 1.

Table 1. Clinical applications of biphasic calcium phosphate bioceramic

CASE	SEX	AGE	SITE	DIAGNOSIS	INFECT	ANTIBIOTIC	EVOLUTION	TIME
1	M	75	tibia	open fracture	present	Clorofenicol	very good	17mo
2	F	23	femur	fract pseudoarthr w. osteomyelitis	present	Keflin	good	16
3	F	70	finger #3	enchondroma	absent	-	very good	6
4	F	46	femur	pseudoarthroses	absent	-	good	6
5	F	13	scapula	osteoblastoma	absent	-	reasonable	9
6	F	66	femur	chronic osteomyelitis	present	Gentamicina	bad (amputation)	13
7	F	56	acetabulum and femur	great osteolysis in arthoplasty rev	absent	-	good	8
8	M	51	acetabulum	great osteolysis in arthoplasty rev	present	Keflin	good	9
9	M	53	femur	great osteolysis	present	Keflin	good	6
10	M	42	femur	open fracture with direct osteomyelitis	present	Keflin	good	13
11	F	8	finger #4	enchondroma	absent	-	very good	13
12	F	26	femur	open comminuted fracture	present	Keflin	very good	13

DISCUSSION and CONCLUSION

The bioceramic applications to obliterate and fulfill spaces and lost structures have been a useful procedure compared to other biomaterial alternatives such as the autologous and homologous materials which have been associated with problems such as unavailability of large quantities of materials needed, morbidity, and risk of disease transmission.

In cases of infection, the alloplastic material has added advantage of serving as an efficient drug delivery system, allowing high drug concentration in the infected site.

In cases where large amounts of bone have been lost, such as trauma pseudoarthrosis cases or in repeated hip prothesis or risk of growth of tumoral tissue, or in osteomyelitis or great fractures, the specific bioceramics have demonstrated a viable alternative compared to the traditionally used materials. Despite a short assessment

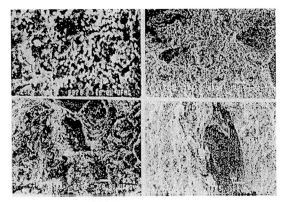

Figure 1. B.C. Ultrastructure a) SEM x1200; b) SEM x1000; c) SEM x100; d) SEM x100

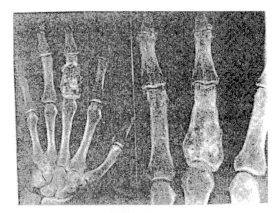

Figure 3. Third hands finger enchonodrom

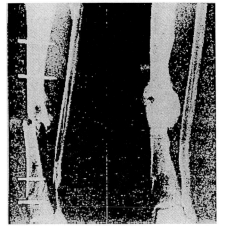

Figure 2. Case 1: Tibia Open Structure

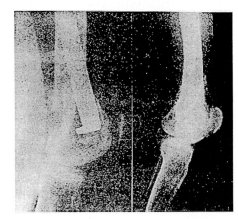

Figure 4. Case 4 femur Pseudoarthrosis

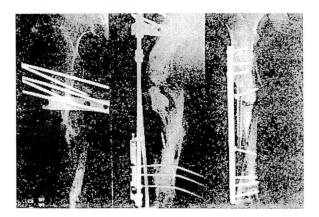

Figure 5. Case 12 femur open comminuted fracture

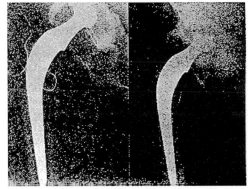

Figure 6. Case 7 Great osteolysis in arthroplasty

period we were able to accomplish positive results with this material.

The cases presented here will continue to be evaluated for a long period, but for the present results, we conclude that the biphasic calcium phosphate material is good for filling or rebuilding procedures and in treating local infections when an immediated response and mechanical resistance are needed.

REFERENCES

1. Nagahara K, Isogai M, Sinibata K. *Int J Oral Maxillofac Implants* **7**: 72-79, 1992.
2. Pollick S, Shors EC, Holmes RE. *Int J Oral Maxillofac Implants* **53**: 915-922, 1995.
3. Ravaglioli A, Krajewski A, Biasini V. *Biomaterials* **13**: 162-167, 1992.
4. LeGeros RZ, LeGeros JP, Daculsi G, Kijkowska R. In: *Handbook of Biomaterials and Applications.* Wise DL (ed) Merkel Publishers, pp. 1429-1463, 1995.
5. LeGeros RZ, Daculsi G. In: *Handbook of Bioactive Ceramics. Vol. 2. Calcium Phosphate Ceramics.* Yamamuro N, Hench L, Wilson-Hench J (eds). CRC Press, Boca Raton, pp. 17-28, 1990.
6. Nery B. LeGeros RZ, Lynch KL, Lee K. *J Periodont* **63**: 729-735, 1992.
7. Daculsi G, Passuti N, Deudon C, LeGeros RZ, Raher S. *J Biomed Mater Res* **24**: 379-396, 1990.
8. Gauthier O, Bouler JM, Aquado E, Pilet P, Daculsi G. Biomaterials **19**: 133-139, 1997
9. Uchida A, Shinto Y. Fourth World Biomaterials Congress, April, 1992

Bioceramics Volume 11, edited by R. Z. LeGeros and J.P. LeGeros
(Proceedings of the 11th International Symposium on Ceramics in Medicine)
New York, NY, USA, November 1998
© 1998 by World Scientific Publishing Co. Pte. Ltd.

Porous AW Glass Ceramic as a Femoral Intramedullary Plug

Hiroshi Fujita[1][2], Kazuhiro Ido[1], Yasutaka Matsuda[1], Hirokazu Iida[1], Masanori Oka[3], and Takashi Nakamura[1]

[1]Department of Orthopaedic Surgery, Faculty of Medicine, Kyoto University, 54 Shogoin-kawaharacho, Sakyo-ku, Kyoto, 606-8397, Japan, [2] Orthopaedic Surgery, Kyoto National Hospital, [3]Research Center for Biomedical Engineering, Kyoto University

ABSTRACT

To improve a survival rate of total hip artyroplasty (THA), modern cement techniques have been advanced. An essential prerequisite to this procedure is adequete plugging of the distal femoral canal. Various methods for plugging the canal have been reported, such as, doughly aclylic cement, bone plug, and manufactured plugs of polyethylene, biodegradable copolymer, and hydroxyapatite. We generally use cancellous bone chips obtained from resected femoral head in primary THA. However, in the cases of revision surgery, porous AW-glass ceramic (AW-GC) has been used. The purpose of this study was to evaluate efficacy and biocompatibility of porous AW-GC as an intramedullary plug in canine THA for up to 24 months. Porous A-W GC rods (70 % porosity, 200 μ m mean pore size) were prepared. 20 adult beagle dogs underwent unilateral THAs and 4 dogs were sacrificed at 1, 3, 6, 12, and 24 months after implantation, respectively. Roentgenographic evaluation showed the efficacy of porous AW-GC as an intramedullary plug. Histological evaluation showed osteoconduction at 1 month and resorption of porous AW-GC which was replaced by newly formed bone at 24 months. On the basis of the present study, porous AW-GC can be used as an intramedullary plug in human THA.

KEYWORDS: AW-glass-ceramic, total hip arthroplasty, canine, bioactivity

INTRODUCTION

Since introduction of polymethylmethacrylate (PMMA) bone cement by Charnley[1] in 1960, PMMA bone cement has come to be considered generally one of the most effective means for the fixation of hip prostheses. Aseptic loosening, however, remains the most serious long term drawback on a multifactorial basis. Modern cement fixation which includes pulsatile lavage, intramedullary plugging, vacuum mixing, retrograde insertion by cement gun, and final compaction have been shown to enhance the fixation of cement to bone. An essential prerequisite to this procedure is adequete plugging of the distal femoral canal. Various methods for plugging the canal have been reported, such as, doughly aclylic cement, bone plug, and manufactured plugs of polyethylene, biodegradable copolymer, and hydroxyapatite.[2] We generally use cancellous bone chips obtained from resected femoral head in primary THA. However, when it is difficult to get bone chips, in the cases of revision surgery, we use porous AW-glass ceramic (AW-GC) as an intramedullary plug. Dense A-W GC has been reported to have high mechanical strength as well as the capability of forming strong chemical bonds with bone tissue. Kawanabe et al. reported on the efficacy of antibiotics-soaked AW-GC blocks as a new drug delivery system (DDS) for osteomyelitis *in vitro* and *in vivo*.[3] The purpose of this study was to evaluate efficacy and biocompatibility of porous AW-GC as an intramedullary plug in canine THA for up to 24 months.

MATERIALS AND METHODS
Porous A-W GC intramedullary plug

Porous A-W GC rods (70 % porosity, 200 μ m mean pore size) were prepared and provided by Nippon Electric Glass Co. Ltd.(Otsu, Japan (Fig. 1)). The chemical composition of porous A-W GC was 4.6% MgO, 44.7% CaO, 34.0% SiO_2, 16.2% P_2O_5, and 0.5% CaF_2, and the crystalized glass-ceramic consisted of 28% residual glass, 38% apatite ($Ca_{10}(PO_4)_6(O, F_2)$), and 34% β-Wollastonite($SiO_2 \cdot$ CaO), as previously described,[3] and was the same as that of dense A-W GC. Its compressive strength was 17.54$\pm$3.82Mpa (mean$\pm$S.D.). We prepared various sizes of cylindrical AW-GC intramedullary plug for various sizes of intramedullary canal of beagle dogs. The sizes were 5×5, 5×10, 6×5, 6×10, 7×5, and 7×10 (mm, diameter×height, respectively).

Hip prosthesis

The hip prosthesis consisted of an acetabular component, 18 mm in outer diameter, made of ultra high molecular weight polyethylene (UHMWPE), a 12 mm femoral head made of stainless steel (SUS-316L), and a straight stemmed, collared femoral component made of stainless steel (SUS-316L). On the outer surface of the acetabular component, circular and centrifugal V-shaped grooves whose depth were 0.8 mm were shaped. The femoral shaft was 4 mm in diameter and 50 mm in length. The surface of the femoral head was finished to a maximum roughness of 0.08 μ m, average roughness of 0.04 μ m. The hip prosthesis was sterilized with gamma irradiation before use.

Bioactive bone cement

Composition of bioactive bone cement (BABC) was descrived in detail elsewhere.[4] Briefly, BABC consists of AW glass-ceramic powder, fused silica glass (SiO_2) powder, and fumed silica powder as the filler (AW glass-ceramic : fused SiO_2 : fumed silica= 73 : 25 : 2, by weight ratio) and Bis-GMA-based resin as the organic matrix. The two pastes (each weight is 40g, 80g in total) were packed and sterilized separately in ethylene oxide gas. In use, they were kneaded together for about one minute using a high-vacuum mixing system, Mixevac II (Stryker Co. Ltd., USA). Both cements polymerized within 8 minutes. Evaluation of BABC in canine THA has been reported elsewhere.[5, 6]

Surgery

We used 20 adult beagle dogs weighing 9.5 to 10.5 kg. Each dog underwent unilateral total hip arthroplasties. The transtrochanteric approach was selected because of its easiness in exposing the acetabulum of dogs. After the fixation of the acetabular component, the femoral canal was serially reamed to remove the spongiosa. Using a special jig, size of the medullary canal was measured to select the largest diameter possible to push in. Syrindrical-shaped intramedullary plug were pushed into the femoral canal until the plug had reached 0.5 to 1.0 cm distal to the femoral component. Bone cement was injected into the femoral canal from the bottom to the top. 4 dogs were sacrificed at 1, 3, 6, 12, and 24 months after implantation, respectively by intravenous overdose of pentobarbital.

Evaluation

The entire femora were harvested and radiographed, antero-posterior and lateral directions. The femur was cut into 5 mm sections, axial to the long axis, using a high speed, water cooled, circular saw with fine diamond coating (BS-3000, EXAKT, Norderstedt, Germany). The 5 mm-thick section was fixed in 10% phosphate-buffered formalin solution and dehydrated in serial concentrations of ethanol and then embedded in polyester resin. Sections 100 μ m thick were prepared for Giemsa surface staining and a scanning electron microscope (SEM)(Hitachi S-800, Hitachi, Tokyo, Japan) equipped with an energy dispersive Xray microanalyzer (EDX)(EMAX-3000, Horiba, Tokyo, Japan).

RESULTS

All dogs were able to bear their body weight within 1 week and walked without a limp by 3 weeks. Neither infection nor abnormal inflammatory reaction of the hip was shown on gross examination, and all the implants appeared to be fixed securely to the skeletons. The radiograph showed neither loosening of the hip prosthesis nor abnormal bone resorption around the cement mantle at 1 to 24 months. No migration of the plug was observed, although small leaks of the cement were tolerated. At 24 months after implantation, the plug became radiolucent, although the cement remained at the level and no subsidence was observed. Giemsa surface staining showed new bone formation in the pores and around the plug at 1 month. Direct contact between newly formed bone and AW-GC was also observed. At 6 months, abundant bone was apparent even in the center of the pores, and direct contact between the plug and the inner surface of endosteum was observed. At 24 months, the wall of the pores became thinner and almost totally resorbed and replaced by newly formed bone. (Fig. 1) When the interface between the bone and AW-GC was observed by SEM, the Ca-P-rich layer whose thickness was 10 μ m was ocserved. SEM-EPMA demonstrated that this layer had a higher phosphorus intensity, lower silicon and magnesium intensities, and almost the same calcium intensity compared with AW-GC, which are the characteristics of the Ca-P-rich layer.

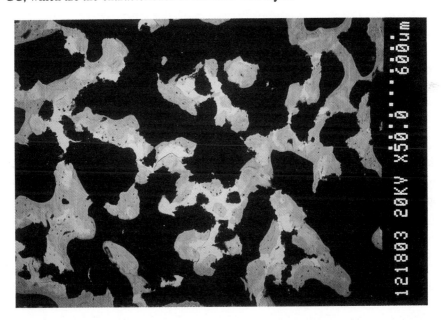

Figure 1 SEM image of porous AW-GC intramedullary plug implanted in canine femoral canal 24 months after surgery. ×50

DISCUSSION

Dense A-W GC has been reported to have high mechanical strength as well as the capability of forming strong chemical bonds with bone tissue. Kawanabe et al. reported on the efficacy of antibiotics-soaked AW-GC blocks as a new drug delivery system (DDS) for osteomyelitis *in vitro* and *in vivo*.[3] They also showed in their pilot clinical study that antibiotics-soaked AW-GC blocks appeared to be useful for the treatment of chronic osteomyelitis or infected arthroplasties with bone defects. On the basis of these two reports porous AW-GC is suitable for the carrier of DDS. Combination of porous AW-GC plug and antibiotics can be used as at THA for preventing an infection. Neo et al. reported that particles (100-220 μ m in diameter) of AW-GC implanted in the rat tibiae have not been resorbed completely even after 96 weeks after implantation. They reported that the resorbed or replaced width of the surface of AW-GC was less than about 50 μ m per year. As the thickness of the wall of porous AW-GC is 30 to70 μ m, it is reasonable that porous AW-GC has been subtotally resorbed within 24 months in the present study. Cancellous bone chips obtained from resected femoral head are generally used in our institute at primary THA. However, when it is difficult to get bone chips, in the cases of revision surgery, we use porous AW-glass ceramic (AW-GC) as an intramedullary plug. Although cylindrical porous AW-GC may be insufficient to occulude the elliptical shape of the femoral canal, by compacting many spherical shaped AW-GC is thought to acheive complete plugging of the femoral canal without any migration or leakage. Raut et al. reported on a one-stage revision of infected THA with discharging sinuses using antibiotics-soaked PMMA bone cement and showed excellent clinical result.[8] Antibiotics-soaked porous AW-GC intramedullary plug may be useful in such situations when femoral head is not available and also antibiotics DDS is essential combined with antibiotics-inpregnated PMMA bone cement.

CONCLUSIONS

The results of our study proved the efficacy of porous AW-GC as an intramedullary plug. AW-GC plugs appear to be good candidates for clinical applications, being biocompatible and having resorbing characteristics within 2 years

ACKNOWLEDGMENTS

The authors thank Mr. Yoshiro Kitamura and Mr. Shunsuke Komatsudani(Nippon Electric Glass, Co., Ltd.) for their technical assistance and Nippon Electric Glass, Co., Ltd. for supply of materials.

REFERENCES

1. J. Charnley, *J. Bone Joint Surg.*, 42-B, 28-30, 1960.
2. M. Maruyama, *Arch Orthop Trauma Surg*, 116, 396-399, 1997.
3. K. Kawanabe, Okada Y, Y. Matsusue, et al., *J. Bone Joint Surg.*, 80-B, 527-530, 1998.
4. H. Fujita, T. Nakamura, J. Tamura et al., *J. Biomed. Mater. Res.*, 40, 145-152, 1998.
5. H. Fujita, T. Nakamura, K. Ido, et al., Bioceramics 9, Elsevier Science, 487-490, 1996.
6. H. Fujita, T. Nakamura, K. Ido, et al., Bioceramics 10, Elsevier Science, 497-500, 1997.
7. M. Neo, T. Nakamura, C. Ohtsuki, et al., *J. Biomed. Mater. Res.*, 28, 365-372, 1994.
8. V. V. Raut, P. D. Siney, and B. M. Wroblewski, *J Bone Joint Surg* 76B:721 -724, 1994.

Bioceramics Volume 11, edited by R. Z. LeGeros and J.P. LeGeros
(Proceedings of the 11th International Symposium on Ceramics in Medicine)
New York, NY, USA, November 1998
© 1998 by World Scientific Publishing Co. Pte. Ltd.

THE IMPROVEMENTS OF THE MATERIAL PROPERTIES OF BIOLOX OFFER BENEFITS FOR TOTAL HIP REPLACEMENT

G. Willmann, W. von Chamier

CeramTec, Medical Product Division, Plochingen, Germany

ABSTRACT

Applications of alumina ceramics in total hip replacement depend on the fact that alumina ceramics provided wear characteristics suitable for bearing surfaces in THR. Resultant orthopaedic use has enjoyed more than 20 years' clinical success.

Material scientists improved the mechanical strength of alumina. There are 3 generation of medical-grade aluminas. The latest one is an alumina that is HIPed, laser marked and proof-tested. Analyzing the clinical experience of the last 20 years it can be concluded that the improvements are offering the option to reduce the wear rate. The fracture rate of femoral heads was reduced from 0.026 % for 1st generation Biolox to 0.004 % for 3rd generation Biolox forte.

KEYWORDS: Total hip replacement, alumina ceramics, femoral heads, reliability

ALUMINA CERAMICS FOR THR

Alumina ceramics are used for femoral heads and acetabular components in total hip replacement (THR). Resultant orthopaedic use has enjoyed more than 20 years' success[3,21]. Material scientists improved alumina's properteies[23]. ISO 6474[6,7] and ASTM F 603[17] were revised.   The question is if all these improvements offer benefits for the patient. Clinical experiences were analyzed to check if the improvements of the material properties are reducing the wear rate and the fracture rate.

IMPROVING ALUMINA CERAMICS

Standard alumina is sintered in air. The mostly used alumina is Biolox manufactured by CeramTec. In 1992 improved raw material were used. Due to that a finer grain size and lower level of impurities could be achieved. 2nd generation Biolox was sintered in air, too. The objective is to improve all properties that are correlated to reliability. This can be achieved by using clean room processing, hot isostatic pressing (HIP), laser marking, and proof-testing[13]. The HIP process allows for the properties relating to material strength such as density, grain size and grain size distribution to be optimized, and creates the prerequisites necessary to improve the materials reliability. For details see [9,13,21,23].

Because of product liability implants need an identification number to trace them back in case of failure. Laser marking used now offers the option to reduce notch effects. Minimizing the notch effects allows for the component strength of the components to be enhanced.

To guarantee safety all ceramic heads and cups are proof-tested. For determining the mechanical load-carrying capacity of ceramic components in a test, random sampling is required, which, however, will yield results relating to the fracture probability only. Testing the fracture load of 100% of the samples is not possible. Proof-testing, however, allows for a low-level limit of the load-carrying capacity to be fixed.

The proof-test is defined as a test in which 100% of the components are tested using a load which is suited to cause component stresses the distribution of which in the test corresponds to the one experienced in practical application, the level of which, however, is higher.

The proof-test allows for defective parts which would have failed under physiological loads (up to 8 times body weight) in practical application to be sorted out as a result of the excess load test. In this way, it is guaranteed that the components having passed the proof-test will stand the loads to which they are exposed in practical application, since the maximum physiological load applied is approx. 8 times body weight which is lower than the load applied in this proof-test.

Proof-testing allows for the probability of failure to be minimized extremely[13]. Components tested in this way are much safer. As was shown above, the properties of Biolox components were still improved by introducing the above mentioned processes. In order to point out to the enhanced safety of Biolox, the trade mark Biolox which has been used for 20 years was changed into Biolox forte (alumina 3rd generation).

WEAR IN THR

One of the major problems in THR is ostolysis caused by polyethylene (PE) wear debris. This problem can be overcome by using alumina-on-PE and alumina-on-alumina. Results about the wear rate in vitro and in vivo had been reviewed by[3,10,11,19,21]. Bos et al.[1] reported that the in vivo wear rate is in the order of 5µm per year when investigating retrieved wear couples[20,24,25]. In vitro tests proved that Biolox forte-on-Biolox forte (3rd generation) has a wear rate that is 5 times less than the old Biolox-on-Biolox[8,12,14].

SURVIVAL RATE OF CERAMIC COMPONENTS

It is well known that ceramics are brittle and fracture easily when not handled correctly. Brittleness is dominating the risk of failure. This is one of the arguments against ceramics in

THR. Statistics prove that Biolox is very reliable. The fracture rate in vivo is much lower than any other reason for revision of a THR, see table 1. Before 1985 the fracture rate of some of the early alumina heads was up to 10% [18]. Because of these failures some companies stopped to offer ceramic heads.

For Biolox alumina heads (1st and 2nd generation) the fracture rate is between 0.01% and 0.02%. These results are based on 200,000 heads[15], 511,000 heads[16], and more than 1.5 million Biolox heads (1st and 2nd generation)[22] used. The analysis discussed is based on CeramTec's and Semlitsch's statistics [15,16].

Fritsch 4 investigated the fracture rate of heads used in combination with the Mittelmeier's monolithic socket. He reported a fracture rate of 0.4% for mushroom shaped femoral heads. This failure rate is due to impingement caused by the very low range of motion (about 87°) of the mushroom shaped femoral heads. For standard femoral heads the failure rate was 0.06%. Recently Geldbach had analyzed more than 60,000 cases Biolox-on-polyethylene [5]. His results prove that the failure rate is in the same order as the one Fritsch had reported.

Ceramics have to classifed as reliable when comparing to the revision rate for septic loosening which is about 1% and the one for aseptic loosening which is about 10% .The fracture rate of Biolox forte heads (3rd generation) is 0.004%[2]. It has to be assumed that not all cases with failed heads have been reported by the hospitals. It is estimated that the factor of known to unknown cases is in the order of 1:3. This estimation seems to be fair when comparing our analysis with th results of Fritsch and Geldbach[4,5].

These results demonstrate that there is a correlation between the improvement of the mechanical strength and the survival rates. It is a fact that the survival rate was improved, too.

Table 1. Revision rate of THRs

Revision rate	due to
about 10 %	aseptic loosening
about 2 %	fracture of stems
about 1 %	septic loosening
up to 10 %	compiled fracture of early alumina heads offered by others manufacturers[18]
0.01 %	compiled fracture of a Biolox heads alone; Semlitsch's analysis for Sulzer[15]
0.015 %	compiled fracture of a Biolox heads alone; Semlitsch's analysis for Sulzer[16]
0.026 %	fracture of a Biolox head (1st generation); CeramTec's analysis[2,22]
0.4 %	fracture of mushroom shaped Biolox heads (neck length XL), Fritsch's investigation is based on the revisions in the hospital in Homburg / Saar[4]
0.014 %	fracture of a Biolox head (2nd generation); CeramTec's analysis[2,22]
0.06 %	fracture of standard Biolox heads (1st and 2nd generation),Fritsch's investigation is based on the revisions in the hospital Homburg / Saar[4]
0.004 %	fracture of a Biolox forte heads (3rd generation); CeramTec's analysis[2,22]

CONCLUSION

Material scientists improved the reliability of alumina. These technical improvements of Biolox forte (alumina of the 3rd generation) offer benefits for the patient, e. g.: Simulator tests prove that the wear of the improved Biolox forte-on-Biolox forte is 5 times lower that the wear rate of the old Biolox generations. The survival rate of ceramic heads was reduced from 0.026 % for 1st generation Biolox to 0.004% for 3rd generation Biolox forte. It is estimated that the factor of known to unknown failures is about 1:3. Analyzing 20 years clinical experiences it an be concluded that the technical improvements are reducing the wear rate and are improving the reliability of ceramic components for THR.

REFERENCES

1. Bos I. in: reference 10; 1996: 24-30
2. Willmann G Chamier W in: refernce 9; 1998: 19-24
3. Clarke IC Willmann G. in: Cameron, HU ed. *Bone Implant Interface.* St. Louis, 1994: 203 - 252
4. Fritsch EW Gleitz M. Clin Orthop Rel Res 1996; **328**: 129-136
5. Geldbach J. Thesis 1998
6. ISO 6474　1st ed 1981
7. ISO 6474　2nd ed 1994
8. Taylor S Serekian S Manley M. 1998; Abstract　51-9
   44th Ann meeting ORS, March 15-19, New Orleans, Lousiana
9. Puhl W ed. Bioceramics in Orthopaedics. 1998 Enke Verlag, Stuttgart
10. Puhl W ed. Die Keramikpaarung BIOLOX in der Hüftendoprothetik.1996 Enke Verlag, Stuttgart
11. Puhl, W ed. Performance of the Wear Couple BIOLOX forte in Hip Arthroplasty. 1997 Enke Verlag Stuttgart
12. Refior J J, Plitz W Walter A. Bioceramics1997; **10**: 127 -130
13. Richter H G, Willmann G. in reference 10; 1996: 1077-88
14. SaikkoV Paff HG. in reference 11; 1997: 117 - 122
15. Semlitsch, M , W Dawihl in: Buchorn, G H, H-G Willert ed. Technical Priniples, Design and Safety of Joint Implants. Hogrefe & Huber Publ, Seattle, 1994: 99-101
16. Semlitsch M Weber H Steger H, Biomed Technik 1995; **40**: 347 - 355
17. ASTM F 603 (1988)
18. Toni A et al. in: Wise D L et al ed. Encyclopedic Handbook of Biomaterials and Bioengineering. Marcel Dekker, Inc New York: Part A, Vol 2; 1995: 1501-1544
19. Walter A. Clin Orthop Rel Res 1992; **282**: 31 - 46
20. Weber BG Fiechter Th. Orthopädie 1989; **18**: 370-376
21. Willmann, G. Orthopaedics 1998; **21**: 173-177
22. Willmann, G. Mat wiss u Werkstofftechnik 1996; **27**: 280 -286
23. Willmann G, Pfaff HG Richter H. Biomed Technik 1995; **40**: 342-346
24. Zichner L Willert HG. Clin Orthop Rel Res 1992; **282**: 86-94
25. Zichner L Lindenfeld Th. Orthopäde 1997; **26**: 129-134

VIII. METHODS: SPECIAL PREPARATIONS AND ANALYSES

Bioceramics Volume 11, edited by R. Z. LeGeros and J.P. LeGeros
(Proceedings of the 11th International Symposium on Ceramics in Medicine)
New York, NY, USA, November 1998
© 1998 by World Scientific Publishing Co. Pte. Ltd.

GRADED SURFACE STRUCTURE OF BIOACTIVE Ti-6Al-4V ALLOY PREPARED BY CHEMICAL TREATMENT

H.-M. Kim,[1] H. Takadama,[1] F. Miyaji,[1] T. Kokubo,[1] S. Nishiguchi[2] and T. Nakamura[2]

[1]Department of Material Chemistry, Faculty of Engineering, Kyoto University, Kyoto 606-8501, Japan; [2]Department of Orthopaedic Surgery, Faculty of Medicine, Kyoto University, Kyoto 606-8507, Japan

ABSTRACT

Ti-6Al-4V alloy can be subjected to NaOH and heat treatments to induce bioactivity on its surface. An Al- and V-free amorphous sodium titanate, which was integrated with the alloy substrate by a graded structure through titanium oxide, was formed *in situ* on the alloy by the NaOH and heat treatments. When exposed to a simulated body fluid, the surface sodium titanate transformed into a hydrated titania via Na^+ ions release to spontaneously induce a bonelike apatite formation on the surface of alloy. In this process, the graded structure of sodium titanate developed one in which the apatite on the top surface gradually changed into interior alloy substrate through hydrated titania and titanium oxide. This graded structure is believed to provide a strong integration of the alloy to a bone through the apatite layer in the body.

KEYWORDS: Ti-6Al-4V alloy, chemical treatment, simulated body fluid (SBF) apatite, bioactivity, graded surface structure

INTRODUCTION

The present authors previously showed that titanium metal forms an amorphous sodium titanate layer on its surface when subjected to NaOH and subsequent heat treatments. Thus-treated metal forms a bonelike apatite layer on its surface in body environment and bonds to living bone through the apatite layer.[1,2] The apatite layer is tightly bonded to the metal substrate because of a graded structure between them.[3]

The above surface treatment is also effective to induce bioactivity on titanium alloys such as Ti-6Al-4V, which is more often used as orthopedic and dental implants.[1] In the present study, surface structural variations of Ti-6Al-4V alloy in the processes of NaOH and heat treatments to induce its bioactivity and subsequent exposure in simulated body fluid were investigated with special interests on effects of the alloying species.

MATERIALS AND METHODS

Ti-6Al-4V alloy substrates (Kobe Steel Ltd., Japan) $10 \times 10 \times 1$ mm^3 in size were soaked in 5 mL of 5.0M-NaOH aqueous solution at 60°C for 24 h. They were then subjected to heat treatment at 600°C for 1 h. Thus-treated substrates were soaked in an acellular simulated body fluid (SBF) with pH (7.40) and ion concentrations (Na$^+$ 142.0, K$^+$ 5.0, Ca^{2+} 2.5, Mg^{2+} 1.5, Cl$^-$ 147.8, HCO^{3-} 4.2, HPO$_4^{2-}$ 1.0, SO$_4^{2-}$ 0.5 mM) nearly equal to those of human blood plasma.

Surface structure and composition of the substrates after the NaOH and heat treatments and subsequent soaking in SBF were analyzed by scanning electron microscopy (SEM: Model S2500CX, Hitachi Co., Japan), thin-film X-ray diffraction (TF-XRD: TF-XRD; Model 2651A1, Rigaku Co., Japan) and Auger electron spectroscopy (AES: Model MT4300, ULVAC-PHI Co., Japan).

RESULTS AND DISCUSSION

Figure 1 shows the SEM photographs and TF XRD patterns of the surfaces of Ti-6Al-4V substrates before and after the NaOH and heat treatments and subsequent soaking in SBF for 5 days. SEM photographs showed that a porous network structure was formed by the NaOH treatment (B) and fairly densified by the subsequent heat treatment (C). On the XRD patterns after the NaOH treatment (B), broad halo patterns were observed around 23-29° and 48° in 2θ. This is due to formation of a sodium titanate hydrogel layer on the metal.[4] After subsequent heat treatment (C), small peaks ascribed to crystalline sodium titanate (Na$_2$Ti$_5$O$_{11}$) and rutile (TiO$_2$) appeared around the halo patterns, indicating that the hydrogel converted into an amorphous sodium titanate containing small amounts of

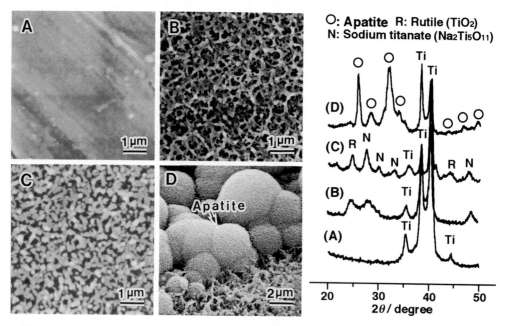

Fig. 1. SEM photographs and TF-XRD patterns of the surfaces of Ti-6Al-4V substrates (A) before and (B) after the NaOH and (C) heat treatments and (D) subsequent soaking in SBF for 5 days.

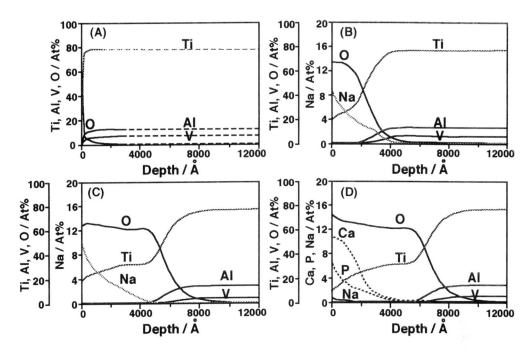

Fig. 2. AES depth profiles of the surfaces of Ti-6Al-4V substrates (A) before and (B) after the NaOH and (C) heat treatments and (D) subsequent soaking in SBF for 5 days.

the above crystalline phases by the heat treatment. After the soaking in SBF, island-like assemblies of tiny apatite crystals were observed on the surface (D) under SEM. XRD peaks appeared after the soaking in SBF (D) were all ascribed to crystalline apatite. The induction period for the apatite formation in SBF was 5 days, which was a little longer than that for pure titanium metal subjected to the same treatments (3 days). The apatite grew into a dense and uniform layer to cover the whole surface of the metal within 7 days of soaking in SBF.

Figure 2 shows the AES depth profiles of the surfaces of Ti-6Al-4V substrates before and after the NaOH and heat treatments and after subsequent soaking in SBF for 5 days. The depth profile after the NaOH treatment (B) showed that a graded structure, in which Na and O concentrations gradually decrease toward the depth about 6000 Å while Ti concentration gradually increases toward the same depth, was formed on the surface of the metal. Alloying species of Al and V were observed to be lack at the top surface, indicating that they were released from the surface of metal by the NaOH treatment. After the subsequent heat treatment (C), the gradient of the Na concentration was not changed but those of O and Ti concentrations were extended to the depth about 10000 Å. It should be noted that the Al and V were observed only in a deeper region than 4500 Å where the Na was negligible. The depth profile after the soaking in SBF (D) showed that Ca and P newly appeared to gradually decrease their concentrations toward the interior. The revelation of Ca and P at the surface is due to the apatite formation on the metal. The Na concentration became negligible, indicating that the Na⁺ ion released into SBF from its surface. The gradients of O, Ti, V and Al concentrations were almost same as those before soaking.

The above results show that, being subjected to the NaOH treatment, Ti-6Al-4V alloy releases Al and V to form a thin Al- and V-free sodium titanate hydrogel layer on its surface. By the subsequent heat treatment, the hydrogel layer is dehydrated and densified to be stabilized into an amorphous sodium titanate.[5] As shown in Fig. 2, thus-formed amorphous sodium titanate is integrated *in situ* with the alloy metal by a graded structure in which it is gradually changes into interior metal through titanium oxide. When this alloy is exposed to SBF, the sodium titanate on its surface releases Na^+ ion via ion exchange with H_3O^+ ion in the surrounding fluid. As the consequence of the ion exchange, a hydrated titania is formed on the surface, and the pH in the fluid increases to increase the ionic activity product of apatite in SBF. Thus-formed hydrated titania induces the apatite nucleation on its surface, and the increased ionic activity product accelerates the apatite nucleation.[6] A large number of apatite nuclei thus-formed on the surface of the alloy spontaneously grow into a dense and uniform surface layer by consuming the calcium and phosphate ions from the surrounding fluid. As a results, the graded structure of sodium titanate converted into one in which the apatite on the top surface gradually decreases into interior alloy substrate through hydrated titania and titanium oxide. In this process, alloying species of Al and V have no effect on the apatite formation on the surface of alloy, since they are lack in the sodium titanate layer. As previously shown for pure titanium metal,[3] thus-formed graded structure may provide a strong integration of the alloy to a bone through the apatite layer in the body.

CONCLUSIONS

Simple NaOH and heat treatments provide bioactive Ti-6Al-V alloy with a graded structure, in which an Al- and V-free amorphous sodium titanate on top surface gradully decreases toward the alloy substrate through titanium oxide. In SBF, the sodium titanate transformed into a hydrated titania via Na^+ ions release to spontaneously induce a bonelike apatite formation on the alloy. The apatite formed in this way was integrated with the metal by a graded structure through hydrated titania and titanium oxide. This graded interfacial structure between the apatite and alloy enables the alloy to bone to and integrate tightly with a bone through the apatite layer in the body.

ACKNOWLEDGMENT

This study was supported by Grant-in-Aid for Scientific Research, the Ministry of Education, Science, Sports, and Culture, Japan.

REFERENCES

1. Kim HM, Miyaji F, Kokubo T, Nakamura T. *J. Biomed. Mater. Res.*, 1996; **32**: 409-417.
2. Yan WQ, Nakamura T, Kobayashi M, Kim HM, Miyaji F, Kokubo T. *J. Biomed. Mater. Res.*, 1997; **37**, 265-275.
3. Kim HM, Miyaji F, Kokubo T, Suzuki T, Itoh F, Nishiguchi S, Nakamura T. In: Sedel L, Rey C, ed. *Bioceramics Vol. 10*, Elsevier, Oxford, 1997: 215-219.
4. Kim HM, Miyaji F, Kokubo T, Nakamura T. *J. Ceram. Soc. Japan*, 1997; **101**: 111-116.
5. Kim HM, Miyaji F, Kokubo T, Nakamura T. *J. Mater. Sci.: Mater. Med.*, 1997; **8**: 341-347.
6. Li P, Ohtsuki C, Kokubo T, Nakanishi K, Soga N, Nakamura T, Yamamuro T, de Groot K. *J. Biomed. Mater. Res.*, 1994; **28**: 7-15.

Bioceramics Volume 11, edited by R. Z. LeGeros and J.P. LeGeros
(Proceedings of the 11th International Symposium on Ceramics in Medicine)
New York, NY, USA, November 1998
© 1998 by World Scientific Publishing Co. Pte. Ltd.

BONE FORMATION AROUND SURFACE MODIFIED TITANIUM IMPLANTS

W.-Q. Yan and J. E. Davies
Institute for Biomaterials and Biomedical Engineering, University of Toronto
170 College Street, Toronto ON, M5S 3E3, Canada.

ABSTRACT

The importance of surface modification of titanium (Ti) implants on bone juxtaposition was studied in rats. A total of 50 custom designed machined (M) commercially pure Ti implants were surface modified by acid etching (AE) with, or without, further alkali (A) or alkali and thermal (AT) treatment. Implant surfaces were examined by scanning electron microscopy (SEM). The AE group exhibited a pitted microtopography, while those in the A and AT groups exhibited a surface oxide of reticulate appearance. Histological examination and back-scattered electron imaging of a total of 46 implants retrieved after 3, 6, and 12 weeks revealed bone enveloping all implant types, at all time points. Bone was directly juxtaposed to the AT surfaces at 3 weeks and no separation occurred at this interface during tissue processing. In the AE and A groups bone was also in close proximity to the surfaces at early periods. In contrast, a tissue space occupied the interface between bone and implants in the M group at early periods and limited bone juxtaposition to the implant surface was seen only at 12 weeks. These results suggest that implant surface microtopography potentiates osteoconduction, whereas AT treatment, as witnessed by the resistance of the bone/implant interface to separate during tissue processing, contributes to bonding osteogenesis.

KEYWORDS: titanium implant, surface modification, acid-etching, alkali, bone-bonding.

INTRODUCTION

Titanium-based metals are commonly used in orthopaedic and dental surgery as load-bearing implants, but they are generally classified as non-bone bonding materials. The use of bioactive coating techniques to modify Ti surfaces has some distinct advantages in enhancing bone-implant bonding. However, physical coatings are not bonded to the underlying Ti substratum, resulting in a weak metal/coating interface, and progressive loss of the coating with time[1]. Recent work has shown that surface modification by chemical treatments of Ti-based metals may render their surfaces bone bonding, and increase bonding strength at the bone-implant interface[2,3]. Despite these results, there is no clear understanding of the surface physicochemical changes induced as result of the chemical treatment which cause this change in biological reaction to the implant. The purpose of the study was to evaluate the independent effects of surface topography and surface chemistry on the bony reaction to Ti implants.

MATERIALS AND METHODS

Custom designed machined (M) implants (n = 50: 5 mm long, 1 mm diameter) manufactured from commercially pure Ti (99.5%) were generously provided by Implant Innovations Inc., FL, of which 38 were acid etched, according the procedure employed for Osseotite™ dental implants. The implants were designed with a parallel-sided medullary component and a threaded trans-cortical portion. All samples were sonicated in a 2% Decon™ solution and dried at 40° for 1 hr. The acid-etched implants were divided into three groups and received the following supplementary treatment: No treatment (AE); alkali-treated - soaked in 10M NaOH aqueous solution at 60° for 24 hr, washed with distilled water and air dried at 40° for 1 hr. (A); and alkali treated, as above, followed by thermal treatment at 600°, for 1 hr (AT). Following cleaning and/or treatment the implants were examined by scanning electron microscopy (SEM – Hitachi model 2500, Japan). Implants were placed aseptically into the anterolateral aspect of mature Wistar rat (320 g) femora, under general anaesthesia. Implants were retrieved at 3, 6 and 12 weeks post-implantation according to the table below.

	M	AE	A	AT
3 Weeks	2(2)	4	4	4
6 Weeks	3(1)	3(1)	4	4
12 Weeks	4	4	5	5

TABLE: Shows the number of implants of each type (M = machined; AE = Acid Etched; A = Acid etched and NaOH treated; AT = Acid etched, NaOH and thermally treated) retrieved after 3, 6, and 12 weeks implantation. The numbers in parentheses indicate the implants not anchored in bone at retrieval).

Retrieved implants were fixed in 10% buffered formaldehyde, dehydrated in serial concentrations of ethanol, embedded in Osteobed™, and polymerized at room temperature. Each block was sectioned approximately perpendicular to the longitudinal axis of the implant with a diamond wheel (1A1-3X, Norton; USA), and thick sections containing the bone-implant interface were obtained. Sections (about 500μm) were further ground to a thickness of 80μm, and stained with Toluidine blue and Van Gieson solutions for observation by light microscopy. The opposing sections were polished with #3000 grit paper, coated with carbon and examined by SEM and backscattered electron imaging (BSEI).

RESULTS and DISCUSSION

SEM of the implants showed that their surfaces were markedly different. The machined surface exhibited distinct ridges and grooves, while the acid-etched surface exhibited a pitted topography at both the 10-and 1-micron scale. Following A and AT treatments the modified oxide surface was of reticulate appearance, as has been demonstrated by others[4]. The micropores of this oxide surface were in the sub-micron range. We have shown, in a parallel study[5] that, following alkali NaOH treatment, the surface oxide increases in thickness from about 10nm in the M and AE groups to 30 and over 200nm in the A and AT groups respectively. Thus, the micron scale topography of the underlying etched surface, which has no undercuts, was obliterated by the growth of the surface oxide with a sub-micron undercut topography. The surface morphology of the oxide surface was almost indistinguishable in the A and AT groups, although the surface chemical composition changed as a result of concentration of sodium ions, following the thermal treatment, to create a surface sodium titanate.[6]

Figure 1. Histological appearance at 6 wks. Left to right: M, AE, A, AT implant types.

Due to the small implant diameter it was generally not possible to orient the diamond wafering blade to produce more than one cut through each embedded tissue block . Thus only two sections (either side of the cut) were produced from each implant producing one sample for histology and the other for BSEI. Furthermore, since the orientation of the cut was variable, sections of varying obliquity, were produced through the implants. Nevertheless, histology demonstrated that the medullary component of all implant types became encapsulated in bone during even the shortest (3 weeks) implantation period, and that the amount of peri-implant bone increased with time. However, the degree of medullary bone/implant contact differed in sample groups. At 3 weeks, the most striking differences were seen between the M and AT groups. In the former only limited bone/implant contact was observed, whereas in the latter a thin seam of bone was in contact with the whole medullary implant surface. A striking feature of the AT group at both this, and later, time periods was that the space often seen at light microscopy between bone and metallic implants, and which is a artifact of tissue processing, was not observed. The AE and A groups exhibited a similar degree of bone contact at three weeks which was greater than that seen in the M group, but less than that of the AT group.

By 6 weeks these differences were less pronounced, due to the overall increase in amount of new inter-medullary bone, although the different pattern of bone/implant contact to the machined surface, which was characterized by a continuous arcade of bone held away from the implant surface by focal areas of bone contact was still clearly visualized (Figure 1). At this time period the A group was similar in appearance to the M group, while the AE group exhibited more evident osteoconduction with a thin seam of bone closely adapted to the medullary implant surface. In the AT group, since bone had already developed in contact with the entire medullary implant surface at 3 weeks, the only obvious difference at the 6 week period was the increase in volume of peri-implant bone. BSEI confirmed the light microscopic observations, as illustrated for M and AT groups at 6 weeks in Figure 2. However, this form of imaging more clearly illustrated the differences in bone healing patterns between implant groups. While it is obvious that bone grew around both the implants in Figure 2, the non-bony tissue spaces occupying the majority of the medullary surface of the machined implant were more clearly visualized. This appearance, of an arcaded (or wavy) seam of bone, apparently separated from the implant surface (Figure 2a), was in sharp contrast to that in the AT group. In the latter, bone was more closely adapted to the entire implant surface. In this implant group, a space could be seen in some sections at the bone/implant interface, but this was a thin parallel-sided defect characteristic of tissue processing artifact, as

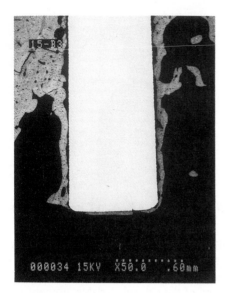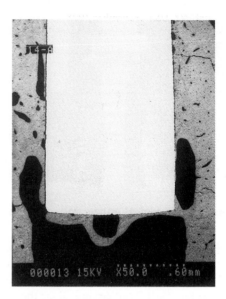

Figure 2. BSEI appearance at 6 weeks. (a) M and (b) AT implant types

illustrated in Figure 2b, and morphologically distinct from the tissue spaces seen in other implant groups. This apparent bone-bonding to the AT surface would corroborate the findings of a previous study[3]. By 12 weeks groups M, AE and A all showed a greater degree of bone/implant contact than seen at earlier time points. As the AT group was already covered with medullary bone at 3 weeks, these histological comparisons indicate that more rapid osteoconduction occurred on AT with respect to the other surfaces, and that the surface modifications in the AE and A groups enhanced osteoconduction with respect to the machined surfaces of the M group.

CONCLUSION

Topographical changes created on the AE, A and AT implant surfaces, and not the surface chemistry of the A and AT groups, increase osteoconduction when compared to machined surfaces.

REFERENCES
1. Bloebaum RD, Beeks D, Dorr LD, Savory CG, Dupont JA, Hofmann AA. Clin.Orthop. 1994, 298:19-26.
2. Kim HM, Miyaji F, Kokubo T, Nakamura T. J.Biomed. Mater. Res., 1996, 32. 409-417.
3. Yan WQ, Nakamura T, Kobayashi M, Kim HM, Miyaji F, Kokubo T. J.Biomed. Mater. Res., 1997, 37:267-275
4. Miyaji F, Zhang X, Yao T, Kukobo T, Ohttsuki O, Kitsugi T, Yamamuro T,Nakamura T. Chemical treatment of Ti metal to induce its bioactivity. In: Andersson ÖH, Happonen R-P,Yli-Urpo A (eds.). Bioceramics 7 Oxford:Pergamon/Butterworth-Heinemann;1994:119-124.
5. Davies JE, Solomon T, Yan W, Dadgostari S, Caudry SD. *In press.*
6. Kokubo T, Miyaji F, Kim H-M, Nakamura T. J. Am. Ceram. Soc. 1996;79:1127-1129.

Bioceramics Volume 11, edited by R. Z. LeGeros and J.P. LeGeros
(Proceedings of the 11th International Symposium on Ceramics in Medicine)
New York, NY, USA, November 1998
© 1998 by World Scientific Publishing Co. Pte. Ltd.

HOW DOES ALKALI-TREATED TITANIUM INDUCE APATITE FORMATION?

H. Takadama[1], H.-M. Kim[1], F. Miyaji[1], T. Kokubo[1], and T. Nakamura[2]

[1]Department of Material Chemistry, Faculty of Engineering, Kyoto University, Sakyo-ku, Kyoto 606-8501, Japan, [2]Department of Orthopedic Surgery, Faculty of Medicine, Kyoto University, Sakyo-ku, Kyoto 606-8507, Japan

ABSTRACT

It was previously shown by the present authors that Ti metal forms a dense and uniform bonelike apatite layer on its surface in a simulated body fluid (SBF) or in the living body and bond to living bone through this apatite layer, when it was previously soaked in 5.0M-NaOH aqueous solution at 60°C for 24 h and then heat treated at 600°C for 1 h. The surface structural changes of the NaOH- and heat- treated Ti metal due to exposure to SBF at 36.5°C were investigated by X-ray photoelectron spectroscopy (XPS). It was found that the sodium ion in the surface amorphous sodium titanate layer was released completely within 2 d. The Ti-OH groups which was formed on the surface by the exchange of the Na^+ ion in the sodium titanate layer with the H_3O^+ ion in SBF combined with only the calcium ion as early as within 30 minutes, and then combined with the phosphate ion 2 d later to form the apatite. This indicates that the Ti-OH groups do not induce the apatite nucleation directly, but through the formation of the calcium titanate.

KEYWORDS: Titanium, chemical treatment, surface structure, X-ray photoelectron spectroscopy (XPS), apatite, simulated body fluid (SBF)

INTRODUCTION

Only a limited kind of ceramics, called bioactive ceramics, had been known to bond to living bone[1]. None of them, however, has fracture toughness as high as that of human cortical bones, and thus they could not be used as load-bearable bone-repairing materials. The present authors showed recently that bioactive Ti metal, which spontaneously bonds to living bone via formation of a bonelike apatite on its surface in the body as the bioactive ceramics do, can be prepared by subjecting the Ti metal to NaOH and subsequent heat treatments.[2-4] Such type of bioactive Ti metal is believed to be truly useful as highly load-bearing artificial bones, since they can provide not only its intrinsic high fracture and fatigue resistances, but also reliable ability to bond to the living bone and integrate with it in the body. The mechanism how apatite is formed on the Ti metal in the body environment has not been, however, clarified yet.

In the present study, the mechanism of the apatite formation on the NaOH- and heat- treated Ti metal was investigated mainly by using X-ray photoelectron spectroscopy (XPS).

MATERIALS AND METHODS

Commercially pure titanium (Ti: Ti > 99.8 %, Kobe Steel Ltd., Kobe, Japan) plates were used in the present study. The metal plates with $10 \times 10 \times 1$ mm^3 in size were abraded with #400 diamond plate, and washed with pure acetone and distilled water in an ultrasonic cleaner. They were treated with 5.0M-NaOH aqueous solution at 60 °C for 24 h, washed gently with distilled water and dried at 40 °C for 24 h. Then they were heated up to 600 °C at a rate of 5 °C / min in an electric furnace, kept at 600 °C for 1 h and allowed to cool in the furnace. Thus-treated Ti substrates were soaked in an acellular simulated body fluid (SBF) with pH (7.40) and ion concentrations (Na^+ 142.0, K^+ 5.0, Ca^{2+} 2.5, Mg^{2+} 1.5, HCO_3^- 4.2, Cl^- 148.0, HPO_4^- 1.0, SO_4^{2-} 0.5 mM) nearly equal to those of human blood plasma to examine the mechanism of the apatite formation on the Ti metal. Each specimen was soaked in 25 ml of SBF at 36.5 °C for various periods, and then removed form the fluid and washed with distilled water and dried at room temperature. Surface structural changes of the NaOH- and heat-treated Ti metal due to exposure to SBF were analyzed by scanning electron microscopy (SEM: Model S2500CX, Hitachi Co., Tokyo, Japan), thin-film X-Ray diffraction (TF-XRD: Model 2651A1, Rigaku Co., Tokoy, Japan) and X-ray photoelectron spectroscopy (XPS: Model MT5500, ULVAC-PHI Co., Ltd., Chigasaki, Japan).

RESULTS AND DISCUSSION

Figure 1 shows SEM photographs and the TF-XRD patterns of the surfaces of the NaOH- and heat-treated Ti metal as a function of soaking time in SBF. It can be seen from Figure 1 that the NaOH- and heat- treated Ti metal shows porous network surface structure. This surface layer is an amorphous sodium titanate layer containing small amounts of the crystalline sodium titanate ($Na_2Ti_5O_{11}$) and rutile (TiO_2) according to the XRD. A broad XRD peak ascribed to the apatite was newly appeared around 32° after soaking in SBF for 2 d. After the soaking in SBF over 3 d, all of the XRD peaks which newly appeared around 25-34°and 46-50° were also ascribed to the apatite. On the SEM photographs after soaking in SBF for 2 d, the tiny spheres of the apatite crystals were observed. The island-like assemblies of these apatite crystals covered the whole surface of the metal after soaking in SBF over 3 d.

Figure 2 shows the Na_{1s}, Ca_{2p}, P_{2p} and O_{1s} XPS spectra of the surfaces of the NaOH- and heat-treated Ti metal as a function of soaking time in SBF. Na_{1s} spectrum was a single peak with a binding energy of 1072.3 ± 0.1 eV. The sodium in the surface amorphous sodium titanate layer decreased its concentration gradually with increasing soaking time and disappeared completely within 2 d. This indicates that the surface sodium titanate layer exchanged its Na^+ ion with H_3O^+ in the fluid to form hydrated titania. The released Na^+ ion increased ionic activity product of apatite in SBF by increasing the pH. Ca_{2p} spectrum was a doublet peak with $Ca_{2p1/2}$ = 350.6 ± 0.4 eV and $Ca_{2p3/2}$ = 347.1 ± 0.3 eV. The calcium was detected as early as within 30 minutes and its intensity

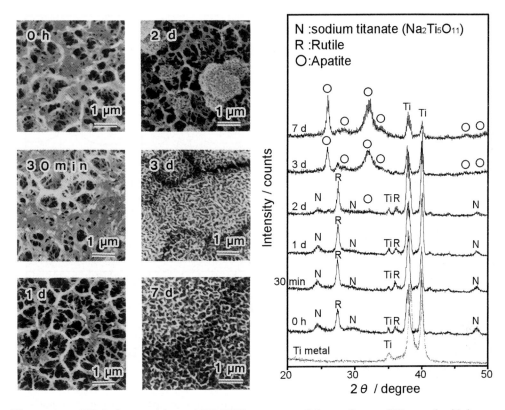

Figure 1. SEM photographs and TF-XRD patterns of the surfaces of Ti metal which were subjected to 5.0M-NaOH treatment at 60℃ for 24 h, and subsequent heat treatment at 600℃ for 1 h as a function of soaking time in SBF.

remarkably increased after 2 d. P_{2p} spectrum was a single peak with a binding energy of 133.0 ± 0.1 eV. The phosphorous was detected about 2 d later than the calcium. This time coincided with the time when the intensity of Ca_{2p} spectra remarkably increased and the time when XRD peaks of apatite became observed. O_{1s} spectrum was a single peak including a probable overlapping peak. The main peak with a binding energy of 530.0 ± 0.2 eV represents the oxygen bonded to the titanium. The shoulder formed at the higher binding energy after soaking in SBF represents the formation of the Ti-OH group. After soaking in SBF for 2 d, this peak sifted to that with a higher binding energy of 531.4 ± 0.3 eV. This peak represents phosphate in the apatite layer on the surface of the Ti metal. The time of this peak-sift coincided with the time of the first detection of the phosphorous. This indicates that the apatite was first formed on the surface of the NaOH- and heat-treated Ti metal after 2 d soaking in SBF.

CONCLUSION

The Ti-OH groups formed on the surface by the exchange of the Na^+ ion in the sodium titanate layer

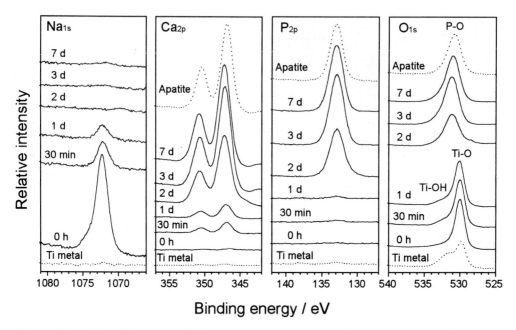

Figure 2. Na$_{1s}$, Ca$_{2p}$, P$_{2p}$ and O$_{1s}$ XPS spectra of the surfaces of Ti metal which were subjected to 5.0M-NaOH treatment at 60°C for 24 h, and subsequent heat treatment at 600°C for 1 h as a function of soaking time in SBF.

with the H$_3$O$^+$ ion in SBF combined with only the calcium ion as early as within 30 minutes, and then combined with the phosphate ion 2 days later to form the apatite. This means that Ti-OH groups do not induce the apatite nucleation directly, but through the formation of the calcium titanate.

ACKNOWLEDGEMENT

This study was supported by Grant-in-Aid for Scientific Research, the Ministry of Education, Science, Sports and Culture, Japan.

REFERENCES

1. Kokubo, T., *J. Ceram. Soc. Japan*, 1991, **99**, 965-973.
2. Kim, H.M., Miyaji, F., Kokubo, T. and Nakamura, T. *J. Biomed. Mater. Res.*, 1996, **32**, 409-417.
3. Yan, W.Q., Nakamura, T., Kobayashi, M., Kim, H.M., Miyaji, F. and Kokubo, T. *J. Biomed. Mater. Res.*, 1997, **37** 1-11.
4. Kim, H.M., Miyaji, F., Kokubo, T., Suzuki, T. Itoh, F., Nishiguthi S. and Nakamura, T., In: *Bioceramics* Volume 10, Elsevier, Oxford 1997, 215-219.

Bioceramics Volume 11, edited by R. Z. LeGeros and J.P. LeGeros
(Proceedings of the 11th International Symposium on Ceramics in Medicine)
New York, NY, USA, November 1998
© 1998 by World Scientific Publishing Co. Pte. Ltd.

BONE-BONDING ABILITY OF TITANIUM METAL CHEMICALLY TREATED WITH HYDROGEN PEROXIDE CONTAINING TANTALUM CHLORIDE: *IN VIVO* EXAMINATION

Shinya Kaneko[1], Hajime Inoue[1], Keizo Kobayashi[2], Chikara Ohtsuki[2] and Akiyoshi Osaka[2]

[1]Department of Orthopaedic Surgery, Okayama University Medical School, Shikata-cho, Okayama-shi 700-8558, Japan; [2]Biomaterials Lab., Faculty of Engineering, Okayama University, Tsushima, Okayama-shi 700-8530, Japan.

ABSTRACT

Apatite formation on implants is important to achieve bone-binding. Ohtsuki *et al.* showed that titanium metal chemically treated with hydrogenperoxide solution containing tantalum chlorides has an ability to form hydroxyapatite layer in a simulated body fluid (Kokubo solution) which had an inorganic ion composition similar to human blood plasma. In our study, titanium cylinder (4.0mm in diameter and 20.0mm in length) treated with Ohtsuki's method was implanted into a hole (4.2mm in diameter) in rabbit's tibia. 4, 8, 12 and 16 weeks after surgery, push-out test was performed to evaluate the shearing force between the titanium metal and bone tissue. The result was compared with those of non-treated titanium. 8 weeks after surgery, shearing force of the treated titanium was significantly stronger than those of the non-treated titanium. Scanning electron microscopic (SEM) observation and energy dispersive X-ray microanalysis (EDX) showed a Ti gel-layer on the surface of the treated titanium and the layer corrected directly to bone tissue. Morever, the shearing force was higher in 4.0mm–hole than that for in 4.2mm–hole for sample-implanted. Thus the titanium implants treated with the hydrogenperoxide solution containing tantalum chlorides had bioactivity *in vivo*.

KEYWORDS: Titanium, bioactivity, *in vivo* study, hydrogenperoxide

INTRODUCTION

Arthroplasty implants inserted without cement should be fixed directly to bone tissue in order to obtain satisfactory clinical outcome to avoid the loosening caused by micromotion at implant-bone interface. Titanium metal and titanium alloys are widely used as implant materials because of their mechanical properties and biocompatibility. These materials do not have the ability to bond to the bone tissue directly. Several studies have been conducted to develop the methods for providing titanium with bioactivity, such as hydroxyapatite coating on the surface of titanium[1-3]. Recently, Ohtsuki *et al.*[4] reported deposition of bone-like apatite on the surface of titanium metal treated with a hydrogenperoxide solution containing tantalum chloride by *in vivo* examination using a simulated body fluid (Kokubo solution). Titanium metal treated with the hydrogenperoxide solution containing tantalum chloride is expected to have a bone-bonding ability (bioactivity), owing to the formation of "bone-like apatite layer" which create the prerequisite condition for bioactivity. The purpose of this study was to estimate bioactivity of the treated titanium metal by *in vivo* examination. The shearing force between metal and bone was measured by push-out test, and interface was studied by scanning electron microscopic observation (SEM) and energy dispersive X-ray micro analysis (EDX).

MATERIALS AND METHODS

Surface treatment

Commercially available pure titanium cylinders, 4.0mm in diameter and 20.0mm in length, were immersed in the hydrogenperoxide solution (30 vol%) containing tantalum chloride in concentration of 5 mmol/dm^3 at 60°C for 24 hours. The treated cylinders were washed with deionized and distilled water, and denoted as H$_2$O$_2$/Ta-Ti. The same titanium cylinders without surface treatment were used as control (denoted as Control-Ti).

Implantation and push-out test

Japanese white rabbits (approximately 3.0kg in weight) were purchased. General anesthesia was performed by using isoflurane and pentobarbital sodium solution, and local anesthesia was performed by 1% lidocaine solution. Penetrating 4.2mm–hole was made in both tibiae of rabbits, 10mm distal from knee joint. H$_2$O$_2$/Ta-Ti was inserted in the hole of right tibia, and Control-Ti in the hole of left tibia. After 4, 8, 12 and 16 weeks, the rabbits were sacrificed, and bone with inserted cylinders were taken out. Shearing force between metal and bone was measured by push-out test (Shimadzu Autograph® AGS-10KNG) with a loading rate of 0.5mm/min. Interface between metal and bone was observed under SEM-EDX. In addition, in order to evaluate the effect of hole size on bone-bonding ability, 4.0mm–holes were applied on the similar examination.

RESULTS AND DISCUSSION

Figure 1 shows shearing force between bone and the titanium implant in 4.2mm–hole for various periods. At 4 weeks after surgery, the shearing force of H$_2$O$_2$/Ta-Ti was almost the same as that of Control-Ti. At 8, 12 and 16 weeks after surgery, the shearing force of H$_2$O$_2$/Ta-Ti was significantly stronger than those of the Control-Ti. At 16 weeks after surgery, the highest force was measured. H$_2$O$_2$/Ta-Ti seemed to achieve bone-bonding between 4 and 8 weeks after surgery.

Figure 2 shows shearing forces on push-out test for implantation in 4.0mmφ hole. Higher rate of increase in shearing force was observed for implantation in 4.0mm–hole, while the highest force was almost the same as in 4.2mm–hole. Tight contact between H$_2$O$_2$/Ta-Ti and bone was considered to be useful for early bonding.

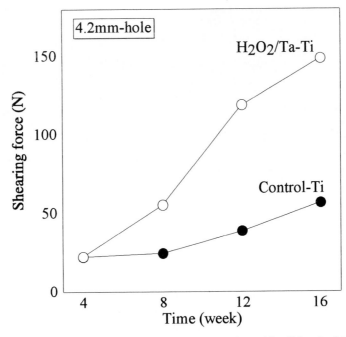

Figure 1. Shearing force between bone and titanium implanted in tibia of rabbit 4, 8, 12 and 16 weeks after surgery. Size of the hole was 4.2mm in diameter.

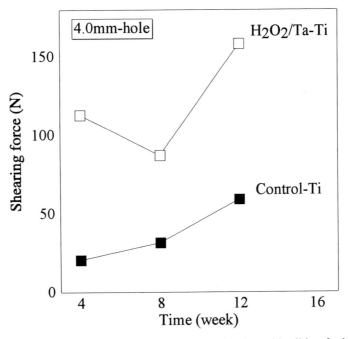

Figure 2. Shearing force between bone and titanium implanted in tibia of rabbit 4, 8 and 12 weeks after surgery. Size of the hole was 4.0mm in diameter.

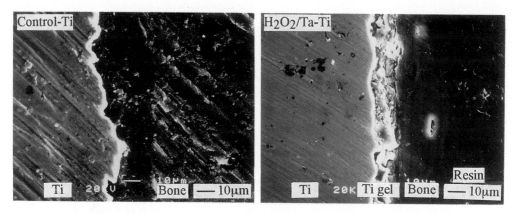

Figure 3. SEM photograghs of cross-section of titanum cylinders, implanted into rabbit's tibiae for 8 weeks. (left)Control-Ti (right)H₂O₂/Ta-Ti

An SEM and EDX study showed that tatamium gel layer was yielded on the surface of H_2O_2/Ta-Ti, such a layer was not observed on the surface of Control-Ti, that contacted directly to bone tissue (Figure 3), whereas a resin-filled gap was observed between the bone and Control-Ti.

It is concluded that titanium metal chemically treated with a hydrogenperoxide solution containing tantalum chloride has an ability to form direct bond to bone.

ACKNOWLEDGEMENT

One of the authors (C.O.) gratefully acknowledges financial support the Grant-in-Aid for Scientific Research, the Ministry of Education, Science, Sports, and Culture, Japan.

REFERENCES

1. Cook SD, Thomas KA, Kay JF, Jarcho M. *Clin Orthop* 1988; **232**: 225-243.
2. Tisdel CL, Goldberg VM, Parr JA, Bensusan JS, Staikoff LS, Stevenson S. *J Bone Joint Surg* 1994; **76A**: 159-171.
3. Oonishi H, Yamamoto M, Ishimaru H, Tsuji E, Kushitani S, Aono M, Ukon Y. *J Bone Joint Surg* 1989; **71B**: 213-216.
4. Ohtsuki C, Iida H, Hayakawa S, Osaka A. *J Biomed Mater Res* 1997; **35**: 39-47.

Bioceramics Volume 11, edited by R. Z. LeGeros and J.P. LeGeros
(Proceedings of the 11th International Symposium on Ceramics in Medicine)
New York, NY, USA, November 1998
© 1998 by World Scientific Publishing Co. Pte. Ltd.

THE EFFECT OF ALKALI AND HEAT TREATMENT ON BONE BONDING ABILITY OF TANTALUM

Hirofumi Kato[1], Takashi Nakamura[1], Shigeru Nishiguchi[1], Hiroshi Fujita[1], Toshiki Miyazaki[2], Fumiaki Miyaji[2], Hyun-Min Kim[2], and Tadashi Kokubo[2]

[1]Department of Orthopaedic Surgery , Faculty of Medicine, Kyoto University,
54 Shogoin-kawaharacho, Sakyo-ku, Kyoto, 606-8397, Japan
[2]Department of Material Chemistry, Faculty of Engineering, Kyoto University,
Yoshida-honmachi, Sakyo-ku, Kyoto, 606-8317, Japan

ABSTRACT

A previous *in vitro* study demonstrated that alkali and heat treatment provide tantalum an ability to form apatite on its surface. The effects of the treatment on the bone-bonding ability of tantalum implants were evaluated in rabbit tibiae. Smooth-surfaced implants (15x10x2 mm) of pure tantalum (Ta) and alkali-and heat-treated Ta were implanted into the tibial metaphyses of mature rabbits. A tensile testing and histological examination of the bone-implant interface were performed at 8 and 16 weeks after implantation. The tensile failure loads between implant and bone were measured by a detaching test. The tensile failure loads of alkali-and heat-treated group were 0.25 kgf and 2.21 kgf, at 8 and 16 weeks, respectively. In contrast, those of control group were nearly 0 kgf even at 16 weeks. Histological examination revealed that alkali-and heat-treated group was in direct contact with bone tissue, but control group had thin intervening fibrous tissue between the implant and bone.

KEY WORDS: Tantalum, alkali and heat treatment, bone-bonding

INTRODUCTION

Tantalum possesses high mechanical strength and can be fabricated in complex shapes(6). It has been reported to be biocompatible due to the surface layer of its oxides. However, being bioinert materials, it does not form a chemical bond to bone. It has been known that apatite formation on the material surface is prerequisite for its bioactivity, that is, direct bone bonding. In *in vitro* study Miyazaki et al showed that via simple chemical treatment of alkali treatment and heat treatment, tantalum formed bonelike apatite on its surface in simulated body fluid (SBF)(2,3), which has ion concentration nearly equal to human blood plasma(1). The purpose of this study is to investigate whether alkali and heat treatment can provide tantalum bone bonding ability.

MATERIALS AND METHODS

Implant preparation   We made two kinds of rectangular tantalum plates (size; 15x10x2 mm).
1) control group; Tantalum plates were abraded with #400 diamond paste and washed with distilled water.

And they were dried at room temperature.

2) alkali-and heat-treated group; Pure tantalum plates were soaked in 0.5 M NaOH aqueous solutions at 60°C for 24 hours, washed with distilled water and dried at 40°C for 24 hours.After above treatment, the plates were heated up to 300 °C at a rate of 5°C/min in an electric furnace, at a given temperature, immediately took out of the furnace, and cooled to room temperature.

Implantation   The implants were conventionally sterilized with ethylene oxide gas. They were implanted into the metaphyses of the tibiae of mature male Japanese white rabbits. The surgical methods were the same as that reported previously(4). Using a dental burr, a 16x2 mm holes were made from the medial cortex to the lateral cortex parallel to the longitudinal axis of the tibial metaphyses. After irrigation of the hole with saline, the tantalum plates were implanted in the frontal direction, perforating the tibiae and protruding from the medial to lateral cortex. Eight rabbits of each group were sacrificed at 8 and 16 weeks after the operation. In this study the guideline for animal experiments of Kyoto University was observed.

Measurement of the detaching failure load   After sacrifice, segments of proximal tibial metaphyses containing the implanted plates were cut out and prepared for the detaching test(Figure 1). Traction through hooks holding the bone segments was applied vertically to the implant surfaces at a cross-head speed of 35 mm/min using an Instron-type autograph (Model 1011, Aikoh Engineering Co., Ltd., Nagoya, Japan)(4). The detaching failure load was measured when the plate was detached from the bone. If the plate was detached before the test, the failure load was defined as 0 Kgf. Data were expressed as mean $\pm$ standard deviation (SD) and assessed using a one-way ANOVA. Differences at $p < 0.05$ were considered to be statistically significant.

Histological Examination   After fhe detatching test, specimens were fixed in 10% phosphate-buffered formalin and dehydrated in serial concentrations of ethanol. Then, they were embedded in polyester resin. Sections 500 μ m thick were cut with a band saw (BS-3000, EXAKT cutting system, Norderstedt, Germany) perpendicular to the axis of the tibia, and were ground to a thickness of 150-180 μ m for CMR and Giemsa surface staining using a grinding-sliding machine(Microgrinding MG-4000, EXAKT, Germany).

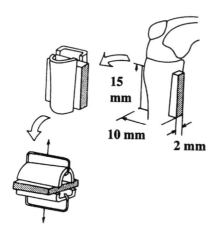

Figure 1.   Detaching test

RESULT

Detaching test   In detaching test breakage always occured at the bone-plate interface. The detaching failure load of each material at 8 and 16 weeks after implantation are summarized in Table 1. At 8 weeks after the operation the failure load of alkali-and heat-treated group did not differ significantly from that of control group. At 16 weeks after the implantation, alkali-and heat-treated group showed a failure load of 2.21 kgf. This value was significantly higer than that of the same group at 8 weeks and that of control group at 16 weeks.

Table 1   Detatching test   failure loads (kgf; mean ± SD)

	8w	16w
alkali-and heat-treated group (n=8)	0.25±0.07	2.21±0.51
control group (n=8)	0	0.01±0.02

Histological examination   Histological examination by Giemsa surface staining and CMR revealed that alkali-and heat-treated group showed direct contact between bone and plate without any intervening fibrous tissue at 8 weeks(Figure 2). And at 16 weeks amount of bone directly contacted to the plate increased. In contrast, there was a fibrous tissue layer between bone and the implant in control group at both 8 and 16 weeks after implantation.

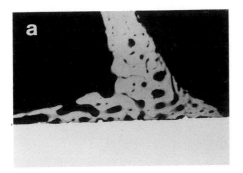 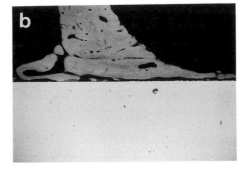

Figure 2. CMR image at 8 weeks after implantation; **a.** Alkali-and heat-treated group. Tantalum implant has direct contact with bone. **b.** Control group. Tantalum implant does not have direct contact with bone.(×100)

DISCUSSION

In this study, the bonding strength of alkali-and heat-treated tantalum increased to 2.21 kgf at 16 weeks by a detaching test. In contrast, pure tantalum did not bond to bone even at 16 weeks. The present chemical treatment improved the bone bonding ability of tantalum implants compared with the untreated tantalum implants. It is considered that the surface bioactivity of tantalum implant is induced by accelerating the formation of tantalum oxide hydrogel on its surface with the chemical treatments. This tantalum oxide hydrogel layer can induce the apatite nucleation on it. Once apatite nucleation occurs, it spontaneously grows by taking calcium and phosphate ions from the surrounding body fluid, and then bonds to bone. In *in vitro* study Miyazaki et al reported that the alkali-and heat-treated tantalum showed almost equal induction period for the apatite formation to that of the substrate without heat treatmaent (3). In the case of the alkali-treated titanium, in *in vivo* study, Nishiguchi et al reported that both alkali and heat treatment are essential for preparation of bone-bonding ability in practical use(5), and hence we did not investigate the influence of heat treatmaent on bone bonding strength of tantalum in this study.

Tantalum shows high malleability and ductility and can be fabricated in complex shapes, either as bulk implant or as an implant coating(6). Alkali-and heat-treated tantalum is supposed to be clinically applicable as orthopedic implant material.

REFERENCES

1.   Kokubo, T., Kushitani, H., Sakka, S., Kitsugi, T., Yamamuro, T. *J. Biomed. Mater. Res.* 1990; **2 4**: 721-734.
2.   Miyazaki, T., Kim, H. M., Miyaji, F., Kokubo, T., Nakamura, T. In: *Bioceramics* Volume 9, Oxford:Elsevier, 1996: 317-320.
3.   Miyazaki, T., Kim, H. M., Miyaji, F., Kokubo, T., Nakamura, T. In: *Bioceramics* Volume 10, Oxford:Elsevier, 1997: 11-14.
4.   Nakamura, T., Yamamuro, T., Higashi, S., Kokubo, T., Ito, S. *J. Biomed. Mater. Res.* 1985; **1 9**: 685-698.
5.   Nishiguchi, S., Nakamura, T., Kobayashi, M., Yan, W. Q., Kim, H. M., Miyaji, F., Kokubo, T. In: *Bioceramics* Volume 10, Oxford:Elsevier, 1997: 561-564.
6.   Stackpool, G. J., Kay, A. B., Morton, P., Harvey, E. J., Tanzer, M., Bobyn, J. D. In: *Proceedings of Combined Ortuopaedic Research Societies Meeting*, San Diego, California 1995: 45.

Bioceramics Volume 11, edited by R. Z. LeGeros and J.P. LeGeros
(Proceedings of the 11th International Symposium on Ceramics in Medicine)
New York, NY, USA, November 1998
© 1998 by World Scientific Publishing Co. Pte. Ltd.

ENHANCEMENT OF BONE BONDING STRENGTHS OF TITANIUM ALLOYS BY ALKALI AND HEAT TREATMENTS

Shigeru Nishiguchi[1], Takashi Nakamura[1], Hirofumi Kato[1], Hiroshi Fujita[1], Hyun-Min Kim[2], Fumiaki Miyaji[2], and Tadashi Kokubo[2]

[1]Department of Orthopaedic Surgery, Faculty of Medicine, Kyoto University, 54 Shogoin-kawaharacho, Sakyo-ku, Kyoto, 606-8397, Japan
[2]Department of Material Chemistry, Faculty of Engineering, Kyoto University, Yoshida-honmachi, Sakyo-ku, Kyoto, 606-8317, Japan

ABSTRACT

The purpose of this study is to investigate whether alkali-and heat-treated titanium alloys can bond to bone. Surface-smoothed rectangular plates of Ti6Al4V, Ti6Al2Nb1Ta, and Ti15Mo5Zr3Al were prepared. The alkali-and heat-treated and untreated each alloy implants were implanted into proximal tibiae of mature rabbits, treated implant for right side and untreated for left. At 8 and 16 weeks after operation detaching test and histological examination were performed. Untreated implants showed almost no bonding even at the 16 weeks after implantation. In contrast treated implants showed bonding to bone both at 8 and 16 weeks. Histological examination showed that alkali-and heat-treated alloys bonded to bone directly. On the other hand untreated implants had intervening fibrous tissue between bone and plate. Although in this study even tentative conditions of treatments enhance bonding strength of titanium alloys, the most suitable conditions of treatments for highest bonding strength should be determined by further experiments. These new bioactive titanium alloys are supposed to be available for weight-bearing and bone-bonding orthopaedic devices.

KEYWORD: Titanium alloy, bone bonding, alkali and heat treatments, bioactivity

INTRODUCTION

Recently Kokubo et al made an another approach to enhance osteointegration of titanium. They showed that titanium forms TiO_2 hydrogel via alkali treatment and thereafter forms biological apatite in simulated body fluid(SBF)(2). Apatite formation on the surface of material surface is believed to be a prerequisite for bone bonding ability. Thus we have performed in vivo study on alkali-treated titanium. As far now it has shown that pure titanium can bond to bone directly after alkali and heat treatment(5) and that the heat treatment is necessary for bone bonding ability(4). Although *in vivo* studies have been carried out mainly on pure titanium, titanium alloys are used in clinical orthopedic implants as well as pure titanium.

In *in vitro* study Kim et al reported that titanium alloys prepared via alkali and heat treatments also has an apatite forming ability in SBF(1). From the point of mechanism of apatite formation of alkali-treated titanium, it seems that titanium alloys will be able to bond to living bone after alkali and heat treatments. However this is not yet verified.

The purpose of this study is to investigate whether alkali-and heat-treated titanium alloys bond to bone earlier than untreated titanium alloys. And difference of the bonding strength among titanium alloys was also studied, if it present.

MATERIALS AND METHODS
Implant preparation

Three kinds of titanium alloys plates (size; $15 \times 10 \times 2$ mm), Ti6Al4V, Ti6Al2Nb1Ta, and Ti15Mo5Zr3Al were abraded with #400 diamond plate and washed with distilled water. Halves of the plates of each alloy were used as untreated. And the other halves of these plates were soaked in NaOH aqueous solution for 24 hours at 60℃ and were dried at room temperature. After alkali treatment, the plates were heated at given temperature for an hour. The concentrations of NaOH solutions and temperature of heat treatment was determined on the basis of *in vitro* study and shown in Table 1. At the condition of these parameters each alloy formed apatite on their surface within 14 days in SBF. (data not shown)

Table 1   Conditions of alkali and heat treatments

	Concentration of NaOH	Temperature of heat treatment
Ti6Al4V	5M	550℃
Ti6Al2Nb1Ta	10M	550℃
Ti15Mo5Zr3Al	5M	600℃

Implantation

Titanium alloy plates were sterilily implanted into proximal tibiae of mature male Japanese white rabbits. The surgical methods was the same as that was reported previously(3). Using a dental bur, a 16×2 mm hole was made from the medial cortex to the lateral one parallel to the longitudinal axis of the tibial metaphysis. After irrigation of the hole with saline, the titanium alloy plates were implanted in the frontal direction, perforating the tibia and protruding from the medial to lateral cortex. A rabbit received an untreated plate of one of three kinds of titanium alloy into left tibia and an alkali-and heat-treated one of the same kind of alloy into the right side. Six rabbits of each group were sacrificed at 8 and 16 weeks after the operation. In this study the guideline for animal experiments of Kyoto University were observed.

Measurement of detaching failure load

After sacrifice, segments of proximal tibial metaphyses containing the implanted plates were retrieved and prepared for the detaching test. The bone tissue surrounding the plates was removed on both sides and at the ends with a dental burr. Traction through hooks holding the bone segments was applied vertically to the implant surfaces at a cross-head speed of 35 mm/min.. The detaching failure load was measured when the plate was detached from the bone. If the plate was detached before the test, the failure load was defined as 0 kgf. Detaching failure loads were analyzed using one-way ANOVA and Fisher PLSD post hoc test. Difference was considered significant when p value was less than 0.05.

Histological examination

After the detaching test, specimens were fixed in 10% phosphate-buffered formalin and dehydrated in serial concentrations of ethanol. Then, they were embedded in polyester resin. Sections 100 μ m thick were prepared for CMR and Giemsa surface staining using a grinding-sliding machine.

RESULTS
Mechanical testing
While preparing for detaching test all untreated samples at 8 weeks and most at 16 weeks detached from bone spontaneously. Detaching failure loads of such samples were defined as 0 kgf. In contrast treated samples did not show spontaneous detaching before testing. In detaching test all samples broke at the interface between bone and plate. The results of detaching test is summarized in Table 2 and 3. At ant time point statistic analysis revealed significantly higher failure loads in alkali-and heat-treated titanium alloys, irrespective of kinds of alloys, in comparison with the untreated implants except Ti6Al2Nb1Ta at 8 weeks. When comparing the strengths of treated alloys, at 8 weeks only Ti15Mo5Zr3Al showed higher strength than the other alloys and at 16 weeks both Ti6Al4V and Ti15Mo5Zr3Al showed higher bonding strength than Ti6Al2Nb1Ta. Failure loads of Ti6Al4V and Ti6Al2Nb1Ta significantly increased from 8 weeks to 16 weeks.

Table 2 Results of detaching test of alkali-and heat-treated alloys (mean ± standard deviation : kgf)

treated alloy	8 weeks	16 weeks
Ti6Al4V	1.41 ± 0.90	2.84 ± 1.66
Ti6Al2Nb1Ta	0.77 ± 0.55	1.61 ± 0.98
Ti15Mo5Zr3Al	2.95 ± 1.36	3.09 ± 0.77

Table 3 Results of detaching test of untreated alloys (mean ± standard deviation : kgf)

untreated alloy	8 weeks	16 weeks
Ti6Al4V	0.00 ± 0.00	0.10 ± 0.24
Ti6Al2Nb1Ta	0.00 ± 0.00	0.11 ± 0.15
Ti15Mo5Zr3Al	0.00 ± 0.00	0.01 ± 0.02

Histological examination
Histological examination showed that alkali-and heat-treated alloys bonded to bone directly(Fig. 1a). On the other hand untreated implants had thin intervening fibrous tissue between bone and plate(Fig.1b).

a.

b.

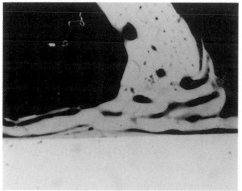
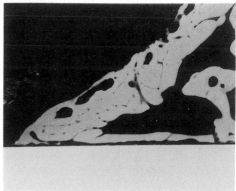

Figure 1 CMR images of Ti15Mo5Zr3Al at 8 weeks after operation a. alkali-and heat-treated b. untreated

DISCUSSION

In this study it was showed that titanium alloys also bond to bone after alkali and heat treatments as well as pure titanium. Although the mechanism of bone bonding of alkali-and heat-treated titanium alloys is still unclear, it must be the same as in the case of alkali-and heat-treated pure titanium. Considering from that all three alloys used in this study increased bone bonding abilities, other titanium base alloys may have bone bonding ability via alkali and heat treatments, although difference in bonding strength may exist.

In this study only tentative condition of treatments was assigned to each alloys. Since single sequence of conditions was tentatively selected for the NaOH and heat treatments in the present study, it is not yet clear how the concentration, the temperature and the period for NaOH treatment as well as the subsequent heat treatment will affect the resultant bone bonding ability for each alloy. However , in view of the results shown here , the conditions given above positively changed bone bonding abilities of titanium alloys. Control of the conditions of NaOH and heat treatment to optimize the bioactivity remained as further task to be investigated .

Titanium alloys have higher mechanical properties than pure titanium. Therefore this alkali-and heat-treated titanium alloys are supposed to be extensively applied to orthopaedic implants as bone bonding materials.

CONCLUSIONS

Alkali and heat treatments enhanced bone bonding abilities of Ti6Al4V, Ti15Mo5Zr3Al, and Ti6Al2Nb1Ta. And with the conditions of treatments in this study Ti15Mo5Zr3Al showed relatively higher bonding strength than the other alloys.

REFERENCES

1. Kim HM, Miyaji F, Kokubo T, Nakamura T. *J.Biomed.Mater.Res.* 1996;**3 2**:409-417

2. Kokubo T, Miyaji F, Kim HM, Nakamura T. *J.Am.Ceram.Soc.* 1996;**7 9**:1127-1129.

3. Nakamura T, Yamarumo T, Higashi S, Kokubo T, Itoo S. *J.Biomed.Mater.Res.* 1985;**19**:631-648.

4. Nishiguchi S, Nakamura T, Kobayashi M, et al. In: Sedel L, Rey C, eds. Bioceramics 10. Elsevier Science Ltd, 1997:561-563.

5. Yan W-Q, Nakamura T, Kobayashi M, Kim HM, Kokubo T. *J.Biomed.Mater.Res.* 1997;**37**: 267-275.

Bioceramics Volume 11, edited by R. Z. LeGeros and J.P. LeGeros
(Proceedings of the 11th International Symposium on Ceramics in Medicine)
New York, NY, USA, November 1998
© 1998 by World Scientific Publishing Co. Pte. Ltd.

CYTOCOMPATIBILITY OF TITANIUM METAL TREATED WITH HYDROGEN PEROXIDE CONTAINING TANTALUM CHLORIDE

Chikara Ohtsuki[1], Keizo Kobayashi[1], Satoshi Hayakawa[1], Akiyoshi Osaka[1] and Hajime Inoue[2]

[1]Biomaterials Lab., Faculty of Engineering, Okayama University, Tsushima, Okayama-shi 700-8530, JAPAN; [2]Department of Orthopaedic Surgery, Okayama University Medical School, Sikata-Cho, Okayama-shi 700-8558, JAPAN.

ABSTRACT

Apatite formation on artificial implants is essential condition to achieve direct boding to bone. We recently showed that titanium metal treated with hydrogenperoxide solution containing tantalum chloride (H_2O_2/Ta) formed an apatite layer on its surface in a simulated body fluid (Kokubo solution). This indicates that the H_2O_2/Ta -treated titanium metal shows bioactivity to bond to living bone. In this study, cytocompatibility of the H_2O_2/Ta -treated specimen was examined, and the results were compared with those for the non-treated titanium and the one treated with 5N-NaOH solution. Osteoblast-like cells (MC3T3-E1) derived from mouse were cultured on the specimens at 36.5°C under 5% CO_2 and 95% humidity. Similar degree of proliferation of the cells was observed at 7 days among the three specimens, while the H_2O_2/Ta-treated titanium after incubation for 5 days showed a lower degree of proliferation than the non-treated titanium and titanium treated with 5N-NaOH. Alkaline phosphatase activity of the cells proliferated on the H_2O_2/Ta-treated titanium was higher than those of the titanium specimens treated with 5N-NaOH, although the degree of proliferation rate was in the order: non-treated titanium > titanium treated with 5N-NaOH > H_2O_2/Ta-treated titanium. These results indicate that the treated titanium with H_2O_2/Ta does not show cytotoxicity and that it rather has high potential for bone formation. The treatment of titanium with H_2O_2/Ta is therefore applicable for providing titanium implants with bioactivity.

KEYWORDS: Titanium, bioactivity, cytocompatibility, hydrogenperoxide, tantalum

INTRODUCTION

Titanium metal and titanium alloy are widely used as implant materials for bone substitutes. They cannot, however, bond to living bone directly. To achieve direct bonding of titanium implants to living bone, several studies have been reported such as hydroxyapatite (HA) coating on the surface of titanium.[1] Still problems are in their difficulty of the interfacial attachment of coating layer with the substrate, as well as controlled composition of coated layer. Recently, we found that bone-like apatite can be provided in a simulated body fluid (denoted as Kokubo solution) on the surface of titanium metal which is chemically treated with a hydrogenperoxide solution containing tantalum chloride.[2] This means that the treated titanium metal has a potential of bonding to living bone, i.e. bioactivity, because formation of a bone-like apatite layer is prerequisite condition for artificial materials to show bioactivity. In the present study we investigated the cytocompatibility of the chemically treated titanium metal by culturing osteoblast-like cell on it. The results were compared with those for such materials as non-treated titanium and the one treated with 5N-NaOH solution.

EXPERIMENTAL

Sample preparation

Rectangular specimens of 10 x 10 x 1 mm^3 were cut from commercially available pure titanium. They were polished with #400 and #2000 abrasive paper before the soaking in a hydrogenperoxide (30 vol%) solution containing tantalum chloride (TaCl$_5$) in concentration of 5 mmol/dm^3 (denoted as H$_2$O$_2$/Ta). The solution was kept at 60°C for 24 hours. The treated specimens were washed with deionized and distilled water. The titanium metal specimens of the same size treated with 5N-NaOH aqueous solution at 60°C for 24 hours and the one without the chemical treatments were also examined for comparison.

Cell culture

Osteoblast-like cells (MC3T3-E1) derived from mouse were seeded on to the specimens placed on the bottom of polystyrene petri dishes containing α-minimum essential medium (α-MEM) supplemented with 10% fetal bovine serum. Initial density of the cell was 1.0 x 10^4 cells/ml. The specimens were incubated at 36.5°C under atmosphere of 5% CO$_2$ and 95% humidity. After incubation for 3, 5 and 7 days, the specimens together with the cells were taken out. The cells were removed from the substrates by immersion in a 0.1M (=mol/dm^3) phosphate-buffered aqueous solution (pH 7.4) containing 0.01wt% actinase E and 0.02wt% EDTA-2Na at 36.5°C for 3 minutes. After centrifuged, the cells were suspended in α-MEM, and the number of the removed cells was measured with hemocytometer.

　　Some of the specimens were also observed under a scanning electron microscope (SEM). Cells on the specimen after culturing were fixed due to immersion in a 0.1M phosphate-buffered solution containing 2% glutaraldehyde for 2 hours at 4°C. After washing with the 0.1M phosphate-buffer solution, the specimens were dehydrated using graded ethanol-water solutions of 50% to 100% concentration in 15 minutes at each step. Then, the specimens were immersed in 100% 3-butanol in 30 minutes. The specimens were freeze-dried at 13.3Pa (0.1Torr), -5°C with ES-2020 (Hitachi, Japan). After coated with thin gold film, specimens were observed with SEM at an accelerating voltage of 10 kV.

　　Alkaline phosphatase (ALP) activity was measured for the cells incubated for 3 and 7 days, as described in the previous report.[3] After incubation at initial density of the cell of 6.0 x 10^4 cells/ml, the specimens were rinsed with the 0.1M phosphate-buffer solution and a 50mM Tris-HCl buffer solution (pH 7.45). Then, the specimens were incubated at 37°C with 100μl solution that contained 2mM Na$_2$-nitrophenylphosphate and 2mM MgCl$_2$ in a 0.1M 2-amino-2methyl-1-propanol buffer (pH 10.5). After 12 hours, the reaction was stopped by adding 100μl of 1N-NaOH. ALP activity was estimated by measuring adsorption at 415 nm of the reacted solution.

RESULTS AND DISCUSSION

Figure 1 shows cell proliferation curves of MC3T3-E1 cultured on non-treated, titanium chemically treated with H_2O_2/Ta, and the one chemically treated with 5N-NaOH. Cell numbers cultured without specimens are also shown on Fig. 1, denoted as "Blank". At the beginning of incubation, apparent increase in the cell number was observed only for non-treated titanium after 3 days. Blank, H_2O_2/Ta-treated and 5N-NaOH treated titanium showed less proliferation than the non-treated titanium. After 5 days incubation the non-treated titanium and Blank showed almost similar proliferation. The cell number on those two specimens was higher than that on 5N-NaOH and H_2O_2/Ta-treated titanium. However, the number of proliferated cells on all the specimens increased to a similar level after 7 days' incubation. These results indicate that the chemical treatment of titanium does not give remarkable cytotoxicity, although the chemically treated titanium specimens showed somewhat lower rate of cell proliferation than non-treated titanium. SEM observation show no significant differences on morphology of the cell among non-treated, H_2O_2/Ta-treated and 5N-NaOH treated titanium. Figure 2 shows ALP activity of cells cultured on the titanium specimens, after incubation for 3 and 7 days. The degree of ALP activity of the cells cultured on H_2O_2/Ta-treated titanium after incubation for 3 days was almost similar to that of non-treated titanium and much higher than that of 5N-NaOH treated titanium. The Cell number after incubation for 3 days on each specimen was in the order: non-treated titanium > H_2O_2/Ta ~ 5N-NaOH. Therefore, the cells cultured on H_2O_2/Ta-treated titanium metal have higher activity than those on non-treated titanium. In addition, H_2O_2/Ta-treated titanium still showed higher ALP activity after 7 days incubation than non-treated and 5N-NaOH treated titanium. These results also support that surface of titanium chemically treated with H_2O_2/Ta has little negative effects on proliferation of the osteoblastic cells. It is interesting that the titanium metal treated with H_2O_2/Ta

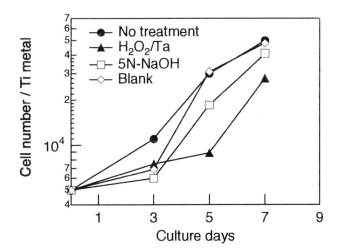

Figure 1. Cell proliferation of MC3T3-E1 cultured on titanium specimens with and without chemical treatment. Non-treated titanium, titanium treated with hydrogenperoxide solution containing tantalum, and titanium treated with 5N-NaOH solution are denoted as No treatment, H_2O_2/Ta and 5N-NaOH, respectively.

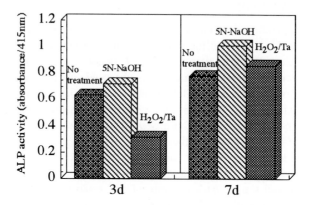

Figure 2. Alkaline phosphatase activity of cultured cell on the titanium specimens, after incubation for 3 and 7 days.

has a such modified surface that can also induce high ALP activity. It should be noted that the titanium treated with H_2O_2/Ta does not show cytotoxicity and that it rather has high potential for bone formation. We have also shown that the higher bonding strength of H_2O_2/Ta-treated titanium than non-treated one by *in vivo* examination with push-out test.[4] Based on these biological tests, the treatment of titanium with the hydrogenperoxide solution containing tantalum chloride is applicable for providing titanium implants with bioactivity.

ACKNOWLEDGEMENT

This research was supported by Grant-in-Aid for Scientific Research, the Ministry of Education, Science, Sports and Culture, Japan. A part of this study was supported by Corning Research Grant.

REFERENCES

1. Lacefield WR. In: Hench LL and Wilson J, ed., *Introduction to Bioceramics*, Singapore: World Scientific, 1993: 223-238.
2. Ohtsuki C, Iida H, Hayakawa S, Osaka A. *J Biomed Mater Res* 1997; **35**: 39-47.
3. Sun ZL, Wataha JC, Hanks CT. *J Biomed Mater Res* 1997; **34**: 29-37.
4. Kaneko S, Inoue H, Kobayashi K, Ohtsuki C, Osaka A. In: *Bioceramics*, 1998; **11**.

Bioceramics Volume 11, edited by R. Z. LeGeros and J.P. LeGeros
(Proceedings of the 11th International Symposium on Ceramics in Medicine)
New York, NY, USA, November 1998
© 1998 by World Scientific Publishing Co. Pte. Ltd.

EFFECT OF ALUMINA AND APATITIC ABRASIVES ON TI ALLOY SUBSTANCES

T.Salgado[a], J.P.LeGeros[a], J.Wang[b]

[a]New York University College of Dentistry and [b]HiMed, Inc., Old Bethpage, New York

ABSTRACT

Titanium and titanium alloy orthopedic and dental implants are grit blasted with abrasives to provide a textured surface thereby increasing the surface area that comes in contact with the bone bed. Grit blasting with abrasive is also used as a surface preparation prior to the application of a coating (e.g., plasma-sprayed HA or titanium). Alumina abrasive was shown to leave residual particles as a contaminant embedded on the implant surface which is difficult, if not practically impossible, to remove. Use of an apatitic calcium phosphate abrasive left a comparatively clean surface. The purpose of this study was to characterize the surfaces roughened by two abrasives: alumina and apatitic calcium phosphate.

Twelve titanium alloy (Ti6Al4V) coupons were used for grit blasting in this experiment: six with alumina and six with apatitic calcium phosphate. The coupon surfaces were characterize using X-ray diffraction, photomicroscopy and scanning electron microscopy before and after grit blasting.

Keywords: implant, grit blasting, alumina, apatitic calcium phosphate, titanium alloy.

INTRODUCTION

Commercially pure titanium (CP-Ti) and titanium alloy (Ti6Al4V) have become the materials of choice for implants because of their biocompatibility with the biological environment, high corrosion resistance, light weight, durability[5] and ease of preparation in many different shapes and textures without affecting their biocompatibility.[3,4,7,8,10] Titanium alloy is often used because of its higher structural strength[5].

The quality of new bone contact with dental and orthopedic implants is an important factor in assuring the sufficient load bearing functions of the implants. Improved anchorage of bone implants is achieved if the implant has a rough surface[9]. One way to produce an increased surface roughness is to grit blast the surface. Abrasive blasting not only increases the surface roughness, but also removes metal surface contaminants and increases metal surface reactivity.[11,12] Brian[1] has suggested that surface preparation of an implant by grit blasting with particles of a material other than that of the implant itself may influence the surface composition and affect the biocompatibility[2], however, grit blasting by titanium is less than effective because of the relatively hardness of this material. Alumina is a commonly used material for grit blasting. Utilization of alumina always leave a residual abrasive as a contaminant embedded in the implant surface and is difficult, if not practically impossible, to remove. Grit blasting with a low grade apatitic calcium phosphate leaves no residue.[6]

METHODS AND MATERIALS

Six titanium alloy coupons were grit blasted with alumina and six other coupons were grit blasted with a low grade apatitic calcium phosphate (obtained from HiMed Inc. Old Bethpage, NY).
Both sets of coupons were grit blasted for one minute using a feed plus auxiliary pressure gun at 60 psi with

using the Trinco Dry Blast Machine (Trinity Tool Co., Fraser, MI). The specimens were washed with distilledand further rinsed with double distilled deionized water. The specimens were then passivated with 12% HNO₃ and washed with alcohol.

The changes in morphology on the titanium surface before and after grit blasting of both groups were evaluated with X-ray diffraction, photomicroscopy (Zeiss photomicroscope) and scanning electron microscopy (Jeol 5400).

X-ray diffraction analysis of the coupon surfaces was carried out by determining the surface residual uniform stress by measuring diffraction peak displacement with a precision of 0.02° 2θ at the back reflection region (100° to 121° 2θ). Non-uniform residual stress was determined by determining differences in diffraction peak broadening for the (203), (211), (114), and (212) peaks. A Philips APD 3720 X-ray diffraction apparatus was used with a fine focus copper target X-ray tube, automatic compensating divergence slit system, and a double crystal monochronometer. A custom step scanning program was used with 0.01° two-theta with 7 seconds counting time per step.

RESULTS

X-ray diffraction patterns in Figure 1 show that non-uniform residual stress is 30% greater for alumina than for the apatitic calcium phosphate grit blasting. On the other hand, alumina grit blasting seems to result in about same amount of <u>uniform</u> residual stress. Evidence with this is shown with the broadening and shifts of the peaks at 102.5, 108, 114. (The peaks for the alumina grit blast had smaller intensities and more broadening than those grit blasted with apatitic calcium phosphate.)

X-ray diffraction patterns and scanning electron microscopy as shown in Figure 2 and Figure 3 that grit blasting by an apatitic calcium phosphate results in a contaminant-free surface and grit blasting with alumina results with alumina and oxide residual contamination (Figure 4).

DISCUSSION

While grit blasting with alumina and with apatitic calcium phosphate can result in the same roughness value (Ra), the difference of the surface profile between the two appears to be significant (Figures 3). LeGeros and Daculsi[6] have reported that greater bone contact and density results in regions immediate to the implant and 50 μm from the implant in dog femurs three weeks after implantation.

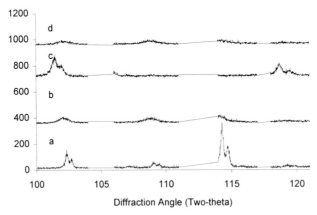

Figure 1 . XRD patterns showing the changes on the surface of the titanium coupons (a) before grit blasting with apatitic calcium phosphate, (b) after grit blasting with apatitic calcium phosphate, (c) before grit blasting with alumina, (d) after grit blasting with alumina.

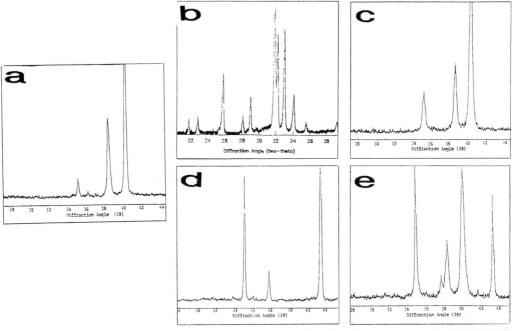

Figure 2. [HiMed, Inc.] XRD peaks on titanium surface (a) titanium peaks, (b) apatitic calcium phosphate sample, (c) titanium after apatitic calcium phosphate grit blast, (d) alumina sample, and (e) titanium after alumina grit blast.

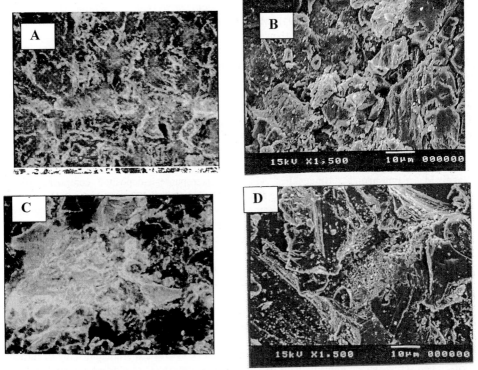

Figure 3. SEM of grit blasted Ti6Al4V surface at 700X and 1,500X (a) and (b) apatitic calcium phosphate grit blast with a contaminant-free surface, 700X and 1,500X. (c) and (d) alumina with oxide residual contamination at 700X and 1,500X.

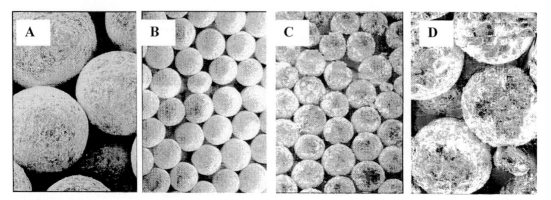

Figure 4. [HiMed, Inc.] Beaded implant (a) apatitic calcium phosphate contaminant-free surface at 90X, and (b) apatitic calcium phosphate contaminant-free surface at 30X (c) alumina grit blast with oxide-residual contamination at 90X, and (d) alumina with oxide-residual contamination.

CONCLUSION

Apatitic calcium phosphate provides a contaminant-free titanium surface while alumina leaves an oxide residual contamination on the titanium surface. Residual uniform and non uniform stress should make the titanium surface more reactive and may have an implication between the bone/implant interface.

Acknowledgement: This study was funded in part by the L Linkow Implant Research Foundation.

References

1. Brian WJO. (1997): Dental Materials and Their Selection. *Quintessence* 2nd edition 315-328.
2. Chern Lin JH, Liu ML, Ju CP (1994): Morphologic variation in plasma-sprayed hydroxyapatite-bioactive glass composite coatings in Hank's solution. *J Biomed Res* **28**:723-730.
3. Inadome T, Hayashi K, Nakashima Y, Tsumura H, Sugioka Y (1995): Comparison of bone-implant surface shear strength of hydroxyapatite-coated and alumina-coated metal implants. *J Biomed Mat Res* **29**:19-24.
4. Kim H, Miyaki F, Kokubo T, Nakamura T (1996): Preparation of bioactive Ti and its alloys via simple chemical surface treatment. *J Biomed Mat Res* **32**:409-417.
5. LeGeros RZ, LeGeros JP, Kim Y, Kijkowska R, Zheng R, Bautista C, and Wang J, (1995) Bioceramics: Materials and Applications Vol 48 pgs. 173-179.
6. LeGeros JP, Daculsi G, LeGeros RZ, (1998) Tissue Response to Grit Blasted Ti Alloy, Proceedings of the 25th Annual International Society of Biomaterials (In Press).
7. Nagai M, Yamashita K, Umegaki T (1991): Electrophoresis-deposited composite films of hydroxyapatite and zirconia. *Phosphorous Research Bulletin* **1**:167-172.
8. Ogiso M, Nakabayashi N, Matsumoto T, Yamamura M, Lee RR (1996): Abrasive improvement of the mechanical properties of a dense HA-cemented Ti dental implant. *J Biomed Mat Res* **30**:109-116.
9. Pimienta C, Dubuc C, Tawashi R (1994): Surface fractal dimension and the quantification of roughness of titanium implant. *Cells and Materials* **4**:379-386.
10. Schwartz Z, Martin JY, Simpson J, Cochran DL, Boyan BD (1996). Effect of titanium surface roughness on chondrocyte proliferation, matrix production, and differentiation depends on the state of cell maturation. *J Biomed Mat* Res **30**:145-155.
11. Wennerberg A, Albrektsson T, Andersson B, Krol JJ (1995): A histomorphometric and removal torque study of screw-shaped titanium implants with three different surface topographies. *Clin Oral Impl Res* **6**:24-30.
12. Wennerberg A, Albrektsson T, Johansson C, Andersson B, (1996) Experimental study of turned and grit-blasted screw-shaped implants with special emphasis on effects of blasting material and surface topography, Biomaterials **17**: 15-22.

Bioceramics Volume 11, edited by R. Z. LeGeros and J.P. LeGeros
(Proceedings of the 11th International Symposium on Ceramics in Medicine)
New York, NY, USA, November 1998
© 1998 by World Scientific Publishing Co. Pte. Ltd.

SURFACE MODIFICATION OF ETHYLENE-VINYLALCOHOL COPOLYMER FOR INDUCING ITS APATITE-FORMING ABILITY

A. Oyane,[1] M. Minoda,[2] T. Miyamoto,[2] K. Nakanishi,[1] H.-M. Kim,[1] F. Miyaji,[1] T. Kokubo,[1] and T. Nakamura[3]

[1]Department of Material Chemistry, Faculty of Engineering, Kyoto University, Kyoto 606-8501, Japan; [2]Institute for Chemical Research, Kyoto University, Uji, 606-0011, Japan; [3]Department of Orthopaedic Surgery, Faculty of Medicine, Kyoto University, Kyoto 606-8507, Japan

ABSTRACT

Silanol (Si-OH) groups on the materials have been believed to induce the apatite nucleation in the body environment. In the present study, the surface of ethylene-vinylalcohol copolymer (EVOH) substrates was modified with Si-OH groups and their apatite-forming ability was examined in a simulated body fluid (SBF) with ion concentrations nearly equal to those of human blood plasma or in a solution (1.5SBF) with ion concentrations 1.5 times those of SBF. The surface modification of EVOH was carried out by reacting 3-isocyanatopropyltriethoxysilane, followed by hydrolysis of ethoxysilyl (Si-O-Et) groups. No apatite formation, however, was observed on the EVOH substrate thus-modified even after 3 w both in SBF and in 1.5SBF. Then the Si-OH modified EVOH substrate was further modified by hydrolysis and polycondensation of tetraethoxysilane (TEOS). It was found that the apatite forms on the TEOS modified substrate within 3 w in 1.5SBF. These results suggest that the presence of a large amount of Si-OH groups and/or their cluster is prerequisite to the apatite formation in body environment. Apatite-EVOH composites prepared by this process would be useful as bone substitutes.

KEYWORDS: Apatite, Silanol group, Ethylene-vinyl alcohol (EVOH) copolymer Simulated body fluid (SBF)

INTRODUCTION

Previously, we reported that a dense and homogeneous bonelike apatite layer is formed on organic polymers when the polymers were placed on granular particles of a CaO, SiO_2-based glass in a simulated body fluid (SBF) and then soaked in another supersaturated solution with respect to the apatite.[1, 2] Apatite nuclei are formed by silicate ions which were released from the glass particles and attached on the polymers during the first process, and they grow spontaneously by consuming the calcium and phosphate ions from the surrounding fluid during the second process. By this method, however, only the surface of the polymer faced to the glass particles is formed with the apatite. In order to obtain a three dimensional apatite-polymer composite analogous to the natural bone, silanol groups effective for the apatite nucleation must be formed on the polymer in solutions without the glass particles.

In the present study, the chemical modification of ethylene vinyl-alcohol copolymer (EVOH) surface with Si-OH groups was attempted using a silane coupling agent, and its apatite-forming ability was examined in SBF with ion concentrations nearly equal to those of human blood plasma and a solution (1.5SBF) with ion concentrations 1.5 times those of SBF. EVOH has a high mechanical strength. The characteristic of this polymer has a large number of reactive hydroxyl groups. Apatite-EVOH composites are expected to exhibit high fracture toughnesses, low elastic moduli and bone-bonding ability similar to the natural bone.

MATERIALS AND METHODS

A substrate ($10 \times 10 \times 1$ mm^3) of EVOH (ethylene content = 32 mol%), supplied by Kuraray Co. Ltd., (Kurashiki, Japan) was soaked in 1 ml toluene solution containing 3-isocyanatopropyltriethoxysilane ($OC(O)NH(CH_2)_3Si(OEt)_3$) : toluene : dibutyltin dilaurate = 1 : 1 : 0.005 by weight at 50°C for 20 h. After the reaction, the substrate was washed and dried for 24 h under vacuum. The silane modified EVOH substrate was then soaked in 1M-HCl aqueous solution at 60°C for 5 d to deprotect the ethoxy groups. The reaction of the silane modified EVOH with TEOS was carried out in solutions with molar ratio of tetraethoxysilane (TEOS) : H_2O : ethanol : HCl = 1.0 : 1.0 - 2.0 : 1.0 : 0.014 at 25°C for 24 h to form Si-OH groups, followed by hydrolysis of ethoxysilyl (Si-OEt) groups on EVOH and partial polycondensation with TEOS. The substrate removed from the solution was washed and dried for 24 h under vacuum.

EVOH substrates modified with silane coupling agent and TEOS were soaked in 30 ml of SBF or 1.5SBF for 3 w. The substrate removed from the solution was washed and dried for 24 h.

The surface of EVOH substrate was examined by X-ray photoelectron spectroscopy (XPS: MT-5500, ULVAC-PHI Co. Ltd., Japan), thin-film X-ray diffraction (TF-XRD: RINT1400, Rigaku Co., Japan) and scanning electron microscope (SEM: Model S2500CX, Hitachi Co., Japan). The silanol group concentrations in TEOS solution aged at 25°C for 24 h were examined by ^{29}Si NMR (NMR: DPX300, Bruker Co., Germany).

RESULTS AND DISCUSSION

Figure 1 shows the XPS survey spectra of the surfaces of EVOH substrates before and after reacting with $OC(O)NH(CH_2)_3Si(OEt)_3$ and TEOS ($H_2O/TEOS$ = 1.5). The appearance of Si peaks after modification indicates that hydroxyl groups on the EVOH substrate were reacted with the isocyanato groups of $OC(O)NH(CH_2)_3Si(OEt)_3$, and Si-OEt groups were introduced by the following reaction.[2]

$$EVOH\text{-}OH \xrightarrow[\text{Dibutyltin dilaurate}]{OCN(CH_2)_3Si(OEt)_3} EVOH\text{-}OC(O)NH(CH_2)_3Si(OEt)_3 \quad (1)$$

Figure 2 shows the C_{1s} XPS spectra of the surfaces of silane modified EVOH substrates before and after HCl treatment. A shoulder assigned to Si-OEt groups at about 286.2 eV was found to disappear after HCl treatment, showing that the Si-OEt groups were completely converted into Si-OH groups according to the Eq. (2).

$$\equiv Si\text{-}O\text{-}Et + H_2O \longrightarrow \equiv Si\text{-}OH + EtOH \quad (2)$$

Figure 1 also shows that Si peaks remarkably increase after TEOS treatment, suggesting

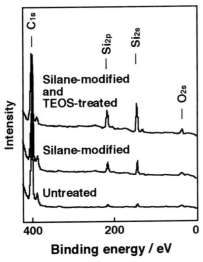

Figure 1. XPS survey spectra of the surfaces of EVOH substrates before and after silane modification and TEOS treatment (H_2O/TEOS = 1.5).

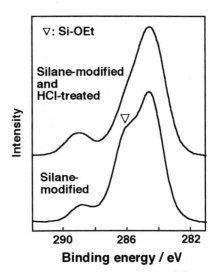

Figure 2. C_{1s} XPS spectra of the surfaces of silane modified EVOH substrates before and after HCl treatment.

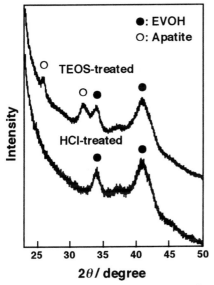

Figures 3. TF-XRD patterns of the surfaces of the silane modified EVOH substrates, which were treated with HCl or TEOS (H_2O/TEOS = 1.5), after soaking in 1.5SBF for 3 w.

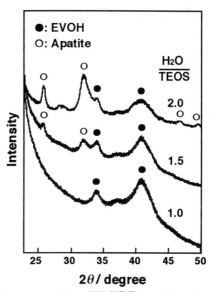

Figures 4. TF-XRD patterns of the surfaces of the silane modified EVOH substrates, which were treated with TEOS (H_2O/TEOS = 1.0 - 2.0), after soaking in 1.5SBF for 3 w.

that part of Si-OH groups on the EVOH substrate reached with TEOS, and silica gel layers were chemically bonded to the EVOH substrate, in other words, the *in situ* sol-gel

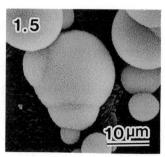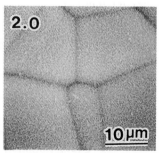

Figure 5. SEM photographs of the surfaces of EVOH substrates modified with TEOS after soaking in 1.5SBF for 3 w.

reaction occurs between the Si-OH modified EVOH and TEOS.

The sample films thus-obtained were soaked in SBF and 1.5SBF at 36.5°C for various periods. No apatite formation was observed for both Si-OH modified and TEOS modified EVOH polymer films in SBF even after 3 w. On the other hand, it was found that the TEOS modified substrate, where a large number of Si-OH groups is introduced, can form the apatite in 1.5SBF, as shown in Fig. 3.

Figures 4 and 5 show the TF-XRD patterns and SEM photographs of the surfaces of EVOH substrates modified with TEOS after soaking in 1.5SBF for 3 w. TEOS treatment was carried out with various H_2O concentrations (H_2O/TEOS = 1.0 - 2.0 by molar ratio). It can be seen that the apatite -forming ability of the substrate increased with increasing the molar ratio of H_2O/TEOS. ^{29}Si NMR analysis revealed that the Si-OH content of the silicate species existing in the solution increases with increasing the H_2O/TEOS ratio. This may be interpreted that the number of Si-OH groups formed on EVOH by TEOS treatment increased with increasing the H_2O/TEOS ratio of the TEOS solution. These results indicate that the presence of a relatively large number of Si-OH groups and/or their cluster is prerequisite to the apatite formation in body environment.

CONCLUSIONS

The EVOH polymer films modified with Si-OH groups by the reaction with a silane coupling agent, $OC(O)NH(CH_2)_3Si(OEt)_3$, followed by hydrolysis of protecting groups with HCl did not form the apatite in SBF and 1.5   F even after 3 w, but the EVOH polymer films further modified by using *in situ* sol   l process with TEOS did form the apatite within 3 w in 1.5SBF, showing that the presence of a relatively large number of Si-OH groups and/or their cluster is prerequisite to the apatite formation in body environment.

ACKNOWLEDGMENT

The authors thank to Dr. R. Takahashi, Chiba University, for ^{29}Si NMR measurements.

REFERENCES

1. Tanahashi M, Yao T, Kokubo T, Minoda M, Miyamoto T, Nakamura T, Yamamuro T. *J. Am. Ceram. Soc.*, 1994; 77: 2805-2808.
2. Jianye W, Garth LW. *Polymer Bulletin*, 1996; 37: 51-57.

Bioceramics Volume 11, edited by R. Z. LeGeros and J.P. LeGeros
(Proceedings of the 11th International Symposium on Ceramics in Medicine)
New York, NY, USA, November 1998
© 1998 by World Scientific Publishing Co. Pte. Ltd.

RESEARCH AND DESIGN OF CERAMIC KNEE REPLACEMENT

D. Sida [1], S. Konvickova,[2] A.Donat[2]
[1]Dept. of Material Science, Technical University of Liberec, Halkova 6,461 17 Liberec, CZ; [2]Laboratory of Human's Biomechanics, Technical University of Prague, CZ.

ABSTRACT
The artificial replacement of the knee joint having the metal femoral component (FC) and UHMWPE tibial plate have been applied for nearly 20 years. The main disadvantage of this type is the relatively high formation of toxic debris of polyethylene resulting from the abrasion of metal/ PE device. The efforts to minimize this abrasion have resulted in the application of ceramic materials to be used for femoral components. Research was carried out in the following areas: (1)FEM stress compar4sion analysis of the metallic and ceramic femoral component and (2) verification of suitability of CIP method of creating intermediate product of ceramics femoral component

Key words: Ceramics, zirconia, rapid prototyping, knee endoprosthesis, FEM analysis

INTRODUCTION
The goals of these experiments were: (1) Lower durability of metal implants (higher quantity UHMWPE debris in knee joint); (2) Successful transplantation of ceramic [alumina] hip endoprostheses (5000 cases in the Czech Republic in 1997); (3) Better tribology of ceramics compared with polyethylene: (4) The successful clinical tests of ceramic [alumina] knee endoprostheses published at Nagoya City University in Japan in 1994 (104 successful transplantation out of 106); (5) High number of metal knee joints transplantation in the Czech Republic (2100 in 1997); Potentially lower prices for series production.

Application of CIP Method for the Creation of Ceramic Femoral Component (FC)

There is a big difference between the geometry of hip joint and knee joints. The hip is a near perfect technical spherical joint, which can be easily produced by known technologies [CIP + HIP]. Due to complications and unsuccessful results with slip casting into combustible molds, injection-molding technology was chosen. Another difficult problem encountered with the production of a knee model and prototype mold is the requirement for five different sizes of knee implants. In addition to this, it is necessary to differentiate the shape of the left from right knee for each type. For this reason, the 3D geometric models were made in CAD system EDS/ Unigraphics. Once the CAD construction of the femoral component was completed, we had to resolve the problems of providing 3D models for mold formation with emphasis on possible direct productions of individual replacement from ceramics. After estimation of all parameters of the methods, **Rapid Prototyping (RP)** and the process of producing warm extrusion (Fused Deposition Modeling - FDM) were made in collaboration with CVUT Prague.
The equipment from Stratasys Co. (USA), type FDM-1650, is able to form 3D objects from plastics ABS (acrylonitrile-butadien-styrene), and Medical ABS.

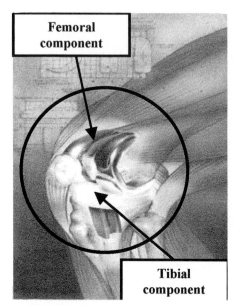

Special extrusion heads were formed using objects from wax, elastomers, as well as ceramics. After rapid installation and putting into operation a number of models FC in different enlargements (1:1; 1:1.3) were made in the course of the 1997. These models were used for the manufacturing of sample molds for CIP pressing of ceramic semi-products FC. Fixation pins (from titanium in future also from Y-TZP ceramics) were anchored by screw connection into titanium nuts, pressed in prepared openings FC.

Based on the results obtained in 1996, priority was given to the technology of forming ceramic powders by method of cold isostatic pressing (CIP) "wet bag" at manufacturing of semi products of femoral component.

To minimize the problem of lower firing into "hard" and therefore hardly machinable shape, preliminary working in bisque fired "chalky" state was required. CNC machining or by 3D copying was used to prepare aspherical, complicated, spatial object

Figure 1. Anatomical endoprothesis of knee joint

The construction of internal areas of the component was adapted in such a way that it could be pressed as exactly as possible, and in "hard" sintered state reground by means of diamond tool. The side of fixation surfaces were coated with bioactive porous, layers of hydroxyapatite (HA) plasma spray (the layer has thickness cca 0.1mm). The internal fixation surfaces as well as Ti pins (pivots) were, for this purpose, roughened with electrocorundum jetting.

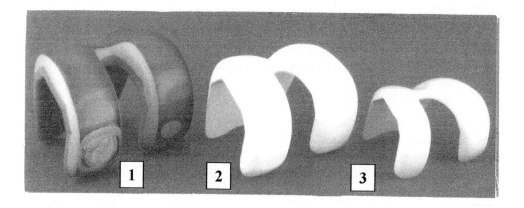

Figure 2. Shrinkage of zirconia (1-model, 2-pressed semi-product, 3-fired sample)

Properties	Units	Alumina	Zirconia Y-TZP
Density	g/cm	3.97	6.07
Grain size	μm	< 2	< 1
Hardness HV 10	daN/ mm	1800	1400
Flexural stength	MPa	450	1250
Abrasions resistance	mm	0.06	0.2
Young's modulus	Gpa	390	205

Table 1. Mechanical properties of zirconia of knee ceramic endoprothesis

Figure 3. Ceramic (ZrO2) Femoral component of knee endoprothesis

FEM ANAYSIS
MATERIALS AND METHODS

Two knee replacement model by Walter a.s. Praha were used in the study. The first model had metallic and the second model ceramic femoral component. The knee joint replacement model consists of two main parts, the femoral part and the tibial plato (see Figure 5). Finite element mesh generation was automatically performed. Each of FE models consisted of 15956 elements and 96057 degrees of freedom.

All analyses were performed using the nonlinear, three-dimensional contact options in ABAQUS (Hibbit, Karlson and Sorensen, Inc.). The present non-linear analyses were performed considering the knee joint in full extension under loading of femoral tibial force, corresponding three times body-weight. The bottom side of tibial plato was fixed.

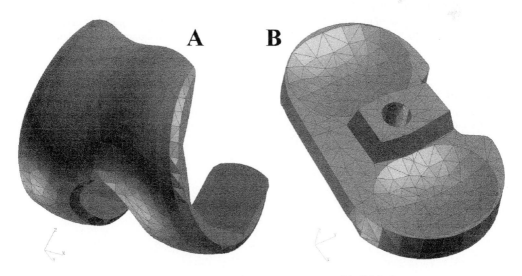

A   **B**

Figure 4. FE model of the knee joint (A) femoral component (B) tibial plato

By means of FEM contact pressures were calculated. Maximum contact pressure in the model with the metalic femoral component was 8.23 MPa and in the model with the ceramics femoral component was 8.19 Mpa. The stress comparison analysis were also carried out (see Figure 5).

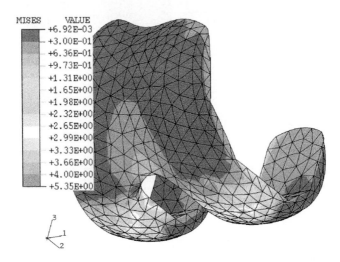

Figure 5. Misses stress distribution in the ceramics femoral component

Maximum Misses stress in the metalic femoral component was computed as 5.73 MPa and in the ceramics femoral component 7.35 MPa. Maximum Misses stress in the tibial plato was 7.04 MPa in the model with metalic femoral component and 7.05 NTa in the model with the ceramics femoral component.

CONCLUSIONS

The cold isostatic pressing (CIP) was shown to be the progressive technology for ceramics to obtain the best mechanical properties of the final components.

FEM analysis: no significant differences between stress distribution in metallic and ceramic femoral components were found Contact pressures was computed to be quantitatively identical in types.

REFERENCES

1. Bendjaballah MZ, Shirazi-Adi A, Zukor DJ. Clinical Biomechanics 1997; 3: 139-148.
2. Chand R, Haug E, Rim K. J. Biomechanics 1976; 9: 417-422.
3. Schwartz M.: Structural Ceramics 1994, 125-140

Bioceramics Volume 11, edited by R. Z. LeGeros and J.P. LeGeros
(Proceedings of the 11th International Symposium on Ceramics in Medicine)
New York, NY, USA, November 1998
© 1998 by World Scientific Publishing Co. Pte. Ltd.

SYNTHESIS OF BLOOD COMPATIBLE CERAMIC POWDERS AND A CONVENIENT METHOD OF EVALUATING AN ANTI-CLOTTING PROPERTY

Seisuke Takashima[1], Chikara Ohtsuki[2], Satoshi Hayakawa[2] and Akiyoshi Osaka[2]

[1]Co-operative Research Center, Okayama University, 5302 Haga, Okayama 701-1221, Japan;
[2]Biomaterials Lab., Faculty of Engineering, Okayama University, 3-1-1 Tsushima-Naka,
Okayama, 700-8530, Japan

ABSTRACT

We attempted to improve blood compatibility of silica-alumina composite powders synthesized through sol-gel processing due to addition of calcium phosphate, coating with poly-hydorxy-ethyl-methacylate (PHEMA). Blood compatibility of the powders was evaluated by measuring coagulation parameters i.e., partial thromboplastin time (PTT), prothrombin time (PT) and amount of fibrin (Fib), when contacted with fresh healthy human serum. Optimum compositions were in the range of $SiO_2/Al_2O_3 = 5/5 \sim 7/3$ of mass ratios with $5 \sim 10$ wt% of calcium phosphate. PHEMA coating remarkably improved blood compatibility of the silica-alumina powders even with low concentration. Moreover, linear correlation was discovered between PTT values and optical absorption intensity of peak in the visible region (515 nm) of 1,1-diphenyl 2-picryhydrazil(DPPH)/methanol solution that is added to serum. This phenomenon proposes a new method for evaluating the blood compatibility.

KEYWORDS: Blood purification therapy, blood compatibility, adsorbent, silica-alumina composites

INTRODUCTION

Extracoporeal blood therapy requires development of adsorbents that has specific properties, like high adsorption activity and high selectivity against the pathogenic substance in the patient serum, as well as high blood compatibility. [1-3] We reported previously that blood compatibility of gel-derived silica-alumina composites was improved by addition of calcium phosphate at low concentration with highly dispersion[3]. In the present study, the detailed synthetic conditions of silica-alumina containing calcium phosphate were investigated to obtain the adsorbent with higher blood compatibility. We examined blood compatibility of the silica-almina composites with various SiO_2/Al_2O_3 mass ratio and those coated with poly-hydorxy-ethyl-methacylate (PHEMA). In addition, a new simple method for evaluating blood compatibility of the adsorbent was discussed by correlating the visible range adsorption spectrum of the serum mixed with methanol solution containing 1,1-diphenyl 2-picryhydrazil(DPPH) to partial thromboplastin time, one of the coagulation parameters.

MATERIALS AND METHODS

Preparation of silica-alumina composite

Silica-alumina composite powders(Si-Al) powders were prepared with various SiO_2/Al_2O_3 mass ratios through sol-gel processing after the previous report[3]. Silica-alumina composite powders containing calcium phosphate (Si-Al-CaP) were also prepared with concentration of calcium phosphate in the range of $3 \sim 10$ wt% with Ca/P atomic ratio of 1.67. After the sol-gel processing, they were calcined at 600 °C for 3 hrs, and cooled to room temperature.

Coating of poly-hydorxy-ethyl-methacylate(PHEMA)

The Si-Al powders with mass ratios of $SiO_2/Al_2O_3 = 0/10$, 5/5 and 10/0 were dispersed in an ethanol (95%)-water (5%) solution of PHEMA (1wt%). The coating was carried out by impregnating method followed by drying at 40°C for 24hrs. Weight ratio of the coated PHEMA was 0.1, 0.3 and 0.5 wt%, based on the silica-alumina composite.

Evaluation for blood compatibility

Blood coagulation parameters, such as partial thromboplastin time (PTT(sec)), prothrombin time (PT(sec)) and amount of fibrin (Fib(mg/dl)), were examined as described previously[3], where 0.1g of the prepared powders were contacted with 1.0ml of mixed healthy serum by using KoaguLab'MJ (Clinical Diagnostic Co. LTD.). The data for the serum free from contact with powder was denoted as "Blank". Those for the serum contacted with PHEMA-coated carbons were also collected for comparison (denoted as PHEMA-A.C.).

New evaluating method for blood compatibility

A methanol (MeOH) solution containing 1,1-diphenyl 2-picryhydrazil(DPPH) (DPPH concentration: ca. 5×10^{-5} g/ml of MeOH) was mixed with 0.1ml of serum, after the contact of the serum with the composite powders. Visible spectra (400~800 nm, λmax: 515nm) were measured for the solutions to determine their absorbance(A). The absorption spectrum of distilled water (0.1 ml) was also measured as the control (A_0). Reaction ratio (R. R_{DPPH}) was estimated from the equation (R. R_{DPPH}) = $(A_0 - A) / A_0$. The values of R. R_{DPPH} were plotted as functions of PTT, PT and Fib.

Characterization of the composite powders

The composite powders prepared were characterized by X-ray diffractometry, gas adsorption (specific surface area), infrared spectroscopy, acid/base titration and scanning electron microscopy.

RESULTS AND DISCUSSION

Blood compatibility of the Si-Al-CaP composites

Figure 1 shows PTT, PT and Fib of the serum for the Si-Al-CaP composites after contacted with the SiO_2/Al_2O_3 of 3 and 10 wt%. PTT shows minimum values at SiO_2/Al_2O_3=7/3 (mass ratio) for both composites of 3 and 10 wt% CaP. However, the blood compatibility of the Si-Al composite powders, when represented with PTT, could not be located in the allowance range, though a wide variety of the mixing ratios SiO_2/Al_2O_3 were attempted, as in the previous paper.[3]

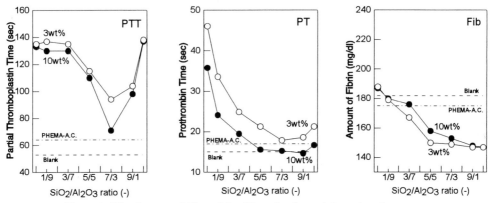

Figure 1. Blood compatibility of the silica-alumina-calcium phosphate.

PT shows minimum values SiO_2/Al_2O_3 = 5/5~7/3. It is noticed that PT for the composites with 10wt% calcium phosphate was in the level of allowance. It is, therefore, concluded that the optimum compositions were SiO_2/Al_2O_3 = 5/5~7/3 with 5~10wt% calcium phosphate.

We attempted to clarify the reasons why the above content ranges of the Si-Al-CaP composite powders had exhibited good blood compatibility. First, blood compatibility of Si-Al composite powders coated with PHEMA in various contents was measured, and PTT, PT and Fib plotted in Figure 2. The PHEMA coated Si-Al powder had good blood compatibility close to that of the positive (Blank) and the negative (PHEMA-A.C.) controls even in the low PHEMA concentration ranges. That is, coated powder did not affected the clotting characteristics of blood with little adsorbing the clotting factors. Blood compatibility was affected by active sites of the very fine area on the surface of the composite powders. Though the original surface of the composite powders was electrically charged the surface of the PHEMA coated composite powders had very weak electrostatic charges, thus the clotting factors in the serum were hard to be adsorbed on the surface of the coated powders since PHEMA has a relatively large molecular size and a relatively strong electrostatic charge. On the other hand, we could not detect significant changes on the profile of the acid-base titration curves and the specific surface area between the PHEMA coated and the non-coated powders. This is due to the small molecular size of the agents relevant to the

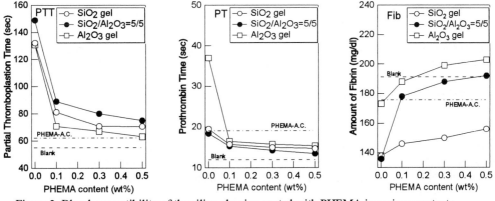

Figure 2. Blood compatibility of the silica-alumina coated with PHEMA in various contents.

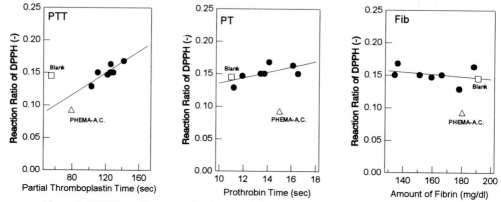

Figure 3. DPPH reactivity vz. blood compatibility of the gel-derived silica-alumina-
calcium phosphate composite powders.

titration and area measurement. Scarce changes were observed on the X-ray diffraction patterns
nor the electrostatic charges was derived from the titration for the surface of the Si-Al composite
powders.

New method for evaluating the blood compatibility

To establish a new method for evaluating blood compatibility, we examined the relationship
between PTT, PT and Fib and discoloring of MeOH solutions containing DPPH. We previously
discovered that discoloring of MeOH solutions proceeded with addition of human body fluid to it [4]
, or the optical adsorption(A_o) of the original MeOH solutions decreased to A when the solution
was contacted with composites. The results are shown on Figure 3. PTT has been correlated to the
reaction ratio (R. R_{DPPH}) = (A_o - A) /A_o in better linearity than PT or Fib. That is, the relation factor
determined for PTT(0.85) was higher than those of another two parameters (PT: 0.65, Fib: 0.29). It
is also noted that the slope of correlation in Figure 3(a) is closer to 45°. Thus R. R_{DPPH} is much
suitable for evaluating PTT than the other parameters.

CONCLUSIONS

1) The optimum compositions for blood compatibility of the Si-Al-CaP composite powder were
   SiO_2/Al_2O_3 = 5/5~7/3 in mass ratio with 5~10wt% of calcium phosphate.
2) The poor blood compatibility of the Si-Al composite powders were markedly improved by the
   coating in low PHEMA.
3) New method for evaluating blood compatibility of the bioceramic composite powders was
   derived by examining the relation between the discoloring of DPPH/MeOH solution in the
   visible range spectrum after the contact with serum and the clotting parameters. PTT can be
   well evaluated by the new method.

REFERENCE

1. Tani N. *Japanese J Artific Organs* 1988; **17**, 266-273.
2. Tanihara M. Nakajima T. Takakura K. *Japanese J Artific Organs* 1989; **18**: 15-18.
3. Takashima S, Ohtsuki C, Hayakawa S, Osaka A, In: *Bioceramics.*, Volume **10**, Pergamon,
   Oxford, 527-530.
4. Takashima S. Hisano A. Suzuki A. Inaba S. *Japanese J Med Instrment* 1998: **68**: 28-34.

Bioceramics Volume 11, edited by R. Z. LeGeros and J.P. LeGeros
(Proceedings of the 11th International Symposium on Ceramics in Medicine)
New York, NY, USA, November 1998
© 1998 by World Scientific Publishing Co. Pte. Ltd.

CERAMIC/METAL JOINING AS A TOOL FOR THE ENCAPSULATION OF TELEMETRIC SYSTEMS TO BE USED IN ORTHOPAEDICS

O. C. Paiva [1,2] and M. A. Barbosa [1,3]

[1]INEB - Institute for Biomedical Engineering, Biomaterials Laboratory, Rua do Campo Alegre 823, 4150 Porto, Portugal; [2]ISEP - Polytechnic Engineering Institute of Porto, Rua de S. Tomé, 4200 Porto, Portugal; [3]FEUP - Faculty of Engineering, University of Porto, Rua dos Bragas, 4099 Porto Codex, Portugal

ABSTRACT

This paper describes optimised methodologies for the bonding of stainless steel or commercially pure titanium to alumina ceramics. The two materials combinations ensure a sufficiently high mechanical strength, a high integrity of the bondings and an inert behaviour in presence of simulated body fluids. Both 316 stainless steel/alumina and Ti/alumina joints were produced by an active metal brazing technique. Two different brazing alloys within the Ag-Cu-Ti system were used. The produced joints were characterised morphological and structurally (by SEM/EDS and XRD), mechanically (by shear strength tests), and for their degradation behaviour (corrosion tests in a simulated physiological solution).

KEY WORDS: encapsulation, orthopaedic device, metal, alumina, active brazing, joining, shear strength, degradation

INTRODUCTION

The clinical follow up of a bone fracture is not an easy task. In fact, it is very difficult to determine precisely when temporary implants must be retrieved [1,2]. There are two ways of solving this problem: the traditional use of periodical checks by radiographic techniques, or the use of instrumented plates, containing a sensor to measure locally the stresses (during the consolidation period), and a telemetric device to transmit the data to outside the human body [2]. The use of the later systems involves the encapsulation of an electronic device in the plate (isolating it from the biological environment), by means of a metal/ceramic lid. The ceramic part of the lid is necessary in order to ensure adequate transparency to radio-frequency signals.

It is possible to produce a strong bond between a metal and a ceramic by several methods. Among those methods, active brazing appears to be one of the most flexible joining techniques to obtain strong interfaces [3-5]. Brazing alloys containing titanium can wet alumina [5-8] in a vacuum or in inert atmospheres, because Ti from the molten filler metal segregates to the ceramic surface and reacts with it. In the present study an active brazing technique, using Ag-Cu-Ti filler metals, was used to produced metal/ceramic joints. Adequate methodologies have been developed and optimised for the bonding of 316 stainless steel and commercially pure titanium to alumina, in order to ensure a sufficiently high mechanical strength, a high integrity of the bondings and an inert behaviour (namely corrosion resistance) in presence of simulated body fluids.

MATERIALS AND METHODS

Commercially pure titanium, grade 2 (Ti) (Titanium Products Limited, UK), and 316 stainless steel (316) (Ferespe, Portugal), and alumina (Al_2O_3) (Degussa, Germany) 99.6% of purity were used on this study. The production of M/C joints was carried out using two brazing filler metals (Frialit-Degussa, Germany), Ag-26.5Cu-3Ti (CB4) and Ag-34.5Cu-1.5Ti (CB5), in the shape of foils with a thickness of 100 μm. The M/C joints were produced at a vacuum level of 10^{-2} Pa at 900°C, using a holding time of 20 minutes. Details of the experimental procedure related to the active metal brazing process have been described elsewhere [9].

The bonding strength of the M/C joints was evaluated by using a previously described [10] shear fracture test. The observation of the M/C joints was carried out by scanning electron microscopy (SEM) using a microscope equipped with a energy dispersive spectroscopy (EDS) device, both on as-brazed cross-sections and mechanically tested fracture surfaces. X-ray diffraction (XRD) analysis of the fracture surfaces was used to identify the reaction products present in the fracture surfaces.

The degradation behaviour of the M/C joints (more precisely of cross-sections) was assessed by electrochemical techniques. These were conducted at 37±2°C, in HBSS (Hank's balanced salt solution). The potentials were measured against the saturated calomel electrode (SCE). The potential as a function of time was monitored for 1 h before initiating the potentiodynamic polarisation. The polarisation potential was scanned from -500 mV to 2000 mV using a scanning rate of 2 mV min^{-1}.

RESULTS AND DISCUSSION

Microstructures of the Metal/Ceramic Joints

Fig.1 presents examples of the M/Al$_2$O$_3$ joints produced with CB4 and CB5 brazing alloys at 900°C, with a holding time of 20 minutes. In both joints a well defined and rich Ti layer (A) was

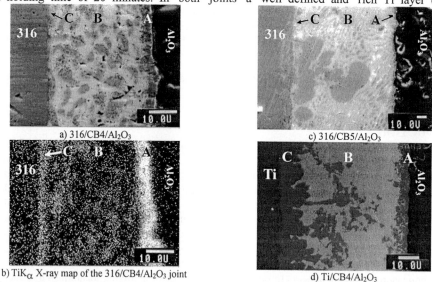

a) 316/CB4/Al$_2$O$_3$

c) 316/CB5/Al$_2$O$_3$

b) TiK$_\alpha$ X-ray map of the 316/CB4/Al$_2$O$_3$ joint

d) Ti/CB4/Al$_2$O$_3$

Figure 1. Typical microstructures of M/C joints produced at 900°C, with a holding time of 20 minutes.

formed at the Al$_2$O$_3$ interface. This segregation of Ti may be attributed to its affinity to oxygen. As the Al$_2$O$_3$ is the main available source of oxygen, Ti tends to diffuse in the direction of the alumina phase. This diffusion of Ti is even more noticeable for the joints produced with the brazing alloy CB4, as it is possible to observe in Fig.1b. By means of analysing the microstructures of the joints, it can be observed that, for both brazing alloys, they are mainly composed by a central area (B) which is very rich in Ag (matrix) and globules of a Ti+Cu mixture. In the case of the Ti/CB5/Al$_2$O$_3$ joints, its microstructures may be divided into two different zones. A globular type structure on the Al$_2$O$_3$ side composed of Cu-Ti in a Ag matrix, and a much thicker layer composed of only Ti-Cu on the Ti side. It may also be suggested, for the Ti/Al$_2$O$_3$ joints, that the Ti detected along the interface is coming not only from the brazing alloy but also from Ti itself.

Mechanical Characterisation of the Ceramic/Metal joints

Table 1 presents the shear strength results for the studied M/C joints. For each condition at least 6 samples were tested. The first comment is that the greater strengths were obtained for 316/Al$_2$O$_3$, as compared to the Ti/Al$_2$O$_3$ system. This result should be due to the higher oxidation at high temperatures of Ti. The best shear strength results, 192±15 MPa, were attained for brazing alloy CB4 used on the 316/Al$_2$O$_3$ system. The better performance achieved with the CB4 may be attributed to the already referred Ti-rich layer (A) in the vicinity of Al$_2$O$_3$ surface. This is owe to the higher amount of Ti, 3 wt%, present in the composition of CB4 relatively to the 1.5 wt% in CB5. In the Ti/Al$_2$O$_3$ system the results attained with CB4 and CB5 are quite similar. The presence of Cu-Ti intermetallic compounds (formed at the interface with Al$_2$O$_3$), which appears to be a barrier to crack propagation, was clear in this case CB5 (more rich in Cu). Furthermore, it was observed by SEM that cracks propagate intergranularly in the Al$_2$O$_3$. The crack propagation occurs in two stages. The fracture nucleation occurs within the Al$_2$O$_3$ and then its propagation through it, with fracture zones within the brazing alloy. In the case of 316/Al$_2$O$_3$ joints the fracture propagation occurs 90-95% within the Al$_2$O$_3$.

Table 1. Bond strengths, obtained in shear solicitation tests.

M/C System	Brazing Alloy	Shear Strength (MPa)
Ti/Al$_2$O$_3$	Ag-26.5Cu-3Ti (CB4)	93 ± 11
	Ag-34.5Cu-1.5Ti (CB5)	105 ± 9
316 SS/Al$_2$O$_3$	Ag-26.5Cu-3Ti (CB4)	192 ± 15
	Ag-34.5Cu-1.5Ti (CB5)	145 ± 12

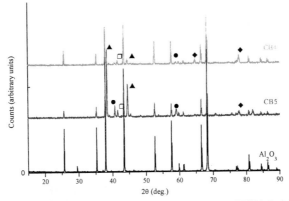

Figure 2. XRD spectra for standard Al$_2$O$_3$ and for the fracture surfaces of Ti/Al$_2$O$_3$ joints. The new phases detected on the fractured surfaces are identified on the spectra: (♦)AlTi$_3$, (●) Ti$_2$Cu$_3$, (□) TiCu$_2$ and (▲) Cu$_2$Ti$_4$O.

Several new phases were detected in the fracture surface of the Ti/Al$_2$O$_3$ brazed joints (e.g. in the exposed fracture path) as shown in the XRD spectra in Fig.2. These new peaks, indicate the presence of AlTi$_3$, Ti$_2$Cu$_3$, TiCu$_2$ and Cu$_2$Ti$_4$O for both brazing alloys. The most important difference between joints produced with CB4 and CB5 is the higher amount of Cu$_2$Ti$_4$O detected in the case of CB5. The formation of the Cu-Ti compounds was to be expected, but their stoichiometry is clearly enriched in Ti, confirming that most of the titanium of the brazing alloy is actively contributing to the brazing reactions. In fact, as stated before, Ti is the main cause of the wetting of the ceramic surface, and for the interfacial reactions that ensure the attained bonding. The presence of Cu$_2$Ti$_4$O indicates that the Ti is getting oxygen from Al$_2$O$_3$ and penetrating on its structure. This reaction of Ti with Al$_2$O$_3$ was further confirmed by the presence of AlTi$_3$.

Degradation of the Ceramic/Metal Joints

Table 2 presents the values obtained for the open circuit potential (E$_{corr}$) and for the corrosion rate (i$_{corr}$) of the several interfaces. As reported in Table 2 the M/Al$_2$O$_3$ joints, disclose an E$_{corr}$ value lower than Ti and stainless steel, but higher than both brazing alloys CB4 and CB5. The joints produced with 316 SS show a more active behaviour than those produced with Ti. In both M/Al$_2$O$_3$ systems, the joints produced using CB4 present a higher E$_{corr}$ than those produced using CB5. This different behaviour is due to the CB4 composition, that contains a higher amount of Ag and Ti than CB5. Ag tends to passivate in Cl⁻ containing solutions forming AgCl [11]. On the contrary, Cu forms soluble complexes and corrodes actively [11].

Table 2. Electrochemical results obtained for the brazing alloys, Ti, 316 SS and respective M/Al_2O_3 joints.

Sample Reference	Open-circuit potential E_{corr} (mV)	Corrosion rate i_{corr} ($\mu A/cm^2$)
Ag-26.5Cu-3Ti (CB4)	-201 ± 21	4.82 ± 1.32
Ag-34.5Cu-1.5Ti (CB5)	-221 ± 11	8.96 ± 1.15
Ti	29 ± 14	0.12 ± 0.08
$Ti/CB4/Al_2O_3$	29 ± 2	8.30 ± 3.51
$Ti/CB5/Al_2O_3$	-39 ± 2	11.5 ± 2.81
316 SS	-96 ± 27	0.56 ± 0.21
$316/CB4/Al_2O_3$	-147 ± 28	1.26 ± 1.02
$316/CB5/Al_2O_3$	-168 ± 4	4.93 ± 3.06

The same explanation applies to the lower i_{corr} values obtained for M/C joints produced with CB4 as compared to those produced with CB5. The Ti/Al_2O_3 joints present higher corrosion rates than the $316/Al_2O_3$, perhaps due to galvanic effects related with their typical microstructures. The microstructures of Ti/Al_2O_3 joints are composed by well defined layers of Cu+Ti (A), Ag-rich (B), Cu+Ti (C) (remember that Cu-rich zones are less noble than Ag based regions) and Ti, which should be compared to the globular structure presented by the $316/Al_2O_3$ joints.

After the electrochemical experiments, the degradation products formed on M/C joints were observed and analysed by SEM/EDS. The presence of higher amounts of Cu and Cl in the degradation products (cross-sections of the joints) was found to be associated with greater i_{corr} values. Also, the joints exhibiting the presence of an Ag-rich film present a more compact morphology. It should also be stressed out that the use of Ag-rich brazings in implant devices was found not to be a problem in previous studies carried out in pigs [12].

CONCLUSIONS

It was possible to develop and optimise active brazing routes to produce Ti/Al_2O_3 and $316/Al_2O_3$ joints. The better compromise between the degradation behaviour and mechanical properties was obtained for $316/Al_2O_3$ brazed joints. These joints may find uses as biocompatible encapsulation systems of implantable electronic devices.

REFERENCES

1. Burny F, Donkerwolcke M, Hinsenkamp M, Schuind F. In: Burny F, Puers R, eds. *Monitoring of Orthopedic Implant Biomaterials/Microelectronics Challenge,* North Holland: E-MRS Monographs, 1993: 7- 22.
2. Puers B, Burny F. In: Muster D, ed. *Biomaterials-Hard Tissue Repair and Replacement,* North Holland: E-MRS Monographs, 1992: 285-306.
3. Schwartz MM. In: Schwartz MM, ed. *Ceramic Joining,* Ohio: ASM International, 1990: 75-140.
4. Nicholas M, Mortimer D. *Materials Science and Technology* 1985; **1**: 657-665.
5. Paiva OC, Barbosa MA. *J. of Materials Science* 1997; **32**: 653-659.
6. Loehamn RE, Tomsia AP. *Acta Metall. Mater.* 1992; **40**: S75-S83.
7. Hao H, Wang Y, Jin Z, Wang X. *J. of Materials Science* 1995; **30**: 1233-1239.
8. Hao H, Wang Y, Jin Z, Wang X. *J. of Materials Science* 1995; **30**: 4107-4111.
9. Paiva OC, Barbosa MA. In: Kossowsky R, Kossovsky N, eds. *Advances in Materials Science and Implant Orthopaedic Surgery,* Dordrecht: Kluwer Academic Publishers, 1995: 275-290.
10. Paiva, OC, Barbosa, MA. Reviewed Proceedings of High Temperature Capillarity'97, *in press*
11. Uhlig HH. *Corrosion and corrosion control.* New York: Wiley, 1967: 145-232.
12. Janssens S, Rocha LA, Bosschaerts L, Barbosa MA, Puers R, Villé H, Geers R. *Prev. Veterinary Med.* 1996; **25**: 249-258.

Bioceramics Volume 11, edited by R. Z. LeGeros and J.P. LeGeros
(Proceedings of the 11th International Symposium on Ceramics in Medicine)
New York, NY, USA, November 1998
© 1998 by World Scientific Publishing Co. Pte. Ltd.

PREPARATION OF ANTIBACTERIAL SILVER-CONTAINING SILICA GLASS BY SOL-GEL METHOD

M. Kawashita[1], S. Tsuneyama[1], F. Miyaji[1], T. Kokubo[1], H. Kozuka[2] and K. Yamamoto[3]

[1]Department of Material Chemistry, Faculty of Engineering, Kyoto University, Sakyo-ku, Kyoto 606-8501, Japan; [2]Department of Materials Science and Engineering, Kansai University, Suita, Osaka 564-8680, Japan; [3]School of Dentistry, Asahi University, Hozumi-cho, Motosu-gun, Gifu-ken 501-0200, Japan.

ABSTRACT

Recently, various inorganic antibacterial materials containing silver have been developed and some of them are in commercial use. Colorless and more chemically durable materials which slowly release the silver ion for a long period are, however, desired to be developed for medical applications such as composite resin for dental restoration. In the present study, $Si(OC_2H_5)_4$-based solutions with various Al/Ag ratios were prepared by using $Si(OC_2H_5)_4$, $Al(NO_3)_3 \cdot 9H_2O$, H_2O, HNO_3, C_2H_5OH and $AgNO_3$ and kept at 40°C for gelation and drying. Thus obtained gels were pulverized into fine powders about 10 μm and then heat-treated at 950 or 1000°C for 2 h. For the composition Al/Ag=0, a yellow-colored glass was formed, since the silver took a form of metallic colloids in the glass, whereas, for the compositions Al/Ag≥1, colorless glasses were successfully obtained, since the silver took a form of Ag^+ ions in the glasses. For the composition Al/Ag=0, the silver ion released rapidly into a water, whereas, for the compositions Al/Ag≥1, it slowly released into the water. A composite of the silica glass powder (Al/Ag=1) with Bis-GMA/TEGDMA in 70:30 weight ratio showed antibacterial activity. Therefore, the sol-gel derived silica glasses containing silver with compositions Al/Ag≥1 are believed to be useful for medical applications such as filler of composite resin for dental restoration.

KEYWORDS: Silver, silica glass, sol-gel method, chemical durability, antibacterial property

INTRODUCTION

It is widely known that materials containing silver show antibacterial property.[1-2] Recently, various inorganic antibacterial materials containing silver have been developed and some of them are in commercial use.[3] Colorless and more chemically durable materials which slowly release the silver ion for a long period are, however, desired to be developed for medical applications such as composite resin for dental restoration.

Silica glass containing silver is potentially a candidate for such medical applications, since it is assumed to show high chemical durability. It is, however, difficult to prepare Ag_2O-SiO_2 glass by the conventional melting method. Although Ag_2O-SiO_2 glasses can be prepared by sol-gel method[4-5], they colored yellow or brown owing to formation of silver colloid particles.

In the present study, silver-containing silica glasses with various Al/Ag ratios were attempted to be prepared by sol-gel method. The states of the silver in the glasses were investigated, and the releases of elements from the glasses were examined. Antibacterial property of composites of the glass powder with Bis-GMA/TEGDMA was also investigated.

MATERIALS AND METHODS

$Si(OC_2H_5)_4$-based solutions with various Al/Ag ratios (See Table 1) were prepared by using $Si(OC_2H_5)_4$, $Al(NO_3)_3 \cdot 9H_2O$, H_2O, HNO_3, C_2H_5OH and $AgNO_3$ and kept at 40°C for 7 d for gelation and drying. The obtained gels were pulverized into fine particles of about 10 μm in diameter, and then the particles were heat-treated at 950°C for the composition Al/Ag=0 and at 1000°C for the compositions Al/Ag=1 and 2 for 2 h.

The state of silver in the specimens were characterized by a powder X-ray diffractometer (RAD-C, Rigaku-Denki Co., Tokyo, Japan). The specimens of 0.1 g were immersed into water of 20 ml at 37°C for 1-14 days. The concentrations of silicon, aluminum and silver released from the specimens were measured by an Inductively Coupled Plasma atomic emission spectrometer (SPS-1500 VR, Seiko Instruments Inc., Tokyo, Japan).

Composite resin was prepared by mixing the heat-treated powder (Al/Ag=1) with Bis-GMA/TEGDMA in 70:30 weight ratio. The composite resin was soaked in the reduced transport fluid[6] (pH 7.2) in which *Streptococcus mutans* ATCC 25175 (*S. mutans*) was cultured at the concentration of 1×10^6 cells·ml^{-1}. After 2-12 h, the cell forming unit (CFU; cells·ml^{-1}) of *S. mutans* was measured.

RESULTS AND DISCUSSION

Figure 1 shows the powder X-ray diffraction patterns of the heat-treated specimens with various Al/Ag ratios. For the composition Al/Ag=0, peaks assigned to metallic silver were

Table 1   Compositions of the starting solution in molar ratio

Al/Ag molar ratio	$Si(OC_2H_5)_4$	C_2H_5OH	H_2O	HNO_3	$AgNO_3$	$Al(NO_3)_3 \cdot 9H_2O$
0	1	2	8	0.01	0.023	—
1	1	2	8	0.01	0.023	0.023
2	1	2	8	0.01	0.023	0.045

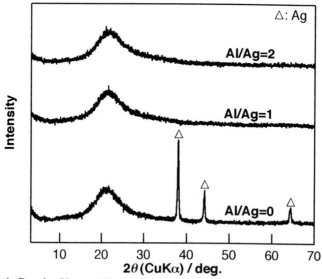

Figure 1. Powder X-ray diffraction patterns of the heat-treated specimens.

observed besides a hallow ascribed to glassy phase, whereas, for the compositions Al/Ag≥1, only the hallow was observed. The specimen with composition Al/Ag=0 colored yellow, whereas the those with compositions Al/Ag≥1 were colorless. These results indicate that, for the composition Al/Ag=0, silica glass containing the silver as metallic colloids is obtained, whereas, for the compositions Al/Ag≥1, those containing the silver as Ag^+ ions were obtained.

Figure 2 shows the concentrations of silicon, aluminum and silver released from the specimens with various Al/Ag ratios. A large amount of silicon was released from the specimens with the composition Al/Ag=0, whereas it was hardly released from those with compositions Al/Ag≥1 (See Fig. 2-(a)). The amount of aluminum released from the specimens with the compositions Al/Ag≥1 was extremely small (See Fig. 2-(b)). These indicate that the chemical durability of the glass can be increased by an addition of alumina. For the composition Al/Ag=0, the silver was rapidly released into the water, whereas, for the compositions Al/Ag≥1, the silver was slowly released into the water in proportional to square root of time (See Fig. 2-(c)). These results can be explained by assuming that the release of silver is controlled by the reaction of the metallic silver colloids with the water for the composition Al/Ag=0, whereas by the diffusion of the silver ions in the glasses for the compositions Al/Ag≥1.

It can be seen from these results that colorless and chemically durable silica glasses which can release the Ag^+ ion slowly at a controlled rate can be obtained, when as-dried gels with Al/Ag≥1 are heat treated at 1000°C.

Figure 3 shows changes in CFU of *S. mutans* cultured in the medium with a composite of the silica glass powder (Al/Ag=1) with Bis-GMA/TEGDMA in 70:30 weight ratio. The concentration of surviving cells remarkably decreased with increasing culture period, and no surviving cell was observed after the soaking for 12 h. It can be seen from this result that thus prepared composite shows a high antibacterial activity.

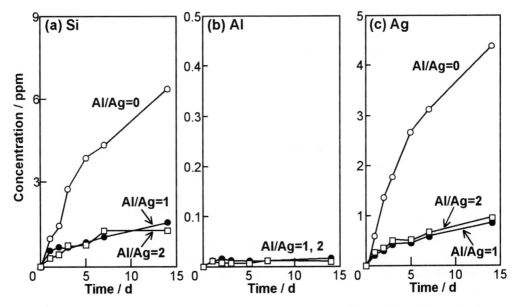

Figure 2. Concentrations of (a) silicon, (b) aluminum and (c) silver released from the heat-treated specimens.

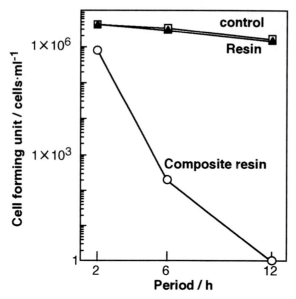

Figure 3. Changes in CFU of *S. mutans* cultured in the medium with a composite of the silica glass powder (Al/Ag=1) with Bis-GMA/TEGDMA in 70:30 weight ratio.

CONCLUSIONS

Colorless and chemically durable silver-containing silica glass, which slowly release the silver ion at a controlled rate for a long period, was successfully prepared by the sol-gel method using $Si(OC_2H_5)$-based solution with Al/Ag≥1.   Thus prepared silica glasses are believed to be useful for medical applications such as composite resin for dental restoration.

ACKNOWLEDGEMENT

This work was supported by a Grant-in-Aid for Scientific Research, The Ministry of Education, Science and Culture, Japan.

REFERENCES

1.   Schreurs WJ, Rosenberg HJ. *Bacteriol.* 1982; **152**: 7-13.
2.   Williams RL, Doherty PJ, Vince DG, Grashoff GJ, Williams DF. *Crit. Rev. Biocompat.* 1989; **5**: 221-243.
3.   Oloffs A, Grosse-Siestrup C, Bisson S, Rinck M, Rudolph R, Gross U. *Biomaterials* 1994; **15**: 753-758.
4.   Innocenzi P, Kozuka H. *J. Sol-Gel Sci. Technol.* 1994; **3**: 229-233.
5.   Hinsch A, Zastrow A. *J. Non-Cryst. Solids* 1992; **147&148**: 579-581.
6.   Syed SA, Loesche WJ. *Appl. Microbiol.* 1967; **24**: 638-644.

Bioceramics Volume 11, edited by R. Z. LeGeros and J.P. LeGeros
(Proceedings of the 11th International Symposium on Ceramics in Medicine)
New York, NY, USA, November 1998
© 1998 by World Scientific Publishing Co. Pte. Ltd.

CATHODOLUMINESCENCE STUDY OF THE APATITE-LIKE LAYER ON BIOACTIVE SOL-GEL GLASSES

A.J. Salinas[1], J. Román[1], M.Vallet-Regí[1], P. Fernández[2] and J. Piqueras[2]

[1]Departamento de Química Inorgánica y Bioinorgánica, Facultad de Farmacia, Universidad Complutense, 28040-Madrid, Spain; [2]Departamento de Fisica de Materiales, Facultad de Físicas, Universidad Complutense, 28040-Madrid, Spain.

ABSTRACT

The small size of crystals forming the calcium phosphate rich layer on the surface of bioactive materials when are exposed to physiological fluids, produce so broad maxima in the X-Ray Diffraction (XRD) patterns that is not possible to identify the crystalline phases formed. To characterise the phases on the layer, cathodoluminescence (CL) appears as a potentially useful characterisation technique in the field of bioceramics. For testing this assumption, two bioactive glasses in the system $SiO_2.P_2O_5.CaO$ were obtained by the sol-gel method. After soaking in a simulated body fluid at 37°C, the surface of the glasses was studied by CL and the results were compared with those obtained for stoichiometric hydroxyapatite (OHAp) and β-tricalcium phosphate (β-TCP), obtained by solid state reaction, that were used as standards. CL images show an inhomogeneous emission intensity distribution suggesting the presence of several phases on the layer. The results show a similarity of the CL spectra of the layer growth on the glasses and the spectrum of β–TCP suggesting that one of the phases present in the layer could be related to the β–TCP standard.

KEYWORDS: Bioactive glasses, sol-gel, cathodoluminescence

INTRODUCTION

The so-called bioactive materials bond to living tissues through a bone-like apatite layer formed in their surface when are implanted[1]. This layer is also formed when such materials are soaked in a solution with ionic concentrations analogous to that of the human plasma[2]. The reaction layer is initially an amorphous calcium phosphate which crystallises after nucleation and growth. However, the small size of crystals produces so broad maxima in the XRD patterns that is not possible to identify the crystalline phases formed. To characterize the phases on the layer CL, widely applied to study insulator and semiconductor materials[3], appears as a potentially useful characterization technique in the field of bioceramics.

In this paper, two sol-gel glasses in the system $SiO_2.P_2O_5.CaO$ were prepared. After soaking the samples in a Simulated Body Fluid[2] (SBF) at 37°C for several days, an apatite-like layer was formed in their surface. The newly formed layer was characterized by XRD, Scanning Electron Microscopy (SEM) and Energy Dispersive Spectroscopy (EDS). In addition, CL, performed in a scanning electron microscope, was used to study the glasses, after soaking in SBF, in order to characterize the crystalline phases formed in their surface and the results were compared with those obtained for the standards OHAp and β–TCP.

EXPERIMENTAL DETAILS

Two sol-gel glasses with the following composition (in mol-%): SiO_2 60-80, CaO 36-16 and P_2O_5 4 in both cases, denoted as 60S and 80S respectively, were prepared by hydrolysis and polycondensation of the appropriate amounts of tetraethyl orthosilicate, triethyl phosphate and calcium nitrate following the method early described[4,5]. The standards $Ca_{10}(PO_4)_6(OH)_2$ (OHAp) and $Ca_3(PO_4)_2$ (TCP), were obtained by solid state reaction from the stoichiometric amounts of $CaCO_3$ and $CaHPO_4.2H_2O$ and heating in air for 14 hours at 1000°C and 900°C, respectively.

Discs (ϕ= 13, h= 2 mm) of 60S, 80S were obtained from the powdered glasses by uniaxial pressure (55 MPa) and then isostatic pressure (150 MPa) followed by a thermal treatment at 700°C for 3 hours. *In vitro* tests were performed by soaking the discs in the SBF proposed by Kokubo[2] at 37°C for several days. XRD analysis were made in a Philips X'Pert MPD difractometer (CAI X-ray Diffraction Complutense University), using Cu Kα radiation. SEM-EDS analysis were made using a JEOL 6400 Microscope-LINK AN100000 System. CL in the visible range was performed in a Hitachi S-2500 scanning electron microscope at 78 K with accelerating voltages of 20 kV.

RESULTS AND DISCUSSION

XRD patterns of 80S before and after soaking in SBF for several days are shown in Figure 1. The XRD diagram of the glass before soaking showed a broad band between 18° and 30° 2θ, and a broad peak between 30° and 36° 2θ with a maximum at about 32°. A sharpening of the broad peak and the apparition of the (002) apatite reflection were observed in XRD patterns of glass after soaking for 1 day. After 3 days of soaking both diffraction maxima (002) and (211) increased the intensity while other diffraction apatite peaks (310), (222), (213), (004) (304) (323) became more evident. The XRD pattern after 7 and 14 days of soaking in SBF are almost identical to that obtained after 3 days of immersion. These results agree with the observed by other authors[6] and indicate the formation of an apatite-like layer. However, the broad maxima in the XRD patterns, due to the small size and/or low perfection or strain of crystals forming the layer, avoid the identification of other crystalline phases that could be present on the layer. For sample 60S the variation of the XRD patterns were analogous.

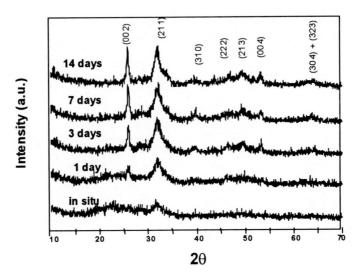

Figure 1. XRD patterns of 80S before and after different soaking times in SBF.

After 7 days in SBF, glasses 60S and 80S showed luminescence emission in the visible spectral range. Both spectra are qualitatively similar, with a peak at about 410 nm and a broad emission extending up to 550 nm with a shoulder at about 500 nm. OHAp showed no luminescent emission while TCP presented a broad emission band peaked at 390 nm with a shoulder at about 500 nm with weaker relative intensity than in the 60S and 80S samples.

The CL spectra of 60S and of TCP are shown in Figure 2. The observed bands have a complex character and the differences between the spectra shown in Figure 2 can be related to the different relative weight of the components, in particular of the 500 nm emission. CL images of all samples show an inhomogeneous intensity distribution which indicates the presence of several phases in the layer. Figure 3 shows the CL image of 60S. The similarity of the CL spectra of the layer grown on the glasses (60S and 80S) and the spectrum of TCP indicates that one of the phases present in the layer would be related to the TCP standard.

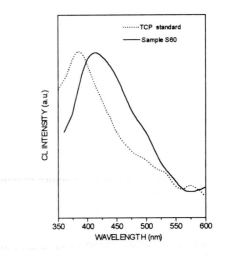

Figure 2. CL spectra of 60S after seven days in SBF and β-TCP standard.

CL images of all samples show an inhomogeneous intensity distribution which indicates the presence of several phases in the layer. Figure 3 shows the CL image of 60S. The similarity of the CL spectra of the layer grown on the glasses (60S and 80S) and the spectrum of TCP indicates that one of the phases present in the layer would be related to the TCP standard.

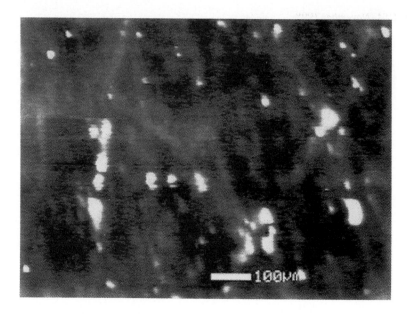

Figure 3. CL image of 60S after seven days in SBF.

CONCLUSIONS

The results indicate that CL in the scanning electron microscope appears as a suitable technique to investigate the phases present in apatite-like layer formed on bioactive materials. However, due to the complexity of the systems investigated here requires further CL studies of the phases present in the apatite layer.

ACKNOWLEDGEMENTS

Financial support of CICYT (Spain) trough Research Project MAT96-0919 is acknowledged.

REFERENCES

1. Hench LL, Wilson J. In: Hench LL, Wilson J eds: *An Introduction to Bioceramics,* Singapore: World Scientific, 1993: 1-24
2. Ebisawa Y, Kokubo T, Ohura K, Yamamuro T, *J Mater Sci: Mater Med,* 1990, **1**, 239-244;
3. Yacobi BG, Holt DB. *Cathodoluminescence Microscopy of Inorganic Solids.* New York: Plenum Press, 1990.
4. Li R, Clark AE, Hench LL. *J Appl Biomaterials* 1991; **2**, 231-239.
5. Pereira MM, Clark AE, Hench LL. *J Biomed Mater Res*1994; **28**, 693-698.
6. Kim H-M, Miyaji F, Kokubo T. *J Am Ceram Soc* 1995; **78**, 2405-2411.

Bioceramics Volume 11, edited by R. Z. LeGeros and J.P. LeGeros
(Proceedings of the 11th International Symposium on Ceramics in Medicine)
New York, NY, USA, November 1998
© 1998 by World Scientific Publishing Co. Pte. Ltd.

EFFECT OF ULTRASONIC VIBRATION ON THE PARTICLE SIZE DISTRIBUTION OF HYDROXYAPATITE CHEMICALLY PRECIPITATED FROM Ca(OH)$_2$ AND H$_3$PO$_4$

G. Vargas, J. López, J. Acevedo, J. Méndez and M. Méndez

CINVESTAV-IPN Unidad Saltillo, Apartado Postal 663, 25000 Saltillo, Coahuila, México, Tel. 52 (84) 88 10 19, Fax. 52 (84) 88 13 00

ABSTRACT

The particle size distribution (PSD) of hydroxyapatite used for the fabrication of biocements has been found to play a very important role due to its strong relationship with the chemical homogeneity and mechanical properties of the resulting product. In the present work, hydroxyapatite was synthesized via chemical precipitation employing Ca(OH)$_2$ and H$_3$PO$_4$ as raw materials. This synthesis method was chosen due to its inherent simplicity, chemical reactants readily available and low cost. In order to reduce the PSD of the hydroxyapatite, ultrasonic vibration (UV) was applied to the reaction vessel during the chemical precipitation process, extending the UV during a posterior aging period. A particle-dispersing agent was used to stabilize the hydroxyapatite aqueous suspensions. X-Ray diffraction (XRD), Laser Light Scattering Particle Size Analysis (LLS) and Scanning Electron Microscopy (SEM) were used for the characterization of the hydroxyapatite chemical composition, PSD and particle morphology. The results showed that by employing UV it is possible to obtain spherical particles of hydroxyapatite showing a narrow PSD with an average value of 7.45 and 5.07μm. In contrast, when neither UV nor a particle-dispersing agent were used, a broader PSD was obtained, with an average value of 22.8μm, due to the formation of agglomerates.

KEYWORDS: Hydroxyapatite, chemical precipitation, particle size, ultrasonic vibration.

INTRODUCTION

Calcium phosphates are very interesting materials for biomedical applications. Since this kind of compounds are present in the human and animal bones naturally, calcium phosphates are among the materials showing the best characteristics of biocompatibility. This makes them good candidates to perform bone repairs and substitutions during reconstructive or aesthetic surgery, as well as for permanent or temporary fixation of dental or orthopaedic implants. Hydroxyapatite [Ca$_{10}$(PO$_4$)$_6$(OH)$_2$] and other calcium phosphates can be obtained from several different sources, namely: sea resources (starfish or coral), calcined and sterilized animal bones, and chemical synthesis. The latter technique may involve the use of a variety of raw materials and processes[1]. The selection of a particular production route depends primarily on factors such as availability and cost of the raw materials, equipment required and properties desired. These properties (such as particle size distribution, particle morphology, solubility in biological media, biointegration properties, etc.) depend in turn on the chosen synthesis route and on the conditions employed. The present work deals with the synthesis of hydroxyapatite via chemical reaction between calcium hydroxide, Ca(OH)$_2$, and phosphoric acid, H$_3$PO$_4$[1,6,8]. This synthesis method was chosen due to its inherent simplicity, chemical reactants readily available and low cost. It has frequently been reported[4] in the literature that hydroxyapatite can be easily synthesized by using this production route. It has been mentioned[6] that the most important processing variables involved in the hydroxyapatite chemical precipitation synthesis process are: the initial Ca/P molar ratio for the raw materials, pH of the reacting aqueous suspensions throughout the process, the reaction temperature, the degree of mixing and the aging conditions of the resulting hydroxyapatite aqueous suspension, as well as the addition rate of phosphoric acid. In the present work, ultrasonic vibration was applied to the reaction vessel (during the aging stage, or during both the acid addition and aging stages) with the aim of obtaining a narrow particle size distribution for hydroxyapatite chemically precipitated. This investigation was motivated by the fact that the particle size distribution of the raw materials has been found[7] to play a key role in the chemical homogeneity and mechanical properties of hydroxyapatite-based biocements.

MATERIALS AND METHODS

Hydroxyapatite was synthesized via chemical precipitation employing reagent grade calcium hydroxide [$Ca(OH)_2$] and phosphoric acid [H_3PO_4] as raw materials. An aqueous solution of phosphoric acid (1M) was added dropwise (at a constant addition rate of ~1.8 ml/min) to a vigorously and continuously stirred aqueous solution of calcium hydroxide (1M). Previously boiled and decarbonated deionized water was used to prepare both aqueous solutions. The relative volumes required for these solutions were determined, according to the volume capacity of the chemical reactor, aiming for a final Ca/P molar ratio of 1.67 for the resulting hydroxyapatite aqueous suspension. The chemical reactor used had a volume capacity of one liter, and was fitted with a rotatory stirrer and an ultrasonic stirrer. Hydroxyapatite synthesis was carried out at room temperature using an air atmosphere, with a slight increase in temperature due to heat released by the exothermic reaction. Both temperature and pH were continuously monitored but not controlled. The reacting aqueous suspension was continuously stirred for a period of 10 hours, starting with the addition of the first drop of phosphoric acid. The stirring period included an aging stage given to the resulting hydroxyapatite aqueous suspensions after complete addition of the acid. The stirring operation was done in three different ways: (1) a rotatory stirring at 400 rpm was applied to the reacting aqueous suspension throughout the stirring period; (2) a rotatory stirring was applied to the reacting aqueous suspension until the addition of phosphoric acid was completed; from that point onwards, ultrasonic vibration was employed throughout the aging stage, using a 47 Khz Bransonic 2210 ultrasonic apparatus; (3) simultaneous application of rotatory stirring and ultrasonic vibration to the reacting aqueous suspension throughout both the acid addition and the aging stages. In the two latter cases, a particle-dispersing agent (polyvinylpolypyrrolidone) was used to stabilize the resulting hydroxyapatite aqueous suspensions. A Philips X-Pert MPD XRD, a Malvern Instruments LLS particle size analyzer, and a JEOL JSM 6300 SEM were used for the characterization of the hydroxyapatite chemical composition, particle size distribution and particle morphology, respectively.

RESULTS AND DISCUSSION

The XRD studies carried out confirmed the formation of hydroxyapatite under all conditions employed in the present work. SEM observations showed spherical hydroxyapatite particles with individual sizes smaller than 1μm. However, much larger agglomerates were also observed, which was attributed to the sample preparation technique employed. From the LLS results, showed in Figures 1-3, it can be seen that the ultrasonic vibration given to the reacting aqueous suspensions had a significant effect on the average particle size as well as on the particle size distribution of the chemically precipitated hydroxyapatite. The hydroxyapatite average particle size decreased, and the corresponding particle size distribution was narrowed, in the same order given above for the three different stirring modalities employed. According to Figure 1, when hydroxyapatite was chemically precipitated at room temperature, and after a 10-hour period of rotatory stirring, which included both the acid addition and the aging stages, the hydroxyapatite particle size ranged from 2 to 100 μm, with an average particle size of 22.8 μm. In contrast, as it can be seen from Figure 2, when a rotatory stirring was applied to the reacting aqueous suspension during the acid addition stage, followed by the application of ultrasonic vibration during the aging stage, the hydroxyapatite particle size ranged from 1 to 50 μm, with an average particle size of 7.45 μm. Similarly, Figure 3 shows that when a simultaneous rotatory stirring and ultrasonic vibration was applied to the reacting aqueous suspension during both the acid addition and the aging stages, the hydroxyapatite particle size ranged from 0.5 to 20μm, with an average particle size of 5.07μm.

It has been pointed out in the literature[1,2,5] that the typical particle size obtained for chemically precipitated hydroxyapatite is < 1μm (which yields characteristically poor x-ray diffraction patterns). It has been also noticed, however, that due to flocculation the particles form aggregates ~ 20 μm in size. The latter particle size is very similar to the largest particle size obtained in the present work, which corresponded precisely to the case in which only a rotatory stirring was applied to the reacting aqueous suspension. Thus, ultrasonic vibration, either applied during the aging period or throughout the chemical synthesis process (aging stage included), caused a significant reduction in the hydroxyapatite particle size by avoiding the formation of larger agglomerates by flocculation. In this case, the resulting hydroxyapatite aqueous suspensions were further stabilized by the particle-dispersing agent employed.

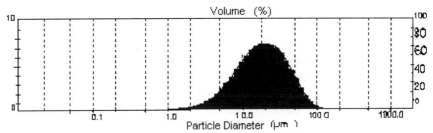

Figure 1. PSD for the application of rotatory stirring.

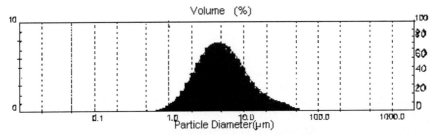

Figure 2. PSD for the application of rotatory stirring followed by ultrasonic vibration.

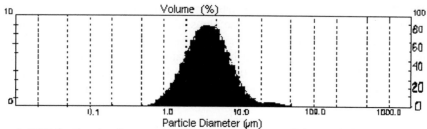

Figure 3. PSD for the simultaneous application of rotatory stirring and ultrasonic vibration.

Thus, the application of ultrasonic vibration is a potentially useful technique to produce fine and deagglomerated powdered hydroxyapatite by chemical precipitation synthesis. However, further research is needed in order to optimize the technique used in the present work. This could be done by a careful consideration of the processing variables involved. According to the relevant literature[3], when ultrasonic waves of sufficient amplitude are introduced into a liquid, the result is cavitation of the liquid at the low pressure points of the sound waves. As waves pass by a given point in the liquid, low pressure areas are replaced by high pressure or "compression" areas. Cavitation bubbles produced under these conditions implode during compression, resulting in the production of extremely small but highly intense shock waves, which are responsible for the deagglomeration of the hydroxyapatite particles observed in this work. Factors which could further increase the cavitation intensity are: an increased ultrasonic power, an increased ultrasonic frequency, an increased temperature, a decreased amount of dissolved gas in the liquid, an increased surface tension and a decreased viscosity of the liquid. The optimum ultrasonic power required must be experimentally determined. Besides, as the ultrasonic frequency is increased, more power must be applied to maintain the same cavitation intensity.

SUMMARY

The application of ultrasonic vibration to the reaction vessel during the hydroxyapatite chemical precipitation had a significant effect on the average particle size as well as on the particle size distribution. This was attributed to the deagglomeration of the hydroxyapatite particles caused by the highly intense shock waves introduced into the reacting aqueous suspension. Thus, this is a potential technique to produce fine and deagglomerated powdered hydroxyapatite.

REFERENCES

1. Berndt CC, Haddad GN, Farmer AJD, Gross KA. Mater Forum 1990; **14**: 161-173.
2. Brown WE, Chow LC. Annu Rev Mater Sci 1976; **6**: 213-236.
3. Fuchs FJ. Metal Finishing 1992; **90**: 134-139.
4. LeGeros RZ, Trautz OR, LeGeros JP, Klein E. Bull Soc Chim Fr 1968; 1712-1718.
5. Posner AS. Physiol Rev 1969; **49**: 760-792.
6. Suwa Y, Banno H, Mizuno M, Saito H. J Ceram Soc Jap 1993; **101**: 642-647.
7. Vargas G. Unpublished work.
8. Young RA, Holcomb DW. Calcif Tissue Int 1982; **34**: S17-S32.

Bioceramics Volume 11, edited by R. Z. LeGeros and J.P. LeGeros
(Proceedings of the 11th International Symposium on Ceramics in Medicine)
New York, NY, USA, November 1998
© 1998 by World Scientific Publishing Co. Pte. Ltd.

PARTICLE SIZING CHARACTERIZATION OF α-TCP AND HYDROXYAPATITE COLLOIDS DURING TRANSFORMATION PROCESS BY ULTRASONIC ATTENUATION SPECTROSCOPY

S. Takeda[1], A. Nakahira[2], S. Yamaguchi[3] and K. Sakamoto[4]

[1]Fac. of Engineering, Okayama University, 3-1-1 Tsushima-naka, Okayama, 700-8530; [2]Kyoto Institute of Technology, Gosho-kaido-cho, Matsugasaki, Sakyo-ku Kyoto, 606-8585; [3]ISIR, Osaka University, 8-1 Mihogaoka, Ibaraki, 567; [4]Osaka Sangyo University, Nakagaito, Daito, Osaka, 574, JAPAN

Keywords: Ultrasonic attenuation spectroscopy, α-TCP, Hydroxyapatite, Colloid

INTRODUCTION

In various fields of applications, there is a need to characterize suspended particles in terms of the particle size distribution (PSD) and to monitor its dynamic changes. Ultrasonic attenuation spectroscopy seems to be most likely to succeed in monitoring the change in PSD for colloidal systems at industrially relevant volume fractions, which are beyond the scope of more conventional techniques such as light scattering. Ultrasonic attenuation spectroscopy is developing rapidly as an alternative to light scattering method for the determining particle size distribution [1-3]. Many new studies related to ultrasonic attenuation spectroscopy have appeared since 1991 when McClement's review of ultrasonic attenuation spectroscopy was published [4].

The development of the automatically measuring instrumentation using ultrasonic attenuation or electroacoustic spectroscopy has also been performed and the instruments were now on market. As the biggest advantage of the ultrasonic attenuation spectroscopy compared with other spectroscopy, such as light scattering technique is the capability to characterize intact concentrated dispersed system.

Since the transformation process of α-TCP to hydroxyapatite in aqueous solutions with and without alcohol was well known to be dependent on pH and existence of alcohol, ultrasonic attenuation spectroscopy was applied to monitor the change in PSD in order to elucidate a mechanism of transformation process. The purpose of this paper is to demonstrate the capability of the monitoring the change in PSD of α-TCP and hydroxyapatite in concentrated suspensions. Characterization of hydroxyapatite after hydrolysis of α-TCP was also performed by XRD, TEM and FT-IR. It is found that ultrasonic attenuation spectroscopy could open the way to obtain some important information in order to elucidate a mechanism of the transformation process investigated here and other systems relevant to the bioceramics fields.

MATERIALS AND METHODS

Powders and prepared suspensions
α-TCP powders (Taihei Chemical Co., Ltd., Japan) was used for all the measurements. Suspensions of 2.5 vol% were prepared by dispersing dry powders in aqueous solutions(pH 11.4, 70°C) and vigorously stirred for transformation to hydroxyapatite.

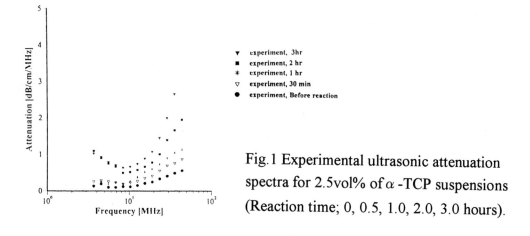

Fig.1 Experimental ultrasonic attenuation spectra for 2.5vol% of α-TCP suspensions (Reaction time; 0, 0.5, 1.0, 2.0, 3.0 hours).

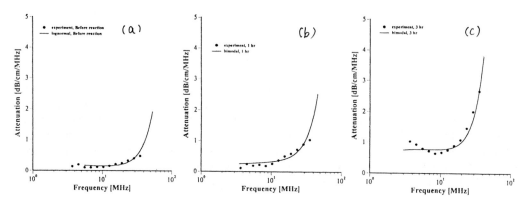

Fig.2 (a)-(c) Experimental and theoretical attenuation spectra for 2.5vol% of α-TCP suspensions (Reaction time; 0, 1.0, 3.0 hours).

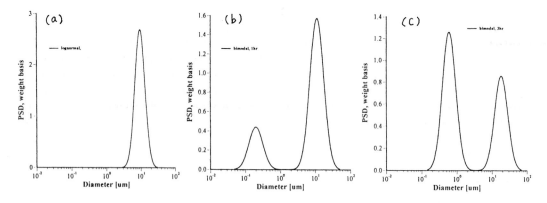

Fig.3 (a)-(c) Particle size distribution for 2.5vol% of α-TCP suspensions (Reaction time; 0, 1.0, 3.0 hours).

Measurement technique

A precise and in detail background of the theory for ultrasonic attenuation spectroscopy has been described in elsewhere [3]. The attenuation spectra of the sample slurries were measured using Acoustophor PK-8000 (Pen Kem, Inc., USA). The attenuation was measured over a wide frequency range of 1 to 100 MHz. The variable gap technique makes it possible to exclude calibration procedures. There is no restriction on the volume fraction but the sample must be fluidic enough so that the peristatic pump to pump the sample through the measuring chamber.

Analysis software converts attenuation spectra into the particle size distribution minimizing the difference between theoretical and measured attenuation spectra. The absolute error of the theoretical fit is the measure of this difference. In the case of the log-normal distribution the absolute error is minimized by adjusting median size and standard deviation of the log-normal distribution. In the case of the bi-modal distribution, the absolute error is also minimized by adjusting median sizes and standard deviations of each particles.

RESULTS AND DISCUSSION

Figure 1 shows the measured attenuation spectra in decibels per centimeter per MHz (dB/cmMHz). Experimental points at the low frequencies (<3MHz) are excluded because of the large errors. It is seen that the measured attenuation curves vary with the reaction time, which suggests that particle size distribution of α-TCP and hydroxyapatite in suspensions changes depending on the reaction time.

Analyzed results are shown in Figure 2: the log-normal distribution provides the good fit to the measured attenuation spectrum for the sample before reaction and bi-modal distribution gives the good fit to the spectra for the samples reacted for 1 hour and 3 hours. The corresponding particle size distributions are shown in Figures 3a to 3c. It is shown that the median size of α-TCP particles before reaction was 9.5 9.5 μm and that the peak at the smaller size appears and its height becomes larger in PSD curve for the samples after reaction depending on the reaction time, which suggests that ultrasonic attenuation spectroscopy can detect the existence of smaller particles resulting from α-TCP and monitor the change in both volume fraction and size in the suspended particulate system.

In order to confirm the capability of the spectroscopy for detecting smaller particles in suspensions, SEM observation was also performed for the same samples which were used for the PSD measurement. It is found that some amounts of smaller particles were observed for the samples after reaction.

CONCLUSION

Particle size distribution in the suspension of α-TCP particles with 2.5 vol% concentration was determined by being converted from the ultrasonic attenuation spectra. The obtained attenuation spectra shows that the peak at the smaller sized particles becomes larger with increase in the reaction time and the change in particle size distribution were observed in SEM as well. This agreement on PSD demonstrated that ultrasonic attenuation spectroscopy makes it possible to monitor the transformation process of α-TCP in the suspensions.

REFERENCES

1. T.A. Strout, Thesis, The university of Maine (1991).
2. A.K. Holmes, R.E. Challis and D.J. Wedlock, *J Colloid Interface Science,* **168** 339-348 (1994).
3. A.S. Dukhin, P.J. Goetz, *Langmuir,* **12**, 4987-4997 (1996).
4. D. McClements, *Colloids Surf,* **90**, 25-35 (1994).

Bioceramics Volume 11, edited by R. Z. LeGeros and J.P. LeGeros
(Proceedings of the 11th International Symposium on Ceramics in Medicine)
New York, NY, USA, November 1998
© 1998 by World Scientific Publishing Co. Pte. Ltd.

CHARACTERISATION OF HYDROXYAPATITE CRYSTAL GROWN ON SELF ASSEMBLED MONOLAYERS VIA ATOMIC FORCE MICROSCOPY

Necesio Costa[1], Cecilia A. C. Zavaglia[1] and Monica A. Cotta[2]

State University of Campinas [1]Faculty of Mechanical Engineering, Department of Materials Engineering, P.O. Box 6122, Campinas - 13083-970; [2]Physics Institute

ABSTRACT

A biomimetic method to grow a hydroxyapatite (HA) layer on a substrate previously functionalized was employed. Atomic Force Microscopy can be a versatile technique for characterising self-assembly (SA) thin films and hydroxyapatite layers. It is a non-destructive test that enables a rapid investigation of film structures to be achieved with minimal sample preparation.

The goal of this research is to use the technique of protein engineering, such as SA, to manipulate size, shape and biochemistry properties.

Characterisation of lysozyme and saccharose using AFM gave a micellar atomic image. These porous structures can work as canals for leading desirable substances or as structure for the blocking of virus and bacterium. The organic template of lysozyme and saccharose seems to be orientating the nucleation of hydroxyapatite.

KEYWORDS: self-assembly, atomic force microscopy, lysozyme, hydroxyapatite.

INTRODUCTION

Organised films such as Langmuir-Blodgett and Self-Assembly (SA) possess defined sites for nucleation and crystallisation of hydroxyapatite crystals[1]. The use of an organic organised monolayer as a template for crystallising ceramic is a biomimic of calcium carbonate formation in abalone shell. This approach provides to the bioceramic HA better functionality of the bioceramics by improving mechanical properties[2]. Altogether, protein membranes can be assembled with the specific ability to act as a positive response when used as a coating for a prosthetic material, e.g. titanium screw-vent implant. Self-Assembly of lyzosyme and saccharose, a designer biological membrane which destroys bacteria by hydrolysing polysaccharides in their cell walls and/or the carbohydrate group, may serve to act against infection as well as to orient HA crystallisation. The binding of saccharine to lysozyme is very weak and does not induce appreciable modifications in the conformational properties of the enzyme[3].

A key factor to be addressed in biomaterial coating is the release of debris, which results from a poor adherence of the coating to the substrate. HA layer produced by the method adopted in this work is very thin, porous and present good adherence.

Much work has attempted to design functional molecules with the aim of immunology. Song et al.[4] have design a synthetic membrane with alpha-hemolysin structure which organise themselves, or self-assemble, into pores which can control the passage of drugs or other molecules. De Grado et al.[5] have synthesised a template-assembled channel forming using tetraphenylporphyrin system as template. The proteins membrane exhibit single channel conductance, ion selectivity and high thermodynamic stability. These characteristics are very helpful for fighting rejection of prosthetic materials when in the human body.

Atomic Force Microscopy (AFM) can be a versatile technique for characterising biological membranes. The main aim of this work was to observe the build-up of the self-assembled lysozyme layer and to study the possibility of having crystallisation of hydroxyapatite on the top of the self-assembled layer.

EXPERIMENTAL

Chicken egg lysozyme (muramidase, mucopeptide N-acetylmuramoylhydrolase) was obtained from Worthington Biochemical Corporation, saccharose ($C_{12}H_{22}O_{11}$) from Merck, the sulphuric acid, the peroxide hydrogen (H_2O_2), ammonium hydroxide (NH_4OH) from LabSynth. All chemicals were used without further purification. The substrate used were polished wafers of semiconductor grade silicon (111) with a nominal surface orientation of (001). The wafers were cleaned and degreased by washing with detergent, rinsing with deionised water in an ultrasonic bath and then rinsing in isopropyl alcohol. The water used in the experiment was distilled and then purified in a millipore purification unit with a two mixed bed ion-exchange cartridges, an activated carbon cartridge, a 0,2 mm filter.

The substrates were previously hydrophilized by immersing them in a solution of 30 ml of H_2O_2 and 70 ml of H_2SO_4, and heated up to 80°C. Lyzosyme and saccharose were dissolved in water [0.042 g egg lys/30 ml H_2O/ 0.1027 g saccharose] by stirring the solution for twelve hours without having the beaker in contact with magnetic stirer plate. The pH was controlled by adding drops of chloridric acid (HCl - 0.01 N). Protein deposition was carried out at two different pHs (pH 4 and 10). The substrates were immersed in SA solution for 72 hours, followed by washing in milli-Q water.

The HA coating procedure used was similar to that described in the literature[1]. Briefly, the silicon wafer substrates were immersed at 37°C for 10 hours in simulated body fluid[6] followed by washing in milli-Q water.

Topography images of the samples were obtained by using an AFM in non contact mode with microfabricated Si_3N_4 cantilever.

RESULTS AND DISCUSSION

It is well known that the saccharides stabilize the folded conformation of lysozyme with respect to the unfolded one and it has also been proved that the denaturation of lysozyme occurs at higher denaturant concentration when compared to the concentration of saccharose used in these experiments[8]. Sugar does not cause substantial structural changes in the lysozyme. The interaction lysozyme and sugar mainly involves changes by the strength of hydrogen bonds provided by the amino acid residues that are part of the binding sites[3].

Atomic Force Images of topological molecules of lysozyme and saccharose, built-up by the self-assembly technique, is presented in the Figure 1. These topological molecules exhibit a channel structure which is probably constrained by the presence of saccharine for the pH used (pH 4). The electrostatic force among chemical groups leads the molecules to assembly on "micelles". Due to bad rinsing a cluster area is also observed in the Fig. 1, inferior middle part. The molecules self-assemblies do not present a uniform rate of deposition, otherwise all "micelles" would have "micelles" would have the same inclination. Probably the depletion of ions in solution during the process of self-assembly causes this inclination. The inclination of the channel-form molecules give us the false impression that they are assembled as different sizes.

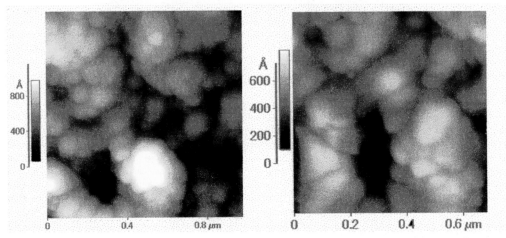

Figure 1 - Atomic Force Microscopy of a self assembled monolayer of .lysozyme and saccharose, a designer biological membrane which destroys bacteria by hydrolysing polysaccharides in their cell walls and/or the carbohydrate group, may also serve to orient HA crystallisation.

Template molecules can play a important role in the molecular recognition at the organic and inorganic interface[8]. The presence of the functional head group at the molecular template presented in Fig. 1, probably an amino acid group, are sites for nucleation and growth of hydroxyapatite crystals when the substrate is immersed in SBF. Figure 2 is an image of hydroxyapatite crystal grown onto self-assembled lysozyme and saccharose. Figure 3 is an 3D image of the hydroxyapatite grown on the same template. As marked in the Figure 3, the hydroxyapatite crystals grow in circles following the pattern of the matrix. Synergically, the self-assembly monolayer acts as an agent against infectious and it also provides the functional head group for hydroxyapatite crystallisation.

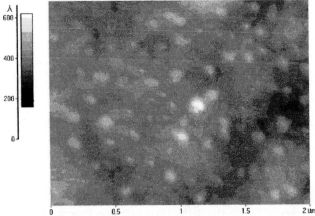

Figure 2 - Atomic Force Image of hydroxyapatite grown on the protein and saccharose template.

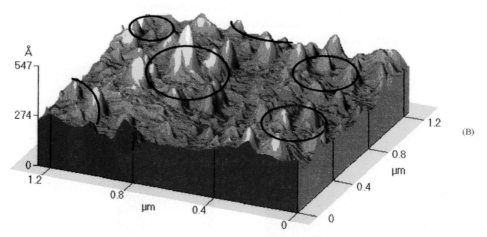

Figure 3 - 3D Atomic Force Image of hydroxyapatite layer deposited on the lysozyme and saccharose self-assembled layer.

CONCLUSIONS

- Under the conditions studied, lysozyme and saccharose self assembles on silicon wafer substrate in a channel-form pattern. These porous structures can work as canals for leading desirable substance or as blocking structure for virus and bacterium.

- The morphology of hydroxyapatite grown on the surface of the lysozyme and saccharose templates suggest that the functional group exerts influence on the nucleation and growth of hydroxyapatite.

REFERENCES

1 - Costa N, Marquis PM, Medical Engineering & Physics, in print.
2 - Wong KKW, Mann S, Curr Opin Colloid, 1998, **3: 1**, 63-68.
3 - Betoluzza A, Bonora S, Fini G, Morelli MA, Canadian Journal of Applied Spectroscopy, 1992; **37: 2**, 58-61.
4 - Song L, Hobaugh MR, Shustak C, Cheley S, Bayley H, Gouaux JE, Science, 1996, **274** ,1859-1866.
5 - De Grado WF, Wassermann ZR and Lear JD, Science, 1989, **243**, 622-628.
6 -Yan WQ, Nakamura T, Kawanabe K, et al. Biomaterials, SEP 1997, **18: (17)**, 1185-1190.
7 - Scheinblatt M, Biopolimers, 1989, **28**, 1913.
8 - Mutter, M, Tuchscherer, G, CMLS, 1997, **53:11/12**, 851-863.

ACKNOWLEDMENTS

The authors would like to thank the "Fundação de Amparo à Pesquisa do Estado de São Paulo - FAPESP" for the financial support of this research project and the CAPES for providing travelling funds.

Bioceramics Volume 11, edited by R. Z. LeGeros and J.P. LeGeros
(Proceedings of the 11th International Symposium on Ceramics in Medicine)
New York, NY, USA, November 1998
© 1998 by World Scientific Publishing Co. Pte. Ltd.

DEVELOPMENT OF A NOVEL ENSTATITE GLASS-CERAMIC BIOMATERIAL

T. Buckland, S. M. Best, K.-A. Hing and W. Bonfield

IRC in Biomedical Materials, Queen Mary and Westfield College, Mile End Road, London E1 4NS

ABSTRACT

Glass-ceramics offer great potential both as bioactive and "bioinert" implant materials. The effect of compositional changes on the crystalline phases precipitated and microstructure of enstatite ($MgSiO_3$) glass-ceramics has been studied. The principle phases precipitated from MgO-SiO_2-Na_2O (MSN) parent glasses were enstatite as the major phase, with cristobalite as the secondary phase. Increasing the amount of Na_2O present in the parent glass resulted in an increase in the proportion of cristobalite precipitated. The phase composition was also strongly affected by the additive used, NaF, resulting in proportionally more enstatite than the TiO_2. The additives strongly influenced the microstructure observed. The TiO_2 glasses produced a fine grain size ($\approx 10\mu m$) with little residual glass and an acicular fracture surface. The NaF glasses produced large ($>100\mu m$), spherulitic grains with interstitial porosity. An MTT assay demonstrated that the TiO_2 containing compositions were not cytotoxic.

KEYWORDS Enstatite, Glass-ceramics

INTRODUCTION

The need for the production of a high toughness, bioinert, easily processable ceramic biomaterial has been identified, with the intention of replacing small joints. The use of a glass-ceramic was proposed due to their ability to be cast to near-net shape and to be crystallised to near 100% densities without the presence of inherent porosity. Of the candidate materials considered, enstatite, $MgSiO_3$, was chosen as a promising material due to its relatively high observed fracture toughness[1]. The effect of using a network modifier on the phase composition and the processing has been studied, as has the use of different additives, TiO_2 and NaF, in order to promote bulk nucleation and crystallisation.

MATERIALS AND METHODS

Glass precursor powders, including the network modifier (Na_2O) and the additives (TiO_2 or NaF) were mixed in a pestle and mortar and were then transferred to a platinum crucible at 1550°C for four hours with intermediate mixing in order to form the parent glasses.

The glasses were cast into a mould at 600°C to form a cylindrical ingot. The castings were annealed for one hour, cooled to room temperature and sectioned into disks using a diamond saw, before being crystallised at an appropriate temperature determined by differential thermal analysis (DTA, Setaram Labsys DSC/DTA 1600). The percentage change from the design composition was calculated from X-ray fluorescence spectroscopy (XRF, Phillips PW1606 spectrometer) of the parent glasses, both for the first and second casts from the melts, while the phase composition of the crystallised glasses was determined using X-ray diffraction (XRD, Siemens D5000 diffractometer with Cu-K_α radiation).

Nucleation and crystallisation studies were performed out on a selectively quenched example of each additive-containing glass. Samples were polished and etched in 48% hydrofluoric acid before being examined in a scanning electron microscope (SEM, Jeol WinSEM6300), which was also used to examine the fractured surfaces of the materials.

An MTT test was performed according to the method devised by Mosmann[2] to assess the cellular viability of MSN+TiO_2 (MSTN) substrates in comparison with hydroxyapatite and a toxic PVC control.

RESULTS

The amount of Na_2O contained in the precursors made a significant difference to the ability of the glasses to be formed by pouring; the greater the amount, the easier the casting process. However, at the higher Na_2O concentrations, undesirable phases were precipitated upon crystallisation.

Figures 1 and 2 show the percentage change from the design compositions measured via XRF for a series of MSTN glasses and the first and second castings, respectively. XRD analysis showed that there were two major phases precipitated, enstatite ($MgSiO_3$) and cristobalite (SiO_2) in all of the glass compositions. The proportions of the phases varied with the additive used as shown in Figures 3 and 4 where the relative intensities of the most intense peaks of each phase are shown for both the TiO_2 and NaF glass-ceramics. XRD results also demonstrated that there was an increase in the amount of enstatite present in the MSTN glass-ceramics when second casting ingots were crystallised, at the expense of the cristobalite present.

Nucleation studies demonstrated that the TiO_2 glasses produced small (<1μm) particles within the glassy matrix (Figure 5) followed by full crystallisation via spherulitic-type crystals in the order of 10μm in diameter, with very little residual glass between the crystals, as shown in Figure 6. The NaF containing glasses transformed very abruptly from fully amorphous to partially crystalline, via the rapid growth of spherulitic-type crystals from very few nucleation sites, until

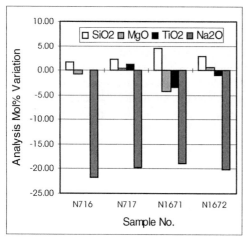

Figure 1: The variation from design composition (by XRF) for four MSTN glasses.

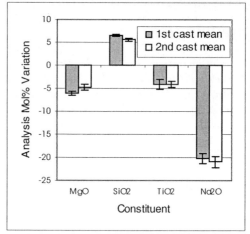

Figure 2: The average and standard deviation of the percentage compositional variation by XRF in first and second castings.

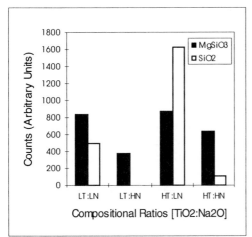

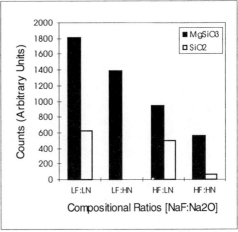

Figure 3: The intensity of the major crystalline peaks in MSTN glasses – L = Low, H = High, T = TiO$_2$, N = Na$_2$O, by XRD.

Figure 4: The intensity of the major crystalline peaks in MSFN glasses – L = Low, H = High, F = NaF, N = Na$_2$O, by XRD.

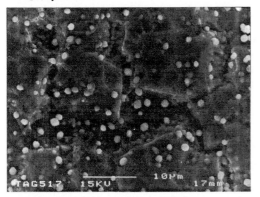

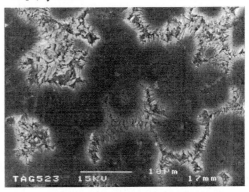

Figure 5: SEM micrograph showing phase separation during the crystallisation of MSTN glass; 820°C quench.

Figure 6: SEM micrograph showing fully crystalline MSTN glass-ceramic; quench after 90 min. dwell.

the final microstructure consisted of large >100µm crystals surrounded by areas of amorphous glass, as shown in Figure 7. The fracture surfaces showed that, although the crack path passed around the grains within the glass-ceramics produced, the fracture surface was characterised by a very fine splintering, on a scale of <1µm.

The MTT results for a TiO$_2$ containing glass-ceramic are shown in Figure 8, along with a PVC control and a pure hydroxyapatite sample. They show that the MSTN glass-ceramic has a similar cellular viability to that of pure hydroxyapatite.

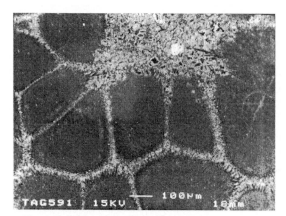

Figure 7: SEM micrograph showing large enstatite grains with an amorphous glassy region (top center) in MSFN glass-ceramic; quench after 90 min. dwell.

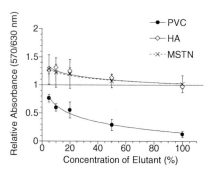

Figure 8: MTT data for MSTN, HA and PVC, showing that the cellular viability of the MSTN glass-ceramics is comparable with that of HA.

DISCUSSION

This study has investigated the variables which affect the production of enstatite glass-ceramics. It has demonstrated that there is an optimal level of Na_2O addition which is a compromise between adequate castability and desired phase composition of the final glass-ceramics. TiO_2 included in the glasses is much more efficient at bulk nucleation of the glass-ceramics, developing a finer microstructure via a phase separation mechanism. The presence of large amounts of Na_2O leads to a residual interstitial SiO_2-Na_2O glass after crystallisation. Finally, enstatite has been precipitated as the major phase and the TiO_2 containing compositions have been shown to have a similar cytotoxicity to that of pure hydroxyapatite.

CONCLUSIONS

The level of Na_2O present is important to the processability of the glass and affects the phase composition of the crystallised glass-ceramic. TiO_2 has been shown to be a more efficient nucleation agent than NaF in these glass systems.

ACKNOWLEDGEMENTS

The support of the EPSRC and De Puy International (UK) Ltd. for the IRC and this project is gratefully acknowledged.

REFERENCES

1.   Beall G.H., *Journal of Non-Crystalline Solids*, 1984; **129**, **3-4**: 317-359.
2.   Mosmann T., *Journal of Immunological Methods*, 1983; **65**: 55.

Bioceramics Volume 11, edited by R. Z. LeGeros and J.P. LeGeros
(Proceedings of the 11th International Symposium on Ceramics in Medicine)
New York, NY, USA, November 1998
© 1998 by World Scientific Publishing Co. Pte. Ltd.

FABRICATION OF CALCIUM PHOSPHATE BASED CERAMICS WITH CONTROLLED POROSITY FOR BONE SCAFFOLDS

Rajesh K. Panda, Patrick Teung, Stephen C. Danforth, and Ahmad Safari

Department of Ceramic and Materials Engineering
Rutgers University, Piscataway, NJ 08855

ABSTRACT

Recent developments in porous calcium phosphate (CaP) based bioceramics appear very promising because of the possibility they offer in promoting the growth of bone tissue. Many researchers have emphasized the importance of the pore size and have claimed that continuous pore channels between 100 and 500 μm are an essential requirement for osteoconduction. In traditional ceramic processing techniques including replamineform, with an increase in the pore size and percent porosity, the compressive strength of the ceramic is observed to fall drastically. Solid Freeform Fabrication (SFF) is a novel prototyping/manufacturing technique that provides a way for making a variety of complex shaped parts. In this study Fused Deposition Modeling (FDM^{TM}) was used to make porous bioceramic scaffolds by a lost mold technique. A high solids loading, water based ceramic slurry was developed for this process. CaP based ceramic structures with 30-60 vol.% macroporosity, with uniform and three dimensionally continuous pore channels varying in size from 200-700 μm have been fabricated. Some of the critical issues in slurry development and the formation of porous structures are discussed in this paper.

KEYWORDS: calcium phosphate, porous, scaffold, honeycomb, solid freeform fabrication

INTRODUCTION

Currently, bioceramics for bone replacement/augmentation consist mostly of ceramic coatings on metal implants. While the coatings do improve the bonding of the metal implant to the bone, there is a desire to produce implants out of a material more closely matching the mechanical properties of bone. Hydroxyapatite (HAp, $Ca_{10}(PO_4)_6 (OH)_2$), and other calcium phosphate (CaP) based ceramics fulfill this latest trend and have become the materials of choice. The design of porous CaP ceramics with large and continuous pore channels is an important criterion for use in clinical applications. Many traditional techniques, including replamineform, gaseous reactions, and variations of the lost mold method have been used to make ceramics with porosities reaching 70 vol.%. [2] However, they show very poor mechanical properties because of uncontrolled and non-uniform pore sizes[3,4].

Solid Freeform Fabrication (SFF) is a novel prototyping/manufacturing technique used for making polymer, ceramic and metal parts without the help of any hard tooling, dies or molds. All the SFF techniques use a CAD data description file as input, and build the final part layer by layer on a fixtureless platform moving along the Z- axis. Hence, the SFF techniques provide ways for making a variety of complex shaped parts or molds which are difficult, costly or sometimes impossible to make by conventional techniques[1].

This research project utilizes the flexibility provided by the SFF techniques to build porous hydroxyapatite structures for bone prostheses. The emphasis has been on getting a high solids loaded ceramic slurry to fabricate high strength scaffolds with pore channels of varying size, shape, distribution and connectivity. The critical issues in slurry development and the fabrication of porous structures with controlled pore network are discussed in this paper.

EXPERIMENTAL

The porous structures were created by combining the lost mold method with SFF techniques. First, sacrificial wax molds having a negative of the desired structure were produced by Fused Deposition Modeling (FDM[TM]). The wax molds were infiltrated with a water based CaP ceramic slurry. The slurry fills the open spaces in the wax. Upon drying, the molds were burned out during the early portion of the binder burnout (BBO) step. After BBO was complete, the CaP ceramic structures were sintered at high temperatures.

For the FDM™ process, commercially available Stratasys™ Investment Casting Wax (ICW-06) filaments were used to make the polymer molds. A high solids loading water based CAP ceramic slurry was specially developed to infiltrate the sacrificial wax molds. The ceramic powder was characterized to determine the particle size distribution, surface area, and morphology. It was calcined to decrease the surface area and then mixed with water, dispersant and antifoaming agent to form a ceramic suspension. Molds were infiltrated with the ceramic suspension and dried overnight in an ambient atmosphere. After drying, the green ceramic structures were kept on a fine zirox powder bed inside an alumina crucible and sintered at 1125°C for 4 hours.

RESULTS AND DISCUSSION

In an earlier paper on this work[6], a 38 vol.% water based calcium phosphate ceramic suspension was used to fabricate a variety of porous scaffolds with very uniform pore channels, including 3-D Honeycomb structures with interconnected and continuous macroporosity in all three orthogonal directions. Figure 1 (a) shows an isometric view of a sintered CaP 3-D Honeycomb structure with cylindrical pores. This scaffold is comprised of straight continuous pore channels of ~ 240 μm diameter propagating along the X, Y, and Z directions. The structure had a total open macroporosity of 56 vol.%. The biggest advantage of using SFF for making scaffolds is the ability to fabricate a desired pore network, which is impossible to accomplish by traditional ceramic processing techniques. For example, researchers have shown that the orientation and geometry of the pore channels greatly influences bone growth and osteogenesis[5]. Figure 1 (b) shows the top view of a calcium phosphate 3-D oriented Honeycomb structure with pore channels oriented 45° to one another. The angular orientation and other parameters, including pore size, shape and wall widths for each layer can be easily changed by incorporating the appropriate parameters in the software program. To test the versatility of the process, computer aided design (CAD) files of actual bone shapes with irregular outlines were used to make many porous CaP specimens of different sizes. Figure 1 (c) shows sintered CaP structures having lengths of about 7.5 cm and 5.5 cm and thickness of 1.5 and 0.5 cm respectively.

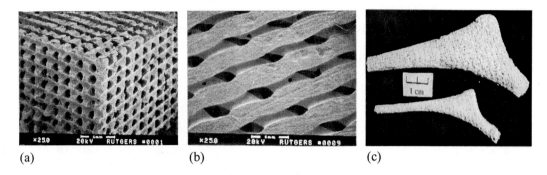

(a)   (b)   (c)

Figure 1: (a) Isometric view of a porous CaP 3-D Honeycomb scaffold with continuous interconnected porosity in three orthogonal directions, (b) top view of scaffold with pore channels oriented 45° to one another and (c) a photograph showing porous scaffolds in the shape of a bone.

The pore networks in the designs shown in Figure 1 should provide good mechanical stability to the scaffolds. However, the ceramic walls of all these sintered CaP structures had a density of only ~ 85% of the theoretical value. Micropores varying in size from 0.5-15 microns could be observed in the sintered specimens, as seen on the polished surface of a bulk cast piece in Figure 2 (a). The appearance of micropores in the samples was attributed to an irregular ceramic powder morphology and presence of agglomerates in the ceramic slurry, which in turn led to a low solids loading of 38 vol.%. This problem could reduce the mechanical strength in spite of the ability of SFF techniques to make a sturdy and mechanically stable 3-D Honeycomb design.

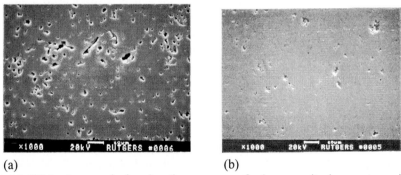

(a)   (b)

Figure 2: (a) SEM micrograph showing the presence of microporosity in a cast specimen that was made from the old powder (source 1), and (b) the polished surface of the sample obtained from new powder (source 2), at the same magnification.

In order to increase the solids loading in the ceramic slurry, CaP powder from a new source was used. The as received powder (from source 2) was spray dried and had a very high specific surface area of 55 m^2/g. It was calcined at 925°C for two hours to lower the surface area to 2.57 m^2/g. The calcined powder was mixed with an appropriate quantity of water, dispersant and defoaming agent and then ball milled for two hours to break any agglomerates. Because of the high quality powder and improved powder processing, the viscosity of the 38 vol.% loaded slurry of the source 2 powder was much lower than the old composition with the same loading (Figure 3 (a)). A 52 vol.% CaP slurry with a workable viscosity was produced for infiltration into the molds. The high powder loading ensured the formation scaffolds with a higher macroporosity and good surface finish, as shown in Figure 3 (b). This 3-D Honeycomb structure had pore channels of 360 μm and a total macroporosity of 60 vol.%. The density of the walls of this structure was ~ 96 % of the theoretical value. The micrograph of a sintered polished surface from this specimen also showed very little microporosity. Hence, by combining a robust design with high density ceramic walls it is possible to make scaffolds with high mechanical integrity.

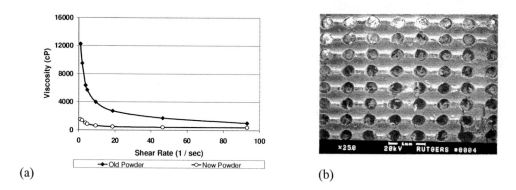

(a)   (b)

Figure 3: (a) Plot showing the viscosity as a function of the shear rate for 38 vol.% loaded CaP slurries obtained from the old and new powder, and (b) photograph showing the side view of a sintered 3-D Honeycomb scaffold obtained from the new powder.

CONCLUSIONS AND FUTURE WORK

In this work, many porous CaP 3-D Honeycomb structures with controlled porosity and pore channel orientation were fabricated by combining the lost mold and FDM^{TM} SFF techniques. Porous scaffolds having the outline of an actual bone and measuring as long as 7.5 cm were also made. The solids loading was enhanced from 38 to 52 vol.% by using a better powder and improved powder processing method. The compressive strengths of the structures described here are being determined at present.

ACKNOWLEDGMENTS

The authors would like to acknowledge the financial support provided by the Johnson and Johnson Corporate Biomaterials Center. They are also thankful to I. Cornejo, T. McNulty, and N. Spratford for help in the processing of the ceramic structures.

REFERENCES

1. Bourell DL, Beamen JJ, Marcus HL, Barlow JW, SFF Proceedings 1990: 1-7
2. Liu DM, Key Engineering Materials 1996; 115: 209-232
3. Liu DM, Ceramics International 1997; 23: 135-139
4. Le Huec JC, Schaeverbeke T, Faber J, Le Reballer A, Biomaterials 1995; 16: 113-118
5. Magan A, Ripamonti U, J Craniofacial Surgery; 7: 71-78
6. Panda RK, Teung P, Danforth SC, Safari A, Submitted to Biomaterials, February 1998

Bioceramics Volume 11, edited by R. Z. LeGeros and J.P. LeGeros
(Proceedings of the 11th International Symposium on Ceramics in Medicine)
New York, NY, USA, November 1998

EFFECT OF Y₂O₃ ADDITIVE ON MICROSTRUCTURE AND SINTERING OF HYDROXYAPATITE

K. Shiba[1], A. Nakahira[1] S. Yamaguchi[2], K. Sakamoto[3], K. Kijima[1] and M. Okazaki[4]

[1]Dept. Chem. and Mater. Eng., Kyoto Institute of Tech., Matsugasaki, Sakyo-ku, Kyoto 606-8585, Japan, [2] ISIR, Osaka Univ., 8-1 Mihogaoka, Ibaraki, Osaka 567-0121, Japan, [3] Osaka Sangyo Univ., 3-1-1 Nakagaito, Daito-shi, Osaka 574-8530, Japan, [4] Dept. of Dentistry, Osaka Univ., 1-1 Yamadaoka, Suita, Osaka 567-0101, Japan.

ABSTRACT

The Effect of rare earth oxide 1-4 wt % Y₂O₃ on sintering behavior and microstructure of hydroxyapatite was investigated Sintering was done at the temperature rang of 1100 to 1200°C for 2h of holding time in air atmosphere by pressureless sintering technique. The composition of the sintered bodies were confirmed by X -ray diffraction. The lattice parameters decreased with the increase of Y₂O₃ as an additive. Hydroxyapatite with 1wt. % Y₂O₃ sintered at 1200°C in air atmosphere showed 98% of the relative density. From the microstructure observations by SEM for hydroxyapatite with Y₂O₃ additive, it was found that addition of Y₂O₃ into hydroxyapatite prevented from grain growth and the densification of hydroxyapatite.

KEYWORDS: Hydroxyapatite, sintering, microstructure, yttrium oxide, additive

INTRODUCTION

Apatite is the basic calcium compound, which has the chemical formula $A_{10}(MO_4)_6(X)_2$ belonging to the hexagonal system with the space group $P63/M^{1,2}$. The lattice sites of A, M, and X were easily substituted by various ions. By using these natures, many studies on apatite ceramics has been done for many practical application in medical and other function field Recently it was reported that apatite ceramics were applicable to electric devices such as various alcoholic and C0₂. gas-sensors by adding various rare earth oxide,'. Nagai et al.[3] succeeded to measure the electric conductivity of hydroxyapatite and reported that the mechanism of electric conductivity for hydroxyapatite was derived .from the diffusion of OH⁻. Owada et al[4] accommodated some cations in solid solution into the apatite structure and evaluated the electric properties and advocated that O^{2-} and proton except OH⁻ could become electric career in the specific system. Therefore, in this study, we especially tried to sinter hydroxyapatite with added Y₂O₃. The relation between sintering behavior and microstructure of hydroxyapatite with Y₂O₃ was examined.

EXPERIMENTAL PROCEDURE

In this study, the starting material was hydroxyapatite (Taihei Chemical Industries Co ., purity > 99.965%) and Y₂O₃ (Shinetsu Chemical Ind., approximately 1-2 μm of particle size). Several properties of hydroxyapatite as a starting powder are shown in Figure 1. Hydroxyapatite crystals were rod-like, 5 μm in length and 1um in diameter. Particle size distribution analyses show about 10μm (see part B of Figure 1) agglomeration of 1-4wt. % Y₂O₃ was added to hydroxyapatite as an additive, mixed with alcohol by ball mill for 6hrs. , The mixed slurry was dried by an evaporator. The dried powders were granulated by a mortar and screened through a 150 μm sieve. The powders obtained were pressed with uniaxial pressing at 50MPa, and then treated with CIP at 200MPa.

This sample was sintered at (1000-1200°C,) in air atmosphere. The heating and cooling speed was 5°C /min, and holding time was for 2hrs.

Density of the sintered bodies was measured using Archimes method in toluene. Identification of the hydroxyapatite with 1-4wt% Y_2O_3 phase was made by X-ray diffraction (XRD), and their lattice constants were measured The microstructure observation of the sintered body was performed by SEM(Hitachi, S-800).

RESULTS AND DISCUSSION

X-ray diffraction patterns of hydroxyapatite with 0-4wt% Y_2O_3 sintered at 1200°C are shown in Figure 2. The diffraction peaks for all samples nearly corresponded with those peaks from JCPDS card of hydroxyapatite. It was found that the component of hydroxyapatite with 0-4wt% Y_2O_3 sintered at 1150°C (not shown here) and 1200°C was hydroxyapatite and no other phases were detected, although small peak shift was observed for hydroxyapatite with 1-4 wt. % Y_2O_3 sintered at 1200°C.

The dependence Of Y_2O_3 additive on lattice parameter of hydroxyapatite with added 1 wt. % Y_2O_3 (a -axis and c-axis) of hydroxyapatite is shown in Figure 3. The lattice constants were not significantly changed below 1150°C. However, the lattice parameters for hydroxyapatite with 1 wt. % Y_2O_3 sintered at 1100 and 1150°C decreased. On the other hand, both a-axis and c-axis parameters of hydroxyapatite with 1-4 wt. % Y_2O_3 sintered at 1200°C with increasing Y_2O_3 content. These parameter changes suggest that Y^{3+} ion of Y_2O_3 were partially replaced with Ca^{2+} ion at A-site of hydroxyapatite sintered at 1200°C, as reported by Yamashita et al[4].

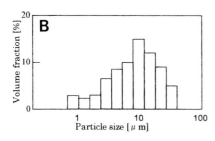

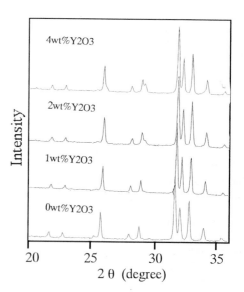

Figure 1. SEM image of (A) hydroxyapatite and (B) particle size distribution.

Figure 2. XRD patterns of hydroxyapatite with 0-4 wt % Y_2O_3 sintered at 1200°C.

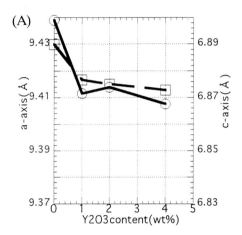 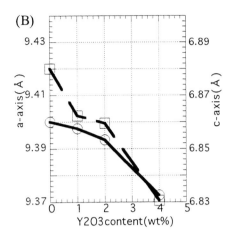

Figure 3. Dependence of Y_2O_3 additive on lattice parameter of hydroxyapatite: (A) a-axis and (B) c-axis

The effects of the Y_2O_3 content on the density for monolithic and hydroxyapatite with Y_2O_3 sintered at several temperatures was examined. The densities of hydroxyapatite at 1100°C indicated about 2.6g/cm³, about 80% of theoretical density. The monolithic hydroxyapatite with about 90% of theoretical density was obtained when sintered at 1150°C. Even sintered at 1200°C, monolithic 3.0g/cm³ hydroxyapatite indicated 3.0g/cm (95%) of density The addition of 1-4 wt. % Y_2O_3 to hydroxyapatite inhibited the sinterability of hydroxyapatite when sintered at 1100 C. However, sintering temperature above 1150 C, (the density of hydroxyapatite with l-4 wt % Y_2O_3) increased. For hydroxyapatite with 2wt.% Y_2O_3 sintered at 1200°C by pressureless sintering, the relative density over 97% was achieved. It was found that the addition of Y_2O_3 into hydroxyapatite enhances the densification of hydroxyapatite

Figure 4 shows the SEM images of hydroxyapatite with 0, 1 and 4wt% Y_2O_3 sintered at 1200 C. SEM image of monolithic hydroxyapatite sintered at 1200°C showed the mixture of equiaxed grains 10- 20 μm in diameter, and elongated grain with 30 μm in length and 10 um in diameter with 10-20 μm in diameter (Figure 5). On the other hand, hydroxyapatite with 4wt% Y_2O_3 showed the relatively dense microstructure, which was composed of equiaxed grains with 10-20μm in diameter and pores about 3 μm in diameter. The incorporation of Y_2O_3 as an additive into hydroxyapatite matrix hindered the grain growth of hydroxyapatite (Figure 4).

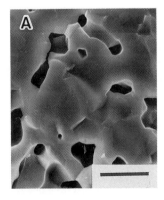 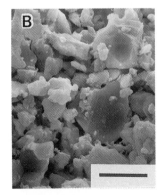 

Figure 4. SEM images of hydroxyapatite with: (A) 0 wt. %, (B) 1 wt. % and (C) 4-wt. % sintered at 1200°C. Bars show 20 μm

SUMMARY

Hydroxyapatite with Y_2O_3 as an additive (1-4wt.%) was prepared by the pressureless sintering technique. Dependence of Y_2O_3 additive on the sintering behavior and microstructures of hydroxyapatite was investigated. The addition Of Y_2O_3 enhanced the sinterability of hydroxyapatite over 1150°C and below 1100°C inhibited the densification of hydroxyapatite. The solid solution of Y^{3+} into hydroxyapatite was successfully made and Y content was controlled by initial Y_2O_3 content.

REFERENCES

1. Hench L L, *J. Am. Ceram. Soc.,* 1991; 74: 1487-1510.
2. Komine Y, Sato K, Fine Ceramics FC Report, 1983; 1: 4-10.
3. Nagai M, Kawai N, Iwanaga Y, Tsuruta Y, Murata Y, Nishino T, Ann Meeting Ceram. Soc. Jpn., 1985; 2J30.
4. Owada H, Yamashita K, Umegaki T, Kanazawa T, Nagai M., *Yogyo-k-yokai-shi,* 1986; 94: 837-841.
5. Yamashita K, Owada H, Nakagawa H, Umegaki T, Kanazawa T, *J. Amer. Ceram. Soc. ,* 1986; 69: 590-594.

Bioceramics Volume 11, edited by R. Z. LeGeros and J.P. LeGeros
(Proceedings of the 11th International Symposium on Ceramics in Medicine)
New York, NY, USA, November 1998
© 1998 by World Scientific Publishing Co. Pte. Ltd.

TWO NEW ROUTES FOR PRODUCING POROUS BIOACTIVE CERAMICS: POLYURETHANE PRECURSORS AND MICROWAVE BAKING

A.S. Ribeiro[1] , P.B. Malafaya,[1] R.L. Reis[1,2]

[1] INEB - Institute for Biomedical Engineering, Biomaterials Laboratory, Rua do Campo Alegre, 823, 4150 Porto, Portugal; [2] Dept. of Metallurgical and Materials Science Eng., Fac. Eng. U. Porto, Rua dos Bragas, 4099 Porto Codex, Portugal

ABSTRACT

There is a need for the development of processing routes for obtaining porous bioactive ceramics with an adequate combination of mechanical properties, associated to a suitable micro and macroporosity. The present work describes two innovative processing routes for producing bioactive porous ceramics. One is based on the use of a typical polyurethane (PU) foaming reaction to build up the original porous structure. The PU is then burn out and the porous ceramic structure obtained by sintering. The second route is based on a microwave baking process using a powder, containing corn starch, sodium carbonate and sodium pyrophosphate, that is added to the bioactive ceramic. The green bodies are then sintered.

By using the developed routes it was possible to produce hydroxylapatite or β-tri-calcium phosphate porous materials, combining and adequate micro and macroporosity with a mechanical performance matching the compressive behaviour of human cancellous bone. The developed porous bioactive ceramics present a combination of mechanical properties and morphological features that may be very useful in bone replacement and drug delivery applications, or to be used as tissue engineering scaffolds.

KEYWORDS: Hydroxylapatite, porous ceramics, processing, bioactive, tissue engineering

INTRODUCTION

Hydroxylapatite (HA) is the major mineral component of the inorganic phase of bone tissues, playing a key role on the calcification and resorption processes.[1] Current research on HA involves several distinct aspects, such as preparation methods (that allow for a wide variety of properties and clinical applications) and the study of the interface and bonding mechanisms with the surrounding tissues. HA and other bioactive porous ceramics have shown to be very useful *in vivo*, due to the similarity of their microstructure with that of cancellous bone.[2-6] It has been shown that a porous material allows for the ingrowth of osteoblasts[7] leading to the formation of osteoids, that eventually would mineralize within the HA pores. During this process, HA implants are resorbed by the organism. An adequate porous structure of the implant allows the angiogenesis to occur in order to promote bone and implant vascularization.[7] The optimum porous size to induce bone growth, and the consequent resorption, is reported as ranging from 100 to 200 μm.[8] Typically, cells tend to form around the edges and span across the diameter of the pores.

The main drawback of porous ceramics is their poor mechanical properties, which deeply narrows their applicability. In order to allow for a wider application of this class of materials, it is necessary to overcome this problem. Bearing this objective in mind, and in an attempt to understand and predict both the mechanical and the biological properties of this type of materials, the study of their microstructure must be a priority. In fact, the porosity is one of the most important parameters to control, and can be divided into micro and macroporosity. Microporosity is defined by the spacial gaps left among particles after complete bonding with one another, as a result of the sintering process. Usually, the original bioactive ceramics particle size is in the micron scale and, as a consequence, the micropores will be of the same dimensional order. These micropores (diameter < 10μm) allow for the circulation of the fluids within them, being determinant for the dissolution and degradation rate of the bioceramics.[9] Macroporosity consists of pores which may host cells, being therefore able to induce bone ingrowth.[9-11] The pore size cannot be exaggerated, and there is a point at which the material mechanical strength becomes insufficient, excluding any practical application.

The present work describes two innovative and simple routes for obtaining porous bioactive materials combining adequate micro and macroporosity with promising mechanical properties.

MATERIALS AND METHODS

In this research, pure HA powders with an average particle size of 6.5 μm (laser granulometry), from Plasma Biotal, Tideswell, UK, were used for producing the porous materials. The first processing route consisted in mixing two liquids, a polyol and an isocyanate (1:1 v/v) at 90 °C, into which the HA powder was added in amounts up to 75% by weight (wt) of the total formulation. When the two liquids were mixed, an expansion reaction was generated and the HA was incorporated in the typical morphology of the resulting polyurethane (PU) foam. The samples were then sintered at 1200 °C for 5h after a previous stage of 1h at 600 °C (to burn out of the PU precursor).

The second processing route consisted in the utilisation of a commercially available baking powder (BP), from Nabisco Iberia Ltd., Barcelona, Spain, containing corn starch, sodium pyrophosphate and sodium carbonate. The baking powder was mixed with HA in amounts ranging from 10 to 50% wt. Water was then added until a consistent slurry dispersion was obtained. The mixture was then processed in a microwave oven. The furnace power set-up and the treatment time was optimized. Finally, samples were sintered using the same thermal cycle referred to above.

The produced samples were characterized morphologically by scanning electronic microscopy (SEM), the chemical composition was evaluated by electron dispersive spectroscopy (EDS), X-ray fluorescence (XRF) and electronic probe microanalysis (EPMA), the resulting mineral phases were identified by X-ray diffraction (XRD), and the respective density and compression strength were measured. The compression tests were carried out in an Instron 4505 universal mechanical testing machine. The cross-head speed was 2 mm/min, and tests were carried out until failure, or up to a maximum reduction of 60 % of the original sample height.

RESULTS AND DISCUSSION

When using the procedure based on the PU precursor, porous ceramics with macropores presenting a diameter ranging from 600 to 1200 μm were obtained. Interconnecting micropores with 3-15 μm in diameter were found between the grains in the macropores. These porous ceramics present a density of about 0.30 g/cm³. The structure of a typical porous ceramic produced from this technique is shown in Figure 1. It is possible to see that individual HA grains were fused together at the grain boundaries during the sintering process.

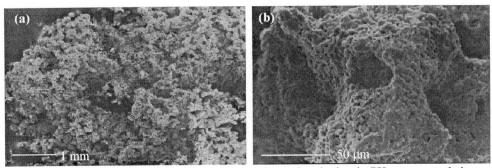

Figure 1. SEM photographs of sintered porous ceramics produced using the PU precursor technique: (a) magnification: 50x; (b) magnification: 500x.

After sintering, the PU precursor was completely burned out leaving no trace elements (originally present in the polyol additives) in the final ceramic structure, as shown by EDS analysis (Fig. 2). XRD analysis confirmed that the porous ceramics were composed of pure HA. An almost perfect match with the standard HA JCPDS file was obtained. EDS, EPMA and XRF analysis indicated that the typical Ca/P ratio was not affected by the developed procedure.

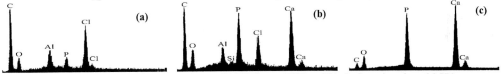

Figure 2. EDS spectra of: (a) PU precursor; (b) PU foam+75% wt HA, before sintering; (c) HA porous ceramic, after sintering.

The microwave baking method generated porous ceramics with an adequate micro (5-20μm) and macroporosity (100-500μm). Densities ranging from 0.40 to 0.70 g/cm^3 were obtained. The best mechanical results have been achieved for the porous materials containing 10% wt of BP: a modulus of 525 MPa and a compression strength of 54 MPa, which are similar to cancellous bone.[12] With increasing amounts of BP the compression properties tend to decrease. Figure 3 presents SEM photographs that show the typical morphology of these porous structures.

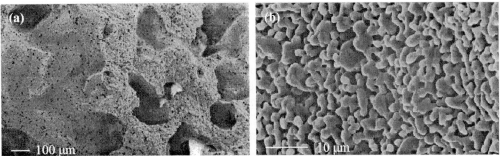

Figure 3. SEM photographs of sintering porous ceramics produced using the microwave baking method: (a) magnification: 50x; (b) magnification: 2000x.

The developed materials exhibit a morphology combining micro and macroporosity (Fig. 3a). At higher magnifications, fused together HA grains are clear (Fig. 3b). This structure is responsible for the good mechanical properties that could be obtained.

EPMA and XRF analysis were used to determine the chemical composition of HA, BP and the porous ceramics obtained before and after sintering. The incorporation of some sodium, coming from BP powder, in the final products was detected. The presence of BP lead to the unstabilisation of the HA sintering mechanism, generating β-tri-calcium phosphate (TCP) and lead to the incorporation of important residual amounts of sodium carbonate and sodium pyrophosphate in the final porous ceramic, as identified by XRD analysis (Fig. 4 a and b). This unstabilisation was also detected in a previous work[13] for systems containing HA and a bioactive glass (i.e. for a liquid phase sintering mechanism). TCP porous ceramics may be advantageous, for the aimed applications, due to their *in-vivo* degradation and resorbability.[5,6]

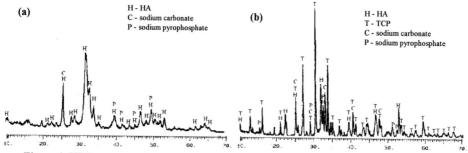

Figure 4. XRD spectras of porous ceramic produced using the microwave baking method:
(a) before sintering; (b) after sintering.

Two innovative methodologies for producing porous bioactive ceramic materials were developed. The developed materials present an interesting combination of morphological and mechanical properties, that may find uses in cancellous bone replacement (filling of bone defects) and drug delivery applications, as well as tissue engineering scaffolds.

REFERENCES

1. Fawcett DW, *A Textbook of Histology*. London: W.B. Company, 1986
2. Holmes RE, Buchholz RW, Mooney V. *J Bone Joint Surg* 1986; **68A**: 904-910
3. Hing KA, Best SM, Tanner KE, Bonfied W, Revell PA. *J Mater Sci: Mater in Med*; 1997; **8**: 731-736
4. Kawanabe K, Okada Y, Iida H, Nakamura T. In: Sedel L, Rey C, ed. *Bioceramics 10*. Oxford: Elsevier Science, 1997: 87-90
5. Lu JX, Flautre B, Anselme K, Gallur A, Descamps M, Thierry B, Hardouin P. In: Sedel, L, Rey, C, ed. *Bioceramics 10*, Oxford: Elsevier Science, 1997: 583-586
6. Ioku K, Goto S, Kurosawa H, Shibuya K, Yokozeki H, Hayashi T, Nakagama T. In: Kokubo,T, Nakamura T, Miyaji F, ed. *Bioceramics 9,* Oxford: Elsevier Science, 1996: 201-204
7. Ball M, Sepulveda P, Downes S, Binner J, 3rd Ceramics, Cells and Tissues Meeting 1996
8. Uchida A, Nade SM, McCartney ER, Ching W. *J Bone Joint Surg* 1984; **66A**: 269-275.
9. Trécant M, Delécrin J, Royer J, Goyenvalle E, Daculsi G. *Clin Materials* 1994; **15**: 233-240.
10. Hench LL In: Ratner BD, Hoffman AS, Schoen FJ, Lemons JE, ed. *Biomaterials Science*, New York: Academic Press, 1996: 73-83.
11. Ravaglioli A, Krajewky A. *Bioceramics*. London: Chapman & Hall, 1992
12. Linde F, Hvid I, Pongsoipetch B. *J Orthop Res* 1989; 7: 432-439
13. Santos JD, Knowles JC, Reis RL, Monteiro FJ, Hastings GW. *Biomaterials* 1994; **15**: 5-10

Bioceramics Volume 11, edited by R. Z. LeGeros and J.P. LeGeros
(Proceedings of the 11th International Symposium on Ceramics in Medicine)
New York, NY, USA, November 1998
© 1998 by World Scientific Publishing Co. Pte. Ltd.

BIOACTIVE SILICA-PHOSPHORIC ACID CONDENSATION REACTIONS: THEORY AND APPLICATION

West, J.K.[1], Zhong J.P.[2], Clark, A.E.[1], and Greenspan D.C.[2]

1. College of Dentistry, University of Florida, Gainesville, FL 32610
2. USBiomaterials Corporation, One Progress Blvd. #23 Alachua, FL 32615, USA

ABSTRACT

The study of hydroxy-carbonate apatite (HCA) formation on bioactive silica surfaces has shown that precipitation of a Ca-P and then, the formation of HCA layer occur rapidly in-vitro. The nucleation mechanism, sites, and initial condensation reactions are not known. Does the phosphorous or the calcium precipitate first and are there any special structural features of the silica gel layer that enhance the process?

In this study, there is an attempt to follow the condensation of ortho-phosphoric acid onto the different ring structures known to exist in silica. The reaction was followed as the phosphoric acid (H_3PO_4) reacted with a silanol on 3-, 4-, 5-, and 6-membered silica rings. The reactants and products for each of the four (4) reactions were optimized using the AM1 semi-empirical molecular orbital method. The transition states were then calculated within the parameters of AM1 which yielded the activation barriers, E_a, for each of the reactions. E_a was found to be +7.7, +17.2, +7.6, and -4.8 for condensation of phosphoric acid onto a 3-, 4-, 5-, and 6-membered ring, respectively. The models indicate that nucleation sites may be on a small number of surface structures making up 6-membered rings and that the reaction is spontaneous and exothermic.

KEYWORDS: AM1, Molecular Orbital Theory, Phosphoric Acid, Bioactive Glass, Silica.

INTRODUCTION

The mechanisms for initiating the cellular response seen for bioactive glass in the healing process have been hypothesized by Larry Hench[1]. The behavior of various bioactive implants is related to the surface reactions kinetics and thermodynamics in physiological solutions. The time scale for the surface reactions for a glass with high bioactivity has been reported previously[1]. Glasses with the highest levels of bioactivity undergo surface reaction Stages 1-5 very rapidly, i.e. within a few hours. A polycrystalline hydroxyl carbonate apatite (HCA) layer is formed on 45S5 Bioglass® (Stages 4 and 5), for example, within 3 hours, both in vitro in simulated body fluids and in vivo. In contrast, compositions with intermediate levels of bioactivity that bond only to bone require 2-3 days to form a crystalline HCA layer on the surface of the material. Composites that are not bioactive and do not form a bond to either bone or soft tissues do not form a crystalline HCA layer even after 3-4 weeks in solution. Modeling and studying the initial period of the condensation of the phoshorous onto the glass surface is the objective of this paper. Such information should prove to be very valuable for the eventual development of complete HCA-tissue bonding models. Molecular modeling, however, provides a very powerful tool to start to investigate plausible molecular level interactions.

MOLECULAR ORBITAL (MO) METHODS

Molecular orbital methods are just one of the approaches used to solve Schroedinger's Equation. We have developed models for silicon based chemistry using a CAChe Worksystem, Beaverton, OR, that provides an interface to ZINDO[2] (Professor M.C. Zerner's Intermediate Neglect of Differential Overlap program) through a Macintosh environment as well as MOPAC[3] that provides an interface to MNDO, AM1 and PM3 semi-empirical methods[4-7].

We have recently shown that various sizes of silica rings calculated by either AM1 or PM3 methods represent the geometries and infrared spectra better than previous MNDO IR spectra and geometries[8]. Our results show that AM1 appears to represent the bulk distribution of rings slightly better than PM3[9], especially the larger clusters. Thus, as a calculational strategy, the geometries for silicate rings used in this study were optimized using the AM1 method. The transition states were calculated using the same AM1 method with Unrestricted Hartree Fock (UHF) Theory in order to better model the condensation of bonds[10].

RESULTS OF THE MODELING

Each of the models of silica rings contain silicon atoms with two bridging oxygen atoms and two non-bridging oxygen atoms terminated with hydrogen atoms. These ring structures are then reacted with an ortho-phosphoric acid monomer. The condensation reaction goes through a transition state where water is being formed and a silicon-oxygen-phosphorous linkage is also being formed.

Figure 1 shows the reaction pathway for the condensation of ortho-phosphoric acid onto a six membered silica ring (cyclohexasiloxane). The structure in figure 1a shows the phosphoric acid monomer hydrogen bonded to the six membered ring. This is a stable configuration that would occur without activation. Condensation, however, requires -4.8 kcal/mol to form the transition state as shown in figure 1b. Table I gives the heat of formation (Hf) for this transition state as -1772.6-4.8=-1777.4 kcal/mol. The formation of a water molecule by proton abstraction can also be seen. The completed condensation reaction structure is shown in figure 1c with a hydrogen bonded water molecule. The silicon-oxygen-phosphorous linkage is clearly shown and the resulting reactants are thermodynamically more stable than the products. The reaction is exothermic, releasing more than +25kcal/mol.

Table I summarizes the reaction paths calculated and the MO models used in the calculation.

TABLE I

Model	Description	(Kcal/mol)	
		Hf	**Δ Hf =Reaction Barrier**
	Cyclotrisillioxane and Ortho-phosphoric acid	-1014.7 (SP6)	+7.7 (SP8)
	Cycloterrasilloxane and Ortho-phosphoric acid	-1278.6 (SP2)	+17.2 (SP4)
	Cyclopentasillioxane and Ortho-phosphoric acid	-1530.2 (SP9)	+7.6 (SP16)
Figure 1	Cyclohexasillioxane and Ortho-phosphoric acid	-1772.6 (SP12)	-4.8 (SP15)

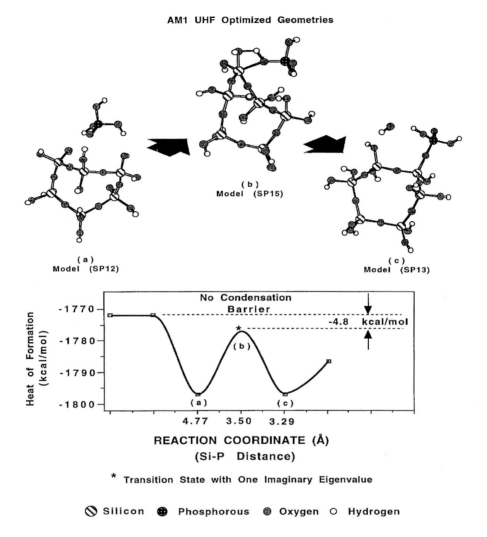

AM1 UHF Optimized Geometries

(b)
Model (SP15)

(a)
Model (SP12)

(c)
Model (SP13)

No Condensation Barrier

-4.8 kcal/mol

* Transition State with One Imaginary Eigenvalue

⊘ Silicon ⊕ Phosphorous ⊛ Oxygen ○ Hydrogen

Fig. 1 Reaction pathway for the condensation of ortho-phosphoric acid onto
a three membered silica ring

Likewise, the condensation of a phosphoric monomer and a four membered silica ring (cyclotetrasiloxane) had the highest barrier to condensation found in this study at +17.2 kcal/mol. The reaction is exothermic but only by +7 kcal/mol. Similar results were found for the five-membered and three-membered silica rings with +7.6 kcal/mol and +7.7 kcal/mol respectively.

For the six-membered ring, there is no barrier. The reaction is spontaneous and it is exothermic, releasing about +25 kcal/mol. The prediction is that condensation should occur on amorphous silica or onto the silica gel-layer in bioactive glasses at room temperature and it should only occur on the sites with cyclohexasiloxane on the surface.

EXPERIMENT AND RESULTS

Pure silica gel with an average pore size of 30Å was reacted in a 4 mM phosphate buffer saline (PBS) solution at 37°C. After 2 weeks, the reacted sample was dried with acetone and surface characterized by FTIR.

FTIR reflection spectroscopy in Fig. 2 shows a slight shift in the primary Si-O-Si transverse optical asymmetric stretch at 1100 cm^{-1} toward the Si-O-P peak at 1020 cm^{-1}. This indicates that condensation is occurring spontaneously as predicted. Experimental verification of these predictions confirmed that small amounts of ortho-phosphoric acid will condense onto pure sol-gel silica.

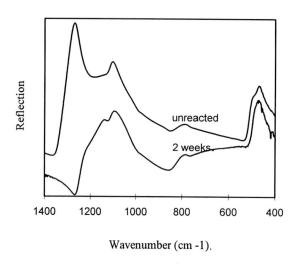

Wavenumber (cm -1).

Fig. 2 FTIR spectra of reacted 30Å silica gel in 4 mM PBS

REFERENCE

1. Hench, L.L., J. Am. Ceram. Soc., 74, 1487, 1991 and Bioceramics 9, 3-6, 1996
2. ZINDO Version 3.0, Oxford Molecular Group (CaChe Scientific), Beaverton, OR, 1994
3. MOPAC Version 94, Oxford Molecular Group (CaChe Scientific), Beaverton, OR, 1994
4. Burggraf, L. W., Davis, L.P. Gordon, M.S., Ultrastructure Processing of Advanced Materials, Wiley, NY, 47-55, 1992
5. Dewar, M.J.S. et al., J. Am. Chem. Soc., 107, 3902-9, 1985
6. Dewar, M.J.S. et al., J. Am. Chem. Soc., 6, 1486-90, 1987
7. Boyd, D.B. "Aspects of Molecular Modeling", in REVIEWS IN COMPUTATIONAL CHEMISTRY, VCH Publishers, Inc., N.Y., 321-354, 1990
8. West, J.K., and Hench, L.L., "A PM3 Molecular Orbital Model of Silica Rings and Their Vibrational Spectra" J.N.C.S., 180, 11-16, 1994
9. West, J.K., and Hench, L.L., "Molecular Orbital Models of Silica Rings and Their Vibrational Spectra" J. Am. Cer. Soc., 78(4), 1093-96, 1995.(1994) Submitted to J. Amer. Ceramic Soc.
10. West, J.K., and Hench, L.L., J. Mater. Sc., Vol. 29, 3601-6, 1994

Bioceramics Volume 11, edited by R. Z. LeGeros and J.P. LeGeros
(Proceedings of the 11th International Symposium on Ceramics in Medicine)
New York, NY, USA, November 1998
© 1998 by World Scientific Publishing Co. Pte. Ltd.

COMPLEX SOL-GEL PROCESS (CSGP) PREPARATION OF CALCIUM PHOSPHATE BIOMATERIALS (POWDERS, MONOLITHS, FIBERS)

A. Deptula[1], W. Lada[1], T. Olczak[1], B. Sarowska[1], R.Z. LeGeros[2] and J.P. LeGeros[2]

[1]Institute of Nuclear Chemistry and Technology, Warsaw, Poland and
[2]New York University College of Dentistry, New York, NY, USA

ABSTRACT

The purpose of this continuing study is to explore the application of complex sol-gel process (CSGP) method previously developed by the authors, in the preparation of potential calcium phosphate biomaterials to be used by itself or as coatings on metallic or non-metallic substrates. The present study investigated the application of CSGP method in the preparation of different physical forms of calcium phosphate materials. The main reagents used were calcium carbonate, phosphoric acid, ammonium hydroxide with ascorbic acid as the complexing agent. Gelation is attained in ambient conditions. Polyethylene oxide was added to promote the formation of fibers. The products of reaction are heat-treated at 900 to 1200°C. The final products were characterized using scanning electron microscopy (SEM) and infrared absorption spectroscopy (IR). SEM analyses demonstrated that the process was successful in preparing materials of different forms: spherical powders, monoliths, fibers, macroporous particles. IR analyses identified the sintered products as hydroxyapatite, CO_3-apatite, HA mixed with $CaCO_3$, or ß-TCP.

Keywords: sol-gel method, hydroxyapatite, CO_3-apatite, ß-TCP

INTRODUCTION

Sol-gel methods [1] are being explored in the preparation of calcium phosphates [2-4]. This method has the advantage of producing calcium phosphate of nanodimensions. Preliminary studies demonstrated that ascorbic acid was an effective complexing agent regulating the HA/ß-TCP in the final product [4]. These studies also showed that this method can be used to deposit thin ceramic coatings on metal substrates.

The purpose of the present study was to explore the application of the sol-gel method developed by Deptula et al [1-4] on the preparation of calcium phosphate in different physical forms, e.g., spherical powders, monoliths, fibers, macroporous particles) as potential biomaterials to be used by itself or as coating on metallic or non-metallic substrates.

METHODS

The flow chart for the preparation is shown in Fig. 1. The main reagents used were calcium carbonate, phosphoric acid, ammonium hydroxide with ascorbic acid as the complexing agent. Gelation is attained in ambient conditions. Polyethylene oxide was added to promote the formation of fibers. The products of reaction are heat-treated at 900 to 1200°C. The final products were characterized using scanning electron microscopy (SEM) and infrared absorption spectroscopy (IR).

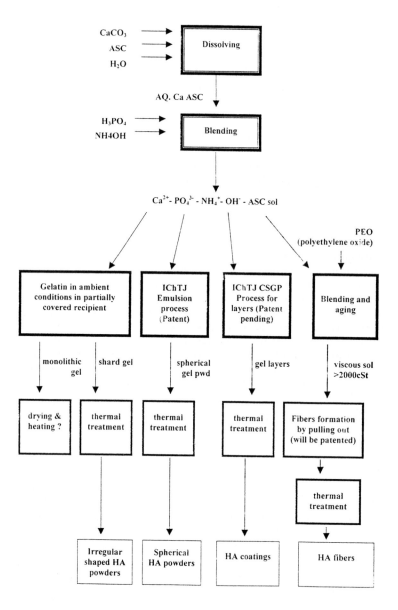

Fig 1: Flow-sheet for the experimental procedure for the preparation of calcium phosphate materials in different sizes and shapes.

RESULTS

SEM micrographs show the different morphology of some of the products obtained (Figs. 2 and 3). Macroporosity was introduced by heat treatment (Fig. 2b compared to Fig. 2a). Well-defined crystals (Fig. 3b) were observed after heat-treatment of the calcium phosphate fiber (Fig. 3a). IR analyses identified the sintered products as consisting of CO_3-apatite (Fig. 4); hydroxyapatite, HA; mixture of HA and $CaCO_3$; and beta-tricalcium phosphate (ß-TCP).

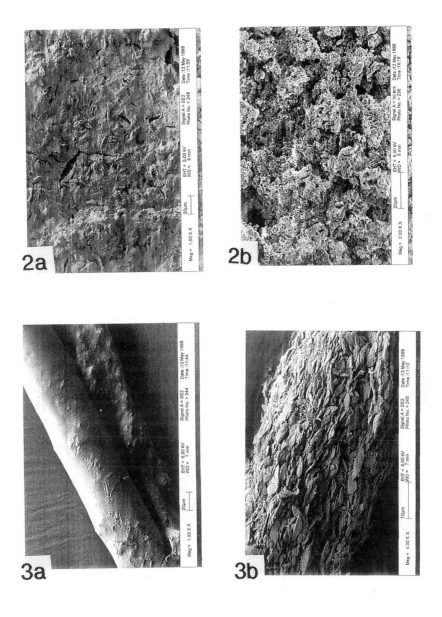

Fig. 2: Products obtained after gelation (a) and after sintering at 1200°C, 3h.
Fig. 3: Product obtained as fiber before (a) and after sintering (b).

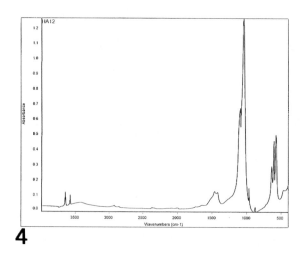

4

Fig. 4: IR absorption analyses identified one of the sintered products as CO_3-apatite.

CONCLUSION

Results of this study demonstrated that the complex sol gel process (CSGP) is a useful method for the preparation of calcium phosphates in different forms (spherical powders, monoliths, fibers) and different calcium phosphate composition (HA, CO_3-AP, ß-TCP or mixtures of HA and $CaCO_3$).

REFERENCES

1. Deptula A, Majani C. *ENEA Report No. TIB/86/25*, Roma, ISSN/0393-6333, 1986.
2. Matsuda Y, Matubara K, Sakka S. *J Ceram Soc Jpn* **98**: 1225, 1990.
3. Deptula A, Lada W, Olczak T, Borello A, Alvani C, DiBartolomeo A. *J Non-cryst Solids* **147**: 537, 1992.
4. Deptula A, Olczak T, Lada W, Alvani C, Lorenzini L, DiBartolomeo A. In: *Hydryxyapatite and Related Materials.* Brown P, Constanz B (eds). CRC Press, Boca Raton, 263, 1994.
5. Deptula A, Lada W, Olczak T, LeGeros RZ, LeGeros JP. In: *Bioceramics Vol 9.* Kokubo T, Nakamura T, Mijaji F (eds). Pergammon, 313, 1996.

Bioceramics Volume 11, edited by R. Z. LeGeros and J.P. LeGeros
(Proceedings of the 11th International Symposium on Ceramics in Medicine)
New York, NY, USA, November 1998
© 1998 by World Scientific Publishing Co. Pte. Ltd.

FORMATION OF APATITES IN THE SYSTEM: KCl-$CaCl_2$-$Ca_3(PO_4)_2$-K_3PO_4-H_2O at 25° C

R. Rokbani, R.Z. LeGeros*, N.K. Ariguib, M. T. Ayedi** and J.P. LeGeros*

Institute National de Recherche Scientifique et Technique, B.P. 95, 2050 Hammam-Lif, Tunisie
*New York University College of Dentistry, New York, NY, USA; **Ecole Normale Superieure, Bizerte, Tunisie

ABSTRACT

Apatites from the system, KCl-$CaCl_2$-$Ca_3(PO_4)_2$-K_3PO_4-H_2O at 25° C were obtained and characterized using x-ray diffraction, infrared absorption spectroscopy and chemical analysis. The crystallinity of the apatite depended on the initial solution composition and on the solution pH at equilibrium. Apatites poor in crystalinity were usually obtained from solutions with high pH. The maximum amount of chloride, Cl^- ion incorporated in the apatite crystals was about 5.0 wt% (1.4 M). This amount was higher than that obtained in previous preparations at 100° C by hydrolysis of $CaHPO_4$ or by precipitation method (about 3 wt% of 1 M); but lower than the amount for a fully substituted chlor-apatite, $Ca_{10}(PO_4)_6Cl_2$ which is 7.0 wt % (2.0 M). The incorporation of potassium in the apatite was limited to 1.2 wt% (0.3 M). Variations in a- and c-axis dimensions (increase and decrease, respectively) indicated a Cl-for-OH substitution: $(Ca,K)_{10}(HPO_4,PO_4)_6(Cl,OH)_2$. The incorporation of K^+ in these apatites appeared to very limited and not related to the incorporation of Cl^- when the pH effect is neglected.

The observed limited incorporation of Cl^- and K^+ ions in synthetic apatites may be relevant to their observed limited concentrations in biological apatites (of enamel, dentin, and bone) in spite of their great abundance in biological fluids.

Keywords: Cl-apatite, potassium, chloride.

INTRODUCTION

Relatively high concentrations of chloride ions (Cl^-) are incorporated in some mineral apatites [1] but to a very limited extent in biological apatites (the mineral phases of enamel, dentin, cementum and bone) [2-4]. The incorporation of chloride ion in synthetic apatites (idealized as $Ca_{10}(PO_4)_6(OH)_2$ have been studied in non-aqueous systems at 1000° C [2,5] and from aqueous systems at 100° C by precipitation or by hydrolysis of monetite, $CaHPO_4$ in chloride-containing solutions [3]. In apatites obtained from both aqueous and non-aqueous systems, a Cl-for-OH substitution in the apatite was determined to have occurred, based on the changes in the unit-cell lattice parameters (increase in a- and decrease in c-parameters) with increasing Cl^- incorporation. A complete (100% or 2 mole Cl) Cl^--for-OH^- substitution, $Ca_{10}(PO_4)_6Cl_2$, was observed in apatites obtained from non-aqueous systems (solid-state reactions), while only a partial substitution (maximum, 50% or 1 mole Cl) in apatites obtained from aqueous systems at 100° C [3]. The purpose of this study was to continue the investigations [6] on the extent of chloride incorporation in apatites obtained at 25° C in the system: KCl-$CaCl_2$-$Ca_3(PO_4)_2$-K_3PO_4-H_2O.

MATERIALS AND METHODS

Solutions containing various concentrations of K^+, Ca^{2+}, PO_4^{3-}, Cl^- ions were prepared and identified as follows: Solution A (Fig. 1, region A): KCl, $CaCl_2$, K_3PO_4: containing, in mole per cent (mol %): KCl, 0.45 to 7.99; K_3PO_4, 0.45 to 3.81; $CaCl_2$, 0.63 to 12.34; H_2O, added to make up the total of 100 mol %, e.g., 98.46 to 75.87. Solution B (Fig. 1, region B): KCl added with $K_4Ca(PO_4)_2$, containing, in mole per cent (mol %): KCl, 1.24 to 7.25; $K_4Ca(PO_4)_2$, 0.23 to 1.49; H_2O, 98.53 to 91.2. Solution C (Fig. 1, region C): KCl added with $KCaPO_4$, containing in mole per cent (mol %): KCl, 0.39 to 0.64; $KCaPO_4$, 10.68 to 1.22; H_2O. 99.22 to 98.15. Solution D (Fig. 1, region D): $CaCl_2$ added with $KCaPO_4$, containing in mole per cent (mol %):

$CaCl_2$, 0.20 to 8.99; $KCaPO_4$, 0.99 to 3.68; H_2O, 98.04 to 87.34. <u>Solution E</u> (Fig. 1, region E): $CaCl_2$ added with β-$Ca_3(PO_4)_2$, containing in mole per cent (mol %): $CaCl_2$, 0.20 to 1.81; β-$Ca_3(PO_4)_2$, 0.06 to 0.61; H_2O, 99.74 to 97.582; and about 1 ml of K_3PO_4 added as catalyst.

Experiments were carried out in an air atmosphere using Merck chemical reagents and decarbonated distilled water. Pure compounds of $KCaPO_4$, $K_4Ca(PO_4)_2$ and β-$Ca_3(PO_4)_2$ were prepared as previously described.

Mixtures of solutions or slurries corresponding to the systems described above were poured in polyethylene bottles and placed in a shaking waterbath maintained at 25° C. Aliquots were taken once a week, press-dried and analyzed with x-ray diffraction (XRD). The equilibrium was considered attained when no further changes in the XRD patterns (in terms of phases present and of the crystallinity of the apatite phase) of the solid phases and no further changes in the solution pH were observed. Because the XRD patterns of the solid phases at equilibrium showed diffraction peaks of apatite mixed with other soluble salts (e.g., KCl), the mixtures were washed with distilled water several times and dried in the oven at 70° C (this temperature was shown by XRD not to have any effect on the apatite crystallinity).

Samples showing only the apatite phase in the XRD patterns were analyzed for chloride (by potentiometric methods); for phosphate (by colorimetric method); for calcium ions (by EDTA complexometric method); and for potassium (by flame spectrometry).

XRD analyses were made on a Philips generator PW 1730/10 system equipped with a copper target. For the determination of lattice parameters, an internal standard (KCl) was used and step-scanning of the designated diffraction peaks for 5 sec per 0.01° 2θ per step was employed. The values of the a- and c-axis dimensions were calculated from the (300) and (002) diffraction peaks, respectively, according to the formula [7]: $a = 2 (3)^{1/2}d_{(300)}$; $c = 2 d_{(002)}$. An accuracy of $\pm 0.003A$ was determined from ten repeated measurements with an internal KCl standard on an apatite sample of comparable crystallinity and calculating the variation from the mean using 95% statistical confidence limits. Multiple regression analyses and analyses of variance (ANOVA) were employed to examine the relationship between a and c axes and the contents of chloride and potassium ions. Differences were considered significant when the probability for error was 1% or less (p < 0.01). (1) $Y_1 = f (Cl, K)$; (2) $Y_2 = f (Cl)$; (3) $Y_3 = f (K)$

The dependent variable, Y_i (where i = 1, 2, 3), was used for the lattice parameters examined and the independent variables are the concentrations of the chloride, [Cl⁻], and potassium, [K⁺] ions in the apatite.

RESULTS

For the system, KCl-$CaCl_2$-K_3PO_4-H_2O (Fig. 1, region A). The apatites obtained in the regions with high proportions of K_3PO_4 had poor crystallinity and contained low amounts of chloride ions (Fig. 2A) compared to those from the regions of high KCl and/or high $CaCl_2$ (Figs. 2B and 2C). The pH of the solutions at equilibrium ranged from 3 to 13. For the system, $K_4Ca(PO_4)_2$-KCl-H_2O (Fig. 1, region B), equilibrium was attained after 10 months; the apatites obtained were poorly crystallized, the crystallinity decreasing in the regions containing decreasing amounts of $K_4Ca(PO_4)_2$ or increasing amounts of KCl. The pH of the solutions at equilibrium ranged from 10 to 12.6. For the system, KCl-$KCaPO_4$-H_2O (Fig. 1, region C), equilibrium was attained after 7 months; the amount of apatite obtained increased and with increasing proportion of $KCa(PO_4)_2$ in the mixture but the amount of Cl⁻ incorporated in the apatite were not significantly different among the apatite samples. The crystallinity of the apatite increased with the time of reaction. The crystallinity of the apatites obtained in this system decreased while the amount of a second phase ($KCaPO_4.H_2O$) increased with increasing concentrations of KCl and decreasing concentrations of $KCaPO_4$. The pH of the solutions at equilibrium ranged from 11.05 to 11.50. For the system, $CaCl_2$ - $KCaPO_4$ - H_2O (Fig. 1, region D), equilibrium was attained after 24 months. The concentrations of the Cl ions were very high (about 5 wt% or 1.4 moles) in apatite samples obtained from regions of high concentrations of $CaCl_2$. The crystallinity of apatite samples were much greater from these regions than from those of high concentrations of $KCaPO_4$. The pH of the solutions at equilibrium ranged from 2.3 to 11. For the system, $CaCl_2$-β-$Ca_3(PO_4)_2$-H_2O with K_3PO_4 as catalyst (Fig. 1, region E), equilibrium was attained after 17 months; the apatite samples obtained contained 1.1 to 2.6 wt % Cl (0.3 to 0.7 moles Cl⁻) and showed good crystallinity. The pH of the solutions at equilibrium ranged from 3.8 to 4.9.

With increasing Cl⁻ incorporation in the apatites, the XRD diffraction peaks exhibited: shifts to lower two

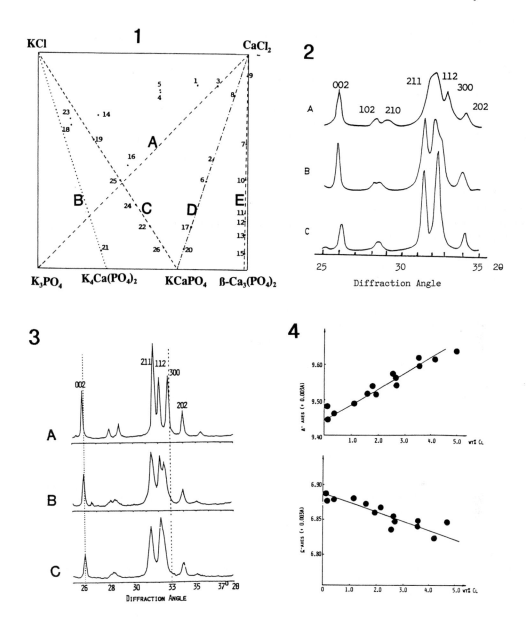

Fig. 1: Schematic representation of the relative composition for the system, KCl-CaCl₂-Ca₃(PO₄)₂-K₃PO₄-H₂O: (region A) KCl-CaCl₂-H₂O; (region B) KCl-K₄Ca(PO₄)₂-H₂O; (region C) KCl-KCaPO₄-H₂O; (region D) CaCl₂KCaPO₄-H₂O; and (region E) CaCl₂-βCa₃(PO₄)₂-H₂O (with small quantity of K₃PO₄ as catalyst). (A) is a mixture of solutions while (B), (C), (D) and (E) are mixtures of solids and H₂O.

Fig. 1: Schematic representation of the relative composition for the system, KCl-$CaCl_2$-$Ca_3(PO_4)_2$-K_3PO_4-H_2O: (region A) KCl-$CaCl_2$-H_2O; (region B) KCl-$K_4Ca(PO_4)_2$-H_2O; (region C) KCl-$KCaPO_4$-H_2O; (region D) $CaCl_2KCaPO_4$-H_2O; and (region E) $CaCl_2$-$\beta Ca_3(PO_4)_2$-H_2O (with small quantity of K_3PO_4 as catalyst). (A) is a mixture of solutions while (B), (C), (D) and (E) are mixtures of solids and H_2O.

Fig. 2: XRD patterns of apatites obtained from system KCl-$CaCl_2$-K_3PO_4-H_2O (Fig. 1, region A) with the following composition:(A) 14.40% KCl, 3.56% $CaCl_2$, 7.77% K_3PO_4, 74.28% H_2O; (B) 16.59% KCl, 4.14% $CaCl_2$, 2.41% K_3PO_4, 76.86% H_2O; (C) 7.40% KCl, 18.34% $CaCl_2$, 7.46% K_3PO_4, 66.80% H_2O. Corresponding lattice parameters, $\underline{a}$ and $\underline{c}$-axes ($\pm$ 0.003 A), respectively, are: (A) 9.438, 6.877; (B) 9.578, 6.885; (C) 9.598, 6.805.

Fig. 3: X-ray diffraction patterns of apatites obtained from combined systems (Fig. 1) showing shifts in the diffraction peaks (300, 211, 112 and 002) reflecting increase in $\underline{a}$- and decrease in $\underline{c}$-axes with increasing Cl content of apatite. The lattice parameters, $\underline{a}$- and $\underline{c}$-axes ($\pm$ 0.003 A) and Cl (wt%) content, respectively, are: (A) 9.43%, 6.88; 0.055; (B) 9.515, 6.875; 1.59; (C) 9.601, 6.846; 5.03.

Fig. 4: Correlation between increase in $\underline{a}$-, decrease in $\underline{c}$-axes with increasing Cl content (wt%) in apatites obtained in all systems. For comparison, the $\underline{a}$- and $\underline{c}$-axes ($\pm$0.003A), respectively, of synthetic Cl-apatite, $Ca_{10}(PO_4)_6Cl_2$, containing 6.8 wt% Cl are: 9.642 and 6.764; for OH-apatite, $Ca_{10}(PO_4)_6(OH)_2$: 9.422, 6.880 [2,5].

theta (2θ) angles of the (300), (211) and (210); shifts to higher two theta (2θ) angles of the (002) and (112); and the merging of the (300) and (112) and of the (210) and (102) (Fig. 3). These shifts reflect the increase in the *a*-parameter and decrease in the *c*-parameter with increasing Cl^- content (Fig. 4). A plot of K^+ concentration, [K], with lattice parameters indicated an inverse relationship between [K] and the a-axis dimensions and an apparent direct relationship with c-axis dimensions with apatites containing very low concentrations (less than 0.3 wt% or 0.08 moles). However, regression analysis of this data failed to show a significant relationship between [K] and the lattice parameters. A significant relationship between changes in the a and c-values and chloride concentration, [Cl], was observed ($0.005 < p < 0.01$), n = 26, $R^2 = 0.90$. The increase in [Cl] (0.03 to 5.0 wt% equivalent to 0.08 to 1.4 moles) did not show a significant positive correlation with that of the K content (0 to 1.2 wt % , equivalent to 0 to 0.3 moles).

DISCUSSION

In this study, the amount of incorporation of Cl^- incorporated in the apatite structure was greater than that previously obtained at 100° C by precipitation or hydrolysis methods [3] but less than that obtained by solid-state reactions at 1000° C [2,5]. The maximum Cl-for-OH substitution (i.e., 2 Cl for 2 OH) can be obtained only by solid state reactions at 1000° C [2, 5]. In the aqueous systems by hydrolysis of monetite ($CaHPO_4$) in Cl-containing solutions, or by precipitation, both at 100° C and both with the simultaneous presence of Na^+ ions, the maximum Cl^- incorporation was about 3.5 wt%, equivalent to 1.0 mole. This amount translates to 50 mole % substitution, i.e., 1 Cl for 1 OH. In the present study, Cl^- incorporation of up to 5.0 wt% (equivalent to 1.4 mole) was obtained in the presence of K^+ ions at lower temperature (25° C) and longer periods of reactions (7 to 24 months compared to 3 to 5 hrs at 100° C). In all these apatites prepared under different conditions and temperature, Cl-for-OH substitution in the apatite structure is observed, idealized as:

$$Ca_{10}(PO_4)_6(OH)_2 \; ----> \; Ca_{10}(PO_4)_6(Cl,OH)_2 \; ----> \; Ca_{10}(PO_4)_6Cl_2$$

This substitution is reflected in the changes in the lattice parameters (increase in a- with concomitant decrease in the c-axis dimensions) with increasing Cl incorporation [2-4]. The incorporation of K^+ ions in the apatite were limited to a maximum of 1.2 wt % (0.3 mole) and an inverse relationship with Cl^- incorporation was apparent. In this study, the increase in carbonate concentrations in cases of elevated pH (pH > 8) may have masked any relationship between K^+ and Cl^- incorporation [4]. Since Cl^- and OH^- ions compete for the same location in the apatite structure, the incorporation of Cl_- ion is expected to be less under conditions of neutral to basic pHs. When the pH effect was considered, a direct relationship between the K^+ and Cl^- incorporation was observed.

The observed limited amount of Cl^- and K^+ ions incorporation in synthetic apatites [3]) may be relevant to the observed limited amounts of these ions in biological apatites (of enamel, dentin and bone), in spite of the great abundance of these ions in biological fluids.

Acknowledgement
This study was supported in part by the National Institute of Dental Research (NIDR) of the National Institutes of Health Research Grant Nos. DE-04123 and DE-07223 (R.Z. LeGeros) and the USA-Tunisia Transfer of Technology from USAID. The authors gratefully acknowledge the valuable technical assistance of W. Torres and D.J. LeGeros.

REFERENCES

1. C. Palache, H. Berman, F. Clifford. *The System of Mineralogy of Dana.* 1946. J. Wiley and Sons, London.
2. E. Dykes, J. C. Elliott, *Calc Tiss Res,* 1971, **3**, 24.
3. R. Z. LeGeros, *Archs oral Biol,* 1974, **20**, 63.
4. R. Z. LeGeros, *Prog Crystal Growth Charact,* 1981, **4**, 1.
5. J. S. Prener, *J Electrochem Soc,* 1967, **114**, 77.
6. R. Rokbani, M. Trabelsi-Ayadi, R. Cohen-Adad, N. Kbir-Ariguib N, *Bull Soc chim Fr* 1990, **127**, 26.
7. H. P. Klug and L. E. Alexander, *X-ray Diffraction Procedures of Polycrystalline and   Amorphous Materials.* 2nd ed. Wiley, New York, 1974, pp. 271-312.

Bioceramics Volume 11, edited by R. Z. LeGeros and J.P. LeGeros
(Proceedings of the 11th International Symposium on Ceramics in Medicine)
New York, NY, USA, November 1998
© 1998 by World Scientific Publishing Co. Pte. Ltd.

HYDROXYAPATITE-ALUMINA PLATELET COMPOSITES

S. Gautier, E. Champion, S. Raynaud, D. Bernache-Assollant

Laboratoire de Matériaux Céramiques et Traitements de Surface, ESA CNRS 6015, 123, avenue Albert Thomas, 87060 Limoges, France.

ABSTRACT

Hydroxyapatite matrix composites containing alumina platelets were produced by slip casting and hot pressing with the aim of achieving a homogeneous and controlled microstructural design to improve the mechanical reliability. With the use of Al_2O_3 platelets of large size ($\Phi \approx 12$ µm), the behaviour of aqueous suspensions of composite mixtures remains quasi-Newtonian. From 30 vol% of small platelets ($\Phi \approx 5$ µm) it becomes shear-thinning. Orientation phenomena of platelets are responsible for the modifications of the flow. Due to the disk-shaped morphology of alumina, a compromise must also be found to optimise particulate rearrangement during casting. After hot pressing, a preferred orientation of Al_2O_3 platelets is obtained. Fracture toughness of composites containing small platelets increases up to 200 % that of the monolithic matrix in the direction parallel to platelet faces and reaches 400 % in the perpendicular direction. Large platelets lead to an increase of residual thermoelastic stresses inducing a microcracking of the matrix. It is concluded that both the size and the aspect ratio of platelets are of prime importance for the toughening of HAP based bioceramics.

KEYWORDS : Composites, Hydroxyapatite, Alumina, Rheology, Toughness.

INTRODUCTION

Dense hydroxyapatite $(Ca_{10}(PO_4)_6(OH)_2$; HAP) is characterised by a low fracture toughness which restricts the use as biological implant.[1] HAP matrices can be toughened by the incorporation of alumina particles.[2] But, as both strength and toughness of ceramics are critically limited by the largest flaws, it is important to avoid initial agglomerates and prevent the formation of microstructural defects during the elaboration process. Therefore, the homogenisation of powder mixtures is a primary important step in the elaboration of composite materials.

In a previous work, we have demonstrated that the incorporation of 20 vol% of alumina platelets could enhance the mechanical reliability of HAP based materials elaborated using slip casting, providing a good control of the slurry composition was performed.[3] From this basis, our work consisted in determining the effect of the size and volume fraction of alumina platelets on the rheological characteristics of the initial composite slurries and on the fracture toughness of slip cast and hot pressed HAP-Al$_2$O$_3$ materials.

MATERIALS AND METHODS

A commercial HAP powder was used in this study (Bioland, France). This powder had a specific surface area of 21.2 m^{2}g^{-1} and was formed of agglomerated elementary particles. The average size of these agglomerates was 20 μm and the largest ones could reach 100 μm. Alumina platelets (Elf Atochem, France) were disk-shaped monocrystals, their main characteristics are listed in table 1.

Table 1. Characteristics of alumina platelets.

Grade (Ref.)	Diameter φ (μm)	Thickness h (μm)	Aspect ratio φ/h	Specific Surface area (m^{2}g^{-1})
T'0	3-7	0.6	5-12	0.8
T2	10-15	1.0	10-15	0.5

Composite mixtures containing up to 40 vol% of alumina platelets were homogenized by ball milling in demineralised water. Ammonium polymethacrylate was used as deflocculant. The suspensions were cast in plaster moulds. The green composite bodies were dried at 40°C for 24 h. Then, they were hot pressed under a compressive stress of 10 MPa for 30 min to 4 h at a temperature ranging from 1100°C to 1250°C to obtain nearly fully dense composites.

The rheological characterization of composite slurries was performed using a coaxial cylinder viscometer (Haake rotovisco RV 20). Viscosity and shear stress of suspensions were determined either from a constant applied shear rate of 350 s^{-1} or from linearly increased shear rates. Scanning electron microscopy on chemically etched surfaces was used for microstructural observations. Fracture toughness of composites was determined by Vickers indentation under a 54 N applied load. K$_{Ic}$ values were calculated from the equation proposed by Evans.[4]

RESULTS AND DISCUSSION

Rheological behavior of suspensions

Figure 1 gives a typical plot of shear stress versus shear rate of a composite suspension after different ball milling duration. Whatever the slurry composition might be, the rheological behavior was shear-thinning and thixotropic for short ball milling time. Thixotropy and shear-thinning decreased with increasing milling time, which corresponds to the progressive breakdown of initial HAP agglomerates. Then, the behavior became time independent. This time required to desagglomerate the slurries varied from 3 h to 4 h, depending on the composite composition. To ensure a constant behavior, suspensions were ball milled during 5 h and the amount of dispersant was adjusted to minimize the viscosity. This quantity of dispersant required for the best dispersion of composite suspensions was found to agree with a single mixture rule on the basis of 2 mg.m^{-2} for the HAP powder and 1.3 mg.m^{-2} for the alumina platelets.

The best rearrangement of solid particles during slip casting was reached for suspensions

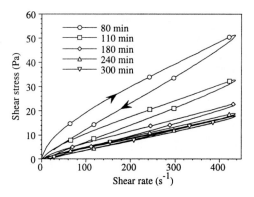

Figure 1. Rheological behavior versus milling time (65 wt% of powder - HAP+10 vol% Al₂O₃ T2 - 3.1 wt% of dispersant).

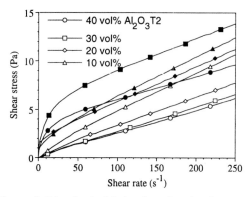

Figure 2. Rheological behavior of optimal suspensions for different composite compositions (filled markers for HAP-Al₂O₃ T'0).

containing 65 wt% of powder ($HAP+Al_2O_3$). In this case, the viscosity is in the range 50 mPa.s to 200 mPa.s, and is compatible with the slip casting process. After casting, alumina platelets tend to lie in parallel planes. This preferred orientation is favored by the ability of alignment of disks under shear stress in the direction of flowing. At lower powder loading, the behavior of the suspensions is Newtonian, but a too important quantity of water has to be removed during casting. At higher loading, interactions between solid particles in the suspensions do not allow an important orientation of alumina platelets. These suspensions result in a low green density of composites (below 50% of the theoretical density).

As shown in Figure 2, optimal composite suspensions (65 wt% of solid content, 5 h milling) behave according to the Ostwald's power law.[5] The shear rate exponent n is close to 1 (i.e. quasi-Newtonian behavior) for all the suspensions except for composites containing at least 30 vol% of small platelets (T'0) for which the exponent is close to 0.5 (i.e. shear-thinning behavior) at low shear rates (<100 s⁻¹). This indicates the increasing difficulty to perform a preferred orientation of platelets as their content in the suspension increases, high shear rates (> 100 s⁻¹) being necessary to obtain a quasi-linear behavior.

Fracture toughness

Figure 3 gives the fracture toughness of hot pressed HAP-Al₂O₃ platelet composites. Because of the preferred orientation of alumina disks, an anisotropic toughening is obtained.

For composites containing small platelets (T'0), the toughness increases with the increase of platelet content. The highest values, obtained for 30 vol% of alumina, correspond to 2 times and 4 times that of the monolithic matrix ($K_{IC} = 0.75$ MPa.m$^{1/2}$) in the directions 90° and 0°, respectively. The most favorable contribution of crack deflection along platelet face during crack propagation explains the higher toughness increment in the direction 0° than in the direction 90°.

When large size platelets are used (T2), the toughening remains much more limited. From 20 vol% of alumina, an important microcracking of the HAP matrix is observed (Fig. 4). This phenomenon is associated to the thermal expansion mismatch between HAP and alumina ($\alpha_{HAP} \approx 16\ 10^{-6}$ K⁻¹; $\alpha_{Al2O3} \approx 8\ 10^{-6}$ K⁻¹) which induces thermoelastic residual stresses during the cooling to room temperature after hot pressing., in agreement with the analysis proposed by Li.[6] This

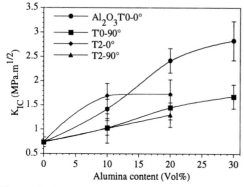

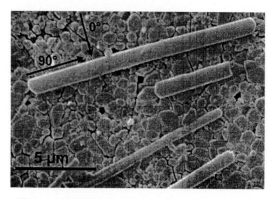

Figure 3. Fracture toughness of composites in the directions 0° and 90° (as referred in Fig. 4).

Figure 4. SEM micrograph of composite HAP-20 vol% Al_2O_3 T2 (H.P. 1200°C-30 min).

analysis indicates the presence of tangential tensile stresses in the matrix whose intensity increases with the increase of the aspect ratio (ϕ/h) of platelets. This would explain that, conversely to composites containing T2 platelets, no microcracking was observed in composites containing T'0 platelets, these last ones having a smaller aspect ratio than T2 platelets (Tab. 1). Therefore, the use of large platelets is detrimental to the reliability of HAP based materials.

CONCLUSION

A more important toughening of HAP matrices can be achieved with the use of alumina platelets than with particles. Slip casting appears as a accurate processing route. But, both the size and volume fraction of added alumina platelets are also of prime importance on the final mechanical characteristics. Platelets should have an aspect ratio (ϕ/h) below 10 to prevent any spontaneous microcracking of the matrix under residual stresses. The behavior of the initial suspension should preferably remain quasi-Newtonian. Indeed, this behavior is associated to an easy orientation of platelets and therefore to an optimal rearrangement of particles in the green body during casting.

ACKNOWLEDGEMENTS

The authors would like to thank Bioland for the financial support provided for this work.

REFERENCES

1. Halouani R, Bernache D, Champion E, Ababou A. *J Mat Sci Mater Med* 1994; **5**: 563-568.
2. Noma T, Shoji N, Wada S, Suzuki T. *J Ceram Soc Jpn* 1993; **101**: 923-927.
3. Gautier S, Champion E, Bernache-Assollant D. In: Sedel L, Rey C, ed. *Bioceramics 10*, Paris: Elsevier Science Ltd, 1997: 549-552.
4. Evans AG, Charles EA. *J Am Ceram Soc* 1976; **59**: 371-372.
5. Couarraze G, Grossiord JL. *Initiation à la rhéologie*. Paris: Lavoisier, 1991.
6. Li Z, Bradt RC. *J Am Ceram Soc* 1989; **72**: 70-77.

Bioceramics Volume 11, edited by R. Z. LeGeros and J.P. LeGeros
(Proceedings of the 11th International Symposium on Ceramics in Medicine)
New York, NY, USA, November 1998
© 1998 by World Scientific Publishing Co. Pte. Ltd.

BONE GRAFT BIOMATERIALS OF ECHINODERMAL ORIGIN

R.Rodríguez[1], J.Gómez[2], F.Blardoni[1], R.Rodríguez–Clemete[2]

[1] "Fructuoso Rodríguez" Orthopedic Hospital. Ave. G y 29 (s/n), Vedado 10400, Ciudad Habana, Cuba.
[2] Institut de Ciència de Materials de Barcelona (CSIC). Campus de la UAB, 08193. Bellaterra. España.

ABSTRACT

A study was initiated to obtain a biomaterial from the sea, specimen *Clypeaster rosaceous,* hydrothermal transformation, and determine its chemical and physical characteristics in relation to its possible application as a bone graft.

The resulting material is a biphasic compound made of 90% hydroxyapatite and 10% calcium carbonate. The average porosity was found to be 50 μm. A Young's modulus of 64.35 Gpa and breaking stress coefficient of 78 Gpa.

Its standard porosity is ideal for the growth of osteocytes and fibrous tissue. Its chemical and physical properties are within parameters. In granulated form, this material may be used for bone filling in case of bone cysts and in concave prosthesis in the skull and ocular orbit.

KEYWORDS: Porous hydroxyapatite, calcium phosphate materials, bone grafts.

EXPERIMENT AND RESULTS

The availability of materials with adequate characteristics for replacement or restoration of bony tissue is still of great research interest. Different kinds of complex materials are used for this purpose and there is a large quantity of great limitations upon current biomedical materials.

Hydroxyapatite $[Ca_{10}(PO_4)_6(OH)_2]$ is very similar- chemically and crystallographically- but not identical- to the human bone and has satisfactory mechanical and biocompatible properties which make it very well accepted as a bone graft material.[1-8,11] However, hydroxyapatite shows poor rate of resorption. Better results are observed in materials of two-phase composition in which hydroxyapatite predominates and small quantities of calcium carbonate or β–TCP are fixed. This improves the resorption helping the new bone formation [9].

Since Niessen's proposal [10] and the works of D.M.Roy,[13] great attention has been given to the porous biomaterial, based on hydroxyapatite obtained from sea corals by hydrothermal transformation with ionic interchange.

Nevertheless, the optimum pore size for the growth of the bone cells and the fibrous tissue has been defined as 40 - 100 μm and 5 - 15 μm respectively [12,14]. Therefore, those investigations are extended to sea echinoderm as a natural source to produce an osteoconductive and bioactive porous biomaterial by means of hydrothermal transformation.

The selected species was the *Clypeaster rosaceous,* which is found abundantly in shallow waters. The porous endoskeletons of these echinoderms were utilized, which have an interconnected macroporous 3-dimensional structure similar to the Haversian system of the human bone. Figures 1 and 2 are SEM images of the product, showing the detail of a pore and the 3-dimensional interconnection of the structure. It was identified as calcium carbonate ($CaCO_3$), calcite type, by X-ray diffraction analysis. Calcium carbonate was transformed by ionic interchange between carbonate ions CO_4^{2-} and phosphate ions PO_4^{3-} in hydrothermal conditions.

Depending on the prefixed initial conditions for the transformation, a two or three phases can be obtained. It is very attractive because it shows a variable solubility. The biphasic compound selected was 90% HAP and 10% $CaCO_3$.

Figures 1 and 2. Pictures of SEM images of material surface.

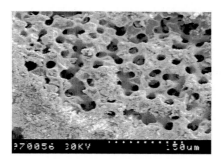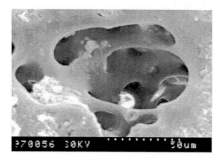

Table 1. Results and conditions of some hydrothermal interchanges.

Sample	Reactive	Temp. (°C)	Press. (atm)	Time (h)	pH	(Ca/P)	Phases
1AT	K_2HPO_4	180	8	24	8.5	1	60% HAP 25% $CaCO_3$ 15% β-TCP
2AT	K_2HPO_4 + NaF	180	10	72	9	1	70% HAP 30% $CaCO_3$
3AT	K_2HPO_4 + NaF	200	12	72	9	1	80% HAP 20% $CaCO_3$
4AT	NaH_2PO_4	160	10	72	9	2	97% HAP 3% β-TCP

The physical properties determined include: average pore size, 50 µm; Young's modulus, 64.35 ± 2.25 Gpa; porosity, of 33 ± 5% and breaking stress, 78 ± 12.6 Gpa. Results of chemical analysis are summarized in table 2.

Table 2. Chemical analysis hydrothermally converted product.

	w.t. %
Calcium (Ca)	41.7 ± 0.3
Phosphorus (P)	17.3 ± 0.2
Magnesium (Mg)	01.4 ± 0.3
Sodium (Na)	0.09 ± 0.02
Iron (Fe)	0.0013 ± 0.0006
Copper (Cu)	0.0012 ± 0.0002
Lead (Pb)	0.0018 ± 0.002
Potassium (K)	< 0.03
Nickel (Ni)	$< 10^{-4}$
Chromium (Cr)	$< 10^{-4}$
Cobalt (Co)	$< 10^{-6}$
Manganese (Mn)	$< 10^{-5}$
Strontium (Sr)	0.2 ± 0.12

No proteins were found in the organic phase, but some amino acids were present (Table 3).

Table 3. Amino acids contents.

glycine	$0.012 \% \pm 0.003 \%$
proline	$0.012 \% \pm 0.0021 \%$
alanine	$0.003 \% \pm 0.001 \%$
valanine	$0.002 \% \pm 0.002 \%$
phenylalanine	$0.001 \% \pm 0.0005 \%$
methionine	$< 10^{-3} \%$

CONCLUSIONS

The obtained material shows satisfactory chemical and physical properties. It is suggested that in granulated form, these materials may be used in bone refilling in cases of cavities caused by cysts or tumors and in concave prosthesis in the skull or in the ocular orbit.

Although this material is presented as a biphasic compound consisting of HAP and $CaCO_3$; the minority phase could be changed to β-TCP; and eventually, three phases may be obtained. Further *in vivo* tests are needed to demonstrate the biocompatibility and efficacy of bone formation of the various mixed phases.

ACKNOWLEDGMENTS

We would like to express sincere thanks to all those persons and Institutions that, in some way, have made this investigation possible. Most of all to Project VIII.6 from CYTED Program under whose coordination this work was done and also to the Institute of Materials and Reactives of the Havana University and the Materials Science Institute of Barcelona for the use of their facilities were utilized.

REFERENCES

1. Canosa R.S, Rev. Ortop. Traum. 1992; 36 1B: 128-134.
2. Drobeck H.P, J. Oral Maxillofac. Srg. 1984; 42: 143-149.
3. González R.S, Quim. Nova 1993; 16:513-516.
4. Holmes R.E, Clin. Orthop. & Rel. Res. 1984; 118: 252-262.
5. Jarcho J, Clin. Orthop. 1981; 157: 259-278.
6. Jarcho J, Dent. Clin. North. Am. 1986; 1: 25-48.
7. Kitsugi T, J. Biomed. Mater. Res. 1987; 21: 1109-1223.
8. Lavernia C, Ceram. Bull. 1991; 70:95-100.
9. LeGeros R.Z, Calcium Phosphates in Oral Biology and Medicine, de. H.M.Myers, N.Y.: Karger, 1991:154-171.
10. Nissen H.U, Science 1969; 166: 1147-1152.
11. Ricci J, Biomedical engineering. Recent developments. New York: Pergamon Press. 1986: 469-474.
12. Roy D.M, U.S.Patent No. 3,929,971.
13. Roy DM. Nature 1974; 247: 220-222.
14. White EW, U.S.Patent No. 3,890,107.

Bioceramics Volume 11, edited by R. Z. LeGeros and J.P. LeGeros
(Proceedings of the 11th International Symposium on Ceramics in Medicine)
New York, NY, USA, November 1998

VALUE-ADDED BIOCERAMIC MATERIALS FROM LOW-COST NATURAL SOURCES: THEIR PROCESSING, CHARACTERISATION AND POTENTIAL APPLICATIONS IN MEDICINE

Michael R. Mucalo[1], Glenn S. Johnson[1], Michel A. Lorier[2], Iain A Anderson[3], Herbert Mucha[4] and Uwe Gieland[4]

[1]Chemistry Department, University of Waikato, Private Bag 3105, Hamilton, New Zealand
[2]Bioprocessing Division, MIRINZ Food Technology and Research, P.O. Box 617, Hamilton, New Zealand; [3]Industrial Research Ltd, P.O. Box 2225, Parnell, Auckland, New Zealand; [4]Institut fuer Verbundwerkstoffe, Chemnitz Technical University, Erfenschlager Str. 73, D-09125, Chemnitz, Germany

ABSTRACT

Sources of material alternative to powders from chemical synthesis for producing bioceramic powders and bodies are described. Materials derived from low cost bone, a meat processing waste product in New Zealand have many applications in medicine. In the present study, a procedure is outlined for preparing cubic implants from excised bovine condyle cancellous bone. In this process, precut cubes are thawed, pressure-cooked in water, soaked in NaOH, microwave heated, solvent extracted in methyl acetate, soaked/ultrasonicated in NaOCl and finally dried to yield an end product that is bleached to the core, has the correct bony architecture and is cuttable to size by surgeons for use in implant applications. Mechanical measurements on the bone to quantify the effects of processing parameters predictably showed a reduction in yield stress as the bone was taken through to the final product. Earlier spectroscopic characterisation of materials produced from bone either by grinding pressure-cooked crushed bone or by acid digestion/reprecipitation revealed that the resultant powders contained residual surface organics and/or collagen, which enhanced their adsorbent properties. Studies involving uptake of drugs and a dye as well as immobilisation of trypsin using a phosphine coupling method have demonstrated the potential of the bone powders as drug delivery systems and enzyme immobilisation substrates. In addition, the reprecipitated powders have shown promise as a feedstock for plasma spraying on titanium substrates.

KEYWORDS

bone, HAP, defatting, deproteination, xenografts, modulus, yield stress, enzymes, plasma coating

INTRODUCTION

Meat products form a major part of New Zealand's export receipts but their production results in large amounts of non-edible waste products. Typically 16-24% of this waste consists of bone, which is often rendered into a low value fertiliser product. This waste bone has the potential to be converted to high value products, in particular, biomedical xenograft materials and bone powders with the powders used as substrates for controlled drug release, enzyme immobilisation, or as plasma spraying feedstocks. In this regard, New Zealand has competitive advantages over other countries because of 1) the absence of a "controlled cattle herd" requirement as in E.C. countries, 2) the absence of BSE-type ailments, and 3) the strict regulation by the meat industry of livestock processed for export. This paper follows a previous report[1] and will very briefly summarise the development of a process for forming xenograft materials from bovine cancellous bone and processes for producing crushed bone and reprecipitated hydroxyapatite powders. In addition, several experiments involving the use of bone-derived powders will demonstrate the potential biomedical application of these materials. There is a well developed literature on the subject of bone processing which has been drawn upon in this study. However, this project has been dominated by the particular need to develop a xenograft material that is bleached to the core of the specimen, aesthetically pleasing and cuttable to size by surgeons.

MATERIALS AND METHODS

Bovine condyles (for xenografts, bone-derived powders) and cervine rib bones (for bone-derived powders) were obtained from local abattoirs and stored at -35°C before processing. The two condyles of different size present on each bovine femur were separated from the femur, cut in half and then sectioned using a sharp band saw into cubes of *ca.* 25 mm^3. An optimum defatting/partial deproteination procedure for the cubes was developed. This involved thawing the cubes in water for 16 hours at 50°C followed by pressure cooking at 15 psi pressure in potable tap water for 6 hours with two water changes. The cubes were subsequently soaked in 0.1 mol L^{-1} NaOH for 16 hours followed by a thorough rinse in water and then microwaved in water to boiling point on high power (850 W) for 2 minutes. The cubes were then transferred to methyl acetate followed by reflux for one hour. The internal liquid was then removed by vigorous manual shaking and the cubes were air-dried on absorbent paper before the final deproteination step. The optimum deproteination procedure involved using a 5% NaOCl solution in a ratio of 50 mL solution/bone cube. Deproteination was carried out at 18-21°C in solutions that were ultrasonicated for 24 hours on the lowest power setting. Rinsing of the cubes followed by manual shaking to remove excess internal water and air-drying completed the procedure.

Spectroscopic characterisation of the bone matrix by FTIR and solid state NMR as a function of processing has already been discussed previously[1]. In mechanical measurements, the angular orientation of bone plates was determined by stereological analysis to give the two optimal final cutting planes for specimens. Following this, columns of bone approximately 20 mm long and 6.0 mm by 6.0 mm in cross section were cut. Bone cube mass, stiffness and yield strength were measured in fresh bone, defatted bone and hypochlorite-bleached bone on a purpose-built compression testing system. Bone specimens were cyclically loaded in the direction of their long axis until the response was stable and then were loaded at a rate of 3.5 to 6 N/s to a maximum strain of 0.6%. At the end of each cube processing step, samples were taken to yield which was defined as the stress resulting in a 1% permanent set.

Preparation of reprecipitated bone powder has been discussed in a previous report[1]. Bone was also converted to powder form directly without any reprecipitation as follows. Pre-cut pieces were crushed with a 100 psi hydraulic press and then pressure cooked at 15 psi for 4 hours to remove tissue and fat. The resultant clean bone chips were then dried for 16 hours in a 105°C oven before further grinding to < 2 mm particle size. Enzyme immobilisation was performed[2] by coupling P(CH$_2$OH)$_3$ to cervine-bone derived powder followed by trypsin adsorption, The activity of the remaining (unadsorbed) trypsin in solutions (extracted after centrifuging) was measured using the standard N-benzoyl-L-arginine-ethyl ester hydrochloride (BAEE) substrate. Activity was determined by following the change in absorbance at 253 nm caused by trypsin interaction with the substrate. Once immobilised, the washed trypsin-coupled cervine bone powder was mixed with a fresh sample of BAEE substrate to measure the activity of the immobilised enzyme. Drug and dye adsorption on the bone-derived powders was followed using a U.V./Vis. method. The change in absorbance of drug and dye stock solutions before and after contact (by shaking for two hours with the powders) was measured, then an adsorption isotherm was calculated based on the simple Langmuir model.

Chlorpheniramine maleate (an antihistaminic drug) and malachite green dye were tested in the adsorption work. Plasma coating of hydroxyapatite using the reprecipitated bone powder as feedstock was performed using a Plasma Technnik LAB 1200 VPS. The bone powder was sieved to between 70 and 220 μm to improve flow and then stirred before radial gravity feed into the plasma. 80 μm plasma coatings were prepared on sandblasted pure titanium plates using a range of powers (18, 22, 26 kW) and were examined by SEM/EDX, ICP, XRD and FTIR to determine the composition and structure of the applied coatings.

RESULTS AND DISCUSSION
General comments on cutting, defatting and deproteination of bone cubes

In general, for cutting the bone matrix samples, a cubic form was the most preferred shape for ease of subsequent processing. Use of a sharp band saw blade and cutting the condyles while frozen greatly improved the success of the subsequent defatting and deproteination steps. Defatting of the bone matrix involved a large number of trials utilising a variety of techniques before the final optimum procedure was settled upon. Pressure cooking the thawed cubes in water followed by sodium hydroxide soaking, was found to be the best method for removing most of the fat and intertrabecular material. Microwaving was a novel defatting technique that allowed rapid removal of residual bulk fat, with methyl acetate being an excellent, relatively low boiling point (60°C), refluxing solvent for removing strongly surface-adsorbed fat. During the aqueous and organic solvent treatments, solvent refreshment was necessary to prevent recontamination of the bone. Successful deproteination, to achieve bleaching to the core and softening of the bone structure to allow cuttability was highly dependent on previous defatting history. Static soaking in hypochlorite gave only gradient bleaching in the cubes with cores remaining unbleached. Penetrability of the hypochlorite solution was much improved by use of ultrasonication which gave core bleaching. A successfully processed final bone product cut to a specific shape is shown in Fig. 1.
Hydroxyapatite powders derived directly from crushed bone or by reprecipitation of acid solution bone digests had residual surface-adsorbed organics or fats that improved drug adsorption and enzyme immobilisation on these materials.

Fig. 1 Final product after shaping for specific implantation purposes

Mechanical properties of the bone cubes as a function of processing

The average modulus of fresh bovine bone depended on the source of the cubes from within the condyle. Values of 0.8-1.3 GPa were obtained. For one group of bone specimens, a 6 hour defatting pressure cook gave a 33% reduction in bone modulus, although an apparent stiffening was observed after only a 1.5 hour pressure cook. Yield stress decreased by > 50% with overall processing. Final deproteinated samples were relatively brittle and yielded rapidly. Thus, processing times (e.g. defatting) can be modified and the effects of these changes on the bone matrix can be monitored in a semi-quantitative fashion by measuring the modulus and yield stress.

Trypsin immobilisation on bone-derived powders

Collagen present on bone particles derived directly from bone crushing provides N-H groups allowing the Mannich-type condensation[2] of $P-CH_2-OH$ groups from $P(CH_2OH)_3$ to occur. $P(CH_2OH)_3$ condensation was most successful on cervine-derived bone due to the high levels of surface-collagen present. Experiments comparing pure collagen and hydroxyapatite confirmed that the former was the principal binding site for phosphine. Assays to monitor trypsin activity in the phosphine-coupled/trypsin solutions showed that with small incremental additions of 16 ppm trypsin, the enzyme became adsorbed relatively quickly. Addition of 1000 ppm trypsin and a 24 hour incubation at *ca.* 4°C indicated a reduction from >>50 trypsin units to just 36 trypsin units for the solution showing strong immobilisation of the trypsin. Rinsing away the source trypsin solution and washing with water followed by refrigeration and then testing of the soaking solution above the enzyme-immobilised bone powders showed a <0.1 trypsin unit activity indicating that the enzyme did not "bleed" from the surface. Trypsin does not lose its enzyme functionality upon immobilisation. Contact of the cervine bone with immobilised trypsin with the BAEE substrate resulted in a rapid increase in activity in the first 3 minutes followed by a decline after 7 minutes.

Drug and dye adsorption and plasma coating using reprecipitated bone powders and bone powders from crushed bone

Malachite green adsorbed very strongly on the reprecipitated bone powder which had residual fat on its surface. The adsorption obeyed Langmuir-type behaviour and was probably enhanced by the dye having a strong affinity for the surface fat on the hydroxyapatite particles. Future studies will use dyes as model compounds to generate characterisation profiles, in order that molecular adsorption on and desorption from the powders can be studied and hence the potential of these powders to act as drug delivery systems can be assessed. Collagen on the surface also enhanced adsorption, as shown by the enzyme immobilisation studies. The antihistaminic drug, chlorpheniramine maleate, adsorbed in Langmuir-type fashion on bone powder derived directly from crushing and pressure cooking/solvent treatment of cervine bone and which contained a significant level of surface-associated collagen.

Plasma spraying with 70-220 μm reprecipitated bone powder produced uniform coatings with a coarse grey appearance. The microstructure of the coatings consisted of glassy smooth splats and various sized spherical particles. From EDX, the coatings had a Ca:P ratio of 1.83 which agreed with ICP analyses of the scraped-off coatings. Some decomposition of the powder to CaO and $Ca_4P_2O_9$ and loss of fat-associated peaks (as shown by XRD and FTIR) had occurred.

ACKNOWLEDGEMENTS
New Zealand Foundation for Research, Science and Technology for funding support.

REFERENCES
1. Mucalo MR, Johnson GS, Lorier MA. In: *Proceedings of 10th International Symposium of Ceramics in Medicine, Paris , France*, Cambridge: Elsevier Science, 1997: 321-325.
2. Petach HH, Henderson W, Olsen GM. *J. Chem. Soc. Chem. Commun.* 1994; 2181-2182

Bioceramics Volume 11, edited by R. Z. LeGeros and J.P. LeGeros
(Proceedings of the 11th International Symposium on Ceramics in Medicine)
New York, NY, USA, November 1998
© 1998 by World Scientific Publishing Co. Pte. Ltd.

PORE VOLUME EXPANSION IN POROUS BIOACTIVE GLASS IMPLANTS DURING *IN VITRO* IMMERSION IN SBF

Heimo Ylänen[1], Clifford Ekholm[1], Kaj H. Karlsson[1], Jukka I. Salonen[2] and Hannu T. Aro[3]
[1]Åbo Akademi, Department of Chemical Engineering, Laboratory of Inorganic Chemistry, Biskopsgatan 8, FIN-20500, Åbo, Finland,
[2] Turku Center for Biomaterials, FIN-20520, Turku, Finland

[3] Department of Surgery, University of Turku, FIN-20520, Turku, Finland

ABSTRACT

Fast and extended bone ingrowth occurs into porous implants made from sintered of bioactive glass microspheres. The unique feature of these implants is their gradually increasing porosity due to the dissolving glass material replaced by new bone. The aim of this work was to determine the pore volume expansion of porous bioactive implants during SBF corrosion test *in vitro* and to compare the results with the corresponding *in vivo* changes of identical bioactive implants in the rabbit femur.

Cylindrical porous bioactive implants were prepared by sintering 250-300 μm bioactive glass microspheres. The implants were corroded under standardized stirred conditions of SBF immersion for 3, 7, 14, 21, 42 and 84 days. At each time interval, the formation of silica gel and apatite layers on the surface of bioactive glass spheres was evaluated by means of SEM/EDXA and the implant porosities were determined by using a computerized image analysis program.

During the *in vitro* corrosion test the porosity of bioactive implants increased significantly only for the first week of immersion. *In vivo*, the porosity increased linearly during the 12-week-period of implant healing with the host bone. Based on these results, the *in vivo* resorption of porous bioactive glass implants is constant and highly predictable. Under the testing conditions of the present study, the *in vitro* test could mimic only the initial stages of the *in vivo* phenomena.

Keyword: Bioactive glass, bone ingrowth, implant, in vitro

INTRODUCTION

Bioactive glasses in the system $Na_2O-K_2O-MgO-CaO-B_2O_3-P_2O_5-SiO_2$ can be used in different sintering processes without devitrification[2]. Thus, for instance, flame-spraying techniques can be applied to produce microspheres. Microspheres can be then sintered into porous implants of different shapes and sizes. The optimum pore size of the implants can be controlled by sintering microspheres of only appropriate diameter obtained by a narrow fractional separation of the raw material.

Our understanding of the basic bonding mechanisms between bone and bioactive glass is still incomplete. Bonding is known to proceed by partial dissolution of the glass surface resulting in formation of a silica-rich gel layer. Subsequently, hydroxyapatite (HA) is found to precipitate on the silica-rich layer[1]. As a result of the process, these reaction layers get thicker as a function of the decreasing amount of the core glass. The silica-rich gel layer obviously is an integral part of the bioactive glass which is Osteoconductive and capable for the chemical bonding with the host tissue. In porous bioactive glass implants, formation of the silica-rich and HA layers occurs inside the three-dimensional implant matrix and provides an anchoring surface for the ingrown new bone. As a unique feature of the biologic incorporation, the gradually decreasing amount of core glass within the porous implants provides an increasing space for the ingrowth of new bone.

Our recent *in vivo* study of the rabbit femur[8] showed that extended bone ingrowth occurs within three weeks into porous implants made by sintering bioactive glass microspheres. Pore volume expansion and subsequent bone ingrowth into pore spaces occurred closely during the first twelve weeks of incorporation. The original section area of the used glass implant contained 73 % glass, while at twelve weeks only 35 % remained. The continuous dissolution process of the bioactive glass and the formation of chemical bond between the reaction layer and bone caused the substitution of glass by new bone.

The aim of this study was to examine whether it is possible to estimate the increase of *in vivo* porosity in bioactive glass implants by means of evaluating the pore volume expansion of identical implants in an *in vitro* corrosion test. Finding of a correlation between *in vitro* and *in vivo* behavior of porous bioactive glass implants would facilitate the evaluation of bone ingrowth into porous bioactive implants *in vivo*.

MATERIALS AND METHODS

In the corrosion test, cylindrical porous implants were immersed in SBF for 3, 7, 14, 21, 42 and 84 days under standardized conditions. The selected composition of the glass has been previously shown to be bioactive[3]. The composition of the glass is given in the Table 1.

Table 1. Composition of the bioactive glass (wt %)

Na_2O	K_2O	MgO	CaO	P_2O_5	SiO_2
6	12	5	20	4	53

The glass was made from analytical grade raw materials and melted twice in a platinum crucible at 1360 °C. The annealed glass was crushed and spherulized by feeding into an acetylene-oxygen flame described by Pitkänen et al[6]. The micro-spheres were sieved to the fraction of 250-300 μm, washed in ethanol and sintered in a graphite mould at 700 °C for 14 min. to porous cylindrical implants with the diameter of 4 mm. Finally, the implants were cut into the length of 4 mm. The composition of SBF was based on analyzed human body fluids[6] and it contained all essential inorganic constituents for formation of hydroxyapatite (HA).

The implants were placed in polystyrene containers, one in each. Seven specimens were studied at each time interval of 3, 7, 14, 21, 42, and 84 days. The implants hung from a thin thread in the middle of the immersion solution, SA/V = 0.4 cm^{-1}. 42 containers were fastened in a rack which was kept in a water bath, at 36.9 °C. The rack was swung in the water at the speed of 1 swing/sec in order to stir the immersion solutions around the implants. At each time interval, seven test implants were removed from the containers, rinsed with ethanol, gently dried and embedded in acrylic resin. The cylindrical implants were ground and polished axially until 2 mm of the implant was left. The section area of each implant showed the corrosion through the whole cross-section of the implant (Figure 1).

During the immersion in SBF, an ion exchange of Na^+ and K^+ for H^+ or H_3O^+ occurs on the surface of the bioactive glass. This leads to the formation of a silica-rich layer on the surface of the glass spheres[5]. After immersion in SBF, the originally glassy spheres consisted of three different material phases: the original glass covered by silica gel and calcium phosphate layers (Figure 2). The original sphere surface could be traced to the outermost surface of the silica-rich layer (Figure 3).

Figure 1. Section area of test implant at 3 days of SBF immersion.

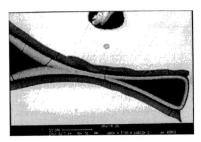

Figure 2. A SEM picture showing glass spheres surface at 3 days with layers of silica gel and HA.

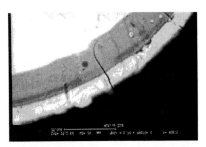

Figure 3. A detail picture of a bioactive sphere at 2 days showing the zones of glass, silica gel and HA Arrow shows original sphere surface befor immersion.

The major difference between the glass and the silica-rich layer was the concentration of K^+ -ions. As shown in the Table 1, the selected bioactive glass contained 12 wt % of K_2O, whereas the silica-rich zone was alkali poor. In the analysis this difference was used to separate the original glass material and the silica-rich layer on its surface. The analysis was made by a scanning electron microscope (SEM) equipped with a backscattered electron detector. For the analysis, an X-ray map was collected on the elements Si and K by energy dispersive X-ray analysis (EDXA). In order to find the thin material layers on the micro-spheres, 512x400 points of each specimen were analyzed with an emission time of 0.02 sec/point. The amount of initial glass and the initial structural porosity could be measured from an implant section image by collecting an X-ray map of all the matters containing Si, i.e. glass and silica-rich gel. The amount of remaining glass after resorption and the final porosity could be evaluated from the potassium mapping. In Figure 4, the two images of Si^{4+} and K^+ mapping were superimposed showing the diminution of the glass area during resorption.

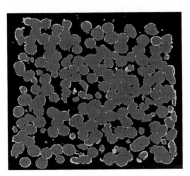

Figure 4. An image consisting of Si^{4+} and K^+ X-ray superimposed maps. The dark gray area indicates glass and the white area the silica layer at 14 days of immersion.

The final calculations of the porosity changes were performed by comparing the two images by means of computerized image analysis (MicroGOP 2000/ContexVision AB, Linköping, Sweden).

The *in vivo* pore volume of identical bioactive glass implants was studied by means of a computerized histomorphometry[4]. The area of porosity was determined as the interspace around the glass microspheres. The time intervals of the *in vivo* study were 21, 42, and 84 days.

The results of the porosity measurements were expressed as the means ± SD and analyzed by means of analysis of variance with a post-hoc test (Tukey/Kramer). P-values less than 0.05 were considered significant.

RESULTS

The porosity of the implants increased steadily during the *in vivo* incorporation with the host bone (Table 2). In contrast, the implants of the in vitro corrosion test showed an increasing porosity only during the early stage of SBF immersion (Table 2).

Table 2. The *in vivo* and *in vitro* pore expansion of porous bioactive glass implants as a function of time. The values represent the mean percentage ± SD, n = 6-7. The superscript letters of both columns indicate significant (p<0.05) differences between the time intervals.

Time in days	*In vivo* pore volume	*In vitro* pore volume
0	27.4 ± 1.6 [a]	27.4 ± 1.6 [a]
3	NA	29.5 ± 0.3 [a]
7	NA	30.7 ± 0.6 [b]
14	NA	32.5 ± 0.8 [b]
21	41.9 ± 4.5 [b]	31.4 ± 0.5 [b]
42	47.4 ± 8.3 [c]	33.5 ± 1.4 [b]
84	64.9 ± 8.6 [d]	31.1 ± 1.1 [b]

(NA = not available)

DISCUSSION

The porosity of sintered implants of bioactive glass microspheres increases during healing, when the dissolving glass is replaced by new bone. How fast this happens depends on the composition of the glass used. The design of any clinical implant device of the bioactive glasses requires information of the rate of the chemical reactions inside the bioactive texture. *In vivo* testing of bioactive structures is time-consuming and financially demanding. Therefore, there is a great need for *in vitro* simulation tests. The present study shows that it is technically laborious to establish an *in vitro* environment, which would mimic the *in vivo* conditions with mechanisms for removing excess matter. The *in vitro* tests failed to simulate the pore volume expansion pattern of the *in vivo* implants. Obviously, the *in vitro* conditions inside the porous bioactive implants were still too static in spite of the continuous stirring of the solution.

REFERENCES

1. Andersson ÖH, Karlsson KH, Yli-Urpo A, Kangasniemi K. *Glastechn Ber* 1988; **61**: 300-305
2. Brink M, Karlsson KH, Yli-Urpo A. Finnish patent application No 950147 (1995).
3. Brink M. Thesis, Åbo Akademi University, Finland, 1997.
4. Hench LL, Andersson ÖH, LaTorre GP. In *Bioceramics 4*, ed. W Bonfield, GW Hastings and KE Tanner, Butterworth-Heinemann Ltd, 1991: 155-162.
5. Heikkilä JT, Beliaev N, Yli-Urpo A and Aho AJ. In *Bioceramics 8*, ed. J Wilson, LL Hench and D Greenspan, Pergamon, 1995; 505-508.
6. Kokubo T, Kushitani H, Sakka S, Kitsugi T and Yamamuro T. *J Biomed Mat Res* 1990; **24**, 721-734.
7. Pitkänen V, Tikkanen M, Graeffe G, Brink M, Karlsson KH. *J. Aerosol Sci.* 1995; **26**: 831.
8. Ylänen H, Karlsson KH, Heikkilä JT, Mattila K and Aro HT. 10th International Symposium on
9. Ceramics in Medicine, Paris 1997.

Author Index

Davies JE: 461,509,659
de Bruijin JD: 497
de Groot K: 41,465
de Pollak C: 537
DeMaeyer EAP: 231
Deng H: 301
Deptula A: 743
Diaz IF: 583
Dimaano F: 181
Di-Silvio L: 285.293
Dohi Y: 262,331,517
Doi Y: 323.395
Dolcini L: 173
Donat A: 691
Dorozhkin SV: 117
Douglas WH: 571
Doyle C: 607,621
Driessens FCM: 231,239,243,247,363
Drouin JM: 73
Ducheyne P: 383,513,529,559
Durucan C: 161

E

Eckert KL: 193,305
Edwards B: 181
Efflandt SE: 571
Ekeberg L: 141
Ekholm C: 763
El-Bassyouni G: 529
Elbel J: 305
Elias A: 223
Elias CN: 223
Ellefterion A: 353
Eppenberger H: 305
Erbe EM: 435,603

F

Faldini C: 617
Fano V: 235
Fernandez MH: 169
Fernandez E: 239,243
Fernandez P: 707
Ferraz MP: 277

Ferreira JMF: 89
Filho JA: 641
Filiaggi MJ: 341
Fisher J: 607
Forest N: 327,457
Fortun Y: 477
Franca VP: 633
Francaviglia N: 637
Francis LF: 571
Franks K: 269
Fraymann JA: 137
Frayssinet P: 353,407
Frondoza CG: 289,309
Fu L: 197
Fujikawa H: 145
Fujimori Y: 335
Fujita H: 391,419,451,645,671.675
Furukawa T: 419

G

Gadaleta SJ: 435,603
Gao Y: 201
Garcia-Menocal JAD: 583
Garcia-Sanz FJ: 209
Garino J: 383
Garrido CA: 641
Gatti AM: 349,399
Gauthier O: 525,563
Gautier S: 751
Giannini S: 617
Gibson IR: 105,223,285,293
Gieland U: 759
Gil FJ: 141,239
Gildenhaar R: 121
Ginebra MP: 141,239.243.247
Gineste L: 353
Gineste M: 353
Giodano R: 265
Gisep A: 193
Gomez J: 755
Gonzalez R: 599
Gonda Y: 403
Greish Y: 161
Greenspan DC: 345,415,739

Grimandi G: 545.563
Gross KA: 101, 177
Gross U: 17
Gruner H: 193
Grynpas MD: 341
Guerra GD: 173
Guicheux J: 525.545
Guilhem A: 353
Guttierrez SA: 583

H

Ha SW: 193
Hall GC: 133,149
Hamagami J: 219,493
Hamadouche M: 427
Hanley L: 101
Harris JJ: 579
Hastings GW: 269
Hayakawa S: 423,489,679,695
Heikkila J: 617
Hench LL: 23.31.285,319,349,501
Hernandez EA: 583
Hernandez JR: 583
Hing KA: 285.293.723
Hino K: 251.439
Hioki Y: 541
Hollinger J: 3
Holy CE: 509
Hornberger H: 579
Horiuchi K: 517
Huang B: 549
Huang J: 165
Huang P-Y: 181
Hungerford DS: 289,309
Huygh A: 559

I

Ichihara J: 113
IIchijima K: 331.521
Ido K: 645
Iida H: 645
Ikeda Y: 323
Ikeuchi M : 517

Imoto K : 411.443
Ingham E: 607
Inoue M: 549,553,667,679
Ishikawa K: 431,447,567
Ishiwari Y: 549,553
Ito A: 97
Iwayama Y: 323

J

Jalisi IJ: 269
Jallot E: 327
Jha LJ: 105
Johnson GS: 759
Jones DW: 133,149
Jones NF: 57

K

Kajimoto T: 323,395
Kameyama T: 189,473
Kamiya A: 189
Kandel RA: 341
Kaneko S: 667
Kannagara K: 101
Karlsson KH: 763
Kasuga T: 145
Kato H: 671.675
Kato K: 541
Katsura Y: 451
Kawagoe K: 251.439
Kawamoto Y: 473
Kawashita M: 703
Khairoun I: 247
Khor KA: 197,227
Kijima K: 731
Kijkowska R: 181
Kikuchi M: 93,153,485
Kikutani : 371
Kim H-M: 77,481,655,663,671,675,687
Kim N: 411.443
Kim S: 205
Kim YE: 181
Kinuta Y: 553
Kitayama N: 403

Mucha H: 759
Muller-Mai C: 17
Murakami A: 251
Muraoka M: 403
Murata N : 411,443

N

Nagai N: 549,553
Naganuma K: 189
Nagaoka N: 553
Nagata F: 473
Nagatsuka H: 549,553,567
Nagle DC: 309
Nagura H: 335
Nakahira A: 113,715,731
Nakajima H: 261,331,521
Nakamura S: 367
Nakamura T: 77,371,391,419,451,481,
          645,655,663,671,675,687
Nakanishi K: 687
Nakano K: 553
Nakashima T: 251,439
Nancollas GH: 469
Nataloni A: 637
Nathason D: 265
Nemoto A: 281,301
Nevelos AB: 607
Nevelos JE: 607
Nies B: 357,363
Nishiguchi S: 655.671.675
Nishizawa K: 473
Niwa M: 575
Nizard RS: 427
Nogami M: 145
Nonami T: 189
Noshi T: 517

O

Ochi T: 251,439
Ohgaki M: 367,493
Ohgushi H: 261,331,505,517,521
Ohtsuki C: 423,489,667,679,695
Oka M: 645

Okada Y: 371,451
Okazaki M: 85,113,731
Okunaga K: 261
Okuno M: 419
Olczak T: 743
Olsen I: 269,277,313
Onuma K: 97
Oonishi H: 23.403,411,443
Ortalli I: 235
Osaka A: 423.489,667,679,695
Ota Y: 145
Oyane A: 687

P

Padrines M: 477
Paiva OC: 699
Panda RK: 727
Pantieri I: 533
Peaker AJS: 285
Peel SAF: 341
Peltola M: 129
Pereira MM: 215
Pérez-Amor M: 209
Pérez-Pariente J: 125
Petite H: 537
Phillips M: 177
Piattelli A: 173,375
Piattelli M: 375
Pilliar RM: 341
Pinasco P: 533
Piqueras J: 707
Planell JA: 141,239,243,247
Ploska U: 121
Polonchuk L: 305
Pou J: 209
Pochkine G: 255
Pozela K: 235
Prado da Silva MH: 223
Prudhommeaux F: 387,621

Q

Qiu Q: 513

R

Radin S: 519
Ravaglioli A: 173,533,637
Raynaud S: 109,751
Reddi AH: 9
Rego MT: 169
Reis RL: 169,735
Revell PA: 501
Rey C: 357,387
Ribeiro AS: 735
Rizkalla AS: 133,149
Rodriguez R: 755
Rodriquez-Clemete R: 755
Rodríguez-Lorenzo LM: 89
Rohanizadeh R: 477
Rokbani R: 747
Roman J: 707
Roncari E: 533
Rouquet N: 353
Routledge T: 133.149

S

Safari A: 727
Saito M: 251,411,439,443
Sakae T: 335
Sakamoto K: 113,715,731
Saku S: 323,295
Salgado T: 683
Salih V: 269
Salinas AJ: 707
Salonen JI: 763
Santos JD: 105,157,277,313
Sapieszko RS: 435
Sarowska B: 743
Sato K: 93,153,485
Sato T: 575
Sautier J-M: 327,457
Scarano A: 173,375
Schepers E: 529,559
Schmitt JM: 3
Schmitt M: 117
Schwartz C: 407
Sedel L: 427,537,621

Shiba K: 731
Shibutani T: 323
Shibuya T: 251.439
Shikinami Y: 419
Shinzato S: 371,391
Shoichet MS: 509
Sida D: 691
Sida V: 69
Siegel RW: 273
Silva RF: 157
Silva SN: 215
Soares EJC: 633
Soares GDA: 223
Sohrabi A: 309
Song L: 509
Sonoda T: 189
Spaziante R: 637
Srisukho K: 595
Stea S: 617
Stumpf S: 633
Suetsugu Y: 93,153,485
Sugaya K: 335
Sugihara F: 23,403
Sugimura M: 517
Suonpaa J: 129
Suwa F: 403
Suzuki K: 431.447.567.629

T

Tabata S: 261
Taira M: 85
Takadama H: 451,655,663
Takahashi J: 85
Takakuda K: 153
Takashima S: 695
Takeda S: 715
Tamai S: 261,331,505,521
Tamamura R: 553
Tanabe T: 395
Tanaka J: 93,153,485
Tanaka T: 153,629
Tanner KE: 165
Tanza D: 349,399
Taoda H: 189

Subject Index